Harper & Row ALGEBRA ONE

Sobel • Maletsky • Lerner • Cohen

Program Overview

STUDENT'S TEXT

- **Concepts and Skills** There are understandable daily lessons, detailed examples clearly worked out, class exercises, exercises for three levels of ability, and starred exercises to challenge top students (see pp. 213–215)

- **Problem Solving** Besides word problems in daily lessons, there are special lessons on Problem Solving (see pp. 111–114) and Strategies for Problem Solving (see p. 91).

- **Applications** A page in each chapter features a concept or skill from that chapter presented in a practical, real-world context (see p. 279).

- **Extension** In addition to level "C" and starred exercises in daily lessons, Extra Topic features (see p. 420) explore mathematical content beyond the standard curriculum. The Challenge feature requires creative thinking and exceptional skill (see p. 53).

- **Technology** Using the Calculator (see p. 207) investigates topics that would be tedious without calculator assistance. A Computer Activity occurs at the end of each chapter (see page 81) and relates a topic from the chapter to the computer. The Computer Handbook at the back of the text (pp. 534–545) can be used to introduce or review BASIC.

- **Review/Maintenance/Testing** There are numerous opportunities for review and for students and teacher to assess progress:

  Before each chapter, Prerequisite Skills Review (see p. 253) and Follow-Up exercises (see p. 503)

  Within each chapter, two or three Checkpoint reviews (see p. 177)

  At the end of each chapter, a Chapter Review (see pp. 198–200)

At the end of each chapter, a Chapter Test (see p. 200)

Four multiple-choice and free-response Cumulative Reviews (see pp. 250–251)

Extra Practice sets in the back of the text (pp. 507–533)

TEACHER'S EDITION

The side columns present a complete lesson plan for each lesson. Every lesson plan includes these features: Warm-Up Exercises, Lesson Notes, Possible Error, Alternate Examples, Daily Quiz, Assignment Guide, and Enrichment Activity (see pp. 66–67). Other features include Prerequisite Skills Reviews Error Analysis (pp. T20–T29); Motivational Activities (pp. T64–T69); an alternate set of Chapter and Cumulative Tests (pp. T30–T63); plus periodic side column features, Using Basic (see p. 115) and Maintaining Skills (see p. 116).

SUPPLEMENTARY MATERIALS

Tests, Duplicating Masters provide an alternate form for chapter and cumulative tests parallel to those that appear in the Teacher's Edition.

Solution Key gives step-by-step solutions to all problems and exercises in the text.

Teacher's Resource Book of over 300 pages contains blacklines masters plus ten transparencies and includes the following:

- Practice and Maintenance
- Motivation and Enrichment
- Activities with Visuals
- Special Topic: Statistics and Probability
- Quizzes
- Chapter and Cumulative Tests
- College Preparatory Tests
- Answer Key

TEACHER'S EDITION

Harper & Row ALGEBRA ONE

TEACHER'S EDITION

Harper & Row ALGEBRA ONE

Authors

MAX A. SOBEL

EVAN M. MALETSKY

NORBERT LERNER

LOUIS S. COHEN

Scribner Educational Publishers
New York

Macmillan Publishing Company
New York

Collier Macmillan Publishers
London

Authors

MAX A. SOBEL
Professor of Mathematics and Computer Science
Montclair State College
Montclair, New Jersey

EVAN M. MALETSKY
Professor of Mathematics and Computer Science
Montclair State College
Montclair, New Jersey

NORBERT LERNER
Professor of Mathematics
State University of New York
Cortland, New York

LOUIS S. COHEN
Teacher of Mathematics
Bloomington Jefferson High School
Bloomington, Minnesota

Acknowledgments

Cover Photo: Taurus Photos: Bob Hahn

Illustrations by: Vantage Art, Inc., John Lind and J&R Services

Scribner Educational Publishers
Macmillan Publishing Company
866 Third Avenue
New York, NY 10022
Collier Macmillan Canada, Inc.

ISBN 06-544200-8   858687MPC098765432

CONTENTS

The Student's Text with Annotations and Teaching Notes

A slightly reduced facsimile of each student page provides answers to exercises. Side columns include teaching suggestions, daily quizzes, assignment guides, enrichment activities, and other teaching resources. An abbreviated Table of Contents for the student's text is shown below. The full Table of Contents appears on pages iii–viii in the student's text and is included in this Teacher's Edition.

A special section consisting of graphs and other answers that would not fit on the annotated pages of the student's text or in the side columns of the lessons.

Dear Colleagues:

We, the authors, are pleased to be your colleagues in the service of educating students. This brief letter is an attempt to acquaint you with some of the basic philosophy that shaped our thoughts as we developed our secondary mathematics series.

In a world where there is such great need for the mastery of basic mathematical skills, it is important that students of all ability levels strive for mathematical excellence. To stimulate such participation on the part of all students, we have attempted to write a text that is complete in its development of concepts and skills but is neither formidable nor frightening. Thus, we have avoided a pedantic, formalistic approach that might lead to "math anxiety."

Each lesson throughout the text has been designed to encourage the understanding of important algebraic concepts and skills. Frequently, concepts are introduced through motivational approaches or illustrative examples before they are stated in precise language. Reasonable mathematical explanations are given where appropriate and are geared to the expected level of ability of your students. Numerous examples are utilized to reinforce the understanding of concepts and skills and to demonstrate how the mathematics is applied in a variety of situations. These illustrative examples not only serve to prepare the students for the exercises in each section, but they also can be used for later reference by the students when working independently on an assignment.

A variety of supplementary features have been included in the text to support and enrich the development as well as to provide additional motivation for the student. The major purpose of all of these features is to interest and involve the student in the learning process.

When students understand the underlying mathematical concepts, then mastery of skills is more readily achieved, and the resulting success leads to a greater appreciation and respect for mathematics. Such positive attitudes are ideals that all teachers of mathematics hope to instill in their students. The authors' major objective was to prepare textbooks that would serve to assist in the pursuit of these goals as our country strives for excellence in education. We trust that you will find using this book a most rewarding experience.

Sincerely,

MAX A. SOBEL
EVAN M. MALETSKY
NORBERT LERNER
LOUIS S. COHEN

THE STUDENT'S TEXT

THE DAILY LESSON

The lessons are structured for the greatest possible clarity and teachability. A careful, step-by-step development characterizes each lesson.

EXAMPLES

Important concepts and skills are illustrated by a variety of carefully sequenced, completely worked Examples. Systematically, the text uses the Examples to prepare the students for different types of mathematical situations. Through the Examples, the students become familiar with all types of exercises, even those that may trouble some average students.

6-3   Common Monomial Factors

OBJECTIVE

To factor the greatest common factor from the terms of a polynomial.

You can factor a polynomial if all of its terms have a common factor. For example, both terms of $6x + 12y$ have 6 as a factor.

$6x + 12y = 6(x) + 6(2y)$ Use the distributive property to factor 6 from each term.

$6x + 12y = 6(x + 2y)$ ← **factored form**

Now consider the common monomial factors of the terms in $4a^3b + 6a^2b^4$.

2 is the greatest common factor (GCF) of the coefficients.

a^2 is the highest power of a common to the two terms.

b^1 is the highest power of b common to the two terms.

The product of 2, a^2, and b^1 is $2a^2b$. This is called the *greatest common factor (GCF)* of the terms of the polynomial $4a^3b + 6a^2b^4$.

Example 1 shows the **greatest common factor** (GCF) of the terms of a polynomial. It is the product of the GCF of the coefficients times the highest powers of the variables common to all terms.

EXAMPLE 1   Find the greatest common factor of the terms of each polynomial.

$8x + 2xy$	$3xy + 5x$	$2x^4 + 6x^3$	$34x^3y + 51x^2y^2$
GCF: $2x$	x	$2x^3$	$17x^2y$

To factor a polynomial completely, be sure to factor the greatest common factor from its terms.

EXAMPLE 2   Factor $10x^2 + 5x$ completely, and check.

The greatest common factor is $5x$.

$10x^2 + 5x = 5x(2x + 1)$

Check $5x(2x + 1) = 10x^2 + 5x$ ✔

EXAMPLE 3   Factor $15a^3 + 10a^2b^2 - 5a^2b$.

The greatest common factor is $5a^2$.

$15a^3 + 10a^2b^2 - 5a^2b = (5a^2)(3a) + (5a^2)(2b^2) - (5a^2)(b)$
$= 5a^2(3a + 2b^2 - b)$

FACTORING   213

PROBLEM SOLVING

Word problems are included in the daily lessons. The ability to solve such problems is developed through regular lessons, special problem-solving lessons, and feature pages called Strategies for Problem Solving.

Through these experiences, students learn to apply various special problem-solving techniques.

Some examples of problem-solving techniques are

— using variables and writing equations

— making a diagram that includes the facts relevant to a problem

— observing a pattern and then finding a general rule based on the pattern

---

3-8   Problem Solving: Organizing Information

OBJECTIVE

To use diagrams and tables for organizing information and solving problems.

A diagram or a table is often used to organize the information in a problem.

EXAMPLE 1   Two sides of a triangle are $7\frac{1}{2}$ inches and $4\frac{1}{4}$ inches long. The triangle has a $16\frac{1}{2}$-inch perimeter. How long is the third side?

the perimeter

sum of the three lengths is $16\frac{1}{2}$.

ong.

l have a total value of

	Number of Coins	Value in Cents
Nickels	1	5
Dimes	8	80
Quarters	x	25x

s, 8 dimes, and a
of $4.10.

111

STRATEGIES for PROBLEM SOLVING

Guessing and Testing

Recently, the square of a man's age was the same number as the year he was born. How old is he now?

One way to find an answer is to **make some guesses and test them.**

Step 1   Try some ages and find their squares.

age 25	$25^2 = 625$	too young
age 35	$35^2 = 1225$	too young
age 45	$45^2 = 2025$	too old

Step 2   Try to improve your guess. Choose ages close to 45, the best of your first guesses.

age 42	$42^2 = 1764$	
age 43	$43^2 = 1849$	
age 44	$44^2 = 1936$	←This is the only possibility for someone living now.

Step 3   You now know that the man was born in 1936. He was 44 in 1980. How old is he now?

Practice this strategy on some other problems.

1. A woman was living at the time Columbus was born. Later, the square of her age was the year of her birth. How old was she in 1492?

2. A certain year during Albert Einstein's life was equal to the square of the number that was 13 less than his age at that time. When was he born?

3. There was a year during George Washington's life that was the square of 10 more than his age then. When was George Washington born?

4. Leonhard Euler was a great mathematician who lived in Switzerland during the 18th century. The year that was 19 years before he died was equal to the square of the quantity that was 15 less than his age then. In what year was he born, and in what year did he die?

POLYNOMIALS   181

T10

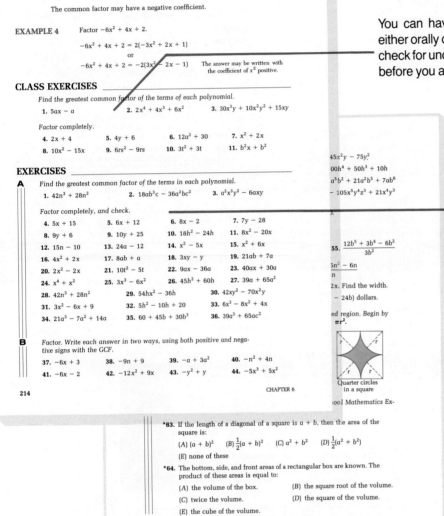

The common factor may have a negative coefficient.

EXAMPLE 4   Factor $-6x^2 + 4x + 2$.

$$-6x^2 + 4x + 2 = 2(-3x^2 + 2x + 1)$$
or
$$-6x^2 + 4x + 2 = -2(3x^2 - 2x - 1)$$ The answer may be written with the coefficient of x^2 positive.

CLASS EXERCISES _____

Find the greatest common factor of the terms of each polynomial.

1. $5ax - a$ **2.** $2x^4 + 4x^3 + 6x^2$ **3.** $30x^3y + 10x^2y^2 + 15xy$

Factor completely.

4. $2x + 4$ **5.** $4y + 6$ **6.** $12a^2 + 30$ **7.** $x^2 + 2x$

8. $10x^2 - 15x$ **9.** $6rs^2 - 9rs$ **10.** $3t^2 + 3t$ **11.** $b^2x + b^2$

EXERCISES _____

A   Find the greatest common factor of the terms in each polynomial.

1. $42n^3 + 28n^2$ **2.** $18ab^3c - 36a^2bc^2$ **3.** $a^2x^3y^2 - 6axy$

Factor completely, and check.

4. $5x + 15$ **5.** $6x + 12$ **6.** $8x - 2$ **7.** $7y - 28$

8. $9y + 6$ **9.** $10y + 25$ **10.** $18h^2 - 24h$ **11.** $8x^2 - 20x$

12. $15n - 10$ **13.** $24a - 12$ **14.** $x^2 - 5x$ **15.** $x^2 + 6x$

16. $4x^2 + 2x$ **17.** $8ab + a$ **18.** $3xy - y$ **19.** $21ab + 7a$

20. $2x^2 - 2x$ **21.** $10t^2 - 5t$ **22.** $9ax - 36a$ **23.** $40ax + 30a$

24. $x^4 + x^2$ **25.** $3x^3 - 6x^2$ **26.** $45h^2 + 60h$ **27.** $39a + 65a^2$

28. $42n^3 + 28n^2$ **29.** $54hx^2 - 36h$ **30.** $42xy^2 - 70x^2y$

31. $3x^2 - 6x + 9$ **32.** $5h^2 - 10h + 20$ **33.** $6x^3 - 8x^2 + 4x$

34. $21a^3 - 7a^2 + 14a$ **35.** $60 + 45b + 30b^3$ **36.** $39a^3 + 65ac^2$

B   Factor. Write each answer in two ways, using both positive and negative signs with the GCF.

37. $-6x + 3$ **38.** $-9n + 9$ **39.** $-a + 3a^2$ **40.** $-n^2 + 4n$

41. $-6x - 2$ **42.** $-12x^2 + 9x$ **43.** $-y^2 + y$ **44.** $-5x^3 + 5x^2$

$45x^2y - 75y^2$

$00h^4 + 50h^3 + 10h$

$a^5b^2 + 21a^2b^5 + 7ab^6$

$- 105x^5y^4z^3 + 21x^4y^3$

55. $\dfrac{12b^5 + 3b^4 - 6b^2}{3b^2}$

$\dfrac{5n^2 - 6n}{n}$

$2x$. Find the width.

$- 24b)$ dollars.

ed region. Begin by πr^2.

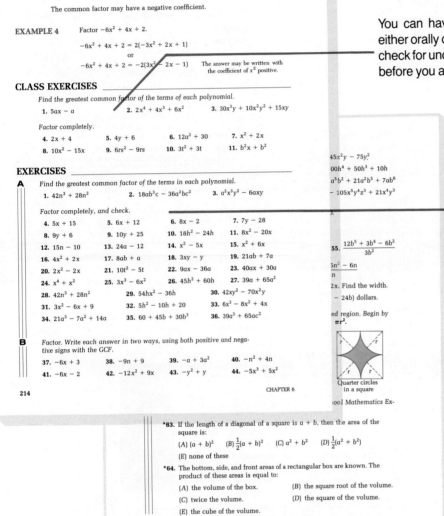
Quarter circles in a square

ool Mathematics Ex-

*63. If the length of a diagonal of a square is $a + b$, then the area of the square is:

   (A) $(a + b)^2$ (B) $\frac{1}{2}(a + b)^2$ (C) $a^2 + b^2$ (D) $\frac{1}{2}(a^2 + b^2)$

   (E) none of these

*64. The bottom, side, and front areas of a rectangular box are known. The product of these areas is equal to:

   (A) the volume of the box.   (B) the square root of the volume.

   (C) twice the volume.   (D) the square of the volume.

   (E) the cube of the volume.

CLASS EXERCISES

You can have students do some of these exercises either orally or with pencil and paper in order to help you check for understanding and identify potential problems before you assign the homework exercises.

EXERCISES

Abundant exercises cover a very wide range of difficulty. Most students will be able to handle all of the A exercises and most of the B exercises. The C exercises are more challenging. Often there also are starred exercises to challenge the most able students.

EXAMPLE 3　Nini's age is 1 year more than twice
Lor's age. If Nini is 19, how old is Lor?

Read the problem to find the key ideas.
Make a table.

	Age
Lor	x
Nini	2x + 1

Use a variable.　　Let x be Lor's age.

Write an equation.　$2x + 1 = 19$　Nini's age expressed in two ways

Find the solution.　　$2x = 18$
　　　　　　　　　　　$x = 9$　Check that 1 more than twice 9 is 19.

Answer the question.　Lor's age is 9.

EXAMPLE 4

Use a variable.

Write an equation.

Find the solution.

Answer the question.

EXAMPLE 5

Use a variable.

Write an equation.

Find the solution.

Answer the question.

112

APPLICATIONS

Break-Even Point

Many businesses have what is called a "break-even point." That is the
number of items they need to sell so that *expenses* just equal *revenues*.
If more items are sold, there is a *profit*. If fewer items are sold, there is
a *loss*.

A weekly magazine has regular expenses of $20,000 per week
and printing expenses of $.25 per copy. It receives $5000 per week
in advertising revenues and charges $1.00 per copy. Find the num-
ber of copies that must be sold to reach the break-even point.

We will show a graphical solution. *Expense and revenue lines are*
drawn on the same set of axes. The break-even point occurs where
these lines meet. That is the point where expenses and revenues are the
same.

Expenses = 20,000 + 0.25n
Revenues = 5000 + 1.00n

(n = number sold)

To simplify the graphing, the
numbers are expressed in thousands.

$y = 20 + 0.25x$

$y = 5 + x$

(x = number sold in thousands)
(y = dollars in thousands)

1. At what value of x does the break-even point occur?　20

2. How many magazines need to be sold to break even?　20,000

3. What are the expenses and revenues at the break-even point?
   Expenses: $25,000, Revenues: $25,000
4. Use the graph to find the profit if 30,000 magazines are sold.
   Profit: $7500
   Hint: Profit = Revenues − Expenses

5. If only 15,000 magazines are sold, what would be the loss?
   Loss: $3750
6. Suppose regular weekly expenses are $15,000 and printing ex-
   penses $.50 per copy. Advertising brings in $9000 weekly and the
   magazine sells for $2.00 per copy. Find the break-even point.
   Hint: A graph is not required!　Break-even point: 4000 copies

SYSTEMS OF LINEAR EQUATIONS　　　　279

APPLICATIONS

Applications are stressed throughout the text. The regular lessons
include applications wherever appropriate, and there are special
features devoted just to applications. These special Applications
pages appear in every chapter.

SPECIAL FEATURES

COMPUTER HANDBOOK

This special section at the back of the text can be used to introduce or review the popular computer language BASIC. Students will find the Computer Handbook a helpful, effective reference.

COMPUTER ACTIVITY

At the end of each chapter, a full-page Computer Activity relates an idea or a topic from the chapter to using a microcomputer.

COMPUTER HANDBOOK

I. Working with BASIC

BASIC is the most popular computer language because it is easy to learn and to use. Computers, however, vary slightly in the BASIC they use. The explanations and programs in this book are designed for use with as many different computers as possible, and can be understood when no computer is available. Because many computers display only capital letters, the programs are written in capitals.

If you enter a program into a computer and find that it does not run properly, first check to see that every line was entered correctly. Even the slightest mistake in entering a program may prevent it from running or may cause an erroneo[...]
sult the section "Some D[...]
sult the manual for the c[...]

In BASIC, each statemen[...]
the statements using mu[...]
tional statements into th[...]

The information imme[...]
affect the program itself.[...]
make the program easier[...]

Here is a program, wr[...]
and displays the sum of[...]
mands the computer to[...]
screen. In order to displ[...]
quotation [...]
in line[...]

```
10  R
20  L
30  L
40  L
50  P
60  P
70  P
80  E
```

The A,[...]
of a lo[...]
20 assi[...]

534

After you have entered the program, you must enter the command RUN. This instructs the computer to run the program, starting with the lowest line number. Here is a sample run of PROGRAM ONE.

```
RUN
THE SUM IS
120
```

If we wish the output to be displayed on one line, as

```
THE SUM IS 120
```

we can combine lines 50 and 60 by using a semicolon.

```
50 PRINT "THE SUM IS "; S
```

EXERCISES   Insert these lines into PROGRAM ONE.

COMPUTER ACTIVITY

Engine Efficiency

Here is a program that helps monitor gasoline consumption. The gasoline tank is filled, and a first reading is taken from the odometer to show how many miles the vehicle has already been driven. When the tank is filled again, the number of gallons used is recorded, and a second reading is taken from the odometer to show the new mileage. This data is then entered into the computer.

The Program	What It Does
`100 REM MILES PER GALLON`	Tells what program will compute.
`110 PRINT "FIRST READING";`	Displays a message or "prompt."
`120 INPUT F`	Waits for entry; assigns first reading to memory location F.
`130 PRINT "SECOND READING";`	
`140 INPUT S`	Assigns second reading to memory location S.
`150 PRINT "NO. OF GALLONS";`	
`160 INPUT G`	Assigns input to memory location G.
`170 LET R = (S - F)/G`	Computes number of miles per gallon obtained.
`180 PRINT "AVERAGED "; R;" MPG"`	Displays the result.
`900 END`	

`RUN`	Instructs computer to run the program.
`FIRST READING? 8643.7`	Assigns 8643.7 to F.
`SECOND READING? 8936.2`	Assigns 8936.2 to S. **Car traveled**
`NO. OF GALLONS? 12.5`	Assigns 12.5 to G. **292.5 miles.**
`AVERAGED 23.4 MPG`	Displays the output.

The letters used in the program (F, S, G, R) are called *variables*. In BASIC, a variable is the name of a location in the computer memory where a value is stored. For example, line 160 stores the number of gallons used in memory location G.

The absolute-value function may be used so that the odometer readings can be entered in any order. This can be done by changing line 170
to: `170 LET R = ABS(S - F)/G`

1. When the program MILES PER GALLON is run, how many memory locations will be used? Name them.

What will the program display for each of these entries?

	First Reading	Second Reading	No. of Gallons
2.	4065.3	4412.7	18.0
3.	12324.7	12715.3	12.4
4.	46385.8	46680.2	23.0

For more information about BASIC, see the Computer Handbook at the back of the book.

COMPUTER ACTIVITY

81

PREREQUISITE SKILLS FOLLOW-UP

EXTRA PRACTICE SETS

COMPUTER HANDBOOK

TABLES

GLOSSARY

ANSWERS TO CHECKPOINTS

ANSWERS TO SELECTED EXERCISES

INDEX

The inequality $2 < x < 4$ can be written as $|x - 3| < 1$. Every point on the graph is less than 1 unit from 3, the midpoint of the interval.

Use the observation above to write an inequality of the form $|x - m| < r$ for the given graph.

40.
1 2 3

41.
2   8

42.
−1   5

43.
−3   2

44. Solve and graph the compound inequality $|x - 2| < 2$ and $|x - 1| > \frac{1}{2}$.

Find the greatest common factor (GCF) of each set of integers.

63. 12, 42, 60   **64.** 42, 56, 70   **65.** 48, 64, 80   **66.** 42, 63, 84

67. 45, 63, 108, 126, 180   **68.** 78, 104, 130, 156, 208

C Factor as the product of two integers, positive or negative, in all possible ways.

69. 15   **70.** 105   **71.** −99   **72.** −165

Write each integer in the form 15,873**n**, where **n** is written in completely factored form.

73. 111,111   **74.** 222,222   **75.** 555,555

From your answers to the preceding exercises, try to predict the following products. Then check by computation or with a calculator.

76. 15,873 × 21   **77.** 15,873 × 28   **78.** 15,873 × 42

79. 15,873 × 49   **80.** 15,873 × 56   **81.** 15,873 × 63

EXTRA TOPIC

This feature allows the students to explore topics or areas of mathematics that enrich or may go beyond the regular classroom curriculum.

EXTRA TOPIC

nd-degree, or **quadratic**
− 4 > 0.
)(x − 4) > 0.
−1 or x = 4, mark the points
w separated into three

part, as follows. For x < −1,
and note:
4) = −2 − 4 = −6 < 0
t (x + 1)(x − 4) is positive.
< 4, and x = 5 for x > 4, to
w.

(x − 4) | (x + 1) (x − 4)
         − | +   +
x < 4 ─────────── x > 4 ──────
         − | 4   +
                  |

d x² − 3x − 4 > 0 are equiv-
> 4
of x² − 3x − 4 < 0?

> 0
x < 0

381

USING THE CALCULATOR

Prim

To test
number

Sar

Use yo

1. 52
5. 77
9. 20

FACTORING

USING THE CALCULATOR

This feature encourages students to explore interesting patterns and gain valuable insights into mathematical concepts that would be too difficult or too tedious to investigate without a calculator.

Express as a difference between a positive and a negative number. Then subtract.

53. The highest recorded temperature on earth is 57.8°C, in Libya. The lowest is −84.4°C, in the Antarctic. What is the difference between the two?

54. Mt. Everest in Nepal is 8848 meters above sea level. The greatest recorded depth in the ocean is 11,033 meters below sea level. Find the difference.

C **55.** You know that 16 − 9 = 7 because 7 added to 9 gives 16. Similarly, you can prove that $a - b = a + (-b)$ by showing that $a + (-b)$ added to b, gives a. Supply reasons for the proof.

(1) $b + [a + (-b)] = b + [(-b) + a]$ Why?
(2) $= [b + (-b)] + a$ Why?
(3) $= 0 + a$ Why?
(4) $= a$ Why?

56. When n is subtracted from 2, the result is −16. What is the value of n?

57. The sum of three numbers is 98. If the first two numbers are 8 and −15, what is the third number?

58. What number can you subtract from 5 in order to get 25?

59. What number must be subtracted from the sum of 16, 18, and −29 to get −2?

60. The numbers n and 12 differ by 30. Find two possible values for n.

CHALLENGE

This feature provides interesting activities and problems that require extensions of skills and creative thinking.

CHALLENGE

A Painted Cube

A cube 3 centimeters on each edge is painted red on all sides. Then it is cut into 1-centimeter cubes, as shown.

3 cm
3 cm
3 cm

1. How many 1-centimeter cubes will there be?

2. How many cubes will have exactly
  a. 0 sides red?   **b.** 1 side red?
  c. 2 sides red?   **d.** 3 sides red?

Answer the same questions for a 4- × 4- × 4-centimeter cube. Now try answering the questions for an n- × n- × n-centimeter cube.

REVIEWS AND TESTS

SYSTEMS OF LINEAR EQUATIONS

Prerequisite Skills Review

Write the letter for the correct answer.

1. In the coordinate plane, which point lies on the x-axis?

   a. $(4, -2)$ **b.** $(-7, -1)$ **c.** $(0, 5)$ **d.** $(-6, 0)$

2. Which point is in Quadrant III?

   a. $(-1, 0)$ **b.** $(-6, -1)$ **c.** $(2, -5)$ **d.** $(-5, 1)$

3. Which line is parallel to the x-axis?

PREREQUISITE SKILLS REVIEW

Each chapter is preceded by a Prerequisite Skills Review. Multiple-choice questions provide a review of the skills that students should have before they begin the chapter. Students who do not perform satisfactorily can get additional help by using the Follow-Up exercises on pages 500–506 of their texts.

with just one exponent.

   20. $(-1)^2(-1)^5(-1)$

   23. $(-7x)(4x^3)(x^2)$

$(-x^5)$ **26.** $-1(x^2y)(xy^2)(-xy)$

   29. $(-2ab^4)^3$

$^2)^2$ **32.** $(-3a^2b^3c^4)^2$

$7)$ **35.** $3x(x^2 - 2x + 3)$

xy^2 **38.** $ab(a^2 - ab + b^2)$

$0.$ $y^2(1 - 2x + 3y)$

$+ 2x^2$ **43.** $5x(x + 1) - 7x^2$

$5.$ $2t^2 - 3(t^2 - 6t^4) + 7t^4$

$7)$ **48.** $(x - 9)(x - 3)$

$+ 3)$ **51.** $(3x - 4)(5x - 1)$

$- 6x)$ **54.** $(a^2 - b)(3a + 2b)$

$x^2 - 5)$ **57.** $(2x - 1)(2x - 1)$

$9.$ $(3x - 1)(x^2 + 5x + 2)$

$- 2s)$ **62.** $(a^2 + b^2)(a^2 - b^2)$

   65. $(3x - 4)^2$

*write **no solution**. If the*

$7.$ $8 - x = 3x - 3(x + 1)$

$9.$ $x(x + 2) - 8 = (x + 4)(x - 2)$

$1.$ $3(2x - 5) = 4(x + 1) - (7 - 2x)$

                          199

CHAPTER 5 REVIEW

VOCABULARY

monomial (p. 166)
polynomial (p. 166)
binomial (p. 166)
trinomial (p. 166)
degree of a monomial (p. 166)

degree of a polynomial in one variable (p. 167)
opposite of a polynomial (p. 170)
product of powers (p. 174)
power of a power (p. 178)
identity (p. 191)

SUMMARY

After classifying various types of polynomials, the basic operations of addition, subtraction, and multiplication of polynomials are studied. The distributive property is used in the multiplication of polynomials, which also requires extensions of the properties of powers. A shortcut for multiplying binomials is presented after the general procedures for multiplying polynomials have been demonstrated. The new algebraic procedures with polynomials are applied to solving equations, and then are used in solving verbal problems.

REVIEW EXERCISES

5-1   *Classify each polynomial as a monomial, binomial, or trinomial.*

  1. $3x + 8$ **2.** $9x^2$ **3.** $x^2 + 5 - 2x$ **4.** $-3x^2 + 5x - x^5$

Simplify each polynomial. Then give the degree.

  5. $2x^2 + 5x - 3x$ **6.** $x^3 + 2x^4 - x - 2x^4$ **7.** $-x^2 + x^4 + 9x^2$

Evaluate $-3x^2 + x - 1$ *for each value of* x.

  8. $x = -2$ **9.** $x = 2$ **10.** $x = \frac{2}{3}$ **11.** $x = 0$

5-2   **12.** Add. $\begin{aligned} 2x^2 + 7x - 9 \\ -5x^2 + x + 4 \end{aligned}$ **13.** Subtract. $\begin{aligned} x^3 - 4x^2 \quad\;\; + 7 \\ 2x^3 - 2x^2 + 5x - 6 \end{aligned}$

  14. Subtract $(x^4 + x^3 - 3x^2 - 2)$ from the sum of $(3x^4 + x^3 - x)$ and $(2x^2 - 7x - 8)$.

Simplify.

  15. $(2x - 9) + (-x + 17)$ **16.** $(n^3 + n + 4) - (4 - n^2 - n^3)$

  17. $(x^2 - 3x) + (5x^2 - 6x + 7) - (4x^2 + 8x - 10)$

198   CHAPTER 5

CHAPTER REVIEW

Vocabulary, Summary, and Review Exercises are provided at the end of each chapter to help students review important terms, concepts, and skills. For the student's reference, the Review Exercises are keyed to the section of the text in which the concept or skill was taught.

CHECKPOINT

Checkpoints occur within the chapters to help students review concepts and skills studied earlier in the chapter. Students may check their answers with those given in the back of their texts.

d b such that $a^b = b^a$.

CHECKPOINT

Simplify. Then give the degree of the polynomial.

  1. $2x + 3x$ **2.** $-11x + 1x$ **3.** $8(3x - x^3) + 3x^3 + x$

  4. $5x + 3(1 + x) - x$ **5.** $4(2x^5 - x^4) - 8x^5$ **6.** $2x - 2(x + 1)$

  7. Evaluate $3x^2 - 2x + 5$ when $x = -1$.

Simplify.

  8. $(9x + 6y + 7) - (-4x + 7y + 9)$ **9.** $(3x + 4y) + (-2y + 7z - 4x)$

  10. $(x^2 - 3xy) - (y^2 - 3xy)$ **11.** $(2x^2 - 17) - (13 - 2x) - (x^2 + 3x)$

  12. $(5a^2)(7a^4)$ **13.** $(-x^5)(3x^3)$ **14.** $(3ab)(2a)$

  15. $(-4b^2)(-ab)$ **16.** $(3x^3y)(x^2y^5)$ **17.** $(4xy)(2x^2y)$

Express each product in exponential form with just one exponent.

  18. $x^3 \cdot x^5$ **19.** $x^4 \cdot x$ **20.** $7^2 \cdot 7^9$ **21.** $a^x \cdot a^y$

POLYNOMIALS   177

5-9 **72.** The sum of two consecutive integers minus the next consecutive integer is 18. Find the integers.

73. Nine more than the square of an integer is the same as the square of the next consecutive integer. Find the integer.

74. A rectangle with a perimeter of 60 meters is 12 meters longer than it is wide. What is the area of the rectangle?

75. The square of a number is 16 more than the square of 2 less than the number. Find the number.

CHAPTER 5 TEST

5-1 Simplify each polynomial. The

1. $2x^2 + 5x - 6x^2 + x^3 + 4x^2$

5-2 **3.** Add. $\begin{array}{r} -3x^2 - 5xy + y^2 \\ -x^2 + 9xy + 4y^2 \end{array}$

5. Simplify $(x^3 + 3x^2 + 1) +$

5-3 Simplify. Then evaluate when

6. $(3^2)(-2x)(4x^2)$

Simplify.

5-4 **8.** $(-2a^2b)^3$

5-5 **10.** Multiply

11. Simplify

5-6 Multiply.

12. $(3x + 4)($

14. $(2x - 3)($

5-7 Expand.

16. $(x + 7)^2$

5-8 Solve for x.

18. $(x + 3)(x$

5-9 **20.** The lengt

CUMULATIVE REVIEW CHAPTERS 1–6

PART I

Write the letter for the correct answer.

Chap. 1 **1.** Which number is an integer but not a whole number?

    a. -1 **b.** 0   **c.** 2   **d.** $\frac{1}{2}$ **e.** -0.2

2. The phrase "5 less than twice a certain number" is represented by $\underline{?}$.

    a. $2(x - 5)$ **b.** $5 - 2x$ **c.** $5x - 2$ **d.** $5(x - 2)$ **e.** $2x - 5$

PART II

Simplify.

Chap. 1 **15.** $19 - 14 + 13$ **16.** $17 - 3 \times 2$ **17.** $36 \div (18 \div 2)$

Chap. 2 **18.** $(-18) + (-19) + 25 + (-33)$ **19.** $-18 + 17 + 26 - 15 - 17$

20. $10y + 12y - 13$ **21.** $-25x - 16x - 21x$ **22.** $x^2y + 9xy^2 - 5x^2y$

23. $-\frac{18x}{12}$ **24.** $\frac{(3x)^2}{9}$ **25.** $\frac{24xy^2}{-4y}$ **26.** $\frac{-300y}{-60y^3}$

Evaluate when x = 3 and y = −5.

27. $8x + 2y$ **28.** y^x **29.** $xy - y^2$ **30.** $(xy)^2 - y^2$

EXTRA PRACTICE SETS

CHAPTER 1

1-1 Simplify.

1. $3 + 9 - 6$ **2.** $5 - 2 + 8$ **3.** $4 \times 3 - 7$

4. $12 - 3 \times 4$ **5.** $10 \div 2 + 9$ **6.** $8 - 4 \div 2$

7. $5 \times 4 \div 5$ **8.** $5 + (7 - 4)$ **9.** $8 \times (15 - 7)$

10. $(4 + 10) \div 2$ **11.** $5 \times (3 + 2) \div 5$ **12.** $11 - (4 - 2) \div 2$

13. $\frac{45 \div (10 - 7)}{5} \div 3$ **14.** $18.5 + \frac{(0.5 - 0.2)}{0.3}$ **15.** $\frac{12 - 4 \times 2}{1 + 6 \div 2} + 5$

16. $48 - [(15 - 10) \times 5]$ **17.** $[18 - (6 + 1)] \times 3$ **18.** $6 \times [16 - (3 + 7)]$

1-2 Evaluate each expression for the given value of the variable.

19. $12 - (3 + n)$ if n = 4   **20.** $4(a + 2)$ if a = 9   **21.** $d(d + 8)$ if d = 5

22. $7(28 - 3p)$ if p = 7   **23.** $16 \div (m + 2)$ if m = 6   **24.** $9(5 - x) - 7$ if x = 3

25. $\frac{3b - 2}{4}$ if b = 6   **26.** $\frac{8z + 14}{z}$ if z = 7   **27.** $\frac{2s + 7}{s + 1}$ if s = 4

Evaluate. Let a = 6, and b = 4.

28. $5a - b$ **29.** $2ab$ **30.** $b(a - 3)$

31. $a(b + 9)$ **32.** $4(2a + 8b)$ **33.** $15a - 3b$

34. $(4a)(ba)$ **35.** $3 + 6ab$ **36.** $\frac{8 + b}{a}$

37. $\frac{a(a + b)}{3b}$ **38.** $\frac{ab + 16}{a + b}$ **39.** $\frac{ab}{2a - (b + 4)}$

Evaluate. Let x = 2, y = 4, and z = 10.

40. xyz **41.** $x(z - y)$ **42.** $2x + 3y - z$

43. $z(x + y)$ **44.** $x(4y - z)$ **45.** $5xy + z$

46. $xy(z + 4)$ **47.** $y(x + z - 7)$ **48.** $\frac{x + y + z}{8}$

49. $\frac{yz}{x}$ **50.** $\frac{x + 3y}{z - 3}$ **51.** $\frac{y(42 - x)}{z}$

EXTRA PRACTICE   507

Tab labels (right side):
PREREQUISITE SKILLS FOLLOW-UP · EXTRA PRACTICE SETS · COMPUTER HANDBOOK · TABLES · GLOSSARY · ANSWERS TO CHECKPOINTS · ANSWERS TO SELECTED EXERCISES · INDEX

1

.6

= 14

(−5, −2)

2

0

RS 1–6

8) + 2y

3)²

− 8

here

251

CHAPTER TEST

These tests appear at the end of each chapter in the student's text. Two independent sets of Chapter Tests are also available, one on pages T30 through T49 of this Teacher's Edition, the other separately in duplicating-master form.

CUMULATIVE REVIEW

Four Cumulative Reviews appear in the student's text. Part I of each is in multiple-choice form, which provides students experience with the type of items found on college entrance tests.

Also available are two independent sets of Cumulative Tests, one on pages T50 through T60 of this Teacher's Edition, the other in duplicating-master form.

EXTRA PRACTICE SETS

At the back of the student's text, there is a section of Extra Practice exercises. These exercises are keyed to the individual chapters and to sections within the chapters.

THE TEACHER'S EDITION

Each page of the student's text is reproduced with annotated answers.

The side columns present a complete lesson plan that includes teaching suggestions, quizzes, assignment guides, enrichment activities, and other teaching resources. All of this is adjacent to the reduced student's pages as you teach them. You do not need to turn to the front of the book for teaching suggestions.

WARM-UP EXERCISES

These exercises are intended to be used as a brief preparation for the lesson. They focus on one previously studied idea or skill that is used in the lesson.

LESSON NOTES

The Lesson Notes provide helpful background material, suggestions for teaching the lesson, or comments about aspects of the lesson that deserve special emphasis.

POSSIBLE ERROR

This feature illustrates mistakes that some students may make as they do the exercises in their text. Where appropriate, procedures for correcting or avoiding the errors are also provided.

EXAMPLE 4 Simplify. Write each expression without parentheses.

a. $a - (b - c)$
$a + (-1)(b - c)$
$a + (-1)b - (-1)c$
$a + (-b) - (-c)$
$a - b + c$

b. $(a + b) - (c + d)$
$(a + b) + (-1)(c + d)$
$a + b + (-1)c + (-1)d$
$a + b + (-c) + (-d)$
$a + b - c - d$

EXAMPLE 5 Evaluate each expression if $a = -3$, $b = -5$, and $c = 4$.

a. $-ab$
$-(-3)(-5)$
$-1(15)$
-15

b. $a - bc$
$(-3) - (-5)(4)$
$(-3) - (-20)$
$(-3) + 20$
17

c. $-(a - b)$
$-[(-3) - (-5)]$
$-1[(-3) + 5]$
$-1(2)$
-2

CLASS EXERCISES

Simplify.

1. $-(-26)$ 26
2. $-(6 - 5)$ -1
3. $-(-30 + 16)$14
4. $-(y - 10)$ $-y + 10$
5. $-(x - y)$ $-x + y$
6. $-(x + y)$ $-x - y$
7. $x - (y + 5)$ $x - y - 5$
8. $y - (x - 3)$ $y - x + 3$

Evaluate for $x = -3$ and $y = 4$.

9. $-x$ 3
10. $-2y$ -8
11. $-5x$ 15
12. $-xy$ 12
13. $x - y$ -7
14. $y - x$ 7
15. $-x - y$ -1
16. $y - xy$ 16

EXERCISES

A Simplify.

1. $-(-14)$ 14
2. $-(4 + 3)$ -7
3. $-(12 - 18)$ 6
4. $-(-11 - 8)$ 19

Simplify. Then evaluate for $x = -3$.

5. $-(x - 8)$ $-x + 8$; 11
6. $-(-x + 8)$ $x - 8$; -11
7. $-(-x - 8)$ $x + 8$; 5
8. $12 - (x + 1)$ $-x + 11$; 14
9. $10 - (x - 8)$ $-x + 18$; 21
10. $10 - (8 - x)$ $x + 2$; -1

B Evaluate $-pq$ for the given values of p and q.

11. $p = -6$, $q = 7$ 42
12. $p = 8$, $q = -15$ 120
13. $p = -10$, $q = -25$ -250

BASIC OPERATIONS   67

EXTRA PRACTICE, page 510

67

ALTERNATE EXAMPLES

An Alternate Example is provided for each Example in the student's text. These alternate examples can be used to provide additional experience with the ideas or skills illustrated by the Examples in the student's text.

DAILY QUIZ

The items in the Daily Quiz are similar to A and B exercises in the lesson. They can be used as suggested or combined to create a weekly quiz.

ASSIGNMENT GUIDE

The daily assignment guide provides suggested assignments for students at three levels of ability.

ENRICHMENT ACTIVITY

The Teacher's Edition provides an enrichment activity for each of the regular lessons. You do not need to look anywhere else to find enrichment suggestions.

OTHER FEATURES

USING BASIC

This feature highlights ways in which activities on a microcomputer can be related to ideas in various lessons in the student's text. Using BASIC supplements the various Computer Activity pages in the text.

MAINTAINING SKILLS

These skills-review exercises appear in the margin at the end of each chapter in the Teacher's Edition. They can be used to supplement the maintenance program built into the student's text.

CHAPTER TESTS AND CUMULATIVE TESTS

A complete set of independent Chapter Tests and independent Cumulative Tests appear on pages T30 through T60. Users of classroom sets of the text are granted permission to reproduce these tests. All answers to the tests appear on pages T61 through T63.

MOTIVATIONAL ACTIVITIES

The Motivational Activities are a special collection of interest-attracting activities that are presented to help motivate students.

---

32. $\dfrac{a^2 + 5a + 4}{a^2 + 8a + 16}$, when $a = 11$ $\frac{a+1}{a+4}; \frac{4}{5}$ 33. $\dfrac{3x^2 + 9x + 6}{x^2 - 4}$, when $x = -1$ $\frac{3(x+1)}{x-2}; 0$

Simplify. State all restrictions on the variables.

34. $\dfrac{xy^5}{-x^3}$ $-\frac{y^5}{x^2}; x \neq 0$ 35. $\dfrac{3a^5b^2}{6a^5b^3}$ $\frac{1}{2b}; \frac{a \neq 0}{b \neq 0}$ 36. $\dfrac{-8a^2b^2}{-12a^5b^{3a}}$ $\frac{a \neq 0}{b \neq 0}$ 37. $\dfrac{2x^2 - 2}{x - 1}$ $2(x+1); x \neq 1$

38. $\dfrac{7n^2 + 14n - 21}{n^2 + 10n + 21}$ 39. $\dfrac{x^2 + 11x + 30}{3ax^2 + 15ax}$ 40. $\dfrac{n^2 - n - 20}{5n^2 + 20n}$

41. $\dfrac{4x^2 - 1}{2x^2 - 5x - 3}$ 42. $\dfrac{6x^2 + 7x + 2}{4x^2 - 1}$ 43. $\dfrac{an^2 + 6an + 9a}{n^2 + 2n - 3}$

44. $\dfrac{2x^2 - 18x}{x^2 + 3x}$ 45. $\dfrac{5x + 20}{15x^2 + 60x}$ 46. $\dfrac{x - 1}{x^2 - 2x + 1}$

47. $\dfrac{x + 1}{x^3 - x}$ 48. $\dfrac{x^2 - x}{x^3 + x^2 - 2x}$ 49. $\dfrac{6x - 30}{x^2 - 7x + 10}$

Using BASIC

The computer can be used to help emphasize the fact that division by zero is not permitted. This program attempts to evaluate $\dfrac{1}{x - 5}$ for each value of x from -10 to 10. When it reaches $x = 5$, the computer stops and displays an error message.

```
10 FOR X = -10 TO 10
20   PRINT "WHEN X IS"; X
30   LET Y = 1/(X - 5)
40   PRINT "1/(X - 5) IS"; Y
50   FOR J = 1 TO 1500
60   NEXT J
70   PRINT
80 NEXT X
90 END
```

Lines 50 and 60 slow down the dis-

MAINTAINING SKILLS

These exercises review basic algebraic skills.

Simplify.
1. $6 - 5 \cdot 3 + 4 \cdot 2$ -1
2. $(-3x^2y^3)(-6xy^2)^2$ $-108x^4y^7$
3. $x^2(x - 1) - x(x^2 - x - 3)$ $3x$

Evaluate when $a = 4$, $b = -5$, and $c = 3$.
4. $-2(a^2bc)$ 480
5. $2a^2 - 3b + c$ 50
6. $\dfrac{ab - bc}{...}$ $\frac{1}{...}$

Solve
7. x
8. 3
9. 6
10. 1
11.
12.
13.

CHAPTER 6 REVIEW

VOCABULARY

prime number (p. 204)
prime factorization (p. 205)
greatest common factor (GCF) of two or more positive integers (p. 205)
greatest common factor (GCF) of the terms of a polynomial (p. 213)

factored form of a polynomial (p. 213)
factoring by grouping (p. 216)
difference of two squares (p. 219)
trinomial square (p. 223)
zero-product rule (p. 236)
double root (p. 237)

Name _____ Date _____ Score _____

CUMULATIVE TEST: CHAPTERS 1–3   **Part I**

Write the letter for the correct answer.
1. Simplify: $36 \div (12 - 3) + 7 \times 2$
   a. 14   b. 18   c. 22   d. 26   e. 32   1. _____
2. Evaluate $ab - (b - 3a)$ if $a = 1$ and $b = 6$.
   a. 3   b. 4   c. 6   d. 7   e. 9   2. _____
3. Write $5x \cdot 3y \cdot y \cdot 2x \cdot x$ in exponential form.
   a. $8x + 4y$ b. $10x^3y^3$ c. $30x^3y^2$ d. $30x^2y^3$ e. $10x^2y^3$ 3. _____
4. Which is the correct expression for the phrase, "8 less than the   4. _____

MOTIVATIONAL ACTIVITIES

The Role of Motivation

Motivation is a key to learning. A suitably motivated student can and will learn mathematics, and an enthusiastic teacher can do much to stimulate interest in the subject.

Although the required subject matter in an algebra course often seems to be too extensive to cover in one year, taking time for the purpose of motivating students is still worthwhile. Many algebra lessons have their own natural appeal or have motivation built through the text approach. At other times it will be up to you to provide the motivation. One way to do this is to use a few minutes at the start of the class period. You may either set the stage for the day's lesson or you may introduce some special motivational aspect of mathematics.

Naturally, it is best to have the introduction linked directly to the lesson for that day, but this need not be a requirement. Students will generally react positively to any attempt to demonstrate an interesting or challenging aspect of mathematics.

Among the ways to provide motivation are the use of a challenging problem, a historical anecdote, a suitable application, an example of mathematics used in the daily newspaper, an opportunity to guess or estimate, a laboratory experiment, a mathematical game or trick, and so forth.

Following are samples of such motivational techniques. As you consider and use these ideas, you will find that other ideas and activities will spring to mind. For additional sources of topics and ideas, consult the Bibliography on page T69.

FALLACIES

1. Students are usually interested in fallacies, especially if these are presented in a dramatic manner. Thus you might announce that a new discovery has been made, namely that $1 = 2$! Then proceed to show the following "proof" of this fact and challenge the students to find the fallacy.

Let $a = b$
Then $a \cdot a = a \cdot b$ Multiply by a.
            $a^2 = ab$ $a \cdot a = a^2$
            $a^2 - b^2 = ab - b^2$ Subtract b^2.
$(a - b)(a + b) = b(a - b)$ Factor.
            $a + b = b$ Divide by $a - b$.
            $2b = b$ Replace a by b ($a = b$).
            $2 = 1$ Divide by b.

Note that the step where both sides of the equation are divided by $a - b$ is not "legal." Since $a = b$, $a - b = 0$, and division by 0 is not permitted. This fallacy is very helpful in providing an effective demonstration that one may not divide by 0.

2. Here is another example of a fallacy based on the same principle, but disguised somewhat better. The fallacy is designed to show that any two numbers are equal!

Assume x and y are two positive numbers with $x > y$. Then $x = y + z$, where z is some positive number.

$x = y + z$
$x(x - y) = (y + z)(x - y)$ Multiply by $x - y$.
$x^2 - xy = xy + xz - y^2 - yz$ By multiplication
$x^2 - xy - xz = xy - y^2 - yz$ Subtract xz.
$x(x - y - z) = y(x - y - z)$ Factor.
$x = y$ Divide by $x - y - z$.

Thus we assumed that $x > y$ and "proved" that $x = y$. Again the fallacy involves the "illegal" procedure of dividing by 0. (Since $x = y + z$, then $x - y - z = 0$.)

MATHEMAGIC

An exceptionally fine way to motivate the learning of mathematics is through the use of mathematical tricks. Many of these can be used to demonstrate concepts of proof and to show how the use of variables can provide explanations as to why the trick works. Here is a sampling of some items that have been used effectively in algebra classes.

1. Students are asked to think of a number, to perform several operations, and are then told the outcomes. They will

---

Name_____ Date_____ Score_____

CHAPTER 5 TEST   Polynomials

5-1   **1.** Give the degree of the polynomial.
$4x^2 - 2x^3 - x^2 + 3$
2. Identify $x^2 - 2x + 3$ as a monomial, a binomial, or a trinomial.

Simplify each polynomial. Then evaluate for $x = 2$.
3. $2x^2 + x^3 - x^2 + 5 - x^3$
4. $4x^4 + x^3 - 3x^2$

5-2   **5.** Find the opposit
6. Add: $-3x^2 - 4x$
$\underline{6x^2 + 3x}$

7. Subtract: $-4x^2$
$\underline{-2x^2}$

8. Simplify: $(4x + 2$

5-3   Simplify. Then evalu
9. $(3^2)(-x)(x^2)$

5-4   Simplify.
11. $(2xy^2)^3$

5-5   **13.** Multiply: $(3x)(x^3$
14. Simplify: $x - 5($

5-6   Multiply.
15. $(3x + 1)$
17. $(x + 1)($

5-7   Expand.
19. $(x - 5)^2$

5-8   Solve for x
equation is
21. $2x + 6($
22. $(x - 3)4$
23. $x + 2(x$
24. $5(x + 2$

5-9   **25.** The len
perimete

Copyright © 1985 Harper

1. _____ 3

2. _____ Trinomial

3. _____ $x^2 + 5; 9$

Name_____ Date_____ Score_____

CUMULATIVE TEST: CHAPTERS 1–6   Part I

Write the letter for the correct answer.

Chap. 1 **1.** Which of the following is *not* always true for real numbers a, b, and c?
a. If $a = b$ and $b = c$, then $a = c$.   **b.** $a + b = b + a$
c. If $a = b$, then $b = a$.   **d.** $a - (b - c) = (a - b) - c$
e. $a = a$

2. Write $x \cdot x \cdot y \cdot y \cdot y$ in exponential form.
a. $x^2 y^3$ **b.** $(xy)^5$ **c.** $2x + 3y$
d. $2xy^3$ **e.** $5x^2 y^3$

Chap. 2 **3.** Simplify: $6 - (-3) + (-1)$
a. 4   **b.** −10   **c.** 8   **d.** 2   **e.** −8
4. Simplify: $-3b - 4 + 5b - 1$

1. _____ d

2. _____ a

3. _____ c

SOLUTION KEY

Harper & Row ALGEBRA ONE

MAX A. SOBEL

EVAN M. MALETSKY

NORBERT LERNER

LOUIS S. COHEN

CHAPTER TESTS AND CUMULATIVE TESTS (DUPLICATING MASTERS)

These duplicating masters provide independent Chapter Tests and Cumulative Tests that are similar to the independent tests in the Teacher's Edition. Use one set as your regular tests and the other for make-up tests. Or use both sets when you have scheduled more than one class for testing.

SOLUTION KEY

The Solution Key includes step-by-step solutions to exercises and problems in the text. All steps of the solutions are presented in a clear, uncluttered format. Thus, the Solution Key can provide significant help in checking assignments.

PREREQUISITE SKILLS REVIEWS: ERROR ANALYSIS

A Prerequisite Skills Review precedes each chapter of the book. The multiple-choice items on that page are designed to help you determine whether students have the skills necessary for succeeding with the various topics of the chapter. For those students who need further practice with such skills, Follow-Up exercises appear on pages 500–506 of the student's text.

To determine the significance of the errors that students make on the Prerequisite Skills Review pages, consult the analyses below. These indicate some possible reasons for a student's choice of a wrong answer for a given item. Since the analyses concentrate on the incorrect choices, the correct choices are not included. Thus, for item 1 on page 1 of the text, only the incorrect choices **a, c,** and **d** are presented and some possible errors indicated. The correct choice, **b,** is not included below; however, it is given as an annotation on page 1.

It is hoped that by referring to the following analyses, you may be able to help students who are having significant difficulties. Often, a few minutes of your timely assistance can make the difference between satisfactory and unsatisfactory performance by a student.

Page 1

1. **a.** Student failed to regroup 18 as $17\frac{3}{3}$; treated $\frac{1}{3}$ as in an addition example and subtracted 5 from 17.
   c. Student treated $\frac{1}{3}$ as in an addition example and subtracted 5 from 18.
   d. Student failed to deduct 1 from 18 when regrouping; used $18\frac{3}{3}$ instead of $17\frac{3}{3}$.
2. **a.** Student added denominators.
   b. Student added numerators and added denominators.
   c. Student added numerators and multiplied denominators.
3. **a.** Student multiplied both numerator and denominator by 7.
   b. Student multiplied the denominator by 7.
   d. Student added 7 and $\frac{2}{3}$; may have difficulty in distinguishing between addition and multiplication.
4. **a.** Student multiplied numerators but added denominators.
   c. Student added numerators and added denominators.
   d. Student added $\frac{1}{2}$ and $\frac{1}{4}$ instead of multiplying them.
5. Student positioned the decimal point incorrectly.
   a. Student may have divided by 100.
   c. Student may have divided by 1.
   d. Student may have multiplied by 10.
6. **b.** Student confused 1 with 0.01, and also incorrectly regrouped (or "borrowed from") the 4.

   c. Student did not recognize that $1 = 1.0$ and aligned the 1 under the 7 in 4.7.
   d. Student may have confused 1 with 0.01.
7. A common error is to overlook the word *not* in the directions. Choices **a, c,** and **d** might be made if the student overlooked that key word. Other possible sources of error are indicated below.

   a. Student failed to recognize that both terms of $\frac{5}{7}$ were divided by 10 to obtain $\frac{0.5}{0.7}$; also, may have failed to recognize that dividing both terms of a fraction by the same nonzero number produces an equal fraction.
   c. Student failed to recognize that multiplying both terms of $\frac{5}{7}$ by 20 (or any nonzero number) produces an equal fraction.
   d. Student failed to recognize that dividing both terms of $\frac{5}{7}$ by 7 (or any nonzero number) produces an equal fraction.
8. **a.** Student disregarded the decimal point and divided 3 by 15 $\left(\text{simplified } \frac{3}{15}\right)$.
   c. Student confused "divided by" with "divided into" and divided 0.15 by 0.3.
   d. Student disregarded the decimal point and also confused "divided by" with "divided into." Student divided 15 by 3.
9. **a.** Student moved the decimal point in the wrong direction.
   b. Student may have misunderstood the word *product*; added instead of multiplying.
   d. Student positioned the decimal point incorrectly; multiplied by 100, either through carelessness or lack of understanding.
10. A common error is to overlook the word *not* in the directions. Choices **a, b,** and **c** might be made if the student overlooked that key word.

   Even if a student does not overlook the word *not,* errors are possible. A student may choose **b** or **c,** assuming incorrectly that the numbers in the verbal expression must appear in the same order that they appear in the numerical expression.

Page 43

1. Difficulties may arise from misinterpreting the word *of* and from confusing a number with its reciprocal.
   a. $\frac{1}{9}$ may have been confused with 9. Student may have thought as follows: $\frac{1}{3}$ of $27 = 9$.

b. Student may have made a random guess; choice **b** does not reflect any common error. (Choice **b** is included among the answers because it fits in the pattern of the other choices; choices **b, c,** and **d** are each $\frac{1}{3}$ of the preceding choice.)

c. Student may have decided to find the missing factor by dividing $\frac{1}{9}$ by $\frac{1}{3}$; and then, instead, the student may have divided 9 by 3, or else inverted the first number, thinking as follows: $\frac{1}{9} \div \frac{1}{3} = \frac{9}{1} \cdot \frac{1}{3}$

2. The word *opposite* and the absolute value symbols may be misunderstood or ignored.

  a. Student may have disregarded the word *opposite* and the absolute value symbols.

  b. Student may have disregarded the absolute value symbols and taken the opposite of $(18 - 3)$.

  c. Student neglected to take the opposite of the sum.

3. A common error is to overlook the word *not* in the directions. Choices **a, b,** and **d** might be made if the student overlooked that key word. Other possible sources of error are indicated below.

  a. Student failed to recognize that numerator and denominator were both divided by 10, and, therefore, that the value of the fraction was unchanged.

  b. Student did not realize that 5.6 is the same as 5.60.

  d. Student may not have recognized that the decimal points in 5.6 and 0.02 were both moved 3 places to the right, which means that the numerator and denominator were multiplied by 1000.

4. a. Student may have thought of $6 + \frac{15}{3}$ as equivalent to $\frac{6 + 15}{3}$ and added as follows: $\frac{6 + 15}{3} + \frac{6 + 15}{3} = 7 + 7 = 14.$

  c. Student may have cancelled incorrectly and thought as follows: $\frac{6 + 15}{3} + 6 + \frac{15}{3} = \frac{6 + \overset{5}{\cancel{15}}}{\cancel{3}} + 6 + 5 = 22$ (order of operations error)

  d. Student may have made the same kind of mistake as in **c** above, thinking as follows: $\frac{6 + 15}{3} + 6 + \frac{15}{3} = \frac{\overset{2}{\cancel{6}} + 15}{\cancel{3}} + 6 + 5 = 28$

5. Errors may arise from incorrect grouping or from incorrect order of operations.

  a. Student may have first added $2 + 1$ and thought as follows: $(12 \div 6) \div 3 = \frac{2}{3}$

  c. Student may have thought as follows: $12 \div (6 \div 2 + 1) = 12 \div (3 + 1) = 12 \div 4 = 3$

  d. Student may have thought as follows: $12 \div 6 \div (2 + 1) = 12 \div (6 \div 3) = 12 \div 2 = 6$

6. Student may have overlooked the word *not*. Other possible errors may arise from incorrect grouping or misunderstanding the meaning of an exponent.

a. Student may have thought as follows: $2^4 \cdot 5 = 8 \cdot 5 = 40$

b. Student may have thought as follows: $2^3 \cdot 10 = 6 \cdot 10 = 60$

d. Student may have multiplied only the 210 by $\frac{1}{3}$; that is, student may have treated choice **d** as if it were the same as choice **c**.

7. a. The 6's may have been cancelled, leaving only the 2.

  b. Student may have confused $(0)(2)$ with $(1)(2)$.

  d. $1 \div 2$ may have been interpreted as 2 divided by 1.

8. b. Student may have substituted 0.5 for $\frac{1}{b}$ instead of for b: $\frac{1}{6} + \frac{1}{2} = \frac{2}{3}$

  c. Student may have thought of $\frac{1}{a} + \frac{1}{b}$ as $\frac{1}{ab}$: $\frac{1}{6(0.5)} = \frac{1}{3}$

  d. Student may have thought of $\frac{1}{a} + \frac{1}{b}$ as $\frac{1}{a + b}$: $\frac{1}{6 + 0.5} = \frac{1}{6.5} = \frac{2}{13}$

9. a. Student may have confused 0 with 1 and thought $4\left(\frac{1}{4}\right)$ equals the required product.

  b. Student may have thought of $\frac{1}{4}$ as the same as 4.

  c. Student may have ignored the y and substituted 4 for x: $4 - 4 = 0$

10. Student may have overlooked the word *not*. *Other possible errors are indicated below.

  a. Student may have failed to apply the distributive property correctly; computed $5(18) - 8$ instead of $5(18) - 5(8)$.

  b. Student might simply have disregarded the n's and computed $45 - 20$.

  c. Student might have subtracted n from n, leaving 26 by itself; that is, student might have thought of $26n - n$ as $26 + n - n$.

Page 83

1. b. Student correctly found the number 124, then incorrectly thought "124 is one-half of what?" and multiplied 124 by 2.

  c. Student misread the problem and multiplied $5 \cdot 620$, then multiplied by $\frac{1}{2}$. Student may also have made a mistake in multiplying $5 \cdot 620$, forgetting to "carry" the 1.

  d. Same error as for **c** except that there was no mistake in "carrying"

2. a. Student made error in multiplying 4.8 by 4.

  c. The $\frac{1}{2}$ was disregarded, and 2.4 was multiplied by 4.

  d. Student multiplied $\frac{1}{2} \cdot 2.4$, then multiplied by 4.

---

* In subsequent Prerequisite Skills Reviews, there are other questions in which the student may overlook the word *not*. Be alert for recognizing students who frequently make this type of error.

3. b. The student forgot to multiply $-\frac{1}{2}$ by $-\frac{1}{3}$ and just multiplied $-\frac{1}{2}$ by -1:

$$\frac{1}{6} - \frac{5}{3} + \frac{1}{2} - \frac{1}{6} - \frac{10}{6} + \frac{3}{6} - \frac{-6}{6} - -1$$

c. The student first subtracted $\frac{1}{3}$ from $\frac{1}{6}$ and thought as follows:

$$\left(\frac{1}{6} - \frac{1}{3}\right)\left(5 - \frac{1}{2}\right) = -\frac{1}{6}\left(\frac{9}{2}\right) = -\frac{9}{12} = -\frac{3}{4}$$

d. The student made an error in multiplying two negative numbers and thought as follows:

$$\frac{1}{6} - \frac{5}{3} + \left(-\frac{1}{3}\right)\left(-\frac{1}{2}\right) = \frac{1}{6} - \frac{5}{3} - \frac{1}{6} = -\frac{5}{3}$$

4. a. Error may be due to two multiplication errors:
$4(300) + 6(700) = 700 + 1300 = 2000$

b. Error may be due to one (careless) multiplication error:
$4(300) + 6(700) = 700 + 4200 = 4900$

d. Error may be due to not applying the distributive property:
$4(300) + 6(1000 - 300) = 1200 + 6000 - 300 = 6900$

5. a. Student may have confused the multiplicative properties of 1 and 0, thinking as follows:
$(8 - 8)8 = (0)8 = 8$

b. Student may not have recognized that 1 and 1.00 name the same number.

d. Student may have confused numerator and denominator and thought that $\frac{0}{5}$ is undefined.

6. The student may have made errors in computing with signed numbers or in applying the distributive property.

a. $3(-4) - 8$ might have been computed as $-12 - 8 = -4$ or as $12 - 8 = 4$.

c. $(6 - x)$ might have been evaluated as 2 rather than as 10; or $-2(6 - x)$ might have first been simplified as $-12 - x$ or as $-12 - 2x$.

d. $3 + (-4)$ might have been simplified incorrectly, or $20(3 + x)$ might have been simplified as $60 + x$.

7. a. $(-8)\left(-\frac{1}{8}\right)$ might have been evaluated as -1.

c. Possible cancellation error, such as $\dfrac{3(5) - 2(5)}{5} = -7$

d. $\left(3\frac{1}{2}\right)\left(\frac{2}{7}\right)$ might have been computed as $3\dfrac{1 \cdot 2}{2 \cdot 7} = 3\frac{1}{7}$.

8. Instead of correctly evaluating the given expression $\left(\dfrac{6}{4 - n} = \dfrac{6}{4 - 4.5} = \dfrac{6}{-0.5} = -12\right)$, the student might have made a mistake in sign $(4 - 4.5 = 0.5)$ or may have confused division by 0.5 with multiplication by 0.5.

a. Error in sign and in division

b. Error in division only

c. Error in sign only

9. a. Student confused $\frac{4}{3}n + \frac{2}{3}$ with $\frac{4n}{3} + \frac{2n}{3}$.

b. Student made a random guess.

c. Student did not apply the distributive property.

10. a. Student did not apply the distributive property.

c. Student was unable to simplify $\frac{3}{4}(8x)$.

d. Student combined $12 - 8x$ as if it were $12x - 8x$, and then multiplied $4x$ by $\frac{3}{4}$.

Page 123

1. b. Student made error in sign or thought:
$$\frac{2}{3} - 1 = \frac{2}{3} - \frac{3}{3} = -\frac{1}{3}$$

c. In simplifying $\frac{2}{3}(2) - 1$, the student may have subtracted the 1 from the 2.

d. Possible error in cancelling; student might have thought of the factor 2 as if it were in the denominator.
$$\frac{\cancel{2}}{3}(\cancel{2}) - 1 = \frac{1}{3} - 1 = -\frac{2}{3}$$

2. All incorrect choices result from errors in sign. Possible errors in thinking are shown below.

a. $-6 + 1 = 5$

c. $-\frac{3}{4}(8) = 6$. Then $6 + 1 = 7$.

d. $-6 + 1 = -7$

3. a. The expression $-\dfrac{3 - 1}{5 - 2}$ might have been mistaken for $\dfrac{-3 - 1}{-5 - 2}$. Then this error would have been followed by an error in dividing a negative number by a negative number.

b. In the expression $\dfrac{-3 - (-1)}{5 - (-2)}$, the numerator $-3 - (-1)$ might have been simplified as $-3 - 1$.

c. Error in dividing a negative number by a negative number

4. a. Student may have substituted 4 (instead of -4) for b.

b. The a's may have been incorrectly cancelled.

c. Student may have made an error in sign in simplifying $\dfrac{7}{-1}$, or student may have made an error in adding $3 + (-4)$ in the denominator.

5. Errors in computing with signed numbers may account for all wrong choices.

a. Student may have thought as follows: $\dfrac{-2}{-2} = -1$

b. Student may have thought as follows: $\dfrac{-2}{4} = -\dfrac{1}{2}$

d. Student may have thought as follows: $\dfrac{-3}{-2} = -\dfrac{3}{2}$

6. a. The question could have been hastily read, as if $-\frac{1}{2}$ were the solution to the equation.

b. The equation $\dfrac{x - 1}{-4} = -\dfrac{1}{2}$ could have been solved incorrectly (with an error in sign) as student multiplied each side by -4: $x - 1 = -2$; $x = -1$

c. Error similar to the one described for **b** except that another error could have been made in the next step: $x - 1 = -2$; $x = -2 - 1$; $x = -3$

7. Errors in multiplying or adding signed numbers account for all wrong choices.

 a. $3(-2) - 5 = 6 - 5 = 1$ [Student may have thought that $3(-2)$ was 6.]

 b. $-6 - 5 = -1$

 c. $-6 - 5 = 11$ (Student may have thought two negatives make a positive.)

8. a. In solving $-2x = 14$, student divided by 2 or else made an error in sign when dividing 14 by -2.

 c. Student solved the equation $-2x + 5 = 14$.

 d. Student substituted 0 for x instead of substituting 0 for y.

9. a. Student solved for $-s$ instead of for s.

 b. Student may have thought of $r - s$ as if it were $s - r$, or student may have made two further errors, first in "putting r on the other side" of the equation and then in solving for $-s$ instead of solving for s.

 d. Student treated $r - s$ as if it were multiplication, $r(-s)$, then divided by r and took the opposite of $2/r$.

10. b. Student made an error in sign, perhaps computing $6 - 10$ as 4; or, student may have divided -4 by -2 and obtained -2.

 c. Student added 10 instead of -10 to the right side of the equation, then made an error in dividing by -2.

 d. Student added 10 instead of -10 to the right side of the equation.

Page 165

1. a. $(-2)^5$ was treated as $5(-2)$; also, student made an error in sign in multiplying.

 b. $(-2)^5$ was treated as $5(-2)$.

 c. Student made an error in sign in computing an odd power of a negative number.

2. a. Error in sign, in multiplying $-5(9)$, or in squaring -3

 c. The exponent was treated as a factor: $2(-5)(-3) = 30$

 d. Error similar to the one described for **c** but with an error in sign in multiplication too

3. a. Student computed $3(0.1)$ instead of $(0.1)^3$.

 b. Student may have misread question as $(0.1)^2$ or may have made a mistake in multiplication with decimals.

 d. Student made a mistake in multiplication with decimals.

4. a. Student evaluated $[4(-2)]^2$ as 16 and then computed $16 - 8$.

 b. Student evaluated $[4(-2)]^2$ as -16 and then computed $-16 - 8$.

d. Student evaluated $[4(-2)]^2$ as -64 and then computed $-64 - 8$.

5. a. The base may have been taken as $\frac{1}{5}(-5)$. Then $\left[\frac{1}{5}(-5)\right]^3 = (-1)^3 = -1$.

 b. The exponent 3 may have been treated as a factor: $3\left(\frac{1}{5}\right)(-5) = -3$

 d. Student made an error in sign in computing an odd power of a negative number.

6. a. Student may have computed $12 + 8 + \frac{1}{3} - \frac{1}{3}$.

 b. The parentheses may have been disregarded, and the expression simplified as $12(8) + \frac{1}{3} - \frac{1}{3}$; then $12(8)$ was incorrectly multiplied, without "carrying."

 c. Error similar to the one described for **b** except that the multiplication was correct.

7. a. The base may have been taken as $3(3)$, with the expression simplified as $3 - [3(3)]^2 = 3 - 81 = -78$.

 c. The exponent was probably treated as a factor: $3 - 2(3)(3) = 3 - 18 = -15$

 d. Student used incorrect order of operations. The expression may have been regarded as $(3 - 3)(3)^2 = 0(9) = 0$.

8. Errors in combining like terms may account for all wrong choices.

 a. The coefficients 3 and 4 were multiplied instead of added.

 c. Distributive property was not applied. Common variable factors were multiplied.

 d. The terms $3x$ and $4x$ were multiplied instead of being added.

9. b. Student treated $3 \cdot x \cdot x$ as if it were $3 \cdot x \cdot x \cdot x$.

 c. Student treated $5 \cdot x \cdot x \cdot x$ as if it were $5 \cdot x \cdot x$.

 d. Student did not recognize like terms or understand how they are combined. The variables of all the terms were multiplied and all coefficients were added.

10. a. The coefficients of the terms $5x^2$ and $2x^2$ were multiplied instead of added.

 b. Error similar to the one described for **a**. Also, the distributive property was not applied.

 c. The distributive property was not applied.

11. a. Several confusions would account for this answer. The 5 and -10 were added to get the coefficient -5. The common factor a "disappeared." The b did not "disappear."

 b. The terms were treated as if they were like terms: $5ab$ and $-10ab$.

 c. The terms were multiplied, though no multiplication was indicated.

12. a. The common factors xy were regarded as separate terms, "disappearing" as if they were $xy - xy$.

   b. The factor x was ignored or treated as the separate terms $x - x$.

   c. The expression $5xy - 7xy + 4y$ may have been regarded as $5x + 5y - 7x - 7y + 4y$. Then the student may have simplified the expression as $-2xy + 2y$ and factored it. The student may have difficulty in distinguishing between multiplication and addition.

13. a. The phrase "more than" was interpreted as "times": x was multiplied by $5(2x)$.

   c. For the length, the 5 was subtracted from $2x$ rather than added to it.

   d. The width x and the length $2x + 5$ were multiplied, but the distributive property was disregarded.

Page 203

1. b. Student made error in sign in multiplying $-2(-9x)$.

   c. Student looked at the equal sign as if it indicated multiplication.

   d. Student confused multiplication with addition and also tried to combine unlike terms, as if $-2(-16x)$ were $-2x - 16x$.

2. a. Student may have misread r^3t as r^2t or may not understand exponents.

   c. Student treated the exponent 3 as a factor.

   d. Student was careless in handling the factor t.

3. a. Student computed $6^2 + 3^2$ as $12 + 9$.

   c. Student tried to follow the rule for squaring a binomial but computed the middle term as $(6)(3)$ instead of $2(6)(3)$.

   d. Student distributed an exponent over the terms of a polynomial and decided that 0 must be the missing number.

4. a. Student distributed an exponent over the terms of a polynomial.

   b. Error similar to the one described for **a** except that the student may have thought $(-1)^2 = 1^2$ for the second term

   c. For the term -9, the student forgot to double the product of the two terms 9 and -1.

5. a. Student made error in sign in multiplying $3x$ and $-x$.

   c. The 3 and 5 were added instead of multiplied.

   d. The 3 was carelessly forgotten in multiplying $3x$ and $-x$.

6. a. The initial minus sign was applied only to $-y$. (The distributive property, or the opposite of a polynomial, was misapplied.)

   b. Writing the terms in a different order was mistaken for taking the opposite of the binomial.

   d. The initial minus sign was applied to the x only, as if no parentheses were there.

7. a. The student made an error in sign in multiplying -2 and $-y$.

   b. The student made an error in sign in multiplying -2 and $-y$; also, the $-5y$ was ignored.

   c. The distributive property was incorrectly applied, and the y's were regarded as $-y - (-y) = 0$.

8. Errors probably arose from rewriting the given expression incorrectly before substituting.

   b. The expression may have been rewritten as $x^2 - 2 - 2x - 2$.

   c. The student may have incorrectly factored out the $(x - 2)$ and obtained $(x - 2)x - 2$ instead of $(x - 2)(x - 2)$.

   d. The expression may have been rewritten as $x^2 - 2 - 2x + 2$.

9. Each error could have been caused by the student failing to check the middle term with the inner and outer products, or by computing the sum of these products incorrectly.

10. Each error could have been caused by the student failing to check the middle term with the inner and outer products. The sum of the inner and outer products was computed incorrectly if an incorrect choice was made.

11. All errors may have involved multiplying two negative numbers incorrectly. Student may have evaluated $-6x$ incorrectly when x is negative.

   b. $-6(-1) = -6$

   c. $-6(-1) = -6$, also $-6(-5) = -30$

   d. $-6(-5) = -30$

12. a. Student may have made a careless error or perhaps checked only the first of the two given numbers.

   b. Error similar to the one described for **a**.

   c. Student may not have looked at choice **d** and may not have recalled (from choice **b**) that -6 was a solution too.

13. a. Student may have subtracted coefficients and subtracted exponents: $5x^3 - x^2 = 4x$. Then $2x(4x) = 8x^2$.

   b. $5x^3 - x^2$ might have been treated as $5x^3 \div x^2$, or $5x$.

   d. Multiplication by $2x$ was not distributed; the grouping symbols were disregarded.

Page 253

1. a. Student has no knowledge of the coordinate plane.

   b. Student has no knowledge of the coordinate plane.

   c. Student may think that since x is 0, the point is on the x-axis.

2. All wrong choices indicate either that the student has forgotten how the quadrants are numbered or has difficulty remembering how points are located in the plane.

3. a. Student may not be able to identify the slope of a line. In particular, student may not realize that $y = 0$ is an equation for the x-axis.
   b. Error similar to the one described for **a.**
   d. Student may have difficulty distinguishing between the graphs for $x = k$ and $y = k$.

4. a. Student may not realize that $x = 0$ is an equation for the y-axis.
   b. Student may have difficulty distinguishing between the graphs for $x = k$ and $y = k$.
   c. Error similar to the one described for **a.**

5. b. Student may have subtracted x-values and y-values in an inconsistent order.
   c. Student may have added the x-values instead of subtracting them; also, may have been inconsistent in the order of subtraction.
   d. Student may have added the x-values instead of subtracting them.

6. a. Student probably made a random guess.
   b. Student may have used $y = mx + b$ form of equation but forgotten to divide by 2 after writing $2y = -3x + 6$.
   d. Student may have confused $y = -3$ with $y = -3x$.

7. b. Student confused slope and y-intercept.
   c. Student forgot to divide by 3.
   d. Student forgot to take the opposite of each side of the equation (or to multiply by -1).

8. a. Student may have overlooked the negative sign in the -1 slope.
   b. Student may have rewritten $y - x = 5$ as $y = -x + 5$.
   c. Student confused the slope and the y-intercept.

9. a. Student may have substituted incorrectly, interchanging the x- and y-values.
   c. Error similar to the one described for **a.**
   d. Student may have made a random guess.

10. a. Student may have substituted 4 (rather than -4) for y.
   b. Student may have substituted -3 (rather than 3) for x.
   d. The x- and y-values may have been interchanged.

11. b. The x- and y-values may have been interchanged.
   c. The x- and y-values may have been interchanged.
   d. Student may not understand that $y = 4$ is satisfied by any ordered pair $(x, 4)$.

12. a. The slope may have been computed as $\frac{2}{-6} = -\frac{1}{3}$, or else the student may have divided the x-differences by the y-differences.

b. The meaning of the y-intercept may not be understood.
   c. The slope-intercept form of a linear equation may not be understood.

Page 285

1. b. Student may have multiplied both the numerator and the denominator of $\frac{4}{3}$ by 3 and obtained the false statement $\frac{12}{9} = 4$.
   c. Student may have multiplied both the numerator and the denominator of $\frac{3}{4}$ by 8 and obtained the false statement $\frac{24}{32} = 2(3)$.
   d. Student may have multiplied both the numerator and the denominator of $\frac{a}{b}$ by 4 and obtained the false statement $\frac{4a}{4b} = \frac{4a}{b}$.

2. a. Student may have simplified denominator incorrectly:
   $$\frac{9 - 6}{2 - (-1)} = \frac{3}{1} = 3$$
   b. Student may have "cancelled" the 6's: $\frac{\cancel{6} - 1}{\cancel{6}} = -1$
   d. Student may have disregarded the parentheses:
   $$\frac{5(-2)}{2(-5)} = \frac{5 - 2}{2 - 5} = \frac{3}{-3} = -1$$

3. a. Student may have misread the directions (failed to notice the word *not*), or student may have made a careless error in arithmetic.
   b. The student might have divided 1.6 by 2 and obtained 0.8 but then not realized that this was equal to $\frac{4}{5}$.
   c. Student may have been puzzled by the form of this complex fraction and simplified it incorrectly.

4. a. Student may have confused 0 and 1, and evaluated the denominator incorrectly: $2\left(\frac{1}{2}\right) = 0$
   b. Student may have thought that a fraction is undefined if the numerator is 0.
   d. $\dfrac{\frac{1}{2}}{\frac{1}{2} - 1}$ may have looked strange to the student and may have been chosen as a guess.

5. a. Student may have forgotten to look for a common factor.
   b. Student may have forgotten how to factor the difference of two squares or may not have recognized that 1 is the square of a whole number.
   d. Student probably misread the direction line.

6. a. Student may not have recognized that this is *not* a factored form.
   c. Student made a random guess since the product does not check with the $2x$ or the -15 in $x^2 + 2x - 15$.

d. Student made an error in sign in adding inner and outer products.

7. a. Student factored 2 rather than -2 from the last term, -18.

    b. Student factored -2 from the first term, $-2x^2$, but left the other terms unfactored.

    d. Student factored 2 rather than -2 from the last two terms of the trinomial.

8. The use of *not* and *opposite* in the directions may cause difficulties for students.

    a. Student probably misread the directions or missed the word *not*.

    b. Student may have misread the directions or may see $5 - x$ and $x - 5$ as equivalent.

    d. The student may have read $-(x - 5)$ as $-x - 5$.

9. a. Student may have forgotten how to multiply a binomial by a binomial.

    b. Error similar to the one described for **a.**

    c. Student forgot to find either the product of the outer terms or the product of the inner terms.

Page 321

1. a. Student may have substituted 9 instead of -9 for x, then cancelled incorrectly, dividing 3 into 6:

$$\frac{\overset{2}{6} - 9}{\cancel{3}} = -7$$

    b. Student may have substituted 9 for x:

$$\frac{6 - 9}{3} = \frac{-3}{3} = -1$$

    d. Student may have cancelled incorrectly:

$$\frac{6 - (-9)}{3} = \frac{6 + \overset{3}{\cancel{9}}}{\cancel{3}} = 9$$

2. a. Student may have made a careless error, ignoring the negative sign, or student may have made an error in sign in multiplying a negative number and a positive number.

    c. Student multiplied by 7 rather than by $\frac{1}{7}$ and also made an error in sign.

    d. Student multiplied by 7 rather than by $\frac{1}{7}$.

3. a. Student may have multiplied both the numerator and the denominator of $\frac{2}{3}$ by 45 and obtained the false statement $\frac{90}{135} = 15(2)$.

    b. Student did not apply the distributive property correctly or did not compute $9\left(\frac{1}{3}\right)$ correctly.

    c. Student may have multiplied both the numerator and the denominator of $\frac{a}{2}$ by 10 and obtained the false statement $\frac{10a}{20} = 5a$.

4. a. The factor 2 was probably not noticed.

c. The factor 2 may have been cancelled with the denominator $x + 2$.

d. The factor 2 was considered to be the same as an exponent 2; $\frac{2(x + 2)(3x)}{x + 2}$ was interpreted as $3x^2$.

5. b. The distributive property was not applied. Student may have thought as follows:

$$6\left(\frac{5x - 2}{3}\right) = 2(5x - 2) = 10x - 2$$

    c. Student may have thought as follows:

$$6\left(\frac{5x - 2}{3}\right) = 6\left(\frac{5x}{3}\right) - \frac{2}{3} = 10x - \frac{2}{3}$$

    d. In cancelling, student may have placed the factor 2 in the denominator:

$$\cancel{6}\left(\frac{5x - 2}{\underset{2}{\cancel{3}}}\right) = \frac{5x - 2}{2}$$

6. a. The student may first have subtracted the 3 from the 9, and also ignored the negative sign:

$$\frac{(9 - 3)\left(\frac{1}{3}\right)}{2} = \frac{2}{2} = 1$$

    b. Error similar to the one described for **a** except that the negative sign was not ignored.

    c. The negative sign was probably not noticed.

7. a. Student may have ignored the third number (8) and simply found the least common multiple of 3 and 4: $3 \times 4 = 12$

    c. 4 and 8 were multiplied.

    d. 3, 4 and 8 were multiplied, yielding a common multiple but not the least common multiple.

8. a. Student chose a common factor rather than a common multiple.

    b. The need to have the factor $(x + 3)$ occur twice in the common multiple was not understood, or perhaps the expressions $(x + 3)^2$ and $2(x + 3)$ were considered equivalent.

    d. Student chose the product of the given expressions; failed to realize that this common multiple was not the least common multiple.

9. b. The need to have $(x - 2)$ occur twice as a factor may not have been understood.

    c. The numerators were multiplied to get the least common multiple of the numerator, not the denominator.

    d. The denominators were added.

10. b. Student did not cancel correctly and misapplied the distributive property.

    c. Student may have ignored the denominator 3 and misapplied the distributive property.

    d. Student made an arithmetical error in applying the distributive property.

1. a. Either the direction line or the inequality symbol was misunderstood.
  c. Student may have compared the denominators rather than the fractions.
  d. Student may not understand the decimal system or may have misunderstood the inequality symbol.

2. b. Student may have misread the direction and thought that the numbers should decrease from left to right.
  c. Student made a random guess.
  d. Student probably ignored the decimal points.

3. a. Student may have interpreted or read the absolute value symbols as parentheses.
  b. Error similar to the one described for **a**.
  d. Student may have subtracted incorrectly:
$$\frac{3}{4} - \frac{1}{2} = \frac{3-1}{4-2} = \frac{2}{2} = 1$$
  Then student would have obtained the statement $1 < \frac{1}{2}$ and chosen **d** as the appropriate answer.

4. b. The absolute value symbols may have been ignored. Student may have thought as follows:
$$8 - 2 - 2 - 8 = -4$$
  c. The absolute value symbols may have been regarded as parentheses.
  d. Error similar to the one described for **c** except that student also made an error in sign in computing:
$$(8-2) - (2-8) = 6 - (-10) = 16$$

5. a. $|x| - 3 = 9$ may have been rewritten as $|x| = 6$.
  b. $|x| - 3 = 9$ may have been rewritten as $|x| = \frac{9}{3}$.
  c. The absolute value symbols may have been ignored, and the equation considered as $x - 3 = 9$.

6. a. The $10 - 5y$ may have been mistakenly combined as $5y$, and the student then solved $5y = 3$.
  b. The $10 - 5y$ may have been mistakenly combined as $-5y$, and the student then solved $-5y = 3$.
  d. Student may have ignored the minus sign on the left side of the equation and then rewritten the operation as $5y = -7$.

7. a. Student may have ignored the minus sign on the left side of the equation and then rewritten the equation as $\frac{1}{2}x = 2$.
  c. Error similar to the one described for **a** combined with an error of adding 3 (rather than -3) to the right side of the given equation.
  d. 3, rather than -3, was probably added to the right side of the given equation.

8. a. In solving for y, the student may have forgotten to multiply the term by -1 or may have forgotten about taking the opposite of a polynomial.

c. Student may have forgotten to multiply $3x$ by -1.
  d. Student may have multiplied the left side by -1 but forgotten to multiply the right side by -1.

9. a. Student may have ignored the minus sign on the left side of the equation.
  b. Student may have correctly simplified the equation to $2x - y = 6$ and to $2x = 6 + y$ and then carelessly thought that this equation was equivalent to $y = 2x + 6$.
  d. Student may have correctly simplified the equation to $y - 2x = -6$ and then carelessly thought that this equation was equivalent to $y = -2x - 6$.

10. a. Student may have made an error in multiplying $(-2)(-3)$, or may have interchanged the x- and y-values in substituting.
  b. Student may have interchanged the x- and y-values in substituting.
  c. Student may have made an error in multiplying $(-2)(-2)$ or may have interchanged the x- and y-values in substituting.

11. Student may have forgotten how to find x- and y-intercepts or may have forgotten what these terms mean.
  a. Student may have substituted -2 for x and obtained $\frac{-2}{2} + y = 1$, which was simplified incorrectly to $y = 0$. Also, the student may have substituted 1 for y and obtained $\frac{x}{2} + 1 = 1$, which was then simplified to $\frac{x}{2} = 0$ and $x = 0$.
  b. Student found y-intercept correctly and may have been careless about the sign in finding the x-intercept.
  d. Student found x-intercept correctly and may have been careless about the sign in finding the y-intercept.

12. a. The student may have checked (3, 5) in the first equation only.
  c. The student may have checked (2, 3) in the first equation only.
  d. The student may have reversed the x- and y-values in substituting in the two equations.

1. Students may make various arithmetical errors in finding the squares of mixed numbers. A common error is to square the whole-number part and square the fraction part and then add.
  b. Student calculated $(2)^2 + \left(\frac{1}{2}\right)^2$ and decided that $4\frac{1}{4} = 6\frac{1}{4}$ is false.
  c. Student calculated $(1)^2 + \left(\frac{2}{3}\right)^2$ and decided that $1\frac{4}{9} = 2\frac{7}{9}$ is false.
  d. Student calculated $(4)^2 + \left(\frac{1}{2}\right)^2$ and decided that $16\frac{1}{4} = 20\frac{1}{4}$ is false.

2. Errors were probably due to thinking of an exponent as a factor.
   a. Student may have calculated $7 \cdot 2 \cdot 10$ and decided that $490 = 140$ is false, or student might have misread the directions and chosen the first true statement (**a**).
   c. Student may have calculated $4 \cdot 2 \cdot 3$ and decided that $48 = 24$ is false.
   d. Student may have calculated $3 \cdot 2 \cdot 3$ and decided that $27 = 18$ is false.

3. a. Student may have forgotten how to move the decimal point in the dividend and the divisor.
   b. Error similar to the one described for **a**.
   d. Student forgot to write the 0 in the quotient after dividing 0 by 8.

4. As in item **3**, student may have forgotten how to move the decimal point in the dividend and the divisor.
   a. Student placed decimal point incorrectly.
   b. Error similar to the one listed in **a**.
   d. Student may simply have ignored the decimal points.

5. a. Student may think that $(0.08)^2 = 0.64$.
   b. Student may have forgotten that $7 = 7^1$.
   c. The exponent may have been thought of as a factor, or $(3r)^4$ may have been interpreted as $3(r^4)$.

6. a. The exponent may have been considered as a factor.
   b. Student may have made an error in sign in calculating an even power of a negative number.
   c. Student may have added exponents.

7. a. Student may have carelessly added the two 5's instead of multiplying them.
   b. Student may have just ignored a 3 in the given expression, or thought that $3 \cdot 10^2$ was the same as $(3 \cdot 10)^2$.
   d. Student may have ignored a 2, or thought that $2 \cdot 15^2 = (2 \cdot 15)^2$.

8. a. Student may have thought of 2 as a factor or may have thought of squaring only one factor in the base.
   b. Student may have forgotten that $5 = 5^1$ or may have added exponents in simplifying $(2^3)^2$.
   d. Student may have read $25 \cdot 10^2$ as $(25 \cdot 10)^2$ or else may have thought of 50^2 as equal to 250.

9. a. Student miscounted the number of times 7 was used as a factor.
   b. Student combined each 2 and 5 into a 10, noted that there were three 10's and three 7's, and thought of the expression as $3(10 \cdot 7) = 3 \cdot 70$.
   c. Student may carelessly have added the 7's.

10. a. The y-values may have been substituted for x.
    c. The coordinates in (2, 9) may have been subtracted instead of subtracting the two x-values.

d. The coordinates in $(-3, 5)$ may have been subtracted instead of subtracting the two x-values.

11. a. The difference of the coordinates in $(0, -2)$ may have been squared.
    c. The difference of x-values, instead of y-values, may have been squared.
    d. The y-values may have been subtracted incorrectly:
    $$[-8 - (-2)]^2 = (-10)^2 = 100$$

Page 433

1. a. Student probably cancelled incorrectly. Division by 2 was not distributed over both terms of the numerator:
   $$\frac{-2 - \overset{0.7}{\cancel{1.4}}}{\cancel{2}} = -2.7$$
   b. Student probably cancelled incorrectly:
   $$\frac{\overset{-1}{\cancel{-2}} - 1.4}{\cancel{2}} = -2.4$$
   d. -2 and -1.4 were incorrectly combined as -1.6.

2. a. Student made error in squaring a negative number: $(-3)^2 = -9$
   b. Careless simplification of $(-3)^2$ as 6.
   d. Student substituted 3 (instead of -3) for x.

3. a. Student probably made a random guess.
   c. Student probably made a random guess.
   d. Student may have made error in squaring $x + 4$: $(x + 4)^2 = x^2 + 4x + 16$. The middle term is not twice the product of x and y.

4. b. Incorrect cancellation: $\dfrac{-\overset{4}{\cancel{8}} + 2\sqrt{22}}{\underset{3}{\cancel{6}}}$
   c. Error in simplifying $64 - (4)(3)(-2)$ as $64 - 24$, or 40.
   d. Errors of **b** and **c** combined.

5. a. Incorrect cancellation: $\dfrac{\overset{3}{\cancel{6}} - 2\sqrt{5}}{\cancel{2}} = 3 - 2\sqrt{5}$
   c. Error in simplifying $\sqrt{20}$ as $2\sqrt{10}$.
   d. Student divided 6 by 2 and ignored the fact that $\sqrt{20}$ must also be divided by 2.

6. a. Student misread question or made a random guess.
   b. Student may have considered only positive values of x.
   c. Student misread question or made a random guess.

7. b. Student probably considered only nonnegative values for x.
   c. Directions may have been misread, with *nonnegative* read as *negative*; also, only positive values for x may have been considered.
   d. Student probably considered only nonnegative values for x.

8. a. The student may have thought only of squaring the two terms, as if $(a + b)^2 = a^2 + b^2$.

b. Student may have divided the product of the two terms by 2 instead of multiplying the product by 2.

c. Student forgot to multiply the product of the two terms by 2.

9. Student may misread the question (ignoring the word *not*) or may not recall the meaning of the term "trinomial square."

a. Student may simply have selected the first choice.

b. Student may have made a random guess.

c. Student may have chosen the trinomial that looks most complicated.

10. **a.** Student may have confused the equal sign in the proportion with a multiplication sign (perhaps thinking of "cross products").

c. Student may have confused division with multiplication.

d. Student may have thought that in a proportion the sum of the means equals the sum of the extremes.

11. **a.** Student solved for n^2, not for n.

c. Instead of multiplying 4 by 2, student may have divided 4 by 2.

d. Student may have confused the exponent 2 with a factor.

Page 475

1. **a.** Student may have confused rationalizing a denominator with taking the reciprocal of a number.

b. Student may have thought only in terms of getting a rational denominator without being concerned about equivalent fractions.

$$\frac{1}{\sqrt{3}} \cdot \frac{1}{\sqrt{3}} = \frac{1}{3} \quad \leftarrow \text{rational denominator}$$

d. Error similar to the one described for **b**; perhaps simply carelessness.

2. **a.** Student confused "reciprocal" with "opposite."

b. Student may have thought of the reciprocal of $\sqrt{2}$ only, and then proceeded incorrectly, as shown below:

$$\text{Reciprocal of } \frac{\sqrt{2}}{2} \text{ is } \frac{1}{\sqrt{2}}.$$

$$\frac{1}{\sqrt{2}} \cdot \frac{1}{2} = \frac{1}{2\sqrt{2}}$$

d. Student may have taken the reciprocal of $\frac{\sqrt{2}}{2}$, simplified, and then taken the reciprocal again; the student may simply have ignored the 2 in the denominator of the given fraction.

3. **a.** Student may have ignored the radical sign.

b. Student may have simplified carelessly after rationalizing the denominator.

d. After rationalizing the denominator and simplifying, the student may have forgotten to cancel the 3 in the denominator.

4. **a.** Student may have chosen the first true statement, overlooking the word *false* in the directions.

b. Student may have ignored the radical sign.

c. Student may have been unable to compare these fractions. Student may not be able to rationalize the denominator.

5. All errors may be due to the student's failure to understand the form of the question. Some students may also fail to realize that $(\sqrt{10})^2 + (3\sqrt{10})^2 = 10 + 9 \cdot 10 = 100$ (and thus $(\sqrt{10})^2 + (3\sqrt{10})^2 = 10^2$).

6. **a.** Student may have thought that $\sqrt{a^2 + b^2} = a + b$, or that $a^2 + b^2 = (a + b)^2$.

b. Student may have regrouped the numbers on the left side as $[(2^2 + 2)\sqrt{3}]^2 = (6\sqrt{3})^2$ and then taken the square root.

d. Student made error in simplifying $\sqrt{16}$.

7. **a.** Student made error in thinking that $a + b = c$ rather than $a^2 + b^2 = c^2$.

c. Student made error in simplifying $\sqrt{45}$ as $5\sqrt{3}$ rather than as $3\sqrt{5}$.

d. Student solved wrong equation: $x^2 = 2^2 + 7^2$

8. **b.** Student may have written as follows:

$$a = \frac{b}{c}$$

$$a \cdot \frac{c}{b} = 1$$

$$\frac{ac}{b} = 1$$

Then student may have *multiplied* the equation by $\frac{a}{b}$ rather than by $\frac{b}{a}$.

c. Student may have subtracted c instead of multiplying by c in the first step:

$$a = \frac{b}{c}$$

$$a - c = b$$

$$-c = b - a$$

$$c = a - b$$

d. Student may have solved $a = \frac{c}{b}$ instead of $a = \frac{b}{c}$.

9. **a.** In combining fractions, the student added the denominators.

b. $a^2 + b^2$ was considered as equivalent to $(a + b)^2$.

c. Error similar to the one described for **a** except that c^2 was substituted for $a^2 + b^2$:

$$\frac{a^2 + b^2}{2c^2} = \frac{c^2}{2c^2} = \frac{1}{2}$$

T29

CHAPTER 1 TEST

1-1 Simplify.

    1. $30 - 5 \times 4$ **2.** $\dfrac{10 - (6 - 1)}{6 - (4 + 1)}$

1-2 Evaluate. Let $x = 3$ and $y = 4$.

    3. $\dfrac{4x - 2y}{y}$ **4.** $x + y \div 2$

1-3   **5.** xy^2 **6.** $(xy)^2 - y$

    7. Write in exponential form: $x \cdot x \cdot x \cdot x \cdot y \cdot y \cdot y$

1-4 Write an algebraic expression for each phrase. Use a as the variable.

    8. 6 times a certain number that has been decreased by 5

    9. 4 more than a number which is divided by 3

1-5   **10.** Which number, 5 or 6, is a solution of $2x - 5 = 7$?

1-6 Using n as a variable, write an equation for each problem. Then solve it.

    11. 12 decreased by a certain number is 8. Find the number.

    12. A \$50 prize is shared equally by 8 winners. How much did each receive?

1-7   **13.** For what whole-number values of n does $\dfrac{7}{n}$ represent a whole number?

    14. Name the first three consecutive even integers greater than 9.

1-8 Give the opposite of each number.

    15. $^-2\dfrac{1}{2}$ **16.** 0

1-9   **17.** List the integers 6, $^-3$, 0, and 3 in order, from least to greatest.

    Use $<$, $>$, or $=$ to make each sentence true.

    18. $^-3 \underline{\ ?\ } ^-8$ **19.** $^-5^2 \underline{\ ?\ } (^-5)^2$

    20. $3(8 - 1) \underline{\ ?\ } 3(6 + 1)$

1. _____
2. _____
3. _____
4. _____
5. _____
6. _____
7. _____
8. _____
9. _____
10. _____
11. _____
12. _____
13. _____
14. _____
15. _____
16. _____
17. _____
18. _____
19. _____
20. _____

CHAPTER 1 TEST (continued)

1-10   **21.** Simplify: $|{}^-7| - |3|$

       22. Try ${}^-2$, ${}^-1$, 0, 1, and 2. Which are solutions to $|x| = 1$?

1-11   Match each equation with the property it illustrates.

       23. $5x + 2y = 2y + 5x$

       24. $(a + b) + c = a + (b + c)$

       25. $xy = yx$

a. Associative property for addition
b. Associative property for multiplication
c. Commutative property for addition
d. Commutative property for multiplication

21. _____

22. _____

23. _____

24. _____

25. _____

CHAPTER 2 TEST

2-1   Find each sum.

        1. $-7 + (-12)$ **2.** $20 + (-8)$ **3.** $12 + (-15)$

2-2   **4.** Is the solution of $x + (-15) = 0$ positive, negative, or zero?

        5. Evaluate $-a + (-b)$ if $a = 5$ and $b = -3$.

2-3   Simplify.

        6. $-7 - (-5)$ **7.** $16 - (-4)$ **8.** $2 - (-4) + (-3)$

        9. Evaluate $-a - b$ if $a = -1$ and $b = -2$.

2-4   Use the distributive property to rewrite each expression.

        10. $8(x + 5)$ **11.** $4(x + y + z)$

2-5   **12.** Tell whether the terms $5n$ and $-2n$ are similar.

        Simplify, if possible.

2-6   **13.** $6a - 3 - 2a + 4$ **14.** $3a - 4 + 2b$ **15.** $5(n + 3) - 3n + 1$

        Multiply.

        16. $7(-8)$ **17.** $(-3)(2)(-5)$

        Evaluate when $x = -2$.

        18. $2x^3$ **19.** $(x - 2)^2$

2-7   **20.** Simplify $3 - (x - 5)$. Then evaluate for $x = -2$.

        21. Simplify. Write without parentheses or brackets.
           $-[-x + (y - z)]$

2-8   **22.** Divide: $\dfrac{-135}{-3}$

        23. Simplify: $\dfrac{(-5) + (-3)}{(-2) + 6}$

        24. Evaluate $\dfrac{xy}{2x}$ when $x = 3$ and $y = 6$.

2-9   **25.** Compound A weighs 36 grams per cubic centimeter. Compound B weighs 4 times as much as compound A, and compound C weighs 5 times more than compound A. Find the weights of compound B and compound C.

1. _____
2. _____
3. _____
4. _____
5. _____
6. _____
7. _____
8. _____
9. _____
10. _____
11. _____
12. _____
13. _____
14. _____
15. _____
16. _____
17. _____
18. _____
19. _____
20. _____
21. _____
22. _____
23. _____
24. _____
25. _____

CHAPTER 3 TEST

3-1   **1.** Write a formula for this geometric relationship:
The volume, V, of a cylinder is π times the square of the radius, r, times the height, h.

Solve each equation.

3-2   **2.** $x + 4 = 13$ **3.** $x + (-5) = -3$ **4.** $y + (-6) = 1$

3-3   **5.** $y - 7 = 18$ **6.** $x + 6 = -2.5$ **7.** $y - 3.5 = 1.2$

3-4   **8.** $4x = -32$ **9.** $3x = 2.85$ **10.** $\frac{3}{5}y = -21$

3-5   **11.** $-7x = 28$ **12.** $\frac{x}{9} = 18$ **13.** $-5x = -62.5$

3-6   **14.** $11x - 3 = 41$ **15.** $8x - 36 = 60$ **16.** $\frac{x}{2} + 5 = 2$

Use an equation to find the number.

17. 14 times a certain number n is 7.

18. Double some number n and add 10 to get 36.

3-7   Solve each equation.

19. $3n = n + 8$ **20.** $5(x - 3) = -5$ **21.** $\frac{2n}{5} + 2 = 8$

Use an equation to solve each problem.

22. 5 times the sum of some number and 11 is 40. Find the number.

23. When a number is increased by 4 and the result is tripled, the final result is equal to 18. What is the number?

3-8   **24.** Robert is 4 years younger than Maria. Together their ages add to 32. How old is Maria?

25. Find two consecutive integers such that 2 times the first, diminished by the second, is equal to 24.

1. _____

2. _____

3. _____

4. _____

5. _____

6. _____

7. _____

8. _____

9. _____

10. _____

11. _____

12. _____

13. _____

14. _____

15. _____

16. _____

17. _____

18. _____

19. _____

20. _____

21. _____

22. _____

23. _____

24. _____

25. _____

CHAPTER 4 TEST

4-1 Write the coordinates of each point.

1. A
2. B
3. C
4. D
5. E

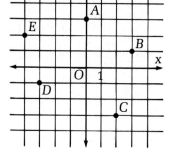

4-2 6. In which quadrant are both coordinates negative?

7. In which quadrant does the point $(-3, 5)$ lie?

8. Which axis is made up of all points with an x-coordinate of 0?

4-3 9. Is $(3, -9)$ a solution of the equation $y = -2x - 3$?

10. Is $(-4, -3)$ a point on the graph of $x - y = 7$?

4-4 11. Find the slope of the line that passes through $(-5, 2)$ and $(2, -7)$.

12. Find the slope of the line that passes through $(-1, 0)$ and $(1, 2)$.

4-5 13. Find the x- and y-intercepts of the line $x - 2y = 10$.

14. The x-intercept of a line is 5. The y-intercept is -2. Find the slope of the line.

4-6 15. Find the slope and the y-intercept of the equation $y = 3x - 5$.

16. Write the equation $3x + y = 7$ in slope-intercept form.

4-7 17. Write, in slope-intercept form, an equation of the line that has a slope of 2 and contains the point $(1, 4)$.

18. Write, in slope-intercept form, an equation of the line that has the same slope as $x - y = -3$ and that contains the origin.

4-8 19. Write the equation $y = \frac{1}{2}x + 1$ in standard form.

20. Write the equation $x + 3y = 15$ in slope-intercept form.

21. Write the equation of the line that passes through $(0, 4)$ and $(6, 1)$.

1. _____
2. _____
3. _____
4. _____
5. _____
6. _____
7. _____
8. _____
9. _____
10. _____
11. _____
12. _____
13. _____
14. _____
15. _____
16. _____
17. _____
18. _____
19. _____
20. _____
21. _____

CHAPTER 4 TEST (continued)

4-9   **22.** Write the equation of the horizontal line passing through $(5, -7)$.

22. _____

23. Write the equation of the line passing through $(3, 7)$ and $(3, -4)$.

23. _____

Graph each equation. Use the coordinate axes that are provided.

24. $y = 3x - 2$

25. $2x + y = 3$

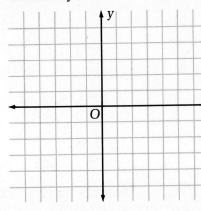

CHAPTER 5 TEST

5-1 **1.** Simplify. Then give the degree of the polynomial.
$5x^3 - 3x^2 + 2x - 5x^3$

2. Identify $6x^2y - 1$ as a monomial, a binomial, or a trinomial.

Simplify each polynomial. Then evaluate for $x = 3$.

3. $3x^3 + 5x^2 - x^3 - x^2 + x$
4. $3x^4 + 2x^2 - 2x^4 - x^2 - x^4$

5-2 **5.** Find the opposite of $-a + b$

6. Add. $\begin{array}{r} -5x^2 + 3xy - y^2 \\ 8x^2 - 2xy + y^2 \end{array}$

7. Subtract. $\begin{array}{r} -4x^2 + 8x - 3 \\ -5x^2 - 3x + 3 \end{array}$

8. Simplify: $(3x - 7y) - (4x - 2y) + (-x - y)$

5-3 Simplify. Then evaluate when $x = -2$.

9. $(2^2)(x^3)(-x)$ **10.** $(2x)(x^3)(-x)$

5-4 Simplify.

11. $(-x^2y^3)^4$ **12.** $(-2n)(3n^2)^2$

5-5 **13.** Multiply: $(2x)(x^2 - 3x - 1)$
14. Simplify: $5x - 3(2 - x)$

5-6 Multiply.

15. $(2x - 3)(3x - 5)$ **16.** $(3a + 2b)(a - 3b)$
17. $(x - 2)(x^2 - x + 1)$ **18.** $(a + 2)(2a^2 + a - 1)$

5-7 Expand.

19. $(x - 3)^2$ **20.** $(3x - y)^2$

5-8 Solve for x and check. If no solution exists, write **no solution.** If the equation is an identity, write **identity.**

21. $5(x - 3) = 5x + 1$
22. $(x + 1)(x + 2) = x^2 - 1$
23. $(x + 1)^2 - 1 = x(x + 2)$
24. $-(x - 3) - (2 + x) = 7$

5-9 **25.** The width of a rectangle is 3 cm less than the length. The perimeter is 26 cm. Find the area.

1. _____
2. _____
3. _____
4. _____
5. _____
6. _____
7. _____
8. _____
9. _____
10. _____
11. _____
12. _____
13. _____
14. _____
15. _____
16. _____
17. _____
18. _____
19. _____
20. _____
21. _____
22. _____
23. _____
24. _____
25. _____

CHAPTER 6 TEST

6-1   **1.** Write the prime factorization of 288.

        2. Find the GCF of 54 and 63.

6-2   Simplify.

        3. $\dfrac{-60a^5b^3}{12a^2b^2}$ **4.** $\dfrac{-27a^2b^2}{-9a^2b}$

        5. Find the missing factor: $-12x^3 = (4x)(\underline{\ ?\ })$

Factor completely.

6-3   **6.** $15x^5 + 45x^4$ **7.** $-14x^3 + 7x^2 + 21x$

6-4   **8.** $x(x - 3) + (3 - x)$ **9.** $10xy + 25x - 6y - 15$

6-5   **10.** $x^2 - 1$ **11.** $49x^2 - 9y^2$

6-6   **12.** $y^2 - 12y + 36$ **13.** $9x^2 + 12xy + 4y^2$

6-7   **14.** $x^2 - 2x - 35$ **15.** $x^2 - 11x + 24$

Factor completely.

6-8   **16.** $5x^2 + 14x - 3$ **17.** $6x^2 - 33x + 15$

6-9   **18.** $5x^2 - 15x - 20$ **19.** $7x^2 - 28$

6-10   Solve for x.

        20. $x(x - 11) = 0$ **21.** $4x^2 - 1 = 0$

        22. $3x^2 - 17x + 10 = 0$ **23.** $x(x - 3) = (x + 2)(x - 2)$

6-11   **24.** The product of two consecutive even integers is 168. Find the integers.

        25. The length of a rectangle exceeds the width by 3 cm. The area of the rectangle is 54 cm². Find the length and the width.

1. _____
2. _____
3. _____
4. _____
5. _____
6. _____
7. _____
8. _____
9. _____
10. _____
11. _____
12. _____
13. _____
14. _____
15. _____
16. _____
17. _____
18. _____
19. _____
20. _____
21. _____
22. _____
23. _____
24. _____
25. _____

CHAPTER 7 TEST

7-1 Dotormino whothor tho point (3, 1) io a oolution of tho oyotomo of equations.

    1. $x - 3y = 0$ **2.** $x + y = 4$ **3.** $x = 5y - 2$
       $x + 2y = 5$ $x = 3y + 1$ $y = 3x$

Solve each system by graphing.

    4. $x + 2y = 1$ **5.** $x = -3$
       $y = x + 2$ $y = x + 1$

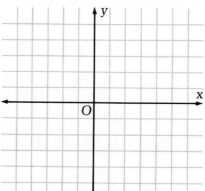

Solve each system.

7-2   **6.** $y = x + 1$ **7.** $y = x - 1$
        $3x + y = 17$ $x + y = 5$

     8. $3x + y = 1$ **9.** $x = 3y + 1$
        $y = x + 5$ $x + y = -7$

Solve each system.

7-3   **10.** $x + y = 6$ **11.** $3x + y = 0$ **12.** $2x - y = -1$
         $x - y = 4$ $-3x + 2y = 9$ $x + y = -5$

7-4   **13.** $3x + y = 1$ **14.** $x - 5y = -2$ **15.** $x = -y + 2$
         $x - 2y = -9$ $-3x + 2y = -7$ $2y + 3x = 9$

7-5   Classify each system as consistent or inconsistent.

    16. $x + 2y = 3$ **17.** $5x - 2y = 4$ **18.** $x + 3y = 5$
        $2x + 4y = 4$ $10x - 4y = 8$ $2x + 3y = 10$

1. _____
2. _____
3. _____
6. _____
7. _____
8. _____
9. _____
10. _____
11. _____
12. _____
13. _____
14. _____
15. _____
16. _____
17. _____
18. _____

CHAPTER 7 TEST (continued)

Select the correct answer.

19. A system is __?__ if it has at least one solution. (consistent, inconsistent)

20. An inconsistent system of equations will graph into __?__ lines. (parallel, intersecting)

21. __?__ equations have different graphs. (dependent, independent)

22. A system of __?__ equations has many solutions. (dependent, independent)

7-6   **23.** Larry is 3 years younger than his brother Peter. The sum of their ages is 31. Find the age of each.

7-7   **24.** Twenty coins in nickels and dimes have a total value of $1.60. How many coins of each type are there?

25. In a two-digit number, the tens digit is 4 more than the units digit. The units digit is half the tens digit. Find the number.

19. _____

20. _____

21. _____

22. _____

23. _____

24. _____

25. _____

CHAPTER 8 TEST

8 1 For what values of x is each expression undefined?

1. $\dfrac{x + 5}{x(x - 3)}$ **2.** $\dfrac{5}{x^2 - x - 30}$ **3.** $\dfrac{x^2 + 5}{x^2 - 25}$

Simplify.

4. $\dfrac{5n^2}{30n^3}$ **5.** $\dfrac{x - 1}{x^2 - 1}$

8-2 **6.** $\dfrac{3 - x}{x^2 - 3x}$ **7.** $\dfrac{x^2 - 7x + 6}{6x - x^2}$

8-3 Multiply. Simplify your answers.

8. $\dfrac{7b}{42a} \cdot \dfrac{a^3}{b^2}$ **9.** $\dfrac{5x^2 - x}{3x} \cdot \dfrac{15x + 3}{25x^2 - 1}$ **10.** $\dfrac{x - 2}{x + 2} \cdot \dfrac{x^2 - 4}{x^2 + 4}$

8-4 Divide and simplify.

11. $\dfrac{16ab^2}{5a^2b^2} \div \dfrac{8a^2}{25ab^3}$ **12.** $\dfrac{2x^2y}{3z^2} \div \dfrac{2xy}{z^3}$ **13.** $\dfrac{x^2 - 3x}{x^2 + 5x} \div \dfrac{x^2 - 9}{x^2 - 25}$

8-5 Divide.

14. $\dfrac{63x^2 - 9x}{9x}$ **15.** $(x^3 - 8x^2 + 14x + 5) \div (x - 5)$

8-6 Add or subtract. Write answers in simplest form.

16. $\dfrac{x^2}{x + 1} + \dfrac{2x + 1}{x + 1}$ **17.** $\dfrac{3x}{9x^2 - 1} - \dfrac{1}{9x^2 - 1}$

Combine and simplify. Where appropriate, write denominators in factored form.

8-7 **18.** $5x + \dfrac{x}{3}$ **19.** $\dfrac{5}{x} - \dfrac{1}{x - 1}$ **20.** $\dfrac{3}{x - 2} + \dfrac{2}{x + 3}$

8-8 **21.** $\dfrac{3}{9x^2 - 1} - \dfrac{1}{3x - 1}$ **22.** $\dfrac{1}{x^2 + 3x + 2} + \dfrac{x}{x + 1}$

8-9 Simplify.

23. $\dfrac{\dfrac{4}{25}}{\dfrac{12}{5}}$ **24.** $\dfrac{4x - \dfrac{1}{x}}{2 + \dfrac{1}{x}}$ **25.** $\dfrac{\dfrac{6}{x - 5}}{\dfrac{-3}{x^2 - 25}}$

1. _____
2. _____
3. _____
4. _____
5. _____
6. _____
7. _____
8. _____
9. _____
10. _____
11. _____
12. _____
13. _____
14. _____
15. _____
16. _____
17. _____
18. _____
19. _____
20. _____
21. _____
22. _____
23. _____
24. _____
25. _____

CHAPTER 9 TEST

Solve and check. Write **no solution** if none exists.

9-1

1. $\dfrac{x}{12} + \dfrac{1}{4} = 1$

2. $\dfrac{2x}{3} - \dfrac{x}{6} = 3$

3. $\dfrac{2}{3}x - \dfrac{5}{2} = \dfrac{1}{4}x + \dfrac{5}{2}$

4. $\dfrac{3x - 2}{4} - \dfrac{x - 5}{2} = 1$

9-2

5. $\dfrac{1}{x} + \dfrac{1}{2x} = 6$

6. $\dfrac{5}{x - 5} = \dfrac{x}{x - 5}$

7. $\dfrac{17}{x} - \dfrac{2}{3} = 5$

8. $\dfrac{6}{x} = 4 - \dfrac{18}{x^2 + 2x}$

9. $\dfrac{-x + 3}{x - 3} = \dfrac{-x}{5}$

10. $\dfrac{5}{x + 2} = \dfrac{3}{x^2 - 4} + \dfrac{2}{x + 2}$

11. $\dfrac{2}{x + 6} = \dfrac{1}{x^2 - 4x} + \dfrac{1}{x + 6}$

12. $\dfrac{x + 1}{x - 1} - \dfrac{1}{x + 2} = \dfrac{51}{x^2 + x - 2}$

9-5 Solve each proportion.

13. $\dfrac{5x}{4} = \dfrac{25}{10}$

14. $\dfrac{x + 5}{3x} = \dfrac{1}{2}$

9-6

15. 8 is 4% of what number?

16. 99 is what percent of 165?

17. Find 7% of 21,300.

18. Find 240% of 160.

9-3

19. The numerator of a fraction is 7 less than 6 times the denominator. If the numerator is decreased by 1, and the denominator is increased by 6, the resulting fraction is equivalent to $\dfrac{1}{2}$. Find the fraction.

9-4

20. If faucets A and B are both opened, an empty tank can be filled in 2.4 hours. If faucet A alone is opened, it will take 4 hours. How long would it take to fill the tank if faucet B alone is opened?

9-5

21. There are 80 members of a school art club. The ratio of the number of boys to the number of girls is 3 : 7. How many boys belong to the club?

1. _____
2. _____
3. _____
4. _____
5. _____
6. _____
7. _____
8. _____
9. _____
10. _____
11. _____
12. _____
13. _____
14. _____
15. _____
16. _____
17. _____
18. _____
19. _____
20. _____
21. _____

CHAPTER 9 TEST (continued)

9-6   **22.** When a roast is cooked, 20% of its original weight is lost. If a roast
       weighs 8 pounds when it is served, what was its original weight?

9-7   **23.** $24,000 is invested at 9% simple interest per year. Find the amount
       of interest paid in 9 months.

9-8   **24.** A mixture of peanuts and cashews weighs 12 pounds. It contains 2
       pounds of cashews. How many pounds of cashews must be added
       to have a mixture that is 25% cashews?

9-9   **25.** Two trains leave the stations in cities A and B and travel toward
       each other along parallel tracks. One train travels 20 miles per hour
       faster than the other. If cities A and B are 630 miles apart, and the
       trains meet after $4\frac{1}{2}$ hours of travel, what is the rate of each train?

22. _____

23. _____

24. _____

25. _____

CHAPTER 10 TEST

10-1 Rewrite each sentence and use an inequality symbol.

    1. x is not more than 7.

    2. x is no less than 0.

Write the inequality for each graph.

  3.   **4.**   **5.**

Solve each inequality. Then graph the solution set on the number line provided.

10-2   **6.** $x - 3 \le 1$

    7. $2(x + 1) < 3(x + 2)$

10-3   **8.** $2x - 3 \ge 3$

    9. $3(x - 1) > 5x - 7$

10-4 **10.** The sum of three consecutive odd integers is greater than 100. Find the set of smallest integers for which this is possible.

    11. Seven times the sum of 11 and three times an integer is less than 245. What is the largest such integer?

10-5 Graph each compound inequality.

    12. $x < -1$ or $x > 1$

    13. $x \ge -5$ and $x \le -2$

Solve each compound inequality.

    14. $-21 < 3x < 15$ **15.** $8 \le 5x - 2 \le 13$

    16. $5 < -2x < 10$

    17. $3x - 2 < 1$ or $x + 5 > 8$

    18. $2 - 3x \ge -7$ and $5 - x \le 6$

10-6 **19.** $|2x - 1| > 5$ **20.** $\left|\dfrac{1}{4}x + 2\right| < 2$

    21. $|5 - 3x| < 20$

1. _____

2. _____

3. _____

4. _____

5. _____

6. _____

7. _____

8. _____

9. _____

10. _____

11. _____

12. _____

13. _____

14. _____

15. _____

16. _____

17. _____

18. _____

19. _____

20. _____

21. _____

CHAPTER 10 TEST (continued)

10-7 Write an inequality for each graph.

22.

23.

22. _____

23. _____

10-8 Graph each system of inequalities.

24. $y > -2$

$x + y \leq -1$

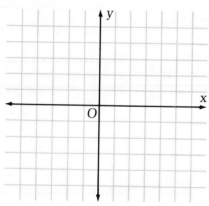

25. $y \leq \dfrac{1}{2}x + 1$

$2x - y > 2$

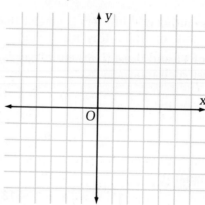

Name _____ Date _____ Score _____

CHAPTER 11 TEST

11-1 Write each rational number as a terminating or repeating decimal.

1. $2\frac{4}{5}$ **2.** $\frac{13}{3}$ **3.** $\frac{11}{12}$

Write each rational number as a fraction in simplest form.

4. 0.08 **5.** $0.\overline{3}$ **6.** $1.\overline{13}$

Simplify each expression.

11-2 **7.** $-\sqrt{441}$ **8.** $\frac{1}{16}\sqrt{16}$

9. Which of the following numbers are irrational?

$\sqrt{1},\ \sqrt{10},\ \sqrt{50},\ \sqrt{100}$

Simplify each expression.

11-3 **10.** $\sqrt{125}$ **11.** $-\sqrt{7}\sqrt{14}$

11-4 **12.** $\frac{7}{\sqrt{7}}$ **13.** $\sqrt{\frac{32}{18}}$

11-5 Simplify each expression. All variables represent positive numbers.

14. $\sqrt{81x^3}$ **15.** $7\sqrt{50x}$ **16.** $\sqrt{\frac{3}{2x}}$

11-6 **17.** $5\sqrt{18} + 2\sqrt{18}$ **18.** $\sqrt{200} - \sqrt{18}$

11-7 Solve for x. Write irrational answers in simplest radical form.

19.   **20.**   **21.**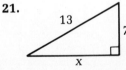

22. A triangle has sides that are 15, 36, and 39 units. Show that it is a right triangle.

11-8 **23.** Find the distance between $(-4, 1)$ and $(3, 7)$. Express your answer in simplest radical form.

11-9 **24.** Solve: $\sqrt{3x - 20} = 4$ **25.** Solve: $5\sqrt{3x} = 1$

1. _____

2. _____

3. _____

4. _____

5. _____

6. _____

7. _____

8. _____

9. _____

10. _____

11. _____

12. _____

13. _____

14. _____

15. _____

16. _____

17. _____

18. _____

19. _____

20. _____

21. _____

22. _____

23. _____

24. _____

25. _____

Name _____ Date _____ Score _____

CHAPTER 12 TEST

12-1 Tell whether each set of ordered pairs is a function. If not, explain why not.

    1. $\{(-3, -1), (3, -1), (1, 3), (2, 0)\}$

    2. $\{(0, 1), (1, 2), (1, 3), (3, 3)\}$

Use the vertical line test to tell whether each graph represents a function.

  3.

      4.

Let $f(x) = x^2 - x - 5$. Evaluate each of the following.

    5. $f(0)$ **6.** $f(-1)$

Give the coordinates of the vertex for each parabola.

12-2   **7.** $y = \dfrac{1}{2}x^2$

12-3   **8.** $y = 3x^2 - 5$

12-4   **9.** $y = (x + 4)^2 + 1$

For each parabola, tell whether the vertex is a maximum or a minimum point.

12-3   **10.** $y = -3x^2 + 5$

12-3   **11.** $y = x^2 - 6$

12-4   **12.** $y = -5(x - 1)^2$

12-5 Write each equation in h, k form. Then: **a.** write the coordinates of the vertex and the equation of the axis of symmetry; **b.** state the domain and range for each function.

  13. $y = 3x^2 - 6x + 2$ **14.** $y = -x^2 - 2x - 6$

Solve each equation by completing the square.

  15. $x^2 - 2x - 1 = 0$ **16.** $2x^2 - 3x + 1 = 0$

  17. $x^2 + 48 = 16x$

1. _____

2. _____

3. _____

4. _____

5. _____

6. _____

7. _____

8. _____

9. _____

10. _____

11. _____

12. _____

13. _____

14. _____

15. _____

16. _____

17. _____

CHAPTER 12 TEST (continued)

12-6   Use the quadratic formula to solve for x.   18. _____

      18. $2x^2 - x - 3 = 0$ **19.** $2x^2 - 3x = 2$

      20. $-3x^2 + 1 = 0$ 19. _____

                                               20. _____

12-7   **21.** Find the value of the discriminant and use it to tell the number of
      roots of the equation $3x^2 + x - 1 = 0$.

                                                 21. _____

12-8   **22.** The sum of a number and twice its reciprocal is $\dfrac{11}{3}$. Find the num-
      ber.

                                                 22. _____

                                                 23. _____

12-9   If y varies directly as x, and x = 11 when y = 3, find y for each value
      of x.

      23. x = 33   **24.** x = 22a   24. _____

                                                 25. _____

12-10   **25.** If y varies inversely with x, and $y = \dfrac{1}{2}$ when x = 40, find x when
        y = 10.

CHAPTER 13 TEST

13-1　**1.** Two supplementary angles have measures of $(x + 20)°$ and $(5x + 40)°$. Find the number of degrees in each angle.

13-2　For each pair of triangles, find x and y.

2.

3.

4.

5. A water tower casts a shadow 45 meters long. At the same time and place a vertical meter stick casts a shadow 30 centimeters long. Find the height of the water tower.

13-3　Complete each ratio for right triangle RST.

6. cos R

7. sin S

8. tan R

9. tan S

13-3　Find each trigonometric ratio.

10. sin A

11. sin B

12. cos A

13. tan A

14. tan B

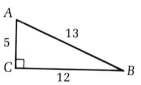

1. _____

2. _____

3. _____

4. _____

5. _____

6. _____

7. _____

8. _____

9. _____

10. _____

11. _____

12. _____

13. _____

14. _____

CHAPTER 13 TEST (continued)

13-4   Find each value. Simplify all radicals.

15. cos 30°   15. _____

16. cos 60°
                                                                                                            16. _____
17. tan 60°

18. tan 45°   17. _____

19. sin 60°
                                                                                                            18. _____
20. cos 45°

21. A ladder leaning against a wall forms a 30° angle with the wall. If   19. _____
      the foot of the ladder is 2 meters from the wall, how high does the
      ladder reach?   20. _____

22. If the diagonal of a square measures 10 cm, what is the measure of
      a side of the square?   21. _____

13-5   **23.** Find the value of x   22. _____
              to the nearest tenth.
                                                                                23. _____

                                                                                24. _____

          24. Find the value of x   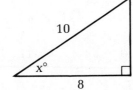   25. _____
              to the nearest degree.

          25. Find the width of the
              river to the nearest foot.

CUMULATIVE TEST: CHAPTERS 1–3   Part I

Write the letter for the correct answer.

1. Simplify: $36 \div (12 - 3) + 7 \times 2$
   a. 14   **b.** 18   **c.** 22   **d.** 26   **e.** 32

2. Evaluate $ab - (b - 3a)$ if $a = 1$ and $b = 6$.
   a. 3   **b.** 4   **c.** 6   **d.** 7   **e.** 9

3. Write $5x \cdot 3y \cdot y \cdot 2x \cdot x$ in exponential form.
   a. $8x + 4y$ **b.** $10x^3y^3$ **c.** $30x^3y^2$ **d.** $30x^2y^3$ **e.** $10x^2y^3$

4. Which is the correct expression for the phrase, "8 less than the product of three times a number and 2"?
   a. $8 - 3x + 2$ **b.** $8 - (3x + 2)$
   c. $(3x + 2) - 8$ **d.** $8 - 6x$ **e.** $6x - 8$

5. On the number line, what are all the integers that lie between -1.5 and 1.5?
   a. 0   **b.** 1 and -1 **c.** -1
   d. -1, 0, and 1   **e.** There are none.

6. Simplify: $-7 - (-5) - 5$
   a. -17 **b.** -7 **c.** -3 **d.** 3   **e.** 7

7. Evaluate $-5x + 3y$ if $x = -6$ and $y = 4$.
   a. -42 **b.** -30 **c.** -18 **d.** 18   **e.** 42

8. Simplify: $6 - 8x - 5 + 3x$
   a. $-4x$ **b.** $6x$ **c.** $-4 + 2x$ **d.** $1 - 5x$ **e.** $11x + 1$

9. Which expression is undefined when $x = 0$?

   a. $\dfrac{2}{5x}$ **b.** $\dfrac{x}{x - 1}$ **c.** $\dfrac{3}{x + 1}$

   d. $\dfrac{5x}{2}$ **e.** $\dfrac{x + 1}{x - 1}$

10. If $a < 0$ and $b < 0$, which of the following is positive?
    a. a^2b **b.** ab^2 **c.** $-ab^2$ **d.** $-ab$ **e.** $-a^2b^2$

11. Evaluate $\dfrac{x^2y}{xy^2}$ when $x = -1$ and $y = -2$.
    a. -1 **b.** $-\dfrac{1}{2}$ **c.** 0   **d.** $\dfrac{1}{2}$ **e.** 1

12. Which term is similar to the term $5x^2y$?
    a. $-5x^2y$ **b.** $5xy$ **c.** $-5xy$
    d. $-5xy^2$ **e.** none of these

1. _____
2. _____
3. _____
4. _____
5. _____
6. _____
7. _____
8. _____
9. _____
10. _____
11. _____
12. _____

CUMULATIVE TEST: CHAPTERS 1–3 (continued)

Write the letter for the correct answer.

13. To solve the equation $\dfrac{x}{5} = -2$, what operation should be performed on each side of the equation?

   a. Add 2.　　　　　　**b.** Subtract 5.　　　　**c.** Add 5.

   d. Multiply by 5.　　**e.** Divide by 5.

14. Which of the following is a solution to the equation $y - \dfrac{1}{2} = \dfrac{1}{2}$?

   a. -1　　**b.** $-\dfrac{1}{2}$　　**c.** 0　　**d.** $\dfrac{1}{2}$　　**e.** 1

15. When a number is increased by 2, the result is -8. What is the number?

   a. -10　　**b.** -8　　**c.** -6　　**d.** 6　　**e.** 8

13. _____

14. _____

15. _____

CUMULATIVE TEST: CHAPTERS 1–3   Part II

Identify the property illustrated.

16. $a + (b + c) = (b + c) + a$

17. $a(b + c) = a(b + c)$

Simplify.

18. -3^4

19. $8 - 6 \times 2$

20. $|-4| - |-3| + 2|0|$

21. $8(3 - x) - 2(x - 1)$

22. $a + (-a) - (-2a)$

23. $x - [-x - (-x + 1)]$

Evaluate.

24. $5x^5$ if $x = -1$

25. $x^3 - 2x^2$ if $x = 2$

26. $\dfrac{2x^2 - 2}{x^2 - 1}$ if $x = 4$

27. $5x^2 - (5x)^2$ if $x = -1$

28. At 12 noon a city's temperature was 12° F. At 12 midnight the temperature was 20° lower. What was the temperature at midnight?

29. Hand calculator A sells for \$120. Calculator B costs $\dfrac{1}{3}$ as much, while calculator C costs $\dfrac{1}{3}$ less than A. What are the costs of B and C?

Solve.

30. $x - 3.5 = 1.5$

31. $\dfrac{x}{3} = -7$

32. $\dfrac{2}{5}x = 10$

33. $6(x - 4) = 3x + 6$

34. $\dfrac{x - 5}{7} = \dfrac{x}{8}$

35. $-(3 - x) = -(x + 1)$

36. $\dfrac{2x + 1}{-1} = -x + 1$

Write as an equation. Then solve for n, and check.

37. 10 less than 8 times the number n is equal to 30.

38. 8 more than half the number n is equal to 2.

39. 3 times the sum of the number n and 5 is equal to half the number.

40. 5 times the number n is equal to 80 less than 4 times the number.

10. _____

17. _____

18. _____

19. _____

20. _____

21. _____

22. _____

23. _____

24. _____

25. _____

26. _____

27. _____

28. _____

29. _____

30. _____

31. _____

32. _____

33. _____

34. _____

35. _____

36. _____

37. _____

38. _____

39. _____

40. _____

CUMULATIVE TEST: CHAPTERS 1–6   Part I

Write the letter for the correct answer.

1. Which of the following is *not* always true for real numbers a, b, and c?
   a. $a(b + c) = ab + ac$ b. $ab = ba$ c. $a + b = b + a$
   d. $a - b = b - a$ e. $(a + b) + c = a + (b + c)$

2. Write $x \cdot x \cdot x \cdot x \cdot y \cdot y$ in exponential form.
   a. $4x + 2y$ b. $(xy)^6$ c. $6x^4y^2$ d. $4x \cdot y^2$ e. x^4y^2

3. Simplify: $-5 - (-5) + (-5)$
   a. -10 b. -5 c. 0 d. 5 e. 10

4. Simplify: $6a - 7 - 3a - 2$
   a. $9a - 9$ b. $9a + 9$ c. $3a - 9$ d. $3a + 9$ e. $-6a$

5. Evaluate $|-2|x - x + |x|$ if $x = -3$.
   a. -6 b. -3 c. 0 d. 3 e. 6

6. The phrase "three years younger than half her father's age" is represented by ? .
   a. $3 - \dfrac{1}{2}x$ b. $\dfrac{1}{2}(x - 3)$ c. $\dfrac{1}{2}(3 - x)$ d. $3x - \dfrac{1}{2}$ e. $\dfrac{1}{2}x - 3$

7. Which point lies in Quadrant IV?
   a. $(0, 0)$ b. $(-1, -1)$ c. $(5, 0)$ d. $(3, -2)$ e. $(0, -5)$

8. Which point is *not* on the graph of $y = -2x$?
   a. $(0, 0)$ b. $(-2, 4)$ c. $(3, 6)$ d. $(3, -6)$ e. $(-1, 2)$

9. What is the equation of the vertical line passing through $(-1, 0)$?
   a. $y = -1$ b. $x = -1$ c. $y = 1$ d. $x = 1$ e. $x + y = -1$

10. Find the slope of the line whose equation is $x + 2y = 3$.
    a. $-\dfrac{1}{2}$ b. $\dfrac{1}{2}$ c. $-\dfrac{2}{3}$ d. $\dfrac{2}{3}$ e. 3

11. Simplify the polynomial $2x^2 - 2x + 3x - x^2$.
    a. $4x - x^2$ b. $3x - 2x^2$ c. $x^2 + x$ d. $x^2 - x$ e. x

12. Subtract $5x - 3$ from $-3x + 4$.
    a. $2x + 1$ b. $-8x + 1$ c. $8x - 7$ d. $-8x + 7$ e. $-8x$

13. Simplify: $(-2x^2y^3)^5$
    a. $-10x^7y^8$ b. $10x^{10}y^{15}$ c. $-32x^7y^8$ d. $-10x^2y^3$ e. $-32x^{10}y^{15}$

14. Find the missing factor: $-27x^5y^3 = (3xy^2)(\underline{\ ?\ })$
    a. $9x^5y$ b. $-9x^4y$ c. $9x^4y$ d. $-9x^6y^5$ e. $9x^6y^5$

15. Solve for x: $x(x - 1) = 0$
    a. 0 only   b. -1 only   c. 1 only   d. 0 or -1 e. 0 or 1

1. _____
2. _____
3. _____
4. _____
5. _____
6. _____
7. _____
8. _____
9. _____
10. _____
11. _____
12. _____
13. _____
14. _____
15. _____

CUMULATIVE TEST: CHAPTERS 1–6   Part II

Simplify.

16. $-8 - 10 + 13$

17. $6 + 4 \times 2 - 8 \div 4$

18. $5(2n + 3) - 2(n - 1)$

19. $\dfrac{-12x^2y^5}{-3xy^5}$

20. $x^2y - 3xy^2 - x^2y + 5xy^2$

Evaluate when $x = -4$ and $y = 2$.

21. $x^2 - y^2 + xy$

22. $(x^2y)^2$

Solve for x.

23. $-8.5 = x + 10$

24. $\dfrac{1}{2} - 2x = 3\dfrac{1}{2}$

25. $6(8 - 3x) = 48$

26. $\dfrac{7x}{2} - 1 = 1.5$

27. Find the slope of a line with an x-intercept of -4 and a y-intercept of -8.

28. Find the y-intercept of the line $4x - y = -20$.

29. Write the equation $x - 6 = -3y$ in standard form.

30. Write the equation, in standard form, of the line having a slope of $\dfrac{2}{3}$ and a y-intercept of -2.

31. Find the equation, in slope-intercept form, of the line shown in the following figure.

32. Graph the equation: $2x + y = 4$

Simplify.

33. $-5x(2x^2)^3 \cdot 2x(x^2)$ **34.** $(x - 5y)(3x + 2y)$ **35.** $(2x - 3y)(2x + 3y)$

Factor completely.

36. $n^2 - 18n + 81$ **37.** $x^2 - 10x + 21$ **38.** $5x^2 - 80$

39. Find two consecutive integers such that 3 times half the first is 3 greater than the second.

40. Mary's age is a third of that of her father. If their ages total 56, how old are Mary and her father?

16. _____
17. _____
18. _____
19. _____
20. _____
21. _____
22. _____
23. _____
24. _____
25. _____
26. _____
27. _____
28. _____
29. _____
30. _____
31. _____
33. _____
34. _____
35. _____
36. _____
37. _____
38. _____
39. _____
40. _____

CUMULATIVE TEST: CHAPTERS 1–9   Part I

Write the letter for the correct answer.

1. Simplify: $20 + 10 \div 5 \times 2$
   a. 3   **b.** 8   **c.** 21   **d.** 24   **e.** 44

2. Evaluate $a(a - 3b)$. Let $a = -1$ and $b = -2$.
   a. -7 **b.** -5 **c.** 0   **d.** 5   **e.** 7

3. Find the slope of the line which has an x-intercept of -2 and which passes through the point $(4, 1)$.
   a. $\dfrac{1}{6}$ **b.** $-\dfrac{1}{6}$ **c.** 6   **d.** -6 **e.** $-\dfrac{3}{2}$

4. Simplify: $(5x^3 - 2x - 1) + (x^2 + 2x) - (x^3 - x^2 - 1)$
   a. $5x^3 + x^2 - 2$ **b.** $4x^3 - 1$ **c.** $4x^3 + 2x^2$
   d. $6x^3$ **e.** $6x^3 + x^2$

5. Multiply: $(3x - 5y)(x + 2y)$
   a. $3x^2 + xy - 10y^2$ **b.** $3x - 5xy + 2y$
   c. $3x^2 - 10y^2$ **d.** $4x - 3y$ **e.** $-30x^2y^2$

6. Evaluate $x^2(-x^2)^2$ when $x = 2$.
   a. -64 **b.** -32 **c.** 0   **d.** 32   **e.** 64

7. Simplify: $\dfrac{63x^{12}y^8z}{9x^4y^2z}$
   a. $54x^3y^4z$ **b.** $7x^3y^4$ **c.** $7x^8y^6$
   d. $7x^{16}y^{10}z^2$ **e.** $54x^8y^6$

8. Factor completely: $x^4 - 2x^3 - 35x^2$
   a. $(x^2 - 7x)(x^2 - 5x)$ **b.** $x^2(x - 7)(x + 5)$
   c. $(x^3 - 7x^2)(x + 5)$ **d.** $(x^4 - 7x)(x + 5x)$
   e. $(x^3 + 5x)(x - 7x)$

9. The length of a rectangle is twice its width. If the area of the rectangle is 72 square units, what is the measure of its length?
   a. 3   **b.** 6   **c.** 9   **d.** 12   **e.** 24

10. If $x - 3y = 2$ is the first equation in a system, which of the following second equations will produce a system which is dependent?
   a. $x + 3y = 2$ **b.** $x + 3y = -2$
   c. $-x - 3y = 2$ **d.** $-x - 3y = -2$
   e. $-x + 3y = -2$

11. Divide and simplify: $\dfrac{x^3y^2}{ab^2} \div \dfrac{x^3y^3}{a^2b^2}$
   a. $\dfrac{a}{y}$ **b.** ay **c.** $\dfrac{y}{a}$ **d.** $\dfrac{b}{a}$ **e.** $\dfrac{a}{b}$

1. _____

2. _____

3. _____

4. _____

5. _____

6. _____

7. _____

8. _____

9. _____

10. _____

11. _____

CUMULATIVE TEST: CHAPTERS 1–9 (continued)

Write the letter for the correct answer.

12. The expression $\dfrac{1}{x^2 - x}$ is undefined for what values of x?

    a. 0   **b.** 1   **c.** 0 and 1

    d. 0 and −1   **e.** 0, 1, and −1

13. Solve the proportion: $\dfrac{5}{3} = \dfrac{x + 1}{x - 1}$

    a. 6   **b.** 4   **c.** 2   **d.** −2   **e.** −4

14. Solve for x: $\dfrac{1}{x} + 3 = -2$

    a. −5   **b.** −1   **c.** $-\dfrac{1}{5}$ **d.** $\dfrac{1}{5}$ **e.** 5

15. How many gallons of water must be added to 10 gallons of a 50% saltwater solution to make the resulting solution a 20% saltwater solution?

    a. 3   **b.** 5   **c.** 6   **d.** 10   **e.** 15

12. _____

13. _____

14. _____

15. _____

CUMULATIVE TEST: CHAPTERS 1–9 **Part II**

16. Simplify: $5 + [3 - (4 - 2 \times 3)]$

17. Find the slope of the line $8x - 2y = 1$.

18. Write the equation of the line that passes through the points $(-8, 3)$ and $(-8, -3)$.

19. What is the y-intercept of the graph of the equation $5x - 2y = 6$?

20. Find the equation in slope-intercept form of the line that passes through the point $(-3, -1)$ and which is parallel to the line $x - y = 0$.

21. Multiply: $(x^2 - 4)(x^2 + 4)$ **22.** Multiply: $(x^2 - 3)(x^4 + 3x^2 + 9)$

Factor completely.

23. $x^6 - x^4$ **24.** $25x^2 + 30x + 9$ **25.** $15x^2 - 19x + 6$

26. $a(x - y) + 2(x - y)$

27. Solve the system: **28.** Solve the system: **29.** Simplify: $\dfrac{\frac{1}{x} + 1}{x + 1}$
$3x - y = 4$ $x - 3y = -18$
$2x + y = 16$ $y = x + 8$

30. 25 is 0.5% of what number?

Solve for x. If no solution exists, write **no solution.** If the equation is an identity, write **identity.**

31. $2x - 1.5 = 3$ **32.** $6(x - 3) = 5 + 6x$

33. $(x - 5)^2 - 3 = x^2 - 10x + 22$

34. $x^2 - 8x + 15 = 0$ **35.** $\dfrac{1}{3x} = \dfrac{x}{27}$

36. Find three consecutive even integers such that the sum of the first and third exceeds the second by 10.

37. The length of a rectangle is 1 cm longer than twice the width. If the perimeter of the rectangle is 35 cm, find the length and width.

38. Twenty-two coins in dimes and quarters have a value of $3.40. How many coins of each type are there?

39. Faucet A will fill a tub in 45 minutes. Faucet B will fill the same tub in 20 minutes. How long will it take to fill the tub if both faucets are opened at the same time?

40. $12,000 is invested at $8\frac{1}{2}$% simple interest per year. How much interest is earned at the end of $1\frac{1}{2}$ years?

16. _____
17. _____
18. _____
19. _____
20. _____
21. _____
22. _____
23. _____
24. _____
25. _____
26. _____
27. _____
28. _____
29. _____
30. _____
31. _____
32. _____
33. _____
34. _____
35. _____
36. _____
37. _____
38. _____
39. _____
40. _____

CUMULATIVE TEST: CHAPTERS 1–13   Part I

Write the letter for the correct answer.

1. Evaluate $a - (4 - a)$ when $a = -5$.
   a. -14 **b.** -9 **c.** -4 **d.** 4 **e.** 9

2. Solve for x: $5(3 - x) = 2x - 6$
   a. -3 **b.** -1 **c.** 0 **d.** 1 **e.** 3

3. Which pair of coordinates satisfies the equation $2x - y = -4$?
   a. $(3, 7)$ **b.** $(5, 6)$ **c.** $(4, 12)$ **d.** $(-4, 12)$ **e.** $(6, 8)$

4. Find the slope of the line that passes through the points $(-8, -3)$ and $(-8, 0)$.
   a. $-\dfrac{3}{8}$ **b.** $-\dfrac{8}{3}$ **c.** 0 **d.** $\dfrac{3}{8}$ **e.** Undefined

5. Find the y-intercept of the line $5x - 2y = 1$.
   a. -2 **b.** $-\dfrac{1}{2}$ **c.** $\dfrac{1}{2}$ **d.** 1 **e.** 2

6. Subtract $-x^2 + x - 1$ from $x^2 - x + 1$.
   a. 0 **b.** $-2x$ **c.** $2x^2$ **d.** $2x^2 - 2x + 2$ **e.** None of these

7. Find the missing factor: $-15x^2y^3 = (3xy)(\underline{\ ?\ })$
   a. $-5x^3y^4$ **b.** $5x^3y^4$ **c.** $-5xy^2$ **d.** $5xy^2$ **e.** $-45x^3y^4$

8. Solve for x: $3x(x - 3) = 0$
   a. 0 and 3   **b.** 0 and -3 **c.** 3 and -3 **d.** Identity   **e.** No solution

9. Multiply: $\dfrac{x^2 + 2x + 1}{x + 1} \cdot \dfrac{x - 1}{x^2 - 1}$
   a. 0 **b.** 1 **c.** $x + 1$ **d.** $x - 1$ **e.** $x^2 + 1$

10. 4 is 8% of what number?
    a. 12   **b.** 32   **c.** 40   **d.** 50   **e.** 100

11. Solve for x: $|x - 1| > 1$
    a. $x < 2$ **b.** $x > 0$ **c.** $x > 2$ or $x < 0$
    d. $x > 0$ and $x < -2$ **e.** $x > 0$ or $x < -2$

12. Which of the following terminating or repeating decimals represents $1\dfrac{5}{11}$?
    a. 0.145 **b.** $1.4\overline{5}$ **c.** $\overline{1.45}$ **d.** $0.1\overline{45}$ **e.** $1.\overline{45}$

13. Solve for x: $\sqrt{x - 5} = -3$

    a. No solution   **b.** -4 **c.** 4 **d.** -8 **e.** 8

14. What is the vertex of the parabola $y = (x - 3)^2 + 1$?
    a. $(0, 0)$ **b.** $(3, 1)$ **c.** $(-3, 1)$ **d.** $(1, 3)$ **e.** $(-1, 3)$

15. If the sides of a square measure 8 cm, what is the measure of a diagonal?
    a. 16   **b.** $8\sqrt{3}$ **c.** $8\sqrt{2}$ **d.** 8   **e.** $4\sqrt{2}$

1. _____
2. _____
3. _____
4. _____
5. _____
6. _____
7. _____
8. _____
9. _____
10. _____
11. _____
12. _____
13. _____
14. _____
15. _____

CUMULATIVE TEST: CHAPTERS 1–13   Part II

16. Evaluate $-x^2 - (-x)^2$ when $x = -3$.

17. Write the equation $\frac{1}{2}y = 2x - 3$ in standard form.

18. Write, in slope-intercept form, the equation of the line that passes through the points $(-5, 1)$ and $(1, -3)$.

Simplify.

19. $(-2x)^3(-xy)^2(x^2y)$

20. $3x(x - 2)^2$

21. $\dfrac{-12x^5y^2}{-18x^3y^3}$

22. $(x - 7)^2 - (x - 7)$

Factor completely.

23. $2x^3 - 5x^2 + 3x$

24. $x^2 - 5x - 3xy + 15y$

25. Solve: $x^2 = 35 - 2x$

26. Solve the system of equations:
$$5x - y = -23$$
$$-4x - 3y = 7$$

27. Divide $3x^2 - 5x - 7$ by $x - 2$.

28. Add: $\dfrac{3}{x} + \dfrac{5}{x - 1}$

29. A faucet takes 20 minutes to fill an empty tub with water. The drain takes 50 minutes to empty the tub when it is full. If both the faucet and the drain are opened, how long will it take to fill the empty tub?

Solve and graph each compound inequality.

30. $2 > 3x - 1$ or $x - 1 > 3$

31. $2x + 3 \geq -5$ and $2 - x > 2$

32. Simplify: $\sqrt{40x} - \sqrt{\dfrac{5x}{2}}$

33. Solve for x: $\sqrt{x} + 1 = 0$

34. Find the vertex of the parabola $y = x^2 - 6x + 6$. Is the vertex a maximum or a minimum?

16. _____
17. _____
18. _____
19. _____
20. _____
21. _____
22. _____
23. _____
24. _____
25. _____
26. _____
27. _____
28. _____
29. _____
30. _____
31. _____
32. _____
33. _____
34. _____

CUMULATIVE TEST: CHAPTERS 1–13 (continued)

35. Use the quadratic formula to solve $2x^2 - 5x + 1 = 0$.

36. If y varies inversely with x, and $y = 18$ when $x = 3$, find y when $x = 12$.

37. For what value(s) of t does the equation $x^2 - x + t = 0$ have no real solution?

38. If the cosine of an acute angle is $\dfrac{3}{8}$, what is the sine of the same angle?

39. A 100-foot flagpole casts a 35-foot shadow at the same time that Wendy casts a 21-inch shadow. How tall is Wendy?

40. Find x to the nearest foot.

Note: sin 50° ≈ 0.77
cos 50° ≈ 0.64
tan 50° ≈ 1.19

35. _____

36. _____

37. _____

38. _____

39. _____

40. _____

ANSWERS FOR THE INDEPENDENT TESTS

CHAPTER 1 TEST

1. 10   **2.** 5   **3.** 1   **4.** 5   **5.** 48   **6.** 140

7. x^4y^3 **8.** $6(a - 5)$ **9.** $\frac{a}{3} + 4$ **10.** 6

11. $12 - n = 8$; 4   **12.** $\frac{50}{8} = n$; $6.25   **13.** 1 and 7

14. 10, 12, and 14   **15.** $2\frac{1}{2}$ **16.** 0

17. ‾3, 0, 3, 6   **18.** >   **19.** <   **20.** =

21. 4   **22.** 1 and ‾1   **23.** c   **24.** a   **25.** d

CHAPTER 2 TEST

1. −19   **2.** 12   **3.** −3   **4.** Postive   **5.** −2

6. −2   **7.** 20   **8.** 3   **9.** 3   **10.** $8x + 40$

11. $4x + 4y + 4z$ **12.** Yes   **13.** $4a + 1$

14. Cannot be simplified.   **15.** $2n + 16$ **16.** −56

17. 30   **18.** −16   **19.** 16   **20.** $8 - x$; 10

21. $x - y + z$ **22.** 45   **23.** −2   **24.** 3

25. B, 144 grams; C, 180 grams

CHAPTER 3 TEST

1. $V = \pi r^2 h$ **2.** 9   **3.** 2   **4.** 7   **5.** 25

6. −8.5   **7.** 4.7   **8.** −8   **9.** 0.95   **10.** −35

11. −4   **12.** 162   **13.** 12.5   **14.** 4   **15.** 12

16. −6   **17.** $14n = 7$; $n = \frac{1}{2}$

18. $2n + 10 = 36$; $n = 13$ **19.** 4   **20.** 2

21. 15   **22.** $5(x + 11) = 40$; $x = -3$

23. $3(x + 4) = 18$; $x = 2$

24. Let x = Maria's age; $x + (x - 4) = 32$; Maria is 18.

25. $2x - (x + 1) = 24$; 25, 26

CHAPTER 4 TEST

1. (0, 3)   **2.** (3, 1)   **3.** (2, −3)   **4.** (−3, −1)

5. (−4, 2)   **6.** III   **7.** II   **8.** y-axis   **9.** Yes

10. No   **11.** $-\frac{9}{7}$ **12.** 1   **13.** 10, −5   **14.** $\frac{2}{5}$

15. 3, −5   **16.** $y = -3x + 7$ **17.** $y = 2x + 2$

18. $y = x$ **19.** $x - 2y = -2$ **20.** $y = -\frac{1}{3}x + 5$

21. $x + 2y = 8$ **22.** $y = -7$ **23.** $x = 3$

24.   **25.**

CHAPTER 5 TEST

1. $-3x^2 + 2x$; 2   **2.** Binomial   **3.** $2x^3 + 4x^2 + x$; 93

4. x^2; 9   **5.** $a - b$ **6.** $3x^2 + xy$

7. $x^2 + 11x - 6$ **8.** $-2x - 6y$ **9.** $-4x^4$; −64

10. $-2x^5$; 64   **11.** x^8y^{12} **12.** $-18n^5$

13. $2x^3 - 6x^2 - 2x$ **14.** $8x - 6$

15. $6x^2 - 19x + 15$ **16.** $3a^2 - 7ab - 6b^2$

17. $x^3 - 3x^2 + 3x - 2$ **18.** $2a^3 + 5a^2 + a - 2$

19. $x^2 - 6x + 9$ **20.** $9x^2 - 6xy + y^2$

21. No solution   **22.** −1   **23.** Identity

24. −3   **25.** 40 cm^2

CHAPTER 6 TEST

1. $2^5 \cdot 3^2$ **2.** 9   **3.** $-5a^3b$ **4.** $3b$ **5.** $-3x^2$

6. $15x^4(x + 3)$ **7.** $-7x(x + 1)(2x - 3)$

8. $(x - 3)(x - 1)$ **9.** $(5x - 3)(2y + 5)$

10. $(x + 1)(x - 1)$ **11.** $(7x + 3y)(7x - 3y)$

12. $(y - 6)^2$ **13.** $(3x + 2y)^2$ **14.** $(x + 5)(x - 7)$

15. $(x - 3)(x - 8)$ **16.** $(5x - 1)(x + 3)$

17. $(6x - 3)(x - 5)$ **18.** $5(x - 4)(x + 1)$

19. $7(x + 2)(x - 2)$ **20.** 0, 11   **21.** $\frac{1}{2}, -\frac{1}{2}$

22. $\frac{2}{3}, 5$ **23.** $\frac{4}{3}$ **24.** 12 and 14, or −14 and −12

25. 9 cm and 6 cm

CHAPTER 7 TEST

1. Yes   **2.** No   **3.** No

4. (−1, 1)   **5.** (−3, −2)

6. (4, 5)   **7.** (3, 2)   **8.** (−1, 4)   **9.** (−5, −2)
10. (5, 1)   **11.** (−1, 3)   **12.** (−2, −3)   **13.** (−1, 4)
14. (3, 1)   **15.** (5, −3)   **16.** Inconsistent
17. Consistent   **18.** Consistent   **19.** Consistent
20. Parallel   **21.** Independent   **22.** Dependent
23. Larry is 14; Peter is 17.   **24.** 8 nickels; 12 dimes
25. 84

1. 0, 3   **2.** 6, −5   **3.** 5, −5   **4.** $\dfrac{1}{6n}$ **5.** $\dfrac{1}{x + 1}$

6. $-\dfrac{1}{x}$ **7.** $\dfrac{1 - x}{x}$ **8.** $\dfrac{a^2}{6b}$ **9.** 1   **10.** $\dfrac{(x - 2)^2}{x^2 + 4}$

11. $\dfrac{10b^3}{a^2}$ **12.** $\dfrac{xz}{3}$ **13.** $\dfrac{x - 5}{x + 3}$ **14.** $7x - 1$

15. $x^2 - 3x - 1$ **16.** $x + 1$ **17.** $\dfrac{1}{3x + 1}$ **18.** $\dfrac{16x}{3}$

19. $\dfrac{4x - 5}{x(x - 1)}$ **20.** $\dfrac{5x + 5}{(x - 2)(x + 3)}$

21. $\dfrac{2 - 3x}{(3x + 1)(3x - 1)}$ **22.** $\dfrac{x + 1}{x + 2}$ **23.** $\dfrac{1}{15}$

24. $2x - 1$ **25.** $-2(x + 5)$

1. 9   **2.** 6   **3.** 12   **4.** −4   **5.** $\dfrac{1}{4}$

6. No solution   **7.** 3   **8.** $\dfrac{5}{2}$, −3   **9.** 5

10. 3   **11.** 6, −1   **12.** 6, −8   **13.** 2   **14.** 10

15. 200   **16.** 60%   **17.** 1,491   **18.** 384   **19.** $\dfrac{5}{2}$

20. 6 hours   **21.** 24   **22.** 10 pounds   **23.** $1620

24. $1\dfrac{1}{3}$ pounds

25. 60 miles per hour; 80 miles per hour

1. $x \le 7$ **2.** $x \ge 0$ **3.** $x > -7$ **4.** $x \le 11$
5. $x < 2$
6. $x \le 4$ **7.** $x > -4$

```
 ◄━━━●━━━►        ◄━━━○━━━►
   0   4           −4   0
```

8. $x \ge 3$ **9.** $x < 2$

```
 ◄━━●━━━━━►        ◄━━━━━○━━►
   0   3             0   2
```

10. 33, 35, 37   **11.** 7

12.   **13.**

```
 ◄━○━━━○━━►        ◄━●━━━━●━━►
  −1    1          −5   −2
```

14. $-7 < x < 5$ **15.** $2 \le x \le 3$

16. $-5 < x < -\dfrac{5}{2}$ **17.** $x < 1$ or $x > 3$

18. $-1 \le x \le 3$ **19.** $x < -2$ or $x > 3$

20. $-16 < x < 0$ **21.** $-5 < x < \dfrac{25}{3}$

22. $y \le x + 1$ **23.** $y > -\dfrac{1}{2}x$

24.   **25.**

1. 2.8   **2.** $4.\overline{3}$ **3.** $0.91\overline{6}$ **4.** $\dfrac{2}{25}$ **5.** $\dfrac{1}{3}$ **6.** $\dfrac{112}{99}$

7. −21   **8.** $\dfrac{1}{4}$ **9.** $\sqrt{10}$ and $\sqrt{50}$ **10.** $5\sqrt{5}$

11. $-7\sqrt{2}$ **12.** $\sqrt{7}$ **13.** $\dfrac{4}{3}$ **14.** $9x\sqrt{x}$

15. $35\sqrt{2x}$ **16.** $\dfrac{\sqrt{6x}}{2x}$ **17.** $21\sqrt{2}$ **18.** $7\sqrt{2}$

19. 35   **20.** $\dfrac{15\sqrt{2}}{2}$ **21.** $2\sqrt{30}$

22. $15^2 + 36^2 \overset{?}{=} 39^2$; $225 + 1296 \overset{?}{=} 1521$; $1521 = 1521$ ✓

23. $\sqrt{85}$ **24.** 12   **25.** $\dfrac{1}{75}$

1. Yes   **2.** No. When $x = 1$, y has values 2 and 3.
3. Yes   **4.** No   **5.** −5   **6.** −3   **7.** (0, 0)
8. (0, −5)   **9.** (−4, 1)   **10.** Max.   **11.** Min.
12. Max.
13. $y = 3(x - 1)^2 - 1$ **14.** $y = -(x + 1)^2 - 5$
    a. (1, −1); $x = 1$ **a.** (−1, 5); $x = -1$
    b. D: x is any real no.   **b.** D: x is any real no.
      R: $f(x) \ge -1$ R: $f(x) \le -5$

15. $1 \pm \sqrt{2}$ **16.** $1, \dfrac{1}{2}$ **17.** 4, 12   **18.** $-1, \dfrac{3}{2}$

19. $2, -\dfrac{1}{2}$ **20.** $\pm\dfrac{\sqrt{3}}{3}$ **21.** $b^2 - 4ac = 13$; 2

22. $\dfrac{2}{3}$ or 3   **23.** 9   **24.** $6a$ **25.** 2

CHAPTER 13 TEST

1. $40°$ and $140°$ 2. $x = 5; y = 16$ 3. $x = 6\frac{2}{3}$; $y = 5$

4. $x = 30; y = 130$ 5. 150 meters 6. $\frac{s}{t}$ 7. $\frac{s}{t}$

8. $\frac{r}{s}$ 9. $\frac{s}{r}$ 10. $\frac{12}{13}$ 11. $\frac{5}{13}$ 12. $\frac{5}{13}$ 13. $\frac{12}{5}$

14. $\frac{5}{12}$ 15. $\frac{\sqrt{3}}{2}$ 16. $\frac{1}{2}$ 17. $\sqrt{3}$ 18. 1 19. $\frac{\sqrt{3}}{2}$

20. $\frac{\sqrt{2}}{2}$ 21. $2\sqrt{3}$ meters 22. $5\sqrt{2}$ cm 23. 10.9

24. 37 25. 175 feet

CUMULATIVE TEST: CHAPTERS 1–3

1. b 2. a 3. c 4. e 5. d 6. b 7. e
8. d 9. a 10. c 11. d 12. a 13. d 14. e
15. a 16. Comm. for add. 17. Reflex. prop. of eq.
18. -81 19. -4 20. 1 21. $26 - 10x$ 22. $2a$
23. $x + 1$ 24. -5 25. 0 26. 2 27. -20
28. $-8°F$ 29. B costs \$40; C costs \$80. 30. 5
31. -21 32. 25 33. 10 34. 40 35. 1
36. -2 37. $8n - 10 = 30; n = 5$

38. $\frac{1}{2}n + 8 = 2; n = -12$ 39. $3(n + 5) = \frac{1}{2}n; n = -6$

40. $5n = 4n - 80; n = -80$

CUMULATIVE TEST: CHAPTERS 1–6

1. d 2. e 3. b 4. c 5. c 6. e 7. d
8. c 9. b 10. a 11. c 12. d 13. e 14. b
15. e 16. -5 17. 12 18. $8n + 17$ 19. $4x$

20. $2xy^2$ 21. 4 22. 1024 23. -18.5 24. $-1\frac{1}{2}$

25. 0 26. $\frac{5}{7}$ 27. -2 28. 20 29. $x + 3y = 6$

30. $2x - 3y = 6$ 31. $y = \frac{2}{3}x + 2$

32.

33. $-80x^{10}$ 34. $3x^2 - 13xy - 10y^2$ 35. $4x^2 - 9y^2$
36. $(n - 9)^2$ 37. $(x - 7)(x - 3)$ 38. $5(x + 4)(x - 4)$
39. 8 and 9 40. Mary is 14; her father is 42.

CUMULATIVE TEST: CHAPTERS 1–9

1. d 2. b 3. a 4. c 5. a 6. e 7. c
8. b 9. d 10. e 11. a 12. c 13. b 14. c
15. e 16. 10 17. 4 18. $x = -8$ 19. -3
20. $y = x + 2$ 21. $x^4 - 16$ 22. $x^6 - 27$
23. $x^4(x + 1)(x - 1)$ 24. $(5x + 3)^2$
25. $(5x - 3)(3x - 2)$ 26. $(x - y)(a + 2)$

27. $x = 4; y = 8$ 28. $x = -3; y = 5$ 29. $\frac{1}{x}$

30. 5000 31. 2.25 32. No solution 33. Identity
34. 3 and 5 35. 3 and -3 36. 8, 10 and 12

37. Length = 12 cm; width = $5\frac{1}{2}$ cm

38. 14 dimes; 8 quarters 39. $13\frac{11}{13}$ minutes

40. \$1530

CUMULATIVE TEST: CHAPTERS 1–13

1. a 2. e 3. c 4. e 5. b 6. d 7. c
8. a 9. b 10. d 11. c 12. e 13. a 14. b

15. c 16. -18 17. $4x - y = 6$ 18. $y = \frac{-2}{3}x - \frac{7}{3}$

19. $-8x^7y^3$ 20. $3x^3 - 12x^2 + 12x$ 21. $\frac{2x^2}{3y}$

22. $x^2 - 15x + 56$ 23. $x(2x - 3)(x - 1)$
24. $(x - 3y)(x - 5)$ 25. 5 and -7 26. $(-4, 3)$

27. $3x + 1 - \frac{5}{x - 2}$ 28. $\frac{8x - 3}{x(x - 1)}$ 29. $33\frac{1}{3}$ minutes

30. $x < 1$ or $x > 4$ 31. $-4 \le x < 0$

32. $\frac{3}{2}\sqrt{10x}$ 33. No solution 34. $(3, -3)$; minimum

35. $\frac{5 \pm \sqrt{17}}{4}$ 36. $4\frac{1}{2}$ 37. $t > \frac{1}{4}$ 38. $\frac{\sqrt{55}}{8}$

39. 5 feet or 60 in. 40. 128 feet

The Role of Motivation

Motivation is a key to learning. A suitably motivated student can and will learn mathematics, and an enthusiastic teacher can do much to stimulate interest in the subject.

Although the required subject matter in an algebra course often seems to be too extensive to cover in one year, taking time for the purpose of motivating students is still worthwhile. Many algebra lessons have their own natural appeal or have motivation built in through the text approach. At other times it will be up to you to provide the motivation. One way to do this is to use a few minutes at the start of the class period. You may either set the stage for the day's lesson or you may introduce some special motivational aspect of mathematics.

Naturally, it is best to have the introduction linked directly to the lesson for that day, but this need not be a requirement. Students will generally react positively to any attempt to demonstrate an interesting or challenging aspect of mathematics.

Among the ways to provide motivation are the use of a challenging problem, a historical anecdote, a suitable application, an example of mathematics used in the daily newspaper, an opportunity to guess or estimate, a laboratory experiment, a mathematical game or trick, and so forth.

Following are samples of such motivational techniques. As you consider and use these ideas, you will find that other ideas and activities will spring to mind. For additional sources of topics and ideas, consult the Bibliography on page T69.

FALLACIES

1. Students are usually interested in fallacies, especially if these are presented in a dramatic manner. Thus you might announce that a new discovery has been made, namely that $1 = 2$! Then proceed to show the following "proof" of this fact and challenge the students to find the fallacy.

Let	$a = b$	
Then	$a \cdot a = a \cdot b$	Multiply by a.
	$a^2 = ab$	$a \cdot a = a^2$
	$a^2 - b^2 = ab - b^2$	Subtract b^2.
	$(a - b)(a + b) = b(a - b)$	Factor.
	$a + b = b$	Divide by $a - b$.
	$2b = b$	Replace a by b ($a = b$).
	$2 = 1$	Divide by b.

Note that the step where both sides of the equation are divided by $a - b$ is not "legal." Since $a = b$, $a - b = 0$, and division by 0 is not permitted. This fallacy is very helpful in providing an effective demonstration that one may not divide by 0.

2. Here is another example of a fallacy based on the same principle, but disguised somewhat better. The fallacy is designed to show that any two numbers are equal!

Assume x and y are two positive numbers with $x > y$. Then $x = y + z$, where z is some positive number.

$x = y + z$	
$x(x - y) = (y + z)(x - y)$	Multiply by $x - y$.
$x^2 - xy = xy + xz - y^2 - yz$	By multiplication
$x^2 - xy - xz = xy - y^2 - yz$	Subtract xz.
$x(x - y - z) = y(x - y - z)$	Factor.
$x = y$	Divide by $x - y - z$.

Thus we assumed that $x > y$ and "proved" that $x = y$. Again the fallacy involves the "illegal" procedure of dividing by 0. (Since $x = y + z$, then $x - y - z = 0$.)

MATHEMAGIC

An exceptionally fine way to motivate the learning of mathematics is through the use of mathematical tricks. Many of these can be used to demonstrate concepts of proof and to show how the use of variables can provide explanations as to why the trick works. Here is a sampling of some items that have been used effectively in algebra classes.

1. Students are asked to think of a number, to perform several operations, and are then told the outcomes. They will enjoy composing their own sets of directions; in each case they should be asked to explain why the trick works. Here is a representative example.

Example	Explanation
Think of a number.	n
Multiply by 3	$3n$
Subtract 7.	$3n - 7$
Add 10.	$3n + 3$
Divide by 3.	$n + 1$
Subtract the original number.	1
The result will always be 1!	

2. Have students write a three-digit number with all digits different, such as 742. They are then to form all possible two-digit numbers from this number and find the sum. Then divide the result by the sum of the three digits. You then can announce their final answer. It will always be 22.

Example	Explanation
Select 742.	Use the number $\underline{a}\ \underline{b}\ \underline{c}$ $(100a + 10b + c)$.
Two digit numbers:	Two-digit numbers:
74	$10a + b$
47	$10b + a$
72	$10a + c$
27	$10c + a$
42	$10b + c$
24	$10c + b$
286	$20a + 20b + 20c + 2a + 2b + 2c = 22a + 22b + 22c = 22(a + b + c)$
$7 + 4 + 2 = 13$	The sum of the digits is $a + b + c$.
$\begin{array}{r} 22 \\ 13\overline{)286} \\ 26 \\ \hline 26 \\ 26 \\ \hline \end{array}$	Thus, $22(a + b + c) \div (a + b + c) = 22$.

This is an excellent "trick" to introduce during chapters concerning factoring and/or addition of polynomials.

3. Have a student at the chalkboard write a number between 50 and 100 while your back is turned. Let the rest of the class observe and check the work to be done. Then give the following directions:

Directions	Sample
Write a two-digit number between 50 and 100.	Assume student begins with 82.
	82
Add 76 to your number.	$\begin{array}{r} + 76 \\ \hline 158 \end{array}$
Cross out the hundreds digit.	$\cancel{1}58$
	58
Add this crossed-out digit to the remaining two-digit number.	$\begin{array}{r} + 1 \\ \hline 59 \end{array}$
Subtract this sum from the original number chosen.	$\begin{array}{r} 82 \\ - 59 \\ \hline 23 \end{array}$

At this point, without looking, you can announce the final result. It will always be 23! To be more dramatic, you can have a sealed envelope with the number 23 enclosed. Or you can have the number 23 written on the back of your hand with soap and have it magically appear by rubbing ashes on it!

The mathematical explanation for the trick is quite simple and appropriate to discuss in a chapter dealing with polynomials. We begin with a two-digit number, $\underline{a}\ \underline{b}\,(10a + b)$, with $a \geq 5$.

Add 76:	$10a + b + 76$
Cross out the hundreds digit:	$10a + b + 76 - 100 = 10a + b - 24$
Add 1:	$10a + b - 23$
Subtract from the original number:	$(10a + b) - (10a + b - 23) = 23$

Note: To alter the problem, note that if the number to be added is x, then the final answer will be $99 - x$.

4. Begin with 20 objects, such as 20 pennies. (If placed on the screen of an overhead projector, this trick will be visible to the entire class.) While your back is turned, ask a student to remove from 1 to 9 pennies. Next ask the student to count the number of pennies that remain, which will be a two-digit number. Ask that they find the sum of these two digits and remove that many more pennies. At this point you can announce the number of pennies that remain. The result will always be 9!

Example	Explanation
Begin with 20 objects.	Remove n objects, where $1 < n < 9$.
Suppose 8 are removed.	There are $20 - n$ left.
There are 12 left.	Write $20 - n$ as $10 + (10 - n)$.
$1 + 2 = 3$; 3 more are removed.	The sum of the digits is $1 + (10 - n)$, or $11 - n$.
$12 - 3 = 9$ There are 9 left.	Subtract this number from $20 - n$: $(20 - n) - (11 - n) = 9$

5. Have all students in the class write in their notebooks a three-digit number with the units and hundreds digits differing by more than 1. Alternatively, have one student work at the chalkboard with the rest of the class serving as observers. Then proceed as follows.

Directions	Sample
Write a three-digit number in which the units and hundreds digits differ by more than 1.	853
Reverse the digits and subtract.	$\begin{array}{r} 853 \\ -\ 358 \\ \hline 495 \end{array}$
Reverse the digits of your answer and add.	$\begin{array}{r} 495 \\ +\ 594 \\ \hline 1089 \end{array}$

At this point, announce that the final result is 1089. That this will always be the final answer can be seen from the following explanation.

Write a three-digit number:	$100a + 10b + c$
Reverse the digits:	$100c + 10b + a$
Subtract:	$100a - 100c + c - a$
*Now add and subtract 100 in this form:	$100a - 100c - 100 + 90 + 10 + c - a$
*Factor:	$100(a - c - 1) + 90 + (10 + c - a)$

Reverse the digits:	$100(10 + c - a) + 90 + (a - c - 1)$
Add:	$\begin{array}{l} 100a - 100c - 100 + 90 + 10 + c - a \\ 1000 + 100c - 100a + 90 + a - c - 1 \end{array}$
Sum =	$900 + 180 + 9 = 1089$

*Note that these two steps are inserted here to explain why the trick works. They are not part of the development of the trick as given above.

6. The Fibonacci sequence is an interesting one in mathematical literature. It begins with the terms 1 and 1. Thereafter, each term is the sum of the two preceding ones. Here are the first ten terms of this sequence:

$$1, 1, 2, 3, 5, 8, 13, 21, 34, 55$$

Although this is the original Fibonacci sequence, you may begin with any two numbers and form a sequence in the same manner. One of the many fascinating properties of such a sequence is that the sum of the first ten terms is equal to 11 times the seventh term. Thus, you may ask a student to write the first ten terms of any Fibonacci sequence in a column on the chalkboard. Before the student is finished, you can magically predict the sum.

Example

1	4	
2	7	
3	11	
4	18	
5	29	
6	47	
7	76	←The sum will be
8	123	$76 \times 11 = 836$
9	199	
10	322	
Sum:	836	

Explanation

1	a
2	b
3	$a + b$
4	$a + 2b$
5	$2a + 3b$
6	$3a + 5b$
7	$5a + 8b$
8	$8a + 13b$
9	$13a + 21b$
10	$21a + 34b$
Sum:	$55a + 88b$

Note that this sum can be factored:

$$55a + 88b = 11(5a + 8b)$$

In factored form, it is clear that the sum is 11 times the seventh term. This is also an excellent item to use during chapters on the subjects of factoring and operations with polynomials.

PATTERNS

A search for patterns can be most rewarding and exciting to students, most of whom will enjoy making discoveries. It is often effective to provide students with a situation and to encourage them to make their own discoveries. However, you will normally have to provide a few examples to indicate the types of discoveries that can be made. In each case, the student should be asked to verify the discovery through some mathematical explanation. Here are several examples.

1. Consider the calendar for the current month. What can the student discover about relationships between numbers on the calendar? Assume that the current month has these dates:

	1	2	3	4	5	6
7	8	9	10	11	12	13
14	15	16	17	18	19	20
21	22	23	24	25	26	27
28	29	30	31			

Enclose a square array of any 9 numbers, such as shown above. Now note such "discoveries" as these:

a. The sum of numbers in opposite corners are equal. That is, $8 + 24 = 10 + 22 = 32$.

b. The sum of all 9 numbers is 9 times the center number. That is, the sum is $9 \times 16 = 144$.

Students should be encouraged to show that such results will hold regardless of where the square array of 9 numbers is chosen. This can be demonstrated by using this generalized array:

$n - 8$	$n - 7$	$n - 6$
$n - 1$	n	$n + 1$
$n + 6$	$n + 7$	$n + 8$

The sum of the numbers in the opposite corners is

$$(n - 8) + (n + 8) = (n - 6) + (n + 6) = 2n$$

Also, by addition, the sum of the nine entries is $9n$.

As an extension, have students investigate the relationship between sums of numbers in opposite corners for rectangular arrays. In each case, they will find that these sums are equal.

2. Now consider a table showing the counting numbers 1 through 100. Again, encourage students to make as many discoveries as they can on their own.

1	2	3	4	5	6	7	8	9	10
11	12	13	14	15	16	17	18	19	20
21	22	23	24	25	26	27	28	29	30
31	32	33	34	35	36	37	38	39	40
41	42	43	44	45	46	47	48	49	50
51	52	53	54	55	56	57	58	59	60
61	62	63	64	65	66	67	68	69	70
71	72	73	74	75	76	77	78	79	80
81	82	83	84	85	86	87	88	89	90
91	92	93	94	95	96	97	98	99	100

Here are some of the discoveries students can be led to make:

a. For any square array, the sum of the numbers in opposite corners are equal. In the square shown,

$$35 + 57 = 37 + 55 = 92$$

This can be shown to be true for square arrays of any size, such as a 4×4 array of 16 numbers, as well as for rectangular arrays.

b. It would be interesting if the products of numbers in the opposite corners were also equal. This is not the case; note that $35 \times 57 = 1995$ and $37 \times 55 = 2035$. However, these products differ by 40. Now ask students to find the difference of such products for other square arrays of nine numbers. In each case, it proves to be 40, as can be shown by using this generalized array:

$n - 11$	$n - 10$	$n - 9$
$n - 1$	n	$n + 1$
$n + 9$	$n + 10$	$n + 11$

The products of numbers in opposite corners are:

$$(n - 11)(n + 11) = n^2 - 121$$
$$(n - 9)(n + 9) = n^2 - 81$$

The difference is $(n^2 - 121) - (n^2 - 81) = 40$.
This is a *proof* that such a difference will always be 40.

As an extension, have students consider other square and rectangular arrays of numbers. Have them compare products of numbers in opposite corners, form generalizations, and attempt to prove these in the manner shown above. For example, consider this generalized form of a rectangular array with three rows and four columns:

n	$n + 1$	$n + 2$	$n + 3$
$n + 10$	$n + 11$	$n + 12$	$n + 13$
$n + 20$	$n + 21$	$n + 22$	$n + 23$

Consider the products of entries in opposite corners:

$$n(n + 23) = n^2 + 23n$$
$$(n + 3)(n + 20) = n^2 + 23n + 60$$

Clearly, the constant difference is 60.

EXPLORATIONS

A good motivational technique is to have students conduct explorations, either individually or in groups. These should lead to some conjecture or discovery that can be expressed algebraically or that has an algebraic flavor to its development. Here are several examples.

1. Have students verify each of the following identities:

$$3^2 - 3 = 2^2 + 2$$
$$4^2 - 4 = 3^2 + 3$$
$$5^2 - 5 = 4^2 + 4$$

At this point, have the students form a conjecture, such as

$$a^2 - a = b^2 + b, \text{ where } a = b + 1$$

Then have them test the conjecture for other values of a and b. For example, for $a = 10$, $b = 9$:

$$10^2 - 10 = 9^2 + 9$$

Finally, ask the students to prove the conjecture. This is a relatively straightforward proof at this grade level:

For $a = b + 1$,
$$a^2 - a = (b + 1)^2 - (b + 1)$$
$$= b^2 + 2b + 1 - b - 1$$
$$= b^2 + b$$
$$= b(b + 1)$$

Thus, we have proved that $a^2 - a = b^2 + b$ for all a and b such that $a = b + 1$.

2. Pose this problem for students:

Mr. Smith looks at his watch at 1 A.M. on January 1. He waits 1 minute and snaps his fingers. Then he waits 2 minutes to snap them again. Thereafter, he snaps them after 4 minutes, 8 minutes, 16 minutes, and so on. That is, he doubles the interval of minutes between snaps. How many times will he snap his fingers in a 365-day year?

In solving the problem, the students will first have to determine the number of minutes in 365 days. (There are 525,600 minutes.) Theoretically, the students must proceed to list the numbers of minutes between snaps and total them until the sum is as close to 525,600 as possible but does not exceed it. In actuality, however, they can try a few sample "totals" and look for a pattern. For example, have them compute these sums:

1	1	1	1
2	2	2	2
4	4	4	4
8	8	8	8
15	16	16	16
	31	32	32
		63	64
			127

At this point, ask the students to make a conjecture concerning the relationship between the sums shown and the number of powers of 2 listed. They should note that in each case the sum is 1 less than the next power of 2. Able students may form this generalization:

$$1 + 2 + 4 + 8 + 16 + 32 + 64 + \ldots + 2^n =$$
$$2^0 + 2^1 + 2^2 + 2^3 + 2^4 + 2^5 + 2^6 + \ldots + 2^n = 2^{n+1} - 1$$

Now the students should be able to list powers of 2 and not have to do the addition each time to see whether a sum of 525,600 has been exceeded. They should find that $2^{19} - 1 = 524,287$. Since there are 19 terms in the expression $2^0 + 2^1 + \ldots + 2^{18}$, Mr. Smith will snap his fingers 19 times in one year.

Bibliography

Bell, Eric T. *Men of Mathematics.* New York: Simon and Schuster, 1937.

Courant, Richard, and Robbins, Herbert. *What Is Mathematics?* Fairlawn, N.J.: Oxford University Press, 1941 (hardcover); 1979 (softcover).

Eves, Howard. *An Introduction to the History of Mathematics.* New York: Holt, Rinehart and Winston, 1976.

Hill, T. J., ed. *Mathematical Challenges II Plus Six.* National Council of Teachers of Mathematics: Reston, Va., 1974.

Jacobs, H. R. *Mathematics, A Human Endeavor.* San Francisco: W. H. Freeman and Company, 1970.

Kasner, Edward, and Newman, James R. *Mathematics and the Imagination.* New York: Simon and Schuster, Touchstone Books, 1962.

Krulik, Stephen, and Rudnick, Jesse A. *Problem Solving: A Handbook for Teachers.* Boston: Allyn & Bacon, 1980.

National Council of Teachers of Mathematics (NCTM). Reston, Va.: Selected publications.

Yearbooks
1969: *Historical Topics for the Mathematics Classroom* (Thirty-first Yearbook).

1970: *The Teaching of Secondary School Mathematics* (Thirty-third Yearbook).

1979: *Applications in School Mathematics.*

1980: *Problem Solving in School Mathematics.*

1984: *Computers in Mathematics Education.*

Other NCTM Publications
A Sourcebook of Applications of School Mathematics. 1980.

Activities from "The Mathematics Teacher." Edited by Evan M. Maletsky and Christian R. Hirsch. 1981.

Polya, George, *How to Solve It.* Princeton, N.J.: Princeton University Press, 1971.

Sobel, Max, and Maletsky, Evan M. *Teaching Mathematics: A Sourcebook of Aids, Activities, and Strategies.* Englewood Cliffs, N.J.: Prentice-Hall, 1975.

For a more extensive bibliography, you may refer to the article "What Every Secondary School Mathematics Teacher Should Read—Twenty-four Opinions" by Lowell Leake in the February 1983 issue of *The Mathematics Teacher,* published by the National Council of Teachers of Mathematics, 1906 Association Drive, Reston, Va. 22091.

ASSIGNMENT CHART

This assignment chart indicates three possible courses based on the text: a minimum course, an average course, and a maximum course. These courses can be modified to meet the needs of your classes.

As you know, students' interests and backgrounds differ significantly from class to class. Therefore, most of the optional features are not listed in this assignment chart. Use those features that you feel are most suited to the students in your classes.

You will observe that the suggested daily assignments make extensive use of odd-numbered exercises. The answers to many odd-numbered exercises appear in the back of the student's book, so the students will be able to check their homework answers independently. However, if you prefer to assign exercises whose answers are not readily accessible to the students, you may easily make similar assignments using even-numbered exercises. For example, instead of

assigning "Ex. 1–49 odd," you might assign "Ex. 2–50 even."

It is also worth noting that the Extra Practice material, which appears on pages 507–533 of the student's book, is not listed in this assignment chart. Rather, it is coded into the daily lessons by simple notations that appear below the reduced student's text pages. In this way, you can assign the Extra Practice material as you see fit.

DAY	MINIMUM COURSE	AVERAGE COURSE	MAXIMUM COURSE
1	Lesson **1-1** p. 2 Ex. 1–49 odd	Lesson **1-1** p. 2 Ex. 1–57 odd, 59, 61	Lesson **1-1** p. 2 Ex. 17–57 odd, 59–65
2	Lesson **1-2** p. 5 Ex. 1–39 odd	Lesson **1-2** p. 5 Ex. 1–59 odd	Lesson **1-2** p. 5 Ex. 17–43 odd, 45–60
3	Lesson **1-3** p. 8 Ex. 1–6, 7–35 odd	Lesson **1-3** p. 8 Ex. 1–43 odd, 45, 46	Lesson **1-3** p. 8 Ex. 1–43 odd, 45–49
4	Lesson **1-3** (second day) Ex. 10–36 even, 37–49 odd	Lesson **1-4** p. 11 Ex. 1–35	Lesson **1-4** p. 11 Ex. 5–40
5	Lesson **1-4** p. 11 Ex. 1–28	Lesson **1-5** p. 14 Ex. 1–45 odd *Checkpoint* review exercises	Lesson **1-5** p. 14 Ex. 7–57 odd *Checkpoint* review exercises
6	Lesson **1-5** p. 14 Ex. 1–6, 7–31 odd *Checkpoint* review exercises	Lesson **1-6** p. 17 Ex. 1–24	Lesson **1-6** p. 17 Ex. 13–32, 33–39 odd
7	Lesson **1-6** p. 17 Ex. 1–16	Lesson **1-6** (second day) Ex. 25–39	Lesson **1-7** p. 21 Ex. 7–23 odd, 25–44 *Strategies for Problem Solving*
8	Lesson **1-6** (second day) Ex. 17–30	Lesson **1-7** p. 21 Ex. 1–13 odd, 14–38 *Strategies for Problem Solving*	Lesson **1-8** p. 25 Ex. 1–32
9	Lesson **1-7** p. 21 Ex. 1–13, 15–35 odd *Strategies for Problem Solving*	Lesson **1-8** p. 25 Ex. 1–26	Lesson **1-9** p. 28 Ex. 13–29 odd, 30–45 *Checkpoint* review exercises

DAY	MINIMUM COURSE	AVERAGE COURSE	MAXIMUM COURSE
10	Lesson 1-8 p. 25 Ex. 1–17, 21–26	Lesson 1-9 p. 28 Ex. 1–12, 13–29 odd, 30–41 *Checkpoint* review exercises	Lesson 1-10 p. 32 Ex. 1–30
11	Lesson 1-9 p. 28 Ex. 1–29 *Checkpoint* review exercises	Lesson 1-10 p. 32 Ex. 1–27	Lesson 1-11 p. 34 Ex. 1–26 odd, 27–37
12	Lesson 1-10 p. 32 Ex. 1–21	Lesson 1-11 p. 34 Ex. 1–16, 17–31 odd	*Applications* p. 37 *Chapter Review*
13	Lesson 1-11 p. 34 Ex. 1–16, 17–26 odd	*Applications* p. 37 *Chapter Review*	*Chapter Test* p. 40
14	*Applications* p. 37 *Chapter Review*	*Chapter Test* p. 40	Lesson 2-1 p. 44 Ex. 15–41
15	*Chapter Test* p. 40	Lesson 2-1 p. 44 Ex. 1–41 odd	Lesson 2-2 p. 47 Ex. 27–49 odd, 50–66
16	Lesson 2-1 p. 44 Ex. 1–30	Lesson 2-2 p. 47 Ex. 13–63 odd	Lesson 2-3 p. 50 Ex. 13–45 odd, 47–60
17	Lesson 2-2 p. 47 Ex. 1–49 odd	Lesson 2-3 p. 50 Ex. 1–45 odd, 47–54	Lesson 2-4 p. 55 Ex. 1–63 odd *Checkpoint* review exercises
18	Lesson 2-3 p. 50 Ex. 1–24, 25–45 odd	Lesson 2-4 p. 55 Ex. 1–41 odd, 43–45 *Checkpoint* review exercises	Lesson 2-5 p. 59 Ex. 5–47 odd, 49–53 *Strategies for Problem Solving*
19	Lesson 2-4 p. 55 Ex. 1–6, 7–33 odd	Lesson 2-5 p. 59 Ex. 1–4, 5–47 odd *Strategies for Problem Solving*	Lesson 2-6 p. 63 Ex. 19–55 odd, 56–64
20	Lesson 2-4 (second day) Ex. 8–34 even, 35, 37, 39, 41 *Checkpoint* review exercises	Lesson 2-6 p. 63 Ex. 1–55 odd	Lesson 2-7 p. 66 Ex. 11–35
21	Lesson 2-5 p. 59 Ex. 1–24, 25, 27, 29, 31 *Strategies for Problem Solving*	Lesson 2-7 p. 66 Ex. 1–13 odd, 14–33	Lesson 2-8 p. 69 Ex. 17–51 odd, 53–54 *Checkpoint* review exercises
22	Lesson 2-6 p. 63 Ex. 1–43 odd	Lesson 2-8 p. 69 Ex. 1–51 odd *Checkpoint* review exercises	Lesson 2-8 (second day) Ex. 42–52 even, 56–61 *Extra Topic*

DAY	MINIMUM COURSE	AVERAGE COURSE	MAXIMUM COURSE
23	Lesson **2-7** p. 66 Ex. 1–21	Lesson **2-8** (second day) Ex. 22–52 even *Extra Topic*	Lesson **2-9** p. 74 Ex. 1–21
24	Lesson **2-8** p. 69 Ex. 1–20, 21–31 odd *Checkpoint* review exercises	Lesson **2-9** p. 74 Ex. 1–14	*Applications* p. 77 *Chapter Review*
25	Lesson **2-8** (second day) *Extra Topic*	Lesson **2-9** (second day) Ex. 15–21	*Chapter Test* p. 80
26	Lesson **2-9** p. 74 Ex. 1–9	*Applications* p. 77 *Chapter Review*	Lesson **3-1** p. 84 Ex. 1–19 odd, 21–29
27	Lesson **2-9** (second day) Ex. 11–17	*Chapter Test* p. 80	Lesson **3-2** p. 87 Ex. 13–63 odd
28	*Appplications* p. 77 *Chapter Review*	Lesson **3-1** p. 84 Ex. 1–11 odd, 13–24, 25, 27, 29	Lesson **3-2** (second day) Ex. 38–62 even, 64–70 *Strategies for Problem Solving*
29	*Chapter Test* p. 80	Lesson **3-2** p. 87 Ex. 1–51 odd	Lesson **3-3** p. 92 Ex. 13–47 odd, 49, 50, 51–61 odd *Checkpoint* review exercises
30	Lesson **3-1** p. 84 Ex. 1–12, 13–23 odd, 27	Lesson **3-2** (second day) Ex. 38–50 even, 53–67 odd *Strategies for Problem Solving*	Lesson **3-4** p. 96 Ex. 13–59 odd
31	Lesson **3-2** p. 87 Ex. 1–35 odd	Lesson **3-3** p. 92 Ex. 1–47 odd, 49, 50 *Checkpoint* review exercises	Lesson **3-5** p. 100 Ex. 21–83 odd
32	Lesson **3-2** (second day) Ex. 14–36 even, 37–53 odd *Strategies for Problem Solving*	Lesson **3-4** p. 96 Ex. 1–49 odd	Lesson **3-6** p. 103 Ex. 1–47 odd
33	Lesson **3-3** p. 92 Ex. 1–35 odd, 39, 43, 47, 49 *Checkpoint* review exercises	Lesson **3-5** p. 100 Ex. 13–75 odd	Lesson **3-7** p. 107 Ex. 1–49 odd, 51–55 *Checkpoint* review exercises
34	Lesson **3-4** p. 96 Ex. 1–35 odd	Lesson **3-6** p. 103 Ex. 1–39 odd	Lesson **3-8** p. 111 Ex. 1–19 odd
35	Lesson **3-5** p. 100 Ex. 1–39 odd, 53, 57, 65, 71	Lesson **3-7** p. 107 Ex. 1–18, 19–29 odd	Lesson **3-8** (second day) Ex. 2–18 even

DAY	MINIMUM COURSE	AVERAGE COURSE	MAXIMUM COURSE
36	Lesson **3-6** p. 103 Ex. 1–17 odd	Lesson **3-7** (second day) Ex. 31–55 odd *Checkpoint* review exercises	Applications p. 115 *Chapter Review*
37	Lesson **3-6** (second day) Ex. 19–37 odd	Lesson **3-8** p. 111 Ex. 1–15 odd	*Chapter Test* p. 118
38	Lesson **3-7** p. 107 Ex. 1–18	Lesson **3-8** (second day) Ex. 2–16 even	*Cumulative Review* p. 120
39	Lesson **3-7** (second day) Ex. 19–51 odd *Checkpoint* review exercises	Applications p. 115 *Chapter Review*	Lesson **4-1** p. 124 Ex. 13–33 odd, 35–54
40	Lesson **3-8** p. 111 Ex. 1–13 odd	*Chapter Test* p. 118	Lesson **4-2** p. 128 Ex. 1–11 odd, 13–31
41	Lesson **3-8** (second day) Ex. 2–14 even	*Cumulative Review* p. 120	Lesson **4-3** p. 132 Ex. 5–39 odd, 41–46 *Checkpoint* review exercises
42	Applications p. 115 *Chapter Review*	Lesson **4-1** p. 124 Ex. 1–11 odd, 13–47	Lesson **4-4** p. 136 Ex. 9–25 odd, 27–31, 33–39 odd
43	*Chapter Test* p. 118	Lesson **4-2** p. 128 Ex. 1–27	Lesson **4-5** p. 141 Ex. 5–47 odd, 49–54
44	*Cumulative Review* p. 120	Lesson **4-3** p. 132 Ex. 1–4, 5–39 odd	Lesson **4-5** (second day) Ex. 32–48 even, 55–58 *Strategies for Problem Solving*
45	Lesson **4-1** p. 124 Ex. 1–34	Lesson **4-3** (second day) Ex. 6–28 even, 41 *Checkpoint* review exercises	Lesson **4-6** p. 145 Ex. 3, 6, 9, 12, 15, 18, 21–53 odd, 55–59 *Checkpoint* review exercises
46	Lesson **4-2** p. 128 Ex. 1–20	Lesson **4-4** p. 136 Ex. 1–25 odd, 27–31	Lesson **4-7** p. 149 Ex. 1–31 odd
47	Lesson **4-3** p. 132 Ex. 1–4, 5–21 odd	Lesson **4-5** p. 141 Ex. 1–3, 5–45 odd	Lesson **4-8** p. 152 Ex. 5–47 odd, 48–56
48	Lesson **4-3** (second day) Ex. 6–16 even, 21–33 odd *Checkpoint* review exercises	Lesson **4-5** (second day) Ex. 32–48 even, 49–54 *Strategies for Problem Solving*	Lesson **4-9** p. 155 Ex. 13–59 odd

DAY	MINIMUM COURSE	AVERAGE COURSE	MAXIMUM COURSE
49	Lesson **4-4** p. 136 Ex. 1–11, 13–23 odd	Lesson **4-6** p. 145 Ex. 1–49 odd *Checkpoint* review exercises	*Applications* p. 159 *Chapter Review*
50	Lesson **4-5** p. 141 Ex. 1–3, 5–31 odd	Lesson **4-7** p. 149 Ex. 1–25 odd	*Chapter Test* p. 162
51	Lesson **4-5** (second day) Ex. 20–38 even, 40–45 *Strategies for Problem Solving*	Lesson **4-8** p. 152 Ex. 1–4, 5–45 odd	Lesson **5-1** p. 166 Ex. 1–69 odd
52	Lesson **4-6** p. 145 Ex. 1–8, 9–31 odd	Lesson **4-9** p. 155 Ex. 1–41 odd, 54, 55	Lesson **5-2** p. 170 Ex. 1–47 odd, 48–50, 55–58
53	Lesson **4-6** (second day) Ex. 22–32 even, 33–39 odd *Checkpoint* review exercises	*Applications* p. 159 *Chapter Review*	Lesson **5-3** p. 174 Ex. 13–87 odd *Checkpoint* review exercises
54	Lesson **4-7** p. 149 Ex. 1–13, 15, 17, 19	*Chapter Test* p. 162	Lesson **5-4** p. 178 Ex. 1–63 odd
55	Lesson **4-8** p. 152 Ex. 1–4, 5–21 odd	Lesson **5-1** p. 166 Ex. 1–65 odd	Lesson **5-4** (second day) Ex. 44–72 even *Strategies for Problem Solving*
56	Lesson **4-8** (second day) Ex. 6–22 even, 23–33 odd	Lesson **5-2** p. 170 Ex. 1–47 odd, 49–54	Lesson **5-5** p. 182 Ex. 1–53 odd
57	Lesson **4-9** p. 155 Ex. 1–27 odd, 32, 33	Lesson **5-3** p. 174 Ex. 9–71 odd, 72 *Checkpoint* review exercises	Lesson **5-6** p. 184 Ex. 11–73 odd
58	*Applications* p. 159 *Chapter Review*	Lesson **5-4** p. 178 Ex. 1–61 odd	Lesson **5-7** p. 187 Ex. 7–77 odd
59	*Chapter Test* p. 162	Lesson **5-4** (second day) Ex. 26–62 even *Strategies for Problem Solving*	Lesson **5-8** p. 190 Ex. 1–25 odd, 27–34 *Checkpoint* review exercises
60	Lesson **5-1** p. 166 Ex. 1–24, 25–51 odd	Lesson **5-5** p. 182 Ex. 1–45 odd, 49, 51	Lesson **5-9** p. 193 Ex. 1–13
61	Lesson **5-2** p. 170 Ex. 1–35 odd, 45, 47, 49	Lesson **5-6** p. 184 Ex. 1–59 odd	Lesson **5-9** (second day) Ex. 14–22

DAY	MINIMUM COURSE	AVERAGE COURSE	MAXIMUM COURSE
62	Lesson **5-3** p. 174 Ex. 1–41 odd, 59–63 odd *Checkpoint* review exercises	Lesson **5-7** p. 187 Ex. 1–63 odd	*Applications* p. 197 *Chapter Review*
63	Lesson **5-4** p. 178 Ex. 1–4, 5–55 odd	Lesson **5-8** p. 190 Ex. 1–15 odd, 17–27 *Checkpoint* review exercises	*Chapter Test* p. 200
64	Lesson **5-4** (second day) Ex. 6–50 even *Strategies for Problem Solving*	Lesson **5-9** p. 193 Ex. 1–12	Lesson **6-1** p. 204 Ex. 1–71 odd, 73–81
65	Lesson **5-5** p. 182 Ex. 1–12, 13–37 odd	Lesson **5-9** (second day) Ex. 13–19	Lesson **6-2** p. 208 Ex. 7–57 odd, 59–64
66	Lesson **5-6** p. 184 Ex. 1–10, 11–37 odd	*Applications* p. 197 *Chapter Review*	*Extra Topic* p. 211
67	Lesson **5-6** (second day) Ex. 12–46 even	*Chapter Test* p. 200	Lesson **6-3** p. 213 Ex. 1–59 odd, 60–62
68	Lesson **5-7** p. 187 Ex. 1–6, 7–53 odd	Lesson **6-1** p. 204 Ex. 1–47 odd, 49–68	Lesson **6-4** p. 216 Ex. 1–51 odd
69	Lesson **5-8** p. 190 Ex. 1–16, 17–21 odd *Checkpoint* review exercises	Lesson **6-2** p. 208 Ex. 1–57 odd	Lesson **6-5** p. 219 Ex. 7–65 odd, 66–69 *Checkpoint* review exercises
70	Lesson **5-9** p. 193 Ex. 1–10	Lesson **6-3** p. 213 Ex. 1–51 odd, 58, 59	Lesson **6-6** p. 223 Ex. 1–53 odd
71	Lesson **5-9** (second day) Ex. 11–18	Lesson **6-4** p. 216 Ex. 1–43 odd	Lesson **6-7** p. 226 Ex. 1–6, 7–47 odd
72	*Applications* p. 197 *Chapter Review*	Lesson **6-5** p. 219 Ex. 1–47 odd, 49, 51, 55	Lesson **6-8** p. 229 Ex. 1–7, 9–49 odd
73	*Chapter Test* p. 200	Lesson **6-6** p. 223 Ex. 1–31 odd, 32–42	Lesson **6-8** (second day) Ex. 8–48 even, 52–54 *Extra Topic*
74	Lesson **6-1** p. 204 Ex. 1–30, 31–57 odd	Lesson **6-7** p. 226 Ex. 1–6, 7–41 odd	Lesson **6-9** p. 233 Ex. 1–57 odd *Checkpoint* review exercises

DAY	MINIMUM COURSE	AVERAGE COURSE	MAXIMUM COURSE
75	Lesson **6-2** p. 208 Ex. 1–47 odd, 55, 57	Lesson **6-8** p. 229 Ex. 1–7, 9–39 odd	Lesson **6-10** p. 236 Ex. 1–61 odd
76	Lesson **6-3** p. 213 Ex. 1–43 odd	Lesson **6-8** (second day) Ex. 8–40 even, 41, 43, 45	Lesson **6-10** (second day) Ex. 30–60 even, 62–76 *Strategies for Problem Solving*
77	Lesson **6-4** p. 216 Ex. 1–8, 9–39 odd	Lesson **6-9** p. 233 Ex. 1–12, 13–43 odd *Checkpoint* review exercises	Lesson **6-11** p. 241 Ex. 1–29 odd
78	Lesson **6-5** p. 219 Ex. 1–39 odd, 49, 51 *Checkpoint* review exercises	Lesson **6-10** p. 236 Ex. 1–57 odd, 59, 60	Lesson **6-11** (second day) Ex. 2–30 even
79	Lesson **6-6** p. 223 Ex. 1–16, 17–31 odd	Lesson **6-10** (second day) Ex. 12–56 even, 62–65 *Strategies for Problem Solving*	*Applications* p. 245 *Chapter Review*
80	Lesson **6-7** p. 226 Ex. 1–6, 7–31 odd	Lesson **6-11** p. 241 Ex. 1–21 odd	*Chapter Test* p. 248
81	Lesson **6-7** (second day) Ex. 8–36 even	Lesson **6-11** (second day) Ex. 2–24 even	*Cumulative Review* p. 250
82	Lesson **6-8** p. 229 Ex. 1–7, 9–31 odd	*Applications* p. 245 *Chapter Review*	Lesson **7-1** p. 254 Ex. 1–41 odd, 43–46
83	Lesson **6-8** (second day) Ex. 8–36 even	*Chapter Test* p. 248	Lesson **7-2** p. 258 Ex. 1–35 odd
84	Lesson **6-9** p. 233 Ex. 1–16, 17–31 odd *Checkpoint* review exercises	*Cumulative Review* p. 250	Lesson **7-3** p. 261 Ex. 1–27 odd *Checkpoint* review exercises
85	Lesson **6-10** p. 236 Ex. 1–45 odd, 59	Lesson **7-1** p. 254 Ex. 1–43 odd	Lesson **7-4** p. 264 Ex. 1–41 odd
86	Lesson **6-10** (second day) Ex. 6–46 even *Strategies for Problem Solving*	Lesson **7-2** p. 258 Ex. 1–31 odd	Lesson **7-4** (second day) Ex. 26–48 even *Strategies for Problem Solving*
87	Lesson **6-11** p. 241 Ex. 1–15 odd	Lesson **7-3** p. 261 Ex. 1–23 odd *Checkpoint* review exercises	Lesson **7-5** p. 268 Ex. 1–33 odd, 34–38 *Checkpoint* review exercises

DAY	MINIMUM COURSE	AVERAGE COURSE	MAXIMUM COURSE
88	Lesson **6-11** (second day) Ex. 2–20 even	Lesson **7-4** p. 264 Ex. 1–35 odd	Lesson **7-6** p. 272 Ex. 1–27 odd
89	Applications p. 245 Chapter Review	Lesson **7-4** (second day) Ex. 26–44 even *Strategies for Problem Solving*	Lesson **7-7** p. 276 Ex. 1–9 odd, 10–18
90	Chapter Test p. 248	Lesson **7-5** p. 268 Ex. 1–33 odd *Checkpoint* review exercises	Applications p. 279 Chapter Review
91	Cumulative Review p. 250	Lesson **7-6** p. 272 Ex. 1–23 odd	Chapter Test p. 282
92	Lesson **7-1** p. 254 Ex. 1–3, 5–33 odd	Lesson **7-6** (second day) Ex. 12–26 even	Lesson **8-1** p. 286 Ex. 1–57 odd, 60–65
93	Lesson **7-2** p. 258 Ex. 1–20	Lesson **7-7** p. 276 Ex. 1–17 odd	Lesson **8-2** p. 290 Ex. 1–31 odd, 32–37
94	Lesson **7-3** p. 261 Ex. 1–12 *Checkpoint* review exercises	Applications p. 279 Chapter Review	Lesson **8-3** p. 293 Ex. 1–49 odd, 51, 52
95	Lesson **7-4** p. 264 Ex. 1–12	Chapter Test p. 282	Lesson **8-4** p. 296 Ex. 1–41 odd, 42–48
96	Lesson **7-4** (second day) Ex. 13–27 odd *Strategies for Problem Solving*	Lesson **8-1** p. 286 Ex. 1–53 odd	Lesson **8-5** p. 299 Ex. 1–35 odd, 36–38
97	Lesson **7-6** p. 272 Ex. 1–8	Lesson **8-2** p. 290 Ex. 1–31 odd, 32, 33	Lesson **8-6** p. 302 Ex. 1–45 odd, 46, 47 *Checkpoint* review exercises
98	Lesson **7-6** (second day) Ex. 9–16	Lesson **8-3** p. 293 Ex. 1–45 odd, 51	Lesson **8-7** p. 305 Ex. 1–41 odd
99	Lesson **7-7** p. 276 Ex. 1–7	Lesson **8-4** p. 296 Ex. 1–35 odd	Lesson **8-7** (second day) Ex. 26–40 even, 44, 45 *Strategies for Problem Solving*
100	Lesson **7-7** (second day) Ex. 8–13	Lesson **8-4** (second day) Ex. 18–36 even, 37–47 odd	Lesson **8-8** p. 309 Ex. 1–33 odd, 34–37 *Checkpoint* review exercises

DAY	MINIMUM COURSE	AVERAGE COURSE	MAXIMUM COURSE
101	Applications p. 279 Chapter Review	Lesson **8-5** p. 299 Ex. 1–33 odd	Lesson **8-9** p. 312 Ex. 1–31 odd
102	Chapter Test p. 282	Lesson **8-6** p. 302 Ex. 1–41 odd, 46 Checkpoint review exercises	Lesson **8-9** (second day) Ex. 18–32 even, 33–39
103	Lesson **8-1** p. 286 Ex. 1–8, 9–37 odd	Lesson **8-7** p. 305 Ex. 1–37 odd	Applications p. 315 Chapter Review
104	Lesson **8-2** p. 290 Ex. 1–6, 7–25 odd	Lesson **8-7** (second day) Ex. 22–40 even, 45 Strategies for Problem Solving	Chapter Test p. 318
105	Lesson **8-3** p. 293 Ex. 1–12, 13–37 odd	Lesson **8-8** p. 309 Ex. 1–6, 7–37 odd Checkpoint review exercises	Lesson **9-1** p. 322 Ex. 1–19 odd, 21–30
106	Lesson **8-4** p. 296 Ex. 1–8, 9–25 odd	Lesson **8-9** p. 312 Ex. 1–20	Lesson **9-2** p. 324 Ex. 1–23 odd, 24–30
107	Lesson **8-4** (second day) Ex. 18–26 even, 27–33 odd	Lesson **8-9** (second day) Ex. 21–39 odd	Lesson **9-3** p. 327 Ex. 1–13 Checkpoint review exercises
108	Lesson **8-5** p. 299 Ex. 1–23 odd	Applications p. 315 Chapter Review	Lesson **9-4** p. 330 Ex. 1–11
109	Lesson **8-5** (second day) Ex. 10–30 even	Chapter Test p. 318	Lesson **9-4** (second day) Ex. 12–17 Strategies for Problem Solving
110	Lesson **8-6** p. 302 Ex. 1–33 odd Checkpoint review exercises	Lesson **9-1** p. 322 Ex. 1–25 odd, 28	Lesson **9-5** p. 335 Ex. 1–43 odd
111	Lesson **8-7** p. 305 Ex. 1–29 odd	Lesson **9-2** p. 324 Ex. 1–23 odd, 28, 29	Lesson **9-6** p. 339 Ex. 1–43 odd Checkpoint review exercises
112	Lesson **8-7** (second day) Ex. 10–30 even Strategies for Problem Solving	Lesson **9-3** p. 327 Ex. 1–13 odd Checkpoint review exercises	Lesson **9-7** p. 343 Ex. 1–17
113	Lesson **8-8** p. 309 Ex. 1–6, 7–27 odd Checkpoint review exercises	Lesson **9-4** p. 330 Ex. 1–8	Lesson **9-8** p. 346 Ex. 1–12

DAY	MINIMUM COURSE	AVERAGE COURSE	MAXIMUM COURSE
114	Applications p. 315 Chapter Review	Lesson **9-4** (second day) Ex. 9-15 Strategies for Problem Solving	Lesson **9-9** p. 349 Ex. 1–15 odd, 16
115	Chapter Test p. 318	Lesson **9-5** p. 335 Ex. 1–35 odd	Lesson **9-9** (second day) Ex. 2–14 even, 17
116	Lesson **9-1** p. 322 Ex. 1–19 odd, 21–23	Lesson **9-6** p. 339 Ex. 1–35 odd Checkpoint review exercises	Applications p. 353 Chapter Review
117	Lesson **9-2** p. 324 Ex. 1–23 odd	Lesson **9-7** p. 343 Ex. 1–14	Chapter Test p. 356
118	Lesson **9-2** (second day) Ex. 2–22 even	Lesson **9-8** p. 346 Ex. 1–10	Cumulative Review p. 358
119	Lesson **9-3** p. 327 Ex. 1–5	Lesson **9-9** p. 349 Ex. 1–13 odd, 14	Lesson **10-1** p. 362 Ex. 1–63 odd
120	Lesson **9-3** (second day) Ex. 6–10 Checkpoint review exercises	Lesson **9-9** (second day) Ex. 2–12 even, 15	Lesson **10-2** p. 366 Ex. 1–29 odd, 30–33
121	Lesson **9-4** p. 330 Ex. 1–6	Applications p. 353 Chapter Review	Lesson **10-3** p. 368 Ex. 1–23 odd, 25–32
122	Lesson **9-4** (second day) Ex. 7–11 Strategies for Problem Solving	Chapter Test p. 356	Lesson **10-3** (second day) Ex. 33–47 Checkpoint review exercises
123	Lesson **9-5** p. 335 Ex. 1–29 odd	Cumulative Review p. 358	Lesson **10-4** p. 371 Ex. 1–4, 5–17 odd
124	Lesson **9-6** p. 339 Ex. 1–29 odd	Lesson **10-1** p. 362 Ex. 1–57 odd	Lesson **10-4** (second day) Ex. 6–18 even
125	Lesson **9-6** (second day) Ex. 16–32 even Checkpoint review exercises	Lesson **10-2** p. 366 Ex. 1–27 odd	Lesson **10-5** p. 375 Ex. 1–49 odd
126	Lesson **9-7** p. 343 Ex. 1–11	Lesson **10-2** (second day) Ex. 2–28 even	Lesson **10-6** p. 379 Ex. 1–33 odd, 34–39, 41, 43 Strategies for Problem Solving

DAY	MINIMUM COURSE		AVERAGE COURSE		MAXIMUM COURSE	
127	Applications Chapter Review	p. 353	Lesson 10-3 Ex. 1–37 odd	p. 368	Lesson 10-7 Ex. 1–51 odd Checkpoint review exercises	p. 383
128	Chapter Test	p. 356	Lesson 10-3 (second day) Ex. 2–38 even Checkpoint review exercises		Lesson 10-8 Ex. 1–26 odd	p. 386
129	Cumulative Review	p. 358	Lesson 10-4 Ex. 1–4, 5–13 odd	p. 371	Applications Chapter Review	p. 389
130	Lesson 10-1 Ex. 1–47 odd	p. 362	Lesson 10-4 (second day) Ex. 6–14 even		Chapter Test	p. 392
131	Lesson 10-1 (second day) Ex. 2–52 even		Lesson 10-5 Ex. 1–9, 11–41 odd	p. 375	Lesson 11-1 Ex. 1–53 odd, 54–59	p. 396
132	Lesson 10-2 Ex. 1–19 odd	p. 366	Lesson 10-6 Ex. 1–12, 13–33 odd Strategies for Problem Solving	p. 379	Extra Topic	p. 399
133	Lesson 10-2 (second day) Ex. 2–20 even		Lesson 10-7 Ex. 1–43 odd Checkpoint review exercises	p. 383	Lesson 11-2 Ex. 7–63 odd, 64, 65, 66 Checkpoint review exercises	p. 401
134	Lesson 10-3 Ex. 1–31 odd	p. 368	Lesson 10-8 Ex. 1–21 odd	p. 386	Lesson 11-3 Ex. 1–57 odd, 59–64	p. 405
135	Lesson 10-3 (second day) Ex. 2–32 even Checkpoint review exercises		Applications Chapter Review	p. 389	Lesson 11-4 Ex. 1–47 odd	p. 408
136	Lesson 10-7 Ex. 1–8, 9–37 odd	p. 383	Chapter Test	p. 392	Lesson 11-5 Ex. 1–57 odd Checkpoint review exercises	p. 411
137	Applications Chapter Review	p. 389	Lesson 11-1 Ex. 1–55 odd	p. 396	Lesson 11-6 Ex. 7–45 odd	p. 414
138	Chapter Test	p. 392	Extra Topic	p. 399	Lesson 11-7 Ex. 1–27 odd	p. 416
139	Lesson 11-1 Ex. 1–37 odd	p. 396	Lesson 11-2 Ex. 1–63 odd Checkpoint review exercises	p. 401	Lesson 11-7 (second day) Ex. 20–28 even, 29–37	

DAY	MINIMUM COURSE	AVERAGE COURSE	MAXIMUM COURSE
140	*Extra Topic* p. 399	Lesson **11-3** p. 405 Ex. 1–57 odd	Lesson **11-8** p. 422 Ex. 1–27 odd
141	Lesson **11-2** p. 401 Ex. 1–51 odd *Checkpoint* review exercises	Lesson **11-4** p. 408 Ex. 1–41 odd	Lesson **11-9** p. 425 Ex. 1–43 odd
142	Lesson **11-3** p. 405 Ex. 1–35 odd	Lesson **11-5** p. 411 Ex. 1–43 odd *Checkpoint* review exercises	*Applications* p. 427 *Chapter Review*
143	Lesson **11-4** p. 408 Ex. 1–25 odd	Lesson **11-6** p. 414 Ex. 1–35 odd	*Chapter Test* p. 430
144	Lesson **11-4** (second day) Ex. 2–30 even	Lesson **11-7** p. 416 Ex. 1–27 odd	Lesson **12-1** p. 434 Ex. 1–29 odd, 30–39
145	Lesson **11-5** p. 411 Ex. 1–31 odd	Lesson **11-7** (second day) Ex. 2–28 even	Lesson **12-2** p. 438 Ex. 1–14 odd, 15–22 *Checkpoint* review exercises
146	Lesson **11-5** (second day) Ex. 2–30 even *Checkpoint* review exercises	Lesson **11-8** p. 422 Ex. 1–15 odd, 16–19	Lesson **12-3** p. 442 Ex. 1–37 odd
147	Lesson **11-6** p. 414 Ex. 1–23 odd	Lesson **11-9** p. 425 Ex. 1–31 odd	Lesson **12-4** p. 445 Ex. 1–25 odd, 27–32
148	Lesson **11-6** (second day) Ex. 2–30 even	*Applications* p. 427 *Chapter Review*	Lesson **12-4** (second day) Ex. 33–46
149	Lesson **11-7** p. 416 Ex. 1–19 odd	*Chapter Test* p. 430	Lesson **12-5** p. 449 Ex. 1–41 odd
150	Lesson **11-8** p. 422 Ex. 1–15 odd	Lesson **12-1** p. 434 Ex. 1–23 odd, 24–29	Lesson **12-6** p. 452 Ex. 1–29 odd, 34–37 *Strategies for Problem Solving*
151	Lesson **11-8** (second day) Ex. 2–16 even	Lesson **12-2** p. 438 Ex. 1–10, 11–17 odd *Checkpoint* review exercises	Lesson **12-7** p. 456 Ex. 7–25 odd, 26–29 *Checkpoint* review exercises
152	*Applications* p. 427 *Chapter Review*	Lesson **12-3** p. 442 Ex. 1–29 odd	Lesson **12-8** p. 459 Ex. 13–23, 25

DAY	MINIMUM COURSE	AVERAGE COURSE	MAXIMUM COURSE
153	Chapter Test p. 430	Lesson **12-4** p. 445 Ex. 1–31 odd	Lesson **12-9** p. 463 Ex. 1 0 odd, 11–19
154	Lesson **12-1** p. 434 Ex. 1–19	Lesson **12-4** (second day) Ex. 33–43	Lesson **12-10** p. 466 Ex. 1–21 odd
155	Lesson **12-2** p. 438 Ex. 1–6 Checkpoint review exercises	Lesson **12-5** p. 449 Ex. 1–35 odd	Applications p. 469 Chapter Review
156	Lesson **12-3** p. 442 Ex. 1–8, 9, 12, 15, 18, 21, 23	Lesson **12-6** p. 452 Ex. 1–29 odd Strategies for Problem Solving	Chapter Test p. 472
157	Lesson **12-4** p. 445 Ex. 1–17 odd	Lesson **12-7** p. 456 Ex. 1–21 odd Checkpoint review exercises	Lesson **13-1** p. 476 Ex. 1–9 odd, 11–22
158	Lesson **12-4** (second day) Ex. 6–12 even, 19–31 odd	Lesson **12-8** p. 459 Ex. 1–17 odd	Lesson **13-2** p. 479 Ex. 1–9 odd, 10–17
159	Lesson **12-6** p. 452 Ex. 1–23 odd	Lesson **12-8** (second day) Ex. 2–18 even	Lesson **13-3** p. 482 Ex. 1–21 odd, 22–28
160	Lesson **12-6** (second day) Ex. 12–28 even Strategies for Problem Solving	Lesson **12-9** p. 463 Ex. 1–17 odd	Lesson **13-4** p. 485 Ex. 1–15 odd, 16–23
161	Lesson **12-8** p. 459 Ex. 1–13 odd	Lesson **12-10** p. 466 Ex. 1–19 odd	Lesson **13-5** p. 489 Ex. 1–31 odd, 32 Strategies for Problem Solving
162	Applications p. 469 Chapter Review	Applications p. 469 Chapter Review	Applications p. 493 Chapter Review
163	Chapter Test p. 472	Chapter Test p. 472	Chapter Test p. 496
164	Cumulative Review p. 498	Cumulative Review p. 498	Cumulative Review p. 498
165	Cumulative Review (second day)	Cumulative Review (second day)	Cumulative Review (second day)

SUMMARY TIME SCHEDULE FOR THE CHAPTERS

To the right is a summary of the number of days suggested for each chapter. Days allocated to *Chapter Reviews, Chapter Tests,* and *Cumulative Reviews* are included in these major subdivisions.

If you wish, an independent testing program can be substituted for the Chapter Tests and Cumulative Reviews in the student's text. See pages T30 to T60.

CHAPTER	MINIMUM COURSE	AVERAGE COURSE	MAXIMUM COURSE
1	15	14	13
2	14	13	12
3	15	14	13
4	15	13	12
5	14	13	13
6	18	17	18
7	11	11	10
8	13	14	13
9	14	14	14
10	9	13	12
11	15	13	13
12	12	16	13
13	0	0	9
TOTAL	165	165	165

Harper & Row ALGEBRA ONE

Authors

MAX A. SOBEL

EVAN M. MALETSKY

NORBERT LERNER

LOUIS S. COHEN

Scribner Educational Publishers
New York

Macmillan Publishing Company
New York

Collier Macmillan Publishers
London

Authors

MAX A. SOBEL
Professor of Mathematics and Computer Science
Montclair State College
Montclair, New Jersey

EVAN M. MALETSKY
Professor of Mathematics and Computer Science
Montclair State College
Montclair, New Jersey

NORBERT LERNER
Professor of Mathematics
State University of New York
Cortland, New York

LOUIS S. COHEN
Teacher of Mathematics
Bloomington Jefferson High School
Bloomington, Minnesota

Editorial Advisors

Donald D. Clark
Utah State Office of Education
South Jordan, Utah

Theodora Romano
Keystone Oaks High School
Pittsburgh, Pennsylvania

Betty Vanden Bosch Shaw
Flint Community School
Flint, Michigan

Thomas E. Clark
Indianapolis Public Schools
Indianapolis, Indiana

John Rucker
Central High School
Phoenix, Arizona

Michael P. Walker
Duval County School Board
Jacksonville, Florida

Steven J. Leinwand
Connecticut State Department of Education
Hartford, Connecticut

Acknowledgments

For permission to reprint copyrighted material, grateful acknowledgment is made to the *Mathematical Association of America* for problems from the American High School Mathematics Examinations, published by the Mathematical Association of America and reprinted by the M.A.A. Committtee on High School Contests.

Page 215   Contest Problem Book I, 1951 Examination Questions 3, 6
Page 263   Contest Problem Book III, 1972 Examination Question 9

Cover Photo: Taurus Photos: Bob Hahn.
Illustrations by: Vantage Art, Inc.

Scribner Educational Publishers
Macmillan Publishing Company
866 Third Avenue
New York, NY 10022
Collier Macmillan Canada, Inc.

ISBN 06-544000-5   858687RRD098765432

CONTENTS

Chapter 6:   Factoring   **202**

Chapter 7:   Systems of Linear Equations   **252**

Chapter 8: Rational Expressions   **284**

Using the Calculator: *Rational Expressions—Equivalent or Not?*, 292;   Strategies for Problem Solving: *Estimating Answers*, 308;   Applications: *Drafting*, 315;   Computer Activity: *Calculating Earnings*, 319

Prerequisite Skills Review, 285;   Checkpoint, 304, 311;   Chapter Review, 316; Chapter Test, 318

Chapter 9:   Applying Fractions: Solving Equations and Problems   **320**

Strategies for Problem Solving: *Starting with a Guess*, 334;   Challenge: *River Currents*, 352;   Applications: *Finance Charges*, 353;   Computer Activity: *Compound Interest*, 357

Prerequisite Skills Review, 321;   Checkpoint, 329, 342;   Chapter Review, 354; Chapter Test, 356;   Cumulative Review, Chapters 1–9, 358

Chapter 10:   Inequalities   **360**

Chapter 11:   Radicals   394

Chapter 12:   Quadratic Functions and Equations   432

Chapter 13: Trigonometry 474

Activity: *Paper Folding*, 478;   Challenge: *More Trigonometric Ratios*, 488;   Strategies for Problem Solving: *Relating a New Problem to a Familiar One*, 492;   Applications: *Architecture*, 493;   Computer Activity: *Arithmetic Mean*, 497

Prerequisite Skills Review, 475;   Chapter Review, 494;   Chapter Test, 496; Cumulative Review, Chapters 1–13, 498

Symbols

$a \cdot b$	a times b
$=$	is equal to
$\neq$	is not equal to
$\approx$	is approximately equal to
$<$	is less than
$>$	is greater than
$\leq$	is less than or equal to
$\geq$	is greater than or equal to
$\sim$	is similar to
$\pm$	plus or minus
$-x$	opposite or additive inverse of x, where $x \neq 0$
$\lvert x \rvert$	absolute value of x
$\sqrt{x}$	principal (positive) square root of x
$\frac{1}{x}$	reciprocal or multiplicative inverse of x
$x : y$	ratio of x to y
(x, y)	ordered pair x, y
$A(x, y)$	point A with coordinates x, y
$2.5\overline{76}$	infinite decimal, with digits 76 repeating without end
2^5	fifth power of 2, or 2 to the fifth power
7^2	second power of 7, or 7 squared
4^3	third power of 4, or 4 cubed
π	pi, approximately $\frac{22}{7}$ or 3.14
$(\ )$	parentheses, a grouping symbol
$[\ ]$	brackets, a grouping symbol
$\{\ \}$	braces, symbol for a set
$\emptyset$	empty set
$\cap$	the intersection of sets
$\cup$	the union of sets
$f(x)$	function of x, the value of f at x
$\%$	percent
$\degree$	degree
$\angle ABC$	angle ABC
$\triangle DEF$	triangle DEF

This chapter reviews some familiar computational skills and properties of arithmetic. Variables are used to express important ideas and properties.

The chapter also provides students with experience in relating algebraic expressions to verbal expressions. Equations are introduced, and simple equations are solved by inspection or by substituting given replacements.

The real number system and its relationship to points on the number line are developed through a study of whole numbers, integers, and rational numbers. This sets the stage for much of the work that follows in the course. For example, basic operations with integers are developed in detail in Chapter 2, and formal procedures for solving equations are developed in Chapter 3.

CHAPTER 1

This physicist is working with pressure gauges in a laboratory. She records the results of an experiment and interprets the data by using appropriate mathematical formulas.

THE LANGUAGE
OF ALGEBRA

PREREQUISITE SKILLS REVIEW

For students who need additional practice with the algebraic skills in this Prerequisite Skills Review, you may assign Follow-Up exercises on page 500 in the students' books.

An item-by-item error analysis of the Prerequisite Skills Review appears on page T20.

Prerequisite Skills Review

Write the letter for the correct answer.

1. $18 - 5\frac{1}{3} = \underline{\ ?\ }$ b

   a. $12\frac{1}{3}$ **b.** $12\frac{2}{3}$ **c.** $13\frac{1}{3}$ **d.** $13\frac{2}{3}$

2. $\frac{1}{3} + \frac{1}{2} = \underline{\ ?\ }$ d

   a. $\frac{1}{5}$ **b.** $\frac{2}{5}$ **c.** $\frac{2}{6}$ **d.** $\frac{5}{6}$

3. $7 \times \frac{2}{3} = \underline{\ ?\ }$ c

   a. $\frac{14}{21}$ **b.** $\frac{2}{21}$ **c.** $4\frac{2}{3}$ **d.** $7\frac{2}{3}$

4. $\frac{1}{2} \times \frac{1}{4} = \underline{\ ?\ }$ b

   a. $\frac{1}{6}$ **b.** $\frac{1}{8}$ **c.** $\frac{2}{6}$ **d.** $\frac{3}{4}$

5. $\frac{4.6}{10} = \underline{\ ?\ }$ b

   a. 0.046   **b.** 0.46   **c.** 4.6   **d.** 46

6. $4.7 - 1 = \underline{\ ?\ }$ a

   a. 3.7   **b.** 3.69   **c.** 4.6   **d.** 4.69

7. Which of the following is *not* equal to $\frac{5}{7}$?   b

   a. $\frac{0.5}{0.7}$ **b.** $\frac{5 + 2}{7 + 2}$ **c.** $\frac{5 \times 20}{7 \times 20}$ **d.** $\frac{5 \div 7}{7 \div 7}$

8. 0.3 divided by 0.15 is equal to $\underline{\ ?\ }$.   b

   a. $\frac{1}{5}$ **b.** 2   **c.** 0.5   **d.** 5

9. The product of 1.45 and 10 is equal to $\underline{\ ?\ }$.   c

   a. 0.145   **b.** 11.45   **c.** 14.5   **d.** 145

10. Which expression does not represent $7 - 3$?   d

   a. 7 less 3   **b.** 3 less than 7   **c.** 3 subtracted from 7   **d.** 7 subtracted from 3

Add, subtract, multiply, or divide.
1. $24 + 8$ 32
2. 24×8 192
3. $24 - 8$ 16
4. $24 \div 8$ 3
5. $8 \times 0 \times 24$ 0

LESSON NOTES

Even though some students may feel they are familiar with order of operations from work in earlier courses, provide careful discussion of the model examples. Emphasize that parentheses, brackets, and fraction bars are grouping symbols.

In discussing Example 3b, point out that when we are simplifying an expression such as $\dfrac{5 \times (3 + 5)}{7 - 5}$, it does not matter whether we simplify the numerator or the denominator first.

POSSIBLE ERROR

Students are likely to follow the correct order of operations when grouping symbols such as parentheses or brackets are used. However, they often work from left to right with all other expressions. Thus, in Example 1b, the expression $10 - 4 \times 2$ might be incorrectly evaluated as 6×2, or 12.

To avoid this type of error, encourage students to scan the entire expression and *think* about the order of operations *before* they begin any computation.

ALTERNATE EXAMPLE

1. Simplify each expression.
   a. $27 - 6 + 3$ 24
   b. $27 - 6 \times 3$ 9
   c. $27 - 6 \div 3 \times 2$ 23

1-1 Order of Operations

OBJECTIVE

To perform operations in a certain order, for given numerical expressions.

Some calculator keys register numbers. Others perform operations such as addition, subtraction, multiplication, and division. How many combinations of keys can you think of that would give a display of 15? For example:

9 plus 6	3 times 5	17 minus 2	60 divided by 4
$9 + 6$	3×5	$17 - 2$	$60 \div 4$

All of the **numerical expressions** above are names for fifteen, but the *simplest name* is **15**.

The equal sign can be used to show that two expressions name the same number.

$$9 + 6 = 15 \qquad 3 \times 5 = 15 \qquad 9 + 6 = 3 \times 5$$

To **simplify** a numerical expression, substitute a simpler name for the same number. How would you simplify the numerical expression $3 + 6 \times 2$? The result depends on the order in which you perform the operations.

If you multiply first and then add, the answer is 15.

$$3 + \underbrace{(6 \times 2)}$$
$$3 + \qquad 12$$
$$15$$

But if you add first and then multiply, the answer is 18.

$$\underbrace{(3 + 6)} \times 2$$
$$9 \quad \times 2$$
$$18$$

To avoid confusion, it is generally agreed to multiply and divide in order from left to right, then add and subtract in order from left to right.

Thus, to simplify $3 + 6 \times 2$ when there are no grouping symbols, multiply and then add.

$$3 + 6 \times 2$$
$$3 + \quad 12$$
$$15$$

EXAMPLE 1   Simplify each expression.

a. $10 - \underbrace{4 + 2}$
   $\quad 6 \quad + 2$
   $\qquad 8$

b. $10 - \underbrace{4 \times 2}$
   $10 - \quad 8$
   $\qquad 2$

c. $10 - \underbrace{4 \div 2} \times 3$
   $10 - \underbrace{2 \quad \times 3}$
   $10 - \qquad 6$
   $\qquad\qquad 4$

When parentheses are used as *grouping symbols,* simplify within them first.

EXAMPLE 2   Simplify each expression.

a. $13 - \underbrace{(6 - 1)}_{5} \div 5$ **b.** $3 \times \underbrace{(7 - 2)}_{5} + 1$

$\quad\quad 13 - \underbrace{5 \div 5}_{1}$ $\quad\quad \underbrace{3 \times 5}_{15} + 1$

$\quad\quad 13 - 1$ $\quad\quad 15 + 1$

$\quad\quad\quad 12$ $\quad\quad\quad\quad 16$

Parentheses, brackets, and fraction bars are all **grouping symbols.**
When one set of grouping symbols occurs inside another, work within
the innermost symbols first.

EXAMPLE 3   Simplify each expression.

a. $7 - [1 + \underbrace{(6 - 4)}_{2}]$ Parentheses are
inside brackets.

$\quad 7 - [1 + \quad 2 \quad]$

$\quad 7 - \quad\quad 3$

$\quad\quad\quad 4$

b. $36 - \dfrac{5 \times (3 + 5)}{7 - 5}$

$\quad\quad 36 - \dfrac{5 \times 8}{2}$

$\quad\quad 36 - \dfrac{40}{2}$

$\quad\quad\quad\quad 16$

EXAMPLE 4   List the operations in the correct order for simplifying the expression
$\dfrac{10 \times [27 - (4 + 2)]}{7}$.

Steps	Add	Subtract	Multiply	Divide
	$4 + 2$	$27 - 6$	10×21	$210 \div 7$

Summary of the Order of Operations

First, simplify expressions within grouping symbols.
Then multiply and divide in order from left to right.
Then add and subtract in order from left to right.

CLASS EXERCISES

Simplify each expression.

1. $5 + 8 - 4$ ⠀9⠀⠀**2.** $10 - 4 + 3$ ⠀9⠀⠀**3.** $3 + 4 \times 5$ ⠀23⠀⠀**4.** $3 \times 1 + 6$ ⠀9

5. $9 - 6 \div 3$ ⠀7⠀⠀**6.** $12 \div 4 - 1$ ⠀2⠀⠀**7.** $5 + (7 - 6)$ ⠀6⠀⠀**8.** $9 - (8 - 7)$ ⠀8

9. $(6 + 8) \div 7$ ⠀2⠀⠀**10.** $20 - (15 - 12)$ ⠀**11.** $4 + (6 - 5) \times 2$⠀⠀**12.** $8 - 8 \div (4 + 4)$
⠀⠀⠀⠀⠀⠀⠀⠀⠀⠀⠀⠀⠀17⠀⠀⠀⠀⠀⠀⠀⠀6⠀⠀⠀⠀⠀⠀⠀⠀⠀7

13. $4 \times (11 - 5) + 6$⠀⠀**14.** $2 \times [14 \div (2 + 5)]$⠀⠀**15.** $8 + \dfrac{6 \times (9 - 3)}{4}$
⠀⠀⠀⠀30⠀⠀⠀⠀⠀⠀⠀⠀⠀⠀4⠀⠀⠀⠀⠀⠀⠀⠀⠀17

THE LANGUAGE OF ALGEBRA ⠀⠀⠀⠀⠀⠀⠀⠀⠀⠀⠀⠀⠀⠀⠀**3**

ALTERNATE EXAMPLES

2. Simplify each expression.
a. $18 - (9 - 3) \div 3$ ⠀16
b. $5 \times (8 + 2) - 10$ ⠀40
3. Simplify each expression.
a. $9 - [8 - (6 - 5)]$ ⠀2
b. $\dfrac{7 - 5}{5 - 3} + \dfrac{3 \times 4}{5 + 1}$ ⠀3
4. List the operations in the correct
order for simplifying the
expression

$\dfrac{11 + [(15 - 9) \div 2]}{7}$

Subtract $15 - 9$; divide $6 \div 2$;
add $11 + 3$; divide $14 \div 7$

DAILY QUIZ

Simplify.
1. $9 + 12 - 8$ ⠀13
2. $13 - 10 \div 5$ ⠀11
3. $20 - 3 \times 2$ ⠀14
4. $\dfrac{4 \times 9}{6} + 2$ ⠀8
5. $[15 + (7 \times 4)] - 22$ ⠀21

ASSIGNMENT GUIDE
(page 4)

Minimum course: 1–49 odd
Average course: 1–57 odd,
59–61
Maximum course: 17–57 odd,
59–65

ENRICHMENT ACTIVITY

Six different orderings are possible
for these three operations:

| Add 12. | Multiply by 4. | Subtract 8. |

Have students write the correct expression for each ordering, assuming that we begin with the number 24.

$24 + 12 \times 4 - 8$ $24 + 12 - 8 \times 4$
$24 \times 4 + 12 - 8$ $24 \times 4 - 8 + 12$
$24 - 8 + 12 \times 4$ $24 - 8 \times 4 + 12$

If a fourth operation is included,

| Divide by 2. |

24 different expressions are possible.

NOTE: In the feature Using BASIC (see below), selected algebraic topics are discussed from the viewpoint of a computer programmer using the BASIC language. These commentaries are intended mainly to illuminate the algebra, not to teach computer programming. You can refer students who are unfamiliar with BASIC to the Computer Handbook starting on page 534.

Using BASIC

Since the order of operations in BASIC is the same as in algebra, the computer may be used to illustrate or to check the exercises. To simplify $6 \div 2 + 4 \times 7$, enter PRINT 6 / 2 + 4 * 7 (followed by pressing the RETURN or ENTER key).

A fraction bar is a grouping symbol; however, on the computer, parentheses must be used when entering a fraction such as $\frac{4+8}{5-1}$. To compute $7 - \frac{4+8}{5-1}$, enter

PRINT 7 - (4 + 8)/(5 - 1)

EXERCISES

A

Simplify each expression.

1. $3 + 7 - 1$ 9   **2.** $9 - 4 + 3$ 8   **3.** $20 - 8 + 6$ 18   **4.** $17 - 10$ 4   0

5. $10 + 6 - 8$ 8   **6.** $9 + 3 \times 5$ 24   **7.** $3 \times 2 - 1$ 5   **8.** $7 - 3 \times 2$ 1

9. $3 \times 1 + 4$ 7   **10.** $8 \times 4 \div 2$ 16   **11.** $7 + 10 \div 5$ 9   **12.** $12 \div 4 \div 3$ 1

13. $7 \div 7 + 7$ 8   **14.** $10 \div 2 \times 5$ 25   **15.** $4 \div 2 - 1$ 1   **16.** $18 \div 6 \div 3$ 1

Simplify. Operate within parentheses first.

17. $(10 - 5) + 3$ 8   **18.** $10 - (5 + 3)$ 2   **19.** $(12 \div 3) \times 4$ 16   **20.** $12 \div (3 \times 4)$ 1

21. $8 - (2 \times 4)$ 0   **22.** $(8 - 2) \times 4$ 24   **23.** $27 - (11 - 8)$ 24   **24.** $(27 - 11) - 8$ 8

25. $(16 \div 4) \div 2$ 2   **26.** $16 \div (4 \div 2)$ 8   **27.** $60 \div (15 - 3)$ 5   **28.** $(60 \div 15) - 3$ 1

Simplify.

29. $(16 + 1) \times (10 - 8)$ 34   **30.** $(13 - 2) \div (18 - 7)$ 1   **31.** $(14 - 7) - 4 - 3$ 0

32. $14 - (7 - 4) - 3$ 8   **33.** $14 - 7 - (4 - 3)$ 6   **34.** $30 - (15 \div 5) \div 3$ 29

35. $(30 - 15) \div 5 \div 3$ 1   **36.** $(30 - 15 \div 5) \div 3$ 9   **37.** $20 - 4 \div 2 - 7$ 11

38. $6 \div 2 + 4 \times 7$ 31   **39.** $5 \times 3 - 8 \div 4$ 13   **40.** $8 + 2 \times 3 - 5$ 9

41. $12 - 6 \div 6 \times 2$ 10   **42.** $24 \div 6 - 16 \div 4$ 0   **43.** $(12 - 6.8) \div 1.3$ 4

44. $\dfrac{4 \times (5 + 4)}{3} - 2$ 10   **45.** $7 - \dfrac{4 + 8}{5 - 1}$ 4   **46.** $\dfrac{8 + 7}{4 - 1} + \dfrac{6 - 2}{2 + 2}$ 6

B

47. $[(20 + 12) \times 4] - 2$ 126   **48.** $[20 + (12 \times 4)] - 2$ 66   **49.** $20 + [12 \times (4 - 2)]$ 44

50. $20 + [(12 \times 4) - 2]$ 66   **51.** $20 + 12 \times 4 - 2$ 66   **52.** $4.8 - 3.2 \div 2$ 3.2

53. $\dfrac{(7 - 2) - [4 - (6 - 3)]}{4}$ 1   **54.** $28 \div [16 - (18 \div 2)]$ 4   **55.** $100 - (3 \times 5 - 3 + 11)$ 77

56. $\dfrac{10 - [5 - (4 - 2)]}{7}$ 1   **57.** $17 - 3 \times \dfrac{4 + 8}{17 - 5}$ 14   **58.** $\dfrac{18 - 3 \times 3}{5 - 4 \div 2} - 3$ 0

Match.

59. $16 \div 8 - 4 \times 3$ c   **a.** Subtract, divide, and then multiply.

60. $16 \div (8 - 4) \times 3$ a   **b.** Subtract, multiply, and then divide.

61. $16 \div [(8 - 4) \times 3]$ b   **c.** Divide, multiply, and then subtract.

C

Copy the expression. Then insert grouping symbols to give the stated value.

62. $18 \div 6 \div 3$ for 1 and for 9
$(18 \div 6) \div 3$; $18 \div (6 \div 3)$

63. $12 \times 2 + 6$ for 30 and for 96
$(12 \times 2) + 6$; $12 \times (2 + 6)$

64. $6 + 24 \div 6 - 3$ for 2 and for 14
$[(6 + 24) \div 6] - 3$; $6 + [24 \div (6 - 3)]$

65. $48 - 28 - 10 \times 2$ for 12 and for 60
$48 - [(28 - 10) \times 2]$; $[48 - (28 - 10)] \times 2$

4

CHAPTER 1

EXTRA PRACTICE, page 507

1-2 Expressions with Variables

OBJECTIVE

To evaluate algebraic expressions.

In a basketball game, each basket is worth 2 points.

One basket	2 × 1	2 points
Two baskets	2 × 2	4 points
Three baskets	2 × 3	6 points
Four baskets	2 × 4	8 points

These expressions fit a pattern that can be used for any number of baskets.

n baskets   2 × n 2n points

The letter n is a **variable**. The score 2 × n is called an **algebraic expression.** Its value depends on the value of n. For any number of baskets, n, the score is 2n points.

In this example, the variable n is a *whole number.*

$$0, 1, 2, 3, 4, 5, 6, \ldots$$

The expression 2n represents an *even number.*

$$0, 2, 4, 6, 8, 10, 12, \ldots$$

Multiplication can be shown in many ways. Each of the following expressions means the same as 2 × n.

$$2n \qquad 2 \cdot n \qquad 2(n) \qquad (2)(n) \qquad (2)n$$

EXAMPLE 1   Find the value of 2n for each value of n.

a. Let $n = 16$.
$$2n = 2(16)$$
$$= 32$$

b. Let $n = 37$.
$$2n = 2(37)$$
$$= 74$$

To **evaluate** an algebraic expression, replace the variable with the number it represents. Then simplify.

EXAMPLE 2   Evaluate for $n = 8$.

a. $3n - 2$
$$3(8) - 2$$
$$24 - 2$$
$$22$$

b. $n(12 - n)$
$$8(12 - 8)$$
$$8(4)$$
$$32$$

c. $\dfrac{1 + 3n}{n - 3}$
$$\frac{1 + 3(8)}{8 - 3}$$
$$\frac{25}{5}$$
$$5$$

THE LANGUAGE OF ALGEBRA   5

WARM-UP EXERCISES

1. If $n = 9$, what is the value of $3 \times n$?   27
2. If $a = 36$, what is the value of $\dfrac{a}{2}$?   18

LESSON NOTES

In this lesson the students work with algebraic expressions that contain one or more variables. Be sure the students understand that each of the following is an algebraic expression:

$$n \qquad 2n \qquad 3n - 2$$
$$a + b \qquad ab \qquad \frac{a + b + c}{2}$$

You may wish to note that an algebraic expression may be a number, a variable, or the sum, difference, product, or quotient of numbers and variables.

POSSIBLE ERROR

The numeral 37 does not mean 3×7. But the algebraic expression 3n *does* mean $3 \times n$. Some students may forget that 3n means $3 \times n$. For example, if $n = 4$ and students evaluate $3n + 6$ as 40, they have incorrectly interpreted 3n as 34 and added 6 to 34. Remind students that, in algebra, multiplication is shown in various ways: 3n, $3 \cdot n$, (3)n, 3(n), and (3)(n) all indicate $3 \times n$.

ALTERNATE EXAMPLES

1. Find the value of 5n for each value of n.
   a. Let $n = 12$.   60
   b. Let $n = 59$.   295
2. Evaluate for $n = 6$.
   a. $2n - 1$ 11
   b. $n(n - 4)$ 12
   c. $\dfrac{n + 18}{3n - 6}$ 2

3. Evaluate $4a - 2(b - 1)$ for $a = 9$ and $b = 6$.   26

Some algebraic expressions contain more than one variable.

EXAMPLE 3   Evaluate $3(a + 5) - 4b$ for $a = 2$ and $b = 3$.

$$3(a + 5) - 4b$$
$$3(2 + 5) - 4(3) \qquad \text{Substitute 2 for } a \text{ and 3 for } b.$$
$$3(7) \quad - \quad 12$$
$$21 \quad - \quad 12$$
$$9$$

4. Evaluate each expression for $a = 8$, $b = 4$, and $c = 1$.
  a. $3ac - b$ 20
  b. $\dfrac{ab - ac}{bc}$ 6

Multiplication symbols are usually omitted from expressions with variables.

Expression	$2 \times a \times b$	$a \times b \times c$	$(a \times b) + c$	$a + (b \times c)$
Usual Form	$2ab$	abc	$ab + c$	$a + bc$

EXAMPLE 4   Evaluate each expression for $a = 2$, $b = 3$, and $c = 6$.

  a. $2ab + c = 2(2)(3) + 6 = 12 + 6 = 18$
  b. $\dfrac{ab + bc}{ac} = \dfrac{(2)(3) + (3)(6)}{(2)(6)} = \dfrac{6 + 18}{12} = \dfrac{24}{12} = 2$

Evaluate each expression for the given value of the variable.
1. $a + 9$ **2.** $10 - (m + 3)$
  if $a = 12$ 21   if $m = 7$ 0
3. $4(p - 6)$ **4.** $7(2t + 1)$
  if $p = 10$ 16   if $t = 4$ 63
5. Evaluate $\dfrac{4 + c}{c - d}$ if $c = 8$ and $d = 5$.   4

CLASS EXERCISES

Evaluate each expression if $n = 6$.

1. $n + 5$ 11	**2.** $n - 4$ 2	**3.** $6n$ 36	**4.** $80n$ 480
5. $15 - n$ 9	**6.** $3n + 1$ 19	**7.** $4n - 5$ 19	**8.** $3 + 2n$ 15
9. $20 - 3n$ 2	**10.** $2(n + 1)$ 14	**11.** $3(n - 2)$ 12	**12.** $7 - (n - 1)$ 2
13. $\dfrac{n}{3}$ 2	**14.** $\dfrac{24}{n}$ 4	**15.** $\dfrac{n + 4}{5}$ 2	**16.** $\dfrac{5n - 10}{8 - n}$ 10

EXERCISES

A   *Evaluate each expression if $a = 10$.*

1. $a + 7$ 17	**2.** $a + 9$ 19	**3.** $a - 4$ 6	**4.** $a - 1$ 9
5. $4a$ 40	**6.** $5a$ 50	**7.** $3a + 7$ 37	**8.** $6a + 8$ 68
9. $30 - 2a$ 10	**10.** $5 + 5a$ 55	**11.** $3(a - 4)$ 18	**12.** $5(a + 1)$ 55
13. $\dfrac{a}{2}$ 5	**14.** $\dfrac{a - 1}{3}$ 3	**15.** $\dfrac{6a}{5}$ 12	**16.** $\dfrac{a + 20}{a - 5}$ 6

6   CHAPTER 1

EXTRA PRACTICE, page 507

Evaluate each expression for the given value of the variable.

17. $8 - (m + 1)$ 2   **18.** $23 + (m - 9)$ 31 **19.** $5(5 + p)$ 60 **20.** $6(p - 8)$ 24
if $m = 5$ if $m = 17$ if $p = 7$ if $p = 12$

21. $7 - (n - 7)$ 3 **22.** $12 - (6 - r)$ 9 **23.** $9(3s - 4)$ 72 **24.** $11(20 - 2s)$ 0
if $n = 11$ if $r = 3$ if $s = 4$ if $s = 10$

25. $12 + 3(t - 5)$ 24 **26.** $8(8 - t) - 8$ 8 **27.** $x - (18 - x)$ 8 **28.** $x(x - 3)$ 40
if $t = 9$ if $t = 6$ if $x = 13$ if $x = 8$

29. $\dfrac{4y - 3}{y}$ 3   **30.** $\dfrac{4y}{4 + y}$ 3   **31.** $\dfrac{6p + 38}{p + 3}$ 8   **32.** $\dfrac{6x - 15}{x - 5}$ 9
if $y = 3$ if $y = 12$ if $p = 7$ if $x = 10$

B *Evaluate. Let $a = 9$ and $b = 6$.*

33. $4a + b$ 42   **34.** $4 + ab$ 58   **35.** $4ab$ 216   **36.** $a(b - 4)$ 18

37. $b(12 - a)$ 18 **38.** $12a - b$ 102 **39.** $12(a + b)$ 180 **40.** $(12a)(12b)$ 7776

41. $\dfrac{3 + a}{b}$ 2   **42.** $\dfrac{ab}{a - b}$ 18   **43.** $\dfrac{6a}{a(a - 7)}$ 3   **44.** $\dfrac{2a + 5b}{a + b + 1}$ 3

Evaluate. Let $x = 5$, $y = 7$, and $z = 8$.

45. $x(y + z)$ 75   **46.** $yz - x$ 51   **47.** xyz 280   **48.** $y(z - y)$ 7

49. $3xy - z$ 97   **50.** $zy(x + z)$ 728 **51.** $y(3x - y)$ 56   **52.** $yz(x - 3)$ 112

53. $\dfrac{x + y + z}{10}$ 2   **54.** $\dfrac{y + z}{x}$ 3   **55.** $\dfrac{xy}{y - 2}$ 7   **56.** $36 - \dfrac{3yz}{x + 1}$ 8

57. The formula for the perimeter of a rectangle is
$P = 2(l + w)$

Find P if $l = 6.4$ and $w = 5.1$.   23

58. The formula for the circumference of a circle is
$C = 2\pi r$

Find C if $r = 150$. Use 3.14 for π.   942

59. The formula for the volume of a rectangular prism is
$V = lwh$

Find V if $l = 1\frac{1}{4}$, $w = \frac{1}{2}$, and $h = \frac{3}{5}$. $\frac{3}{8}$, or 0.375

60. The formula for the lateral area of a cone is
$L = \pi rs$

Find L if $r = \frac{3}{4}$ and $s = \frac{7}{8}$. Use $\frac{22}{7}$ for π. $2\frac{1}{16}$, or 2.0625

THE LANGUAGE OF ALGEBRA

7

Find the value of each expression if
$a = 4$ and $b = 3$.
1. $b \cdot b$ 9
2. $a \cdot a \cdot a$ 64
3. $b \cdot a \cdot a$ 48
4. $a \cdot a \cdot a \cdot a$ 256

LESSON NOTES

Students will have had experience with exponents in earlier grade levels. This lesson reviews the basic ideas of exponents and extends the rules of order of operations to include expressions that involve exponents.

As you review exponents, you may wish to use patterns to help rationalize the definition of the zero power.

$$10^3 = 1000$$
$$10^2 = 100$$
$$10^1 = 10$$
$$10^0 = ?$$ 1

Each product is one-tenth of the preceding product; so it is reasonable that $10^0 = 1$.

A similar pattern can be explored, using 2 as the base.

$$2^3 = 8$$
$$2^2 = 4$$
$$2^1 = 2$$
$$2^0 = ?$$ 1

ALTERNATE EXAMPLES

1. Write in factored form. Then simplify.
   a. 2^3 $2 \cdot 2 \cdot 2 = 8$
   b. $\left(\frac{1}{4}\right)^4$ $\frac{1}{4} \cdot \frac{1}{4} \cdot \frac{1}{4} \cdot \frac{1}{4} = \frac{1}{256}$
   c. The second power of 5
      $5 \cdot 5 =$ 25
   d. The first power of 8 $8^1 = 8$
2. Write each expression in exponential form.
   a. $x \cdot x \cdot x \cdot x$ x^4
   b. $4 \cdot x \cdot x \cdot x$ $4x^3$
   c. $4x \cdot 4x \cdot 4x$ $(4x)^3$
   d. $3 \cdot a \cdot a \cdot a \cdot b$ $3a^3b$

1-3   Exponents and Factors

OBJECTIVES

To evaluate expressions with exponents.
To write expressions with repeated factors in exponential form.

Here are numbers you can name using two 4's.

zero	one	eight	sixteen	forty-four
$4 - 4$	$\frac{4}{4}$	$4 + 4$	$4 \cdot 4$	44

But to express a much greater number, use one of the 4's as an *exponent*.

two hundred fifty-six: $4^4 = 4 \cdot 4 \cdot 4 \cdot 4$

An **exponent** tells you how many times a number, the **base**, is used as a factor.

$$\text{base} \to 2^{5 \leftarrow \text{exponent}} = \overbrace{2 \cdot 2 \cdot 2 \cdot 2 \cdot 2}^{\text{5 factors of 2}}$$

Here are some expressions in *exponential form*. Note that the terms *squared* and *cubed* are commonly used instead of *second power* and *third power*.

Exponential Form	Factored Form	Description
x^1	x	x to the first power The exponent 1 need not be written.
x^2	$x \cdot x$	x to the second power, or x squared
x^3	$x \cdot x \cdot x$	x to the third power, or x cubed
x^4	$x \cdot x \cdot x \cdot x$	x to the fourth power

Zero can also be used as an exponent in a very special way. Any number, except 0, raised to the zero power is *defined* to be 1.

EXAMPLE 1   Write in factored form. Then simplify.

a. $3^4 = 3 \cdot 3 \cdot 3 \cdot 3 = 81$ b. $\left(\frac{1}{2}\right)^3 = \frac{1}{2} \cdot \frac{1}{2} \cdot \frac{1}{2} = \frac{1}{8}$

c. **The fifth power of 4**   d. **The zero power of 15**
   $4 \cdot 4 \cdot 4 \cdot 4 \cdot 4 = 1024$ $15^0 = 1$

EXAMPLE 2   Write each expression in exponential form.

a. $b \cdot b \cdot b \cdot b \cdot b = b^5$ b. $2 \cdot b \cdot b \cdot b = 2b^3$
c. $2b \cdot 2b \cdot 2b \cdot 2b = (2b)^4$ d. $4 \cdot x \cdot x \cdot y \cdot y = 4x^2y^2$

8   CHAPTER 1

When expressions have exponents, another step is needed in the *order of operations*. First simplify within grouping symbols, and then apply exponents. Follow with multiplication and division, and then with addition and subtraction.

EXAMPLE 3 Simplify each expression.

a. $3 + 4 \cdot 5^2$

$3 + 4(5 \cdot 5)$

$3 + 4 \cdot 25$

$3 + 100$

103

b. $3 + 2(4 + 5)^2$

$3 + 2(9)^2$

$3 + 2 \cdot 81$

$3 + 162$

165

c. $3 + \dfrac{(4 \cdot 5)^2}{10}$

$3 + \dfrac{(20)^2}{10}$

$3 + \dfrac{400}{10}$

$3 + 40$

43

EXAMPLE 4 Evaluate each algebraic expression for $n = 10$.

a. $5n^2 = 5 \cdot n \cdot n$

$= 5 \cdot 10 \cdot 10$

$= 50 \cdot 10$

$= 500$

b. $(5n)^2 = (5n)(5n)$

$= (5 \cdot 10)(5 \cdot 10)$

$= (50)(50)$

$= 2500$

c. $\dfrac{n^2}{5} = \dfrac{n \cdot n}{5}$

$= \dfrac{10 \cdot 10}{5}$

$= 20$

Be careful to apply the exponent to the correct base.

$2a^2$	$(2a)^2$	a^2b	ab^2	$(ab)^2$
$2(a \cdot a)$	$(2a)(2a)$	$(a \cdot a)b$	$a(b \cdot b)$	$(a \cdot b)(a \cdot b)$
Base: a	Base: $2a$	Base: a	Base: b	Base: ab

EXAMPLE 5 Evaluate $xy^2 + (xy)^2$ when $x = 3$ and $y = 4$.

$xy^2 + (xy)^2 = 3 \cdot 4^2 + (3 \cdot 4)^2 = 3 \cdot 16 + 12^2 = 48 + 144 = 192$

CLASS EXERCISES

Simplify.

1. 5^2 25

2. 7^2 49

3. 3^3 27

4. 12^0 1

Evaluate each algebraic expression if $n = 3$.

5. n^4 81

6. $4n^2 - 20$ 16

7. $(n + 7)^2$ 100

8. $\dfrac{(4n)^2}{4n^2}$ 4

Write in exponential form.

9. $x \cdot x \cdot x$ x^3

10. $4 \cdot a \cdot a$ $4a^2$

11. $a \cdot b \cdot b \cdot b \cdot b$ ab^4

12. $5 \cdot x \cdot x \cdot x \cdot y$ $5x^3y$

THE LANGUAGE OF ALGEBRA

9

ENRICHMENT ACTIVITY

Have students find the greatest number that can be written with two 9's. The answer is 9^9, which equals 387,420,489.

Then ask if n^n is always the greatest number that can be written using any digit twice. The answer is *no*. For example, 1^1 is less than $1 + 1$, and 2^2 is less than 22.

ADDITIONAL ANSWERS

Exercises
19. x^6 20. a^2b^3
21. $3xz^2$ 22. $4bc^3$

EXERCISES

A   *Simplify.*

1. 2^3 8   2. 6^2 36   3. 3^2 9   4. 10^3 1000   5. 25^0 1   6. 1^4 256

*Evaluate each algebraic expression if **x** = 3.*

7. x^5 243   8. $4x^2$ 36   9. $(4x)^2$ 144   10. $x^2 - 1$ 8

11. $(7 - x)^2$ 16   12. $3x^2 + 5$ 32   13. $4x + x^2$ 21   14. $2x^2 - x$ 15

15. $\dfrac{x^2}{3}$ 3   16. $\left(\dfrac{x}{3}\right)^2$ 1   17. $\dfrac{2x^3}{3x^2}$ 2   18. $\dfrac{(2x)^2}{2x^2}$ 2

Write in exponential form.

19. $x \cdot x \cdot x \cdot x \cdot x \cdot x$ 20. $a \cdot a \cdot b \cdot b \cdot b$ 21. $3 \cdot z \cdot z \cdot x$ 22. $4 \cdot b \cdot c \cdot c \cdot c$

23. $4 \cdot d \cdot d$ $4d^2$ 24. $4d \cdot 4d$ $(4d)^2$ 25. $7e \cdot 7e \cdot 7e$ $(7e)^3$ 26. $x \cdot 2y \cdot 2y$ $x(2y)^2$

B   27. The square of $5s$ $(5s)^2$ 28. The sum of the squares of 5 and s $5^2 + s^2$

*Evaluate each expression if **a** = 2 and **b** = 4.*

29. $a^3 + b$ 12   30. $a + b^3$ 66   31. $(a + b)^3$ 216   32. $(b - a)^3$ 8

33. a^3b 32   34. ab^3 128   35. $(ab)^3$ 512   36. a^3b^3 512

37. $3a^2b$ 48   38. $3ab^2$ 96   39. $3(ab)^2$ 192   40. $(3ab)^2$ 576

C   41. $(b^3 - b)^2$ 3600   42. $(2a^3 - b^2)^2$ 0   43. $2a^b$ 32   44. $(2b)^a$ 64

*Write an algebraic expression, and then evaluate it if **a** = 2 and **b** = 4.*

45. The sum of the square of a and the square of b $a^2 + b^2 = 20$

46. The square of the sum of a and b 47. The square of the product of a and b
    $(a + b)^2 = 36$ $(ab)^2 = 64$

48. The product of the square of a and the square of b $a^2b^2 = 64$

49. The formula for the volume of a cube is $V = e^3$. Find V if $e = 1.2$.
    1.728

CHALLENGE

Consecutive Counting Numbers

The counting numbers are 1, 2, 3, 4, 5, and so on. Consecutive counting numbers are successive numbers, one immediately following the other.

1. What is the next year that will be equal to the square of the sum of two consecutive counting numbers? $2025 = (22 + 23)^2$

2. What year in the 20th century is equal to the sum of the squares of two consecutive counting numbers? $1985 = 31^2 + 32^2$

EXTRA PRACTICE, page 508

1-4 From Words to Algebraic Expressions

OBJECTIVE

To translate phrases into algebraic expressions and algebraic expressions into phrases.

These phrases are written as algebraic expressions using n as the variable.

Phrase	Algebraic Expression
The sum of n and 4, n increased by 4, 4 more than n	$n + 4$
The difference n minus 4, 4 less than n, n decreased by 4	$n - 4$
4 more than the product of 3 and n	$3n + 4$
3 times the sum of some number and 4	$3(n + 4)$
4 times the cube of n	$4n^3$
The sum of some number and 3, divided by 8	$\dfrac{n + 3}{8}$

Certain key words can sometimes help you know which operations to use.

Add:	sum; increased by; more than
Subtract:	difference; less than; decreased by; minus
Multiply:	product; times
Divide:	quotient

EXAMPLE 1   Write an algebraic expression for each phrase.

Phrase	Algebraic Expression
1 less than some number	$x - 1$
A certain number increased by 2	$x + 2$
The product of some number and 3	$3x$
The quotient x divided by 4	$\dfrac{x}{4}$
4 more than the cube of x	$x^3 + 4$
3 more than the product of 5 and x	$5x + 3$

THE LANGUAGE OF ALGEBRA

11

2. Write a phrase for each algebraic expression.

$\frac{n}{25}$	Some number divided by 25
$n + 25$	Some number increased by 25
$5(n + 2)$	5 times the sum of a number and 2
$5n + 2$	2 more than the product of 5 and some number
$n^3 - 4$	4 less than the cube of some number

POSSIBLE ERROR

Students sometimes translate these two kinds of expressions with the same words.

$$4x + 3 \qquad 4(x + 3)$$

Point out that the first expression indicates "3 more than the product of 4 and some number x"; in contrast, the second expression indicates "4 times the sum of some number and 3." Provide additional practice with such expressions, and let the students evaluate the expressions for different values of the variable.

DAILY QUIZ

Find the number.
1. 32 decreased by 17   15
2. 3 less than the product of 7 and 2   11

Write an algebraic expression for each phrase.
3. 4 times x $4x$
4. 4 decreased by x $4 - x$
5. 4 more than the square of x $x^2 + 4$

ASSIGNMENT GUIDE
(pages 12–13)

Minimum course: 1–28
Average course: 1–35
Maximum course: 5–40

EXAMPLE 2   Write a phrase for each algebraic expression.

Algebraic Expression	Phrase
$\frac{50}{n}$	50 divided by some number
$20 - n$	20 decreased by some number
$3(n + 6)$	3 times the sum of some number and 6
$3n + 6$	6 more than the product of 3 and some number
$n^2 - 5$	5 less than the square of some number

CLASS EXERCISES

Find the number.

1. 12 increased by 8   20

2. 3 times the sum of 7 and 3   30

3. 7 less than 15   8

4. 2 more than the product of 4 and 5   22

*Write an algebraic expression for each phrase. Use **x** as the variable.*

5. 5 more than some number $x + 5$

6. 5 less than some number $x - 5$

7. The sum of 5 and a number $5 + x$

8. 5 divided by some number $\frac{5}{x}$, or $5 \div x$

9. 5 more than the product of 5 and some number $5x + 5$

10. 5 times the sum of a number and 5 $5(x + 5)$

11. 5 minus the quotient of some number divided by 5 $5 - \frac{x}{5}$

EXERCISES

A   *Find the number.*

1. 20 decreased by 6   14

2. 6 times the sum of 1 and 8   54

3. 3 more than 42   45

4. 2 more than the product of 15 and 2   32

Write an algebraic expression for each phrase.

5. 6 times n $6n$

6. The sum of n and 6 $n + 6$

7. 6 decreased by n $6 - n$

8. 6 less than n $n - 6$

9. $6n$ increased by 6 $6n + 6$

10. 6 decreased by $6n$ $6 - 6n$

11. 6 divided by n $\frac{6}{n}$, or $6 \div n$

12. n divided by 6 $\frac{n}{6}$, or $n \div 6$

12

*Write an expression for each phrase. Use **a** as the variable.*

13. 15 more than some number $a + 15$ **14.** The product of a number and 6 $6a$

15. 8 divided by some number $\frac{8}{a}$ **16.** 12 minus a certain number $12 - a$

17. 7 more than the product of 6 and a number $6a + 7$

18. 4 times the sum of a number and 5 $4(a + 5)$

19. 11 divided by 6 more than some number $\frac{11}{a + 6}$

Write a phrase for each expression.   Answers will vary.

20. $5b$ **21.** $b + 5$ **22.** $\frac{5}{b}$ 5 divided by   **23.** $b - 5$ 5 less than
5 times a number   5 more than a number   a number   a number

B   *Let **x** and **y** represent two numbers, with **x** greater than **y**. Write an expression for each phrase.*

24. The greater number decreased by the lesser $x - y$

25. The greater number divided by the lesser $x \div y$, or $\frac{x}{y}$

26. The lesser number increased by twice the greater number $y + 2x$

Write a phrase for each expression.   Answers will vary.

27. $5p + 6$ **28.** $5 - 6q$ **29.** $5(r + 6)$ **30.** $\frac{(5 + s)}{6}$

Using exponents, write an expression for each phrase.

31. 1 more than the square of x $x^2 + 1$

32. 3 less than the cube of y $y^3 - 3$

33. The square of the sum of x and y $(x + y)^2$

34. The sum of the square of x and the square of y $x^2 + y^2$

35. y decreased by the fourth power of x $y - x^4$

C   *Let **s** represent your school's football score. Write an expression, in terms of **s**, to represent the score of the opposing team.*

Home	Visitors
s	?

36. Their team won by 1 point. $s + 1$

37. Your team won by 6 points. $s - 6$

38. Their team's score was 3 more than twice yours. $2s + 3$

39. Your team's score was half of their score. $2s$

40. Your team's score was twice their score. $\frac{1}{2}s$

THE LANGUAGE OF ALGEBRA   13

WARM-UP EXERCISES

Substitute 7 for *n*. Tell whether the sentence is true or false.
1. $3n = 21$ True
2. $16 - n = 8$ False
3. $\frac{56}{n} = 7$ False

LESSON NOTES

In Chapter 3, the students will learn to solve equations by adding, subtracting, multiplying, or dividing both sides of an equation by the same number (multiplying and dividing by 0 are excluded). In this lesson, the students solve simple equations by (a) substituting values in the given equation or (b) inspection.

Be sure the students understand that an equation such as $x + 5 = 13$ is neither true nor false as it stands; when we find a value for *x* that makes the equation true, we have solved the equation.

[Lesson notes continue on page 15.]

ALTERNATE EXAMPLES

1. Is 11 a solution of $\frac{n}{2} + 1 = 7$?
   Is 12?   11 is not a solution.
              12 is a solution.
2. Is 0 a solution of $5(10 - n) = 40$?
   Is 1? Is 2?   0 is not a solution.
              1 is not a solution.
              2 is a solution.

3. Solve the equation
   $27 - n = 19$.   8

1-5   Equations

OBJECTIVE

To solve simple equations by inspection.

An **equation** consists of two expressions with an equal sign between them. If the equation contains a variable, it is called an **open sentence.**

$n + 5 = 13$	This equation is an open sentence, with *n* as the variable.
$7 + 5 = 13$	When *n* is 7, the equation is false.
$8 + 5 = 13$	When *n* is 8, the equation is true.

$n + 5 = 13$ becomes true when $n = 8$. Therefore, 8 is a **solution.** A solution is also called a **root** of the equation.

EXAMPLE 1   Is 5 a solution of $8n + 2 = 50$? Is 6?

$8n + 2 = 50$	Write the open sentence.
$8(5) + 2 = 50$	Substitute 5 for *n*. The equation is false. Therefore, 5 is *not* a solution of $8n + 2 = 50$.
$8(6) + 2 = 50$	Now substitute 6 for *n*. This equation is true. Therefore, 6 is a solution of $8n + 2 = 50$.

EXAMPLE 2   Is 2 a solution of $4(7 - n) = 16$? Is 3? Is 4?

Substitute 2 for *n*.   Substitute 3.   Substitute 4.

$4(7 - n) = 16$ $4(7 - n) = 16$ $4(7 - n) = 16$

$4(7 - 2) = 16$ $4(7 - 3) = 16$ $4(7 - 4) = 16$

$4(5) = 16$ $4(4) = 16$ $4(3) = 16$

$20 = 16$ *False* $16 = 16$ *True* $12 = 16$ *False*

Thus, 3 is a solution. 2 and 4 are not solutions.

To *solve* an equation means to find its solution. Solutions to simple equations can often be found by inspection.

EXAMPLE 3   Solve the equation $12 + n = 17$.

$12 + n = 17$ Think: What number added to 12 equals 17? The solution is 5. 5 is the only value for *n* that makes the equation true.

EXAMPLE 4   Find the solution for the equation $8n = 72$.

$8n = 72$ Think: What number times 8 equals 72?
The solution is 9.

CLASS EXERCISES

1. Is 3 a solution of $n + 4 = 7$? Yes

2. Is 5 a solution of $2n + 3 = 15$? No

3. Is 8 a solution of $\dfrac{56}{n} = 7$? Yes

4. Is 9 a solution of $\dfrac{17 - x}{2} = 3$? No

5. Is 4 a solution of $21 = 5n$? No

6. Is 7 a solution of $3(x - 5) = 6$? Yes

Tell whether 1, 2, or 3 is the solution of the equation.

7. $3 + 4x = 11$ 2

8. $10 - n = 7$ 3

9. $18 = 9x$ 2

10. $8n - 2 = 22$ 3

11. $4(n + 1) = 16$ 3

12. $3y + 5 = 8$ 1

EXERCISES

A

1. Is 6 a solution of $8n = 48$?   Yes

2. Is 4 a solution of $21 + 2x = 29$?   Yes

3. Is 4 a solution of $\dfrac{9 - n}{5} = 2$? No

4. Is 13 a solution of $\dfrac{1 + 3n}{10} = 4$?   Yes

5. Is 7 a solution of $7 - n = 0$? Yes

6. Is 9 a solution of $8x + 9 = 81$?   Yes

Tell whether 1, 2, or 3 is the solution of the equation.

7. $x + 5 = 7$ 2

8. $n - 1 = 1$ 2

9. $6 = 7 - n$ 1

10. $13 + x = 15$ 2

11. $5a = 15$ 3

12. $7x = 14$ 2

13. $2(n + 6) = 14$ 1

14. $4(x + 5) = 28$ 2

15. $3a + 4 = 10$ 2

16. $8 + 6a = 14$ 1

17. $7n - 4 = 17$ 3

18. $6n - 1 = 11$ 2

19. $\dfrac{1}{3}x + 6 = 7$ 3

20. $\dfrac{1}{2}x - \dfrac{1}{2} = 0$ 1

21. $4x - 3\dfrac{1}{2} = 4\dfrac{1}{2}$ 2

B   *Is the number in parentheses a solution of the equation? Write **yes** or **no**.*

22. $8x - 12 = 108$;   (15)   Yes

23. $102 - 5x = 47$;   (12)   No

24. $35 - 3(n + 4) = 5$;   (6)   Yes

25. $2(4n + 1) = 58$;   (6)   No

26. $75 - (3a - 1) = 52$;   (8)   Yes

27. $28 - 2(3a + 4) = 8$;   (2) Yes

28. $(16 - 3a) + 4 = 5$;   (5)   Yes

29. $(13 + a) - 6 = 13$;   (13)   No

THE LANGUAGE OF ALGEBRA

15

4. Find the solution for the equation $\dfrac{n}{3} = 2$.   6

LESSON NOTES (continued)

Sometimes, substituting a value in an equation results in an expression that is undefined. For example, consider $\dfrac{12}{x - 1} = 6$. If we substitute 1 for x, $\dfrac{12}{x - 1}$ becomes $\dfrac{12}{1 - 1}$, or $\dfrac{12}{0}$, which is undefined, since division by zero is undefined. In Exercise 44, substituting 0 for x results in $\dfrac{5}{0}$, which is undefined; in Exercise 57, substituting 4 for x results in $\dfrac{4}{0}$, which is undefined.

DAILY QUIZ

Tell whether 1, 2, or 3 is the solution of the equation.

1. $3x - 4 = 2$ 2

2. $2(x + 8) = 18$ 1

3. $\dfrac{1}{3}x - 1 = 0$ 3

Is the number in parentheses a solution of the equation? Write *yes* or *no*.

4. $7y - 15 = 48$ (9) Yes

5. $\dfrac{n + 20}{2n} = 1$ (10) No

ASSIGNMENT GUIDE
(pages 15–16)

Minimum course: 1–6, 7–31 odd
Average course: 1–45 odd
Maximum course: 7–57 odd
All courses: *Checkpoint* review exercises

EXTRA PRACTICE, page 508

Have students use substitution to
find which of the counting numbers
from 1 to 10 are solutions to these
equations.

$x^2 + 5x - 24 = 0$ 3
$x^2 - 6x - 16 = 0$ 8
   $x^2 + 30 = 11x$ 5 or 6

Tell students to each make up similar equations, to write the solutions
on separate sheets of paper, and
then to challenge a classmate to
solve the problems.

30. $\dfrac{3x + 2}{7} = 2;$ (4)   Yes   **31.** $\dfrac{5x - 20}{6} = 5;$ (10)   Yes

32. $\dfrac{4x}{9} + 2 = 6;$ (9)   Yes   **33.** $\dfrac{2x}{3} - 1 = 1;$ (3)   Yes

34. $3n + n = 44;$ (11)   Yes   **35.** $n(2n) = 2;$ (1)   Yes

36. $4(n + 1) + n = 4;$ (0)   Yes   **37.** $\dfrac{n + 7}{n} = 7;$ (7)   No

38. $\dfrac{3x + 4}{x - 2} = 5;$ (7)   Yes   **39.** $2 + \dfrac{x + 19}{3x - 3} = 3;$ (11)   Yes

C The first six whole numbers are 0, 1, 2, 3, 4, and 5. Use these numbers
to find two solutions for each equation.

40. $x(7 - x) = 12$ 3; 4   **41.** $x(x - 3) = 0$ 0; 3   **42.** $(3 - x)x = 2$ 1; 2

43. $x^2 = x$ 0; 1   **44.** $6 - x = \dfrac{5}{x}$ 1; 5   **45.** $\dfrac{20}{9 - x} = x$ 4; 5

Find the solution. It is a whole number between 1 and 10.

46. $2n - 8 = 2$ 5   **47.** $3x + 4 = 25$ 7   **48.** $17 - x = 11$ 6

49. $3(a + 2) = 33$ 9   **50.** $20 - 3b = 5$ 5   **51.** $38 - (13 - n) = 28$ 3

52. $4(3 + x) - 2 = 30$ 5   **53.** $21 - (n + 11) = 3$ 7   **54.** $3(x - 8) - 2 = 1$ 9

55. $\dfrac{x + 4}{12 - x} = 1$ 4   **56.** $7 + \dfrac{x + 8}{2} = 12$ 2   **57.** $27 - \dfrac{x}{x - 4} = 24$ 6

Checkpoint

Students may check their answers
with those given in the back of their
books.

CHECKPOINT

Simplify each expression.

1. $7 + 9 - 6$ 10   **2.** $18 - 6 + 4$ 16   **3.** $(12 - 7) + 5$ 10

4. $12 - (7 + 5)$ 0   **5.** $(14 \div 2) \times 7$ 49   **6.** $30 - 5 \times 3 - 3$ 12

Evaluate. Let $a = 8$, $b = 4$, and $c = 6$.

7. $a + 7$ 15   **8.** $25 - 3a$ 1   **9.** $ab + b$ 36   **10.** $6b + a$ 32

11. $6ab$ 192   **12.** $a(b + c)$ 80   **13.** $b + ac$ 52   **14.** $(2c)^2$ 144

15. The sum of a and b multiplied by c 72

16. The product of a and b divided by one-third the sum of a and b 8

16   CHAPTER 1

1-6 Problem Solving: Using Equations

OBJECTIVE

To write equations and use the solutions to answer number problems.

Most of the problems solved in mathematics involve numerical relationships. To plan the solutions, read carefully before deciding which operation to use.

A number is 7 more than 26. What is the number?

The number you are looking for is *more than* 26; add to find the answer.

26 + 7 = 33   33 is the correct number, since 33 is 7 more than 26.

Here is another problem that uses the words *more than*. Will you add to find the answer?

7 more than a number is 26. What is the number?

In this problem, the number you are looking for is *less than* 26, so you must subtract to find the number.

26 − 7 = 19   19 is the correct number, since 7 more than 19 is 26.

In algebraic problems, numbers and operations are often shown in *equations*. The *solutions* to the equations are used to answer the questions asked in the problems. The problems shown above can also be solved by using equations.

EXAMPLE 1

Strategy: Write and solve an equation.

a. A number is 7 more than 26. What is the number?

b. 7 more than a number is 26. What is the number?

Read the problem to find the key ideas.

A number *is more than* 26.

A number *is less than* 26.

Use a variable.

Let n be the number.

Let n be the number.

Write an equation.

n = 26 + 7

n + 7 = 26

Find the solution.

n = 33

n = 19

Always check to see that the solution to the equation satisfies the problem.

33 is 7 more than 26.

7 more than 19 is 26.

Answer the question.

The number is 33.

The number is 19.

2. If today's date is October 20, what will be the date two weeks from today?   November 3

3. Seth worked part-time for 4 weeks and earned a total of $180. How much money did he earn per week? $45

POSSIBLE ERROR

Students often think that when a problem uses the word *more*, they will add to find the answer. Similarly, they think that if the word *less* is used, they will sub- tract to find the answer. Use Ex- ample 1 and Class Exercises 1–8 as reminders to students that each problem must be ana- lyzed individually to determine whether to add, subtract, multi- ply, or divide. Provide other pairs of exercises similar to Class Exercises 1–8 if additional experiences of this type seem necessary.

DAILY QUIZ

Using *n* as the variable, write an equation for each problem. Then solve it.

1. Three times some number is 96. What is the number? $3n = 96$; 32

2. Keith is 17, which is 6 years younger than his cousin Dana. How old is Dana? $17 = n - 6$; 23

3. In 11 years, Anne will be 30. How old is she now? $n + 11 = 30$; 19

4. A certain amount of money was divided equally among 8 people. Each person received $20. What was the original amount of money? $\frac{n}{8} = 20$; $160

Be careful. Sometimes the solution to an equation does not answer the problem. It only helps you to find the answer.

EXAMPLE 2   The date of a party is 7 days after September 26. When is the party?

Use a variable.	Let *n* be the date of the party.
Write an equation.	$n = 26 + 7$
Find the solution.	$n = 33$ But the answer is not September 33. September has 30 days.
Answer the question.	The date of the party is October 3.

EXAMPLE 3   Jane earned $135 delivering papers at $15 per week. How many weeks did she work?

The problem can be solved directly by division. It can also be solved by using an equation.

Use a variable.	Let *n* be the number of weeks worked.
Write an equation.	$15n = 135$
Find the solution.	$n = 9$ Check to see that $15 times 9 is $135.
Answer the question.	Jane worked for 9 weeks.

CLASS EXERCISES

Decide what operation is needed to find the number. Then find the number.

1. A number is 12 less than 37.   Sub.; 25 **2.** 12 less than a number is 37.   Add.; 49

3. A number is 9 more than 19.   Add.; 28 **4.** 9 more than a number is 19.   Sub.; 10

5. 8 times a number is 400.   Div.; 50 **6.** A number is 8 times 400.   Mult.; 3200

7. A number divided by 30 is 6. Mult.; 180 **8.** 30 divided by a number is 6.   Div.; 5

*Using **n** as the variable, write an equation for each problem. Then solve it.*

9. In 3 years John will be 17. How old is he now? $n + 3 = 17$; 14

10. Jill is 18, which is 2 years younger than Jack. How old is Jack? $18 = n - 2$; 20

11. Jed is 4 times as old as Judy. If Judy is 9, how old is Jed? $n = 4(9)$; 36

12. José is 5 times as old as Jeremy. If José is 45, how old is Jeremy? $45 = 5n$; 9

13. Four weeks ago today, it was July 4. What is the date today? $4 + 4(7) = n$; 32; Aug. 1

14. Abraham Lincoln was born 33 years after the United States' inde- pendence. When was he born? $1776 + 33 = n$; 1809

EXERCISES

A *Decide which operations are needed to find the numbers. Then find each number.*

1. A number is 8 more than 88. Add; 96
2. 88 is 8 more than a number. Sub.; 80
3. A number is 25 less than 65. Sub.; 40
4. 25 less than a number is 65. Add.; 90
5. 7 times a number is 77. Div.; 11
6. A number is 7 times 77. Mult.; 539
7. A number divided by 4 is 20. Mult.; 80
8. A number divided by 20 is 4. Mult.; 80
9. 20 divided by a number is 4. Div.; 5
10. A number is 45 more than the sum of 15 and 45. Add.; 105
11. A number is 15 less than 45 increased by 25. Add., sub.; 55
12. A number is 25 times the sum of 15 and 45. Add., mult.; 1500

*Using **n** as the variable, write an equation for each problem. Then solve it.*

13. Brook's earnings increased from $18 to $35 a week. What was the increase? $n + 18 = 35$; $17
14. Lena's weekly earnings decreased by $18 a week to $35. What was she earning before the decrease? $n - 18 = 35$; $53
15. Mei-ling bought 8 items for $1.20. What was the price per item? $8n = 1.20$; 15¢
16. Phyllis bought 8 items at $1.20 each. How much did she spend? $n = 8(1.20)$; $9.60
17. Twelve bills of a certain denomination totaled $600. What was the value of each bill? $12n = 600$; $50
18. Six hundred dollars was divided equally among 40 people. How much did each person receive? $40n = 600$; $15
19. A certain amount divided by 25 equals $6. What is the amount? $\frac{n}{25} = 6$; $150
20. Some number less the sum of 14 and 15 is 70. What is the number? $n - (14 + 15) = 70$; 99

B
21. In 16 years, Mike will be 40. How old is he now? $n + 16 = 40$; 24
22. Eleven years ago, Tora was 11. How old is she now? $n - 11 = 11$; 22
23. Maria is $\frac{1}{6}$ as old as her grandmother, who is 96. How old is Maria? $6n = 96$; 16
24. Barry is 64, or 4 times Kevin's age. How old is Kevin? $64 = 4n$; 16

In 9 years, Matt will be half a century old.

25. How old will he be in 25 years? 66
26. How old was he 25 years ago? 16

George Washington died in 1799 at the age of 67.

27. In what year was he born? 1732
28. How old would he have been if he had lived until 1850? 118

THE LANGUAGE OF ALGEBRA

19

EXTRA PRACTICE, page 508

ENRICHMENT ACTIVITY

Have the students find all the possible solutions to this problem.

In a certain room there are chairs with four legs and some three-legged stools. The total number of legs in the room is 50. How many chairs and stools could there be?

11 chairs, 2 stools;
8 chairs, 6 stools;
5 chairs, 10 stools;
2 chairs, 14 stools

Note that Exercises 29–32 present a practical situation with data used in a variety of ways. Exercises 29 and 30 are straightforward problems that require division. However, to solve Exercise 31 correctly, the students must bear in mind that the prices given (78¢ a dozen and $4.50 a gross) apply only to buying those particular quantities. Thus, to buy 180 pencils most economically, a person must buy 1 gross ($4.50) and 3 dozen ($2.34); the total cost is $6.84. To solve Exercise 32, the students must multiply 12 times 78¢ ($9.36) and then find the difference between $9.36 and $4.50; the difference is $4.86.

Pencils sell for 78¢ a dozen or for $4.50 a gross, which is 12 dozen.

29. How much does each pencil cost when buying a dozen? $6\frac{1}{2}$¢, or 6.5¢

30. How much does each pencil cost when buying a gross? $3\frac{1}{8}$¢, or 3.125¢

31. What is the price of 180 pencils bought by the less expensive method? $6.84

32. How much can be saved by buying a gross rather than buying an equal amount by the dozen? $4.86

What year or years in the 1980's are represented by a number with the property given?

33. The product of the digits is 0. 1980 **34.** The sum of its digits is 25. 1987

35. Two digits are the same. 1981; 1988; 1989 **36.** The product of its digits is 288. 1984

37. Two pairs of digits differ by 1. 1980; 1982

38. The sum of 3 of its digits times the fourth is 90. 1981; 1985

C **39.** Theodore Roosevelt was 42 years old at the turn of the century and died in 1919. Franklin Roosevelt was 18 at the turn of the century and died in 1945. Who lived longer and by how much? Franklin Roosevelt; 2 years

 USING THE CALCULATOR

Sums of Counting Numbers, of Squares, of Cubes

Think of the first 10 counting numbers. Use a calculator to find these sums.

1. $1 + 2 + 3 + 4 + 5 + 6 + 7 + 8 + 9 + 10 = \underline{?}$ 55

2. $1^2 + 2^2 + 3^2 + 4^2 + 5^2 + 6^2 + 7^2 + 8^2 + 9^2 + 10^2 = \underline{?}$ 385

3. $1^3 + 2^3 + 3^3 + 4^3 + 5^3 + 6^3 + 7^3 + 8^3 + 9^3 + 10^3 = \underline{?}$ 3025

The following formulas can be used to find the sums of the first n consecutive counting numbers, their squares, and their cubes.

Sum: first n counting numbers	**Sum:** squares of first n counting numbers	**Sum:** cubes of first n counting numbers
$\dfrac{n(n + 1)}{2}$	$\dfrac{n(n + 1)(2n + 1)}{6}$	$\dfrac{n^2(n + 1)^2}{4}$

4. Use these formulas to check your answers to Exercises 1–3. The answers are the same; 55, 385, and 3025.

5. Find the sum of the first 75 counting numbers. 2850

6. Find the sum of the squares of the first 75 counting numbers. 143,450

7. Find the sum of the cubes of the first 75 counting numbers. 8,122,500

20

CHAPTER 1

1-7 The Whole Numbers

OBJECTIVES

To identify whole numbers.
To write algebraic expressions for whole numbers, for even numbers, and
for odd numbers.

The whole numbers are the natural, or counting numbers, and zero.
That is, the set of **whole numbers** starts with 0 and increases by 1,
without end.

0,   1,   2,   3,   4,   5,   6,   7,   8,   9,   10, . . .

The least whole number is 0.   There is no greatest whole number.

The three dots indicate that the whole numbers continue without end.
On the number line, each whole number is represented by a point.

If n is a whole number, then n + 1 is the next whole number. If 1 is
added again and again, **consecutive whole numbers** are the result. For
instance, the four consecutive whole numbers that follow 100 are

101, 102, 103, 104

EXAMPLE 1   Let n represent a whole number. Write expressions for the given
numbers.
  a. The next three consecutive whole numbers
  b. A whole number twice as great as n
  c. A whole number 10 greater than n

Answers   **a.** n + 1, n + 2, n + 3   **b.** 2n   **c.** n + 10

EXAMPLE 2   Evaluate for n = 50. Is the result a whole number?
  a. 2n − 1   **b.** 0.6n   **c.** n ÷ 3   **d.** $\dfrac{2.5n}{5}$

Answers   **a.** Yes, since 2(50) − 1 = 100 − 1 = 99.
  b. Yes, since 0.6(50) = 30.
  c. No, since $50 \div 3 = \dfrac{50}{3} = 16\dfrac{2}{3}$.
  d. Yes, since $\dfrac{2.5(50)}{5} = \dfrac{125}{5} = 25$.

THE LANGUAGE OF ALGEBRA   21

WARM-UP EXERCISES

Evaluate for n = 25.
1. n + 15   40   **2.** $\dfrac{4n}{3}$ $33\dfrac{1}{3}$

LESSON NOTES

In this lesson, the students use
algebraic expressions in exploring
basic ideas about whole numbers.
Notice that the students find: In
some expressions, when the variable is replaced by any whole number, the result is always a whole
number; in other cases, the result is
sometimes a whole number and
sometimes not a whole number; in
still other cases, the result is never
a whole number.
    Exercises 37–38 use the idea of
between. You may wish to remind
the students:

  "The numbers from a to c"
  include both a and c.

  "The numbers between a and c"
  do not include either a or c.

Thus, "the odd numbers between 9
and 15" are 11 and 13.

ALTERNATE EXAMPLES

  1. Let *n* represent a whole number. Write expressions for the
  given numbers.
    a. The next four consecutive
    whole numbers   n + 1,
    n + 2, n + 3, n + 4
    b. A whole number that is 5
    times as great as n   5n
    c. A whole number that is 6
    greater than n   n + 6
  2. Evaluate for n = 100. Is the result a whole number?
    a. 3n + 2   Yes **b.** 0.75n   Yes
    c. n ÷ 3   No   **d.** $\dfrac{0.5n}{8}$ No

3. Let n represent a whole number. For what values of n will the expression be a whole number?

a. $\dfrac{n}{5}$ A whole number only when n is 0, 5, 10, 15, . . .

b. $\dfrac{10}{n}$ A whole number only when n is 1, 2, 5, or 10

c. $n + 0.25$ Never a whole number if n is a whole number

d. $8n$ Always a whole number if n is a whole number

e. $1\dfrac{1}{3}n$ A whole number only when n is 0, 3, 6, 9 . . .

****For an expression in which substituting whole numbers sometimes results in a value that is less than 0, use

$3 - n$ A whole number only when n is 0, 1, 2, 3

(See Class Exercises 9, 10, 16; A Exercises 18, 21.)

4. Let $2n$ equal any even number. Write expressions for the next three

a. whole numbers $2n + 1$, $2n + 2$, $2n + 3$

b. even numbers $2n + 2$, $2n + 4$, $2n + 6$

c. odd numbers $2n + 1$, $2n + 3$, $2n + 5$

POSSIBLE ERROR

When working with whole numbers, some students forget to consider 0. Thus, in Class Exercises 9–16, they may forget to use 0 as a possible value for n. In Class Exercise 9, for example, they may give their answer as "any number from 1 to 24." To help students avoid this type of error, contrast the whole numbers (0, 1, 2, 3, . . .) with the counting numbers (1, 2, 3, . . .).

EXAMPLE 3   Let n represent a whole number. For what values of n will the expression also be a whole number?

a. $\dfrac{n}{3}$ A whole number only when n is 0, 3, 6, 9, . . .

b. $\dfrac{4}{n}$ A whole number only when n is 1, 2, or 4

c. $n + 7$ Always a whole number if n is a whole number

d. $n + 0.5$ Never a whole number if n is a whole number

e. $2\dfrac{1}{2}n$ A whole number only when n is 0, 2, 4, 6, . . .

Whole numbers are either *even* or *odd*. If n is a whole number, then $2n$ must be an **even number**.

	2(0)	2(1)	2(2)	2(3)	2(4)	2(5)	
	↓	↓	↓	↓	↓	↓	
Even Numbers	0	2	4	6	8	10	. . .
Odd Numbers	1	3	5	7	9	11	. . .

Numbers such as 12, 14, 16, 18 are **consecutive even numbers,** while numbers such as 13, 15, 17, 19 are **consecutive odd numbers.** Notice that consecutive even or odd numbers differ by 2.

EXAMPLE 4   Let n equal any even number. Write expressions for the next two

a. even numbers.   **b. odd numbers.**   **c. whole numbers.**

$n + 2, n + 4$ $n + 1, n + 3$ $n + 1, n + 2$

CLASS EXERCISES

Evaluate for $n = 12$. *Is the result a whole number?*

1. $7n$ 84; yes   **2.** $3n - 2$ 34; yes   **3.** $0.4n - 0.6$ 4.2; no   **4.** $n - 6$ 6; yes

5. $\dfrac{1}{3}n$ 4; yes   **6.** $\dfrac{1}{3}n + 2$ 6; yes   **7.** $\dfrac{1}{3}n - 2$ 2; yes   **8.** $n - \dfrac{1}{3}$ $11\dfrac{2}{3}$; no

Let n *equal a whole number. For what values of* n *will the expression also be a whole number?*

9. $24 - n$ 0, 1, 2, . . . , 24

10. $n - 3.5$ No values

11. $n + 1$ All whole numbers: 0, 1, 2, . . .

12. $n + \dfrac{1}{2}$ No values

13. $2n$ All whole numbers: 0, 1, 2, . . .

14. $\dfrac{1}{2}n$ 0, 2, 4, 6, . . .

15. $\dfrac{1}{3}n$ 0, 3, 6, 9, . . .

16. $n - 3$ 3, 4, 5, . . .

22

EXERCISES

A *Tell whether the given number is a whole number.*

1. 7.4 No   **2.** 5.0 Yes   **3.** 76 Yes   **4.** 100 Yes   **5.** $3\frac{1}{3}$ No

Evaluate for $n = 9$. *Is the result a whole number?*

6. $2n + 7$ 25; yes **7.** $11n$ 99; yes **8.** $6(n - 5)$ 24; yes **9.** $6n - 5$ 49; yes

10. $n - 9$ 0; yes **11.** $0.9 - 0.1n$ 0; yes **12.** $\dfrac{n}{6}$ 1.5; no **13.** $\dfrac{n + 9}{9}$ 2; yes

Let n *equal a whole number. For what values of* n *will the expression also be a whole number?*

14. $\dfrac{n}{5}$ $0, 5, 10, 15, \ldots$ **15.** $3n$ All whole numbers **16.** $\dfrac{12}{n}$ $1, 2, 3, 4, 6, 12$ **17.** $n + 0.1$ No values

18. $n - 10$ $10, 11, 12, \ldots$ **19.** $\dfrac{10}{n}$ $1, 2, 5, 10$ **20.** $\dfrac{n}{10}$ $0, 10, 20, \ldots$ **21.** $5 - n$ $0, 1, 2, 3, 4, 5$

Name the next three consecutive even numbers

22. greater than 12. $14, 16, 18$ **23.** greater than 997. $998, 1000, 1002$

24. equal to or greater than one million. $1,000,000; 1,000,002; 1,000,004$

B *Let* n *be an odd number. Write expressions for the next three*

25. odd numbers. **26.** even numbers. **27.** whole numbers.
$n + 2, n + 4, n + 6$ $n + 1, n + 3, n + 5$ $n + 1, n + 2, n + 3$

Let n *be an odd whole number. Does the given expression represent an odd number or an even number?*

28. $n + 7$ Even **29.** $2n$ Even **30.** $2n + 1$ Odd **31.** $n + 2$ Odd

32. $2(n + 1)$ Even **33.** n^2 Odd **34.** $(n + 1)^2$ Even **35.** $n(n + 1)$ Even

36. Which whole numbers from 0 through 10 will make $\dfrac{100 + n}{n}$ a whole number?
$1, 2, 4, 5, 10$

Represent all odd numbers between $n + 3$ *and* $n + 10$

37. if n is an odd number. **38.** if n is an even number.
$n + 4, n + 6, n + 8$ $n + 5, n + 7, n + 9$

C *For what whole-number values of* n *does the expression represent a whole number?*

39. $\dfrac{n + 8}{8}$ $0, 8, 16, \ldots$ **40.** $\dfrac{3n + 5}{2}$ $1, 3, 5, \ldots$ **41.** $\dfrac{2n}{3}$ $0, 3, 6, 9, \ldots$

42. n^2 $0, 1, 2, 3, \ldots$ **43.** $n(n + 1)$ $0, 1, 2, \ldots$ **44.** $\left(\dfrac{n + 4}{5}\right)^2$ $1, 6, 11, 16, \ldots$

THE LANGUAGE OF ALGEBRA

23

In science, in mathematics, and in daily life, many problem-solving situations are solved *not* by the use of "formal" procedures, but by techniques that involve reasoning, pattern analysis and extension, and/or trial and error.

In this work with the sum of consecutive odd numbers, the students have the opportunity to work with patterns and to generalize. They also have the opportunity to apply a pattern "in reverse."

Using BASIC

The computer can be used to demonstrate the use of algebraic expressions for consecutive odd numbers, consecutive even numbers, and so on. To display the consecutive odd numbers, enter and RUN this program:

```
10  LET N = 1
20  PRINT N
30  LET N = N + 2
40  GO TO 20
```

This program generates an infinite loop. Every computer has a procedure for getting out of such a loop; for example, on the Apple IIe, use the CTRL and RESET keys.

To display the consecutive even numbers, simply change line 10:

```
10  LET N = 0
```

STRATEGIES for PROBLEM SOLVING

Searching for Patterns

The sums of consecutive odd numbers have an interesting pattern.

Try to discover a pattern.

Start with several simple sums.

The first odd number	1		=	1	=	$1 \cdot 1$	=	1^2
The first two odd numbers	$1 + 3$		=	4	=	$2 \cdot 2$	=	2^2
The first three odd numbers	$1 + 3 + 5$		=	9	=	$3 \cdot 3$	=	3^2
The first four odd numbers	$1 + 3 + 5 + 7$		=	16	=	$4 \cdot 4$	=	4^2

Use the pattern.

Find the sum of these odd numbers without adding.

1. The first 5 odd numbers   25 **2.** The first 10 odd numbers   100

3. The first 100 odd numbers 10,000 **4.** The first n odd numbers n^2

Reverse the pattern.

How many consecutive odd numbers, starting with 1, have this sum?

5. 64 8   **6.** 169 13   **7.** 2500 50   **8.** k^2 k

Apply the pattern.

9. Add the first million odd numbers. The sum is _?_.   1,000,000,000,000

10. Add the first _?_ odd numbers. The sum is 1 million.   1000

11. Use the pattern to find the sum of all these numbers.   3600

1	21	41	61	81	101
3	23	43	63	83	103
5	25	45	65	85	105
7	27	47	67	87	107
9	29	49	69	89	109
11	31	51	71	91	111
13	33	53	73	93	113
15	35	55	75	95	115
17	37	57	77	97	117
19	39	59	79	99	119

CHAPTER 1

1-8 The Integers

OBJECTIVES

To identify integers and their opposites.
To order a set of integers.

The set of **integers** continues without end in both directions from 0.

$$\ldots, \; ^-5, \; ^-4, \; ^-3, \; ^-2, \; ^-1, \; 0, \; ^+1, \; ^+2, \; ^+3, \; ^+4, \; ^+5, \; \ldots$$

There is no least integer.   **There is no greatest integer.**

These integers increase by 1 as you read to the right. $^+3$ is read *positive three,* and is the same as 3. All positive integers are to the *right* of 0 on the number line. $^-5$ is read *negative five.* All negative integers are to the *left* of 0 on the number line.

Every integer has an **opposite.** The **graph** of the opposite of an integer is the same distance from the **origin** but in the opposite direction. The opposite of 3 is $^-3$. The opposite of $^-5$ is 5. The opposite of 0 is 0, and 0 is neither positive nor negative.

EXAMPLE 1   Give the opposite of each integer.

Integer	$^+4$	$^-5$	0	4	25
Opposite	$^-4$	5	0	$^-4$	$^-25$

You can use a dot as a graph of a number on a number line.

EXAMPLE 2   **a.** Graph the integers $^-4$, $^-3$, and 1 on a number line.
              b. Graph their opposites on a different number line.

Answers   **a.**   **b.**

Integers increase in value from left to right on the number line.

     1 is to the right of $^-4$. $^-2$ is to the left of $^-1$.
     1 *is greater than* $^-4$. $^-2$ *is less than* $^-1$.
         $1 > {}^-4$ $^-2 < {}^-1$

The symbols $>$ and $<$ are *inequality symbols.* A third inequality symbol is $\neq$. The number sentence $4 \neq {}^-4$ is read, "4 *is not equal to* $^-4$." Other inequality symbols are $\geq$ (is greater than or equal to) and $\leq$ (is less than or equal to).

THE LANGUAGE OF ALGEBRA   **25**

WARM-UP EXERCISES

1. What is the least whole number?   0
2. Name all the whole numbers between 3 and 7.   4, 5, 6

LESSON NOTES

The text indicates that $^+3$, which is read as *positive three,* corresponds to the whole number 3. The set of integers can be thought of as the whole numbers and their opposites (with 0 acting as its own opposite).

Following the discussion of the inequality symbols, you might wish to use the symbol $<$ to define betweenness. If $a < b$ and $b < c$, then b is between a and c. We can write $a < b < c$, and read it as **b** *is between* **a** *and* **c**. The idea of betweenness is used in Example 5b and in Exercises 11–13.

POSSIBLE ERROR

Some students order negative integers incorrectly by using distance from 0. For example, they may think that $^-6$ is greater than $^-4$ because $^-6$ is farther from 0. Repeatedly remind the students that as we move from left to right on the number line, the numbers increase in value. If x is to the right of y on the number line, $x > y$.

ALTERNATE EXAMPLES

1. Give the opposite of each integer.

$^+5$	$^-6$	0	8	$^-99$
$^-5$	6	0	$^-8$	99

2. **a.** Graph the integers $^-1$, 0, and 2 on a number line.

    b. Graph their opposites on a different number line.

3. Tell whether the sentence is true or false.
   a. ⁻5 > ⁻6   True
   b. 1(1) − 1 ≠ 1   False
   c. 0 < ⁻3   False
   d. 7(8) ≠ 9(6)   True
4. List each set of integers.
   a. Four consecutive integers, starting with ⁻2. ⁻2, ⁻1, 0, 1
   b. Four consecutive odd integers, starting with ⁻5. ⁻5, ⁻3, ⁻1, 1
   c. Four consecutive even integers, starting with ⁻6. ⁻6, ⁻4, ⁻2, 0
   d. The integers 0, ⁻3, ⁻4, 2, ⁻11, 10 in order, least to greatest. ⁻11, ⁻4, ⁻3, 0, 2, 10
5. Refer to a number line.
   a. Name the two integers that are five units from ⁻3. ⁻8 and 2
   b. How many integers are there between ⁻1 and 4? Four

6. What integer would you use to describe each of these?
   a. A business loss of $250   ⁻250
   b. A 3-foot rise in the water level   ⁺3
   c. A 7-yard gain in football   ⁺7

Give the opposite of each integer.
1. ⁻8 8   2. 32 ⁻32
3. 0 0   4. 175 ⁻175
5. What integer would you use to describe a 12-yard loss in football? ⁻12

EXAMPLE 3   Tell whether the sentence is *true* or *false*.
   a. ⁻3 < ⁻4   b. 3·1 = 3 + 0   c. 4 ≥ 0   d. 4·0 ≠ 4 + 0
        False   True   True   True

EXAMPLE 4   List each set of integers.
   a. Five consecutive integers, starting with ⁻3
   b. Five consecutive even integers, starting with ⁻8
   c. Five consecutive odd integers, starting with ⁻1
   d. The integers ⁻2, ⁻5, 1, 6, ⁻7, 0 in order, least to greatest

   Answers   a. ⁻3, ⁻2, ⁻1, 0, 1   b. ⁻8, ⁻6, ⁻4, ⁻2, 0
              c. ⁻1, 1, 3, 5, 7   d. ⁻7, ⁻5, ⁻2, 0, 1, 6

EXAMPLE 5   Refer to a number line.
   a. Name the two integers that are three units from 2.
   b. How many integers are there *between* ⁻3 and 5?

   Answers   a. ⁻1 and 5   b. Seven

Integers are often used when two directions can be associated with a number.

Savings Account	A deposit of $150	⁺150
Temperature Change	A drop of 8 degrees	⁻8
Stock Prices	A loss of 2 points	⁻2

EXAMPLE 6   What integer would you use to describe each of these?
   a. A withdrawal from a savings account of $50
   b. A rise in temperature of 10°
   c. A gain in stock prices of 3 points

   Answers   a. ⁻50   b. ⁺10   c. ⁺3

CLASS EXERCISES

Is the given number an integer?

1. ⁻21 Yes   2. 13 Yes   3. 1.83 No   4. ⁻1$\frac{1}{2}$ No   5. ⁺100 Yes

Give the opposite of each integer.

6. 6   ⁻6   7. ⁺9   ⁻9   8. 0   0   9. ⁻1   1   10. ⁻11   11

Name the integer that corresponds to each point, A–E.

11.

EXERCISES

A

1. Which numbers shown at the right are whole numbers?
   13, 49, 0
2. Which numbers at the right are integers?
   13, ⁻7, 49, 0

13	⁻7	49
$\frac{1}{2}$	⁻0.2	0

Give the opposite of each integer.

3. ⁻2   2   **4.** 25 ⁻25   **5.** ⁻257 257   **6.** 0 0

Name the integer that corresponds to each point, A–H.

7.
A B C D
⁻8 ⁻6 ⁻4 ⁻3   0 1   4   7 8

8.
E   F   G   H
⁻20 ⁻18   ⁻11 ⁻10   ⁻5   0   7 10   20

9. Graph the integers ⁻5, ⁻3, ⁻2, and 1 on a number line. Graph their
   opposites on another line.

   0 1
   0 1

10. Name six consecutive even integers, starting with ⁻4.
    ⁻4, ⁻2, 0, 2, 4, 6

Name all of the integers between the given numbers.

11. 8 and 14   **12.** ⁻5 and 3   **13.** ⁻6 and ⁻2
9, 10, 11, 12, 13   ⁻4, ⁻3, ⁻2, ⁻1, 0, 1, 2   ⁻5, ⁻4, ⁻3

*Is the sentence **true** or is it **false**?*

14. ⁻6 > ⁻12 True   **15.** ⁻9 < 0 True   **16.** ⁻10 ≥ 2 False

17. List the integers 0, ⁻1, 1, ⁻4, 3, ⁻7 in order, least to greatest.   ⁻7, ⁻4, ⁻1, 0, 1, 3

B

*Name two integers on the number line that are three units from the
given integer.*

18. 0   ⁻3, 3   **19.** 3   0, 6   **20.** ⁻6   ⁻9, ⁻3

What integer would you use to describe each of these?

21. A 9-yard gain in football   ⁺9   **22.** A price markdown of $25   ⁻25

23. A business loss of $5000   ⁻5000   **24.** An investment profit of $1000   ⁺1000

25. A 2-foot drop in water level   ⁻2   **26.** 30 seconds before blast-off   ⁻30

C

*Let **n** be an odd integer. Write expressions for the next two*

27. greater integers.   **28.** consecutive odd integers.   **29.** even integers.
n + 1, n + 2   n + 2, n + 4   n + 1, n + 3

*If **n** is an even integer, does the expression represent an odd or an even integer?*

30. n + 1   Odd   **31.** n − 1   Odd   **32.** n + 4   Even

THE LANGUAGE OF ALGEBRA   27

LESSON NOTES

To show students the relationships of various sets of numbers within the set of real numbers, you can sketch the following diagram for them.

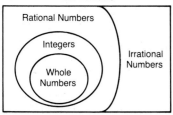

The diagram shows that every whole number is an integer, that every integer is a rational number, and that every rational number is a real number. It also shows other relationships—for example, no whole number is an irrational number.

Point out that such a number as ⁻2 is located inside the ring for the "Integers" but not inside the ring for the "Whole Numbers." Ask where such numbers as $\frac{1}{2}$ and $\sqrt{3}$ are located.

ALTERNATE EXAMPLE

1. Arrange each set of rational numbers from least to greatest.
   a. ⁻3.2, 1.1, 0, ⁻3, ⁻4.5 ⁻4.5, ⁻3.2, ⁻3, 0, 1.1
   b. $2\frac{1}{2}$, 1, ⁻2.1, ⁻0.9, $\frac{-1}{2}$ ⁻2.1, ⁻0.9, $\frac{-1}{2}$, 1, $2\frac{1}{2}$

28

1-9   Real Numbers and the Number Line

OBJECTIVES

To order real numbers from least to greatest.
To locate real numbers on the number line.

A **rational number** is a number that can be expressed as a ratio of two integers.

$$0.875 = \frac{7}{8} \qquad 1\frac{1}{2} = \frac{3}{2} \qquad 2 = \frac{2}{1} \qquad ^-3 = \frac{^-3}{1}$$

Every whole number and every integer is a rational number. Every rational number has an *opposite* that is also a rational number.

⁻0.875 is the opposite of 0.875. $^-1\frac{1}{2}$ is the opposite of $1\frac{1}{2}$.

A rational number can be located as a point on the number line. The number is called the **coordinate** of the point.

The number line helps you to *order* rational numbers. As you move to the right, the numbers increase. As you move to the left, the numbers decrease.

$$^-3 < \,^-1\frac{1}{2} \qquad\qquad 0.875 > \,^-1\frac{1}{2}$$

⁻3 is less than $^-1\frac{1}{2}$.   0.875 is greater than $^-1\frac{1}{2}$.

EXAMPLE 1   Arrange each set of rational numbers from least to greatest.

a. **⁻2.5, 0, ⁻1, 2, ⁻5**   b. $\frac{1}{2}, \,^-3, 4, \frac{1}{4}, \,^-3.7$

⁻5, ⁻2.5, ⁻1, 0, 2 $^-3.7, \,^-3, \frac{1}{4}, \frac{1}{2}, 4$

Some points on the number line have coordinates that are *not* rational numbers. These numbers are called **irrational numbers.** They cannot be represented as the ratio of two integers. They can, however, be approximated by rational numbers.

28

Here are approximations for $\sqrt{2}$ and $^-\sqrt{3}$. These square roots are irrational numbers, given here to three decimal places.

$$\sqrt{2} \approx 1.414 \qquad ^-\sqrt{3} \approx ^-1.732$$

The symbol $\approx$ is read "is approximately equal to."

The *approximation* 3.14 is commonly used for *pi*, which is another familiar irrational number. The symbol for pi is π.

The rational and irrational numbers together form the set of **real numbers.** Every real number can be represented by a point on the number line. Every point on the number line can be named by a real number, rational or irrational.

EXAMPLE 2

Name the real number. Refer to a number line.

a. Halfway between $^-2$ and 1

b. Halfway between $^-1\frac{1}{2}$ and $^-3$.

c. Three units to the left of 2.25

d. Three units to the right of $^-2.1$

Answers   **a.** $\dfrac{^-1}{2}$ **b.** $^-2\dfrac{1}{4}$ **c.** $^-0.75$ **d.** 0.9

Every real number is positive, negative, or zero. Those located to the right of 0 on the number line are positive real numbers. Those located to the left of 0 are negative real numbers.

EXAMPLE 3

Is the real number positive, negative, or zero?

a. 2 more than $\sqrt{2}$

b. 3 less than $\sqrt{3}$

c. 4 times π

d. Halfway between $^-\sqrt{5}$ and $\sqrt{5}$

Answers   **a.** positive   **b.** negative   **c.** positive   **d.** zero

CLASS EXERCISES

What lettered point represents the rational number given?

1. $^-1\frac{1}{2}$ B

2. $\frac{1}{2}$ F

3. $^-3$ A

4. $^-\frac{1}{4}$ E

THE LANGUAGE OF ALGEBRA

Using BASIC
For an approximation of $\sqrt{2}$ that is more precise than 1.414, enter:

    PRINT SQR (2)

ALTERNATE EXAMPLES

2. Name the real number. Refer to a number line.

a. Halfway between $^-3$ and 0 $^-1\frac{1}{2}$

b. Halfway between $^-3$ and $^-4$ $^-3\frac{1}{2}$

c. Four units to the left of 1.75 $^-2.25$

d. Four units to the right of $^-1.2$ 2.8

3. Is the real number positive, negative, or zero?

a. 1 less than $\sqrt{2}$ Positive; $\sqrt{2} - 1$

b. 2 less than $\sqrt{2}$ Negative; $\sqrt{2} - 2$

c. 2 times π Positive; 2π

d. One-third of the way from $^-1$ to 2   Zero; 0

DAILY QUIZ

Use < or > to complete each sentence.

1. 6 ? $^-10$ >

2. $^-3\frac{1}{2}$? $^-5$ >

3. $^-4.3$? 2.7   <

4. $\dfrac{^-2}{3}$? $\dfrac{^-1}{3}$ <

5. Arrange in order from least to greatest: $^-2$, $^-2.3$, $^-\pi$, $^-\sqrt{3}$
$^-\pi$, $^-2.3$, $^-2$, $^-\sqrt{3}$

ASSIGNMENT GUIDE
(pages 30–31)

Minimum course: 1–29
Average course: 1–12,
13–29 odd,
30–41
Maximum course: 13–29 odd,
30–45
All courses: *Checkpoint*
review
exercises

ENRICHMENT ACTIVITY

Remind the students that all rational numbers can be expressed as infinite repeating decimals. For example, $\frac{1}{3}$ = 0.33333. . . (which can be written as $0.\overline{3}$), $\frac{3}{4}$ = 0.75000. . . (which can be written as $0.75\overline{0}$ or 0.75), and $\frac{12}{99}$ = 0.121212. . . (which can be written as $0.\overline{12}$). Explain that irrational numbers have non-repeating nonterminating decimal representations. For example, 0.454554555. . . is the decimal representation of an irrational number.

Challenge the students to use only the digits 0 and 1 to represent

a. a rational number
b. an irrational number

Then have them order the two numbers and find a rational number that is between these two numbers.

Answers will vary. One possible rational number is 0.010101. . . ; one possible irrational number is 0.010010001. . . . A rational number between these two numbers is 0.01002.

Between which two of the integers would you locate the irrational number?

5. $\sqrt{3}$ 1, 2   **6.** $^-\sqrt{2}$ $^-1, ^-2$ **7.** $\frac{\pi}{2}$ 1, 2   **8.** $\pi - 2.5$ 0, 1

Arrange in order from least to greatest.

9. 3, $^-$1.7, $^-$2, 1.5 $^-$2, $^-$1.7, 1.5, 3   **10.** $-\frac{3}{4}$, $^-$1, $\frac{1}{2}$, $-\frac{1}{4}$ $^-$1, $-\frac{3}{4}$, $-\frac{1}{4}$, $\frac{1}{2}$

EXERCISES

A   Match a point on the number line with each coordinate.

1. $\frac{1}{2}$ G   **2.** $^-$1.5   C

3. 2   J   **4.** $^-$0.5   E

5. $^-1\frac{1}{2}$ C   **6.** $^-$2.5   A

Graph each set of numbers on a separate number line.

7. $^-$1, $^-$4, 0, 3, $^-$3   **8.** $^-$1.2, $\frac{4}{5}$, $-\frac{1}{5}$, $^-$0.8

Express each rational number as a ratio of two integers.

9. 0.3 $\frac{3}{10}$ **10.** 2 $\frac{2}{1}$ **11.** $^-$0.65 $-\frac{65}{100}$ **12.** $^-1\frac{1}{4}$ $-\frac{5}{4}$

Use > or < to complete each sentence.

13. 12 ? $^-$8   >   **14.** 8 ? $^-$12   >   **15.** $^-$12 ? $^-$8   <

16. 1.0 ? 1.1   <   **17.** $^-$1.2 ? $^-$1.1   <   **18.** $-\frac{1}{2}$? $-\frac{1}{4}$ <

19. $3\frac{3}{4}$? $1\frac{5}{8}$ >   **20.** $1\frac{3}{4}$? $1\frac{5}{8}$ >   **21.** $1\frac{3}{4}$? 1.5   >

Arrange in order from least to greatest.

22. 6, 2, $^-$3 $-3, 2, 6$ **23.** $^-$3, $^-$5, 8 $-5, -3, 8$ **24.** $^-$1, $^-$7, $^-$10 $-10, -7, -1$

25. 0, $^-$1, $-\frac{1}{2}$ $-1, -\frac{1}{2}, 0$ **26.** $-\frac{1}{2}$, $\frac{1}{4}$, $-\frac{1}{10}$ $-\frac{1}{2}, -\frac{1}{10}, \frac{1}{4}$ **27.** 0.9, $^-$1.1, $^-$0.8 $-1.1, -0.8, 0.9$

B   **28.** $1\frac{4}{9}$, π, $\sqrt{2}$, $\sqrt{3}$, 1.5 $\sqrt{2}, 1\frac{4}{9}, 1.5, \sqrt{3}, \pi$ **29.** $^-1\frac{4}{9}$, $^-\pi$, $^-\sqrt{2}$, $^-\sqrt{3}$, $^-$1.5 $-\pi, -\sqrt{3}, -1.5, -1\frac{4}{9}, -\sqrt{2}$

CHAPTER 1

EXTRA PRACTICE, page 508

Match each real number to its best representation on the number line below.

30. ⁻0.9 E **31.** $-\dfrac{3}{4}$ F **32.** $-\dfrac{\pi}{2}$ C **33.** ⁻√3 B

34. ⁻√2 D **35.** $-\dfrac{2}{5}$ H **36.** $-\dfrac{1}{2}$ G **37.** ⁻1.75 A

```
          A B   C    D            E   F    G H
    ←──────┼────────────────────────┼────────────────┼──→
        ⁻2                         ⁻1                 0
```

Name the real number that is

38. halfway between ⁻0.4 and 0.5. 0.05 **39.** halfway between ⁻$1\dfrac{1}{2}$ and ⁻$1\dfrac{3}{4}$. $-1\dfrac{5}{8}$

40. $\dfrac{1}{2}$ more than ⁻$1\dfrac{1}{4}$. $-\dfrac{3}{4}$ **41.** 1.5 less than ⁻2.5. −4

C Is the real number positive or negative?

42. ⁻√3 + √3 **43.** √3 more than ⁻√2 **44.** (√3)² **45.** ⁻√2 divided by √3
 0; neither   Positive   Positive   Negative

CHECKPOINT

Simplify.

1. 16 ÷ 8 − 2 + 3 3 **2.** 28 ÷ 7 − 20 ÷ 5 0 **3.** (64 − 4) ÷ (2 + 4) 10

Evaluate. Let **x** = 1, **y** = 2, and **z** = 3.

4. yz − xy + xz 7 **5.** y² − xz 1 **6.** z³y²x¹⁰⁰ 108

Write an algebraic expression for each phrase.

7. Two times some number 2x **8.** Two more than some number x + 2

9. Two less than some number x − 2 **10.** Some number divided by 2 $\dfrac{x}{2}$

Use the variable **x** to write an equation for each sentence. Then solve it.

11. A certain number increased by 5 equals 13. x + 5 = 13; x = 8

12. Some number decreased by 11 equals 21. x − 11 = 21; x = 32

13. Three times some number equals 51. 3x = 51; x = 17

For what whole-number values of **x** does the expression represent a whole number?

14. 2 − x **15.** x − 3 **16.** $\dfrac{6}{x}$ 1, 2, 3, 6 **17.** $\dfrac{x + 2}{x}$ 1, 2 **18.** 7 − 2x
 0, 1, 2   3, 4, 5, 6, . . .   0, 1, 2, 3

THE LANGUAGE OF ALGEBRA 31

Checkpoint

Students may check their answers with those given in the back of their books.

1-10 Absolute Value

OBJECTIVES

To find the absolute values of numbers.
To solve equations that involve absolute values.

The numbers ⁻3 and 3 are opposites. They both are 3 units from 0 on the number line, but in opposite directions.

The **absolute value** of a number is its distance from 0 on the number line.

$|\overline{5}| = 5$ The absolute value of ⁻5 is 5, since ⁻5 is 5 units from 0.

$|\overline{+}5| = 5$ The absolute value of ⁺5 is 5, since it also is 5 units from 0.

The absolute value of a number is *positive* or *zero*. It is never negative.

$|\overline{+}12| = 12$ The absolute value of a positive number is the number itself.

$|\overline{12}| = 12$ The absolute value of a negative number is the opposite of that number.

$|0| = 0$ The absolute value of 0 is 0.

EXAMPLE 1   Give the absolute value of each number.

a. ⁺7   b. ⁻4   c. $1\frac{1}{2}$ d. ⁻0.3

$|\overline{+}7| = 7$ $|\overline{4}| = 4$ $\left|1\frac{1}{2}\right| = 1\frac{1}{2}$ $|\overline{0.3}| = 0.3$

EXAMPLE 2   Simplify each expression.

a. $|\overline{7}| + 1$ b. $|9| - |\overline{7}|$ c. $5|\overline{9}| + 2$

$7 + 1 = 8$ $9 - 7 = 2$ $45 + 2 = 47$

EXAMPLE 3   Try the values ⁻2, ⁻1, 0, 1, 2 for x. Which are solutions for the given equation?

a. $6 - |x| = 5$ b. $2|x| = 4$ c. $|x| = x$

1 and ⁻1   2 and ⁻2   0, 1, and 2

For the equation $x + 3 = 5$, the only value for x that makes the sentence true is 2. There is *one* solution to the equation.

The equation $|x| + 3 = 5$ has *two* solutions. They are 2 and ¯2. Both values for x make the sentence true.

$$|2| + 3 \overset{?}{=} 5 \qquad\qquad |{}^-2| + 3 \overset{?}{=} 5$$
$$2 + 3 \overset{?}{=} 5 \qquad\qquad 2 + 3 \overset{?}{=} 5$$
$$5 = 5 \quad \text{True} \qquad\qquad 5 = 5 \quad \text{True}$$

CLASS EXERCISES

Simplify.

1. $|{}^-6|$ 6   **2.** $|4|$ 4   **3.** $|{}^+3|$ 3   **4.** $\left|{}^-2\frac{1}{2}\right|$ $2\frac{1}{2}$

5. $|{}^-3| + |{}^-4|$ 7   **6.** $|2| - |{}^-2|$ 0   **7.** $|{}^-4.5| - |1.5|$ 3   **8.** $|100| + |{}^-1|$ 101

Try ¯1, 0, and 1. Which are solutions to the given equation?

9. $x = 1$ 1   **10.** $|x| = 1$ 1 and ¯1   **11.** $|x| - 1 = 0$ 1 and ¯1

12. $|x| + 1 = 0$ None   **13.** $6|x| = 6$ 1 and ¯1   **14.** $|x| + |x| = 0$ 0

EXERCISES

A

Find the absolute value of each number.

1. ¯5   5   **2.** 21   21   **3.** 12.7   12.7   **4.** ¯1.8   1.8   **5.** $\frac{0}{2}$ 0

Simplify.

6. $|{}^-12|$ 12   **7.** $|10|$ 10   **8.** $|{}^-1|$ 1   **9.** $|0|$ 0

10. $|3| + |4|$ 7   **11.** $|{}^-1| + |7|$ 8   **12.** $|2| + |{}^-8|$ 10   **13.** $|{}^-7| \cdot |3|$ 21

14. $|8| \div |{}^-4|$ 2   **15.** $3|{}^-5|$ 15   **16.** $2|1| - 1$ 1   **17.** $3 + 4|{}^-6|$ 27

B

Try ¯3, ¯2, ¯1, 0, 1, 2, and 3. Which are solutions to the given equation?

18. $|x| = 2$ **19.** $|x| + 1 = 2$ **20.** $4 - |x| = 3$ **21.** $|x| - 2 = {}^-3$
   2 and ¯2   1 and ¯1   1 and ¯1   None

Find the solutions.

22. $|x| = 10$ 10 and ¯10   **23.** $|x| + 4 = 5$ 1 and ¯1   **24.** $|x| - 2 = 3$ 5 and ¯5

25. $|x| - 4 = |{}^-3|$ 7 and ¯7   **26.** $|x| - 3 = |{}^-4|$ 7 and ¯7   **27.** $5|x| + 2 = 47$ 9 and ¯9

C

For what values of x is the sentence true?

28. $|x| = x$ **29.** $|x| \neq x$ **30.** $|x| = -x$ ***31.** $|x| \geq x$
Positive values and 0   Negative values   Negative values and 0   Positive and negative
                                                               values and 0

THE LANGUAGE OF ALGEBRA   **33**

Are the expressions equal?
1. $(54 \div 6) \div 3$
$\overset{?}{=} 54 \div (6 \div 3)$ No
2. $(3 \times 8) \times 7$
$\overset{?}{=} 3 \times (8 \times 7)$ Yes

LESSON NOTES

As the text indicates, the properties of addition and multiplication are accepted without proof. In effect, they are postulated.

Students should be familiar with the commutative and associative properties from their work at earlier grade levels. However, the closure properties may be less familiar to them.

In discussing Example 1, point out that one example, $8 \div 2 \neq 2 \div 8$, is sufficient to show that division is *not* commutative. You may also wish to point out that $8 - 2 = 6$ but $2 - 8$ does *not* equal 6. So $8 - 2 \neq 2 - 8$; this one example is sufficient to show that subtraction is *not* commutative.

The reflexive, symmetric, and transitive properties will be new to nearly all students. Spend some time distinguishing among these properties.

ALTERNATE EXAMPLE

1. If the expressions are equal, state the illustrated property.
   a. $7 + 2.5 \overset{?}{=} 2.5 + 7$
   $9.5 = 9.5$
   The commutative property for addition is illustrated.
   b. $[(6)(2)](\frac{1}{4}) \overset{?}{=} 6[(2)(\frac{1}{4})]$
   $3 = 3$
   The associative property of multiplication is illustrated.
   c. $(24 \div 4) \div 2 \overset{?}{=} 24 \div (4 \div 2)$
   $3 \neq 12$
   This shows that division is not associative.

1-11 Properties

OBJECTIVE

To identify the properties of real numbers and the properties of equality.

We have been using, without question, certain basic properties of addition and multiplication of real numbers. For example, when two real numbers are added or multiplied, only one sum or product is possible, and it is always a real number. This is because of the **closure properties.** Each of the following gives a *unique* real number as the answer.

$$17 + 3 = 20 \qquad 17 \times 3 = 51$$

You know that the order in which two numbers are added or multiplied does not affect the sum or the product. This results from the **commutative properties.**

$$19 + 6 = 25 \quad \text{and} \quad 6 + 19 = 25 \qquad 24 \times \frac{1}{4} = 6 \quad \text{and} \quad \frac{1}{4} \times 24 = 6$$

Suppose there are three or more numbers to add or multiply. The way in which they are grouped does not change the sum or product. The **associative properties** allow such regrouping.

$$(8 + 3) + 14 = 25 \quad \text{and} \quad 8 + (3 + 14) = 25$$
$$\left(8 \times \frac{1}{2}\right) \times 3 = 12 \quad \text{and} \quad 8 \times \left(\frac{1}{2} \times 3\right) = 12$$

Let a, b, and c be any real numbers.

Closure Properties: $a + b$ is a unique real number, and ab is a unique real number.

Commutative Properties: $a + b = b + a$ and $ab = ba$

Associative Properties: $(a + b) + c = a + (b + c)$ and $(ab)c = a(bc)$

EXAMPLE 1

If the expressions are equal, state the illustrated property.

a. $(5 + 6) + 3.4 \overset{?}{=} 5 + (6 + 3.4)$
$14.4 = 14.4$

The associative property for addition is illustrated.

b. $\left(3\frac{1}{2}\right)(2) \overset{?}{=} 2\left(3\frac{1}{2}\right)$
$7 = 7$

The commutative property for multiplication is illustrated.

c. $8 \div 2 \overset{?}{=} 2 \div 8$
$4 \neq \frac{1}{4}$

This shows that division is not commutative.

CHAPTER 1

EXAMPLE 2   Simplify mentally.

a. 15 + 7 + 25

15 + 25 + 7   Reorder.

40 + 7, or 47

b. 25 × (9 × 4)

25 × (4 × 9)   Reorder.

(25 × 4) × 9   Regroup.

100 × 9, or 900

In this book, the word *number* will now be used to mean *real number*. Likewise, solutions will be from the set of real numbers unless otherwise stated.

EXAMPLE 3   For what number x is it true that:

$$\sqrt{2} + (\pi + \sqrt{3}) = (\sqrt{2} + x) + \sqrt{3}$$

The equality sign indicates that the two expressions name the same number. Therefore, because of the associative property, π on the left and x on the right also name the same number. Hence, x = π.

The following properties of equality are regularly used in algebra.

Let *a*, *b*, and *c* be any numbers.

$a = a$ **Reflexive Property**

If $a = b$, then $b = a$. **Symmetric Property**

If $a = b$ and $b = c$, then $a = c$. **Transitive Property**

EXAMPLE 4   What property of equality is illustrated?

a. If 17 = x, then x = 17.   **b.** If x = y and y = 17, then x = 17.

Answers   Symmetric Property   Transitive Property

CLASS EXERCISES

Name the property illustrated.

1. 15 + 55 = 55 + 15   Comm. for add.   **2.** 3 × (4.5 × 2) = (3 × 4.5) × 2   Assoc. for mult.

3. $(3c)d = 3(cd)$ Assoc. for mult.   **4.** $c \times 2\frac{1}{4} = 2\frac{1}{4} \times c$ Comm. for mult.

5. $\left(c + \frac{1}{2}\right) + 3 = c + \left(\frac{1}{2} + 3\right)$ **6.** $5(cd) = 5(dc)$ Comm. for mult.

Assoc. for add.

7. $c + (d + e) = (d + e) + c$ **8.** $cd + e = e + cd$ Comm. for add.

Comm. for add.

9. If 22.5 = d, then d = 22.5. Symmetric   **10.** $e + \pi = e + \pi$ Reflexive

2. Simplify mentally.
  a. 93 + 89 + 7
    93 + 7 + 89; 100 + 89; 189
  b. 2 × (16 × 50)
    2 × (50 × 16); (2 × 50) × 16; 100 × 16; 1600
3. For what number y is it true that
  $\pi \times (\sqrt{3} \times \sqrt{2})$
  $= (\pi \times y) \times \sqrt{2}$ $\sqrt{3}$
4. What property of equality is illustrated?
  a. If $2\frac{1}{2} = d$, then $d = 2\frac{1}{2}$.
    Symmetric property
  b. If $c = d$ and $d = 2\frac{1}{2}$, then $c = 2\frac{1}{2}$. Transitive property

---

POSSIBLE ERROR

Students often mistakenly assume that if an equation seems to show different groupings of the same three numbers, it must illustrate the associative property. This is not necessarily true.
$(a + b) + c = a + (b + c)$
does illustrate the associative property of addition. However, $(a + b) + c = c + (a + b)$ illustrates the commutative property of addition, since $(a + b)$ has been treated as one addend and c has been treated as the other addend, and the order of the addends has been changed. Use Class Exercises 6–8 to discuss this idea.

DAILY QUIZ

Name the property illustrated.
1. 6 + (5 + 2) = (6 + 5) + 2
  Assoc. for add.
2. cd = dc Comm. for mult.
3. If $^-3 = x$, then $x = ^-3$.
  Symmetric
4. If $a = b$ and $b = ^-5$, then $a = ^-5$. Transitive
5. For what number y is it true that $3 + \left(y + \frac{1}{2}\right) = \left(3 + \frac{2}{3}\right) + \frac{1}{2}$? $\frac{2}{3}$

EXERCISES

A   *Name the property of addition or multiplication illustrated.*

1. $8 + (7 + 2) = (8 + 7) + 2$ Assoc. for add.
2. $6 + (4 + 0.1) = 6 + (0.1 + 4)$ Comm. for add.

3. $3 \times \left(\frac{1}{2} \times \frac{1}{4}\right) = \left(3 \times \frac{1}{2}\right) \times \frac{1}{4}$ Assoc. for mult.
4. $5 \times \frac{1}{4} = \frac{1}{4} \times 5$ Comm. for mult.

5. $(2 \times 0.8) \times 3 = 2 \times (0.8 \times 3)$ Assoc. for mult.
6. $11 + (6 + 3) = 11 + (3 + 6)$ Comm. for add.

7. $(p + q) + 4 = p + (q + 4)$ Assoc. for add.
8. $15(pq) = 15(qp)$ Comm. for mult.

9. $(pq)r = p(qr)$ Assoc. for mult.
10. $p + q + r = q + p + r$ Comm. for add.

11. $3 \times \sqrt{3}$ is a unique real number. Closure for mult.

12. $p + \sqrt{3}$ is a unique real number for every real number p. Closure for add.

Name the property of equality illustrated.

13. If $x = \sqrt{7}$, then $\sqrt{7} = x$. Symmetric
14. If $x = z$ and $z = \sqrt{2}$, then $x = \sqrt{2}$. Transitive

15. $\sqrt{7} + \sqrt{3} = \sqrt{7} + \sqrt{3}$ Reflexive
16. If $x = y$ and $z = x$, then $z = y$. Transitive

B   *Evaluate each pair of expressions. State the property illustrated whenever the two are equal.*

17. $(7 + 6) + 2$ and $7 + (6 + 2)$
18. $(9 - 6) + 3$ and $9 - (6 + 3)$

19. $0.5 + 1.6$ and $1.6 + 0.5$
20. $3 \div 4$ and $4 \div 3$

21. $5 \times (4 \times 3)$ and $(5 \times 4) \times 3$
22. $8 + (7 + 2)$ and $(7 + 2) + 8$

23. $\frac{2}{3}(9)$ and $9\left(\frac{2}{3}\right)$ 6; 6; comm. for mult.
24. $(4 \times 3) \times \frac{1}{2}$ and $4 \times \left(3 \times \frac{1}{2}\right)$ 6; 6; assoc. for mult.

25. $3\left(2 + \frac{1}{4}\right)$ and $3\left(\frac{1}{4} + 2\right)$
$6\frac{3}{4}$; $6\frac{3}{4}$; comm. for add.
26. $(16 - 4) - 2$ and $16 - (4 - 2)$
10; 14; not equal

*For what number **y** is the equation true?*

27. $2\frac{1}{4} + \frac{1}{2} = \frac{1}{2} + y$ $2\frac{1}{4}$
28. $2 + \left(y + \frac{1}{4}\right) = \left(2 + \frac{1}{2}\right) + \frac{1}{4}$ $\frac{1}{2}$

29. $5 \times (0.4 \times 3) = (5 \times y) \times 3$ 0.4
30. $0.75y = (13)(0.75)$ 13

31. $33 \times y = 33 \times 67$ 67
32. $2(0.7 + 1.1) = 2(y + 0.7)$ 1.1

C   *Let ↑ represent **exponentiation.** Thus, 3 ↑ 2 means 3^2, or 3 raised to the second power. Is exponentiation*

33. commutative? No
34. associative? No

Consider the relationship "is greater than," >. Does > have the

35. reflexive property? No   **36.** symmetric property? No   **37.** transitive property? Yes

Pictorial Graphs

Illustrators are frequently asked to draw representations of data in the form of graphs. Mathematics is important in much of this work. The manner in which the data are presented is also important.

PROBLEM There was a striking increase in the average price of a new home between 1970 and 1980. Illustrate this data in a graph.

| 1970—$24,000 |
| 1975—$40,000 |
| 1980—$64,000 |

A bar graph can be used.

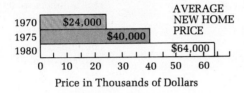

1970 $24,000
1975 $40,000
1980 $64,000

AVERAGE NEW HOME PRICE

0   10   20   30   40   50   60

Price in Thousands of Dollars

Here are two representations of the data in a more pictorial form.

1. Which of the three graphs do you think communicates the information best?

2. What is similar about the presentation of data in the three graphs?

3. What could be misleading about the presentation of data in the graph that pictures the houses?

Applications

Graphic representations of data—and the ability to read and interpret graphs—are important in our society. This Applications page raises interesting and significant questions about graphs and the manner in which the data is presented or pictured. You may wish to suggest that students collect other examples of graphs, including some graphs that are misleading. Then the various graphs could be brought to class and discussed.

ADDITIONAL ANSWERS

Applications
1. Answers may vary.
2. The lengths of the bars, the heights of the stacks of coins, and the heights of the houses all correspond to the prices.
3. The areas are not in the same ratio as the heights.

These exercises review basic algebraic skills. Evaluate. Let $a = 6$ and $b = 3$.

1. $2a + b$ 15

2. $a - 2b$ 0

3. $5ab$ 90

4. $\dfrac{a}{b}$ 2

5. $\dfrac{5a - 2b}{4b}$ 2

6. b^2 9

7. $2a^2$ 72

8. $(4b)^2 - 1$ 143

Using x as the variable, write and solve an equation for each problem.

9. Twelve less than a number is 15. Find the number.
$x - 12 = 15;\ 27$

10. A certain number multiplied by 5 is 85. Find the number.
$5x = 85;\ 17$

11. Fourteen more than a number is 30. What is the number?
$n + 14 = 30;\ 16$

12. A certain number divided by 8 is 12. What is the number?
$\dfrac{x}{8} = 12;\ 96$

Give the opposite of each number.

13. $^-7$ 7

14. 250 $^-250$

15. $^-0.5$ 0.5

Simplify.

16. $|\,^-3\,|$ 3

17. $|\,^-8\,| - |\,6\,|$ 2

18. $|\,^-12\,| + |\,^-7\,|$ 19

Arrange in order from least to greatest.

19. $^-4,\ ^-6,\ 2$ $^-6,\ ^-4,\ 2$

20. $0,\ \dfrac{^-1}{2},\ \dfrac{1}{4},\ \dfrac{1}{10},\ ^-1$ $^-1,\ \dfrac{^-1}{2},\ 0,\ \dfrac{1}{10},\ \dfrac{1}{4}$

CHAPTER 1 REVIEW

VOCABULARY

numerical expression (p. 2)
simplify (p. 2)
grouping symbols (p. 3)
order of operations (p. 3)
variable (p. 5)
algebraic expression (p. 5)
evaluate (p. 5)
exponent (p. 8)
base (p. 8)
exponential form (p. 8)
power (p. 8)
factored form (p. 8)
equation (p. 14)
open sentence (p. 14)

solution (p. 14)
root (p. 14)
whole numbers (p. 21)
consecutive whole numbers (p. 21)
integers (p. 25)
opposite (p. 25)
rational numbers (p. 28)
coordinate (p. 28)
irrational numbers (p. 28)
real numbers (p. 29)
absolute value (p. 32)
closure (p. 34)
commutative (p. 34)
associative (p. 34)

SUMMARY

This chapter reviews some basic properties of various sets of numbers that will be fundamental to the study of algebra. Exponents, absolute value, and ordering concepts are also presented. Variables are used in writing algebraic phrases which, in turn, lead to writing and solving equations. A highlight of this chapter is the introductory work to problem solving. Solving verbal problems is an important theme throughout this course, and the basic guidelines used to help with solving such problems are introduced in this chapter.

REVIEW EXERCISES

1-1   *Simplify.*

1. $15 - 9 + 2$ 8   **2.** $66 - 11 \times 2$ 44   **3.** $28 - (9 - 5)$ 24

4. $40 + 18 \div 3$ 46   **5.** $36 \div 6 \times (4 + 11)$ 90   **6.** $\dfrac{[27 - (18 + 6)]}{3}$ 1

1-2   *Evaluate. Let $a = 5$ and $b = 10$.*

7. $5a + b$ 35   **8.** $2(a + b)$ 30   **9.** $4(b - a) + 2b$ 40

10. $\dfrac{a + b}{a}$ 3   **11.** $\dfrac{5(4a + b)}{2a}$ 15   **12.** $\dfrac{30 - 2a}{b - 5}$ 4

38

1-3 *Evaluate. Let* **x** = 4.

13. x^3 64   **14.** $(x - 1)^3$ 27   **15.** $10x^2$ 160

16. $(10x)^2$ 1600   **17.** $(6 - x)^3$ 8   **18.** $2x^2 - 3x$ 20

1-4 *Write an algebraic expression for each phrase.*

19. One less than the sum of x and y $(x + y) - 1$

20. Three divided by the product of 5 and n $\frac{3}{5n}$, or $3 \div (5n)$

21. Two times the sum of x and 12 $2(x + 12)$

1-5 *Tell whether 3, 4, or 5 is the solution of the equation.*

22. $2(x - 1) + 12 = 18$ 4   **23.** $15 - 3b = 0$ 5   **24.** $25 + 5(y + 1) = 50$ 4

1-6 *Using* **n** *as the variable, write and solve an equation for each problem.*

25. Sixteen more than a number is 39. Find the number. $n + 16 = 39$; 23

26. A number decreased by 16 is 39. Find the number. $n - 16 = 39$; 55

27. A certain amount divided by 12 is \$7. Find the amount. $\frac{n}{12} = 7$; \$84

28. Jed bought 9 boxes for \$1.35. How much did each box cost? $9n = 1.35$; \$.15

1-7 *Let* **n** *equal a whole number. For what values of* **n** *will the expression also be a whole number?*

29. $5 - n$ **30.** $2(n - 5)$ **31.** $\frac{12}{n}$ 1, 2, 3, 4, 6, 12   **32.** $\frac{n}{2}$ 0, 2, 4, 6, . . .
     0, 1, 2, 3, 4, 5   5, 6, 7, . . .

1-8 *Which of the following are integers?*

33. 8   Yes   **34.** $^-3$ Yes   **35.** 0   Yes   **36.** $-\frac{1}{4}$ No

37. What is the opposite of 5? -5 **38.** What is the opposite of $^-120$?   120

39. Identify the point halfway between any two opposites on the number line.   0

40. Name two integers on the number line that are 4 units from $^-1$. -5 and 3

1-9 *Use* < *or* > *to make each sentence true.*

41. 5 $\underline{\ ?\ }$ $^-8$ >   **42.** $^-1$ $\underline{\ ?\ }$ $^-3$ >   **43.** $^-2$ $\underline{\ ?\ }$ 1.3   <   **44.** $-\frac{1}{2}$ $\underline{\ ?\ }$ $-\frac{1}{4}$ <

1-10 *Simplify.*

45. $|^-0.6|$ 0.6   **46.** $|5| + |^-7|$ 12   **47.** $|2 + 9|$ 11   **48.** $3|^-1| - |2|$ 1

1-11 *Name the property of addition or multiplication illustrated.*

49. $3(ab) = 3(ba)$ **50.** $n + 5 = 5 + n$ **51.** $(3x)y = 3(xy)$
     Commut. prop.   Commut. prop.   Assoc. prop.
     for multiplication   for addition   for multiplication

REVIEW   **39**

Name the property of equality illustrated.

52. If $x = y$ and $y = 1.5$, then $x = 1.5$. **53.** $y + 1.5 = y + 1.5$ Reflexive
Transitive
54. If $1.5 = y$, then $y = 1.5$.   Symmetric **55.** If $5 = n + 3$, then $n + 3 = 5$. Symmetric

≡ C̲HAPTER 1 ≡
T̲EST

1-1 *Simplify.*

   1. $5 + 8 \times 4$ 37   **2.** $17 - [8 - (3 + 1)]$ 13   **3.** $\dfrac{2(5 - 3)}{8 - (3 + 1)}$ 1

Evaluate. Let $x = 5$ *and* $y = 2$.

1-2   **4.** $\dfrac{2x - 1}{y}$ $4\frac{1}{2}$ **5.** $xy \div (y + 3)$ 2   **6.** $\dfrac{3(2x - y)}{xy + 2}$ 2

1-3   **7.** $3y^2$ 12   **8.** $(3y)^2 - 25$ 11   **9.** $(x - y)^2$ 9

1-4 *Write an algebraic expression for each phrase in Exercises 10 and 11.*

  10. One less than the product of 3 and some number x $3x - 1$

  11. A certain number x divided by 4 more than the number $\frac{x}{4 + x}$, or $x \div (4 + x)$

1-5 **12.** Which number, 2 or 10, is a solution of $5(4 + x) = 30$?   2

1-6 *Using* **n** *as the variable, write and solve an equation for each problem.*

  13. 30 decreased by a certain number is 13. Find the number. $30 - n = 13$; 17

  14. Jan bought 12 of a certain item for $3.00. What was the cost per item? $12n = 3.00$; $.25

1-7 **15.** For what values of n does $\frac{25}{n}$ represent a whole number?   1, 5, 25

Give the opposite of each number.

1-8 **16.** 7.5 -7.5 **17.** 0   0   **18.** $-2\frac{1}{2}$ $2\frac{1}{2}$

1-9 *Use* $<$, $>$, *or* $=$ *to make each sentence true.*

  19. $-8 \underline{\ ?\ } -3$ $<$ **20.** $2(3)^2 \underline{\ ?\ } 3(2)^2$ $>$ **21.** $2(3 + 4) \underline{\ ?\ } 10$ $>$

1-10 **22.** True or false? $|1| + |-7| = |7| + |-1|$ True

1-11 *Match each equation with the property it illustrates.*

  23. $3y + 3x = 3x + 3y$ c

  24. $xy = yx$ d

  25. $3 + (x + y) = (3 + x) + y$ a

     a. Associative property for addition
     b. Associative property for multiplication
     c. Commutative property for addition
     d. Commutative property for multiplication

Circumference

Every computer must be given a detailed set of instructions, called a *program*, written in a language that the computer can understand. Since most personal computers use BASIC (Beginner's All-purpose Symbolic Instruction Code), all programs in this book are written in that language. In BASIC, the order of performing operations is the same as in algebra. However, the symbol * is used to indicate multiplication, and the symbol / is used to indicate division.

Once a program is entered and you press RUN, the computer starts at the least line number. Line numbers are often multiples of ten. This makes it easy to insert additional statements.

Since a REM statement does not affect the program itself, we can include explanations of what the program does.

The program below instructs the computer to compute and display the circumference of a circle when its radius is entered. If you have difficulty understanding the program, see the Computer Handbook starting on page 534.

The Program	What It Does
10 REM CIRCUMFERENCE	Gives the program a title.
20 PRINT "RADIUS";	Asks for the radius of the circle.
30 INPUT R	Stops and waits for an entry.
40 LET C = 2 * 3.14 * R	Computes $C = 2\pi r$.
50 PRINT "CIRCUMFERENCE IS "; C	Displays the circumference.
90 END	Ends the program.
RUN	This is a sample RUN, displayed by a typical computer. You must enter RUN.
RADIUS? 20	You enter, or input, a radius of 20.
CIRCUMFERENCE IS 125.6	The computer displays the answer.

Messages that follow PRINT must always be enclosed in quotation marks. The semicolon in line 50 instructs the computer to print the circumference C right after the word IS.

What will the above program display for each of these entries?

1. 40   **2.** 15   **3.** 6.5   **4.** 1275   **5.** 67.25   **6.** 0.75

Insert these lines into the above program:

```
60 LET A = 3.14 * R * R          Computes the area of the circle.
70 PRINT "AREA IS "; A; " SQUARE UNITS"
```

What will the revised program display for each of these entries?

7. 20   **8.** 5   **9.** 100   **10.** 2.5   **11.** 9

12. Write a program that displays the perimeter of a square when you enter the length of a side.

Computer Activity

Note the blank space after the word IS in line 50. This is not required on all computers. However, on a computer with a limited screen display, you may wish to insert additional spaces so that the length of the circumference is printed on one line. This kind of display modification can be made after the program is entered and run.

ADDITIONAL ANSWERS

Computer Activity

1. CIRCUMFERENCE IS 251.2
2. CIRCUMFERENCE IS 94.2
3. CIRCUMFERENCE IS 40.82
4. CIRCUMFERENCE IS 8007
5. CIRCUMFERENCE IS 422.33
6. CIRCUMFERENCE IS 4.71
7. CIRCUMFERENCE IS 125.6
   AREA IS 1256 SQUARE UNITS
8. CIRCUMFERENCE IS 31.4
   AREA IS 78.5 SQUARE UNITS
9. CIRCUMFERENCE IS 628
   AREA IS 31400 SQUARE UNITS
10. CIRCUMFERENCE IS 15.7
    AREA IS 19.625 SQUARE UNITS
11. CIRCUMFERENCE IS 56.52
    AREA IS 254.34 SQUARE UNITS
12. PROGRAMS MAY VARY.
    ```
    10 REM PERIMETER OF SQUARE
    20 PRINT "SIDE ";
    30 INPUT S
    40 LET P = 4 * S
    50 PRINT "PERIMETER IS "; P
    90 END
    ```

This chapter deals with the basic operations of addition, subtraction, multiplication, and division of real numbers, with major emphasis on integers.

First, addition is shown on the number line, and mental computation is encouraged; subsequently, the rules for addition are defined in terms of absolute value.

Subtraction is related to addition, and the students learn that to subtract a number, they can add its opposite (additive inverse). The text also gives attention to the important distinction between a negative number and the opposite of a number, which may be positive, negative, or zero.

Multiplication and division are taught, and the rules for multiplication and division are stated and used. Special attention is given to the multiplication properties of 1 and ⁻1.

Various forms of the distributive property are studied in detail, and the students learn to simplify expressions by combining like terms. The chapter ends with a problem-solving lesson that involves integers and formulas.

Extensive practice is needed with basic operations on integers (and all signed numbers). Mastery of these skills by the students will increase their ability to succeed in the work with equation solving, graphing, polynomials, and so forth.

CHAPTER 2

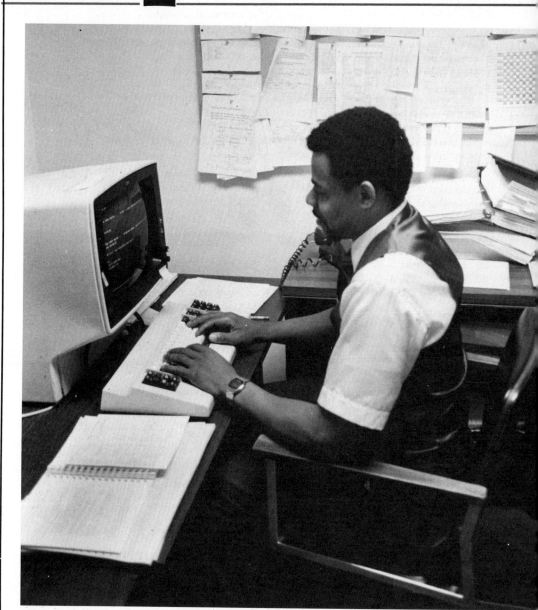

In solving complex problems, today's large computers can perform millions of arithmetic operations per second.

BASIC OPERATIONS

Prerequisite Skills Review

Write the letter for the correct answer.

1. $\frac{1}{3}$ of what number is equal to $\frac{1}{9}$?   d

   a. 27   **b.** 9   **c.** 3   **d.** $\frac{1}{3}$

2. The opposite of the sum $|18| + |-3|$ is ? .   d

   a. 15   **b.** -15 **c.** 21   **d.** -21

3. Which fraction is *not* equal to $\frac{5.6}{0.02}$?   c

   a. $\frac{0.56}{0.002}$ **b.** $\frac{5.60}{0.02}$ **c.** $\frac{56}{2}$ **d.** $\frac{5600}{20}$

4. Simplify $\frac{6 + 15}{3} + 6 + \frac{15}{3}$.   b

   a. 14   **b.** 18   **c.** 22   **d.** 28

5. $12 \div 6 \div 2 + 1 = $?   b

   a. $\frac{2}{3}$ **b.** 2   **c.** 3   **d.** 6

6. Which expression is *not* equal to 80?   c

   a. $2^4 \cdot 5$ **b.** $2^3 \cdot 10$ **c.** $\frac{1}{3}(210) + 30$ **d.** $\frac{1}{3}(210 + 30)$

7. Which expression is equal to 2?   c

   a. $\frac{2 + 6}{6}$ **b.** $(0)(2)$ **c.** $\frac{(2)(5)}{5}$ **d.** $1 \div 2$

8. If $a = 6$ and $b = 0.5$, then $\frac{1}{a} + \frac{1}{b} = $? .   a

   a. $2\frac{1}{6}$ **b.** $\frac{2}{3}$ **c.** $\frac{1}{3}$ **d.** $\frac{2}{13}$

9. If $x = 4$ and $y = \frac{1}{4}$, which expression is equal to 0?   d

   a. xy **b.** $x - y$ **c.** $x - 4y$ **d.** $x - 16y$

10. If $n = 2$, which expression is *not* equal to 50?   d

    a. $5(9n - 4n)$ **b.** $45n - 20n$ **c.** $26n - n$ **d.** $9(5n - 4n)$

BASIC OPERATIONS

43

PREREQUISITE SKILLS REVIEW

For students who need additional practice with the algebraic skills in this Prerequisite Skills Review, you may assign Follow-Up exercises on page 500 in the students' books.

An item-by-item error analysis of the Prerequisite Skills Review appears on page T20.

Are you east or west of your starting point?

1. You walk 5 miles east, then 2 miles west,   East
2. You walk 2 miles east, then 5 miles west.   West

LESSON NOTES

Number-line drawings provide a helpful visual model in adding real numbers. Compare the drawings and the results for ⁻2 + 3 and 2 + (⁻3) [the third and fourth illustrations]. In discussing Example 1, too, give extra attention to the addition of addends that have unlike signs; use number-line drawings for ⁻7 + (⁺5) and ⁺7 + (⁻5).

Most of the Class Exercises involve addition of integers only. However, Class Exercises 17, 18, and 22–26 include rational numbers in fraction or decimal form. It will be worthwhile to discuss some of these exercises before overall assignments are made.

ALTERNATE EXAMPLES

1. Find each sum.
   a. ⁺6 + (⁺2)   ⁺8
   b. ⁻6 + (⁻2)   ⁻8
   c. ⁻6 + (⁺2)   ⁻4
   d. ⁺6 + (⁻2)   ⁺4
2. Find the sum:
   ⁻8 + 12 + (⁻9) + 3   ⁻2

2-1   Addition on the Number Line

OBJECTIVES

To add real numbers.
To evaluate −a when a is positive, negative, or 0.

You can show the addition of real numbers on a number line. Start at 0. To add a positive number, move to the right. To add a negative number, move left.

The sum of any two positive numbers is positive, as in   2 + 3 = 5.

The sum of any two negative numbers is negative, as in   ⁻2 + (⁻3) = ⁻5.

For   ⁻2 + 3, move 2 units left and then 3 units right. The sum is positive.

$$^-2 + 3 = 1$$

For   2 + (⁻3), move 2 units right and then 3 units left. The sum is negative.

$$2 + (^-3) = ^-1$$

EXAMPLE 1   Find each sum.

a. ⁺7 + (⁺5)   b. ⁻7 + (⁻5)   c. ⁻7 + (⁺5)   d. ⁺7 + (⁻5)
   ⁺12   ⁻12   ⁻2   ⁺2

EXAMPLE 2   Find the sum: ⁻16 + 9 + 5 + (⁻1)

Method I	**Method II**
Add from left to right.	Add positive and negative numbers separately.
⁻16 + 9 + 5 + (⁻1)	
⁻7 + 5 + (⁻1)	9 + 5 + ⁻16 + ⁻1
⁻2 + (⁻1)	14 + ⁻17
⁻3	⁻3

When 0 is added to a number, the sum equals the same number. For example, ⁻7 + 0 = ⁻7   and   0 + (⁻7) = ⁻7. Therefore, 0 is called the **additive identity.** It preserves the identity of the number to which it is added.

The sum of **opposites** is 0. For example, 2 + (⁻2) = 0. The opposite of a number is also called its **additive inverse.** So 2 and ⁻2 are additive

44

inverses, as are ⁻3 and 3. The additive inverse of 0 is 0. The symbol −a means the opposite, or additive inverse, of a. Thus,

If $a = 2$, then −a is −2, which equals ⁻2.
If $a = ⁻3$, then −a is − (⁻3), which equals 3.
If $a = 0$, then −a is −0, which equals 0.

Notice the lowered sign in −2 and the raised sign in ⁻2. They both name the same number, since the opposite of 2 is negative 2. For convenience, the lowered sign in −2 will be used to mean both *negative 2* and *the opposite of 2*.

We can use −a to name a negative number, a positive number, or 0, but the sum of a and −a is always 0. We can state these addition properties that involve zero.

Addition Property of Zero

Let a be any number. Then $a + 0 = a$ and $0 + a = a$.

Addition Property of Opposites

Let a be any number. Then $a + (-a) = 0$ and $-a + a = 0$.

EXAMPLE 3   Evaluate each expression when $x = -5$ and $y = \dfrac{1}{2}$.

a. $-x + y = -(-5) + \dfrac{1}{2}$ **b.** $-x + (-y) = -(-5) + \left(-\dfrac{1}{2}\right)$

$\quad\quad\quad = 5 + \dfrac{1}{2} = 5\dfrac{1}{2}$ $\quad\quad\quad\quad = 5 + \left(-\dfrac{1}{2}\right) = 4\dfrac{1}{2}$

CLASS EXERCISES

Name the additive inverse of each number.

1. 6   −6   **2.** −1   1   **3.** −15   15   **4.** 0   0

Write the addition sentence shown on each number line.

5. $1 + 4 = 5$ **6.** $-3 + 7 = 4$

Find each sum. Think of the number line.

7. $3 + 2$ 5   **8.** $6 + (-4)$ 2   **9.** $-7 + 1$ −6   **10.** $-5 + (-2)$ −7

11. $5 + (-3)$ 2   **12.** $-2 + (-1)$ −3   **13.** $8 + (-8)$ 0   **14.** $-6 + 0$ −6

15. $-9 + 11$ 2   **16.** $0 + (-14)$ −14 **17.** $-3.0 + 6.2$ 3.2 **18.** $-3.5 + (-7)$ −10.5

BASIC OPERATIONS

Using BASIC

The symbol - may be used to display the additive inverse of a number or an expression that involves two or more numbers. For example:

```
PRINT -ABS(-4)    −4
PRINT -(4 - 7)    3
```

ALTERNATE EXAMPLE

3. Evaluate each expression when $x = \dfrac{1}{4}$ and $y = -7$.
a. $-y + x$ $7\dfrac{1}{4}$
b. $-y + (-x)$ $6\dfrac{3}{4}$

DAILY QUIZ

Find each sum.
1. $5 + 3$ 8
2. $-5 + (-5)$ −10
3. $-7 + 9$ 2
4. $6 + (-10)$ −4
5. $[-7 + (-6) + 12] + (-21)$ −22

19. $-2 + 3 + (-6) + (-3)$ -8 20. $15 + (-1) + (-1) + 2$ 15

21. $2 + [3 + (-4)] + 1$ 2   22. $\left[-6 + \left(5 + \frac{1}{2}\right)\right] + 18$ $17\frac{1}{2}$

Evaluate if $u = -4$ and $b = \frac{1}{4}$.

23. $-b$ $-\frac{1}{4}$ 24. $-a$ 4   25. $a + (-b)$ $-4\frac{1}{4}$ 26. $-a + (-b)$ $3\frac{3}{4}$

ENRICHMENT ACTIVITY

Tell the students to use trial and error to solve exercises such as the ones below.

Identify all the integers that make the sentence true.

1. $x + 12 = -7$ -19
2. $x + 5 = -11$ -16
3. $8 + x = 6$ -2
4. $9 + (-5) < x$ $5, 6, 7, 8, \ldots$
5. $9 + (-5) > x$ $3, 2, 1, 0, \ldots$
6. $-6 + 4 < x$ $-1, 0, 1, 2, \ldots$
7. $-6 + 4 > x$
   $-3, -4, -5, -6, \ldots$

EXERCISES

A *Write the addition sentence shown on each number line.*

1.
$(-2) + (-2) = -4$

2.
$-5 + 3 = -2$

Find each sum.

3. $3 + 1$ 4   4. $-3 + (-1)$ -4 5. $-3 + 1$ -2 6. $-3 + 3$ 0

7. $-3 + (-3)$ -6 8. $-1 + (-3)$ -4 9. $5 + (-7)$ -2 10. $-5 + (-7)$ -12

11. $-5 + 7$ 2   12. $-7 + (-5)$ -12 13. $-8 + 3$ -5 14. $9 + (-9)$ 0

15. $8 + (-4)$ 4   16. $-6 + 2$ -4 17. $-3 + (-7)$ -10 18. $-4 + 6$ 2

19. $5 + \left(-\frac{1}{2}\right)$ $4\frac{1}{2}$ 20. $-8 + \left(\frac{1}{4}\right)$ $-7\frac{3}{4}$ 21. $-10 + 6.7$ -3.3 22. $-6 + 7.4$ 1.4

23. $(-4) + (-3) + 4 + (-5)$ -8 24. $-60 + 45 + 36 + (-96)$ -75

B 25. $[-8 + (-9 + 15)] + (-23)$ -25 26. $-8 + [(-9 + 15) + (-23)]$ -25

27. $[5 + 17 + (-9)] + (-14)$ -1 28. $-16 + [(-17) + (-18) + 24]$ -27

29. $-8 + 7 + 16 + (-5) + (-7)$ 3   30. $10 + 3 + (-5) + (-7) + 15$ 16

31. $-11 + 5 + (-11) + (-12) + (-8)$ -37 32. $16 + (-6) + (-6) + 16 + (-6)$ 14

33. $-0.2 + 4.5 + (-1.6) + 7.4$ 10.1   34. $0.2 + (-0.5) + (-0.7) + 5.5$ 4.5

35. $\frac{1}{2} + 2 + \left(-\frac{1}{4}\right) + 6$ $8\frac{1}{4}$ 36. $-\frac{7}{10} + \left(-\frac{1}{5}\right) + \frac{1}{2} + \left(-\frac{4}{5}\right)$ $-1\frac{1}{5}$

Evaluate if $a = 3$ and $b = -\frac{1}{5}$.

37. $a + b$ $2\frac{4}{5}$ 38. $-a + b$ $-3\frac{1}{5}$ 39. $a + (-b)$ $3\frac{1}{5}$ 40. $-a + (-b)$ $-2\frac{4}{5}$

C *Write the problem as a sum of positive and negative numbers. Then add.*

41. The football is on your team's 36-yard line. In three plays your team gains 4 yards and then loses 3 yards and 6 yards. The last play is a completed 17-yard pass. Where is the ball now?
$36 + 4 + (-3) + (-6) + 17 = 48$; on your team's 48-yard line

46

2-2 Addition of Real Numbers

OBJECTIVE

To apply rules for the addition of real numbers.

Recall that the absolute value of a number is its distance from 0 on the number line. The definition of absolute value can be expressed as follows:

$|x| = x$ when $x \geq 0$ Example: $|3| = 3$, since $3 \geq 0$.

$|x| = -x$ when $x < 0$ Example: $|-3| = -(-3) = 3$, since $-3 < 0$.

The absolute value of any number, positive or negative, is positive. The absolute value of 0 is 0. The rules for adding real numbers can be given in terms of their absolute values.

> **To add two numbers with the *same sign*,** add their absolute values. Then give that same sign to the sum.
>
> **To add two numbers with *different* signs,** subtract their absolute values, lesser from greater. Then give the result the same sign as the number with the greater absolute value.

EXAMPLE 1   Add.

a. $18 + 7 = +(|18| + |7|)$ Both numbers are positive.
$= +(18 + 7)$ Make the sum positive.
$= +25$, or simply 25

b. $-21 + (-11) = -(|-21| + |-11|)$ Both numbers are negative.
$= -(21 + 11)$ Make the sum negative.
$= -32$

EXAMPLE 2   Add.

a. $-31 + 9 = -(|-31| - |9|)$ -31 has the greater absolute value.
$= -(31 - 9)$ Make the sum negative.
$= -22$

b. $31 + (-9) = +(|31| - |-9|)$ 31 has the greater absolute value.
$= +(31 - 9)$ Make the sum positive.
$= +22$, or 22

BASIC OPERATIONS

WARM-UP EXERCISES

Find the correct value.
1. $|5| = n$ 5
2. $|-5| = n$ 5
3. $|0| = n$ 0
4. $|-7| - |1| = n$ 6

LESSON NOTES

After you review the meaning of absolute value, discuss the generalization for using absolute value in adding real numbers. The rule for addition of addends with different signs is sometimes difficult for students. Use Example 2a and 2b to illustrate the rule. Then give an additional pair of examples, such as $-11 + 30$ and $11 + (-30)$.

[Lesson notes continue on page 48.]

> **POSSIBLE ERROR**
>
> Students often have trouble with the second part of the definition of absolute value:
>
> $|x| = -x$ when $x < 0$
>
> Restate this part of the definition in words: "The absolute value of x is the *opposite* of x when x is negative." This restatement will help them understand "$-x$" is not negative. Illustrate the idea repeatedly with various negative numerical values for x.
>
> $|-6| = -(-6) = 6$
> $|-11| = -(-11) = 11$
> $|-2.3| = -(-2.3) = 2.3$

ALTERNATE EXAMPLES

1. Add.
   a. $16 + 5$ $+21$, or 21
   b. $-17 + (-12)$ -29
2. Add.
   a. $-24 + 8$ -16
   b. $24 + (-8)$ $+16$, or 16

Example 3 provides simple equations to be solved informally, by *thinking* about the numbers (rather than by formal procedures). Exercises 17–25 and 38–58 provide similar experiences for the students.

Most students can learn to add real numbers *without* writing expressions involving absolute value. Except in cases in which they are specifically directed to show the work using absolute value, encourage them to find sums mentally.

ALTERNATE EXAMPLE

3. Find each solution.
  a. $x + 7 = -5$ $x = -12$
  b. $-4 + x = 2$ $x = 6$

DAILY QUIZ

Find each sum.
  1. $-19 + 10$ -9
  2. $-8 + 24$ 16
  3. $100 + (-40) + (-15)$ 45
Complete.
  4. $8 + \underline{?} = 0$ -8
  5. $6 + \underline{?} + (-5) = 1$ 0

```
┌─────────────────────────────┐
│      ASSIGNMENT GUIDE        │
│       (pages 48–49)          │
│  Minimum course: 1–49 odd    │
│  Average course: 13–63 odd   │
│  Maximum course: 26–49 odd,  │
│             50–66            │
└─────────────────────────────┘
```

EXAMPLE 3   Find each solution.

a. $x + 6 = -2$ 6 added to what number is -2?
       $x = -8$ The solution must be negative.

b. $-9 + x = 5$ What number added to -9 is 5?
       $x = 14$ The solution must be positive.

CLASS EXERCISES

Give the correct sign for each sum.

1. $16 + 20$ $+$ **2.** $4 + (-9)$ $-$ **3.** $-5 + 3$ $-$

4. $-8 + (-22)$ $-$ **5.** $-15 + (-11)$ $-$ **6.** $-2.0 + 2.1$ $+$

Find each sum.

7. $18 + (-12)$ 6 **8.** $-18 + 12$ -6 **9.** $-18 + (-12)$ -30

10. $-4 + 5 + (-3)$ -2 **11.** $16 + (-7) + 5$ 14 **12.** $8 + (-8) + (-10)$ -10

13. $-3 + 2 + (-5) + (-7)$ -13 **14.** $12 + (-2) + (-2) + 1$ 9

15. $(-6) + (-5) + 3 + \dfrac{1}{2}$ $-7\frac{1}{2}$ **16.** $(-5) + (-11) + \left(-\dfrac{1}{3}\right) + (-9)$ $-25\frac{1}{3}$

Complete.

17. $\underline{?} + 0 = -5$ -5 **18.** $\underline{?} + 11 = 11$ 0 **19.** $\underline{?} + 7 = 0$ -7

20. $6 + \underline{?} = 4$ -2 **21.** $-2 + \underline{?} = -5$ -3 **22.** $8 + \underline{?} = -8$ -16

EXERCISES

A   *Find each sum.*

1. $-42 + (-16)$ -58 **2.** $-80 + 50$ -30 **3.** $100 + (-99)$ 1

4. $35 + (-40)$ -5 **5.** $-72 + (-36)$ -108 **6.** $-400 + 500$ 100

7. $-4 + 5 + (-30)$ -29 **8.** $16 + (-7) + 5$ 14 **9.** $8 + (-8) + (-100)$ -100

10. $20 + (-12) + 7$ 15 **11.** $(-40) + (-8) + 6$ -42 **12.** $12 + (-15) + (-8)$ -11

13. $200 + (-40) + 20 + (-100)$ 80 **14.** $-300 + (-30) + 45 + (-5)$ -290

15. $-100 + 55 + (-75) + (-200)$ -320 **16.** $-75 + (-14) + (-25) + (-400)$ -514

Complete.

17. $6 + \underline{?} = 0$ -6 **18.** $8 + \underline{?} = -1$ -9 **19.** $-15 + \underline{?} = 3$ 18

48

EXTRA PRACTICE, page 509

20. $\underline{?} + (-8) = 5$ 13   **21.** $\underline{?} + 0 = -17$ -17 **22.** $\underline{?} + (-6) = 10$ 16

23. $-4 + \underline{?} = -1$ 3   **24.** $-7 + \underline{?} = -12$ -5 **25.** $\underline{?} + (-35) = 0$ 35

Simplify.

26. $+(|12| + |5|)$ 17   **27.** $+(|-8| + |-7|)$ 15   **28.** $+(|13| - |-4|)$ 9

29. $-(|6| + |16|)$ -22 **30.** $-(|-3| - |-2|)$ -1 **31.** $-(|17| - |-14|)$ -3

Use absolute values to find each sum.

32. $-30 + (-12)$ **33.** $-5 + 78$ **34.** $16 + (-23)$

35. $-8 + (-1.5)$ **36.** $-8 + (1.5)$ **37.** $8 + (-1.5)$

   $-(|-8| + |-1.5|) = -9.5$ $-(|-8| - |1.5|) = -6.5$ $+(|8| - |-1.5|) = 6.5$

B   *Complete.*

38. $4 + (-3) + \underline{?} = 0$ (-1) **39.** $-9 + \underline{?} + (-1) = -5$ 5

40. $\underline{?} + (-4) + (-7) = 11$ 22   **41.** $-2 + (-11) + \underline{?} = -6$ 7

42. $3 + \underline{?} + (-5) = -2$ 0   **43.** $\underline{?} + 10 + (-12) = -30$ -28

Is the solution positive, negative, or zero?

44. $x + 4 = -12$ Neg.   **45.** $x + (-5) = -3$ Pos.   **46.** $x + (-3) = 2$ Pos.

47. $-6 + x = -7$ Neg.   **48.** $-8 + x = -4$ Pos.   **49.** $-12 + x = -12$ 0

Find the solution.

50. $x + 1 = -3$ -4 **51.** $x + (-1) = -3$ -2 **52.** $x + (-1) = 3$ 4

53. $5 + x = 0$ -5 **54.** $-6 + x = -5$ 1   **55.** $-8 + x = -10$ -2

56. $-x + 2 = 1$ 1   **57.** $3 + (-x) = -1$ 4   **58.** $-x + (-4) = -3$ -1

C   *Evaluate for* $a = -2$, $b = \frac{1}{4}$, *and* $c = -\frac{1}{2}$.

59. $a + b + c$ $-2\frac{1}{4}$ **60.** $a + (-b) + c$ $-2\frac{3}{4}$ **61.** $-a + b + (-c)$ $2\frac{3}{4}$

62. $-a + (-b) + c$ $1\frac{1}{4}$ **63.** $-a + b + c$ $1\frac{3}{4}$ **64.** $a + (-b) + (-c)$ $-1\frac{3}{4}$

65. Starting from Homeside dock, Kay rowed 540 yards upstream, then 220 yards downstream, 60 yards upstream, and 400 yards downstream. At that point, how far was Kay from Homeside dock? In which direction, upstream or downstream?   20 yds; downstream

66. Rita added every other integer from -9 through 13. Tom added every other integer from -10 through 12. If both additions were correct, whose sum was greater? How much greater was it?   Rita's; 12

*67. How far must the numbers in the pattern $3, -6, 9, -12, 15, \ldots$ continue for the sum to reach 30? $-18, 21, -24, 27, -30, 33, -36, 39, -42, 45, -48, 51, -54, 57$

LESSON NOTES

In discussing $13 - 9$ and $13 + (-9)$, you may wish to use a number-line drawing on the board:

Students will recognize that the drawing shows $13 + (-9)$. From their work in earlier grades, they will also see that the drawing can be thought of as showing $13 - 9$.

   As you discuss the Subtraction Rule, remind students that $-b$ indicates the opposite (or additive inverse) of b. It is not necessarily negative.

ALTERNATE EXAMPLE

1. Use addition to rewrite each expression. Then simplify.

a. $3 - 11$
$\quad 3 + (-11)$
$\quad -8$

b. $3 - (-11)$
$\quad 3 + 11$
$\quad 14$

c. $-3 - 11$
$\quad -3 + (-11)$
$\quad -14$

d. $-3 - (-11)$
$\quad -3 + 11$
$\quad 8$

2-3   Subtraction

OBJECTIVES

To subtract real numbers.
To simplify expressions that include sums and differences.

Every subtraction expression can be rewritten using addition. In the example at the right, notice that the answer is the same whether 9 is subtracted from 13 or -9 is added to 13.

Subtract $13 - 9 = 4$
Add $13 + (-9) = 4$

To subtract a number, add its opposite.

In both cases, the result is -2.

Subtraction Rule

Let a and b be any numbers. Then $a - b = a + (-b)$.

EXAMPLE 1   Use addition to rewrite each expression. Then simplify.

a. $4 - 9$
$\quad 4 + (-9)$
$\quad -5$

b. $4 - (-9)$
$\quad 4 + 9$
$\quad 13$

c. $-4 - 9$
$\quad -4 + (-9)$
$\quad -13$

d. $-4 - (-9)$
$\quad -4 + 9$
$\quad 5$

Expressions that have both sums and differences may be rewritten in terms of addition only. Then you can either add from left to right or group like signs together. Remember that the commutative and associative properties for addition allow you to reorder and to group terms in any way.

50

EXAMPLE 2 Simplify $16 - 3 + (-4) - (-5) - 2$. First, replace each difference with a sum.

| **Method I** | **Method II** |
| Add from left to right. | Group like signs together. |

Method I
Add from left to right.
$16 + (-3) + (-4) + 5 + (-2)$
$\quad 13 \quad + (-4) + 5 + (-2)$
$\qquad\quad 9 \qquad + 5 + (-2)$
$\qquad\qquad\qquad 12$

Method II
Group like signs together.
$16 + (-3) + (-4) + 5 + (-2)$
$(16 + 5) + [(-3) + (-4) + (-2)]$
$\quad 21 \quad + \qquad (-9)$
$\qquad\qquad 12$

EXAMPLE 3 Simplify.

a. $8 - [(-7) - (-6)]$
$8 - [(-7) + 6]$
$8 - (-1)$
$8 + 1$
9

Note that you can simplify without rewriting.
Think of $4 + 6 - 8 - 10$ as the sum of 4, 6, -8, and -10.

b. $4 + 6 - 8 - 10$
$4 + 6 + (-8) + (-10)$
$\quad 10 \quad + (-18)$
$\qquad -8$

$4 + 6 - 8 - 10$
$\quad 10 \quad - 8 - 10$
$\qquad 2 \quad - 10$
$\qquad -8$

EXAMPLE 4 Evaluate if $a = -4$ and $b = 7.5$.

a. $a - b$
$-4 - 7.5$
$-4 + (-7.5)$
-11.5

b. $b - a$
$7.5 - (-4)$
$7.5 + 4$
11.5

c. $-a - b$
$-(-4) - 7.5$
$4 + (-7.5)$
-3.5

ALTERNATE EXAMPLES

2. Simplify $-14 + 6 - (-2) - 4 - (-3)$. First, replace each difference with a sum.
$-14 + 6 + 2 + (-4) + 3$; -7

3. Simplify.
   a. $4 - [(-2) - (-9)]$ -3
   b. $3 + 7 - 9 - 6$ -5

4. Evaluate if $x = -2\frac{1}{2}$ and $y = 6$.
   a. $x - y$ $-8\frac{1}{2}$ b. $y - x$ $8\frac{1}{2}$
   c. $-x - y$ $-3\frac{1}{2}$

DAILY QUIZ

Simplify.

1. $8 - 5$ 3   2. $6 - 11$ -5
3. $-4 - 5$ -9 4. $6 - (-6)$ 12
5. $-2 - (-3) - 8$ -7

CLASS EXERCISES

Write an addition sentence and a subtraction sentence for each figure.

1.
$-3\ -2\ -1\ \ 0\ \ 1\ \ 2\ \ 3\ \ 4\ \ 5$
$3 + (-5) = -2$ $3 - 5 = -2$

2.
$-2\ -1\ \ 0\ \ 1\ \ 2\ \ 3\ \ 4\ \ 5\ \ 6$
$5 + (-2) = 3$ $5 - 2 = 3$

Rewrite as an addition expression. Then simplify.

3. $9 - 5$
$\quad 9 + (-5) = 4$

4. $-9 - 5$
$\quad -9 + (-5) = -14$

5. $9 - (-5)$
$\quad 9 + 5 = 14$

6. $-9 - (-5)$
$\quad -9 + 5 = -4$

7. $5 - 9$
$\quad 5 + (-9) = -4$

8. $-5 - 9$
$\quad -5 + (-9) = -14$

9. $5 - (-9)$
$\quad 5 + 9 = 14$

10. $-5 - (-9)$
$\quad -5 + 9 = 4$

BASIC OPERATIONS

51

Simplify.

11. $8 - 12$ -4 **12.** $7 - 16$ -9 **13.** $18 - 11\frac{1}{2}$ $6\frac{1}{2}$ **14.** $6 - 25$ -19

15. $-3 - 11$ -14 **16.** $5 - (-8)$ 13 **17.** $-4 - (-6)$ 2 **18.** $-7\frac{1}{4} - (-3)$ $-4\frac{1}{4}$

19. $1 - 2 - 3 - 4 - 5$ -13 **20.** $-1 + (-2) - (-3) + (-4) - (-5)$ 1

EXERCISES

A   *Rewrite as an addition expression. Then simplify.*

1. $2 - 3$ **2.** $7 - 5$ **3.** $-2 - 3$ **4.** $2 - (-3)$
   $2 + (-3) = -1$ $7 + (-5) = 2$ $-2 + (-3) = -5$ $2 + 3 = 5$

Simplify.

5. $6 - 3$ 3 **6.** $-8 - 6$ -14 **7.** $6 - 6$ 0 **8.** $3 - 8$ -5

9. $4 - 9$ -5 **10.** $1 - 11$ -10 **11.** $2 - 10$ -8 **12.** $8 - 9$ -1

13. $-2 - 3$ -5 **14.** $-6 - 1$ -7 **15.** $-8 - 7$ -15 **16.** $-9 - 4$ -13

17. $4 - (-4)$ 8 **18.** $2 - (-3)$ 5 **19.** $1 - (-2)$ 3 **20.** $6 - (-7)$ 13

21. $-2\frac{1}{2} - (-5)$ $2\frac{1}{2}$ **22.** $-\frac{8}{3} - \left(-\frac{8}{3}\right)$ 0 **23.** $-7\frac{1}{4} - \left(-6\frac{1}{4}\right)$ **24.** $-5 - (-11)$ 6
                                                           -1

B   **25.** $13 - 6 - 5$ 2 **26.** $-8 - 4\frac{1}{3} - (-2)$ $-10\frac{1}{3}$

27. $14 - 8 - 3 + 7$ 10 **28.** $20 - 15 - (-10) + 5 - 0$ 20

29. $12 - (-9) - 7 + (-6)$ 8 **30.** $-3 - (-13) + 8 - 12$ 6

31. $20 - (-6) - 7 + 8 - 15$ 12 **32.** $-(-30) + (-5) - 25 + 15 - 20$ -5

33. $7 - [(-3) - 4]$ 14 **34.** $[7 - (-3)] - 4$ 6

35. $5 - [2 - (-11)] - 6$ -14 **36.** $5 - [2 - (-1) - 6]$ 8

Evaluate for $a = -6.8$ *and* $b = -2.8$.

37. $a - b$ -4 **38.** $a - (-b)$ -9.6 **39.** $-a - b$ 9.6 **40.** $-a - (-b)$ 4

Evaluate for $x = -5$, $y = 4$, *and* $z = -3$.

41. $x + y + z$ -4 **42.** $x - y - z$ -6 **43.** $x - y + z$ -12

44. $-x + y - z$ 12 **45.** $x - (-y) - z$ 2 **46.** $-x - y - z$ 4

Find each difference.

47. 18 **48.** -3 **49.** 24.6 **50.** -83.4
     $\underline{- \ (-13)}$ $\underline{- \ 15}$ $\underline{- \ 40.0}$ $\underline{- \ (-11.5)}$
       31 -18 -15.4 -71.9

51. Simplify $6 - (8 - 11)$ and $(6 - 8) - 11$. Is subtraction associative? 9; -13; no

52. Simplify $18 - 24$ and $24 - 18$. Is subtraction commutative? -6; 6; no

52

EXTRA PRACTICE, page 509

POSSIBLE ERROR

Some students change the operation sign when they are subtracting but forget to change the sign of the number being subtracted. For example, in Exercise 18, they may write $2 - (-3) = 2 + (-3)$, which is incorrect.

Emphasize that to subtract a number, we add its opposite. Point out that $a - b$ is not $a + b$; rather, $a - b = a + (-b)$.

ENRICHMENT ACTIVITY

Have the students refer to a number line and state the conditions under which each of these statements is true:

$a - b < 0$ $a - b = 0$ $a - b > 0$

Tell them to state their findings in terms of the location of a and b.

$a - b < 0$ if a is to the left of b.
$a - b = 0$ if a and b locate the same point.
$a - b > 0$ if a is to the right of b.

You can also challenge them with this problem:

If $a - b - c = 0$, must a be farther from 0 than each of the other numbers? If your answer is no, give an example that supports your answer.

No. For instance, $6 - (-2) - 8 = 0$, but 8 is farther from 0 than 6.

Express as a difference between a positive and a negative number. Then subtract.

53. The highest recorded temperature on earth is 57.8°C, in Libya. The lowest is −84.4°C, in the Antarctic. What is the difference between the two? $57.8 − (−84.4) = 142.2; 142.2°$

54. Mt. Everest in Nepal is 8848 meters above sea level. The greatest recorded depth in the ocean is 11,033 meters below sea level. Find the difference.

$8848 − (−11,033) = 19,881; 19,881$ m

55. You know that $16 − 9 = 7$ because 7 added to 9 gives 16. Similarly, you can prove that $a − b = a + (−b)$ by showing that $a + (−b)$ added to b, gives a. Supply reasons for the proof.

(1) $b + [a + (−b)] = b + [(−b) + a]$ Why?   Comm. prop. for addition

(2) $= [b + (−b)] + a$ Why?   Assoc. prop. for addition

(3) $= 0 + a$ Why?   Addition prop. of opposites

(4) $= a$ Why?   Addition property of 0

56. When n is subtracted from 2, the result is −16. What is the value of n?   18

57. The sum of three numbers is 98. If the first two numbers are 8 and −15, what is the third number?   105

58. What number can you subtract from 5 in order to get 25?   −20

59. What number must be subtracted from the sum of 16, 18, and −29 to get −2?   7

60. The numbers n and 12 differ by 30. Find two possible values for n.   42 and −18

CHALLENGE

A Painted Cube

A cube 3 centimeters on each edge is painted red on all sides. Then it is cut into 1-centimeter cubes, as shown.

3 cm

3 cm

3 cm

1. How many 1-centimeter cubes will there be?   27

2. How many cubes will have exactly

   a. 0 sides red?   1   **b.** 1 side red?   6

   c. 2 sides red?   12   **d.** 3 sides red?   8

Answer the same questions for a 4- × 4- × 4-centimeter cube. Now try answering the questions for an n- × n- × n-centimeter cube.   64; 8; 24; 24;8

n^3; $(n − 2)^3$; $6(n − 2)^2$; $12(n − 2)$; 8

BASIC OPERATIONS

53

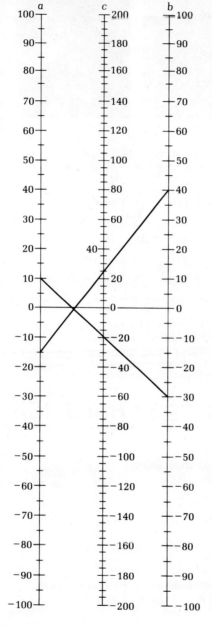

Adding and Subtracting on a Nomograph

This nomograph can be used to add integers between −100 and 100. Locate two integers on the a and b scales. The line connecting them crosses the c scale at their sum.

$$a + b = c$$

To find the sum −15 + 40, read along the line connecting −15 and 40. It crosses the c scale at 25.

$$-15 + 40 = 25$$

To find the sum 10 + (−30), read along the line connecting 10 and −30. It crosses the c scale at −20.

$$10 + (-30) = -20$$

Find these sums on the nomograph.

1. 45 + 75	120	**2.** 30 + 95	125
3. −50 + (−50)	−100	**4.** −25 + (−85)	−110
5. −60 + 35	−25	**6.** −10 + 70	60
7. 90 + (−15)	75	**8.** 20 + (−40)	−20
9. 25 + 0	25	**10.** 0 + (−90)	−90
11. 40 + (−40)	0	**12.** −65 + 65	0

To subtract an integer, add its opposite.

Find these differences on the nomograph.

13. 35 − 45	−10	**14.** 60 − 35	25
15. −15 − 20	−35	**16.** −85 − 10	−95
17. −75 − (−75)	0	**18.** −55 − (−25)	−30
19. 20 − 15	5	**20.** 20 − (−15)	35
21. −25 − 50	−75	**22.** 25 − 50	−25
23. −60 − 5	−65	**24.** 60 − 5	55
25. 5 − 60	−55	**26.** −25 − 5	−30

CHAPTER 2

2-4 The Distributive Property

OBJECTIVE

To rewrite expressions by using the distributive property.

Liang usually jogs 2 miles on a path around the park. If he has time, he follows a detour and jogs 0.5 of a mile farther. What is his distance for 5 trips on the longer path?

Method I	Method II
Add the distances. Then multiply by 5.	Multiply each distance by 5. Then add.
$5(2 + 0.5)$	$5(2) + 5(0.5)$
$5(2.5)$	$10 + 2.5$
12.5	12.5

These are **equivalent expressions** because they have the same value. They are equal.

$$5(2 + 0.5) = 5(2) + 5(0.5)$$

The multiplication by 5 is *distributed* over the addends 2 and 0.5. This illustrates the **distributive property of multiplication over addition.**

Let a, b, and c be any numbers.

Then $a(b + c) = ab + ac$ and $(b + c)a = ba + ca$.

EXAMPLE 1 Use the distributive property to rewrite each expression.

a. $3(x + 4)$	b. $6(a + b)$	c. $(r + s)t$
$3x + 3(4)$	$6a + 6b$	$rt + st$
or $3x + 12$		

The distributive property also applies to subtraction. For any numbers a, b, and c:

$$a(b - c) = ab - ac$$

BASIC OPERATIONS

55

Suppose that when Liang, the jogger, is late, he takes a 0.2-mile shortcut. What is his distance for 5 trips on this shorter path?

Method I	Method II
Subtract the distances. Then multiply by 5.	Multiply each distance by 5. Then subtract.
$5(2 - 0.2)$	$5(2) - 5(0.2)$
$5(1.8)$	$10 - 1.0$
9.0	9.0

The two expressions are equal.

EXAMPLE 2   Use the distributive property to rewrite each expression.

   a. $3(5 - a)$ **b.** $8(a + b - c)$ **c.** $(q - r)s$

   $3(5) - 3a$ $8a + 8b - 8c$ $qs - rs$
   or $15 - 3a$

EXAMPLE 3   Use the distributive property to simplify.

   a. $7(100 - 5) = 7(100) - 7(5)$ **b.** $60\left(5 + \frac{1}{2}\right) = 60(5) + 60\left(\frac{1}{2}\right)$

   $= 700 - 35$ $= 300 + 30$
   $= 665$ $= 330$

The distributive property can be used in reverse when a factor is already distributed.

Property	Reverse
$a(b + c) = ab + ac$	$ab + ac = a(b + c)$

EXAMPLE 4   Use the distributive property in reverse.

   a. $3x + 3y = 3(x + y)$ **b.** $5n - 3n = (5 - 3)n$

CLASS EXERCISES

Copy and complete.

1. $4(8 + 3) = 4(8) + 4(\underline{?})$ 3
2. $7(8 - 6) = 7(\underline{?}) - 7(\underline{?})$ 8; 6
3. $5(4 - y) = 5(4) - (\underline{?})(y)$ 5
4. $9(x + 5) = 9(\underline{?}) + 9(\underline{?})$ x; 5
5. $(2 + 3)y = 2y + (\underline{?})(y)$ 3
6. $(5 - \underline{?})n = 5n - 9n$ 9

Use the distributive property to rewrite each expression.

7. $3(x + 4)$ $3x + 12$ 8. $5(x + y)$ $5x + 5y$ 9. $\frac{2}{3}(y + k)$ $\frac{2}{3}y + \frac{2}{3}k$ 10. $b(x + y)$ $bx + by$

11. $11(x - y)$ 12. $4(x - 2)$ $4x - 8$ 13. $(x - 5)t$ $xt - 5t$ 14. $(x - y)b$ $xb - yb$
    $11x - 11y$

CHAPTER 2

Use the distributive property to simplify.

15. $5(3 + 2) = 5(3) + 5(2) = \underline{?}$ 25   **16.** $9(7 - 4) = 63 - \underline{?} = \underline{?}$ 36; 27

17. $12(11 + 5)$ **18.** $20(10 + 15)$ **19.** $8(12 - 5)$ **20.** $(16 - 5)9$
$132 + 60 = 192$ $200 + 300 = 500$ $96 - 40 = 56$ $144 - 45 = 99$

EXERCISES

A   *Copy and complete.*

1. $5(6 + 4) = 5(6) + 5(\underline{?})$ 4   **2.** $11(3 + 8) = 11(\underline{?}) + 11(\underline{?})$ 3; 8

3. $14(10 + 2) = \underline{?}(10) + \underline{?}(2)$ 14; 14   **4.** $\frac{7}{8}(5 - 1) = \frac{7}{8}(\underline{?}) - \underline{?}(1)$ $5; \frac{7}{8}$

5. $(5 + 8)x = 5x + (\underline{?})x$ 8   **6.** $(\underline{?} - 8)y = 3y - 8y$ 3

Use the distributive property to rewrite each expression.

7. $3(p + q)$ $3p + 3q$ **8.** $5(a + b)$ $5a + 5b$ **9.** $6(m + t)$ $6m + 6t$ **10.** $7(x + y)$ $7x + 7y$

11. $a(x + p)$ $ax + ap$ **12.** $b(y + q)$ $by + bq$ **13.** $a(x - p)$ $ax - ap$ **14.** $n(r + s)$ $nr + ns$

15. $3(x - y)$ $3x - 3y$ **16.** $4(a - b)$ $4a - 4b$ **17.** $8(x - r)$ $8x - 8r$ **18.** $3(n + 8)$ $3n + 24$

19. $\frac{1}{2}(x + 8)$ $\frac{1}{2}x + 4$ **20.** $5(p + 3)$ $5p + 15$ **21.** $3(y - 5)$ $3y - 15$ **22.** $5(x - 1)$ $5x - 5$

23. $6(a + b + c)$ **24.** $d(e - f - y)$ **25.** $7(k + n + 2)$ **26.** $9(r - s + 8)$
$6a + 6b + 6c$ $de - df - dy$ $7k + 7n + 14$ $9r - 9s + 72$

B   *Copy and complete.*

27. $6x + 6y = 6(x + \underline{?})$ y **28.** $\frac{1}{2}a + \frac{1}{2}b = \frac{1}{2}(a + \underline{?})$ b

29. $7p - 7q = 7(\underline{?} - q)$ p **30.** $8x - 8y = \underline{?}(x - y)$ 8

31. $xc + xd = \underline{?}(c + d)$ x **32.** $xc - xd = x(\underline{?} - \underline{?})$ $c; d$

33. $-4x + 15x = (-4 + \underline{?})\underline{?}$ $15; x$ **34.** $pr + qr = (\underline{?} + q)\underline{?}$ $p; r$

Use the distributive property to rewrite each expression.

35. $0.7(t + k)$ **36.** $0.5(3 + x)$ **37.** $0.2(y + 25)$ **38.** $1.2(x - 0.4)$
$0.7t + 0.7k$ $1.5 + 0.5x$ $0.2y + 5$ $1.2x - 0.48$

39. $8\left(y - \frac{1}{4}\right)$ **40.** $12\left(\frac{1}{3} - x\right)$ **41.** $\frac{2}{3}(x + 6)$ **42.** $\frac{3}{4}(12 + y)$
$8y - 2$ $4 - 12x$ $\frac{2}{3}x + 4$ $9 + \frac{3}{4}y$

Copy and complete.

43. $4(25) = 4(20 + 5) = \underline{?} + \underline{?} = \underline{?}$ $80 + 20 = 100$

44. $4(257) = 4(200 + 50 + 7) = \underline{?} + \underline{?} + \underline{?} = \underline{?}$ $800 + 200 + 28 = 1028$

45. $4(2573) = 4(\underline{?} + \underline{?} + \underline{?} + \underline{?}) = \underline{?} + \underline{?} + \underline{?} + \underline{?} = \underline{?}$
$4(2000 + 500 + 70 + 3) = 8000 + 2000 + 280 + 12 = 10,292$

EXTRA PRACTICE, page 509

ASSIGNMENT GUIDE
(pages 57–58)

Minimum course: 1–6,
　　　　　　　7–33 odd
Second day: 8–34 even,
　　　　　35, 37, 39, 41
Average course: 1–41 odd,
　　　　　　　43–45
Maximum course: 1–63 odd
All courses: *Checkpoint*
　　　　　review
　　　　　exercises

ENRICHMENT ACTIVITY

Have the students evaluate the following expressions for various values of *a* and *b*. Then challenge them to use the distributive property to simplify each expression.

1. $\frac{1}{5}(5a + 5b)$ $a + b$

2. $\frac{1}{3}(6a + 6b)$ $2a + 2b$

3. $\frac{3}{4}(8a + 12b)$ $6a + 9b$

4. $\frac{2}{3}(9a + 3b)$ $6a + 2b$

Use the distributive property to rewrite each product. Then evaluate mentally.

Samples $7(52) = 7(50 + 2) = 350 + 14 = 364$

$6(99) = 6(100 - 1) = 600 - 6 = 594$

46. $5(81)$ **47.** $8(98)$ **48.** $6(203)$ **49.** $10(199)$

50. $10(304)$ **51.** $7(499)$ **52.** $100(81)$ **53.** $50(2001)$

Use two methods.

   I. Use the distributive property to rewrite the expression. Then simplify.

   II. Combine terms inside the parentheses first. Then simplify.

Samples **I.** $9(8 + 2) = 72 + 18 = 90$ **II.** $9(8 + 2) = 9(10) = 90$

54. $4(2 + 3)$ **55.** $3(4 + 7)$ **56.** $2(20 + 8)$ **57.** $10(5 + 15)$

58. $(6 + 9)3$ **59.** $(7 + 11)2$ **60.** $(9 + 16)5$ **61.** $\left(\frac{1}{2} + \frac{1}{4}\right)20$

62. $4(9 - 8)$ **63.** $5(9 + 8 - 7)$ **64.** $6(9 - 8 + 7 - 6 + 5 - 4 + 3)$

CHECKPOINT

Simplify.

1. $-6 + 4$ -2 **2.** $2 + (-7)$ -5 **3.** $-3 + 6$ 3 **4.** $-13 - 8$ -21

5. $89 - 89$ 0 **6.** $6 - (-6)$ 12 **7.** $5 - (-3)$ 8 **8.** $-3 - 7$ -10

9. $(-12 + 7) + (-7)$ -12 **10.** $17 - (-14) - 12$ 19 **11.** $14 - (-12) - 13$ 13

12. $-(|-3| + |5|)$ -8 **13.** $-(|-12| + |-61|)$ -73 **14.** $-(|-3| - |-17|)$ 14

15. $2 + [3 + (-4)]$ 1 **16.** $(-6 + 5) + 1$ 0 **17.** $-8 - (-18) + 13$ 23

18. $300 + (-50) + 30 + (-200)$ 80 **19.** $-10 + 5.5 + (-7.5) + (-2)$ -14

20. $14 - (-12) - 13 - 21$ -8 **21.** $-(-36) + (-11) - 31 + 21 - 26$ -11

Evaluate for $a = 2.5$ and $b = -3$.

22. $a + b$ -0.5 **23.** $a - b$ 5.5 **24.** $-a + b$ -5.5 **25.** $-a - (-b)$ -5.5

26. $b - a$ -5.5 **27.** $b - (-a)$ -0.5 **28.** $-b - (-a)$ 5.5 **29.** $-[b + (-a)]$ 5.5

Copy and complete.

30. $7(4 + 9) = 7(\underline{\,?\,}) + 7(9)$ 4 **31.** $(2 + 4)a = 2a + 4(\underline{\,?\,})$ a

Use the distributive property to rewrite each expression.

32. $4(x + 3)$ $4x + 12$ **33.** $15(x + y)$ **34.** $x(y - 7)$ $xy - 7x$ **35.** $x(y + z)$ $xy + xz$
                                       $15x + 15y$

CHAPTER 2

2-5 Like Terms

OBJECTIVES

To identify like terms.
To simplify expressions by combining like terms.

A **term** is a number, a variable, or the product or quotient of numbers and variables. Each of the following expressions is a term.

$$2 \qquad x \qquad -3x \qquad xy \qquad -y^2 \qquad \frac{x}{y}$$

A number alone is called a *constant term*, or simply a **constant**. A **numerical coefficient** is the numerical factor of a term.

Term	Coefficient
$3x$	3
$-5x^2y$	-5
y	1, since $y = 1y$

Terms with fractional coefficients can be written in various ways.

$\frac{x}{3}$ has the same meaning as $\frac{1}{3}x$.   The coefficient is $\frac{1}{3}$.

Like terms are identical, or differ only in their numerical coefficients. They either have the same variables with the same exponents, or they are constants. Like terms may also be called *similar terms*.

EXAMPLE 1   Decide whether the given terms are like terms.

Terms	Are they like terms?	Explanation
$6x, \ -7x, \ x$	Yes	Each term has the same variable, x. Exponents are understood to be 1.
$4a^3, \ 4a^2$	No	Variables are the same, but exponents are different.
$-2ab, \ 3ac$	No	Not all variables are the same.
$8, \ -16$	Yes	Constants are like terms.

You can add or subtract like terms that have variables by adding or subtracting their coefficients. This is called *combining* like terms.

$$2x + 3x = (2 + 3)x = 5x$$

The distributive property allows the terms to be combined.

BASIC OPERATIONS

59

WARM-UP EXERCISES

Evaluate each expression if $x = 5$.
1. $4x + 3x$ 35 **2.** $(4 + 3)x$ 35
3. $7x$ 35

LESSON NOTES

Some students may wonder whether an expression and a term are the same. Explain that an expression is a number, a variable, or the sum, difference, product, or quotient of numbers and variables. Comparing this definition with the definition of a term, we see: every term is an expression; however, an expression is not necessarily a term. For example, $a + 3b$ is an expression; it is not a single term; it consists of two terms.
  Stress the use of the distributive property in combining like terms. In simplifying an expression such as $n + 5n + 3$ (Example 2), it may be useful to rewrite the expression as $1n + 5n + 3$ and then apply the distributive property to the first two terms.

POSSIBLE ERROR

Students often think that if two terms have the same variable(s), then the terms are similar. Thus, in Class Exercise 5, they may incorrectly identify $-3x$ and $-3x^2$ as similar terms. Stress that similar terms must have the same variable(s) with the same exponents, or else they must be constants.

ALTERNATE EXAMPLE

1. Decide whether the given terms are like terms.
   $-3y, y, 5y$ Yes
   $5x, 5x^2$ No
   $-9, 12$ Yes
   $4bc, 2c$ No

3. Simplify: $3 - 8y - (-2y) - 5$
$-6y - 2$

4. Simplify each expression, if possible.
   a. $8ab + 6ab$ $14ab$
   b. $4y + 2xy - 9y$ $-5y + 2xy$
   c. $3y^2 - 5y + 6$ Simplified form, since no terms are similar.

5. Simplify: $\frac{3y}{2} - y + \frac{y}{4}$ $\frac{3}{4}y$ or $\frac{3y}{4}$

DAILY QUIZ

Simplify, if possible.

1. $3x + 8x$ $11x$
2. $-7y + (-6y)$ $-13y$
3. $2xy + 3xy$ $5xy$
4. $3x - 5y$ Cannot be simplified.
5. $-3x + 9x + 5$ $6x + 5$

ASSIGNMENT GUIDE
(pages 60–61)
Minimum course: 1–24, 25, 27, 29, 31
Average course: 1–4, 5–47 odd
Maximum course: 5–47 odd, 49–53
All courses: *Strategies for Problem Solving*

To *simplify* a sum or difference means to combine like terms. Note that the expression $2x + 3x$ and the expression $5x$ are **equivalent.** For any replacement of x, these expressions have the same value.

EXAMPLE 2   Simplify $n + 5n + 3$.

$n + 5n + 3$ Combine the like terms n and $5n$.

$6n + 3$ Simplified form, since the terms are unlike

EXAMPLE 3   Simplify $1 - 7x - 7 - 9x$.

Method I	**Method II**
$1 - 7x - 7 - 9x$	Think of the expression as the
$1 + (-7x) + (-7) + (-9x)$	sum of 1, $-7x$, -7, and $-9x$.
$-16x + (-6)$	Combine like terms mentally.
$-16x - 6$	$1 - 7x - 7 - 9x = -16x - 6$

EXAMPLE 4   Simplify each expression, if possible.

   a. $5xy + 6xy$ **b.** $2x - 5x + 3xy$ **c.** $2x^2 + 3x + 5$

   $11xy$ $-3x + 3xy$ Simplified form, since no terms are similar

EXAMPLE 5   Simplify $\frac{x}{10} + x - \frac{4x}{5}$.

$$\frac{x}{10} + x - \frac{4x}{5} = \frac{1}{10}x + 1x - \frac{4}{5}x = \left(\frac{1}{10} + 1 - \frac{4}{5}\right)x = \frac{3}{10}x$$

CLASS EXERCISES

Tell whether the terms are similar.

1. $3a, -4a$ Yes   **2.** $2ab, -4a$ No   **3.** $-4, -4a$ No   **4.** $a, -4a$ Yes

5. $-3x, 3x^2$ No   **6.** $4xy, 3x^2$ No   **7.** $x^2, 3x^2$ Yes   **8.** $3x^3, 3x^2$ No

Simplify, if possible.

9. $\frac{1}{2}a + \frac{1}{2}a$ $1a$, or a **10.** $11b + b$ $12b$ **11.** $2c - 5c$ $-3c$ **12.** $-7x + (-9x)$ $-16x$

EXERCISES

A   *Match each term with all terms at the right that are similar.*

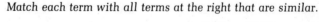

1. $3a$ $a, -4a$ **2.** b $\frac{1}{5}b, -3b$

3. $-5ab$ **4.** 6 $1, 17$
$ab, -ab, 6ab$

17	ab	1	$6ab$	a^2	$-4a$
$\frac{1}{5}b$	$-ab$	a	$3ab^2$	b^2	$-3b$

EXTRA PRACTICE, page 570

Simplify, if possible.

5. $2x + 7x$ *9x*   **6.** $5x + x$ *6x*   **7.** $12x - 7x$ *5x*   **8.** $-3y + y$ *−2y*

9. $-6y + (-5y)$
   −11y   **10.** $x - 4y$ *Cannot be simplified*   **11.** $-3xy + 9xy$ *6xy*   **12.** $-7xy + xy$ *−6xy*

13. $xy + xy$ *2xy*   **14.** $a + (-10a)$ *−9a*   **15.** $3b + (-2b)$ *b*   **16.** $-6c - 3c$ *−9c*

17. $r - 3r$ *−2r*   **18.** $-11r + 12r$ *r*   **19.** $-\dfrac{1}{5}s + \dfrac{1}{5}s$ *0*   **20.** $6u^2 + 8v^2$ *Cannot be simplified*

21. $-5u^2 + 3v^2$ **22.** $-6v^2 - 9v^2$ **23.** $x + x + 5x$ *7x*   **24.** $7y + y + y$ *9y*
   Cannot be simplified   *−15v²*

B

Simplify.

25. $z + 2z - 3z$ **26.** $-3a - 4a + a$ **27.** $-2b + (-2b) - (-2b)$

28. $-11c - 10c - 5c$ **29.** $5st + 8st - 3st$ **30.** $-3uv - 8uv - (-9uv)$

31. $-15w - 6w - 11w$ **32.** $13m - 13m - 3m$ **33.** $6pqr - 9pqr - 2pqr$

34. $4m + 9m + 3$ **35.** $-7n + 4 + n$ **36.** $-2x + 7x + (-1)$

37. $8mn + m - 6 - 5mn$ **38.** $-4 + (-5m^2) + (-8m^2)$ **39.** $5x^2 - 3x + x^2 - 10$

40. $-2ab + a + b + ab$ **41.** $3 - 8x - 5 - 17x$ **42.** $4a^2 - 7a - 4a^2 + 7a$

43. $x + \dfrac{x}{2} + \dfrac{x}{4}$ $1\frac{3}{4}x$ **44.** $6x - 3x + \dfrac{x}{3}$ $3\frac{1}{3}x$ **45.** $5a + \dfrac{1}{3} - a$ $4a + \frac{1}{3}$

Simplify. Use the distributive property twice.

46. $9(x + 15) + 2(x + 1)$ **47.** $6(x - 3) + 4(x + 3)$ **48.** $3(n - 5) + 2(n - 6)$
   11x + 137   *10x − 6*   *5n − 27*

C

Express each sum algebraically, using a single variable. Then simplify.

Hint: To represent two consecutive integers, let n be the lesser integer.
       Then $n + 1$ is the next integer.

49. The sum of three consecutive integers   *3n + 3*

50. The sum of three consecutive even numbers   *3n + 6*

51. The perimeter of a rectangle whose length is twice
as long as the width w *6w*

52. The perimeter of a triangle with two equal sides,
each 3 times as long as the third   *7x*

53. The sum of the perimeters of two squares, where
each side of one square is twice as long as each side
of the other   *12x*

STRATEGIES for PROBLEM SOLVING

Making a List

Making a list can be a very helpful problem-solving strategy.

Read the problem.

How many decimals can be formed using all these cards?

Make a list.

Arrange the two digits in all possible ways.

Next, place the decimal point in all possible positions for each arrangement. Then make all the decimals negative.

Use the list.

There are six decimals in the list, so the answer to the problem is 6.

Modify the problem.

1. Suppose any number of the cards can be used. Then how many decimals can be found?

   The answer is 20. Try to list them all.

2. Suppose another digit is added. How many decimals can be formed using all five cards? 24

   Use the listing strategy. Methods of listing may vary.

3. Try Question 2 again, but this time use any number of cards. 96

   One method to use is listing. But if you're clever, maybe you can figure out the answer using the work you did above!

2-6 Multiplication

OBJECTIVES

To multiply two or more real numbers.
To evaluate expressions that contain products and powers.

The product of two positive numbers is always positive.

$$3(4) = 4 + 4 + 4 = 12$$

The product of a positive number and a negative number is always negative.

$$3(-4) = (-4) + (-4) + (-4) = -12$$
$$(-3)4 = 4(-3) = (-3) + (-3) + (-3) + (-3) = -12$$

But what is the product of two negative numbers, such as $(-3)(-4)$? The reasoning in the following steps suggests that the product of two negative numbers is always positive.

$$-3[4 + (-4)] = -3(4) + (-3)(-4) \qquad \text{Use the distributive property.}$$
$$\underbrace{-3(0)} \quad = -12 \; + \underbrace{(-3)(-4)}$$
$$0 \quad = -12 \; + \quad \underline{?} \qquad \text{Since their sum is 0, the two}$$
$$\text{addends must be opposites.}$$

Therefore, $(-3)(-4) = 12$.

We know also that the product of a number and 0 is always equal to 0.

$$5(0) = 0 \qquad (0)(-3) = 0 \qquad (0)(0) = 0$$

EXAMPLE 1 Find each product.

a. $6(-2) = -12$ **b.** $-6(2) = -12$ **c.** $-6(-2) = 12$ **d.** $-2(0) = 0$

EXAMPLE 2 Simplify each expression.

a. $-2(-8)(4)(-5)$
$$16(4)(-5)$$
$$64(-5)$$
$$-320$$

b. $-3(-4)(-2)(-10)$
$$12(-2)(-10)$$
$$-24(-10)$$
$$240$$

Why is the product of any *odd* number of negative factors always negative?
Why is the product of any *even* number of negative factors always positive?

EXAMPLE 3 Evaluate if $n = -2$ and $t = 7$.

a. $5n^3 = 5(-2)^3$
$$= 5(-2)(-2)(-2)$$
$$= -40$$

b. $n^4 + t^2 = (-2)^4 + 7^2$
$$= (-2)(-2)(-2)(-2) + 7(7)$$
$$= 16 + 49 = 65$$

BASIC OPERATIONS

63

Solve
1. $5 + 5 + 5 = n$ 15
2. $(-2) + (-2) + (-2) = n$ −6
3. $(-9) + (-9) + (-9) + (-9)$
   $= n$ −36

LESSON NOTES

Students will readily accept the fact that the product of two positive numbers is positive, and the product of a positive number and a negative number is negative. However, the rationalization for the product of two negative numbers is sometimes difficult for students. You may wish to use a pattern to help students accept the idea.

$$-3(3) = -9$$
$$-3(2) = -6 \qquad \text{The products are}$$
$$-3(1) = -3 \qquad \text{increasing by 3; so}$$
$$-3(0) = 0 \qquad \text{it is reasonable to}$$
$$-3(-1) = ? \;\; 3 \quad \text{think: } -3(-1) = 3;$$
$$-3(-2) = ? \;\; 6 \quad -3(-2) = 6; \text{ and}$$
$$-3(-3) = ? \;\; 9 \quad -3(-3) = 9.$$

ALTERNATE EXAMPLES

1. Find each product.
   a. $7(-3)$ −21 **b.** $-7(3)$ −21
   c. $-7(-3)$ 21 **d.** $0(-6)$ 0

2. Simplify each expression.
   a. $5(-4)(-3)(-2)$ −120
   b. $-10(-2)(-3)(-10)$ 600

3. Evaluate if $x = -3$ and $y = 5$.
   a. $2x^4$ 162 **b.** $x^3 + y^2$ −2
   **For an example that involves finding the value of a term with two variables, use the following:
   $$xy^2 \;\; -75$$
   (See B Exercises 34–37.)

EXAMPLE 4

Use the distributive property. Then combine like terms.

a. $3(-4a + b) + 5a$

$-12a + 3b + 5a$

$-7a + 3b$

b. $-2(x + 4) + 5(-3 + x)$

$-2x + (-8) + (-15) + 5x$

$3x + (-23)$

$3x - 23$

Multiplication Rules

If a and b are both positive or both negative numbers, then ab is positive.
If either a or b is positive and the other is negative, then ab is negative.
If either a or b is 0, then $ab = 0$.

CLASS EXERCISES

Multiply.

1. $(8)(-7)$ -56 **2.** $(-9)(3)$ -27 **3.** $\left(\frac{6}{10}\right)\left(\frac{1}{10}\right)$ $\frac{6}{100}$ **4.** $(-2)(-10)$ 20

5. $(-5)(-6)$ 30 **6.** $(7)(-7)$ -49 **7.** $(8)(-3)$ -24 **8.** $(-30)(4)$ -120

9. $(-10)(-20)$ 200 **10.** $(-30)(40)$ -1200 **11.** $(100)(-50)$ -5000 **12.** $(-15)(-5)$ 75

Evaluate. Let $x = 7$ and $y = -9$.

13. $-3x$ -21 **14.** $-5y$ 45 **15.** $3x + y$ 12 **16.** $x + 5y$ -38

EXERCISES

A Multiply.

1. $(7)(9)$ 63 **2.** $(-7)(9)$ -63 **3.** $(7)(-9)$ -63 **4.** $(-7)(-9)$ 63

5. $(-10)(-50)$ 500 **6.** $(-5)(100)$ -500 **7.** $(500)(-10)$ -5000 **8.** $(-500)(0)$ 0

9. $(3)(4)(0)$ 0 **10.** $(3)(4)(-5)$ -60 **11.** $(-3)(-4)(5)$ 60

12. $(-3)(-4)(-5)$ -60 **13.** $(4)(3)(2)(1)$ 24 **14.** $(-5)(4)(-3)(2)$ 120

15. $(-10)(-9)(5)(-2)$ -900 **16.** $(-3)(-3)(-3)(-3)$ 81 **17.** $(-6)(-5)(-2)(-20)$ 1200

Evaluate when $x = -5$ and $y = 6$.

18. $5x$ -25 **19.** $-5x$ 25 **20.** $5x - 5$ -30 **21.** $5 - 5x$ 30

22. $-4y$ -24 **23.** $4y$ 24 **24.** $4y - 3$ 21 **25.** $3 - 4y$ -21

B **26.** $7x + y$ -29 **27.** $3x - 4y$ -39 **28.** $6y + 8x$ -4 **29.** $5y - 9x$ 75

64

EXTRA PRACTICE, page 510

30. y^2 36   **31.** x^2 25   **32.** $3x^2$ 75   **33.** $(3x)^2$ 225

34. $xy - 1$ -31 **35.** x^2y 150   **36.** xy^2 -180 **37.** $(xy)^2$ 900

Evaluate for the given value of the variable.

38. $\frac{1}{2}(r - 3)^2$ for $r = 11$ 32   **39.** $(-2d)^6$ for $d = -1$ 64

40. $t^2 - t^3$ for $t = 10$ -900 **41.** $n - 2n^2$ for $n = -6$ -78

42. $w^2(w - 4)$ for $w = 3$ -9 **43.** $x^3 + x^{100}$ for $x = -1$ 0

Use the distributive property. Then combine like terms.

44. $\frac{1}{4}(n + 8) - 6n$ $-5\frac{3}{4}n + 2$ **45.** $15 + 7(x - 2)$ $7x + 1$

46. $8(a + 9) + 2(a - 6)$ $10a + 60$ **47.** $7y + 2(y - 18)$ $9y - 36$

48. $8(x - 3) - 5(6 - x)$ $13x - 54$ **49.** $-4(8 + x) + 6x + 4$ $2x - 28$

C   *Simplify. Then evaluate for $n = -3$.*

50. $3(n + 2) - 2n$ $n + 6; 3$ **51.** $n^2 - 2n^2 + 3n^2$ $2n^2; 18$ **52.** $n(n + 1) - n^2$ $n; -3$

53. $3n + 5 - 4(n + 2)$ **54.** $\frac{1}{3}n + 6 + \frac{1}{3}(n + 6)$ **55.** $4n^3 - 5n^3 + 6n^3$
    $-1n - 3; 0$ $\frac{2}{3}n + 8; 6$ $5n^3; -135$

*Determine if the following are **true** or **false**.*

56. The product of any two numbers must be positive or negative.   False

57. The product of four numbers is negative. All of the numbers are negative.   False

58. The product of five numbers is positive. All of the numbers are positive.   False

59. The product of six numbers is positive. At least one is positive.   False

60. The product of seven numbers is negative. At least one is negative.   True

61. If one million -1's are multiplied together, the product is 1.   True

Write a numerical expression to describe each situation. Then find the answer.

62. Ben began the year with $3000 in a savings account. He deposited $360 a month, but withdrew $175 a month for rent. What was his balance after 12 months? $3000 + 12(360 - 175)$; $5220

63. Charlene's expenses for driving to work are $12.40 per week. She gives a ride to two friends, who each pay her $5 a week. How much will Charlene spend for travel in 6 weeks? $6[12.40 - 2(5)]$; $14.40

64. Mrs. Olson earns $62 in interest every 3 months, but pays $13 each month on a loan. How much money will she gain in a year? $4[62 - 3(13)]$; $92

---

1. $1(36) = n$ 36
2. $1(-20) = n$ -20
3. $-1(15) = n$ -15
4. $-1(-24) = n$ 24

LESSON NOTES

This lesson uses the multiplication properties of 1 and -1 to help increase the students' understanding of opposites and addition and subtraction of algebraic expressions. The understandings developed here will be valuable in later work with polynomials.

Give careful attention to Examples 2, 3, and 4 because they provide helpful experiences with procedures for simplifying expressions that involve subtraction.

POSSIBLE ERROR

In simplifying an expression such as $y - (x - 3)$, students often forget to make a change in the sign that precedes the 3. Thus, they may write:

$y - (x - 3) = y - x - 3$
                  (incorrect)

Use multiplication by -1 and the distributive property to rationalize the correct simplification of the expression.

$y - (x - 3)$
$= y + (-1)(x - 3)$
$= y + (-1)x - (-1)3$
$= y + (-x) - (-3)$
$= y - x + 3$

ALTERNATE EXAMPLES

1. Simplify $-(-8)$ by two different methods.
   Method I $-(-8) = -1(-8) = 8$
   Method II $-(-8) = 8$
2. Simplify: $-(x + 5)$ $-x - 5$
3. Simplify:
   $-7 + 5y + 2 - y$ $4y - 5$

2-7   Multiplication Properties of 1 and -1

OBJECTIVES

To substitute -1 times a number for the opposite of a number.
To use multiplication properties of 1 and -1 when simplifying expressions.

The number 1 is called the **multiplicative identity.** Multiplying a number by 1 produces the same number.

$$1(3) = 3 \qquad 1(-300) = -300$$

Multiplying a number by -1 produces the *opposite* of the number.

$$-1(3) = -3 \qquad -1(-300) = 300$$

> **Multiplication Properties of 1 and -1**
>
> **Let a be any number.**
> **Then $a = 1(a) = a(1)$**
> $-a = -1(a) = a(-1)$
> $-1(-a) = -(-a) = a$

These properties of 1 and -1 are useful in simplifying expressions.

EXAMPLE 1   Simplify $-(-5)$ by two different methods.

Method I $-(-5) = -1(-5) = 5$ Multiplication property of -1
Method II $-(-5) = 5$ The opposite of -5 is 5.

EXAMPLE 2   Simplify $-(4 + n)$.

$-(4 + n) = -1(4 + n)$ Multiplication property of -1
$= -1(4) + (-1)(n)$ Distributive property
$= -4 + (-n)$ Multiplication property of -1
$= -4 - n$ Subtraction rule

EXAMPLE 3   Simplify $-8 + 4y + 5 - y$.

$-8 + 4y + 5 - y = -8 + 4y + 5 + (-y)$ Definition of subtraction
$= -8 + 4y + 5 + (-1)y$ Multiplication property of -1
$= 3y - 3$

CHAPTER 2

EXAMPLE 4   Simplify. Write each expression without parentheses.

a. $a - (b - c)$

$a + (-1)(b - c)$

$a + (-1)b - (-1)c$

$a + (-b) - (-c)$

$a - b + c$

b. $(a + b) - (c + d)$

$(a + b) + (-1)(c + d)$

$a + b + (-1)c + (-1)d$

$a + b + (-c) + (-d)$

$a + b - c - d$

EXAMPLE 5   Evaluate each expression if $a = -3$, $b = -5$, and $c = 4$.

a. $-ab$

$-(-3)(-5)$

$-1(15)$

-15

b. $a - bc$

$(-3) - (-5)(4)$

$(-3) - (-20)$

$(-3) + 20$

17

c. $-(a - b)$

$-[(-3) - (-5)]$

$-1[(-3) + 5]$

$-1(2)$

-2

CLASS EXERCISES

Simplify.

1. $-(-26)$ 26   **2.** $-(6 - 5)$ -1 **3.** $-(-30 + 16)$ 14   **4.** $-(y - 10)$ $-y + 10$

5. $-(x - y)$
$-x + y$

6. $-(x + y)$
$-x - y$

7. $x - (y + 5)$
$x - y - 5$

8. $y - (x - 3)$
$y - x + 3$

Evaluate for $x = -3$ and $y = 4$.

9. $-x$ 3   **10.** $-2y$ -8 **11.** $-5x$ 15   **12.** $-xy$ 12

13. $x - y$ -7 **14.** $y - x$ 7   **15.** $-x - y$ -1 **16.** $y - xy$ 16

EXERCISES

Simplify.

1. $-(-14)$ 14   **2.** $-(4 + 3)$ -7 **3.** $-(12 - 18)$ 6   **4.** $-(-11 - 8)$ 19

Simplify. Then evaluate for $x = -3$.

5. $-(x - 8)$ $-x + 8$; 11   **6.** $-(-x + 8)$ $x - 8$; -11 **7.** $-(-x - 8)$ $x + 8$; 5

8. $12 - (x + 1)$
$-x + 11$; 14

9. $10 - (x - 8)$
$-x + 18$; 21

10. $10 - (8 - x)$
$x + 2$; -1

Evaluate $-pq$ for the given values of p and q.

11. $p = -6$, $q = 7$ 42   **12.** $p = 8$, $q = -15$ 120   **13.** $p = -10$, $q = -25$ -250

BASIC OPERATIONS

ALTERNATE EXAMPLES

4. Simplify. Write each expression without parentheses.
   a. $x - (y + z)$ $x - y - z$
   b. $(w - x) - (y - z)$
   $w - x - y + z$

5. Evaluate each expression if $a = -2$, $b = 3$, and $c = -6$.
   a. $-bc$ 18
   b. $c - ab$ 0
   c. $-(a - c)$ -4

DAILY QUIZ

Simplify.

1. $-(-15)$ 15
2. $-(9 - 7)$ -2
3. $x - (y - 4)$ $x - y + 4$
Simplify. Write each answer without parentheses or brackets.
4. $-(a + b) + c$ $-a - b + c$
5. $-[y + (-x)]$ $-y + x$

ASSIGNMENT GUIDE
(pages 67–68)

Minimum course: 1–21
Average course: 1–13 odd,
14–33
Maximum course: 11–35

Evaluate each expression when $a = -5$, $b = 6$, and $c = -10$.

14. $-ab$ 30   **15.** $ab + c$ -40 **16.** $-(b + c)$ 4   **17.** $-(a - c)$ -5

18. $-abc^2$ 3000   **19.** $a^2 - bc$ 85   **20.** $-(ab)^2 - c$ -890 **21.** $-(a - b)^2$ -121

Simplify. Write each answer without parentheses or brackets.

22. $-(-x)$ x **23.** $-[-(-y)]$ $-y$ **24.** $-[y - (-x)]$ $-y - x$

25. $x - (y - z)$ $x - y + z$ **26.** $-(x + y) + z$ **27.** $-(xy - z)$ $-xy + z$
                             $-x - y + z$

28. $-[(x - y) - z]$ **29.** $-[x - (y - z)]$ **30.** $8x + 2y - y + x$ $9x + y$
     $-x + y + z$ $-x + y - z$

31. $-y - y - y + 5$ **32.** $(x + 5) - (x - 3)$ 8   **33.** $-(2x + 8) + 5x$ $3x - 8$
     $-3y + 5$

C   **34.** Supply reasons for the proof that $-(a - b) = -a + b$.

Proof	(1) $-(a - b) = (-1)(a - b)$	Why?	Multiplication prop. of -1
	(2) $= (-1)[a + (-b)]$	Why?	Subtraction rule
	(3) $= (-1)a + (-1)(-b)$	Why?	Distributive prop.
	(4) $= -a + b$	Why?	Multiplication prop. of -1

35. Prove $-(a + b - c - d + e) = -a - b + c + d - e$

*36. Prove $a(-b) = -ab$ ***37. Prove** $-a(-b) = ab$

USING THE CALCULATOR

Guess and Test

A calculator is useful for finding answers by trial and error.

Example   Find two consecutive whole numbers with squares whose sum is 6613.

Estimate mentally. Start with $50^2 + 50^2$, or $2(50^2)$.

$2(50^2) = 2(2500) = 5000$ $2(60^2) = 2(3600) = 7200$
               └──too small   └──too large

So the consecutive numbers are between 50 and 60. Now use a calculator.

$55^2 + 56^2 = 6161$ $56^2 + 57^2 = 6385$ $57^2 + 58^2 = 6613$

The numbers are 57 and 58. Are -58 and -57 also solutions?   Yes

Make a rough estimate. Then use a calculator.

1. Find two consecutive numbers with squares whose sum is 9385.
   68 and 69; also -69 and -68
2. Find two consecutive numbers whose product is 1332.   36 and 37; also -37 and -36

3. Find three consecutive even numbers with a product of 73,920. 40, 42, and 44

4. Find three consecutive even numbers with squares whose sum is 47,636.
   124, 126, and 128; also -128, -126, and -124

68

2-8 Division

OBJECTIVES

To use the division rule: $\frac{a}{b} = a \cdot \frac{1}{b}$, where $b \neq 0$.

To evaluate algebraic expressions that involve division.

Fractions can illustrate how division is related to multiplication.

$$\frac{3}{7} = 3 \div 7 \quad \text{or} \quad \frac{3}{7} = \frac{1}{7} + \frac{1}{7} + \frac{1}{7} = 3\left(\frac{1}{7}\right)$$

This can be stated as a general rule for every number a and every nonzero number b.

> **To divide a by b, multiply a by the reciprocal of b.**
>
> $$\frac{a}{b} = a \cdot \frac{1}{b}, \text{ where } \frac{1}{b} \text{ is the reciprocal of } b.$$

Two numbers are **reciprocals** if their product is 1.

$$4 \text{ and } \frac{1}{4} \text{ are reciprocals, since } 4\left(\frac{1}{4}\right) = 1.$$

$$\frac{3}{4} \text{ and } \frac{4}{3} \text{ are reciprocals, since } \frac{3}{4} \times \frac{4}{3} = \frac{12}{12} = 1.$$

$$-5 \text{ and } -\frac{1}{5} \text{ are reciprocals, since } (-5)\left(-\frac{1}{5}\right) = 1.$$

The only number that has no reciprocal is 0, since there is no possible replacement for x in the sentence $0 \cdot x = 1$. There is no number that gives a product of 1 when it is multiplied with 0. However, you *can* divide 0 by any nonzero number.

$$\frac{3}{0} \text{ is undefined.} \quad \frac{0}{3} \text{ is defined as 0, since } \frac{0}{3} = 0 \times \frac{1}{3} = 0.$$

The reciprocal of a number is also called its **multiplicative inverse.**

EXAMPLE 1   Find the reciprocal, or multiplicative inverse, of each number.

Number	3	1	$\frac{3}{5}$	-2	$-1\frac{1}{2}$	-1
Multiplicative Inverse	$\frac{1}{3}$	1	$\frac{5}{3}$	$-\frac{1}{2}$	$-\frac{2}{3}$	-1

Notice that a number and its reciprocal have the same sign.

BASIC OPERATIONS

69

69

WARM-UP EXERCISES

Solve.

1. $2(\frac{1}{2}) = n$ 1

2. $-4(-\frac{1}{4}) = n$ 1

3. $\frac{3}{8}(-6) = n$ $-2\frac{1}{4}$

4. $-\frac{5}{3}(-\frac{1}{10}) = n$ $\frac{1}{6}$

LESSON NOTES

The generalization shows how division can be expressed in terms of multiplication. As you consider the generalization, use a familiar example such as $15 \div 3 = 15 \times \frac{1}{3}$ to illustrate the generalization.

Review the idea of reciprocals and point out that the reciprocal of a positive number is positive; the reciprocal of a negative number is negative. Example 1 can be used to emphasize this idea. You may need to remind some students that to find the reciprocal of a number such as $-1\frac{1}{2}$, they first express the number in fraction form, $\frac{a}{b}$, and then name the reciprocal.

After discussing all the model examples, you might wish to consider some division examples in which the divisor is not an integer. For example, use $4\frac{1}{2} \div \frac{3}{4}$ or $\frac{2}{3} \div \left(-\frac{1}{6}\right)$.

ALTERNATE EXAMPLE

1. Find the reciprocal, or multiplicative inverse, of each number.

5	-1	$\frac{7}{8}$	1	4	$-2\frac{2}{3}$
$\frac{1}{5}$	-1	$\frac{8}{7}$	1	$\frac{1}{4}$	$-\frac{3}{8}$

2. Rewrite each division expression, using multiplication.

a. $8 \div \dfrac{4}{5}$ $8 \times \dfrac{5}{4}$

b. $\dfrac{9}{10} \div (-3)$ $\dfrac{9}{10} \times \left(-\dfrac{1}{3}\right)$

c. $-4 \div n$ $-4 \times \dfrac{1}{n}$

d. $\dfrac{0}{-12}$ $0 \times \left(-\dfrac{1}{12}\right)$

3. Write a related multiplication expression. Then simplify.

a. $\dfrac{12}{3}$ $12 \times \dfrac{1}{3}$; 4

b. $\dfrac{-12}{3}$ $-12 \times \dfrac{1}{3}$; -4

c. $\dfrac{12}{-3}$ $12 \times \left(-\dfrac{1}{3}\right)$; -4

d. $\dfrac{-12}{-3}$ $-12 \times \left(-\dfrac{1}{3}\right)$; 4

4. Evaluate when $x = 6$ and $y = -30$.

a. $\dfrac{2y}{5}$ -12 **b.** $\dfrac{y}{x - 56}$ $\dfrac{3}{5}$

c. $(2y \div 10) \div x$ -1

POSSIBLE ERROR

In division with fractions, students may forget to use the reciprocal. If students solve $6 \div \left(-\dfrac{1}{3}\right)$ and obtain -2 as the answer, they have made that type of error.

$6 \div \left(-\dfrac{1}{3}\right) = 6 \times \left(-\dfrac{1}{3}\right) = -2$

(incorrect)

Emphasize that when a division example is rewritten as a multiplication example, we must multiply by the *reciprocal* of the divisor (the reciprocal of the second number). It may be worthwhile to show the generalization using the $\div$ sign and fractions for each of the numbers.

$\dfrac{a}{c} \div \dfrac{b}{d} = \dfrac{a}{c} \times \dfrac{d}{b}$

EXAMPLE 2 Rewrite each division expression, using multiplication.

a. $4 \div \dfrac{2}{3}$ **b.** $\dfrac{3}{5} \div (-10)$ **c.** $-6 \div y$ **d.** $\dfrac{0}{7}$

$4 \times \dfrac{3}{2}$ $\dfrac{3}{5} \times \left(-\dfrac{1}{10}\right)$ $-6 \times \dfrac{1}{y}$ $0 \times \dfrac{1}{7}$

EXAMPLE 3 Write a related multiplication expression. Then simplify.

a. $\dfrac{10}{2}$ **b.** $\dfrac{-10}{2}$ **c.** $\dfrac{10}{-2}$ **d.** $\dfrac{-10}{-2}$

$(10)\left(\dfrac{1}{2}\right)$ $(-10)\left(\dfrac{1}{2}\right)$ $(10)\left(-\dfrac{1}{2}\right)$ $(-10)\left(-\dfrac{1}{2}\right)$

5   -5 -5 5

This suggests that division and multiplication rules for signs are similar.

Division Rules

If a and b are both positive or both negative numbers, then $\dfrac{a}{b}$ is positive.

If either a or b is positive and the other is negative, then $\dfrac{a}{b}$ is negative.

If $a = 0$ and $b \neq 0$, then $\dfrac{a}{b} = 0$. Division by 0 is undefined.

EXAMPLE 4 Evaluate when $x = -5$ and $y = 20$.

a. $\dfrac{-5y}{4} = \dfrac{-5(20)}{4} = \dfrac{-100}{4} = -25$ **b.** $\dfrac{x}{10 - y} = \dfrac{-5}{10 - 20} = \dfrac{-5}{-10} = \dfrac{1}{2}$

c. $(y \div 2) \div x = (20 \div 2) \div (-5) = 10 \div (-5) = -2$

CLASS EXERCISES

Write a related multiplication expression. Then simplify.

1. $\dfrac{-12}{3}$ $-12\left(\dfrac{1}{3}\right) = -4$ **2.** $\dfrac{-24}{-8}$ $-24\left(-\dfrac{1}{8}\right) = 3$ **3.** $\dfrac{48}{-6}$ $48 \times \left(-\dfrac{1}{6}\right) = -8$ **4.** $\dfrac{-500}{-25}$ $-500\left(-\dfrac{1}{25}\right) = 20$

5. $\dfrac{18}{-6}$ $18\left(-\dfrac{1}{6}\right) = -3$ **6.** $\dfrac{-45}{-9}$ $-45\left(-\dfrac{1}{9}\right) = 5$ **7.** $\dfrac{200 - 500}{60}$ **8.** $\dfrac{(5)(-30)}{5 - 20}$

$(200 - 500)\dfrac{1}{60} = -5$ $(5)(-30)\left(\dfrac{1}{5 - 20}\right) = 10$

Evaluate when $a = 6$ and $b = 4$.

9. $\dfrac{4a}{b}$ 6 **10.** $\dfrac{-3b}{a}$ -2 **11.** $\dfrac{a - b}{b - a}$ -1 **12.** $\dfrac{ab}{a + b}$ 2.4, or $2\dfrac{2}{5}$

EXERCISES

A   Write a related multiplication expression. Then simplify.

1. $\dfrac{80}{5}$ **2.** $\dfrac{-80}{5}$ **3.** $\dfrac{80}{-5}$ **4.** $\dfrac{-80}{-5}$

5. $\dfrac{400}{20}$ **6.** $\dfrac{400}{-20}$ **7.** $\dfrac{-400}{20}$ **8.** $\dfrac{-400}{-20}$

9. $\dfrac{24}{6}$ **10.** $\dfrac{-16}{2}$ **11.** $\dfrac{-48}{-8}$ **12.** $\dfrac{-100}{-4}$

13. $\dfrac{-60}{-5}$ **14.** $\dfrac{72}{-9}$ **15.** $\dfrac{-63}{7}$ **16.** $\dfrac{84}{-12}$

Simplify.

17. $\dfrac{100-25}{-5}$ -15 **18.** $\dfrac{(-6)(9)}{-18}$ 3 **19.** $\dfrac{-36}{-12+3}$ 4 **20.** $\dfrac{(-6)(-6)}{-6+(-6)}$ -3

Evaluate when $x = -8$ and $y = 4$.

21. $\dfrac{x}{2}$ -4 **22.** $\dfrac{y}{-4}$ -1 **23.** $\dfrac{x}{y}$ -2 **24.** $\dfrac{-y}{x}$ $\frac{1}{2}$

B   **25.** $\dfrac{x+2}{y+2}$ -1 **26.** $\dfrac{y-10}{y+10}$ $-\frac{3}{7}$ **27.** $\dfrac{xy}{4x}$ 1 **28.** $\dfrac{x-y}{x+y}$ 3

29. $\dfrac{-3x}{-2y}$ -3 **30.** $\dfrac{4y-4}{x-4}$ -1 **31.** $\dfrac{5x+y}{x+7}$ 36 **32.** $\dfrac{x^2}{-xy}$ 2

Write a related multiplication expression and simplify.

33. $4 \div 2$ $4 \cdot \frac{1}{2} = 2$ **34.** $0 \div 2$ $0 \cdot \frac{1}{2} = 0$ **35.** $\frac{1}{4} \div \frac{1}{2}$ $\frac{1}{4} \cdot 2 = \frac{1}{2}$ **36.** $4 \div \left(-\dfrac{1}{2}\right)$

$4 \cdot (-2) = -8$

Simplify each division expression or write **undefined.**

37. $\dfrac{0}{1}$ 0 **38.** $\dfrac{1}{0}$ Undefined   **39.** $\dfrac{0}{0}$ Undefined   **40.** $\dfrac{2a-(-2a)}{7+(-7)}$

Undefined

Evaluate when $a = -\frac{1}{4}$ and $b = 2\frac{1}{2}$.

41. $\dfrac{-8a}{2}$ 1 **42.** $\dfrac{-24b}{8}$ $-7\frac{1}{2}$ **43.** $\dfrac{50b}{-5b}$ -10 **44.** $\dfrac{-20a^3}{-4a}$ $\frac{5}{16}$

45. $\dfrac{a^2b}{a}$ $-\frac{5}{8}$ **46.** $\dfrac{ab^3}{b}$ $-1\frac{9}{16}$ **47.** $\dfrac{ab}{b}$ $-\frac{1}{4}$ **48.** $\dfrac{a^3b^2}{a^2b^2}$ $-\frac{1}{4}$

49. $\dfrac{-a^3b}{a^2}$ $\frac{5}{8}$ **50.** $\dfrac{(4a)^2}{8}$ $\frac{1}{8}$ **51.** $\dfrac{-12ab^2}{3b}$ $\frac{5}{2}$ **52.** $\dfrac{30b}{-6b^3}$ $-\frac{4}{5}$

BASIC OPERATIONS

71

EXTRA PRACTICE, page 510

71

C

53. Simplify $(-100 \div 50) \div (-2)$ and $-100 \div [50 \div (-2)]$. Is division associative?   1; 4; No

54. Simplify $-50 \div 10$ and $10 \div (-50)$. Is division commutative? $-5; -\frac{1}{5}$; No

*55. Evaluate $\dfrac{\frac{1}{x^2} - \frac{1}{y^2}}{x - y}$ when $x = 3$ and $y = -2$. $-\frac{1}{36}$

Evaluate by direct substitution. Then evaluate again, but this time after first simplifying the expression. Both results should be the same.

56. $\dfrac{x^3 y}{xy^2}$ for $x = 2$ and $y = 3$ $\frac{x^2}{y}; \frac{4}{3}$

57. $\dfrac{28x}{-7y}$ for $x = 3$ and $y = -2$ $-\frac{4x}{y}; 6$

58. $\dfrac{-5x^2}{xy}$ for $x = -1$ and $y = -1$ $-\frac{5x}{y}; -5$

59. $\dfrac{-24xy}{-6x^2 y}$ for $x = 2$ and $y = -2$ $\frac{4}{x}; 2$

60. $\dfrac{-80x^3 y^3}{-5(xy)^3}$ for $x = 2$ and $y = 2$ 16; 16

61. $\dfrac{-60x(x + y)}{12x^2}$ for $x = -2$ and $y = -3$ $-\frac{5(x + y)}{x}; -12\frac{1}{2}$

*62. For what values of x does $\dfrac{|x|}{-x} = 1$?   For all negative numbers

CHECKPOINT

Simplify.

1. $15 + 27 + (-19)$ 23   **2.** $-26 + (-27) + 34$ -19 **3.** $17 - (-3) - 4$ 16

4. $15 - 2 - (-21) - 16$ 18   **5.** $15 - 12 - (-11) - 16$ -2

6. $(6)(8)$ 48   **7.** $(6)(-8)$ -48 **8.** $(-6)(8)$ -48 **9.** $(-6)(-8)$ 48

10. $4 \div (-2)$ -2 **11.** $\frac{1}{4} \div 2$ $\frac{1}{8}$ **12.** $(-1)(-2)(-3)$ -6 **13.** $(-1)(2)(3)$ -6

Use the distributive property to rewrite each expression.

14. $3(x + 1)$ $3x + 3$ **15.** $4(a + b)$ $4a + 4b$ **16.** $g(6 + 2)$ $6g + 2g$ **17.** $q(r - t)$ $qr - qt$

Solve.

18. $n + 3 = -7$ -10 **19.** $n - 3 = -1$ 2   **20.** $n - 1 = 2$ 3   **21.** $-n - 5 = -9$ 4

Simplify, if possible.

22. $6x + 7x + 5x$ $18x$ **23.** $-7y - 9y - 2y$ $-18y$ **24.** $-3a - 4a - a$ $-8a$

25. $-17k^2 - 8k^2 - 5k^2$ **26.** $1 - 7h - 7 - 9h$ **27.** $5p^2 q + 7pq^2 - 3pq$
   $-30k^2$ $-6 - 16h$ Cannot be simplified

Evaluate when $x = -3$, $y = 4$, and $z = -5$.

28. $-(xyz)$ -60 **29.** $-x - y - z$ 4   **30.** $-(xy) - z$ 17   **31.** $-(xy - z)$ 7

72

A Mean, or Average

An *average* is a measure of central tendency—a typical, or representative, value. The average that is used most often is the *mean*. To find a mean, add all of the numbers. Then divide the sum by the number of numbers.

Find the mean of the numbers $-2, 1, 5, -1, -4$.

$$\text{mean} = \frac{-2 + 1 + 5 - 1 - 4}{5} = \frac{-1}{5} = -0.2$$

Ike opened a bike shop. Use the frequency distribution table to find the mean of the weekly sales. First multiply each number by its frequency.

Number Sold Weekly	0	1	2	3	4	5	6	7	8
Frequency	1	1	5	10	14	9	7	2	3

$$\text{mean} = \frac{1(0) + 1(1) + 5(2) + 10(3) + 14(4) + 9(5) + 7(6) + 2(7) + 3(8)}{52} = \frac{222}{52} \approx 4.26$$

The mean number of bikes sold weekly was 4.3, to the nearest tenth.

EXERCISES

Find the mean for each set of numbers.

1. $\frac{1}{8}, \frac{3}{8}, \frac{1}{4}$ $\frac{1}{4}$, or 0.25

2. $0^5, 1^4, 2^3, 3^2, 4^1$ 4.4

3. $(0.1)^3, (0.3)^2, (0.5)^1$ 0.197

4. $(-3)^2, (0)^2, (3)^2$ 6

5. $3^1, 3^2, 3^3, 3^4$ 30

6. $(-2)^0, (-2)^1, (-2)^2, (-2)^3$ $-\frac{5}{4}$ or -1.25

7. $\pi, 3\pi, 5\pi$ 3π

8. $-4, -6, 1, 3$ $-\frac{3}{2}$, or -1.5

9. $|-4|, |-6|, |1|, |3|$ $\frac{7}{2}$, or 3.5

10. Low temperatures in degrees Celsius for 14 consecutive days:
    $-12, -6, 0, 3, 2, -2, 4, -4, -5, -3, 2, 5, 5, -3$. $-1°C$

11. Test Scores for 50 Students   82

Score	60	70	80	90	100
Frequency	1	10	24	8	7

12. Ages of 30 Students   14

Age	12	13	14	15
Frequency	1	7	13	9

13. What is the mean of any number and its opposite?   0

Each set of numbers has a mean of 10. Find the missing number.

14. $10, 10, 10, \underline{\ ?\ }, 10$ 10

15. $12, 6, 8, \underline{\ ?\ }$ 14

16. $30, 5, -15, \underline{\ ?\ }$ 20

Extra Topic

Students should be familiar with the basic concept of an average, or *mean*. Similarly, most students will have had some experience with a frequency distribution table in their work in earlier grades. However, be sure they understand that the frequency of an item indicates how often it occurs in a set of data. Thus, the first pair of numbers in the frequency distribution table indicates that weekly sales of 0 bicycles occurred in just 1 week; the second pair of numbers indicates that weekly sales of 1 bicycle occurred in just 1 week; and so on.

Notice that in Exercises 1–10, the students find the average by simply adding the given numbers and then dividing. In Exercises 11–12, they make use of frequency distribution tables. (Of course, in Exercise 10, the students could decide to make a frequency distribution table and then use it; this would not be a very effective approach because most of the numbers occur only once in the set of data.)

WARM-UP EXERCISES

Use x as the variable. Write an expression for each phrase.

1. 8 less than the number $x - 8$

2. The number decreased by 7 $x - 7$

3. 5 more than the number $x + 5$

4. Three fourths of the number $\frac{3}{4}x$

LESSON NOTES

After you discuss the introductory problem and Example 1, devote attention to the material at the top of page 75. Often in daily life, mistakes are made because a problem is not fully understood, or because the "solution" that we find is not examined carefully or reinterpreted correctly in terms of the given problem.

In solving Exercise 3, some students may write the equation $2 - (4)(3) = n$, and give their answer as $-10°C$. However, this exercise does not ask for the final temperature; it asks, "How much below 0° was the final temperature?" Therefore, the correct answer is "10° below 0°C."

ALTERNATE EXAMPLE

1. At 1 A.M., the temperature was $-5°C$. Temperature in degrees Fahrenheit is 32 more than $\frac{9}{5}$ times the corresponding temperature in degrees Celsius. What was the temperature at 1 A.M. in degrees Fahrenheit? 23°F

2-9 Problem Solving: Using Formulas

OBJECTIVES

To look for key words in a problem.
To write and use formulas to answer number problems.

In problem solving it is important to read carefully to make sure you understand what useful information is given and what you are to find. Often there are key words that are helpful.

A normal room temperature is 20°C. Dry ice used in refrigeration is 99° colder than normal room temperature. What is the temperature of dry ice?

Colder means *lower*, so you should subtract. The answer must be negative.

$$20 - 99 = -79$$

The temperature of dry ice is $-79°C$, which is 99° lower than 20°C.

Many problems can be solved by writing an equation or a formula.

EXAMPLE 1

Dry ice has a temperature of $-79°C$. Its temperature in degrees Fahrenheit is 32 more than $\frac{9}{5}$ times its temperature in degrees Celsius. What is its Fahrenheit temperature to the nearest degree?

Strategy: Use a formula.

Read the problem to find the key relationship.
   °F is 32 more than $\frac{9}{5}$ times °C.

Use variables.
   Let $F = $ °Fahrenheit.
   Let $C = $ °Celsius.

Write a formula.
   $$F = \frac{9}{5}C + 32$$

Find the solution (substitute and evaluate).
   $$F = \frac{9}{5}(-79) + 32$$
   $$= -110.2$$

Answer the question.
   Dry ice has a temperature of about $-110°F$.

74

EXAMPLE 2   The profit is equal to the selling price less the cost. Find the profit if the selling price is $445, but the cost is $529.

Read the problem to find the key relationships.

The selling price less (minus) the cost (expenses) equals the profit.

Use variables.   Let p be the profit.
Let s be the selling price.
Let c be the cost.

Write a formula. $p = s - c$

Find the solution. $p = 445 - 529$
$= -84$

Answer the question.   There is no profit. The loss is $84.

CLASS EXERCISES

Liquid hydrogen is used as a rocket fuel. Hydrogen gas becomes a liquid at 70° lower than the boiling point of oxygen.

1. Is a use for liquid hydrogen given?   for liquid oxygen?
Yes; No
2. Is the boiling point for oxygen higher or lower than for hydrogen?   Higher
3. Use variables to identify the boiling points of hydrogen and oxygen.   Answers may vary. Sample: Let x = boiling pt. of oxygen; y = boiling pt. of hydrogen.
4. Write a formula relating the two boiling points. $y = x - 70$
5. Liquid hydrogen becomes a gas at −253°C. Use the formula to find the temperature at which oxygen changes from a liquid to a gas.   −183°C

Gas
← Boiling Point

Liquid

← Freezing Point

Solid

EXERCISES

A   *Solve the problem.*

1. From a reading of −4°C, the temperature dropped 7° and then rose 5°. What was the final temperature?   −6°C

2. From a reading of 8°C, the temperature rose 4° and then dropped 12°. What was the final temperature?   0°C

3. The temperature started at 2°C and dropped 3° in each of the next four hours. How much below 0°C was the final temperature?   10° below 0°C

Chemical A freezes at 17° lower than chemical B.

4. Use variables to write a formula relating the two freezing points. $a = b - 17$

5. If chemical A freezes at −25°C, at what temperature does chemical B freeze?   −8°C

BASIC OPERATIONS

75

EXTRA PRACTICE, pages 510–511

Write a formula. Then solve the problem.

6. The range r is the highest value h minus the lowest value l. Find the range if the highest value is -12.5 and the lowest is -27.3. $r = h - l$; 14.8

7. The number of degrees Celsius is $\frac{5}{9}$ times the difference, 32 less than the number of degrees Fahrenheit. Express 85°F in degrees Celsius.
   $C = \frac{5}{9}(F - 32)$; about 29°C

B

Two pieces of metal start at the same length but contract at different rates when cooled. The first piece contracts 3.6 mm. Find the difference in their lengths if the second piece contracts

8. 1.8 mm.   1.8 mm   9. 1.8 mm more.   10. 0.7 mm more than 3 times as much.
                                  1.8 mm   7.9 mm

Use the table of values.

11. At -240°C, is oxygen a solid, a liquid, or a gas?   Solid

12. At -240°C, is hydrogen a solid, a liquid, or a gas?   Gas

	Freezing point	Boiling point
Oxygen	-218°C	-183°C
Hydrogen	-259°C	-253°C

13. How many degrees warmer is the boiling point of oxygen than of hydrogen?   70°

14. Over how many more degrees will oxygen maintain a liquid state than hydrogen?   29° more

Compound A weighs 3 times as much as compound B. Compound C weighs 24 grams more than compound B.

15. Write a formula for the weight of compound A in terms of the weight of compound C. $a = 3(c - 24)$

16. If compound A weighs 48 grams per cubic centimeter, how much does compound C weigh per cubic centimeter?   40 grams per cubic centimeter

Product D costs $\frac{1}{4}$ as much as product E, while product F costs $\frac{1}{4}$ less than product E. Write a formula for the cost of:

17. D in terms of E $d = \frac{1}{4}e$ 18. E in terms of F $e = \frac{4}{3}f$ 19. F in terms of D $f = 3d$

C

The weight of a liter of oxygen is 0.079 gram more than 15 times as heavy as hydrogen. The weight of a liter of carbon dioxide is 0.003 gram less than 22 times as heavy as hydrogen.

20. Use formulas to express the weights of oxygen and carbon dioxide in terms of that of hydrogen.

21. If a liter of oxygen weighs 1.429 grams, find the weight of a liter of hydrogen and of carbon dioxide.   0.09 g; 1.977 g

Measurement and Cost

Stanley Ortiz is a carpet salesman. He has to measure carefully and compute areas and prices accurately. He sells carpeting by the square yard, and the prices vary widely, depending on the quality.

Example Find the cost of carpeting a room that is 9 ft by 13 ft at $7.77 per square yard. Assume that installation is included in the price.

Change the length and width to yards: 9 ft = 3 yd, 13 ft = $4\frac{1}{3}$ yd.

Step 1
$$A = lw$$
$$= \left(4\frac{1}{3}\right)(3)$$
$$= 13$$
The area is 13 sq. yd.

Step 2
$$\begin{array}{r} \$ \ 7.77 \\ \times \quad 13 \\ \hline \$101.01 \end{array}$$
Cost per sq. yd
Number of sq. yd

The cost is $101.01.

Find the cost, assuming that installation is included in the price.

1. Bedroom: 15 ft by 15 ft, at $8.89 per square yard $222.25

2. Living room: 12 ft by 18 ft, at $24.29 per square yard $582.96

3. Hallway: a feet by b feet, at c dollars per square yard $\frac{a}{3} \times \frac{b}{3} \times c$, or $\frac{abc}{9}$, dollars

Stanley makes a 15% commission on each sale. How much does he make from each of these sales?

4. $11.99 per square yard for the carpet and $3.25 per square yard for the carpet pad

5. $13.50 per square yard for carpeting and pad combined

These exercises review basic algebraic skills.

Use < or > to make each sentence true.

1. $-3 \underline{\ ?\ } -4$ $>$
2. $-0.5 \underline{\ ?\ } 0.2$ $<$

Evaluate when $a = 5$ and $b = -15$.

3. $a + b$ -10
4. $a - b$ 20
5. $b - a$ -20
6. ab -75
7. b^2 225
8. $\dfrac{b}{a}$ -3
9. $\dfrac{12b}{18a}$ -2
10. $-8ab$ 600

Simplify

11. $-3 - 9 - (-10)$ -2
12. $8 + (-23) - (-4) - 11$ -22

Use the distributive property to rewrite each expression.

13. $1.5(3 + y)$ $4.5 + 1.5y$
14. $\dfrac{1}{2}(8 - x)$ $4 - \dfrac{1}{2}x$

Simplify.

15. $12n - (-4n)$ $16n$
16. $-9y + y$ $-8y$
17. $6x + 3 + (-5x)$ $x + 3$
18. $3n - (6 - 2n)$ $5n - 6$

Solve the problem.

19. Twelve more than a number is 71. What is the number? 59
20. A certain number multiplied by 3 is -42. What is the number? -14

CHAPTER 2 REVIEW

VOCABULARY

additive identity (p. 44)
additive inverse (p. 44)
addition property of zero (p. 45)
addition property of opposites (p. 45)
distributive property (p. 55)
term (p. 59)
numerical coefficient (p. 59)
like terms (p. 59)

similar terms (p. 59)
constant term (p. 59)
multiplicative identity (p. 66)
multiplication property of 1 (p. 66)
multiplication property of -1 (p. 66)
reciprocal (p. 69)
multiplicative inverse (p. 69)

SUMMARY

In this chapter the four basic operations with signed numbers are explained and illustrated. The number line and the absolute-value concept are used in these discussions. Some additional properties of numbers are introduced, including the all-important distributive property. The algebraic work with variables and expressions, introduced in Chapter One, is extended here. In particular, like terms are combined by using the distributive property. The study of problem solving also continues in this chapter, here focusing on the use of formulas.

REVIEW EXERCISES

2-1   *Find each sum.*

1. $-5 + 17 + 0$ 12
2. $-8 + \dfrac{1}{2} + 1$ $-6\dfrac{1}{2}$
3. $6 + (-3) + (-10)$ -7
4. $21 + (-14) + (-7)$ 0
5. $-0.2 + 4$ 3.8
6. $12 + 24 + (-16) + (-26)$ -6

2-2   *Is the solution positive, negative, or zero?*

7. $x + 6 = -10$ Neg.
8. $x + (-3) = -1$ Pos.
9. $x + (-1) = 4$ Pos.
10. $-4 + x = -5$ Neg.
11. $10 + x = -2$ Neg.
12. $-10 + x = -10$ Zero

2-3   *Simplify.*

13. $15 - 8 - 7$ 0
14. $-10 - 6 - (-4)$ -12
15. $14 - (-11) - 9 + (-8)$ 8
16. $-5 - (-15) + 10 - 14$ 6
17. $-(-32) + (-7) - 27 - 22$ -24

2-4   *Use the distributive property to rewrite each expression.*

18. $23(a + b)$ $23a + 23b$
19. $0.7(5 - x)$ $3.5 - 0.7x$
20. $x(y + 12)$ $xy + 12x$

2-5 *Simplify.*

21. $-7a^2 - 10a^2$ $-17a^2$ **22.** $13x - (-5x)$ $18x$ **23.** $c + (-9c)$ $-8c$

24. $-9m + 5 + 3m$ $-6m + 5$**25.** $-4z + 9z + (-3)$ $5z - 3$**26.** $8w - 5w + \dfrac{v}{4}$ $3w + \dfrac{v}{4}$

2-6 *Multiply.*

27. $(5)(60)$ 300 **28.** $(15)(-3)$ -45 **29.** $(-9)(6)$ -54 **30.** $(-9)(-10)$ 90

31. $(-7)(-5)(2)$ 70 **32.** $(-3)(-12)(-10)$ -360 **33.** $(-3)(-3)(-3)(-3)$ 81

Evaluate for $a = -2$ and $b = 5$.

34. $-2a$ 4 **35.** $4a - b$ -13 **36.** $2a + 3b$ 11 **37.** $-2b^2$ -50

2-7 *Simplify. Then evaluate for $g = -3$ and $h = -1$.*

38. $-(-g)$ $g; -3$ **39.** $-[-(-h)]$ $-h; 1$ **40.** $-[h - (-g)]$ $-h - g; 4$

41. $g - (h - g)$ $2g - h; -5$ **42.** $-(g + h) + h$ $-g; 3$ **43.** $-(gh - h)$ $-gh + h; -4$

2-8 *Simplify.*

44. $\dfrac{320}{-40}$ -8 **45.** $\dfrac{-72}{-3}$ 24 **46.** $\dfrac{(-5)(-12)}{-10}$ -6 **47.** $\dfrac{2 - 72}{2}$ -35

Evaluate when $a = -6$ and $b = 3$.

48. $\dfrac{a}{2}$ -3 **49.** $\dfrac{b}{-3}$ -1 **50.** $\dfrac{a}{b}$ -2 **51.** $\dfrac{-b}{a}$ $\frac{1}{2}$ **52.** $\dfrac{a + 2}{b + 2}$ $-\frac{4}{5}$

53. $\dfrac{b - 10}{b + 10}$ $-\frac{7}{13}$ **54.** $\dfrac{ab}{3a}$ 1 **55.** $\dfrac{a - b}{a + b}$ 3 **56.** $\dfrac{-3a}{-2b}$ -3 **57.** $\dfrac{a^2}{b^2}$ 4

Extra Topic *Find the mean for each set of numbers.*

58. 23, 41, 18, 72, 17, 60 38.5 **59.** 13, -9, -3, 6, 8, 7, 9, 9 5

2-9 *Solve the problem.*

60. The high temperature for the day was 15°F. At night the temperature dropped 28°. How cold was it at night? $-13°F$

61. The theater made a profit of \$135 on the evening show but lost \$69 on the matinee. What was the total gain?   \$66

62. John bought 350 new stamps for his collection. Then he gave away 475 to a friend. Express the final result as an integer. -125

REVIEW   79

63. One month a family received the following bills and checks:

Check for $182.58, check for $309.17, bill for $299.36, check for $99.09, bill for $111.17, bill for $35.05, bill for $469.19, check for $887.62.

The family's balance was $116.72 at the start of the month. What was the balance at the end of the month? $680.41

CHAPTER 2 TEST

2-1   *Find each sum.*

1. $-8 + (-7)$ -15 **2.** $13 + (-6)$ 7 **3.** $-21 + 4$ -17 **4.** $14 + (-2)$ 12

2-2   **5.** Is the solution to $x + (-5) = -4$ positive, negative, or zero?   Pos.

2-3   *Simplify.*

6. $18 - (-2)$ 20 **7.** $-17 - (-9)$ -8

8. $20 - (-6) + 7$ 33 **9.** $-13 + (-8) - (-9)$ -12

2-4   *Use the distributive property to rewrite each expression.*

10. $12(x + 3)$ $12x + 36$ **11.** $x(5 - y)$ $5x - xy$ **12.** $7(a + b - c)$ $7a + 7b - 7c$

2-5   *Simplify.*

13. $4a - 1 - 2a + 5$ $2a + 4$ **14.** $3(n - 4) - 2n$ $n - 12$

15. $3x^2 - 4x^2 + 6x^2$ $5x^2$ **16.** $x(1 + y) + 2(x - xy)$ $3x - xy$

2-6   **17.** Multiply $(-2)(-5)(-6)$. -60

Evaluate when $x = -3$.

18. x^3 -27 **19.** $(x - 1)^2$ 16 **20.** $-5(x + 1)$ 10

2-7   **21.** Simplify $6 - (x - 8)$.   Then evaluate for $x = -5$. $14 - x$; 19

2-8   *Simplify.*

22. $\dfrac{(-6)(-3)}{-9}$ -2 **23.** $\dfrac{(-4) - (-7)}{12 + (-15)}$ -1

24. Evaluate $\dfrac{b^2}{ab}$ when $a = -6$ and $b = -2$. $\dfrac{1}{3}$

2-9   **25.** In January 225 people started a social club. By the end of June, 27 people had dropped out of the club while 78 new members had enrolled. How many people were members as of the end of June?   276

80

Engine Efficiency

Here is a program that helps monitor gasoline consumption. The gasoline tank is filled, and a first reading is taken from the odometer to show how many miles the vehicle has already been driven. When the tank is filled again, the number of gallons used is recorded, and a second reading is taken from the odometer to show the new mileage. This data is then entered into the computer.

The Program	What It Does
`100 REM MILES PER GALLON`	Tells what program will compute.
`110 PRINT "FIRST READING";`	Displays a message or "prompt."
`120 INPUT F`	Waits for entry; assigns first reading to memory location F.
`130 PRINT "SECOND READING";`	
`140 INPUT S`	Assigns second reading to memory location S.
`150 PRINT "NO, OF GALLONS";`	
`160 INPUT G`	Assigns input to memory location G.
`170 LET R = (S - F)/G`	Computes number of miles per gallon obtained.
`180 PRINT "AVERAGED "; R;" MPG"`	Displays the result.
`900 END`	

```
RUN
FIRST READING? 8643.7
SECOND READING? 8936.2
NO, OF GALLONS? 12.5
AVERAGED 23.4 MPG
```

Instructs computer to run the program.
Assigns 8643.7 to F.
Assigns 8936.2 to S. **Car traveled 292.5 miles.**
Assigns 12.5 to G.
Displays the output.

The letters used in the program (F, S, G, R) are called *variables*. In BASIC, a variable is the name of a location in the computer memory where a value is stored. For example, line 160 stores the number of gallons used in memory location G.

The absolute-value function may be used so that the odometer readings can be entered in any order. This can be done by changing line 170 to: `170 LET R = ABS(S - F)/G`

1. When the program MILES PER GALLON is run, how many memory locations will be used? Name them.

What will the program display for each of these entries?

	First Reading	Second Reading	No. of Gallons
2.	4065.3	4412.7	18.0
3.	12324.7	12715.3	12.4
4.	46385.8	46680.2	23.0

For more information about BASIC, see the Computer Handbook at the back of the book.

The chapter opens with a lesson that focuses on the relationship between word sentences and the corresponding equations. This translation from one form to another deserves careful attention because it is fundamental to the work in this chapter.

The addition and multiplication properties of equality are then developed separately and used extensively to solve equations of the form $x + a = b$ and $ax = c$. The chapter also discusses alternate methods for solving equations by using inverse operations.

Equations of the form $ax + b = c$ are solved by using both the addition and multiplication properties. Subsequently, a special lesson is devoted to equations that require various techniques of simplification.

The chapter closes with a problem-solving lesson in which the students apply algebraic methods for solving equations. Diagrams and tables are suggested as aids in clarifying problems or organizing data. Emphasis is placed on writing appropriate equations as well as on solving the equations.

Solving equations is at the heart of algebra, so this is a critical chapter in the program. Be sure your students develop the necessary skills.

CHAPTER 3

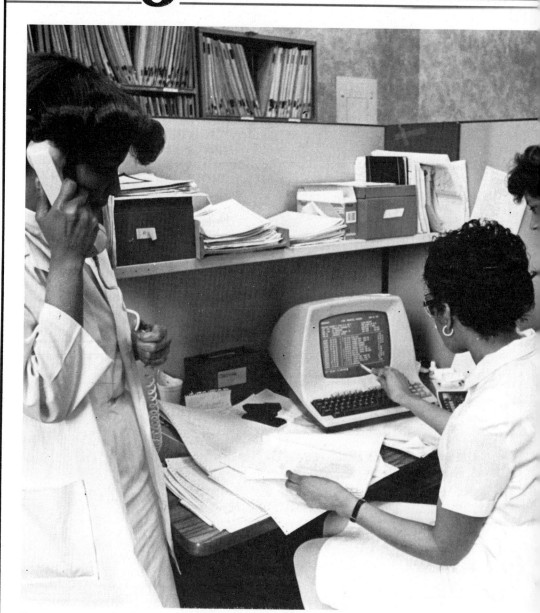

Computers are used to keep track of accounts in professional offices.

EQUATIONS

PREREQUISITE SKILLS REVIEW

For students who need additional practice with the algebraic skills in this *Prerequisite Skills Review,* you may assign *Follow-Up* exercises on page 501 in the students' books.

An item-by-item error analysis of the *Prerequisite Skills Review* appears on page T21.

Prerequisite Skills Review

Write the letter for the correct answer.

1. If 5 times a number is 620, then $\frac{1}{2}$ of the number is ? .   a

   a. 62 **b.** 248 **c.** 1500 **d.** 1550

2. If $\frac{1}{2}$ of a number is 2.4, then 4 times the number is ? .   b

   a. 19.6 **b.** 19.2 **c.** 9.6 **d.** 4.8

3. Simplify $\frac{1}{6} - \frac{1}{3}\left(5 - \frac{1}{2}\right)$.   a

   a. $-1\frac{1}{3}$ **b.** -1 **c.** $-\frac{3}{4}$ **d.** $-1\frac{2}{3}$

4. If $x = 300$, then $4x + 6(1000 - x) =$? .   c

   a. 2000 **b.** 4900 **c.** 5400 **d.** 6900

5. Which expression is *not* equal to 0?   c

   a. $(8 - 8)8$ **b.** $1 - 4(0.25)$ **c.** $\frac{6}{2(3) - 6}$ **d.** $\frac{2(5) - 10}{5}$

6. If $x = -4$, which expression is *not* equal to -20?   b

   a. $3x - 8$ **b.** $28 - 2x$ **c.** $-2(6 - x)$ **d.** $20(3 + x)$

7. Which expression is *not* equal to 1?   b

   a. $(-8)\left(-\frac{1}{8}\right)$ **b.** $\frac{1}{2} \cdot \frac{1}{2}$ **c.** $\frac{3(5) - 2(5)}{5}$ **d.** $\left(3\frac{1}{2}\right)\left(\frac{2}{7}\right)$

8. If $n = 4.5$, then $\frac{6}{4 - n} =$? .   d

   a. 3 **b.** -3 **c.** 12 **d.** -12

9. $\frac{4}{3}n + \frac{2}{3}$ is equivalent to ? .   d

   a. $2n$ **b.** $n\left(\frac{4}{3} + \frac{2}{3}\right)$ **c.** $\frac{4}{3}\left(n + \frac{2}{3}\right)$ **d.** $\frac{2}{3}(2n + 1)$

10. Simplify $\frac{3}{4}(12 - 8x)$.   b

    a. $9 - 8x$ **b.** $9 - 6x$ **c.** $9 - 6\left(\frac{3}{4}x\right)$ **d.** $3x$

EQUATIONS

83

84

WARM-UP EXERCISES

Beth is *x* years old. Write an algebraic expression to represent the age of

1. a friend who is 2 years younger than Beth. $x - 2$
2. an uncle who is 3 times as old as Beth. $3x$

LESSON NOTES

The ability to translate word sentences or other information into mathematical sentences is crucial in problem solving.

In discussing Example 1, remind students that the same equation can represent different word sentences. For instance, $n + 7 = 18$ represents "the sum of some number and 7 is 18" as well as "7 more than some number is equal to 18."

In a similar way, the equations in Example 2 can be expressed in different ways, each of which may be correct. For the exercises that the students do independently, accept any answers that are essentially correct even if they are different from the annotated answers.

ALTERNATE EXAMPLES

1. Translate each sentence into an equation. Use *n* as the variable.
   a. 10 more than some number is equal to 21. $n + 10 = 21$
   b. 3 less than some number is equal to 2. $n - 3 = 2$
   c. The product of 4 and some number is equal to -32. $4n = -32$
   d. Some number divided by 2 is equal to -5. $\frac{n}{2} = -5$
   e. 20 less some number is equal to 8. $20 - n = 8$
2. Express each equation in words.
   a. $n + 82 = 150$ c. $6n = 54$
   b. $5(n + 2) = 30$ d. $3 = \frac{n}{8}$

   82 added to some number *n* is equal to 150; 5 times the quantity, *n* plus 2, is equal to 30; 6 times some number *n* is equal to 54; 3 is equal to some number *n* divided by 8.

3-1   Reading and Writing Equations

OBJECTIVES

To translate word sentences or other information into equations.
To express equations in words.
To express measurement relationships as formulas.

In algebra it is often necessary to translate information into equations.

A record that usually sells for $6 is reduced by x dollars. The sale price is $4.

$6 - x = 4$ 6 decreased by the number *x* is equal to 4.

The usual price of x dollars is reduced $5. The sale price is $6.

$x - 5 = 6$ 5 less than the number *x* is equal to 6.

A record is on sale for $x, but only if you buy 3 records for $14.

$3x = 14$ 3 times the number *x* is equal to 14.

EXAMPLE 1   Translate each sentence into an equation. Use n as the variable.

		Equation
a.	7 more than some number is equal to 18.	$n + 7 = 18$
b.	5 less than some number is equal to -1.	$n - 5 = -1$
c.	Some number multiplied by 9 is equal to 54.	$9n = 54$
d.	Some number divided by 6 is equal to 8.	$\frac{n}{6} = 8$
e.	18 less some number is equal to -3.	$18 - n = -3$

EXAMPLE 2   Express each equation in words.

a. $145 + x = 50$ b. $3(x - 14) = -3$ c. $36 = 4x$ d. $\frac{72}{x} = 8$

a. The sum of 145 and some number x is equal to 50.
b. 3 times the quantity, x minus 14, is equal to -3.
c. 36 is equal to the product of 4 and some number x.
d. 72 divided by a certain number x is equal to 8.

There are many formulas used in geometry that can be written as equations.

The perimeter P of a rectangle is equal to twice the sum of the length l and the width w.

$$P = 2(l + w)$$

The area A of a triangle is equal to one-half the product of the base b and the height h.

$$A = \frac{1}{2}bh$$

EXAMPLE 3 Write the formula for the perimeter of a triangle.

The perimeter P of a triangle is the sum of the lengths of the three sides.

$$P = a + b + c$$

CLASS EXERCISES

Write each sentence as an equation.

1. The sum of the number a and 16 is equal to 84. $a + 16 = 84$

2. 12 decreased by the number b is equal to -5. $12 - b = -5$

3. The number c divided by 4 is equal to 7. $\frac{c}{4} = 7$

4. The product of 9 and the number d is equal to 144. $9d = 144$

5. 6 times the number e is equal to -78. $6e = -78$

6. 8 times the sum of 8 and the number f is equal to 160. $8(8 + f) = 160$

Express each equation in words.

7. $9 - n = 17$ 8. $n + 10 = -3$ 9. $14n = 84$ 10. $\frac{n}{-8} = 9$

EXERCISES

A

Write each sentence as an equation.

1. 6 decreased by the number y is equal to -3. $6 - y = -3$

2. 11 times the number z is equal to 99. $11z = 99$

3. The number x, increased by 7, is equal to $3\frac{1}{2}$. $x + 7 = 3\frac{1}{2}$

4. 4 less than the number n is equal to 10. $n - 4 = 10$

EQUATIONS

85

ENRICHMENT ACTIVITY

Mark these symbols on separate pieces of paper. Place them in the order shown. When read from the top down, the steps indicate this equation:

$3(x + 3) - 9 = 12$

"3 times the sum of x and 3 decreased by 9 is equal to 12."

If the rectangular pieces of paper are rearranged, new equations are indicated. Six different equations are possible. Have the students find and write each of the possible equations.

For a more challenging activity, use a fourth rectangular piece of paper with "Divide by 6" on it. In this case, 24 equations are possible.

ADDITIONAL ANSWERS

Exercises

Answers for Exercises 13–20 may vary. Sample answers are given below.

13. The number n increased by 14 is equal to 39.
14. 18 minus some number n is equal to 42.
15. 3 increased by n is equal to 21.
16. Some number n minus 6 is equal to −90.
17. 5 times n is equal to 65.
18. A number n divided by 8 is equal to −16.
19. Twice some number n plus 3 is equal to 25.
20. Twice the sum of n and 3 is equal to 24.

---

5. The sum of 2 and the number p is equal to −1. $2 + p = -1$

6. The number q divided by 4 is equal to 14.75. $\frac{q}{4} = 14.75$

7. The product of 9 and the number r is equal to 3. $9r = 3$

8. 4 divided by the number a is equal to 1. $\frac{4}{a} = 1$

9. 66 less the number b is equal to −6.5. $66 - b = -6.5$

10. $\frac{1}{4}$ times the sum of the number c and 5 is equal to 8. $\frac{1}{4}(c + 5) = 8$

11. 5 more than the product of the number c and 5 is equal to 8. $5c + 5 = 8$

12. 8 is equal to 9 times the quantity, s plus 4. $8 = 9(s + 4)$

Express each equation in words.

13. $n + 14 = 39$ **14.** $18 - n = 42$ **15.** $3 + n = 21$ **16.** $n - 6 = -90$

17. $5n = 65$ **18.** $\frac{n}{8} = -16$ **19.** $2n + 3 = 25$ **20.** $2(n + 3) = 24$

B   *Write a formula for each geometric relationship.*

21. The perimeter P of a square is 4 times the length of a side s. $P = 4s$

22. The area A of a square is the square of the length of a side s. $A = s^2$

23. The volume V of a rectangular prism is the product of the length l, the width w, and the height h. $V = lwh$

24. The area A of a trapezoid is one-half the height h times the sum of the bases, a and b. $A = \frac{1}{2}h(a + b)$

C   **25.** A temperature is 212° Fahrenheit. Write an equation that shows how to find the corresponding Celsius reading C. To find C, subtract 32 from the Fahrenheit reading, then multiply by $\frac{5}{9}$. $C = (212 - 32)\frac{5}{9}$

26. If the temperature is 30° Celsius, write an equation that shows how to find the Fahrenheit reading F. To find F, multiply the Celsius reading by $\frac{9}{5}$, then add 32. $F = \left(\frac{9}{5}\right)30 + 32$

27. Yoko is y years old. Hiroshi is 10 years younger. Write an equation to show that the sum of their ages is 36. $y + (y - 10) = 36$

28. Katie is k years old. Leon is 20 years old. Write an equation to show that Leon's age is 4 years more than twice Katie's age. $20 = 2k + 4$

29. Matt is m years old. Vince is 3 years older. Write an equation to show that the product of their ages is 550. $m(m + 3) = 550$

***30.** Robert buys x twenty-cent stamps and y fifteen-cent stamps. Write an equation to show that the total cost of the stamps is $13.00. $0.20x + 0.15y = 13.00$

3-2 Addition Property of Equality

OBJECTIVE

To solve equations of the forms $x + a = b$ and $x + (-a) = b$ for x, by using the addition property of equality.

A savings account with x dollars is increased by a deposit. Can you find the value of x in each equation by looking at the deposit and the new balance?

amount	+	deposit	=	new balance
x	+	20	=	150
x	+	30	=	160
x	+	100	=	230

You can see that in each equation, $x = 130$. As the deposit on the left side increases, the balance on the right side increases by the same amount. But the solution is unchanged. Equations with the same solution are **equivalent.**

If you add the same quantity to each side of an equation, the new equation is equivalent to the original equation.

Addition Property of Equality

Let a, b, and c be any numbers.

If $a = b$, then $a + c = b + c$.

The addition property of equality helps you to find an equivalent equation with the variable alone on one side. This is the clearest way to state the value of the variable.

EXAMPLE 1 Solve the equation $x + 7 = 12$. Then check your answer.

$$x + 7 = 12$$
$$x + 7 + (-7) = 12 + (-7)$$ The opposite of 7 is -7. So add -7 to each side of the equation and simplify.
$$x + 0 = 5$$
$$x = 5$$ In this equation, x is alone on the left side.

To check this value, substitute 5 for x in the original equation.

Check
$$x + 7 = 12$$
$$5 + 7 \stackrel{?}{=} 12$$
$$12 = 12 ✔$$

The solution is 5.

Write the opposite of each number.

1. 11 -11 2. -5 5
3. $-\frac{1}{2}$ $\frac{1}{2}$ 4. 25 -25

LESSON NOTES

The equations dealing with the savings deposit may be restated to emphasize the addition property of equality:

$$x = 130$$
$$x + 20 = 130 + 20$$
$$x + 30 = 130 + 30$$
$$x + 100 = 130 + 100$$

Notice that in Examples 1–3, we solve equations by adding the opposite of a number to both sides of the equation. It does not matter whether the equation is $x + 7 = 12$ or $n + (-6) = 21$. The procedure is the same; we see what number has been added to the variable in the given equation, and then we add its opposite to both sides.

Example 3 presents an equation in which the variable is on the right side of the equal sign; this type of equation is more difficult for some students, so discuss it in detail.

In Example 4, explain that solving $x + y = 5$ for x means that we re-express the equation in the form $x = \_$, where $\_$ is some expression involving the other variable. The ability to re-express equations this way is useful in work with formulas, in graphing, and in systems of equations.

ALTERNATE EXAMPLE

1. Solve the equation $x + 5 = 11$. Then check your answer. $x = 6$

2. Solve $n + (-7) = 2$, and check.
$n = 9$

3. Solve $-3 = 4 + n$. $n = -7$
4. Solve $x + y = -8$.
   a. for x $x = -8 - y$
   b. for y $y = -8 - x$

POSSIBLE ERROR

Some students will use the wrong number in trying to solve an equation such as $x + (-7) = 26$. Adding -26 to both sides may cause confusion.

$x + (-7) + (-26)$
$\qquad = 26 + (-26)$
$\quad x + (-33) = 0$

Of course, the solution is still 33. However, emphasize that in solving $x + a = b$, we add the opposite of a (the opposite of the number that is on the same side of the equation as the variable is).

Solve each equation, and check.

1. $x + 5 = 19$ $x = 14$
2. $13 + x = 32$ $x = 19$
3. $17 = x + 6.5$ $x = 10.5$
4. $-6 + x = -7$ $x = -1$
5. $x + (-5) = 6$ $x = 11$

EXAMPLE 2

Solve $n + (-6) = 21$ and check.

$$n + (-6) = 21$$
$$n + (-6) + 6 = 21 + 6$$
$$n + 0 = 27$$
$$n = 27$$

The opposite of -6 is 6. So add 6 to each side of the equation, and simplify.

Check
$$27 + (-6) \overset{?}{=} 21$$
$$21 = 21 \ \checkmark$$

Thus, the solution is 27.

The variable may be on the right side of an equation.

EXAMPLE 3

Solve $15 = -7 + n$.

Method I	**Method II**
Solve with the variable on the right side of the equation.	Reverse sides, using the symmetric property of equality.

Method I	Method II
$15 = -7 + n$	$15 = -7 + n$
$15 + 7 = -7 + n + 7$	$-7 + n = 15$
$22 = n$	$-7 + n + 7 = 15 + 7$
	$n = 22$

The solution is the same by either method.
The check is left to you.

In the next example, solve for one variable in terms of another.

EXAMPLE 4

Solve $x + y = 5$.   **a.** for x **b.** for y

a. To solve for x, add $-y$ to each side.

$$x + y = 5$$
$$x + y + (-y) = 5 + (-y)$$
$$x = 5 - y$$

b. To solve for y, add $-x$ to each side.

$$x + y = 5$$
$$x + y + (-x) = 5 + (-x)$$
$$y = 5 - x$$

Check

$(5 - y) + y \overset{?}{=} 5$	$x + (5 - x) \overset{?}{=} 5$
$5 = 5 \ \checkmark$	$5 = 5 \ \checkmark$

CLASS EXERCISES

*Tell what number you would add to each side of the equation to solve for **n**. Then solve the equation and check.*

1. $n + 7 = 19$ $-7; 12$ **2.** $n + 3 = 2$ $-3; -1$ **3.** $5 + n = 1$ $-5; -4$

4. $n + (-3) = 7$ $3; 10$ **5.** $n + (-9) = 3$ $9; 12$ **6.** $-4 + n = -5$ $4; -1$

CHAPTER 3

7. $n + (-6) = 8$ 6; 14 **8.** $n + (-8) = 5$ 8; 13 **9.** $-12 + n = 11$ 12; 23

10. $3 = n + 4$ $-4; -1$ **11.** $7 = n + (-9)$ 9; 16 **12.** $0 = -1 + n$ 1; 1

EXERCISES

A *What number would you add to each side of the equation to solve for **x**?*

1. $x + 2 = 8$ -2 **2.** $x + 5 = 11$ -5 **3.** $x + 9 = 16$ -9

4. $3 + x = 9$ -3 **5.** $-7 + x = 15$ 7 **6.** $-6 + x = 10$ 6

7. $7 = x + 4$ -4 **8.** $6 = x + 6$ -6 **9.** $15 = x + 8$ -8

10. $x + (-3) = 10$ 3 **11.** $x + (-4) = 2\frac{1}{2}$ 4 **12.** $x + 7 = -1$ -7

Solve each equation and check.

13. $x + 3 = 17$ 14 **14.** $x + (-7) = 26$ 33 **15.** $x + (-8) = 19$ 27

16. $11 + x = 30$ 19 **17.** $9 + x = -4$ -13 **18.** $-3 + x = 0$ 3

19. $23 = x + 3.75$ 19.25 **20.** $18 = x + (-13)$ 31 **21.** $17 = x + 28$ -11

22. $-4 + y = -5$ -1 **23.** $y + (-7) = 6$ 13 **24.** $y + (-12) = -15$ -3

25. $y + 6 = 15$ 9 **26.** $y + 9 = 12$ 3 **27.** $y + (-4) = 20$ 24

28. $-5 + x = -2$ 3 **29.** $7 + x = 3\frac{1}{2}$ $-3\frac{1}{2}$ **30.** $1 = 8 + x$ -7

31. $-6 = y + \frac{1}{2}$ $-6\frac{1}{2}$ **32.** $\frac{4}{9} = \frac{4}{9} + y$ 0 **33.** $y + (-3) = -2.5$ 0.5

34. $r + (-3) = 4$ 7 **35.** $t + \left(-5\frac{1}{4}\right) = 5$ $10\frac{1}{4}$ **36.** $-7 + s = -1$ 6

B *Solve for **x** and check.*

37. $181 = x + 92$ 89 **38.** $-333 = 177 + x$ -510 **39.** $-122 = x + (-45)$ -77

40. $x + (-0.1) = 1$ 1.1 **41.** $x + 2 = -0.5$ -2.5 **42.** $-1.6 + x = 2$ 3.6

43. $x + (-1.3) = -1.5$ -0.2 **44.** $-4.1 = x + 1.1$ -5.2 **45.** $-5.9 = -3.1 + x$ -2.8

46. $x + \frac{1}{2} = \frac{1}{4}$ $-\frac{1}{4}$ **47.** $\frac{1}{3} + x = -\frac{1}{2}$ $-\frac{5}{6}$ **48.** $-\frac{1}{4} = -\frac{1}{5} + x$ $-\frac{1}{20}$

49. $\frac{1}{3} + x = \frac{1}{9}$ $-\frac{2}{9}$ **50.** $x + \frac{1}{5} = -\frac{1}{10}$ $-\frac{3}{10}$ **51.** $\frac{1}{6} = -\frac{1}{2} + x$ $\frac{2}{3}$

*Solve for **a** in terms of **b** and check.*

52. $a + 5 = b$ $a = b - 5$ **53.** $a + b = 10$ $a = 10 - b$ **54.** $a + (-b) = 15$ $a = b + 15$

55. $-20 + a = b$
$a = b + 20$

56. $-b + a = -25$
$a = b - 25$

57. $-30 = a + b$
$a = -b - 30$

EQUATIONS

89

ENRICHMENT ACTIVITY

Provide pairs of equations such as:

$$y = x + 3$$
$$z = y - 5$$

Have the students express z in terms of x. $z = x - 2$

Other pairs of equations might include:

$$y = 4x - 1$$
$$z = 3y + 2 \quad z = 12x - 1$$
$$y = 6 - 2x$$
$$z = 4y + 5 \quad z = 29 - 8x$$

Let the students invent other pairs of equations of this type. They can exchange papers and solve each other's exercises.

*Solve for **y** in terms of **x**, and check.*

58. $y + (-6) = x$
$y = x + 6$

59. $x + y = 18$
$y = 18 - x$

60. $x + (-5) = y + (-5)$
$y = x$

61. $x + y + 7 = 15$
$y = 8 - x$

62. $2x + y = 9$
$y = 9 - 2x$

63. $24 = x + y$
$y = 24 - x$

Solve the equation $p = a + b + c$ for the indicated variable.

64. Solve for a.
$a = p - b - c$

65. Solve for b.
$b = p - a - c$

66. Solve for c.
$c = p - a - b$

C *Name the property that justifies each step, **a** through **c**.*

67. $x + 15 = 42$

    a. $x + 15 + (-15) = 42 + (-15)$
        Add. prop. of equality
    b. $x + 0 = 42 + (-15)$
        Add. prop. of opposites
    c. $x = 27$
        Add. prop. of 0

68. $-12 + x = 71$

    a. $12 + (-12) + x = 12 + 71$
        Add. prop. of equality
    b. $0 + x = 12 + 71$
        Add. prop. of opposites
    c. $x = 83$
        Add. prop. of 0

Complete each step.

69. $2x + 3 = x + 4$

    a. $\underline{\ ?\ } + 2x + 3 = \underline{\ ?\ } + x + 4$ $-x; -x$
    b. $x + 3 = \underline{\ ?\ }$ 4
    c. $x + 3 + \underline{\ ?\ } = \underline{\ ?\ } + \underline{\ ?\ }$ $(-3); 4; (-3)$
    d. $x = \underline{\ ?\ }$ 1

70. $3 + 2x = 5 + 3x$

    a. $3 + 2x + \underline{\ ?\ } = 5 + 3x + \underline{\ ?\ }$ $(-2x); (-2x)$
    b. $\underline{\ ?\ } = 5 + x$ 3
    c. $\underline{\ ?\ } + \underline{\ ?\ } = \underline{\ ?\ } + 5 + x$ $-5; 3; -5$
    d. $\underline{\ ?\ } = x$ -2

EXTRA TOPIC

The Language of Sets

A **replacement set** is a set of numbers that may be used as replacements for a variable. Suppose that any real number may replace x in the equation $x^2 = 49$. The *replacement set* is the set of real numbers and the **solution set** is $\{7, -7\}$. The solution set must be a **subset,** or part, of the replacement set.

Example Solve, using the replacement set $\{-2, -1, 0, 1, 2\}$.

    a. $\dfrac{x}{2} + 5 = 4$ The solution is -2, the solution set is $\{-2\}$.

    b. $|2x| = 2$ The solutions are 1 and -1, the solution set is $\{1, -1\}$.

    c. $3x = 15$ There is no solution. The solution set is the *empty set*.

    The **empty set** is a set with no members, and is denoted by $\emptyset$ or $\{\}$.

Find the solution set if the replacement set is $\{-8, -4, 0, 4, 8\}$.

1. $x + 6 = -2$ **2.** $3 + |x| = 7$ **3.** $x - 2 = 9$ **4.** $x^2 - 64 = 0$

Drawing a Sketch

Many problems are easier to solve when a sketch is drawn first.

PROBLEM A certain rectangular paper, folded in half, forms a square with a perimeter of n centimeters. Find the area of the rectangle.

STRATEGY Draw and label a picture to help visualize the problem.

 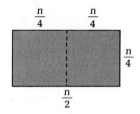

SOLUTION Multiply the length and width of the rectangle to find its area. Express the area in terms of n.

$$l = \frac{n}{4} + \frac{n}{4} = \frac{n}{2} \qquad\qquad A = lw$$

$$w = \frac{n}{4} \qquad\qquad\qquad A = \frac{n}{2} \cdot \frac{n}{4} = \frac{n^2}{8}$$

The area of the rectangle is $\frac{n^2}{8}$ cm^2.

Use the rectangle described above.

1. Find the area of the rectangle if the perimeter of the square is 12 cm. 18 cm²

2. If the area of the rectangle is 50 cm², find the perimeter of the square. 20 cm

*Try these problems, which are similar. Draw and label new sketches. Express all answers in terms of **n**.*

3. A square paper is folded in half. Without unfolding, it is folded again, in the same direction. Find the area of the resulting figure if the perimeter of the original square was n centimeters. $\frac{n^2}{64}$ cm²

4. When a square paper is folded in half, it forms a rectangle with a perimeter of n centimeters. Find the perimeter of the square. Find the area of the square.   Perimeter, $\frac{4}{3}n$ cm; area, $\frac{n^2}{9}$ cm²

Strategies for Problem Solving

Often, a diagram can help a person clarify a problem. With the aid of a diagram, the students may find the relationship of the data easier to understand, and they may be better able to write an appropriate equation for the problem.

The use of diagrams is encouraged as a problem-solving strategy throughout the book. For example, it is mentioned again in Lesson 3–8, on page 111.

LESSON NOTES

The opening paragraphs of this lesson review the use of the addition property of equality and extend its use to solving an equation of the form $x - a = b$. Be sure the students understand how $x - a = b$ is expressed as $x + (-a) - b$ and the addition property of equality is applied. Use the equation $n - 6 = -9$ to discuss this idea.

Then show how inverse operations can be used to solve equations of the form $x + a = b$ or $x - a = b$ (Examples 1 and 2). Note that the text deliberately uses the same equations presented near the top of the page.

After discussing Example 3, it may be useful to show that the same solution can be obtained *without* rewriting $n - (-6)$ as $n + 6$:

$$n - (-6) = -9$$
$$n - (-6) + (-6) = -9 + (-6)$$
$$n = -15$$

Example 5 presents an equation in which terms involving the variable are on both sides of the equal sign. Point out that it is helpful to subtract the term that has the smaller coefficient. Thus, in an equation such as $3y + 2 = 4y$, we can subtract $3y$ from both sides and obtain $2 = y$.

ALTERNATE EXAMPLES

1. Solve $n + 7 = 13$. Use subtraction, the inverse of the operation of addition. Subtract 7 to "undo" the addition of 7. $n = 6$
2. Solve $n - 3 = -7$. Use addition, the inverse of the operation of subtraction. Add 3 to "undo" the subtraction of 3. $n = -4$

3-3 Using Addition and Subtraction

OBJECTIVE

To solve equations by using the inverse operations of addition and subtraction.

You have used the addition property of equality to solve equations.

$$\mathbf{n + 6 = 9}$$
$$n + 6 + (-6) = 9 + (-6)$$
$$n = 3$$

The sum of a number n and 6 is equal to 9.
Add -6, the opposite of 6, to find n.

$$\mathbf{n - 6 = -9}$$
$$n + (-6) = -9$$
$$n + (-6) + 6 = -9 + 6$$
$$n = -3$$

The difference, n minus 6, is -9.
If you write $n - 6$ as $n + (-6)$, you can use the addition property here as well.

You may also use *inverse operations* to solve such equations. Adding a number and subtracting the same number are **inverse operations.** One "undoes" the other.

EXAMPLE 1 Solve $n + 6 = 9$. Use subtraction, the inverse of the operation of addition. Subtract 6 to "undo" the addition of 6.

$$n + 6 = 9$$
$$n + 6 - 6 = 9 - 6 \qquad \text{Subtract 6 from each side of the equation.}$$
$$n + 0 = 3$$
$$n = 3$$

Check $\qquad 3 + 6 \overset{?}{=} 9$
$\qquad\qquad 9 = 9 \ \checkmark$

The solution is 3.

EXAMPLE 2 Solve $n - 6 = -9$. Use addition, the inverse of the operation of subtraction. Add 6 to "undo" the subtraction of 6.

$$n - 6 = -9$$
$$n - 6 + 6 = -9 + 6 \qquad \text{Add 6 to each side of the equation.}$$
$$n + 0 = -3$$
$$n = -3$$

Check $\qquad -3 - 6 \overset{?}{=} -9$
$\qquad\qquad -9 = -9 \ \checkmark$

The solution is -3.

EXAMPLE 3 Solve $n - (-6) = -9$.

Rather than add (-6) to both sides, rewrite $n - (-6)$ as $n + 6$.

$$n - (-6) = -9$$
$$n + 6 = -9$$
$$n + 6 - 6 = -9 - 6 \qquad \text{Subtract 6 from each side.}$$
$$n = -15$$

To check, substitute -15 for n in $n - (-6) = -9$.

EXAMPLE 4 Use the inverse operation to solve each equation. Then check.

a. $\qquad \mathbf{0.4 + s = 3.2}$
$$0.4 - 0.4 + s = 3.2 - 0.4$$
$$s = 2.8$$

b. $\qquad t - \dfrac{1}{2} = 2\dfrac{3}{4}$
$$t - \frac{1}{2} + \frac{1}{2} = 2\frac{3}{4} + \frac{1}{2}$$
$$t = 3\frac{1}{4}$$

Check $\qquad 0.4 + 2.8 \stackrel{?}{=} 3.2$
$$3.2 = 3.2 \ \checkmark$$

$$3\frac{1}{4} - \frac{1}{2} \stackrel{?}{=} 2\frac{3}{4}$$
$$2\frac{3}{4} = 2\frac{3}{4} \ \checkmark$$

The solution is 2.8.

The solution is $3\frac{1}{4}$.

Some equations have variables on both sides of the equal sign.

EXAMPLE 5 Solve $2n = n + 4$.

Method I	**Method II**
Add $-n$ to each side.	Subtract n from each side.
$2n = n + 4$	$2n = n + 4$
$2n + (-n) = n + (-n) + 4$	$2n - n = n - n + 4$
$n = 0 + 4$	$n = 0 + 4$
$n = 4$	$n = 4$

Check $2(4) \stackrel{?}{=} 4 + 4$
$$8 = 8 \ \checkmark$$
The solution is 4.

CLASS EXERCISES

Solve for **x** and check.

1. $x - 3 = 7$ $\quad$ 10

2. $x - 6 = 4\dfrac{1}{2}$ $\quad$ $10\frac{1}{2}$

3. $x - 5 = -1$ $\qquad$ 4

4. $x + 7 = 1$ $\quad$ -6

5. $x + 5 = -3$ $\quad$ -8

6. $-4.1 + x = 12$ $\quad$ 16.1

EQUATIONS

93

3. Solve $n - (-3) = -1$. Rewrite $n - (-3)$ as $n + 3$. Then use subtraction. $\quad n = -4$

4. Use the inverse operation to solve each equation. Then check.
  a. $0.7 + x = 6.5$ $\quad x = 5.8$
  b. $y - \dfrac{3}{5} = 1\dfrac{1}{10}$ $\quad y = 1\dfrac{7}{10}$

5. Solve $5n = 4n + 8$. $\quad n = 8$

POSSIBLE ERROR

Watch for students who mistakenly combine inverse operations with adding the opposite. For example:

$$n - (-6) = -9$$
$$n - (-6) + 6 = -9 + 6$$
$$n = -3 \qquad \text{(incorrect)}$$

Be sure to discuss the mistakes that have been made. The step $n - (-6) + 6 = -9 + 6$ is *not* mathematically incorrect, but it does not result in an equation in the form $n = c$ (where c is some number). Point out that $n - (-6) + 6$ is $n + 12$, not n. Also make it clear that the inverse of subtracting -6 is adding -6.

DAILY QUIZ

Solve each equation and check.

1. $x - 7 = 3$ $\quad x = 10$
2. $x + 5 = 1$ $\quad x = -4$
3. $x - 10 = -10$ $\quad x = 0$
4. $-5 = x + 3$ $\quad x = -8$
5. $x - (-7) = 12$ $\quad x = 5$

7. $-15 = x + 1$ -16 **8.** $x - 6 = -13$ -7 **9.** $-4 = x - 7$ 3

10. $x - 15 = -7$ 8 **11.** $x - (-4) = 9$ 5 **12.** $x - (-12) = 20$ 8

13. $10 = x - 3$ 13 **14.** $9 = x + 4\frac{3}{8}$ $4\frac{5}{8}$ **15.** $x - 1 = 0.5$ 1.5

EXERCISES

A   *Solve each equation and check.*

1. $x - 5 = 1$ 6 **2.** $x - 7 = 7$ 14 **3.** $x - 9 = 11$ 20

4. $x + 3 = 6$ 3 **5.** $6 + x = -19$ -25 **6.** $5 = x + 13$ -8

7. $x - 8 = -8$ 0 **8.** $x - 6 = -4$ 2 **9.** $x - 4 = -5$ -1

10. $-3 = x + 1$ -4 **11.** $x - 8\frac{1}{2} = 0$ $8\frac{1}{2}$ **12.** $x - \left(-8\frac{1}{3}\right) = 0$ $-8\frac{1}{3}$

13. $n - 5 = 10$ 15 **14.** $n - (-2) = -1$ -3 **15.** $n - 2 = -1$ 1

16. $n + 5 = 15$ 10 **17.** $1 + n = -4$ -5 **18.** $6 = n + 12$ -6

19. $-5 = n + 3$ -8 **20.** $n + 5 = 0$ -5 **21.** $n + 0.5 = 1.5$ 1.0

22. $y + 7 = 3\frac{3}{4}$ $-3\frac{1}{4}$ **23.** $2 + y = 8$ 6 **24.** $11 = y + 5$ 6

25. $4 + y = 4$ 0 **26.** $y + (-4) = 3$ 7 **27.** $y - 5 = 5.8$ 10.8

28. $14 = y - 4$ 18 **29.** $-4 + y = 9$ 13 **30.** $-5 + y = -4$ 1

31. $9 = a - 12$ 21 **32.** $1 = 8 + t$ -7 **33.** $-2 + z = -5$ -3

34. $b - 1 = -7$ -6 **35.** $-2 = r + 6$ -8 **36.** $0 = y - 2$ 2

B   **37.** $-4 = y - 3$ -1 **38.** $12.7 = y + 35.0$ -22.3 **39.** $-21.4 = 13.3 + y$ -34.7

40. $x - 0.54 = 1.42$ 1.96 **41.** $x - 1.5 = -1.3$ 0.2 **42.** $-3.4 = x + 2.2$ -5.6

43. $\frac{1}{6} + n = -\frac{2}{3}$ $-\frac{5}{6}$ **44.** $n + \frac{1}{4} = \frac{1}{2}$ $\frac{1}{4}$ **45.** $\frac{1}{3} + y = \frac{1}{2}$ $\frac{1}{6}$

46. $-4 = x + 2\frac{2}{3}$ $-6\frac{2}{3}$ **47.** $-\frac{1}{2} + x = -\frac{1}{3}$ $\frac{1}{6}$ **48.** $-\frac{1}{3} = -\frac{1}{4} + x$ $-\frac{1}{12}$

Use the given information to write an equation. Then solve it and answer the question.

49. A coat costs $174.95. With the sales tax, *t*, the total cost is $187.25. How much is the sales tax? $174.95 + t = 187.25$; $12.30

50. The delivery charge, x dollars, is added to $187.25, giving a total cost of $192.50. How much is the delivery charge? $x + 187.25 = 192.50$; $5.25

94

ENRICHMENT ACTIVITY

Have the students solve for *c* in terms of *a*, *b*, and *d*:

$a = b + c - d$
$c = a - b + d$

$-a = -b + c + d$
$c = b - a - d$

$a + b = b + c - d$
$c = a + d$

$a + 2b - 3d = -d + c + b$
$c = a + b - 2d$

Solve for **s**.

51. $s + 8 = p$
$s = p - 8$

52. $s - 2 = p$
$s = p + 2$

53. $s + p = 4$
$s = 4 - p$

54. $s + p = 0$
$s = -p$

Solve and check.

55. $3n = 2n - 18$ -18 **56.** $7p = 6p + 17$ 17 **57.** $3 + 4y = 5y$ 3

C

Solve and check.

58. $6x - 9 - 2x = 12 + 3x$ 21 **59.** $7 - 4x + 6 = x + 20 - 6x$ 7

60. $2 + 8x + 59 + 2x = 30 - x - 2 + 10x$ -33

61. $-x + 9 - 7x - 25 = -10x + 25 + 3x - 48$ 7

*62. Karin bought 3 cans of corn and paid 26¢ less than Maryanne, who bought 4 cans of corn but got a 12¢ coupon discount. What was the price for 1 can of corn?   38¢

CHECKPOINT

Checkpoint

Students may check their answers with those given in the back of their books.

Translate each sentence into an equation. Use the variable **x**.

1. 17 more than some number is equal to 29. $x + 17 = 29$

2. 12 less than some number is equal to 10. $x - 12 = 10$

3. Some number added to 3 is equal to -2. $3 + x = -2$

4. 6 less some number is equal to 8. $6 - x = 8$

Express each equation in words.

5. $3n = 18$
Three times some number is equal to 18.

6. $2n + 5 = 16$
Five more than twice a number is equal to 16.

7. $4(n + 2) = 10$
Four times the sum of n and 2 is equal to 10.

Solve and check.

8. $n + (-8) = 3$ 11 **9.** $-6 + n = 1.8$ 7.8 **10.** $n - 5.4 = 0$ 5.4

11. $x - (-2.3) = 0$ -2.3 **12.** $26 = x + 11$ 15 **13.** $y - 3 = -11$ -8

14. $\frac{1}{4} + n = \frac{3}{8}$ $\frac{1}{8}$ **15.** $-\frac{1}{3} + x = \frac{1}{6}$ $\frac{1}{2}$ **16.** $x - \frac{2}{3} = -\frac{5}{6}$ $-\frac{1}{6}$

Use an equation to find the number. Then check your answer.

17. 13 subtracted from some number is equal to 9. $x - 13 = 9$; 22

18. The sum of 11 and some number is equal to 4. $11 + x = 4$; -7

19. 1 is the sum when -8 is added to some number. $1 = x + (-8)$; 9

20. 3 is the result when -8 is subtracted from some number. $3 = x - (-8)$; -5

EQUATIONS

95

Find the missing numbers.

1. $\frac{3}{5} \cdot n = 1$ $\frac{5}{3}$ **2.** $4 \cdot n = 1$ $\frac{1}{4}$

3. $-8 \cdot n = 1$ $-\frac{1}{8}$ **4.** $-\frac{1}{3} \cdot n = 1$
-3

5. What do we call two numbers whose product is 1?   Reciprocals

LESSON NOTES

To illustrate the multiplication property of equality, you can write $8x = 24$ on the chalkboard, then multiply both sides by $\frac{1}{2}, \frac{1}{4},$ and $\frac{1}{8},$ and simplify.

$$8x = 24$$
$$\frac{1}{2}(8x) = \frac{1}{2}(24) \;\rightarrow\; 4x = 12$$
$$\frac{1}{4}(8x) = \frac{1}{4}(24) \;\rightarrow\; 2x = 6$$
$$\frac{1}{8}(8x) = \frac{1}{8}(24) \;\rightarrow\; x = 3$$

Students should readily see that the solution to each equation is 3. The equations $8x = 24$, $4x = 12$, $2x = 6$, and $x = 3$ are equivalent.

Use Example 1 to emphasize this important point: our goal is to have the variable (with coefficient 1) alone on one side of the equal sign, so we multiply by the reciprocal of the coefficient of the variable in the given equation. In Example 1b and 1d, be sure the students understand why we multiply by $-\frac{1}{6}$ and $-\frac{8}{5}\Big($not $\frac{1}{6}$ and $\frac{8}{5}\Big)$. In Example 1e, you may need to remind students that to find the reciprocal of a mixed number such as $2\frac{1}{2}$, we first express $2\frac{1}{2}$ as $\frac{5}{2}$; then the reciprocal is easily named.

In Example 3b, some students may suggest an alternate approach: "There is no need to multiply by -1. We can just think: If the opposite of x is 17, then x is -17." This approach is acceptable; it shows understanding of the meaning of $-x$.

3-4   Multiplication Property of Equality

OBJECTIVE

To solve equations of the forms $ax = c$ and $\frac{a}{b}x = c$ by using reciprocals.

Len has 85 cents in his pocket.

All of the coins are nickels.
How many nickels are there?

n	The number of nickels
$5n$	The value of the nickels, in cents
$5n = 85$	The value of the nickels is 85¢.

To solve the equation $5n = 85$, multiply each side by $\frac{1}{5}$, the reciprocal of 5. This leads to an equivalent equation that has n alone on one side of the equal sign.

$$5n = 85$$
$$\frac{1}{5}(5n) = \frac{1}{5}(85) \qquad \text{Multiply each side by } \tfrac{1}{5}.$$
$$1n = 17$$
$$n = 17$$

Check the value of n in the problem. Are 17 nickels worth 85 cents? Len has 17 nickels.

If you multiply each side of an equation by the same nonzero number, the new equation is equivalent to the original equation. This is possible because of the following property.

Multiplication Property of Equality

Let a, b, and c be any numbers.

If $a = b$, then $ac = bc$.

CHAPTER 3

EXAMPLE 1   State how to use the multiplication property of equality to solve each equation.

    a.   **7n = 56**   Multiply each side by $\frac{1}{7}$.

    b. **−6n = 51**   Multiply each side by $-\frac{1}{6}$.

    c.   **52 = $\frac{1}{4}$n**   Multiply each side by 4.

    d. **$-\frac{5}{8}$n = 36**   Multiply each side by $-\frac{8}{5}$.

    e. **$2\frac{1}{2}$n = 20**   Multiply each side by $\frac{2}{5}$.

When an equation is in the form $ax = b$, you can solve for x by multiplying each side by the reciprocal of a.

EXAMPLE 2   Solve the equation $\frac{3}{4}n = 15$ and check.

$$\frac{3}{4}n = 15 \qquad \text{The coefficient of } n \text{ is } \frac{3}{4}.$$

$$\frac{4}{3}\left(\frac{3}{4}n\right) = \frac{4}{3}(15) \qquad \text{Multiply each side by } \frac{4}{3}, \text{ the reciprocal of } \frac{3}{4}.$$

$$1(n) = 20$$

$$n = 20$$

Check $\frac{3}{4}(20) \overset{?}{=} 15$

             $15 = 15$ ✔

The solution is 20.

EXAMPLE 3   Solve for x and check.

    a.   **−2x = −8**   **b.**   **−x = 17**

    Multiply each side by $-\frac{1}{2}$.   Multiply each side by −1.

    $\left(-\frac{1}{2}\right)(-2x) = \left(-\frac{1}{2}\right)(-8)$ $(-1)(-x) = (-1)(17)$

             $x = 4$ $x = -17$

Check $-2(4) \overset{?}{=} -8$ $-(-17) \overset{?}{=} 17$

             $-8 = -8$ ✔ $17 = 17$ ✔

    The solution is 4.   The solution is −17.

EQUATIONS   **97**

ALTERNATE EXAMPLES

1. State how to use the multiplication property of equality to solve each equation.
    a. $6n = -42$
    b. $-15n = 105$
    c. $2 = -5n$
    d. $\frac{3}{7}n = 27$
    e. $1\frac{1}{4}n = 10$

    a. Multiply each side by $\frac{1}{6}$.

    b. Multiply each side by $-\frac{1}{15}$.

    c. Multiply each side by $-\frac{1}{5}$.

    d. Multiply each side by $\frac{7}{3}$.

    e. Multiply each side by $\frac{4}{5}$.

2. Solve the equation $\frac{3}{7}n = 21$, and check. $n = 49$

3. Solve for x, and check.
    a. $-4x = -1$ **b.** $-x = 0.5$
        $x = \frac{1}{4}$ $x = -0.5$

4. Solve for x, and check.

a. $\frac{2}{5}x = -3$ **b.** $-9x = 5$

$x = -\frac{15}{2}$ $x = -\frac{5}{9}$

POSSIBLE ERROR

Some students persist in forgetting that the reciprocal of a negative number is negative. Thus, in solving $-7x = 28$, they may multiply both sides by $\frac{1}{7}$ and unthinkingly write $x = 4$ as the resulting equation. Point out that if they multiply by $\frac{1}{7}$, the resulting equation is $-x = 4$, which in turn can be written as the equivalent equation $x = -4$. Emphasize that if a coefficient is negative, its reciprocal is negative, and multiplying by the reciprocal gives the solution $x = c$ in one step.

DAILY QUIZ

Solve each equation, and check.

1. $9x = 27$ **2.** $-11x = -44$
     $x = 3$ $x = 4$

3. $\frac{1}{7}x = 2$ **4.** $\frac{2}{3}x = -10$
     $x = 14$ $x = -15$

5. $-\frac{3}{4}x = 9$ $x = -12$

ASSIGNMENT GUIDE
(pages 98–99)

Minimum course: 1–35 odd
Average course: 1–49 odd
Maximum course: 13–59 odd

ADDITIONAL ANSWERS

Exercises

	Mult. by	Sol.		Mult. by	Sol.
1.	$\frac{1}{7}$	3	**2.**	$\frac{1}{2}$	25

[Answers continue on page 99.]

EXAMPLE 4   Solve for x and check.

a. $\frac{2}{3}x = -3$

$$\frac{3}{2}\left(\frac{2}{3}x\right) = \frac{3}{2}(-3)$$

$$x = -\frac{9}{2}$$

b. $-5x = 2$

$$\left(-\frac{1}{5}\right)(-5x) = \left(-\frac{1}{5}\right)(2)$$

$$x = -\frac{2}{5}$$

Check $\frac{2}{3}\left(-\frac{9}{2}\right) \stackrel{?}{=} -3$

$-3 = -3$ ✔

$-5\left(-\frac{2}{5}\right) \stackrel{?}{=} 2$

$2 = 2$ ✔

The solution is $-\frac{9}{2}$.

The solution is $-\frac{2}{5}$.

CLASS EXERCISES

State how to use the multiplication property of equality to solve each equation.

1. $4x = 20$
Mult. by $\frac{1}{4}$.

2. $-3x = 15$
Mult. by $-\frac{1}{3}$.

3. $-2x = 1$
Mult. by $-\frac{1}{2}$.

4. $25 = 5x$
Mult. by $\frac{1}{5}$.

5. $\frac{1}{2}x = -6$
Mult. by 2.

6. $\frac{2}{3}x = \frac{1}{2}$
Mult. by $\frac{3}{2}$.

7. $-\frac{3}{5}x = 9$
Mult. by $-\frac{5}{3}$.

8. $42 = -1\frac{1}{3}x$
Mult. by $-\frac{3}{4}$.

*Solve for **x** and check.*

9. $4x = 12$ 3

10. $7x = -21$ -3

11. $-2x = -6$ 3

12. $51 = -3x$ -17

13. $\frac{3}{4}x = 1$ $\frac{4}{3}$

14. $\frac{2}{5}x = -4$ -10

15. $-1 = \frac{3}{2}x$ $-\frac{2}{3}$

16. $1\frac{2}{3}x = 35$ 21

EXERCISES

A   *State how to use the multiplication property of equality to solve each equation. Then solve and check.*

1. $7x = 21$

2. $2x = 50$

3. $4x = 30$

4. $3x = 39$

5. $9x = 0$

6. $-11x = 11$

7. $5x = -55$

8. $-7x = 28$

9. $-12x = -60$

10. $-8x = -24$

11. $-42 = 6x$

12. $20 = -x$

13. $16x = 96$

14. $-6x = 120$

15. $4x = -52$

16. $-13x = 273$

17. $-21x = -441$

18. $45 = 3x$

19. $-200 = 40y$

20. $13y = -156$

21. $-8 = 64y$

22. $\frac{1}{4}y = 24$

23. $1\frac{1}{7}y = 56$

24. $\frac{1}{2}y = -18$

25. $-3y = 4$

26. $-5y = 8$

27. $-12y = -18$

28. $15a = 9$

29. $8a = -720$

30. $-6a = -45$

31. $81 = -900a$

32. $-200 = 5a$

B

Solve and check.

33. $-120 = -15a$ ___8___ **34.** $-121 = 11x$ ___−11___ **35.** $340 = -17x$ ___−20___ **36.** $-600 = 15x$ ___−40___

37. $\frac{1}{4}x = 16$ ___64___ **38.** $\frac{2}{3}x = -10$ ___−15___ **39.** $-1\frac{3}{5}x = 40$ ___−25___ **40.** $\frac{1}{2}x = -\frac{3}{4}$ ___$-\frac{3}{2}$___

41. $-\frac{9}{10}x = \frac{1}{3}$ ___$-\frac{10}{27}$___ **42.** $-\frac{4}{5}x = -\frac{4}{5}$ ___1___ **43.** $5x = 0.1$ ___0.02___ **44.** $2x = -1.6$ ___−0.8___

45. $-4n = -8.8$ ___2.2___ **46.** $\frac{2}{3}n = -3$ ___$-\frac{9}{2}$___ **47.** $-50 = \frac{1}{2}n$ ___−100___ **48.** $-2.5n = -10$ ___4___

C

*Combine like terms. Then solve for **n**.*

49. $n + n = -6$ ___−3___ **50.** $2n + n = 30$ ___10___ **51.** $-5n + 2n = 6$ ___−2___

52. $-2(3n) + 15n = 18$ ___2___ **53.** $3n + 2n + n = 3$ ___$\frac{1}{2}$___ **54.** $-42 = -10n + 3n$ ___6___

55. $-30 = -(2n + 3n)$ ___6___ **56.** $2(n + 3n) = -24$ ___−3___ **57.** $n - (3n + n) = -1$ ___$\frac{1}{3}$___

*Name the property that justifies each step, **a** through **d**.*

58. $5x = 65$

   a. $\frac{1}{5}(5x) = \frac{1}{5}(65)$ Mult. prop. of equality

   b. $\left(\frac{1}{5} \cdot 5\right)x = \frac{1}{5}(65)$ Assoc. prop. of mult.

   c. $1x = \frac{1}{5}(65)$ Def. of reciprocals

   d. $x = 13$ Mult. property of 1

59. $54 = -6x$

   a. $-\frac{1}{6}(54) = -\frac{1}{6}(-6x)$ Mult. prop. of equality

   b. $-\frac{1}{6}(54) = \left[-\frac{1}{6}(-6)\right]x$ Assoc. prop. of mult.

   c. $-\frac{1}{6}(54) = 1x$ Def. of reciprocals

   d. $-9 = x$ Mult. property of 1

USING THE CALCULATOR

Patterns and Predictions

Use a calculator to find the answers. Look for a pattern. Then make the prediction without doing any calculation.

1. $9 \times 3 = $ _?_ 27 $99 \times 3 = $ _?_ 297 $999 \times 3 = $ _?_ 2997 $9999 \times 3 = $ _?_ 29,997

   Prediction: $99,999,999 \times 3 = $ _?_ 299,999,997

2. $1 + (1 \times 8) = $ _?_ 9 $2 + (12 \times 8) = $ _?_ 98 $3 + (123 \times 8) = $ _?_ 987

   Prediction: $9 + (123,456,789 \times 8) = $ _?_ 987,654,321

3. $[(1 \times 9) + 2]^2 = $ _?_ 121 $[(12 \times 9) + 3]^2 = $ _?_ 12,321 $[(123 \times 9) + 4]^2 = $ _?_ 1,234,321

   Prediction: $[(12,345,678 \times 9) + 9]^2 = $ _?_ 12,345,678,987,654,321

EQUATIONS

99

Divide.

1. $\dfrac{-54}{-9}$ 6   2. $\dfrac{-24}{3}$ -8 3. $\dfrac{8}{-4}$ -2

LESSON NOTES

The opening paragraphs of this lesson review the use of the multiplication property of equality and extend its use to solving an equation of the form $\dfrac{x}{a} = c$. Be sure students understand how $\dfrac{x}{a} = c$ is expressed as $\dfrac{1}{a}x = c$ and the multiplication property of equality is applied. Use the equation $\dfrac{n}{3} = 13$ when discussing this idea.

Then discuss how inverse operations are used to solve equations of the form $ax = c$ and $\dfrac{x}{a} = c$ (Examples 1 and 2).

Example 3 provides illustrations that involve negative numbers. Note that in Example 3b the variable is on the right side of the equal sign; give special attention to this example to be sure students understand why we multiply both sides by -10, not by 5.

You might also wish to discuss an equation such as $\dfrac{n}{1.4} = 8$ so the students can see that the procedure is the same even if the variable is divided by a number that is not an integer.

ALTERNATE EXAMPLES

1. Solve $7x = -56$. Use division, the inverse of the operation of multiplication. Divide by 7 to "undo" multiplication by 7.
   $x = -8$
2. Solve $\dfrac{n}{9} = 8$. Use multiplication, the inverse of the operation of division. Multiply by 9 to "undo" the division by 9. $n = 72$

3-5 Using Multiplication and Division

OBJECTIVE

To solve equations by using the inverse operations of multiplication and division.

You have used the multiplication property of equality to solve equations.

$$4x = -24 \qquad \text{The product of 4 and a number } x \text{ is } -24.$$

$$\frac{1}{4}\left(4x\right) = \frac{1}{4}(-24) \qquad \text{To find } x \text{, multiply by } \tfrac{1}{4}, \text{ the reciprocal of 4.}$$

$$x = -6$$

$$\frac{n}{3} = 13 \qquad \text{The quotient, } n \text{ divided by 3, is 13.}$$

$$\frac{1}{3}n = 13 \qquad \text{If you rewrite } \tfrac{n}{3} \text{ as } \tfrac{1}{3}n, \text{ you can use the}$$
$$\text{multiplication property here as well.}$$

$$3\left(\frac{1}{3}n\right) = 3(13)$$

$$n = 39$$

You can also use inverse operations to find the solutions. Multiplying by a number and dividing by the same number are *inverse operations*. One "undoes" the other.

EXAMPLE 1   Solve $4x = -24$. Use division, the inverse of the operation of multiplication. Divide by 4 to "undo" multiplication by 4.

$$4x = -24$$

$$\frac{4x}{4} = \frac{-24}{4} \qquad \text{Divide each side of the equation by 4.}$$

$$1x = -6$$

$$x = -6$$

EXAMPLE 2   Solve $\dfrac{n}{3} = 13$. Use multiplication, the inverse of the operation of division. Multiply by 3 to "undo" the division by 3.

$$\frac{n}{3} = 13$$

$$3\left(\frac{n}{3}\right) = 3(13) \qquad \text{Multiply each side of the equation by 3.}$$

$$n = 39$$

EXAMPLE 3 Use the inverse operation to solve each equation. Then check.

a. $\dfrac{n}{4} = -12$

$4\left(\dfrac{n}{4}\right) = 4(-12)$

$n = -48$

Check $\dfrac{-48}{4} \overset{?}{=} -12$

$-12 = -12$ ✔

The solution is -48.

b. $\dfrac{1}{5} = \dfrac{n}{-10}$

$-10\left(\dfrac{1}{5}\right) = -10\left(\dfrac{n}{-10}\right)$

$-2 = n$

$\dfrac{1}{5} \overset{?}{=} \dfrac{-2}{-10}$

$\dfrac{1}{5} = \dfrac{1}{5}$ ✔

The solution is -2.

c. $-5x = -2$

$\dfrac{-5x}{-5} = \dfrac{-2}{-5}$

$x = \dfrac{2}{5}$

$-5\left(\dfrac{2}{5}\right) \overset{?}{=} -2$

$-2 = -2$ ✔

The solution is $\dfrac{2}{5}$.

CLASS EXERCISES

*Solve for **x** and check.*

1. $\dfrac{x}{4} = 4$ 16   **2.** $\dfrac{x}{6} = 9$ 54   **3.** $\dfrac{x}{3} = -7$ -21 **4.** $\dfrac{x}{4} = 100$ 400

5. $\dfrac{x}{-20} = 6$ -120 **6.** $\dfrac{x}{-3} = -2$ 6   **7.** $8x = -16$ -2 **8.** $5x = 12$ $\dfrac{12}{5}$

9. $7x = 420$ 60   **10.** $36 = -4x$ -9 **11.** $2 = 5x$ $\dfrac{2}{5}$ **12.** $4x = 18$ $\dfrac{9}{2}$

Solve each equation by two methods, multiplication and division.

13. $-3x = -21$ 7   **14.** $-6x = 1$ $-\dfrac{1}{6}$ **15.** $60x = 9$ $\dfrac{3}{20}$ **16.** $-4x = -30$ $\dfrac{15}{2}$

17. $3x = -1$ $-\dfrac{1}{3}$ **18.** $-6x = -3$ $\dfrac{1}{2}$ **19.** $-15 = 3x$ -5 **20.** $4 = -5x$ $-\dfrac{4}{5}$

EXERCISES

A *Solve and check.*

1. $\dfrac{y}{5} = 7$ 35   **2.** $\dfrac{y}{9} = 5$ 45   **3.** $\dfrac{y}{7} = 6$ 42   **4.** $\dfrac{y}{7} = -7$ -49

5. $\dfrac{y}{-5} = 6$ -30 **6.** $\dfrac{y}{-5} = -8$ 40   **7.** $\dfrac{y}{-6} = -8$ 48   **8.** $\dfrac{y}{9} = -6$ -54

9. $\dfrac{y}{-9} = 8$ -72 **10.** $\dfrac{y}{-6} = 20$ -120 **11.** $\dfrac{y}{-7} = -20$ 140   **12.** $\dfrac{y}{31} = -7$ -217

Solve each equation by two methods, multiplication and division.

13. $7w = -42$ -6 **14.** $-7w = 49$ -7 **15.** $-5a = -30$ 6   **16.** $-5w = 40$ -8

17. $-6t = -54$ 9   **18.** $6t = -48$ -8 **19.** $8t = 1$ $\dfrac{1}{8}$ **20.** $3t = -5$ $-\dfrac{5}{3}$

Solve each equation.

21. $\dfrac{x}{8} = 31$ 248   **22.** $13 = \dfrac{x}{9}$ 117   **23.** $\dfrac{x}{16} = 8$ 128   **24.** $\dfrac{x}{4} = -59$ -236

EQUATIONS

EXTRA PRACTICE, page 511–512

ALTERNATE EXAMPLE

3. Use the inverse operation to solve each equation. Then check.

a. $\dfrac{n}{3} = -8$ **b.** $\dfrac{3}{7} = \dfrac{n}{-21}$

$n = -24$ $n = -9$

c. $-3x = -7$

$x = \dfrac{7}{3}$

POSSIBLE ERROR

In solving an equation such as $-1.6 = -0.8t$, some students will divide both sides by -1.6. To help students avoid dividing by the wrong number, stress that the coefficient of the variable is used as the divisor.

DAILY QUIZ

Solve each equation, and check.

1. $\dfrac{y}{7} = 9$ $y = 63$

2. $\dfrac{y}{-3} = 6$ $y = -18$

3. $\dfrac{x}{-8} = -10$ $x = 80$

4. $0.7x = 2.1$ $x = 3$

5. $7.5 = -1.5x$ $x = -5$

ASSIGNMENT GUIDE
(pages 101–102)

Minimum course: 1–39 odd, 53, 57, 65, 71

Average course: 13–75 odd

Maximum course: 21–83 odd

25. $\dfrac{x}{-4} = 13$ -52 **26.** $-5 = \dfrac{x}{-12}$ 60 **27.** $-6x = 120$ -20 **28.** $7x = -14$ -2

29. $21 = 7x$ 3 **30.** $\dfrac{x}{-12} = 13$ -156 **31.** $-8x = -248$ 31 **32.** $\dfrac{x}{-14} = 3$ -42

33. $-8y = 128$ -16 **34.** $144 = 9y$ 16 **35.** $4y = 36$ 9 **36.** $-4y = 236$ -59

37. $\dfrac{y}{3} = 45$ 135 **38.** $\dfrac{y}{35} = -3$ -105 **39.** $\dfrac{y}{-13} = 5$ -65 **40.** $\dfrac{y}{39} = -1$ -39

41. $16 = 12y$ $\dfrac{4}{3}$ **42.** $29y = 87$ 3 **43.** $-12y = 156$ -13 **44.** $35y = -140$ -4

45. $\dfrac{s}{3} = -87$ -261 **46.** $5 = \dfrac{s}{-17}$ -85 **47.** $\dfrac{s}{59} = 1$ 59 **48.** $\dfrac{s}{76} = -13$ -988

49. $17t = -238$ -14 **50.** $-741 = 39t$ -19 **51.** $-49t = 931$ -19 **52.** $-1t = 542$ -542

B

53. $\dfrac{x}{4} = \dfrac{1}{2}$ 2 **54.** $\dfrac{x}{-6} = \dfrac{1}{3}$ -2 **55.** $\dfrac{x}{8} = -\dfrac{1}{4}$ -2 **56.** $\dfrac{1}{2} = \dfrac{x}{-8}$ -4

57. $-2y = \dfrac{1}{4}$ $-\dfrac{1}{8}$ **58.** $3y = \dfrac{1}{5}$ $\dfrac{1}{15}$ **59.** $\dfrac{y}{-9} = -1.7$ 15.3 **60.** $\dfrac{y}{7} = -1.3$ -9.1

61. $\dfrac{a}{-12} = 2.4$ -28.8 **62.** $-3.4 = \dfrac{a}{1.5}$ -5.1 **63.** $\dfrac{n}{1.2} = -3.1$ -3.72 **64.** $\dfrac{n}{-1.7} = 4.2$ -7.14

65. $0.7r = -1.4$ -2 **66.** $-1.6 = -0.8t$ 2 **67.** $-1.5x = 4.5$ -3

68. $3.2 = -0.4y$ -8 **69.** $-0.6v = 7.2$ -12 **70.** $-2.4 = -0.8w$ 3

Write and solve an equation to find each answer.

71. The product of a certain number x and 3.4 is 105.4. Find x. $3.4x = 105.4;\ 31$

72. If y is divided by 1.7, the quotient equals 9. Find y. $\dfrac{y}{1.7} = 9;\ 15.3$

73. Solve for h: $A = bh$ $h = \dfrac{A}{b}$ **74.** Solve for l: $A = lw$ $l = \dfrac{A}{w}$

75. Solve for d: $C = \pi d$ $d = \dfrac{C}{\pi}$ **76.** Solve for h: $V = lwh$ $h = \dfrac{V}{lw}$

77. Solve for t: $d = rt$ $t = \dfrac{d}{r}$ **78.** Solve for r: $d = rt$ $r = \dfrac{d}{t}$

79. Solve for b: $a = \dfrac{b}{c}$ $b = ac$ **80.** Solve for c: $a = \dfrac{b}{c}$ $c = \dfrac{b}{a}$

C

Use two properties of equality to solve each equation.

81. $2x - 5x = 7 - x$ $-\dfrac{7}{2}$ **82.** $12 - 3x = 2x - 3$ 3

83. $11x - 42 - 72 - 8x$ 6 **84.** $15 - 12x + 2 = 6x + 5 - 2x$ $\dfrac{3}{4}$

*85. According to Einstein's Theory of Relativity, a quantity of energy, E, can be considered to have a mass, m, equal to E divided by the square of c, where c represents the speed of light. Write an equation for m in terms of E and c. Then solve for E. $m = \dfrac{E}{c^2};\ E = mc^2$

102

3-6 Using Two Properties of Equality

Simplify.
1. $2n + 3 - 3$ $2n$
2. $5x - 6 + 6$ $5x$
3. $4\left(\dfrac{y}{4}\right)$ y
4. $\dfrac{1}{3}(3x)$ x

OBJECTIVE

To write an equation by following a series of directions, and then to solve the equation by reversing the steps.

The following directions lead to an equation.

Start with n.   n
Multiply by 2.   2n
    Add 9.   2n + 9
The result is equal to 15. $2n + 9 = 15$

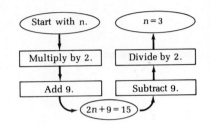

To solve the equation $2n + 9 = 15$, simply undo the directions. Work in the reverse order.

First subtract 9, which is the inverse of adding 9.

Then divide by 2, which is the inverse of multiplying by 2.

$$2n + 9 = 15$$
$$2n + 9 - 9 = 15 - 9$$
$$2n = 6$$
$$\frac{2n}{2} = \frac{6}{2}$$
$$n = 3$$

LESSON NOTES

In this lesson students learn how to solve equations of the form $ax + b = c$. Use the introductory material involving $2n + 9 = 15$ to emphasize the importance of understanding the order of operations used in constructing the equation; once this order is understood, the reverse order can be used for applying the inverse operations.

Note that the text carefully uses Examples 1 and 2 to develop the procedure for using inverse operations in solving $ax + b = c$. Then, in Examples 3 and 4, the text recalls the addition property of equality and the multiplication property of equality and uses them to solve equations of the same type. Actually, even in the earlier examples, the two properties were used, since the addition property can be thought of as including addition and subtraction, and the multiplication property can be thought of as including multiplication and division.

EXAMPLE 1   Start with n. Multiply by 3, then add 5. The result is 44. Write and then solve the corresponding equation.

Write the equation.
Start with n.   n
Multiply by 3.   3n
    Add 5.   3n + 5
The result is 44. $3n + 5 = 44$

Solve the equation.
$$3n + 5 = 44$$
$$3n + 5 - 5 = 44 - 5 \qquad \text{Subtract 5 from each side.}$$
$$3n = 39$$
$$\frac{3n}{3} = \frac{39}{3} \qquad \text{Divide each side by 3.}$$
$$n = 13$$

Check $3(13) + 5 \overset{?}{=} 44$
$39 + 5 \overset{?}{=} 44$
$44 = 44 \; ✔$

Thus, the solution is 13.

ALTERNATE EXAMPLE

1. Start with n. Multiply by 7, then add 3. The result is 38. Write and then solve the corresponding equation. $7n + 3 = 38$; $n = 5$

EQUATIONS

103

2. Start with x. Divide by 6, then subtract 3. The result is 0. Write and then solve the corresponding equation.
$\frac{x}{6} - 3 = 0;\ x = 18$

3. Solve the equation $9x + 7 = 52$, and check. $x = 5$

4. Solve $-3x + (-5) = 16$, and check. $x = -7$

POSSIBLE ERROR

As they work with two-step equations in this lesson, some students may develop the feeling that addition or subtraction is always used before multiplication or division. This is true for an equation of the form $ax + b = c$. However, in Lesson 3–7, many of the equations are *not* of the form $ax + b = c$, so addition or subtraction may not be applied first. Caution the students to avoid working mechanically. Encourage them to *think* about the order of operations implied in each equation *before* they begin to solve the equation.

EXAMPLE 2

Start with x. Divide by 5, then subtract 2. The result is 3. Write and then solve the corresponding equation.

Write the equation.

Start with x. x

Divide by 5. $\frac{x}{5}$

Subtract 2. $\frac{x}{5} - 2$

The result is 3. $\frac{x}{5} - 2 = 3$

Solve the equation.

$$\frac{x}{5} - 2 = 3$$
$$\frac{x}{5} - 2 + 2 = 3 + 2 \qquad \text{Add 2 to each side.}$$
$$\frac{x}{5} = 5$$
$$5\left(\frac{x}{5}\right) = 5(5) \qquad \text{Multiply each side by 5.}$$
$$x = 25$$

Check $\frac{25}{5} - 2 = 5 - 2 = 3$ The solution is 25.

Opposites and reciprocals are used to solve equations in the next examples. You may sometimes choose to use this method instead of inverse operations.

EXAMPLE 3

Solve the equation $3x + 1 = 7$ and check.

$$3x + 1 = 7$$
$$3x + 1 + (-1) = 7 + (-1) \qquad \text{Add } -1, \text{ the opposite of 1, to each side.}$$
$$3x = 6$$
$$\frac{1}{3}(3x) = \frac{1}{3}(6) \qquad \text{Multiply each side by } \frac{1}{3}, \text{ the reciprocal of 3.}$$
$$x = 2$$

Check $3(2) + 1 = 6 + 1 = 7$ The solution is 2.

EXAMPLE 4

Solve $-5x + (-2) = 18$.

$$-5x + (-2) = 18$$
$$-5x + (-2) + 2 = 18 + 2 \qquad \text{Add 2, the opposite of } -2.$$
$$-5x = 20$$
$$\left(-\frac{1}{5}\right)(-5x) = \left(-\frac{1}{5}\right)(20) \qquad \text{Multiply by } -\frac{1}{5}, \text{ the reciprocal of } -5.$$
$$x = -4$$

CLASS EXERCISES

Write as an equation.

1. Start with n. Multiply by 3. Then add 6. The result is 30. $3n + 6 = 30$

2. Start with n. Multiply by 5. Then subtract 15. The result is 40. $5n - 15 = 40$

3. Start with n. Divide by 6. Then add 4. The result is 10. $\frac{n}{6} + 4 = 10$

Solve each equation for x.

4. $2x + 5 = 9$ 2	5. $3x - 2 = 10$ 4	6. $5x + 7 = 2$ -1
7. $4x + 5 = -3$ -2	8. $9x - 4 = 104$ 12	9. $-14x + 2 = 30$ -2
10. $\frac{x}{3} + 7 = 15$ 24	11. $\frac{x}{2} + 5 = -1$ -12	12. $\frac{x}{5} - 3 = 9$ 60
13. $2x + 3\frac{5}{8} = 8\frac{5}{8}$ $2\frac{1}{2}$	14. $-8 = \frac{1}{2}x + 2$ -20	15. $\frac{3}{5}x - 2 = 13$ 25

EXERCISES

A

Write as an equation.

1. Start with a. Multiply by 5. Then add 3. The result is 28. $5a + 3 = 28$

2. Start with b. Multiply by 4. Then subtract 7. The result is 17. $4b - 7 = 17$

3. Start with c. Multiply by $2\frac{1}{2}$. Then add 6. The result is 31. $2\frac{1}{2}c + 6 = 31$

4. Start with d. Divide by 2. Then add 10. The result is 25. $\frac{d}{2} + 10 = 25$

5. Start with e. Divide by 3. Then subtract 7. The result is 12. $\frac{e}{3} - 7 = 12$

6. Start with f. Multiply by -4. Then subtract -3. The result is 7. $-4f - (-3) = 7$

Solve each equation. Check your answers.

7. $2x + 1 = 5$ 2	8. $3x + 4 = 16$ 4	9. $5x + 2 = -3$ -1
10. $4x + 7 = 35$ 7	11. $8x - 1 = 23$ 3	12. $6x - 5 = -11$ -1
13. $9 + 2x = 17$ 4	14. $5 + 5x = 55$ 10	15. $7x - 6 = 36$ 6
16. $2x + 4\frac{3}{5} = 10\frac{3}{5}$ 3	17. $8 = 2\frac{1}{3}x + 1$ 3	18. $-16 = 5x - 1$ -3

B

19. $-2x + 3 = -9$ 6	20. $-5x - 7 = 48$ -11	21. $0.5x - 7.5 = 10$ 35
22. $0.8x - 0.2 = 7$ 9	23. $2.6x + 8 = 60$ 20	24. $0.3 - 2.5x = 7.8$ -3
25. $-x + 4 = \frac{1}{2}$ $3\frac{1}{2}$	26. $\frac{x}{3} - 1 = 12$ 39	27. $\frac{2}{5}x + 4 = 10$ 15

EQUATIONS

EXTRA PRACTICE, page 512

Have the students write word problems whose solutions require the use of equations of the form $ax + b = c$ (or any of the types of equations studied earlier). Each student should solve the problems he or she has written. Then the students can exchange papers and solve the problems written by one of their classmates.

*Write as an equation. Then solve for **n** and check.*

28. 7 more than 3 times some number n is equal to 34. $3n + 7 = 34; 9$

29. 6 more than twice some number n is equal to 24. $2n + 6 = 24; 9$

30. 19 more than 3 times some number n is 100. $3n + 19 = 100; 27$

31. 9 less than 5 times some number n is 76. $5n - 9 = 76; 17$

32. 4 times some number n, less 25, is equal to 11. $4n - 25 = 11; 9$

*Write an equation and solve it. Use **x** as the variable.*

33. Double some number and add 18 to get 150. $2x + 18 = 150; 66$

34. Triple some number and subtract 9 to get 120. $3x - 9 = 120; 43$

35. Add 50 to twice some number to get 500. $2x + 50 = 500; 225$

36. Multiply a number by 12 and then subtract 40 to get 200. $12x - 40 = 200; 20$

37. Double some number and add 25 to get −5. $2x + 25 = -5; -15$

C

Simplify, solve, and check.

38. $3x + x + 2 = 10$ 2   39. $5x + 7 - 2x = 11$ $\frac{4}{3}$ 40. $-x + 4x + 4 = 16$ 4

41. $2x + 3 - 8x = 75$ −12   42. $x + 15 + 3x = -1$ −4   43. $36 = 2x - 9 + 7x$ 5

44. $2\frac{1}{2}x - x - \frac{1}{2} = \frac{1}{4}$ $\frac{1}{2}$ 45. $\frac{1}{2}x + 2x - 7 = 3$ 4   46. $\frac{1}{2}x + \frac{1}{3}x = \frac{1}{6}$ $\frac{1}{5}$

*Solve for **x**.*

47. $ax + b = c$ $x = \frac{c - b}{a}$ 48. $\frac{x}{a} - b = c$ $x = a(b + c)$ *49. $xa + b = cx$ $x = \frac{b}{c - a}$

CHALLENGE

A Choice of Solutions

These problems can be solved using arithmetic or algebra.

1. A store buys cans of soda at a wholesale price of 6 for 62¢ and sells them at a retail price of 10 for $2.70. How many cans must the store sell to realize a $10 profit?   60 cans

2. Suppose you sell your $500 microcomputer at a 10% profit. Six months later you buy it back at a 10% loss to the person who bought it from you. Have you gained, lost, or broken even as a result of these two transactions? If there is a gain or loss, what is the amount? $55 gain

106

CHAPTER 3

3-7 Solving More Equations

OBJECTIVES

To solve equations that first need to be simplified.
To compare alternate methods of solving equations.

Some equations should be simplified before the properties of equality are applied.

EXAMPLE 1 Solve the equation $4x - 5 + 2x + 3 = 7$. First, combine *like terms*.

$$4x - 5 + 2x + 3 = 7 \qquad \text{Combine } 4x \text{ and } 2x. \text{ Combine } -5 \text{ and } 3.$$
$$6x - 2 = 7$$
$$6x - 2 + 2 = 7 + 2 \qquad \text{Add 2 to each side.}$$
$$6x = 9$$
$$\frac{6x}{6} = \frac{9}{6}$$
$$x = \frac{3}{2}$$

Check $4\left(\dfrac{3}{2}\right) - 5 + 2\left(\dfrac{3}{2}\right) + 3 = 6 - 5 + 3 + 3 = 7$

The solution is $\frac{3}{2}$.

EXAMPLE 2 Solve the equation $3 - (2x + 5) = 8$.

$$3 - (2x + 5) = 8$$
$$3 + (-1)(2x + 5) = 8 \qquad \text{Use the multiplication property of } -1.$$
$$3 - 2x - 5 = 8 \qquad \text{Use the distributive property.}$$
$$-2x - 2 = 8 \qquad \text{Combine like terms.}$$
$$-2x = 10 \qquad \text{Add 2 to each side.}$$
$$x = -5 \qquad \text{Divide each side by } -2.$$

Check $3 - [2(-5) + 5] = 3 - (-10 + 5) = 3 - (-5) = 8$

The solution is -5.

EQUATIONS

107

LESSON NOTES

When discussing Example 2, be sure the students understand the step that re-expresses
$3 - (2x + 5) = 8$ as
$3 + (-1)(2x + 5) = 8$.
To subtract $2x - 5$, we are adding its opposite; to find the opposite, we are using the multiplication property of -1. Multiplying any expression by -1 yields the opposite of that expression. Once the opposite has been found, the procedure for solving the equation is similar to the procedure used in Example 1.

Example 3 shows two methods of solving an equation in which terms with the variable are on both sides of the equal sign. In Method I, we subtract $3n$ from both sides of the equation; since $3 < 7$, we obtain the variable with a positive coefficient on the right side of the equation. In Method II, subtracting $7n$ from both sides results in the variable with a negative coefficient on the left side of the equation. In Method II notice that division by a negative number (or multiplication by a negative number) is needed next. Many students will prefer to avoid this type of situation; they can be encouraged to begin by subtracting the variable-term that has the lesser coefficient.

In Example 4, Method II involves thinking of the expression $(x - 2)$ as a single quantity. In effect,
$3(x - 2) = 33$ is thought of as
$3(\underline{\;?\;}) = 33$ or $3n = 33$ and both sides of the equation are multiplied by the reciprocal of 3. Be sure the students understand this fact.

ALTERNATE EXAMPLES

1. Solve the equation:
   $5x - 3 - 2x + 1 = 1$. First combine the like terms. $x = 1$
2. Solve the equation:
   $4 - (3x + 1) = 9$ $x = -2$

There is often more than one way to solve an equation. Different methods are shown in the following examples.

EXAMPLE 3   Solve $3n = 7n - 8$ by two methods.

Method I

On the right side of the equation, collect all terms containing the variable by subtracting $3n$ from each side.

$$3n = 7n - 8$$
$$3n - 3n = 7n - 3n - 8$$
$$0 = 4n - 8$$
$$0 + 8 = 4n - 8 + 8$$
$$8 = 4n$$
$$2 = n$$

Method II

On the left side of the equation, collect all terms containing the variable by subtracting $7n$ from each side.

$$3n = 7n - 8$$
$$3n - 7n = 7n - 7n - 8$$
$$-4n = -8$$
$$\frac{-4n}{-4} = \frac{-8}{-4}$$
$$n = 2$$

EXAMPLE 4   Solve the equation $3(x - 2) = 33$.

4. Solve the equation:
$5(x + 4) = 80$ $x = 12$

Method I

Use the distributive property.

$$3(x - 2) = 33$$
$$3x - 6 = 33$$
$$3x - 6 + 6 = 33 + 6$$
$$3x = 39$$
$$\frac{1}{3}(3x) = \frac{1}{3}(39)$$
$$x = 13$$

Method II

Multiply each side by $\frac{1}{3}$, the reciprocal of 3.

$$3(x - 2) = 33$$
$$\frac{1}{3}[3(x - 2)] = \frac{1}{3}(33)$$
$$x - 2 = 11$$
$$x - 2 + 2 = 11 + 2$$
$$x = 13$$

5. Solve: $\dfrac{2x}{5} = 30$ $x = 75$

EXAMPLE 5   Solve $\frac{5x}{6} = 15$.

Method I

Rewrite $\frac{5x}{6}$ as $\frac{5}{6}x$. Then multiply each side by $\frac{6}{5}$.

$$\frac{5x}{6} = 15$$
$$\frac{5}{6}x = 15$$
$$\frac{6}{5}\left(\frac{5}{6}x\right) = \frac{6}{5}(15)$$
$$x = 18$$

Method II

Multiply each side by 6, then divide each side by 5.

$$\frac{5x}{6} = 15$$
$$6\left(\frac{5x}{6}\right) = 6(15)$$
$$5x = 90$$
$$\frac{5x}{5} = \frac{90}{5}$$
$$x = 18$$

POSSIBLE ERROR

Students are sometimes puzzled by equations such as $(5y - 1) - (3y - 2) = -17$ [Exercise 38]. Occasionally, they are unsure about what step to take first. Review the idea that they have learned to solve equations of the form $x + a = b$, $ax = b$, and $ax + b = c$. The first step(s) in solving an equation such as $(5y - 1) - (3y - 2) = -17$ involve simplifying the equation. When it has been simplified, it becomes $2y + 1 = -17$, which can be solved by using inverse operations or two properties of equality.

108

CLASS EXERCISES

*Solve for **x**, and check.*

1. $3(x - 4) = 6$ 6
2. $2(x + 3) = 7$ $\frac{1}{2}$
3. $-(x - 1) = 5$ -4

4. $\frac{2x}{3} = 8$ 12
5. $\frac{4x}{5} = 4$ 5
6. $\frac{3x}{4} = 18$ 24

7. $3x - 6 = x$ 3
8. $7x + 4 = 3x$ -1
9. $15 - 2x = 3x$ 3

10. $(2x - 1) + (x + 3) = 8$ 2
11. $(2x - 1) - (x + 3) = 8$ 12

EXERCISES

A   *Solve for **x**, and check.*

1. $2(x + 3) = 8$ 1
2. $2(x - 3) = 8$ 7
3. $-2(x - 3) = 8$ -1

4. $3(x - 1) = 6$ 3
5. $-3(x + 1) = 6$ -3
6. $3(x + 1) = -6$ -3

7. $\frac{5x}{6} = 15$ 18
8. $\frac{3x}{4} = -1$ $-\frac{4}{3}$
9. $\frac{2x}{3} = 40$ 60

10. $2x + 5 = 7x$ 1
11. $-2x + 5 = -7x$ -1
12. $2x - 5 = 7x$ -1

13. $-3x - 8 = x$ -2
14. $3x + 8 = x$ -4
15. $-3x = x + 8$ -2

16. $x + 7 = \frac{1}{2}x + 1$ -12
17. $x - 7 = \frac{1}{2}x + 1$ 16
18. $x - 7 = \frac{1}{2}x - 1$ 12

B   *Solve and check.*

19. $4x + 8 = 20$ 3
20. $4(x + 8) = 20$ -3
21. $3x + 9 = -21$ -10

22. $3(x + 9) = -21$ -16
23. $6(x - 7) = 24$ 11
24. $-2(x - 5) = 18$ -4

25. $6\left(x - \frac{1}{2}\right) = 9$ 2
26. $4\left(x + \frac{1}{4}\right) = -15$ -4
27. $2(x - 1) = \frac{1}{2}$ $\frac{5}{4}$

28. $2x - 1 = \frac{1}{2}$ $\frac{3}{4}$
29. $-\left(x - \frac{1}{2}\right) = 1$ $-\frac{1}{2}$
30. $-x - \frac{1}{2} = 1$ $-\frac{3}{2}$

31. $x + (x + 1) = 5$ 2
32. $3x + x + 2 = 10$ 2

33. $4 + 3(x + 2) = 22$ 4
34. $2(y - 4) = 3y$ -8

35. $3(y + 5) = 2y$ -15
36. $x + 2(x - 2) = 8$ 4

37. $(5y + 1) + (3y - 2) = -17$ -2
38. $(5y - 1) - (3y - 2) = -17$ -9

39. $1 - (y + 1) = 4$ -4
40. $3 - (y + 5) = 9$ -11

41. $2(x - 1) - x = 81$ 83
42. $3x + 4 = 2(x + 5)$ 6

43. $6x - 2 = 4x + 2$ 2
44. $3x + 5 = x - 2$ $-\frac{7}{2}$

45. $5(x - 6) = 3 + 4x$ 33
46. $2(x + 1) = 3x + 2$ 0

EQUATIONS

EXTRA PRACTICE, page 512

Have the students solve for x, and
then check.

$$a + b(x - c) = d$$

$$x = \frac{d - a + bc}{b}$$

$$b(x + c) - a = d$$

$$x = \frac{d + a - bc}{b}$$

You can also provide equations in x
and y, and have the students solve
for y.

$$2x + 3y = 6 \qquad y = -\frac{2}{3}x + 2$$

$$5x - 2y = 8 \qquad y = \frac{5}{2}x - 4$$

$$-6x + 4y = 12 \qquad y = \frac{3}{2}x + 3$$

Checkpoint

Students may check their answers
with those given in the back of their
books.

47. $3(x - 1) = 5(x + 3)$ -9 **48.** $2x - (1 + x) = 13$ 14

49. $5t - 3 = -2(4 - 3t)$ 5 **50.** $2x - 3 = 5(x - 3)$ 4

C

51. 9 less than 3 times a certain number n is equal to 4 more than twice the number. Find the number. 13

52. Add 3 to a certain number x and multiply this sum by 4. The result is the same as you would get if you decreased x by 9. Find x. -7

53. If x is decreased by 4, the result is equal to 6 times the sum of x and 1. Find x. -2

54. Twice the sum of some number n and 3 is equal to the product of the number and 6. Find the number. $\frac{3}{2}$

55. Let c be the list price of a certain small car. The car dealer established his total selling price, \$6741, by multiplying the list price by $\frac{21}{20}$. Find the list price, c.   \$6420

*56. Solve for x, and check: $|2x - 2| = 3$ $x = \frac{5}{2}$ or $x = -\frac{1}{2}$

CHECKPOINT

Solve and check.

1. $x + 14 = -16$ -30 **2.** $-9 + x = -10$ -1 **3.** $x - 5 = -2$ 3

4. $-2x = 18$ -9 **5.** $4x = \frac{1}{2}$ $\frac{1}{8}$ **6.** $\frac{x}{-8} = -1$ 8

7. $6x - 1 = 35$ 6 **8.** $8x - 6 = 34$ 5 **9.** $9x + 2 = 74$ 8

10. $-18 = 3x + 60$ -26 **11.** $0.6x - 1.4 = 1$ 4 **12.** $4x = 6 + x$ 2

13. $4x + x + 7 = 22$ 3 **14.** $\frac{x}{3} = x - 2$ 3 **15.** $\frac{3}{4}x + 12 = 21$ 12

16. $5(x + 16) = 65$ -3 **17.** $8\left(x + \frac{1}{2}\right) = -12$ -2 **18.** $8 + 4(x + 11) = 0$ -13

Use an equation to find the number. Then check your answer.

19. 8 times a number, less 50, is equal to 6. $8x - 50 = 6$; 7

20. 3 times the sum of some number and 2 is equal to 9. $3(x + 2) = 9$; 1

21. 15 less than twice a number is equal to 75. $2x - 15 = 75$; 45

22. One-half the sum of some number and 13 is equal to 3 times the result of subtracting that number from 1. $\frac{1}{2}(x + 13) = 3(1 - x)$; -1

110

3-8 Problem Solving: Organizing Information

OBJECTIVE

To use diagrams and tables for organizing information and solving problems.

A diagram or a table is often used to organize the information in a problem.

EXAMPLE 1

Two sides of a triangle are $7\frac{1}{2}$ inches and $4\frac{1}{4}$ inches long. The triangle has a $16\frac{1}{2}$-inch perimeter. How long is the third side?

Strategy:
Draw a diagram; write and solve an equation.

Read the problem to find the key ideas.

Use a variable.

Let x = length of the third side.

Write an equation.

$$7\frac{1}{2} + 4\frac{1}{4} + x = 16\frac{1}{2}$$ Equal expressions for the perimeter

Find the solution.

$$x = 4\frac{3}{4}$$ Check to see that the sum of the three lengths is $16\frac{1}{2}$.

Answer the question.

The third side of the triangle is $4\frac{3}{4}$ inches long.

EXAMPLE 2

A stack of quarters plus 8 dimes and a nickel have a total value of $4.10. How many quarters are in the stack?

Strategy:
Make a table.

Read the problem to find the key ideas.

Use a variable.

Let x be the number of quarters.

Write an equation.

$$5 + 80 + 25x = 410$$ Equal expressions for the total value

	Number of Coins	Value in Cents
Nickels	1	5
Dimes	8	80
Quarters	x	25x

Find the solution.

$$85 + 25x = 410$$
$$85 - 85 + 25x = 410 - 85$$
$$25x = 325$$
$$x = 13$$ Check that 13 quarters, 8 dimes, and a nickel have a value of $4.10.

Answer the question.

There are 13 quarters in the stack.

EQUATIONS

111

3. Peggy's age is 3 years less than twice Jane's age. If Peggy is 15, how old is Jane?   Jane is 9.

4. Find two consecutive integers such that the greater number, increased by three times the lesser, is 49.   The integers are 12 and 13.

5. The perimeter of a rectangle is 50 cm. If the length is 1 more than twice the width, find the length and width.   The width of the rectangle is 8 cm. The length is 17 cm.

EXAMPLE 3

Nini's age is 1 year more than twice Lor's age. If Nini is 19, how old is Lor?

Read the problem to find the key ideas. Make a table.

	Age
Lor	x
Nini	$2x + 1$

Use a variable. Let x be Lor's age.

Write an equation. $2x + 1 = 19$ Nini's age expressed in two ways

Find the solution. $2x = 18$

$x = 9$ Check that 1 more than twice 9 is 19.

Answer the question. Lor's age is 9.

EXAMPLE 4

Find two consecutive integers such that the lesser number increased by twice the greater, is 50.

Read the problem to find the key ideas. List the values in a table.

Lesser Integer	Greater Integer	Lesser Integer Increased by Twice the Greater
n	$n + 1$	$n + 2(n + 1)$

Use a variable. Let n be the lesser integer.

Write an equation.
$$n + 2(n + 1) = 50$$
$$n + 2n + 2 = 50$$
$$3n + 2 = 50$$
$$3n = 48$$

Find the solution. $n = 16$ and $n + 1 = 17$ Check that 16 increased by twice 17 is equal to 50.

Answer the question. The integers are 16 and 17.

EXAMPLE 5

The perimeter of a rectangle is 36 cm. If the length is 3 less than twice the width, find the length and width.

Read the problem to find the key ideas. Draw and label a picture.

Use a variable. Let x be the width of the rectangle.
The length of the rectangle is $2x - 3$
The perimeter of the rectangle is $2x + 2(2x - 3)$

Write an equation.
$$2x + 2(2x - 3) = 36$$
$$2x + 4x - 6 = 36$$
$$6x - 6 = 36$$
$$6x = 42$$

Find the solution. $x = 7$ and $2x - 3 = 11$ Check that the perimeter is 36.

Answer the question. The width of the rectangle is 7 cm. The length is 11 cm.

112

CLASS EXERCISES

The sum of two consecutive integers is 97.

1. If the lesser integer is n, express the greater integer in terms of n. $n + 1$

2. Find two different expressions for the sum of the integers. $n + (n + 1)$; 97

3. Write an equation and solve it to find the two integers. $2n + 1 = 97$; 48, 49

Mark is 2 years less than 3 times as old as Fran.

4. How old is Mark if Fran is 28? 82

5. How old is Fran if Mark is 28? 10

*Write an equation to solve each problem. Use **x** as the variable.*

6. Kim is 3 years more than twice as old as Katie. If Kim is 21, how old is Katie? 9

Katie	Kim
x	2x + 3

7. The width of a rectangle is 12 meters less than its length. The perimeter is 400 meters. Find its dimensions. Width is 94 m; length is 106 m.

8. A stack of nickels and stacks of the same number of dimes and quarters have a total value of $10.00. How many coins are in each stack? 25

	Number of Coins	Value in Cents
Nickels	x	5x
Dimes	x	10x
Quarters	x	25x

EXERCISES

A *Write an equation to solve each problem. Check the answer.*

1. Alison is 7 years younger than Dean. Together their ages add to 39. How old is each one? Dean is 23. Alison is 16.

Dean	Alison
x	x − 7

2. Diane's age is 2 years less than twice the age of Janice. If Diane is 34, how old is Janice? 18

3. Jack is 9 years more than twice as old as David. If Jack is 37, how old is David? 14

4. There are 12 more dimes than nickels. Find the number of each if together they have a value of $4.20. 20 nickels; 32 dimes

	Number of Coins	Value in Cents
Nickels	x	5x
Dimes	x + 12	10(x + 12)

5. There are 8 fewer dimes than nickels. Find the number of each if together they have a value of $10.00. 72 nickels; 64 dimes

6. Some nickels and pennies have a total value of $1.21. Find the number of each if there are twice as many nickels as pennies. 11 pennies; 22 nickels

EQUATIONS

113

Write an equation to solve each problem. Check the answers.

1. Barbara is 9 years younger than Adam. Together their ages add to 23. How old is each person? $x + (x - 9) = 23$; $x = 16$ and $x - 9 = 7$. Adam is 16 and Barbara is 7.

2. Naomi's age is 4 years less than twice the age of Jennifer. If Naomi is 24, how old is Jennifer? $2x - 4 = 24$; $x = 14$ Jennifer is 14.

3. There are 14 more nickels than dimes. Find the number of each if together they have a value of $1.75. $10x + 5(x + 14) = 15$ $x = 7$ and $x + 14 = 21$ There are 7 dimes and 21 nickels.

4. Some quarters and nickels have a total value of $6.05. Find the number of each if there are two times as many quarters as nickels. $25(2x) + 5(x) = 605$; $x = 11$ and $2x = 22$. There are 11 nickels and 22 quarters.

5. The perimeter of a rectangle is 64 cm. The width of the rectangle is 6 cm less than the length. Find the dimensions of the rectangle. $2(x) + 2(x - 6) = 64$ $x = 19$ and $x - 6 = 13$. The length is 19 cm and the width is 13 cm.

Using BASIC

In general, a different program must be written for each type of problem. Therefore, a computer may not be the most efficient tool when many types of problems must be solved.

EXTRA PRACTICE, page 513

B

C

7. A stack of nickels and pennies is worth 70 cents. Find the number of each if there are twice as many pennies as nickels.   20 pennies; 10 nickels

8. A rectangle is 8 meters longer than it is wide. Find its length and width if the perimeter is 80 meters.   Width is 16 m; length is 24 m.

9. The perimeter of a rectangle is 48 cm. Its width is 5 cm less than its length. Find its length and width.   Width is $9\frac{1}{2}$ cm; length is $14\frac{1}{2}$ cm.

10. Two consecutive even integers add up to 54. Find the integers.   26, 28

First Even Integer	n
Next Even Integer	$n + 2$

11. Find two consecutive even integers if twice the lesser integer is 16 more than the greater.   18, 20

12. Find three consecutive integers if the sum of the first two lesser integers, added to twice the third, is equal to 33.   7, 8, 9

13. An odd integer is added to 3 times the next consecutive odd integer. If the sum is 66, find the two odd integers.   15, 17

14. One side of an isosceles triangle is 9 cm shorter than the other two sides. Find the length of each side if the perimeter is 69 cm.   17, 26, 26

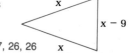

15. Two sides of an isosceles triangle are each 3 cm shorter than the third side. Find the length of each side if the perimeter is 30 cm.   9, 9, 12

16. Lee is 12 years older than Dee. In 8 years, Lee will be twice as old as Dee will be then. How old is each one now?   Dee is 4. Lee is 16.

	Age Now	Age in 8 Years
Dee	x	? $x + 8$
Lee	? $x + 12$	? $x + 20$

17. Mel is 16 years older than Merv. In 3 years, he will be twice as old as Merv will be then. How old is each one now?   Merv is 13. Mel is 29.

18. Find four consecutive even integers if the sum of the first three integers is 80 more than the greatest integer.   40, 42, 44, 46

19. If the sum of three consecutive odd integers is decreased by 130, the result is equal to the second odd integer. Find the three integers.   63, 65, 67

*20. A buoy is between a dock and a boat. The distance from the dock to the boat is three times the distance from the buoy to the boat. How far is the boat from the buoy if the buoy is 5.5 km from the dock?   2.75 km

114

Meteorology

Meterologists study weather conditions. They know that normally the higher the altitude, the lower the temperature of the air.

The average decrease in air temperature is about 5°F for every 1000 feet of altitude. The following formula shows this relationship.

$$T = t - 5\left(\frac{A}{1000}\right)$$

In the formula, t represents the ground temperature. A is the altitude, in *feet*. T is the temperature at altitude A in degrees *Fahrenheit*.

Example   Estimate the temperature T at an altitude A of 12,000 feet if the ground temperature t is 70°F.

$$T = t - 5\left(\frac{A}{1000}\right)$$
$$= 70 - 5\left(\frac{12,000}{1000}\right)$$
$$= 70 - 5(12)$$
$$= 70 - 60$$
$$= 10$$

?° ——————12,000 ft——————

55° ——————3000 ft——————
60°
65° ——————1000 ft——————
70° ——————ground level——————

The temperature is 10° Fahrenheit.

1. Simplify the right side of the equation $T = t - 5\left(\frac{A}{1000}\right)$. $t - \frac{A}{200}$

2. Estimate the temperature at an altitude of 7600 feet if the ground temperature is 22°F. $-16°F$

3. At 5500 feet, the temperature is −5°F.   Estimate the ground temperature.
   $22.5°F$

4. In the metric system the relationship between temperature and altitude can be expressed as follows.

The temperature drops about 9 degrees *Celsius* for every 1000 meters increase in altitude.

Write a formula that expresses this relationship. Let x stand for the ground temperature. Let y stand for the temperature at altitude a, in meters. $y = x - 9\left(\frac{a}{1000}\right)$

Using BASIC

When the same formula must be evaluated many times, the computer can help minimize the time required for the computations. The meteorological formula in this *Applications* lesson can be evaluated by using this program:

```
10  PRINT "ENTER GROUND
    TEMP"
20  INPUT G
30  PRINT "ENTER DESIRED
    ALT"
40  INPUT A
50  LET T = G - 5 * A
    / 1000
60  PRINT "TEMP  IS  "; T
70  PRINT
80  PRINT "ANOTHER? (1 =
    YES, 0 = NO)"
85  INPUT Z
90  IF Z = 1 THEN 10
99  END
```

Note that the variable G has been substituted for the t in the formula. This is because many computers treat T and t as the same variable.

These exercises review basic algebraic skills.

Evaluate for $x = 4$ and $y = -8$.

1. $|x| + |y|$ 12
2. $|y| - |x|$ 4
3. $x + y$ -4
4. xy -32
5. $-3x^2y$ 384
6. $\dfrac{x}{2y}$ $-\dfrac{1}{4}$

Simplify.

7. $-5b^2 - 12b^2$ $-17b^2$
8. $n - (-8n)$ $9n$
9. $y + (-3) - 5y$ $-4y - 3$
10. $9 - (2 + 6x)$ $7 - 6x$

Use the distributive property to rewrite each expression.

11. $15(a + 2b)$ $15a + 30b$
12. $9(7 - 3x)$ $63 - 27x$
13. $-1(y - 3)$ $-y + 3$
14. $a(-b - c)$ $-ab - ac$

Solve and check.

15. $x - (-4) = 7$ 3
16. $8y = -6$ $-\dfrac{3}{4}$
17. $15 = 23 + n$ -8
18. $\dfrac{x}{5} = \dfrac{2}{3}$ $\dfrac{10}{3}$
19. $\dfrac{1}{2}x - 3 = 12$ 30
20. $9y = 15y - 6 - 2y$ $\dfrac{3}{2}$

CHAPTER 3 REVIEW

VOCABULARY

equivalent equations (p. 87)
addition property of equality (p. 87)
inverse operations (pp. 92, 100)

reciprocal (p. 69)
multiplication property
  of equality (p. 96)

SUMMARY

The addition and multiplication properties of equality are introduced in this chapter and used to extend procedures for solving equations. With the aid of these properties, it is possible to solve more complicated equations than before. Substantial work is included for the purpose of strengthening the ability to translate from verbal to algebraic form. The new algebraic methods for solving equations are applied–to solve verbal problems in which diagrams and tables serve as aids to organizing and clarifying the problems.

REVIEW EXERCISES

3-1   *Write each sentence as an equation. Use **y** for the unknown number.*

1. 11 more than some number is equal to 15. $y + 11 = 15$
2. 9 less than a number is equal to 6. $y - 9 = 6$
3. 10 times some number is equal to 2700. $10y = 2700$
4. A number divided by 12 is equal to 144. $\frac{y}{12} = 144$
5. 8 times the sum of a number and 5 is equal to 200. $8(y + 5) = 200$
6. 16 times 3 less than a number is equal to 80. $16(y - 3) = 80$

3-2   *Solve each equation and check.*

7. $x + 15 = 27$ 12	8. $x + (-3) = 2$ 5	9. $x + 3.1 = 2.5$ -0.6
3-3 10. $x - 7 = 19$ 26	11. $x - 4 = -15$ -11	12. $5 + x = 2.2$ -2.8
13. $n + 5 = -2.6$ -7.6	14. $x - (-4) = 1$ -3	15. $6 + x = 2.3$ -3.7
16. $x - \frac{1}{4} = \frac{3}{4}$ 1	17. $\frac{1}{5} + x = -\frac{3}{10}$ $-\frac{1}{2}$	18. $3x = 2x + 5$ 5
3-4 19. $9x = 108$ 12	20. $3x = -51$ -17	21. $4n = 10.4$ 2.6
22. $\frac{1}{6}y = -12$ -72	23. $-165 = 15n$ -11	24. $y + 4y = 45$ 9

116

3-5 Solve each equation by two methods, multiplication and division.

25. $-5t = 40$ -8

26. $10x = 3$ $\frac{3}{10}$

27. $4t = -5.2$ -1.3

Solve and check.

28. $\frac{x}{4} = -14$ -56

29. $\frac{y}{3} = \frac{5}{6}$ $2\frac{1}{2}$

30. $2x = \frac{1}{3}$ $\frac{1}{6}$

Use an equation to find the answer. Then check.

31. The product of a number n and 12.25 is 49. Find n. $12.25n = 49$; 4

32. If n is divided by 2.3, the quotient is equal to 6. Find n. $\frac{n}{2.3} = 6$; 13.8

3-6 Solve and check.

33. $8x + 5 = 37$ 4

34. $3x - 9 = 33$ 14

35. $11 + 2x = -7$ -9

36. $7 - 2x = 15$ -4

37. $\frac{n}{5} + 2 = 6$ 20

38. $10 = \frac{n}{4} - 1$ 44

Use an equation to find the number. Then check.

39. 15 more than 4 times some number is equal to 47. $4x + 15 = 47$; 8

40. 8 less than twice a number is equal to 14. $2x - 8 = 14$; 11

41. Twice some number added to -3 is equal to 11. $2x + (-3) = 11$; 7

42. Multiply a number by -4 and add 10 to get 2. $-4x + 10 = 2$; 2

43. 2.8 is equal to the quotient obtained when 7 times a number is divided by 13. $2.8 = \frac{7x}{13}$; 5.2

3-7 Solve and check.

44. $5(x - 2) = 35$ 9

45. $7(x + 6) = -42$ -12

46. $-2(n + 3) = 4$ -5

47. $3(x - 5) = -15$ 0

48. $8x = 5x + 21$ 7

49. $4n = 9n - 10$ 2

50. $2x + 5 = x - 3$ -8

51. $x - 2 = \frac{1}{2}x + 4$ 12

52. $\frac{y}{4} = 1.6$ 6.4

53. $\frac{4x}{3} = 60$ 45

54. $\frac{8x}{7} = -24$ -21

55. $\frac{3n}{5} = -15$ -25

56. $(x + 6) + (3x - 4) = 14$ 3

57. $(2x - 8) - (x - 12) = 11$ 7

3-8 Use an equation to solve each problem.

58. Jennifer has 2 more dimes than Adam. How many dimes has each one if the total value of their dimes is $2.40? Adam has 11 dimes. Jennifer has 13 dimes.

59. Find two consecutive integers such that 3 times the lesser integer, added to the greater integer, is 81.   20, 21

REVIEW

60. Mia is 2 years more than 6 times as old as Pat. If Mia is 26 years old, how old is Pat?   4 years old

61. Norman has a dollar in change, consisting of nickels, dimes, and quarters. He has 2 more dimes than quarters and 6 more nickels than dimes. How many coins of each type does he have?   9 nickels, 3 dimes, 1 quarter

62. The perimeter of a rectangle is 62 cm. If the length is 7 cm more than the width, find the dimensions of the rectangle.   Width is 12 cm; length is 19 cm.

CHAPTER 3
TEST

Solve each equation.

3-2   **1.** $x + 3 = 7$ 4   **2.** $x + (-2) = 3$ 5   **3.** $y + (-1) = -10$ −9

3-3   **4.** $y - 3 = 50$ 53   **5.** $x + 8 = -1.2$ −9.2   **6.** $y - \dfrac{2}{3} = \dfrac{10}{3}$ 4

3-4   **7.** $4x = -16$ −4   **8.** $3x = 4.26$ 1.42   **9.** $\dfrac{4}{5}x = -80$ −100

3-5   **10.** $5x = -35$ −7   **11.** $\dfrac{x}{12} = 3$ 36   **12.** $-8y = 16.8$ −2.1

3-6   **13.** $6x + 2 = 86$ 14   **14.** $4 - 3x = -8$ 4   **15.** $\dfrac{x}{3} + 8 = 2$ −18

Use an equation to find the number.

16. 19 times some number is equal to 57. $19x = 57; x = 3$

17. Double some number and subtract 5 to get 27. $2x - 5 = 27; x = 16$

18. Multiply a number by 5 and add 14 to get 59. $5x + 14 = 59; x = 9$

3-7   *Solve each equation.*

19. $3(x + 1) = -9$ −4   **20.** $3n = n - 14$ −7   **21.** $\dfrac{2n}{5} = 18$ 45

Use an equation to solve each problem.

22. 3 times the sum of some number and 6 is 45. What is the number? $3(x + 6) = 45; 9$

23. When a number is decreased by 4 and the difference is doubled, the result is equal to 16. What is the number? $2(x - 4) = 16; 12$

3-8   **24.** Amy is 3 years less than twice as old as Carlos. If Amy is 17, how old is Carlos?   Let x = Carlos's age. $2x - 3 = 17; x = 10$ Carlos is 10.

25. Find two consecutive integers such that the lesser number, increased by 3 times the greater, is 79. $x + 3(x + 1) = 79; 19, 20$

Equations

When $Ax + B = C$ is solved for x, the solution is $x = \dfrac{C - B}{A}$. If we use this solution to write a program in BASIC, we must use parentheses since the numerator has more than one term. The expression $\dfrac{C - B}{A}$ is written in BASIC as $(C - B)/A$.

The Program	What It Does
`10 REM SOLVE AX + B = C`	Tells what program will do.
`20 PRINT "ENTER A, B, C"`	Waits for 3 numbers separated by commas.
`30 INPUT A, B, C`	
`40 LET X = (C - B)/A`	Solves for x.
`50 PRINT "X = "; X`	Displays the solution.
`60 PRINT`	Leaves a blank line.
`70 PRINT "ANOTHER?(1 = YES, 0 = NO)"`	Gives you a choice.
`80 INPUT Z`	Waits for 1 (yes) or 0 (no).
`90 IF Z = 1 THEN 20`	If 1 is entered, returns to line 20. If not, continues to the next line.
`99 END`	

```
RUN
ENTER A, B, C
? 4, -9, 43

X = 13

ANOTHER?(1 = YES, 0 = NO)
```

This sample run is for $4x - 9 = 43$.

Values of A, B, and C are entered, in order, separated by commas.

Displays the solution.

Asks whether you have another equation to solve.

Line 30 assigns the first number entered to A, the second to B, and the third to C. The order of entering the numbers is important.

Lines 70 to 90 help communicate a decision to the computer. If we enter 1, to represent "yes," then the computer jumps back to line 20 for another equation. If not, it continues to line 99.

To use the above program, what values should be entered (input) to solve these equations? What solutions will be displayed?

1. $2x + 13 = 55$ 2. $9x - 13 = 59$ 3. $5x + 2 = 6$ 4. $4 - 3x = 7$

5. $8x = 32$ 6. $7x - 56 = 0$ 7. $8x + 16 = 68$ 8. $15 - 7x = -13$

9. If the parentheses in line 40 are omitted, what will the computer display as the solution for each of the above?

*Enter these values of **A**, **B**, and **C** in the original program. Write the equation that has been solved and its solution.*

10. 9, 8, 44   11. 5, −12, 23   12. 2.5, 77, 22   13. 1, 1, 1

14. The general equation $Ax + B = Cx + D$ has the solution $x = \dfrac{D - B}{A - C}$.

Write a program to solve equations of the form $Ax + B = Cx + D$.

For more information about BASIC, see the Computer Handbook at the back of the book.

Computer Activity

Statements similar to those in lines 60 through 90 may be inserted in many programs in this book. However, when this procedure for running a program again is used, the value of the variables is left unchanged. When RUN is entered, all variables are automatically set to zero.

ADDITIONAL ANSWERS

Computer Activity

	Input	Solution
1.	2, 13, 55	x = 21
2.	9, −13, 59	x = 8
3.	5, 2, 6	x = .8
4.	−3, 4, 7	x = −1
5.	8, 0, 32	x = 4
6.	7, −56, 0	x = 8
7.	8, 16, 68	x = 6.5
8.	−7, 15, −13	x = 4

9. Answers may vary slightly on some computers.
   - (1) X = 48.5
   - (2) X = 60.4444444
   - (3) X = 5.6
   - (4) X = 8.33333333
   - (5) X = 32
   - (6) X = 8
   - (7) X = 66
   - (8) X = −10.8571429

10. 9X + 8 = 44; X = 4
11. 5X − 12 = 23; X = 7
12. 2.5X + 77 = 22; X = −22
13. X + 1 = 1; X = 0
14. Programs may vary. Sample is given below.

```
10  REM SOLVE AX + B = CX
    + D
20  PRINT "ENTER A, B, C,
    D"
30  INPUT A, B, C, D
40  LET X = (D - B)/
    (A - C)
50  PRINT "X = "; X
60  PRINT
70  PRINT "ANOTHER? (1 =
    YES, 0 = NO)"
80  INPUT Z
90  IF Z = 1 THEN 20
99  END
```

PART I

Write the letter for the correct answer.

Chap. 1

1. Simplify: $18 - 3 \times 4 \div (3 - 1)$ **b**

    a. 3   **b.** 12   **c.** 15   **d.** 19   **e.** 30

2. Evaluate: $2(a - b) + ab$ if $a = 5$ and $b = 1$ **b**

    a. 14   **b.** 13   **c.** 12   **d.** 11   **e.** 10

3. Write $3x \cdot 3x \cdot 3x \cdot 2y \cdot 2y$ in exponential form.   **e**

    a. $3^3 x \, 2^2 y$ **b.** $3x^3 2y^2$ **c.** $6x^3 y^2$ **d.** $27x^3 y^2$ **e.** $108x^3 y^2$

4. Write an expression for the phrase "5 less than the product of n and 3."   **d**

    a. $5n - 3$ **b.** $3n + 5$ **c.** $5n + 3$ **d.** $3n - 5$ **e.** $5 - 3n$

5. Write an expression for the phrase "3 times the sum of x and 6."   **d**

    a. $3x + 6$ **b.** $(3x + 3)6$ **c.** $(3 + x)6$ **d.** $3(x + 6)$ **e.** $3x + 6x$

6. Simplify: $2(3x + 2y)$ **a**

    a. $6x + 4y$ **b.** $2(5xy)$ **c.** $4x + 6y$ **d.** $6x + 2y$ **e.** $5x + 4y$

7. Which of the following numbers is a solution of $3(x - 1) = 24$?   **d**

    a. 7   **b.** 8   **c.** $8\frac{1}{3}$ **d.** 9   **e.** 12

8. Which of the following numbers is greater than -3.7 and less than -2.5?   **c**

    a. -2 **b.** -2.1 **c.** -3.5 **d.** -3.75 **e.** -4

9. Simplify: $-6 + |-4|$ **d**

    a. 24   **b.** 10   **c.** 2   **d.** -2 **e.** -10

10. Which two integers on the number line are 6 units from -4?   **b**

    a. $-10, -2$ **b.** $-10, 2$ **c.** $-6, -4$ **d.** $-2, 10$ **e.** 2, 10

Chap. 2

11. Evaluate $-2x - 3y$ if $x = 4$ and $y = -3$.   **b**

    a. 17   **b.** 1   **c.** -1 **d.** -3 **e.** -17

12. Simplify: $4n - 3 - 7n + 5$ **e**

    a. $n - 2$ **b.** $3n - 8$ **c.** $-3n + 8$ **d.** $3n + 2$ **e.** $-3n + 2$

13. If $a < 0$ and $b > 0$, which of the following is positive?   **c**

    a. ab **b.** ab^2 **c.** $-2ab$ **d.** $3ab$ **e.** $a|b|$

14. Which expression is undefined when $x = 0$?   **b**

    a. $\dfrac{x}{-2}$ **b.** $\dfrac{-2}{x}$ **c.** $\dfrac{x}{x + 1}$ **d.** $\dfrac{x^2}{2}$ **e.** $\dfrac{x - 1}{x - 1}$

PART II

Chap. 1   *Identify the property illustrated.*

15. $a(b + c) = ab + ac$ Dist. prop. of mult. over add.   **16.** $a + (b + c) = (a + b) + c$ Assoc. for addition

17. $a(bc) = a(cb)$ Comm. for mult.   **18.** If $d = e$, then $e = d$.   Symmetric property of equality

Simplify.

19. $24 - 6 \times 2$ 12   **20.** 2^4 16   **21.** $|-4| + 2|3|$ 10

Chap. 2   **22.** $2(-3) + (-1)(-4)$ −2   **23.** $4(x - 5) + x$ $5x - 20$ **24.** $-a - [(-a) - (-a)]$ −a

Chap. 3   *Evaluate.*

25. $x^4 + 0^3$ if $x = 1$ 1   **26.** $4x^2$ if $x = 3$ 36   **27.** $(3x)^2$ if $x = -4$ 144

28. $\dfrac{2x - 1}{x - 3}$ if $x = 8$ 3   **29.** $\dfrac{x - 1}{x + 1}$ if $x = -2$ 3   **30.** $\dfrac{3(x - 3)}{3x - 3}$ if $x = -3$ $1\frac{1}{2}$

Chap. 2   **31.** Mr. Peeler sells apples for \$.35 each. What amount will he receive, in dollars, if he sells n apples?   \$.35n

Chap. 2   **32.** The temperature range during one day was from 14° below zero to 11° above zero. By how many degrees did the low differ from the high?   25°

Chap. 3   *Solve.*

33. $x - 7 = 13$ 20   **34.** $25 + x = 3$ −22   **35.** $2x + 1 = -5$ −3

36. $3x - 5 = 28$ 11   **37.** $\dfrac{3}{4}x = \dfrac{3}{8}$ $\frac{1}{2}$ **38.** $\dfrac{2n}{5} = 4$ 10

39. $3(n + 1) = 15$ 4   **40.** $5(2x - 3) = 75$ 9   **41.** $4(x - 1) = x - 4$ 0

42. $\dfrac{n}{10} - 5 = 0$ 50   **43.** $-6x - (x - 1) = 8$ 1   **44.** $\dfrac{x + 1}{2} = \dfrac{x - 1}{4}$ −3

45. The length of a rectangle is 4 units longer than the width. The perimeter is 64 units. Find the measurements of the sides.   14 units and 18 units

*Write as an equation. Then solve for **n**, and check.*

46. 6 more than 4 times the number n is equal to 42. $4n + 6 = 42$; $n = 9$

47. 7 more than twice the number n is equal to 39. $2n + 7 = 39$; $n = 16$

48. 11 less than 3 times the number n is equal to that number n added to 5.
$3n - 11 = 5 + n$; $n = 8$

49. 5 times the sum of the number n and 3 is equal to the product of that number n and 2. $5(n + 3) = 2n$; $n = -5$

50. Twice the number n added to 3 times the sum of n and 4 is equal to −3.
$3(n + 4) + 2n = -3$; $n = -3$

This chapter deals with some fundamental ideas of coordinate geometry. As you know, coordinate geometry brings together algebraic equations and their geometric representations; it is an extremely powerful tool in mathematics. Therefore, the contents of this chapter are of particular importance.

The first two lessons in this chapter introduce the coordinate plane and develop skill in locating points and identifying coordinates. Following this work, the students learn to graph linear equations by constructing tables of values and plotting the corresponding points. Slopes and intercepts are studied as properties of lines drawn in the coordinate plane; then the students learn to use slopes and intercepts as aids in graphing equations. The students also find that they can use the *slope-intercept form*, $y = mx + b$, to write the equation of a line when certain data is given—for example, when any point and the slope is given or when any two points are given.

To help students develop greater understanding of linear equations, the text also discusses and provides experience with the *standard form* for such equations, $Ax + By = C$. The chapter ends with a lesson that devotes special attention to horizontal and vertical lines and their equations.

CHAPTER 4

A meteorologist locates high and low pressure areas, storm systems, and other atmospheric patterns by using a computer screen weather grid.

122

LINEAR EQUATIONS

PREREQUISITE SKILLS REVIEW

For students who need additional practice with the algebraic skills in this Prerequisite Skills Review, you may assign Follow-Up exercises on pages 501–502 in the students' books.

An item-by-item error analysis of the Prerequisite Skills Review appears on page T22.

Prerequisite Skills Review

Write the letter for the correct answer.

1. $\frac{2}{3}(2) - 1 = \underline{\ ?\ }$ **a**

   a. $\frac{1}{3}$　　　　**b.** $-\frac{1}{3}$　　　　**c.** $\frac{2}{3}$　　　　**d.** $-\frac{2}{3}$

2. $-\frac{3}{4}(8) + 1 = \underline{\ ?\ }$ **b**

   a. 5　　　　**b.** -5　　　　**c.** 7　　　　**d.** -7

3. Which expression is equal to $-\frac{4}{7}$? **d**

   a. $-\frac{3 - 1}{5 - 2}$　　**b.** $\frac{-3 - (-1)}{5 - (-2)}$　　**c.** $\frac{-3 - 1}{-5 - 2}$　　**d.** $\frac{-3 - 1}{5 - (-2)}$

4. If $a = 3$ and $b = -4$, then $\frac{a - b}{a + b} = \underline{\ ?\ }$. **d**

   a. $-\frac{1}{7}$　　　　**b.** -1　　　　**c.** 7　　　　**d.** -7

5. Which expression represents a negative number? **c**

   a. $\frac{0 - 2}{7 - 9}$　　**b.** $\frac{4 - (-2)}{6 - 2}$　　**c.** $\frac{7 - (-1)}{-1 - 7}$　　**d.** $\frac{-1 - 2}{-3 + 1}$

6. $\frac{x - 1}{-4}$ is equal to $-\frac{1}{2}$ if $x = \underline{\ ?\ }$. **d**

   a. $-\frac{1}{2}$　　　　**b.** -1　　　　**c.** -3　　　　**d.** 3

7. If $x = -2$ and $y = 5$, then $3x - y = \underline{\ ?\ }$. **d**

   a. 1　　　　**b.** -1　　　　**c.** 11　　　　**d.** -11

8. If $-2x + 5y = 14$ and $y = 0$, then $x = \underline{\ ?\ }$. **b**

   a. 7　　　　**b.** -7　　　　**c.** $-\frac{9}{2}$　　　　**d.** $\frac{14}{5}$

9. If $r - s = 2$, then $s = \underline{\ ?\ }$. **c**

   a. $2 - r$　　　　**b.** $2 + r$　　　　**c.** $r - 2$　　　　**d.** $-\frac{2}{r}$

10. If $5t - 2k = 6$, and $t = 2$, then $k = \underline{\ ?\ }$. **a**

    a. 2　　　　**b.** -2　　　　**c.** 8　　　　**d.** -8

On a map, which direction do you
move to go
1. east?   Right   2. west?   Left
3. north?   Up   4. south?   Down

LESSON NOTES

In Lessons 4-1 and 4-2, students
are introduced to the coordinate
plane. They have already worked
with a horizontal number line; now
they work with a horizontal line and
a vertical line that are perpendicular
to each other and have a common
origin.

The emphasis in this first lesson
is on understanding the coordinate
plane. Terminology is minimized.
The students are simply asked to
think in terms of horizontal and vertical movements: right, left, up, and
down. (In Lesson 4-2, the axes will
be identified as *x*- and *y*-axes, and
the students will learn more of the
mathematical terminology—including
abscissa, ordinate, and so on.)

In this lesson, Examples 1–3 deal
with locating points for given ordered pairs of numbers. Example 4
deals with naming the coordinates
of given points. As you discuss Example 4, you can note that for a
point such as *A*, the first coordinate
can be found by imagining a perpendicular to the horizontal axis,
and the second coordinate can be
found by imagining a perpendicular
to the vertical axis.

4-1   The Coordinate Plane

OBJECTIVES

To locate points whose coordinates are ordered pairs of numbers.
To identify the coordinates of given points in a plane.

A **line** extends without end in both directions. On a number line, every
point corresponds to a particular number.

In the diagram above, point P is the **graph** of 2, and 2 is the **coordinate**
of point P.

A **plane** is a flat surface that extends endlessly in all directions. A **coordinate plane**
has two number lines, called **axes.** One axis
is horizontal, and the other is vertical. The
point where the axes meet is called the **origin.**

Each point in a coordinate plane is the graph of *two* coordinates
given in a definite order. Follow these steps to locate the point with
coordinates (4, 3).

Step 1   Start at the origin. The first coordinate
tells how far to move in a horizontal
direction. Since 4 is positive, move 4
units *right.*

Step 2   The second coordinate tells how far
to move in a vertical direction. Since
3 is positive, move 3 units *up.*

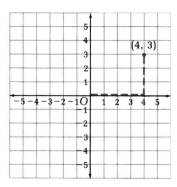

124

In Example 1, the **ordered pairs** (6, 2) and (2, 6) represent two different points. The numbers are the same but their order is reversed.

EXAMPLE 1   Locate each point.

a. (6, 2)

b. (2, 6)

If the first coordinate is negative, move *left* instead of right. If the second coordinate is negative, move *down* instead of up.

EXAMPLE 2   Locate each point.

a. (4, −2)

b. (−4, 2)

c. (−4, −2)

d. (4, 2)

EXAMPLE 3   For each ordered pair, state the two moves needed to locate the point, beginning at the origin.

a. (−4, 1)   **b. (8, −2)**   **c. (0, −5)**

left 4   right 8   no move right or left

up 1   down 2   down 5

ALTERNATE EXAMPLE

4. Give the coordinates of each point shown.

$A(1, 1)$;
$B(-2, 3)$;
$C(-2, -1)$;
$D(0, -3)$;
$E(0, 3)$;
$F(3, 3)$;
$G(3, -2)$;
$H(2, 0)$

DAILY QUIZ

Write the coordinates of each point.

$A(-3, 0)$;
$B(2, 5)$;
$C(5, -2)$;
$D(0, -2)$;
$E(-2, -3)$

ADDITIONAL ANSWERS

Class Exercises

9. No move right or left, up 3
10. Right 3, no move up or down
11. Left 2, no move up or down
12. No move right or left, down 2

Exercises

1. No move right or left, down 2
2. Right 1, up 2

[Answers continue on page 127.]

Remember to give the coordinates of a point in the correct order.

EXAMPLE 4   Give the coordinates of each point shown.

Answers

$A(2, 3)$ $B(-3, 2)$

$C(-4, -2)$ $D(4, -2)$

$E(2, 0)$ $F(0, 2)$

$O(0, 0)$ $H(-2, 0)$

CLASS EXERCISES

For each ordered pair, state the two moves needed to locate the point, beginning at the origin.

1. (5, 4)
Right 5, up 4
2. (4, 5)
Right 4, up 5
3. (−1, 3)
Left 1, up 3
4. (3, −1)
Right 3, down 1
5. (−5, −2)
Left 5, down 2
6. (−2, −5)
Left 2, down 5
7. (1, −6)
Right 1, down 6
8. (−6, 1)
Left 6, up 1
9. (0, 3)
10. (3, 0)
11. (−2, 0)
12. (0, −2)

Write the coordinates of each point.

13. J   (−1, 1)   **14.** K   (2, 4)

15. L   (0, 3)   **16.** M   (−4, −1)

17. N   (3, 0)   **18.** P   (2, −2)

19. Q   (0, −3)   **20.** R   (−4, 0)

EXERCISES

A   *For each ordered pair, state the two moves needed to locate the point.*

1. (0, −2)   **2.** (1, 2)   **3.** (−4, −1)   **4.** (3, 0)

5. (0, 2)   **6.** (−4, 0)   **7.** (0, 0)   **8.** (2.5, −1.5)

9. $\left(1\frac{1}{2}, 1\right)$ **10.** $\left(-3\frac{1}{2}, 1\right)$ **11.** $\left(\frac{3}{4}, -\frac{1}{4}\right)$ **12.** $\left(-\frac{1}{2}, 0\right)$

126

Write the coordinates of each point.

13. A $(-2, 1)$

14. B $(4, -1)$

15. C $(0, -3)$

16. D $(0, 2)$

17. E $(-1, -1)$

18. O $(0, 0)$

19. G $(-4, 0)$

20. H $(2, 2)$

21. J $\left(3, \frac{1}{2}\right)$

22. K $\left(-3, -3\frac{1}{2}\right)$

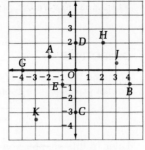

Name the corresponding point.

23. $(-4, 1)$ G

24. $(4, -1)$ D

25. $(3, -2)$ B

26. $(-3, 2)$ J

27. $(1, 1)$ F

28. $(-1, 1)$ L

29. $(0, 3)$ K

30. $(-2, -1)$ H

31. $(-2, -2.5)$ E

32. $(0, -3.5)$ M

33. $\left(1\frac{1}{2}, -1\right)$ C

34. $\left(\frac{1}{2}, -1\frac{1}{2}\right)$ A

B

Draw horizontal and vertical axes. Then graph and label points A through L.

35. $A(4, 4)$

36. $B(-4, 4)$

37. $C(-2, -3)$

38. $D(4, -3)$

39. $E(2, 3)$

40. $F(3, 2)$

41. $G(-2, 3)$

42. $H(-3, 1)$

43. $I(2, 0)$

44. $J(-4, 0)$

45. $K(0, -2)$

46. $L(0, 3)$

47. Draw a new set of axes. Connect, in order, the points $A(0, 4)$, $B(1, 1)$, $C(4, 0)$, $D(1, -1)$, $E(0, -4)$, $F(-1, -1)$, $G(-4, 0)$, $H(-1, 1)$, and $A(0, 4)$. What kind of figure have you drawn? A star

Find the number of units between each pair of points.

48. $(5, 1), (2, 1)$ 3 units

49. $(-4, 2), (3, 2)$ 7 units

50. $(-1, -7), (-1, 5)$ 12 units

C

51. Find the distance from $A(4, 3)$ to $C(-7, -2)$, going through $B(-7, 3)$. 16 units

52. Find the perimeter of a rectangle whose vertices are $(-2, 3)$, $(5, 3)$, $(5, -1)$, and $(-2, -1)$. 22 units

53. A square has four vertices. Three of them are $(0, 0)$, $(0, 4)$, and $(4, 0)$. Find the coordinates of the fourth vertex. $(4, 4)$

54. A rectangle has four vertices. Three of them are $(5, 7)$, $(-3, 7)$, and $(5, -9)$. Find the coordinates of the fourth vertex. $(-3, -9)$

*55. A parallelogram has three vertices at $(0, 0)$, $(-2, -3)$, and $(6, -3)$. The first coordinate of the fourth vertex is 4. What is the second coordinate? -6

LINEAR EQUATIONS

127

ENRICHMENT ACTIVITY

Have the students draw coordinate grids and mark the points $(-2, -1)$ and $(1, 1)$. Tell them the object of the game is to travel along grid lines only, from the point $(-2, -1)$ to the point $(1, 1)$. However, the moves can only be upward or to the right.

The challenge is to discover how many different paths can be followed. There are 10 possible paths. For example, one possible path is $(-2, -1) \rightarrow (-2, 0) \rightarrow (0, 0) \rightarrow (0, 1) \rightarrow (1, 1)$.

ADDITIONAL ANSWERS
(continued)

3. Left 4, down 1

4. Right 3, no move up or down

5. No move right or left, up 2

6. Left 4, no move up or down

7. No move, right, left, up, or down

8. Right 2.5, down 1.5

9. Right $1\frac{1}{2}$, up 1

10. Left $3\frac{1}{2}$, up 1

11. Right $\frac{3}{4}$, down $\frac{1}{4}$

12. Left $\frac{1}{2}$, no move up or down

35.–46.

State the two moves needed to locate each point.
1. (6, −2) Right 6, down 2
2. (−2, 8) Left 2, up 8
3. (5, 4) Right 5, up 4
4. (−5, −4) Left 5, down 4

LESSON NOTES

In this lesson the four quadrants are
identified and numbered. You might
wish to use a sketch such as this to
emphasize the positive and negative
values in each quadrant.

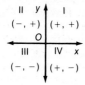

Point out that the *y*-value, or ordinate, of every point on the *x*-axis is
0. The *x*-value, or abscissa, of every
point on the *y*-axis is 0.

[*Lesson notes continue on page 129.*]

ALTERNATE EXAMPLES

1. Name the *x*-coordinate and the
   y-coordinate of each of these
   points in the coordinate plane.

   A(−3, 1)   *B*(6, 0)
   −3 is the *x*-co-   6 is the *x*-coor-
   ordinate. 1 is   dinate. 0 is the
   the *y*-coordinate. *y*-coordinate.

2. In which quadrant (I, II, III, or
   IV) or on which axis does each
   point lie?
   A(−3, 0) *B*(1, 5)   *C*(−1, −1)
    x-axis   I   III
   D(0, −1) *E*(−3, 4) *F*(4, −3)
    y-axis   II   IV

4-2 Plotting Points with Coordinates (*x, y*)

OBJECTIVES

To name the quadrant or the axis in which a given point lies.
To plot points whose coordinates satisfy a given description.

Later in this chapter you will graph algebraic equations with two variables, usually *x* and *y*. In such cases, the horizontal axis is called the
x-axis and the vertical axis is called the **y-axis.**

The x-axis and y-axis separate the plane into four **quadrants**—I, II,
III, and IV.

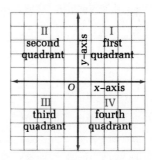

Points are located by the ordered pair (*x, y*) where the first number is
the **x-coordinate,** or **abscissa,** and the second number is the **y-coordinate,**
or **ordinate.**

EXAMPLE 1   Name the x-coordinate and the y-coordinate of each of these points in
the coordinate plane.

A(5, 2)   5 is the x-coordinate, or abscissa.
             2 is the y-coordinate, or ordinate.

B(0, −3)   0 is the x-coordinate, or abscissa.
             −3 is the y-coordinate, or ordinate.

EXAMPLE 2   In what quadrant (I, II, III, or IV) or on which axis does each point lie?

A(−1, 5)   *B*(−7, −2)   *C*(3, 3)   *D*(0, 1)   *E*(3, −2)   *F*(4, 0)
   II   III   I   y-axis   IV   x-axis

128   CHAPTER 4

It is often convenient to name a point by giving only its coordinates.

Points $(-4, 1)$, $(0, 1)$, $(2, 1)$ and $(3\frac{1}{2}, 1)$ all have a y-coordinate of 1. There are many such points and they all lie on a straight line. To show all such points, plot several and then draw a straight line through them.

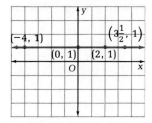

EXAMPLE 3

Graph all points in the coordinate plane whose x- and y-coordinates are equal.

Plot several points that have equal x- and y-coordinates such as $(0, 0)$, $(1, 1)$, $(-2, -2)$, and $(2\frac{1}{2}, 2\frac{1}{2})$.

There are many more points whose coordinates are equal. To show them all, draw the line through the plotted points.

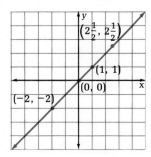

The arrowheads show that the line continues in both directions.

EXAMPLE 4

Find the y-coordinate of each point if the sum of the coordinates is -2. Then draw a graph of all such points.

Answers

a. $(0, \underline{\ ?\ })$ $(0, -2)$

b. $(-2, \underline{\ ?\ })$ $(-2, 0)$

c. $(-3, \underline{\ ?\ })$ $(-3, 1)$

d. $(0.4, \underline{\ ?\ })$ $(0.4, -2.4)$

LESSON NOTES (continued)

In discussing Example 3, note that the text asks for the graphs of all points that have equal x- and y-coordinates. Point out that it is impossible to draw every point that satisfies such a condition. We use arrowheads to show that the line extends infinitely in both directions.

Examples 3–4 and Exercises 23–26 are an important preliminary to the graphing of linear equations in the next lesson.

ALTERNATE EXAMPLES

3. Graph all the points in the coordinate plane whose y-coordinates are 1 more than their x-coordinates.

4. Find the y-coordinate of each point if the sum of the coordinates is 1. Then draw a graph of all such points.
$A(0, ?)$ $B(-3, ?)$ $C(-1, ?)$
$D(3, ?)$
$(0, 1)$ $(-3, 4)$ $(-1, 2)$
$(3, -2)$

CLASS EXERCISES

*In what quadrant (I, II, III, or IV) or on which axis (**x** or **y**) does each point lie?*

1. (2, 5)   I   **2.** (0, 1)   *y*-axis   **3.** (−4, 3)   II   **4.** (−5, 0) *x*-axis   **5.** (7, −2)   IV

6. (0, −6) *y*-axis   **7.** (−4, −3)   III   **8.** (−8, −8)   III   **9.** $\left(\frac{1}{2}, 0\right)$ *x*-axis   **10.** $\left(5, -2\frac{1}{2}\right)$ IV

Draw a single set of axes. Then graph all points that have

11. an x-coordinate of 2.   **12.** a y-coordinate of −1.

EXERCISES

A   *In what quadrant or on which axis does each point lie?*

1. (−1, −3)   III   **2.** (0, 0)   *x*-axis and *y*-axis   **3.** (15, 1)   I   **4.** (−4, 9)   II

5. (5, −7)   IV   **6.** (1, 1)   I   **7.** (−3, 0)   *x*-axis   **8.** (0, −8)   *y*-axis

9. (−1, −6)   III   **10.** (7, 3)   I   **11.** (−8, 1)   II   **12.** (4, −7)   IV

Draw a separate set of axes for each exercise. Then graph all points that have

13. a y-coordinate of 5.   **14.** an x-coordinate of 3.

15. an x-coordinate of −2.   **16.** a y-coordinate of −4.

B   *Complete the following statements about a point (**x, y**).*

17. If the x-coordinate is positive and the y-coordinate is negative, the point lies in quadrant ? .   IV

18. If both coordinates are negative, the point lies in quadrant ? .   III

19. If the x-coordinate is 0, the point must lie on the ? axis.   *y*

20. If the y-coordinate is 0, the point must lie on the ? axis.   *x*

21. All points whose y-coordinates are 2 lie on a ? (horizontal, vertical) line.   horizontal

22. All points whose x-coordinates are 3 lie on a ? (horizontal, vertical) line.   vertical

Write the coordinates of four of the points described. Plot them, and then draw a line through all such points.   Answers will vary.

23. The x-coordinate is 2 more than the y-coordinate.   (3, 1), (2, 0), (0, −2), (−3, −5)

24. The y-coordinate is 3 less than the x-coordinate.   (4, 1), (3, 0), (1, −2), (0, −3)

CHAPTER 4

25. The x-coordinate is twice the y-coordinate. $(-4, -2), (0, 0), (2, 1), (4, 2)$

26. The sum of the x- and y-coordinates is 5. $(0, 5), (1, 4), (3, 2), (5, 0)$

C *Name the quadrant or quadrants in which a point (x, y) must lie, under each of the following conditions.*

27. $x > 0$ and $y > 0$ I **28.** $x < 0$ and $y > 0$ II **29.** $x > 0$ and $y < 0$ IV

30. $x < 0$ and $y < 0$ III **31.** $xy > 0$ I or III ***32.** $2x + y = 1$ and $x > \frac{1}{2}$ IV

CHALLENGE

Symmetry

Connect these points, in order, on a grid. The figure formed is a rectangle.

$(-2, 3) \rightarrow (2, 3) \rightarrow (2, -3) \rightarrow (-2, -3) \rightarrow (-2, 3)$

The rectangle has *line symmetry*. For every point on one side of the x-axis, there is another point the same distance on the other side of the axis. It has the same x-value, but the opposite y-value.

The rectangle is also symmetric about the y-axis, for similar reasons.

The same rectangle has *point symmetry*. It is symmetric about the origin. For every point on the rectangle, there is another point with the opposite x-value *and* the opposite y-value.

Connect the points, in order, on the grid. Does the resulting figure have line symmetry? Does it have point symmetry?

1. $(4, 1) \rightarrow (4, -1) \rightarrow (-4, -1) \rightarrow (-4, 1) \rightarrow (4, 1)$ Yes; yes

2. $(0, 0) \rightarrow (0, 2) \rightarrow (1, 2) \rightarrow (1, 0) \rightarrow (-1, 0) \rightarrow (-1, -2) \rightarrow (0, -2) \rightarrow (0, 0)$ No; yes

3. $(-1, -1) \rightarrow (-1, 0) \rightarrow (0, 0) \rightarrow (0, -2) \rightarrow (-2, -2) \rightarrow (-2, 1) \rightarrow (1, 1) \rightarrow (1, 0) \rightarrow (0, 0) \rightarrow (0, 2) \rightarrow (2, 2) \rightarrow (2, -1) \rightarrow (-1, -1)$ No; yes

LINEAR EQUATIONS

131

[*Answers for Exercises and for the Challenge continue on page A1.*]

WARM-UP EXERCISES

Does the pair of values make the
equation $x - y = 3$ true?
1. $x = 5, y = 8$ No
2. $x = 10, y - 7$ Yoo
3. $x = -8, y = -11$ Yes

LESSON NOTES

Point out to the students that an
equation such as $y = x + 1$ has an
unlimited number of solutions, and
that its graph has an unlimited number of points.

To graph a straight line, only two
points are actually needed. Still, we
use additional points to check our
work. If all the points do not line up,
we know that a mistake has been
made somewhere.

Example 3 illustrates the fact that
if the coordinates of a point *do not*
satisfy a given equation, the point
does not lie on the graph of the
equation.

Notice that Exercises 43–46 prepare the way for the concept of
slope, which is introduced in the
next lesson.

ALTERNATE EXAMPLE

1. Graph the equation of
$y = x + 3$.

4-3   Graphing Linear Equations

OBJECTIVES

To graph linear equations.
To determine whether the coordinates of a point satisfy a given equation.

Each equation below is a **linear equation** because its graph is a straight
line. The variables occur in the first degree only, so they are sometimes
called *first-degree equations*.

$$y = x + 1 \qquad y = -2x \qquad y = 2 - 3x$$

To graph a linear equation, plot several points whose coordinates satisfy the equation. Then draw the line through these points.

EXAMPLE 1   Graph the equation $y = x + 1$.

Step 1   Make a table containing
several values of x.

x	−2	−1	0	1	2
y	?	?	?	?	?

Step 2   Find the y-coordinate that corresponds to each x-coordinate. To do this,
substitute the values for x in the equation.

Let $x = -2$.	Let $x = -1$.	Let $x = 0$.	Let $x = 1$.	Let $x = 2$.
$y = x + 1$	$y = x + 1$	$y = x + 1$	$y = x + 1$	$y = x + 1$
$y = -2 + 1$	$y = -1 + 1$	$y = 0 + 1$	$y = 1 + 1$	$y = 2 + 1$
$y = -1$	$y = 0$	$y = 1$	$y = 2$	$y = 3$

Step 3   Each pair of numbers gives the coordinates of a point. Plot each point.

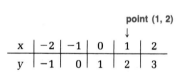

point (1, 2)

x	−2	−1	0	1	2
y	−1	0	1	2	3

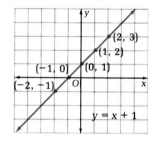

Step 4   Draw a line through the points. The line is the graph of $y = x + 1$.
This equation can also be written in other forms, such as

$$y - x = 1 \text{ or } y - x - 1 = 0.$$

It is often convenient to refer to a line by its equation. Note that the
next example is about "line" $y = -2x$.

132

EXAMPLE 2 Graph the line $y = -2x$.

Step 1 Select several values for x.

Step 2 Complete a table showing y-values that correspond to the x-values you chose.

x	-2	-1	0	1	2
y	4	2	0	-2	-4

Step 3 Plot the points. Draw a line through the points.

The **solution set** of a linear equation is the set of ordered pairs that satisfy the equation. Each **solution,** or ordered pair, represents the coordinates of a point on the line.

EXAMPLE 3 Tell whether the ordered pair *is* or *is not* a solution of the equation $y = 2 - 3x$.

a. (−1, 5)

$y = 2 - 3x$
$5 \overset{?}{=} 2 - 3(-1)$
$5 = 5$ ✔ true

The ordered pair $(-1, 5)$ is a solution. The point is on the line.

b. (4, −12)

$y = 2 - 3x$
$-12 \overset{?}{=} 2 - 3(4)$
$-12 = -10$ false

The ordered pair $(4, -12)$ is *not* a solution. The point is not on the line.

CLASS EXERCISES

Complete the table for each equation. Then draw the corresponding graph.

1. $y = 2x$

x	-3	-2	-1	0	1	2
y	-6	-4	?	?	?	?
			-2	0	2	4

2. $y = x - 2$

x	-2	-1	0	1	2	3
y	?	?	?	?	?	?
	-4	-3	-2	-1	0	1

3. $y = -x + 1$

x	-5	-3	-1	1	3	5
y	?	?	?	?	?	?
	6	4	2	0	-2	-4

4. $y = \frac{1}{2}x$

x	0	1	2	3	4	5
y	?	?	?	?	?	?
	0	$\frac{1}{2}$	1	$1\frac{1}{2}$	2	$2\frac{1}{2}$

*Does the given ordered pair satisfy the equation? Write **yes** or **no**.*

5. $y = x + 5$ $(-2, 7)$ No

6. $y = x - 7$ $(7, 0)$ Yes

7. $y = -5x - 1$ $(0, -1)$ Yes

8. $y = x - \frac{1}{2}$ $(2\frac{1}{2}, 2)$ Yes

LINEAR EQUATIONS

133

EXERCISES

A *Complete the table for each equation.*

1. $y = x + 2$

x	-3	-2	-1	0	1	2	3
y	?	?	?	?	?	?	?
	-1	0	1	2	3	4	5

2. $y = 3x$

x	-2	-1	0	1	2
y	?	?	?	?	?
	-6	-3	0	3	6

3. $y = -x + 2$

x	-3	-2	-1	0	1	2	3
y	?	?	?	?	?	?	?
	5	4	3	2	1	0	-1

4. $y = -3x$

x	-2	-1	0	1	2
y	?	?	?	?	?
	6	3	0	-3	-6

Graph each equation. First plot and label at least three points on the graph.

5. $y = x + 3$ 6. $y = x - 3$ 7. $y = -x - 3$ 8. $y = -x + 4$

9. $y = -x + 5$ 10. $y = x - 1$ 11. $y = x - 4$ 12. $y = -x - 4$

13. $y = -x - 6$ 14. $y = 3x$ 15. $y = 4x$ 16. $y = -2x$

B 17. $y = 2x + 1$ 18. $y = 2x - 1$ 19. $y = -2x + 1$

20. $y = -2x - 1$ 21. $y = 2x + 3$ 22. $y = 3x + 2$

23. $y = 5x - 3$ 24. $y = 4x - 1$ 25. $y = -2x + 2$

26. $y = -5x + 5$ 27. $y = -2x - 3$ 28. $y = -3x - 2$

*Is the given ordered pair a solution of the equation? Write **yes** or **no**.*

29. $y = \frac{1}{2}x$ $(4, 4)$ No   30. $y = \frac{1}{2}x + 2$ $(4, 4)$ Yes

31. $y = \frac{1}{4}x$ $(-4, 1)$ No   32. $y = -\frac{1}{4}x - 4$ $(-4, 0)$ No

33. $y = \frac{1}{2}x + \frac{1}{2}$ $\left(0, \frac{1}{2}\right)$ Yes   34. $y = \frac{1}{4}x + \frac{1}{4}$ $(7, 2)$ Yes

35. $4x - 3y = 0$ $(0, 0)$ Yes   36. $2x + 3y = 9$ $(0, 9)$ No

37. $x + 3y - 6 = 0$ $(0, 2)$ Yes   38. $3x - 2y = 8$ $(0, 8)$ No

39. $3x + 2y = 10$ $(0, 5)$ Yes   40. $2x + 4y = 1$ $\left(\frac{1}{4}, \frac{1}{8}\right)$ Yes

C 41. Find k if $(3, k)$ is a point on the line $y = -\frac{2}{5}x + \frac{1}{5}$. -1

42. Which of these three points are on the line $y = -4x + 6$?
    $A(2.2, -2.8)$, $B(2.5, 4)$, $C(1.5, 0)$ *A and C*

134

Match the following equations with the lines at the right. For each exercise, write *l*, *m*, *n*, or *p*.

43. $y = 2x + 2$ *m*

44. $y = 2x$ *n*

45. $y = 2x - 2$ *p*

46. $y = 2x + 4$ *l*

*47. Find the point that is on each of the lines $y - x = 2$ and $x + y = 0$. $(-1, 1)$

CHECKPOINT

Write the coordinates of each point.

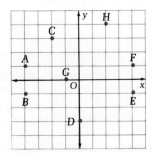

1. A $(-4, 1)$ **2.** B $(-4, -1)$

3. C $(-2, 3)$ **4.** D $(0, -3)$

5. E $(4, -1)$ **6.** F $(4, 1)$

7. G $(-1, 0)$ **8.** H $(2, 4)$

In what quadrant or on which axis does each point lie?

9. $(1, 2)$ I   **10.** $(-2, 0)$ *x*-axis   **11.** $(-4, -3)$ III   **12.** $(0, 0)$ *x* and *y* axes

13. $(-3, 8)$ II   **14.** $(4, -2)$ IV   **15.** $(0, 3)$ *y*-axis   **16.** $(25, 64)$ I

Plot four of the points described. Then draw a line through all such points.

17. The *y*-coordinate is 2 more than the *x*-coordinate.

18. The *x*-coordinate is $\frac{1}{2}$ the *y*-coordinate.

Graph each equation. First plot and label at least four points on the graph.

19. $y = 4x + 4$ **20.** $y = -\frac{1}{2}x + 6$ **21.** $y = -3x - 3$

Is the given ordered pair a solution of the equation? Write **yes** or **no**.

22. $y = 2x$ $(0.5, 1)$ Yes   **23.** $y = -x$ $(-3, 3)$ Yes   **24.** $y = -6x + 1$ $(1, 5)$ No

LINEAR EQUATIONS   **135**

In each group, which two ratios are equivalent?

1. $\dfrac{6}{10}, \dfrac{4}{6}, \dfrac{3}{5}$ $\dfrac{6}{10}$ and $\dfrac{3}{5}$

2. $\dfrac{-2}{-4}, \dfrac{1}{2}, -\dfrac{1}{2}$ $\dfrac{-2}{-4}$ and $\dfrac{1}{2}$

3. $\dfrac{-8}{12}, \dfrac{-6}{8}, \dfrac{-3}{4}$ $\dfrac{-6}{8}$ and $\dfrac{-3}{4}$

LESSON NOTES

In discussing the formula $m = \dfrac{y_2 - y_1}{x_2 - x_1}$, point out that the subscripts provide a way of referring to the co-ordinates of the two points. (x_1, y_1) are the coordinates of one point, P. (x_2, y_2) are the coordinates of the other point, Q.

Emphasize that when we subtract x-coordinates and y-coordinates, we must use the coordinates in the same order. We must find $\dfrac{y_2 - y_1}{x_2 - x_1}$, or we must find $\dfrac{y_1 - y_2}{x_1 - x_2}$.

ALTERNATE EXAMPLE

1. Find the slope of each line.

slope $= \dfrac{1}{6}$

slope $= 3$

4-4   Slope of a Line

OBJECTIVES

To find the slope of a line that contains two given points.
To tell whether the slope of a given line is positive, negative, or 0.

Which path is steeper?

This path rises 240 feet over a horizontal run of 600 feet.

$$\dfrac{\text{rise}}{\text{run}} = \dfrac{240}{600} = \dfrac{2}{5}$$

This path rises 120 feet over a horizontal run of 300 feet.

$$\dfrac{\text{rise}}{\text{run}} = \dfrac{120}{300} = \dfrac{2}{5}$$

Both ratios of rise to run are $\dfrac{2}{5}$. This means that the paths are equally steep.

The steepness, or **slope**, of a line is given by the ratio of *rise* to *run*. *Rise* refers to units of *vertical* change between any two points on the line. *Run* refers to the corresponding *horizontal* change between the same two points.

EXAMPLE 1   Find the slope of each line.

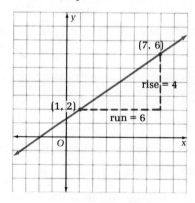

$$\text{slope} = \dfrac{\text{rise}}{\text{run}} = \dfrac{4}{6} = \dfrac{2}{3}$$

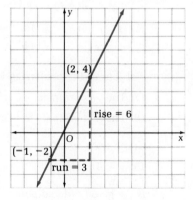

$$\text{slope} = \dfrac{\text{rise}}{\text{run}} = \dfrac{6}{3} = 2$$

You can also find the rise by subtracting the y-coordinates of any two points on the line. To find the run, subtract the corresponding x-coordinates, in the same order.

EXAMPLE 2   Find the slope of the line containing the points with coordinates (2, 7) and (8, 10).

$$\text{slope} = \frac{\text{vertical change}}{\text{horizontal change}} = \frac{\text{difference of } y\text{-coordinates}}{\text{difference of } x\text{-coordinates}}$$

$$\text{slope} = \frac{10 - 7}{8 - 2} = \frac{3}{6} = \frac{1}{2}$$

The ratio is the same if the coordinates are subtracted in reverse order.

$$\frac{7 - 10}{2 - 8} = \frac{-3}{-6} = \frac{1}{2}$$

Let $P(x_1, y_1)$ and $Q(x_2, y_2)$ be any two different points on a line, with $x_1 \neq x_2$. Then the slope m of the line is given by the formula:

$$m = \frac{y_2 - y_1}{x_2 - x_1}$$

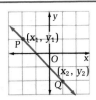

The slope of a line can be positive, zero, or negative. The slope of a line that goes "uphill" from left to right is positive. The slope of a horizonal line is 0. The slope of a line that goes "downhill" from left to right is negative.

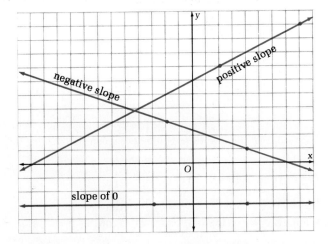

2. Find the slope of the line containing the points with coordinates (5, 8) and (7, 11).

$$\text{slope} = \frac{3}{2}$$

POSSIBLE ERROR

In finding slopes, some students will carelessly subtract the y-values in one order, and the x-values in the other order.

For instance, in Example 3, they might write

$$m = \frac{1 - 3}{-2 - 4} = \frac{-2}{-6} = \frac{1}{3}$$
(incorrect)

To help them avoid this type of error, stress the need for them to check the *order* they have used. The first number used in the numerator and the first number used in the denominator must be obtained from the same ordered pair. Similarly, the second numbers in the numerator and denominator must be obtained from another ordered pair.

3. Find the slope of the line that contains the points $(-3, 5)$ and $(2, -1)$. Use the formula $m = \dfrac{y_2 - y_1}{x_2 - x_1}$. $m = -\dfrac{6}{5}$

4. Find the slope of the line that contains $(6, -2)$ and $(5, -2)$. $m = 0$

Find the slope of the line through the two given points.

1. $(-3, 7)$ and $(5, 4)$ $-\dfrac{3}{8}$

2. $(6, 8)$ and $(-4, 5)$ $\dfrac{3}{10}$

3. $(7, -5)$ and $(-3, 6)$ $-\dfrac{11}{10}$

4. $(-5, -4)$ and $(-4, -7)$ -3

5. $(2, 2)$ and $(6, 2)$ 0

EXAMPLE 3   Find the slope of the line that contains $(-2, 3)$ and $(4, 1)$.

Use the formula: $m = \dfrac{y_2 - y_1}{x_2 - x_1}$

$$m = \frac{1 - 3}{4 - (-2)} = \frac{-2}{6} = -\frac{1}{3}$$

The slope is the same if you use the points in reverse order.

$$m = \frac{3 - 1}{-2 - 4} = \frac{2}{-6} = -\frac{1}{3}$$

Since the slope is negative, the line goes from upper left to lower right in the coordinate plane.

EXAMPLE 4   Find the slope of the line that contains $(-3, -3)$ and $(4, -3)$.

$$m = \frac{-3 - (-3)}{4 - (-3)} = \frac{0}{7} = 0 \qquad \text{A line with slope 0 is horizontal.}$$

CLASS EXERCISES

Simplify each ratio.

1. $\dfrac{6 - 3}{9 - 5}$ $\dfrac{3}{4}$
2. $\dfrac{4 - 7}{3 - 8}$ $\dfrac{3}{5}$
3. $\dfrac{3 - (-5)}{5 - (-7)}$ $\dfrac{2}{3}$
4. $\dfrac{4 - 5}{6 - 2}$ $-\dfrac{1}{4}$
5. $\dfrac{-4 - (-4)}{3 - (-4)}$ 0

6. For each line a–d, tell whether the slope is positive, 0, or negative.

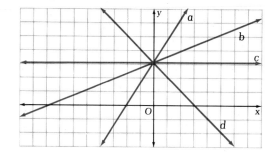

a. Positive
b. Positive
c. 0
d. Negative

Find the slope of the line through the two given points.

7. $(3, 4), (5, 6)$ 1
8. $(1, 7), (4, 13)$ 2
9. $(2, 1), (7, 3)$ $\dfrac{2}{5}$

10. $(-2, -1), (6, -1)$ 0
11. $(3, 1), (-2, 6)$ -1
12. $(-4, -1), (0, -3)$ $-\dfrac{1}{2}$

13. $(0, 0), (1, 2)$ 2
14. $(0, 0), (1, 4)$ 4
15. $(0, 0), (1, -5)$ -5

16. $(0, 0), (2, 7)$ $\dfrac{7}{2}$
17. $(3, -4), (0, 0)$ $-\dfrac{4}{3}$
18. $(0, 0), (-6, -2)$ $\dfrac{1}{3}$

EXERCISES

A *Simplify each ratio.*

1. $\dfrac{5-2}{8-4}$ $\dfrac{3}{4}$ 2. $\dfrac{3-7}{5-8}$ $\dfrac{4}{3}$ 3. $\dfrac{4-(-3)}{9-(-5)}$ $\dfrac{1}{2}$ 4. $\dfrac{2-(-8)}{5-(-5)}$ 1

5. $\dfrac{2-5}{7-2}$ $-\dfrac{3}{5}$ 6. $\dfrac{-3-3}{5-1}$ $-\dfrac{3}{2}$ 7. $\dfrac{10-0}{-2-2}$ $-\dfrac{5}{2}$ 8. $\dfrac{7-7}{6-5}$ 0

Find the slope of each line.

9.

10.

11.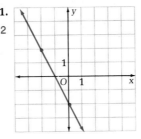

Find the slope of the line through the two given points.

12. $(-1, 5), (3, 2)$ $-\dfrac{3}{4}$ 13. $(4, 6), (-2, 3)$ $\dfrac{1}{2}$ 14. $(5, -3), (-1, 4)$ $-\dfrac{7}{6}$

15. $(2, 3), (-1, -2)$ $\dfrac{5}{3}$ 16. $(-3, -2), (-2, -5)$ -3 17. $(-1, -5), (-2, -7)$ 2

18. $(3, -8), (-1, -5)$ $-\dfrac{3}{4}$ 19. $(4, -3), (-1, -8)$ 1 20. $(10, -5), (6, -2)$ $-\dfrac{3}{4}$

21. $(3, 1), (5, 1)$ 0 22. $(0, 0), \left(-\dfrac{1}{2}, \dfrac{1}{4}\right)$ $-\dfrac{1}{2}$ 23. $\left(-\dfrac{1}{4}, -\dfrac{1}{4}\right), \left(\dfrac{1}{2}, \dfrac{1}{2}\right)$ 1

B 24. $(0, 0), \left(3\dfrac{1}{2}, -5\dfrac{1}{4}\right)$ $-\dfrac{3}{2}$ 25. $(0, 0), (4, 0)$ 0 26. $\left(3\dfrac{1}{2}, -5\dfrac{1}{4}\right), \left(-\dfrac{1}{2}, \dfrac{1}{4}\right)$ $-\dfrac{11}{8}$

*Refer to lines **a–e** at the right.*

27. Which line has a slope that is equal to 1?   *a*

28. Which line has a slope of 0?   *d*

29. Which line has a slope that is a negative number?   *e*

30. Which line has a slope that is equal to the slope of line *b*?   *c*

31. Which lines have slopes that are opposites?   *a* and *e*

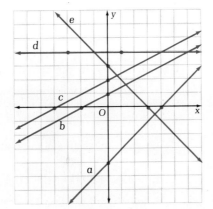

LINEAR EQUATIONS

ASSIGNMENT GUIDE
(pages 139–140)

Minimum course: 1–11, 13–23 odd

Average course: 1–25 odd, 27–31

Maximum course: 9–25 odd, 27–31, 33–39 odd

ENRICHMENT ACTIVITY

The slope of a vertical line is undefined because division by 0 is undefined. However, it is less obvious that the slope can be made as large as one desires.

Illustrate this by selecting a point. Then have students give another point such that the slope of the line connecting them is some large given value. For example:

The original point is (2, 3) and the slope is 1000.

Possible responses: (3, 1003), (1, −997), and others.

Using BASIC

The following program may be used to compute and display the slope of a line from two of its points. Note that the slope will be displayed in decimal form rather than in fraction form.

```
10 PRINT "ENTER
   COORDINATES"
20 PRINT "FIRST POINT"
30 INPUT X1, Y1
40 PRINT "SECOND POINT"
50 INPUT X2, Y2
60 LET S = (Y2 - Y1) / (X2 -
   X1)
70 PRINT "SLOPE IS "; S
90 END
```

Each pair of coordinates should be entered without parentheses, but separated by a comma.

EXTRA PRACTICE, page 514

32.

33.

34.

35.

36.

37.

C

Graph the line that contains the given point and has the given slope.

Sample point: (2, 1)
slope: 3

To graph the line, first plot the point (2, 1). Then use the rise and the run from that point to locate another point.

Another point on the line is (2 + 1, 1 + 3), or (3, 4).

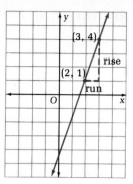

32. point: (1, 3)

slope: $\frac{1}{2}$

33. point: (3, 5)

slope: $-\frac{1}{3}$

34. point: (2, 3)

slope: 2

35. point: (−2, 3)

slope: 3

36. point: (−2, 4)

slope: −1

37. point: (1, 1)

slope: 0

*Find the slope of the line that contains the given points. Both **a** and **b** are nonzero, with **a** ≠ **b**.*

38. (a, b), (2a, b)   0

39. (a, b), (3a, 3b) $\frac{b}{a}$

40. (a + b, a − b), (2a + b, 2a − b)   1

*41. Three vertices of a parallelogram are located at (−1, −1), (−2, 3), and (3, 6). Find all possible choices for the fourth vertex.   (4, 2), (2, 10), (−6, −4)

USING THE CALCULATOR

Slope of a Line

Calculator results can be fast and accurate *if* you give correct directions.

1. Think of the line through points (0.2, 3.5) and (1.8, 1). List the keys in the sequence you would use them to find the slope of the line, doing all of the work on a calculator.   Answers may vary.

The coordinates of two points on a line are given. Find the slope of the line, to the nearest hundredth.

2. (−4.80, 1.36), (4.73, −9.01)   −1.09

3. (8.04, 13.98), (−3.44, −14.66) 2.49

4. (−0.01, −0.07), (−3.18, 2.09) −0.68

5. (0.68, −4.72), (2.73, −9.50)   −2.33

140

4-5   x- and y-Intercepts

OBJECTIVES

To determine the x- and y-intercepts of a line from the graph of the line or from its equation.

To use the x- and y-intercepts to draw a line.

The line shown at the right crosses the x-axis at $A(-5, 0)$ and the y-axis at $B(0, 3)$.

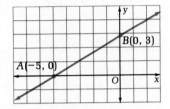

The x-intercept is -5.

The y-intercept is 3.

> The *x-intercept* of a line is the x-coordinate when $y = 0$.
>
> The *y-intercept* of a line is the y-coordinate when $x = 0$.

EXAMPLE 1   Find the x- and y-intercepts for $y = 4x - 2$.

Substitute 0 for y. Solve for x.	Substitute 0 for x. Solve for y.
$y = 4x - 2$	$y = 4x - 2$
$0 = 4x - 2$	$y = 4(0) - 2$
$2 = 4x$	$y = -2$ **y-intercept**
$\frac{1}{2} = x$ **x-intercept**	

The line crosses the x-axis at $(\frac{1}{2}, 0)$ and the y-axis at $(0, -2)$.

EXAMPLE 2   Find the x- and y-intercepts for $3x + 2y = -6$, and draw the graph.

Let y = 0.	Let x = 0.
$3x + 2y = -6$	$3x + 2y = -6$
$3x + 2(0) = -6$	$3(0) + 2y = -6$
$3x + 0 = -6$	$0 + 2y = -6$
$3x = -6$	$2y = -6$
$x = -2$	$y = -3$

The x-intercept is -2. The line crosses the x-axis at $(-2, 0)$.
The y-intercept is -3. The line crosses the y-axis at $(0, -3)$.

LINEAR EQUATIONS

141

3. The x-intercept of a line is −5. The y-intercept is 1. Find the slope of the line. **Slope is $\frac{1}{5}$.**

POSSIBLE ERROR

Students sometimes make errors with intercepts by reversing the definitions. They incorrectly assume that the x-intercept has an x-value of 0, and that the y-intercept has a y-value of 0. This is a serious mistake.

You can use additional problems similar to the Examples to help correct this error. Repeat often that the x-intercept has a y-value of 0, and the y-intercept has an x-value of 0.

DAILY QUIZ

Find the x- and y-intercepts for each equation.

1. $y = 2x + 4$ −2; 4

2. $y = 4x + 2$ $-\frac{1}{2}$; 2

3. $y = -6x - 7$ $-\frac{7}{6}$; −7

4. $y = -7x - 6$ $-\frac{6}{7}$; −6

5. $x - y = 2$ 2; −2

ASSIGNMENT GUIDE
(pages 142–144)

Minimum course: 1–3, 5–31 odd
   second day: 20–38 even,
      40–45
Average course: 1–3, 5–45 odd
   second day: 32–48 even,
      49–54
Maximum course: 5–47 odd,
      49–54
   second day: 32–48 even,
      55–58
All courses: *Strategies for
   Problem
   Solving*

EXAMPLE 3 The x-intercept of a line is −6. The y-intercept is 3. Find the slope of the line.

To find the slope, use the points (−6, 0) and (0, 3).

$$m = \frac{3 - 0}{0 - (-6)} = \frac{3}{6} = \frac{1}{2}$$

The slope is $\frac{1}{2}$.

CLASS EXERCISES

*Find the **x-intercept** and the **y-intercept** for each graph or equation.*

1.

x-int. −2; y-int. 1

2.

x-int. −1; y-int. −3

3.

x-int. 3; y-int. 2

4. $y = 3x + 6$
x-int. −2; y-int. 6

5. $y = 2x + 5$
x-int. $-\frac{5}{2}$; y-int. 5

6. $y = \frac{2}{3}x - 4$
x-int. 6; y-int. −4

7. $x + y = 1$
x-int. 1; y-int. 1

8. $2x - y = -4$
x-int. −2; y-int. 4

9. $y - x - 2 = 0$
x-int. −2; y-int. 2

EXERCISES

A *Find the **x-intercept** and the **y-intercept** for each line.*

1.

1; 2

2.

−3; 3

3.

−2; −1

*Find the **y-intercept** for each equation.*

4. $y = 4x + 3$ 3 **5.** $y = 3x + 4$ 4 **6.** $y = -2x + 4$ 4 **7.** $y = 7x + 6$ 6

8. $y = 7x - 3$ −3 **9.** $y = -8x - 3$ −3 **10.** $y = -8x - 5$ −5 **11.** $y = 6x$ 0

*Find the **x-intercept** for each equation.*

12. $y = 2x$ 0 **13.** $y = 2x + 2$ −1 **14.** $y = 2x - 2$ 1 **15.** $y = 3x + 6$ −2

16. $y = 3x - 6$ 2 **17.** $y = -4x - 2$ $-\frac{1}{2}$ **18.** $y = -4x + 2$ $\frac{1}{2}$ **19.** $y = 8x + 4$ $-\frac{1}{2}$

CHAPTER 4

EXTRA PRACTICE, page 514

Find the **x**-intercept and the **y**-intercept for each equation.

20. $y = 5x - 2\frac{2}{5}$; -2 **21.** $y = 2x - 5$ $\frac{5}{2}$; -5 **22.** $y = -4x - 5$ $-\frac{5}{4}$; **23.** $y = -5x - 4$ $-\frac{4}{5}$;

24. $y = 3x$ $0; 0$ **25.** $y = 3x + 1$ $-\frac{1}{3}$; 1 **26.** $y = x$ -5 **27.** $y = -x$ -4

$0; 0$ $0; 0$

28. $y = -2x$ $0; 0$ **29.** $x + y = 2$ $2; 2$ **30.** $3x - y = 6$ **31.** $x - y - 3 = 0$

$2; -6$ $3; -3$

B **32.** $y - x = \frac{1}{2}$ $-\frac{1}{2}; \frac{1}{2}$ **33.** $2x - y = -\frac{1}{2}$ $-\frac{1}{4}; \frac{1}{2}$ **34.** $y - 2 = \frac{1}{2}x$ $-4; 2$ **35.** $2x + 3y = 5$ $\frac{5}{2}; \frac{5}{3}$

36. $3x - 5y = 2$ $\frac{2}{3}; -\frac{2}{5}$ **37.** $x - 4y + 3 = 0$ $-3; \frac{3}{4}$ **38.** $1.5x = 3y$ $0; 0$ **39.** $5x + 1.5 = 3y$ $-0.3; 0.5$

Find the slope for each line. Then draw the graph.

40. x-intercept: 3
y-intercept: 2 $-\frac{2}{3}$

41. x-intercept: -2
y-intercept: 5 $\frac{5}{2}$

42. x-intercept: -4
y-intercept: -4 -1

Find the intercepts for each line.

43.

y-int. 2

44.

x-int. 2

45.

y-int. -1

46.

x-int. -1

47.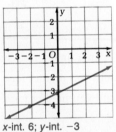

x-int. 6; y-int. -3

48.

x-int. 6; y-int. 6

Find the **x**- and **y**-intercepts. Use the intercepts to graph each equation.

49. $y = -2x + 4$ x-int. 2 y-int. 4 **50.** $y = -3x + 6$ x-int. 2 y-int. 6 **51.** $3x + 2y = 12$ x-int. 4 y-int. 6

52. $y = -2x - 2$ x-int. -1 y-int. -2 **53.** $y - 5x - 5 = 0$ x-int. -1 y-int. 5 **54.** $y - 3 = 3x$ x-int. -1 y-int. 3

C Use the **x**- and **y**-intercepts to graph each linear equation.

55. $\frac{x}{5} + \frac{y}{3} = 1$ x-int. 5; y-int. 3 **56.** $-\frac{x}{2} + \frac{y}{4} = 1$ x-int. -2; y-int. 4 **57.** $\frac{x}{6} - \frac{y}{4} = 1$ x-int. 6; y-int. -4 **58.** $x + \frac{y}{5} = 1$ x-int. 1; y-int. 5

LINEAR EQUATIONS 143

ENRICHMENT ACTIVITY

Have the students mark these four points in the coordinate plane.

$A(0, 4)$ $B(5, 0)$
$C(0, -4)$ $D(-5, 0)$

Then have them give the equations for all the lines that contain pairs of these points.

$y = -\frac{4}{5}x + 4$, $y = \frac{4}{5}x + 4$,

$y = -\frac{4}{5}x - 4$, $y = \frac{4}{5}x - 4$,

$y = 0, x = 0$

ADDITIONAL ANSWERS

Exercises

40.

41.

42.

[Answers continue on page A2.]

Strategies for Problem Solving

Organizing and graphing data is a procedure often used in science and industry. The discovery of patterns sometimes makes it possible to predict other data.

In this Strategies for Problem Solving, students discover that the ordered pairs (height, weight) correspond to points that lie on a line.

When graphing data in real-life situations, it is highly unlikely that the points will be exactly collinear. To determine whether a linear relationship exists, it is sufficient if the points tend to cluster about a straight line.

Stress the use of graphs such as this as a helpful aid in recognizing trends and making predictions.

ADDITIONAL ANSWERS

Strategies for Problem Solving

1. (69, 150), (65, 132), (75, 177), (71, 159)

6. No. These data apply to men of age 25 and of medium frame. They do not represent a trend for women or for men of other ages or frames.

7. The slope is $\frac{9}{2}$.

8. No. Neither a height nor a weight of 0 would have any application.

STRATEGIES for PROBLEM SOLVING

Organizing and Interpreting Data

Organizing data often leads to the discovery of a pattern or trend.

Here are the heights and weights of four men, age 25 and of medium frame. Is there a connection between their heights and their weights?

	Height	Weight
A	69 in.	150 lb
B	65 in.	132 lb
C	75 in.	177 lb
D	71 in.	159 lb

Draw a graph.

1. Make number pairs from the data and plot each point. Let the horizontal axis show height and the vertical axis show weight.

Look for a trend.

2. Are all the points on a line?   Yes, the points are collinear.

3. What weight would you predict for a height of 73 in.?   168 lb

4. What height would you predict for a weight of 141 lb?   67 in.

Interpret the results.

5. For the data given, what appears to be the weight increase in pounds for each additional inch of height? $4\frac{1}{2}$ pounds increase

6. Does everybody's height and weight fit the trend for these data? Explain your answer.

7. How would you describe the slope for these data?

8. Would intercepts have any meaning in this problem?

144

144

4-6　Slope-Intercept Form

OBJECTIVES

To find the slope and the y-intercept of a line when its equation is in the form $y = mx + b$.

To write a linear equation, given the slope and the y-intercept.

To rewrite an equation in the slope-intercept form.

Every linear equation in the form $y = mx$ represents a line through the origin, with slope m. The line $y = 2x$ passes through the origin and has a slope of 2. Its y-intercept is 0, as shown at the left below.

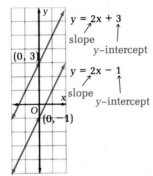

As shown at the right, if every y-value in $y = 2x$ is increased by 3, the new equation is $y = 2x + 3$. Its slope is 2, but its y-intercept is 3. If every y-value in $y = 2x$ is decreased by 1, the new equation is $y = 2x - 1$. Its slope is 2, but its y-intercept is −1.

When two lines have the same slope but different y-intercepts, they are *parallel*. The lines $y = 2x + 3$ and $y = 2x - 1$, shown above, are parallel. Both have the same slope, but different y-intercepts.

Slope-Intercept Form of a Linear Equation

$$y = mx + b$$

The slope is m. The y-intercept is b.

EXAMPLE 1　　Find the slope and the y-intercept for each equation.

$y = 4x + 1$	$y = -3x + 2$	$y = x - 5$
slope: 4	slope: −3	slope:　1
y-intercept: 1	y-intercept:　2	y-intercept: −5

LINEAR EQUATIONS

145

Solve for y.
1. $2y = 6x + 4$　$y = 3x + 2$
2. $y - x = 8$　$y = x + 8$
3. $4y - 3x = 0$　$y = \dfrac{3x}{4}$

LESSON NOTES

Discuss the fact that a linear equation can be written in many forms. Point out, however, that the slope-intercept form, $y = mx + b$, is extremely useful. In this form, the slope and the y-intercept of the line are obvious. This makes the graphing of the equation easy.

　Note that Example 4 shows the procedure for graphing an equation when the slope and y-intercept are known. As you discuss Example 4, be sure the students understand that when the y-intercept is given as a single number such as 1, we are really referring to the ordered pair (0, 1).

　Exercises 45–47 provide valuable experiences for the students. To decide if three points lie on the same line, the students can calculate the slope by using the first and second points, and then calculate it again by using the second and third (or first and third) points. If the slope is the same in both calculations, then the points are collinear.

ALTERNATE EXAMPLE

1. Find the slope and the y-intercept for each equation.
   a. $y = -2x - 3$　b. $y = x - 1$
   　slope: −2　　　 slope: 1
   　y-int.: −3　　　 y-int.: −1
   c. $y = 5x$
   　slope: 5
   　y-int.: 0

2. The slope of a line is 4, and its y-intercept is -1. Write an equation for the line.
$y = 4x - 1$

3. Rewrite the equation $5x - 3y = 9$ in slope-intercept form. Then find the slope and y-intercept. $y = \frac{5}{3}x - 3$; slope $\frac{5}{3}$; y-int. -3

4. Use the slope and the y-intercept to graph the equation $y = \frac{5}{2}x - 2$.

(0, −2)

146

EXAMPLE 2   The slope of a line is 3 and its y-intercept is -4. Write an equation for the line.

$$y = mx + b$$
$$y = 3x + (-4)$$
$$y = 3x - 4$$

EXAMPLE 3   Rewrite the equation $3x + 2y = 4$ in slope-intercept form. Then find the slope and the y-intercept.

$3x + 2y = 4$	Solve the equation for y.
$2y = -3x + 4$	Subtract $3x$ from each side.
$\frac{1}{2}(2y) = \frac{1}{2}(-3x + 4)$	Multiply each side by $\frac{1}{2}$.
$y = -\frac{3}{2}x + 2$	The slope-intercept form of the equation

The slope is $-\frac{3}{2}$. The y-intercept is 2.

EXAMPLE 4   Use the slope and the y-intercept to graph the equation $y = \frac{1}{2}x + 1$.

Since the y-intercept is 1, plot $(0, 1)$.
   The slope, $\frac{1}{2}$, is the ratio of rise to run. Therefore, from the point $(0, 1)$, go 2 units to the right and 1 unit up to locate another point.

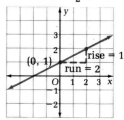

CLASS EXERCISES

Find the slope and the y-intercept for each equation.

1. $y = \frac{1}{2}x$ $\frac{1}{2}$; 0   **2.** $y = -8x$ -8; 0   **3.** $y = 2x + 9$ 2; 9   **4.** $y = 6x - 3$ 6; -3

5. $y = -\frac{1}{3}x + 2$ **6.** $y = -x - 5$ **7.** $y = \frac{2}{3}x + 3$ **8.** $y = -2x$
$-\frac{1}{3}$; 2 -1; -5 $\frac{2}{3}$; 3 -2; 0

Write the equation for each line in slope-intercept form.

9. $m = 4$; $b = 1$ **10.** $m = 1$; $b = 4$ **11.** $m = 1$; $b = 4.5$ **12.** $m = -2$; $b = \frac{3}{4}$
$y = 4x + 1$ $y = x + 4$ $y = x + 4.5$ $y = -2x + \frac{3}{4}$

Rewrite in slope-intercept form. Then find the slope and the y-intercept.

13. $y + 3x = 9$ **14.** $2y = 8x - 6$ **15.** $3 - y = x$ **16.** $3x - 2y = 12$
$y = -3x + 9$; -3, 9 $y = 4x - 3$; 4, -3 $y = -x + 3$; -1, 3 $y = \frac{3}{2}x - 6$; $\frac{3}{2}$, -6

146

EXERCISES

A *Find the slope and the **y**-intercept for each equation.*

1. $y = -2x$ **2.** $y = 2x + 5$ **3.** $y = 5x - 2$ **4.** $y = 3x - 4$

5. $y = \frac{2}{3}x$ **6.** $y = \frac{4}{3}x - \frac{2}{3}$ **7.** $y = \frac{1}{2}x - 1$ **8.** $y = -\frac{1}{2}x + 2$

Write the equation for each line in slope-intercept form.

9. $m = 3, b = 0$
$y = 3x$

10. $m = -5, b = -3$
$y = -5x - 3$

11. $m = -3, b = -5$
$y = -3x - 5$

12. $m = -2, b = 0$
$y = -2x$

13. $m = 0, b = 3$
$y = 3$

14. $m = 0, b = 72$
$y = 72$

15. $m = \frac{1}{4}, b = 3$
$y = \frac{1}{4}x + 3$

16. $m = \frac{1}{2}, b = -16$
$y = \frac{1}{2}x - 16$

17. $m = -\frac{2}{3}, b = -5$
$y = -\frac{2}{3}x - 5$

18. $m = \frac{3}{4}, b = -3$
$y = \frac{3}{4}x - 3$

19. $m = 1.2, b = 1$
$y = 1.2x + 1$

20. $m = 0.5, b = 5$
$y = 0.5x + 5$

*Rewrite in slope-intercept form. Then find the slope and the **y**-intercept.*

21. $4x + y = 7$ **22.** $3y - x = 6$ **23.** $y - 3x = 4$

24. $3y - 4x = -2$ **25.** $10y - 15x = 4$ **26.** $4x - 4y = 3$

27. $2y - x = 1$ **28.** $x - 4y = -1$ **29.** $y - 4x = 6$

30. $2x + y = -1$ **31.** $x - 3y = 12$ **32.** $x - y - 1 = 0$

B *Use the slope and the **y**-intercept to graph each equation without using a table of values.*

33. $y = 3x + 2$ **34.** $y = x - 4$ **35.** $y = 2x - 3$ **36.** $y = 2x - 1$

37. $y = \frac{1}{2}x + 1$ **38.** $y = 2x - \frac{1}{2}$ **39.** $y = \frac{1}{4}x + \frac{1}{2}$ **40.** $y = \frac{1}{2}x$

*Find the value of **b** if the line **y = 5x + b** contains the given point.*

Hint: Substitute the x- and y- values in $y = 5x + b$. Then solve for b.

41. $(3, 18)$ 3   **42.** $(-4, -30)$ −10   **43.** $(2, 10)$ 0   **44.** $(-2, 10)$ 20

Without graphing, determine whether the given points lie on a straight line. If they do, give the slope of the line.

45.

x	0	1	2
y	3	5	7

They do. $m = 2$

46.

x	−3	−1	0
y	2	3	4

They don't.

47.

x	−4	2	6
y	2	−1	−3

They do. $m = -\frac{1}{2}$

LINEAR EQUATIONS

EXTRA PRACTICE, page 514

---

48. The three points $A(2, 1)$, $B(-1, -2)$, and $C(-6, 3)$ determine a triangle. Find the slopes of the three lines containing the sides of the triangle. For line AB, $m = 1$. For line BC, $m = -1$. For line AC, $m = -\frac{1}{4}$.

49. A triangle is determined by points $D(2, -2)$, $E(6, 4)$, and $F(-4, 2)$. Find the slopes of the sides DE, EF, and DF. For side DE, $m = \frac{3}{2}$. For side EF, $m = \frac{1}{5}$. For side DF, $m = -\frac{2}{3}$.

Write the equation of the line satisfying the given conditions.

50. Has a y-intercept of 3 and the same slope as $y = x + 2$ $y = x + 3$

51. Has a y-intercept of 2 and the same slope as $y = 4x + 6$ $y = 4x + 2$

52. Contains $(0, 3)$ and has the same slope as $y - 2x = 4$ $y - 2x = 3$, or $y = 2x + 3$

53. Contains $(0, 2)$ and has the same slope as $y + 2x = 7$ $y + 2x = 2$, or $y = -2x + 2$

54. Has the same y-intercept as $y - 3x = 5$ and the same slope as $2y + 4x = 3$ $y = -2x + 5$

*Write **true** or **false**. Each statement refers to the graph of $y = mx + b$.*

55. If $m > 0$ and $b > 0$, then the x-intercept is to the right of the origin. False

56. If $m < 0$ and $b < 0$, then the x-intercept is to the left of the origin. True

57. If $m < 0$ and $b > 0$, then the x-intercept is to the right of the origin. True

58. If $m > 0$ and $b < 0$, then the x-intercept is to the left of the origin. False

59. If $m \neq 0$ and $b = 0$, then the x-intercept and y-intercept are the same number. True

CHECKPOINT

1. In what quadrant does a point lie if the x-coordinate is positive and the y-coordinate is negative? IV

Find the slope of the line through the two given points.

2. $(-3, -4)$, $(4, 7)$ $\frac{11}{7}$ **3.** $(5, 8)$, $(2, 8)$ 0   **4.** $(6, -3)$, $(-5, 9)$ $-\frac{12}{11}$

Find the x- and y-intercepts for each equation.

5. $y = 3x + 1$ $-\frac{1}{3}$; 1   **6.** $2x - y = -4$ -2; 4   **7.** $x - 2y = 6$ 6; -3

Find the slope and y-intercept for each equation. Then draw its graph.

8. $y = 2x + 3$ 2; 3   **9.** $y = -4x$ -4; 0   **10.** $y = \frac{2}{3}x - 3$ $\frac{2}{3}$; -3

11. Find the slope of the line with x-intercept 2 and y-intercept 3. $-\frac{3}{2}$

Exercises

1. Slope -2, y-int. 0
2. Slope 2, y-int. 5
3. Slope 5, y-int. -2
4. Slope 3, y-int. -4
5. Slope $\frac{2}{3}$, y-int. 0
6. Slope $\frac{4}{3}$, y-int. $-\frac{2}{3}$
7. Slope $\frac{1}{2}$, y-int. -1
8. Slope $-\frac{1}{2}$, y-int. 2

21. $y = -4x + 7$, $m = -4$, $b = 7$
22. $y = \frac{1}{3}x + 2$, $m = \frac{1}{3}$, $b = 2$
23. $y = 3x + 4$, $m = 3$, $b = 4$
24. $y = \frac{4}{3}x - \frac{2}{3}$, $m = \frac{4}{3}$, $b = -\frac{2}{3}$
25. $y = \frac{3}{2}x + \frac{2}{5}$, $m = \frac{3}{2}$, $b = \frac{2}{5}$
26. $y = x - \frac{3}{4}$, $m = 1$, $b = -\frac{3}{4}$
27. $y = \frac{1}{2}x + \frac{1}{2}$, $m = \frac{1}{2}$, $b = \frac{1}{2}$
28. $y = \frac{1}{4}x + \frac{1}{4}$, $m = \frac{1}{4}$, $b = \frac{1}{4}$
29. $y = 4x + 6$, $m = 4$, $b = 6$
30. $y = -2x - 1$, $m = -2$, $b = -1$
31. $y = \frac{1}{3}x - 4$, $m = \frac{1}{3}$, $b = -4$
32. $y = x - 1$, $m = 1$, $b = -1$
33.

[*Answers for Exercises and the Checkpoint continue on page A3.*]

Checkpoint
Students may check their answers with those given in the back of their books.

4-7 Point and Slope: Writing Linear Equations

OBJECTIVE

To use the slope and any point on a line to write an equation of the line.

There are many different lines through the point $(-2, 1)$.

Only one of these lines has a slope that is equal to $\frac{1}{2}$. You can write an equation for that line because you know its slope and a single point on the line. Begin by finding the y-intercept, as shown in Example 1.

EXAMPLE 1   A line contains the point $(-2, 1)$; its slope is $\frac{1}{2}$. Find the y-intercept for that line, write an equation, and draw the graph.

$y = mx + b$

$1 = \frac{1}{2}(-2) + b$ Substitute values for m, x, and y in the slope-intercept formula.

$1 = -1 + b$ Simplify and solve for the y-intercept, b.
$2 = b$

Write the equation of the line.

$y = \frac{1}{2}x + 2$

Draw the graph of the line by plotting $(-2, 1)$ and the y-intercept.

Check   Does $(-2, 1)$ satisfy the equation?

$1 \overset{?}{=} \frac{1}{2}(-2) + 2$

$1 \overset{?}{=} -1 + 2$

$1 = 1$ ✔

EXAMPLE 2   Write an equation of the line that contains the point $(2, -3)$ and has the same slope as the line $y = -2x + 7$.

$y = mx + b$
$-3 = -2(2) + b$ Substitute: $m = -2$, $x = 2$, $y = -3$
$-3 = -4 + b$ Simplify and solve for the y-intercept, b.
$1 = b$

The equation of the line is $y = -2x + 1$.

Check   Show that $(2, -3)$ is a solution of the equation $y = -2x + 1$.

LINEAR EQUATIONS

149

WARM-UP EXERCISES

Consider the equation $y = 3x - 2$
1. What is its slope?   3
2. What is its y-intercept? -2

LESSON NOTES

In this lesson the students learn to find the equation of a line when the slope of the line and the coordinates of a point on the line are known.

Two steps are required. First, the slope is substituted for m in the formula, $y = mx + b$. Then the coordinates of the known point are substituted for x and y in the formula, thus enabling us to calculate the value of b.

Example 2 uses the fact that parallel lines have the same slope. Since $y = -2x + 7$ has a slope of -2, the value -2 is substituted for m in $y = mx + b$.

Example 3 requires that $3y + x = 15$ be put in the form $y = -\frac{1}{3}x + 5$; then the slope, $-\frac{1}{3}$, becomes evident.

[*Lesson Notes continue on page 150.*]

ALTERNATE EXAMPLES

1. A line contains the point $(-1, 2)$; its slope is $\frac{2}{3}$. Find the y-intercept for that line, write an equation, and draw the graph.
$b = \frac{8}{3}$; $y = \frac{2}{3}x + \frac{8}{3}$

2. Write an equation of the line that contains the point $(-1, 1)$ and has the same slope as the line $y = 4x + 1$. $y = 4x + 5$

Exercise 27 develops the point-slope form of the linear equation, $y - y_1 = m(x - x_1)$. Encourage the students to learn this form. With it, they can find the equation of a line when its slope and the coordinates of a point on the line are known. (There is no need to calculate the y-intercept.)

ALTERNATE EXAMPLE

3. Write an equation of the line that is parallel to the line $4x - 2y = 3$ and contains the point $(1, 1)$. $y = 2x - 1$

DAILY QUIZ

The slope and one point on the line are given. Find the y-intercept. Then write an equation for that line.
1. $m = 3$; $(2, 4)$ $b = -2$; $y = 3x - 2$
2. $m = -1$; $(0, -2)$ $b = -2$; $y = -x - 2$

Write an equation of the line satisfying the given conditions.
3. Same slope as $y = 4x - 3$ and containing $(-5, 5)$ $y = 4x + 25$
4. Same slope as $3x - 2y = 6$ and containing the origin
   $3x - 2y = 0$, or $y = \frac{3}{2}x$
5. Passing through $(3, 8)$; $m = 0$ $y = 8$

ASSIGNMENT GUIDE
(pages 150–151)

Minimum course: 1–13, 15, 17, 19
Average course: 1–25 odd
Maximum course: 1–31 odd

EXAMPLE 3   Write an equation of the line that is parallel to the line $3y + x = 15$ and contains the point $(5, -1)$.

Find the slope.   Parallel lines have the same slope. Rewrite $3y + x = 15$ as $y = -\frac{1}{3}x + 5$. The slope is $-\frac{1}{3}$.

Find the y-intercept.
$$y = mx + b$$
$$-1 = -\frac{1}{3}(5) + b \quad \text{Substitute: } m = -\frac{1}{3}, \ x = 5, \ y = -1$$
$$-1 = -\frac{5}{3} + b \quad \text{Solve for } b.$$
$$\frac{2}{3} = b \quad \text{The } y\text{-intercept is } \frac{2}{3}. \text{ The slope is } -\frac{1}{3}.$$
$$y = -\frac{1}{3}x + \frac{2}{3} \quad \text{The equation of the line}$$

Check to be sure that $(5, -1)$ is a solution of $y = -\frac{1}{3}x + \frac{2}{3}$.

CLASS EXERCISES

The slope and one point on a line are given.
Find the y-intercept. Then write an equation for the line.

1. $m = 3$; $(1, 2)$ $b = -1$; $y = 3x - 1$
2. $m = 1$; $(-3, 1)$ $b = 4$; $y = x + 4$
3. $m = -1$; $(-2, -4)$ $b = -6$; $y = -x - 6$
4. $m = 3$; $(-3, -2)$ $b = 7$; $y = 3x + 7$
5. $m = \frac{3}{5}$; $(5, 2)$ $b = -1$; $y = \frac{3}{5}x - 1$
6. $m = 2$; $(-2, -4)$ $b = 0$; $y = 2x$

EXERCISES

A   *The slope and one point on a line are given.*
Find the y-intercept. Then write an equation for the line.

1. $m = 1$; $(0, 2)$ $b = 2$; $y = x + 2$
2. $m = -1$; $(2, -2)$ $b = 0$; $y = -x$
3. $m = \frac{1}{2}$; $(4, -2)$ $b = -4$; $y = \frac{1}{2}x - 4$
4. $m = \frac{1}{4}$; $(4, 5)$ $b = 4$; $(y = \frac{1}{4}x + 4)$4
5. $m = -2$; $(-4, 5)$ $b = -3$; $y = -2x - 3$
6. $m = 4$; $(-1, 4)$ $b = 8$; $y = 4x + 8$
7. $m = \frac{1}{2}$; $(-1, -1)$ $b = -\frac{1}{2}$; $y = \frac{1}{2}x - \frac{1}{2}$
8. $m = \frac{3}{2}$; $(-6, -2)$ $b = 7$; $2 \ y = \frac{3}{2}x + 7$
9. $m = 0$; $(3, 3)$ $b = 3$; $y = 3$

Write the equation of the line satisfying the given conditions.

10. Same slope as $y = 2x - 5$ and containing $(-3, 3)$ $y = 2x + 9$

11. Same slope as $y - 3x = 6$ and containing $(1, 7)$ $y - 3x = 4$, or $y = 3x + 4$

12. Same slope as $2x - 3y = 6$ and containing the origin $2x - 3y = 0$, or $y = \frac{2}{3}x$

13. Same slope as $3x + 2y = 8$ and containing the origin $3x + 2y = 0$, or $y = -\frac{3}{2}x$

CHAPTER 4

EXTRA PRACTICE, page 514

B *The slope and one point of a line are given. Write an equation for each line and then draw its graph.*

14. $m = 0$; $(2, 7)$ $y = 7$ **15.** $m = 1$; $(1, 0)$ $y = x - 1$ **16.** $m = -1$; $(2, 2)$ $y = -x + 4$

17. Parallel to $y = \frac{1}{2}x - 5$, with the same y-intercept as $y = 3x - 2$ $y = \frac{1}{2}x - 2$

18. Parallel to $y = \frac{1}{4}x + 3$, with the same y-intercept as $y = -2x + 8$ $y = \frac{1}{4}x - 8$

19. Parallel to $2x + 3y = 7$, with the same y-intercept as $-4x + 2y = 8$ $2x + 3y = 12$ or $y = -\frac{2}{3}x + 4$

20. Parallel to $5x - 7y - 14 = 0$, with the same y-intercept as $2x + 3y + 9 = 0$ $5x - 7y - 21 = 0$, or $y = \frac{5}{7}x - 3$

C
21. Write the equation of the line with the same slope as $y = ax + c$ and the same y-intercept as $y = dx - e$. $y = ax - e$

22. Write the equation of the line with the same slope as $y = -dx - f$ and the same y-intercept as $y = rx + h$. $y = -dx + h$

23. Find the value of k for which the graph of $y = kx + 2$ will have the same slope as the graph of $y + 3x + 2 = 0$. -3

24. Find the value of k for which the graph of $y = 3x + k$ will have the same y-intercept as the graph of $5x - 9 - y = 0$. -9

25. Find the value of k for which the point $(-2, 1)$ lies on the line $y = 2x + k$. 5

26. Find the value of k for which the point $(1, -2)$ lies on the line $2y = 3x + k$. -7

27. A line contains the point (x_1, y_1) and has a slope m. Follow these steps to write the *point-slope form* of a linear equation in two variables.

Let (x, y) represent any other point on the line.

Then the slope can be written as $m = \dfrac{y - y_1}{x - x_1}$.

Multiply each side of the equation by $(x - x_1)$.
The result is the **point-slope form** of a linear equation.
$m(x - x_1) = y - y_1$, or $y - y_1 = m(x - x_1)$

*The slope and one point on a line are given. Write the equation of the line in **point-slope form**.*

28. $m = -4$; $(-2, -3)$ **29.** $m = \frac{3}{4}$; $\left(\frac{1}{2}, -\frac{1}{4}\right)$ **30.** $m = 0$; $\left(\frac{2}{3}, \frac{3}{4}\right)$

Find the slope of the line through the two points. Write the equation of the line in point-slope form and then in slope-intercept form.

31. $(-2, -2)$ and $(1, 1)$ **32.** $(-2, 2)$ and $(2, -2)$

*33. Write the point-slope form of $2y = -5x + 1$, using the point on the line where $x = 3$. $y + 7 = -\frac{5}{2}(x - 3)$

LINEAR EQUATIONS   **151**

ENRICHMENT ACTIVITY

Let the students experiment with finding the midpoints of line segments drawn in the coordinate plane. Use segments with endpoints such as the following:

1. $(4, 2)$ and $(4, 5)$ Mdpt. $\left(4, 3\frac{1}{2}\right)$

2. $(3, 1)$ and $(-4, 1)$ Mdpt. $\left(-\frac{1}{2}, 1\right)$

3. $(-1, -2)$ and $(7, 6)$ Mdpt. $(3, 2)$

4. $(-2, 9)$ and $(2, 13)$ Mdpt. $(0, 11)$
Let them try to generalize by using these coordinates for the endpoints:
(x_1, y_1) and (x_2, y_2)
Mdpt. $\left(\dfrac{x_1 + x_2}{2}, \dfrac{y_1 + y_2}{2}\right)$

ADDITIONAL ANSWERS

Exercises

14.

15.

16.

[Answers continue on page A3.]

Find the slope of the following:
1. the line that passes through
   (1, 5) and (2, 6) $m = 1$
2. the line that passes through
   (0, 0) and (−2, −4) $m = 2$

LESSON NOTES

This lesson identifies two forms of the linear equation, the *standard* form and the *two-point* form. The standard form, $Ax + By = C$, is sometimes used as the definition of a linear equation. That is, a linear equation is one that can be written in the form $Ax + By = C$, in which A, B, and C are integers, A and B not both 0.

The two-point form of the linear equation, $y - y_1 = \dfrac{y_1 - y_2}{x_1 - x_2}(x - x_1)$, is developed in Exercise 53. It can be thought of as a variation of the point-slope form,

$$y - y_1 = m(x - x_1).$$

POSSIBLE ERROR

Students may make various types of errors in the algebraic manipulations used in changing equations from slope-intercept form to standard form. One common type of error is shown below.

$$y = -\frac{1}{2}x + 5$$

$$2(y) = 2\left(-\frac{1}{2}x\right) + 5 \text{ (incorrect)}$$

Point out that when the equation is multiplied by 2, the entire expression on each side of the equation must be multiplied by 2. Thus:

$$2(y) = 2\left(-\frac{1}{2}x + 5\right)$$

$$2(y) = 2\left(-\frac{1}{2}x\right) + 2(5)$$

$$2y = -x + 10$$

$$x + 2y = 10$$

ALTERNATE EXAMPLE

Write the equation $y = \dfrac{3}{2}x + \dfrac{5}{2}$ in standard form. $3x - 2y = -5$

4-8 Two Points: Writing Linear Equations

OBJECTIVES

To write the equation of a line, given two points on the line.
To rewrite an equation in standard form, $Ax + By = C$.

Just one line passes through any two points. Given the coordinates of two points, you can write an equation for the line that contains those points.

Consider the line shown at the right, which contains the points $(-2, 3)$ and $(4, 1)$. To write the equation of this line, first find the slope.

$$m = \frac{3 - 1}{-2 - 4} = \frac{2}{-6} = -\frac{1}{3}$$

Now solve for the y-intercept b. Substitute the x- and y-values of *either* point. Here the point $(4, 1)$ is used.

$$y = mx + b$$

$$1 = -\frac{1}{3}(4) + b$$

$$1 = -\frac{4}{3} + b$$

$$\frac{7}{3} = b$$

$$y = -\frac{1}{3}x + \frac{7}{3}$$

To check, verify that both $(-2, 3)$ and $(4, 1)$ are solutions of $y = -\frac{1}{3}x + \frac{7}{3}$.

Further, look at the graph above. Does it appear that the line crosses the y-axis at $\frac{7}{3}$?

A linear equation in two variables can be written as $Ax + By = C$, A and B not both 0. If A, B, and C are integers, the equation is in **standard form.**

The equation of the line through points $(-2, 3)$ and $(4, 1)$ is given above in *slope-intercept* form. The Example shows how to write it in standard form.

EXAMPLE Write the equation $y = -\frac{1}{3}x + \frac{7}{3}$ in standard form.

$$y = -\frac{1}{3}x + \frac{7}{3}$$

$$3(y) = 3\left(-\frac{1}{3}x + \frac{7}{3}\right) \quad \text{Multiply each side by the least common denominator, 3.}$$

$$3y = -x + 7 \quad \text{Next, add } x \text{ to each side.}$$

$$x + 3y = 7 \quad \text{Equation in standard form; } A = 1, B = 3, C = 7$$

Check Show that $(-2, 3)$ and $(4, 1)$ are both solutions of $x + 3y = 7$.

For $(-2, 3)$: $-2 + 3(3) \overset{?}{=} 7$ \qquad For $(4, 1)$: $4 + 3(1) \overset{?}{=} 7$

$7 = 7 ✔$ \qquad\qquad\qquad\qquad $7 = 7 ✔$

152

CLASS EXERCISES

A line passes through the points (−2, −3) and (4, 3).

1. Find the slope.   1
2. Find the y-intercept.   −1
3. Write an equation for the line in slope-intercept form. $y = x - 1$
4. Write the equation in standard form. $x - y = 1$

A line contains the points (−2, 2) and (4, −1).

5. Find the slope. $-\frac{1}{2}$
6. Find the y-intercept.   1
7. Write an equation for the line in slope-intercept form. $y = -\frac{1}{2}x + 1$
8. Write the equation in standard form. $x + 2y = 2$

EXERCISES

A

A line passes through the points (5, 7) and (7, 11).

1. Find the slope.   2
2. Find the y-intercept.   −3
3. Write the equation of the line in slope-intercept form. $y = 2x - 3$
4. Write the equation in standard form. $2x - y = 3$

Write the equation, in slope-intercept form, of the line passing through the given pair of points.

5. (3, 1), (5, 3) $y = x - 2$
6. (3, 1), (8, 4) $y = \frac{3}{5}x - \frac{4}{5}$
7. (3, 2), (6, 3) $y = \frac{1}{3}x + 1$
8. (−3, −2), (−1, 2) $y = 2x + 4$
9. (1, −1), (3, 3) $y = 2x - 3$
10. (0, 0), (−3, 5) $y = -\frac{5}{3}x$
11. (2, −4), (−6, 2) $y = -\frac{3}{4}x - \frac{5}{2}$
12. (0, 4), (3, 0) $y = -\frac{4}{3}x + 4$
13. (0, 0), (−4, −6) $y = \frac{3}{2}x$

Write each equation in standard form.

14. $y = \frac{1}{5}x + 1$ $x - 5y = -5$
15. $y = -x + 8$ $x + y = 8$
16. $y = \frac{2}{3}x + \frac{1}{3}$ $2x - 3y = -1$
17. $y = 2x + 6$ $2x - y = -6$
18. $y = -x + 4$ $x + y = 4$
19. $y = \frac{1}{3}x - 4$ $x - 3y = 12$
20. $y = \frac{1}{2}x - \frac{3}{2}$ $x - 2y = 3$
21. $y = -\frac{2}{3}x + 2$ $2x + 3y = 6$
22. $y = -\frac{3}{2}x + 3$ $3x + 2y = 6$

B

Two points are given. Use the standard form to write the equation of the line that contains them. Then check that both ordered pairs satisfy the equation. Draw the graph.

23. (−1, −2), (3, −8)
24. (3, 0), (−5, 2)
25. (0, 5), (−3, 7)
26. (6, 3), (−4, −2)
27. (4, −4), (−2, 0)
28. (−2, 5), (4, 5)
29. (−4, 1), (−2, −3)
30. (1, 7), (−2, 3)
31. (4, −3), (5, 0)

LINEAR EQUATIONS

153

Write an equation in standard form for each line.

32.

$x - 2y = -2$

33.

$4x + y = -4$

34.
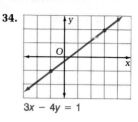

$3x - 4y = 1$

Write each equation in slope-intercept form.

35. $3x + 2y = 6$
$y = -\frac{3}{2}x + 3$

36. $-x - 3y = 6$
$y = -\frac{1}{3}x - 2$

37. $-\frac{1}{2}x + \frac{1}{3}y = 1$ $y = \frac{3}{2}x + 3$

Write the equation, in slope-intercept form, of the line containing the given pair of points.

38. $(-5, 2), (0, 2)$ $y = 2$

39. $(-3, 4), (1, 4)$ $y = 4$

40. $(-2, a), (5, a)$ $y = a$

41. $\left(\frac{1}{2}, \frac{1}{3}\right), (3, 2)$ $y = \frac{2}{3}x$

42. $\left(\frac{1}{2}, -\frac{1}{4}\right), \left(\frac{1}{4}, \frac{1}{2}\right)$
$y = -3x + \frac{5}{4}$

43. $\left(-\frac{1}{3}, 1\right), \left(\frac{1}{4}, -\frac{4}{3}\right)$
$y = -4x - \frac{1}{3}$

44. $\left(2\frac{1}{4}, 1\frac{1}{2}\right), \left(1\frac{1}{4}, -2\frac{1}{2}\right)$ $y = 4x - 7\frac{1}{2}$

45. $\left(3\frac{2}{5}, -\frac{1}{2}\right), \left(2\frac{2}{5}, 1\frac{1}{2}\right)$ $y = -2x + \frac{63}{10}$

46. $(1.2, -2.4), (-1.4, 2.8)$ $y = -2x$

47. $(c, d), (c + f, d + f)$ $y = x + d - c$

C Answer the following questions about the slope of the line $Ax + By = C$.

48. If $A = 0$ and $B \neq 0$, is the slope positive, negative, or 0? 0

49. If $A < 0$ and $B < 0$, is the slope positive, negative, or 0? Negative

50. If $A > 0$ and $B > 0$, is the slope positive, negative, or 0? Negative

51. If $A > 0$ and $B < 0$, is the slope positive, negative, or 0? Positive

52. If $A < 0$ and $B > 0$, is the slope positive, negative, or 0? Positive

53. Follow these steps to write the *two-point form* of a linear equation.

Step 1 Find the slope using the two points (x_1, y_1) and (x_2, y_2). $\frac{y_1 - y_2}{x_1 - x_2}$

Step 2 Find the slope using an arbitrary point (x, y) on the line and the point (x_1, y_1). $\frac{y - y_1}{x - x_1}$

Step 3 Set the two slopes equal to each other and solve for $y - y_1$. The result is the **two-point form** of a linear equation.

$$y - y_1 = \left(\frac{y_1 - y_2}{x_1 - x_2}\right)(x - x_1)$$

Write the equation of the line through the two points. Use the *two-point form*.

54. $(4, 6), (1, 18)$

55. $(7, 2), (5, -8)$

56. $(2, 9), (4, 11)$

CHAPTER 4

4-9 Horizontal and Vertical Lines

OBJECTIVE

To write the equation of a horizontal line or a vertical line and tell whether the slope of the line is 0 or is undefined.

What is the slope of this horizontal line?

$$m = \frac{2 - 2}{-3 - 1} = \frac{0}{-4} = 0$$

The slope is 0. Note that every y-coordinate is 2, so clearly the y-intercept is 2. Thus, the equation of the line is

$$y = 0(x) + 2, \text{ or } y = 2$$

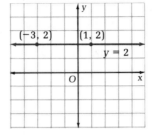

> Every horizontal line has an equation of the form
> $$y = k$$
> The y-intercept is k and the slope is 0.

Observe that this equation is a special case of the standard form $Ax + By = C$, where $A = 0$, $B = 1$, and $C = k$.

The slope is 0 for all horizontal lines, but what about vertical lines? Can you find the slope of this line?

$$m = \frac{3 - (-1)}{2 - 2} = \frac{4}{0} = \frac{?}{}$$

Since division by 0 is undefined, $\frac{4}{0}$ is not a number. Thus, the slope of this vertical line is undefined.

Every point on this vertical line has an x-coordinate of 2. Therefore, the equation of the line is $x = 2$.

> Every vertical line has an equation of the form
> $$x = h$$
> The x-intercept is h and the slope is undefined.

This equation is a special case of the standard form $Ax + By = C$, where $A = 1$, $B = 0$, and $C = h$.

LINEAR EQUATIONS

155

1. Write the equation of each line. Then give the slope of the line or indicate that the slope is undefined.

Line a: The equation is $y = 3$. The slope is 0.

Line b: The equation is $y = -4$. The slope is 0.

Line c: The equation is $x = -2$. The slope is undefined.

Line d: The equation is $x = 3$. The slope is undefined.

2. Write the equation for each line shown through A (3, 2). Then tell whether the slope is 0 or undefined.

The vertical line through A: $x = 3$. Slope is undef.

The horizontal line through A: $y = 2$. Slope is 0.

3. Write the equation of the line that contains the two points given. Give the direction of the line (vertical, horizontal). Tell whether the slope is 0 or is undefined.

   a. The line through (2, 3) and (0, 3) $y = 3$; horizontal; slope 0

   b. The line through $(-1, -1)$ and $(-1, 0)$ $x = -1$; vertical; slope undefined

   c. The line through (5, 10) and (10, 10) $y = 10$; horizontal; slope 0

EXAMPLE 1 Write the equation of each line. Then give the slope of the line, or indicate that the slope is undefined.

 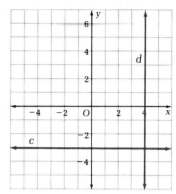

Line a   The equation is $x = -5$. The slope is undefined.

Line b   The equation is $y = 2$. The slope is 0.

Line c   The equation is $y = -3$. The slope is 0.

Line d   The equation is $x = 4$. The slope is undefined.

EXAMPLE 2 Write the equation for each line shown through $A(2, -5)$. Then tell whether the slope is 0 or is undefined.

The vertical line through $A(2, -5)$:

$x = 2$

The slope is undefined.

The horizontal line through $A(2, -5)$:

$y = -5$

The slope is 0.

EXAMPLE 3 Write the equation of the line that contains the two points given. Give the direction of the line (vertical, horizontal). Tell whether the slope is 0 or is undefined.

	a. The line through (3, 5) and (3, 9)	b. The line through (2, −3) and (7, −3)	c. The line through (0, 0) and 5, 0)
Equation	$x = 3$	$y = -3$	$y = 0$
Direction	vertical	horizontal	horizontal
Slope	undefined	0	0

CLASS EXERCISES

Two points on a line are given. Write the equation of the line. Then tell whether the slope is 0 or is undefined.

1. $(-4, 0), (7, 0)$ $y = 0$, slope is 0   **2.** $(0, 2), (0, 6)$ $x = 0$; slope is undefined   **3.** $(0, -9), (0, 7)$ $x = 0$; slope is undefined

4. $(0, 0), (0, -6)$ $x = 0$; slope is undefined   **5.** $(-2, 0), (-1, 0)$ $y = 0$; slope is 0.   **6.** $(3, 0), (0, 0)$ $y = 0$; slope is 0.

7. Write the equation for each line *a–f*.

a. $y = 4$
b. $x = -8$
c. $x = -4$
d. $y = -1$
e. $x = 5$
f. $x = 7$

EXERCISES

A

Two points are given. Tell whether the slope of the line through the points is 0 or is undefined.

1. $(3, 0), (3, 1)$ Undefined   **2.** $(0, -6), (5, -6)$ 0   **3.** $(3, -4), (0, -4)$ 0

4. $(5, 2), (1, 2)$ 0   **5.** $(10, 1), (10, -3)$ Undefined   **6.** $(4, -1), (4, -3)$ Undefined

7. $(1, 6), (-5, 6)$ 0   **8.** $(8, -5), (8, 4)$ Undefined   **9.** $(8, 14), (8, -14)$ Undefined

10. $(-15, -10), (-10, -10)$ 0   **11.** $(-8, 12), (12, 12)$ 0

Write the equation of the line containing the given pair of points.

12. $(2, 3), (2, -2)$ $x = 2$ **13.** $(5, 1), (-4, 1)$ $y = 1$ **14.** $(8, 5), (-1, 5)$ $y = 5$

15. $(-3, 6), (-7, 6)$ $y = 6$ **16.** $(4, 1), (4, 2)$ $x = 4$ **17.** $(3, 0), (0, 0)$ $y = 0$

18. $(8, 5), (13, 5)$ $y = 5$ **19.** $(6, -4), (-1, -4)$ $y = -4$ **20.** $(7, 1), (7, 6)$ $x = 7$

21. $(0, 3), (0, 12)$ $x = 0$ **22.** $(0, 3), (-12, 3)$ $y = 3$ **23.** $(9, 5), (9, 1)$ $x = 9$

Graph each equation. Use a separate pair of axes for each graph.

24. $x = 5$ **25.** $y = 3$ **26.** $x = -1$ **27.** $y = 0$

28. $x = 0$ **29.** $y = -5$ **30.** $x = 2\frac{1}{2}$ **31.** $y = 4\frac{1}{2}$

B

Write the equation of the line satisfying the given conditions.

32. Vertical, with *x*-intercept -3 $x = -3$ **33.** Horizontal, with *y*-intercept 6 $y = 6$

34. Horizontal, containing $(1, 5)$ $y = 5$ **35.** Vertical, containing $(3, 2)$ $x = 3$

LINEAR EQUATIONS   **157**

25.

26.

27.

28.

29.

[Answers for Exercises and for the
Challenge continue on page A4.]

36. Write the equation of the x-axis. $y = 0$ **37.** Write the equation of the y-axis. $x = 0$

Does the line with the given equation contain the point (2, 6)?

38. $x = 2$ Yes   **39.** $y = 3x$ Yes   **40.** $y = 6$ Yes   **41.** $y = 6x$ No

42. $y = 2$ No   **43.** $x = 6$ No   **44.** $y - x = 4$ Yes   **45.** $y - 8 = x$ No

Does the line with the given equation pass through the origin?

46. $y = 3x$ Yes **47.** $x = 0$ · Yes **48.** $y = 0$ Yes **49.** $y = 5x + 2$ No

50. $y - 3x = 0$ Yes **51.** $y + x = 0$ Yes **52.** $y - 5 = 0$ No **53.** $x = 3$ No

C

54. Write the equation of the line through (5, 7) and parallel to $y = 4$. $y = 7$

55. Write the equation of the line through $\left(-\frac{1}{2}, -\frac{1}{2}\right)$ and perpendicular to $x = -3$. $y = -\frac{1}{2}$

56. Write the equations of two lines parallel to $y = -2$ and three units away. $y = -5$ and $y = 1$

57. Write the equations of two lines parallel to $x = \frac{1}{3}$ and $\frac{1}{2}$ unit away. $x = \frac{5}{6}$ and $x = -\frac{1}{6}$

58. On the same pair of axes, draw lines with equations $y = 3$, $y = -2$, $x = 5$, and $x = 1$. On your graph show the coordinates of the intersection points.

59. What are the coordinates of the point where the lines $x = 4$ and $y = 4$ intersect?   (4,4)

60. What are the coordinates of the point where the lines $x = -3$ and $y = 2$ intersect?   (−3, 2)

CHALLENGE

A Clockwise Pattern

Follow this clockwise pattern of 1-, 2-, and 3-unit moves. Connect the points that have the following coordinates, in order, on a grid.

Start at

(0, 2) → (1, 2) → (1, 0) → (−2, 0) → (−2, 1) → (0, 1) → (0, −2)
     1 right   2 down   3 left   1 up   2 right   3 down

Continue the repeating clockwise pattern of 1-, 2-, and 3-unit moves. What are the next six points? (−1, −2), (−1, 0), (2, 0), (2, −1), (0, −1), (0, 2)

Plot and connect those points on the same grid. You should come back to the starting point, (0, 2).

Now make up a similar pattern of your own.

158

Taxi Fares

In one city, the cost of hiring a taxicab is as follows.

The first $\frac{1}{9}$ mile: $1.00

Each additional $\frac{1}{9}$ mile: $ .10

The cost C in dollars for a ride that covers a distance of d miles is given by the formula

$$C = 1 + \frac{9}{10}\left(d - \frac{1}{9}\right)$$

Example   Find the cost of a taxi ride of 2 miles.

$$C = 1 + \frac{9}{10}\left(2 - \frac{1}{9}\right)$$

$$= 1 + \frac{9}{10}\left(\frac{17}{9}\right)$$

$$= 2\frac{7}{10}, \text{ or } 2.70$$

The cost is $2.70.

Find the cost of a taxi ride that covers each of the following distances.

1. $\frac{2}{9}$ mile $1.10   **2.** 1 mile $1.80   **3.** 5 miles $5.40   **4.** $\frac{2}{3}$ mile $1.50

5. A ride costs $6.60. Find the distance covered. $6\frac{1}{3}$ miles

You must pay the full 10 cents for the last $\frac{1}{9}$ mile of a trip, even if you only use part of it. Therefore, if the formula gives the cost at $2.03, you pay $2.10. Always round up to the next dime. Find the cost of these trips.

6. $\frac{1}{2}$ mile $1.40   **7.** $1\frac{1}{4}$ miles $2.10   **8.** $3\frac{4}{5}$ miles $4.40   **9.** $6\frac{1}{2}$ miles $6.80

10. Write a formula for the cost C of a taxi ride if the first $\frac{1}{3}$ mile costs $2.00 and each additional $\frac{1}{3}$ mile costs 50¢. $C = 2 + \frac{3}{2}\left(d - \frac{1}{3}\right)$

Applications

This Applications page illustrates the way in which a mathematical formula can summarize a real-life situation.

Before the students begin the exercises, be certain that they *understand* the formula. They should see that the $\frac{9}{10}$ represents 90 cents, and that $\frac{1}{9}$ is subtracted from d because the rider has already been charged for the first $\frac{1}{9}$ mile. Notice that once the formula has been established, it can be used to calculate cost (Exercises 1–4) or distance (Exercise 5).

Exercise 10 provides students with an opportunity to write their own formula for a different taxi-rate specification.

These exercises review basic algebraic skills.

Simplify.

1. $8 - (-3) + (-2)$
$- (-1) + 4$ 14

2. $31 - 11 \cdot 2 + 3$ 12

3. $-|-3| - |5 - 8| +$
$|-6|$ 0

4. $7x^2y - 5xy^2$
$- x^2y + xy^2$ $6x^2y - 4xy^2$

5. $3(5 - x) - 2(x - 3) + (1 - x)$
$-6x + 22$

Evaluate when $a = -5$, $b = -2$, and $c = 4$.

6. $8b - 2a$ -6

7. $\dfrac{5bc + 2ab}{abc}$ $-\dfrac{1}{2}$

8. $a^2b - b^2c + a^2c^2$ 334

Solve for x.

9. $5x - 7 = -3$ $\dfrac{4}{5}$

10. $6x - 5 = 7 + 9x$ -4

11. $x - (5 - 2x) = -(1 - 2x)$ 4

12. 7 more than 3 times a certain number is 3 less than the number. Find the number. -5

13. There are 6 fewer nickels than dimes. Find the number of each if together they have a value of $3.30.   18 nickels, 24 dimes

14. Find three consecutive integers if the sum of the first two lesser integers, added to the third, is equal to 54.   17, 18, 19

[*Maintaining Skills continues on page 161.*]

ADDITIONAL ANSWERS

Review Exercises

See page 161.

CHAPTER 4 REVIEW

VOCABULARY

line (p. 124)
coordinate (p. 124)
plane (p. 124)
coordinate plane (p. 124)
axes (p. 124)
origin (p. 124)
ordered pair (p. 125)
x-axis (p. 128)
y-axis (p. 128)
quadrant (p. 128)
x-coordinate (p. 128)
abscissa (p. 128)
y-coordinate (p. 128)
ordinate (p. 128)

linear equation (p. 132)
solution of a linear equation (p. 133)
slope (p. 136)
rise (p. 136)
run (p. 136)
x-intercept (p. 141)
y-intercept (p. 141)
slope-intercept form of a linear
    equation (p. 145)
slope of parallel lines (p. 145)
standard form of a linear
    equation (p. 152)
equation of a horizontal line (p. 155)
equation of a vertical line (p. 155)

SUMMARY

In this chapter algebra takes on a geometric aspect in the form of graphs. Ordered pairs of numbers are used to identify and plot points on the coordinate plane. Linear equations in two variables are first graphed by using tables of values. After defining the slope of a line, new forms of linear equations are developed. The slope-intercept form, along with the point-slope form and the two-point form, is used in the study of linear equations and their graphs.

REVIEW EXERCISES

4-1   *Write the coordinates of each point.*

1. A (0, 2)   **2.** B (2, −3)   **3.** C (−2, 0)

4. D (−2, 3)   **5.** E (2, 0)   **6.** F (0, −2)

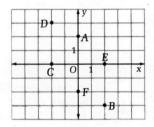

4-2   *In what quadrant or on which axis does each point lie?*

7. (5, 7) I   **8.** (0, 7) y-axis   **9.** (−4, 5) II   **10.** (−5, 0) x-axis   **11.** (9, −2) IV

4-3   *Graph each equation. First plot and label at least three points on the graph.*
Points may vary.

12. $y = 2x - 1$ **13.** $y = -3x + 2$ **14.** $y = -\dfrac{3}{2}x + 4$

160

CHAPTER 4

*Is the given ordered pair a solution of the equation? Write **yes** or **no**.*

15. $y = 2x - 3$; $(1, -1)$ Yes   **16.** $y = -2x + 3$; $(-1, 1)$ No

4-4   *Find the slope of the line through the two given points.*

17. $(5, 2)$, $(-4, 5)$ $-\frac{1}{3}$ **18.** $(-7, 8)$, $(12, 8)$ 0   **19.** $(-1, -3)$, $(1, 3)$ 3

Find the slope of each line.

20.   **21.**   **22.**

1   0 $-\frac{3}{2}$

4-5   *Find the **x**- and **y**-intercepts for each equation.*

23. $y = -7x + 21$ 3; 21   **24.** $x - y = -2$ $-2; 2$ **25.** $3x + 2y = 6$ 2; 3

Find the slope for each line.

26. x-intercept: 2 $-\frac{3}{2}$ **27.** x-intercept: -5 $-\frac{7}{5}$ **28.** x-intercept: -3 2
     y-intercept: 3   y-intercept: -7 y-intercept: 6

4-6   *Find the slope and **y**-intercept for each equation.*

29. $y = 15x - 37$ 15; -37 **30.** $y = -29x$ $-29; 0$ **31.** $y = 72x + 101$ 72; 101

Write an equation, using the information given, for each line.

32. $m = -92$, $b = 0$ **33.** $m = 1$, $b = 18$ **34.** $m = 0$, $b = -6$
     $y = -92x$ $y = x + 18$ $y = -6$

Rewrite in slope-intercept form. Then graph each equation.

35. $x + 2y = 8$ **36.** $4x - y = -12$ **37.** $-3x + 6y = 9$
     $y = -\frac{1}{2}x + 4$ $y = 4x + 12$ $y = \frac{1}{2}x + \frac{3}{2}$

4-7   *The slope **m** and the coordinates of one point on a line are given.*
      Write the equation in slope-intercept form.

38. $m = 4$; $(-2, -3)$ **39.** $m = -1$; $(-5, 6)$ **40.** $m = 0$; $(3, 7)$
     $y = 4x + 5$ $y = -x + 1$ $y = 7$

Write an equation of the line satisfying the given conditions.

41. Same slope as $x - y = -4$ **42.** Parallel to $2x - 3y = 12$, with the
     and containing $(-4, 0)$.   same y-intercept as $x + 2y = 18$.
     $y = x + 4$ $y = \frac{2}{3}x + 9$

4-8   *Write the equation that contains the given points.*

43. $(-1, 7)$, $(-2, 11)$ **44.** $(-6, -4)$, $(3, 8)$ **45.** $(4, -3)$, $(-5, 3)$
     $y = -4x + 3$ $y = \frac{4}{3}x + 4$ $y = -\frac{2}{3}x - \frac{1}{3}$

REVIEW   **161**

23.

24.

25.

Write each equation in standard form, $Ax + By = C$.

46. $y = \frac{3}{8}x + \frac{1}{4}$
$3x - 8y = -2$

47. $y = -\frac{1}{2}x + \frac{2}{5}$
$5x + 10y = 4$

48. $y = 5x - \frac{1}{2}$ $10x - 2y = 1$

4-9 Determine the slope of the line through the two given points. Then write its equation.

49. $(-9, 5), (11, 5)$ $0; y = 5$ **50.** $(-1, -7), (-1, 9)$ **51.** $(-1, -7), (9, -7)$ $0; y = -7$
Undefined; $x = -1$

≡ C**HAPTER 4** ≡
  TEST

4-1 Write the coordinates of each point.

1. A $(-3, 0)$ **2.** B $(2, 2)$ **3.** O $(0, 0)$

4. D $(3, -2)$ **5.** E $(-2, -1)$ **6.** F $(0, -2)$

4-2 In what quadrant or on which axis does each point lie?

7. $(0, 6)$ y-axis   **8.** $(-2, -7)$ III   **9.** $(4, -1)$ IV

4-3 Is the given ordered pair a solution of the equation? Write **yes** or **no**.

10. $y + 3x = 1$; $(-2, 5)$ No   **11.** $y = \frac{1}{2}x - 1$; $(10, 4)$ Yes

4-4 **12.** Find the slope of the line through the points $(3, -5)$ and $(2, -1)$. -4

4-5 **13.** Find the x- and y-intercepts for the equation $2x - 3y = 12$. $6; -4$

4-6 **14.** Find the slope and y-intercept for the equation $y = -11x + 15$. $-11; 15$

4-7 Write an equation of the line that satisfies the given conditions.

15. A slope of -1 and containing $(3, 2)$ $y = -x + 5$

16. Parallel to $x - 2y - 6 = 0$, with the same y-intercept as $\frac{1}{2}x - \frac{1}{4}y + 8 = 0$
$y = \frac{1}{2}x + 32$

4-8 Write the equation, in slope-intercept form, of the line containing the given two points.

17. $(0, 0), (2, 2)$ $y = x$ **18.** $(0, -3), (-3, 0)$ **19.** $(3, -2), (0, -3)$ $y = \frac{1}{3}x - 3$
$y = -x - 3$

20. Write the equation $y = \frac{1}{3}x + 2$ in standard form. $x - 3y = -6$

4-9 **21.** Write the equation of the vertical line containing $(3, 2)$. $x = 3$

22. Write the equation of the horizontal line containing $(3, 2)$. $y = 2$

Graph each equation.

23. $y = 2x - 6$ **24.** $x + 2y = 4$ **25.** $x + 4 = 0$

CHAPTER 4

Ordered Pairs

If you are drawing graphs of linear equations in the form $Ax + By = C$, the program below can help you by computing ordered pairs.

Lines 130 and 160 contain a FOR . . . NEXT . . . statement. To begin, FOR X = −5 TO 5 STEP 1 assigns −5 to X. When the computer reaches NEXT X (line 160), it jumps, or "loops," back to line 130 where STEP 1 increases the value assigned to X by 1. The computer continues in this loop until the value assigned to X exceeds 5. Then the computer exits the loop and continues to the next line, which is line 200.

The Program	What It Does
100 REM ORDERED PAIRS AX + BY = C	
110 PRINT "ENTER A, B, C"	
120 INPUT A, B, C	Waits for A, B, C to be entered in order, separated by commas.
130 FOR X = −5 TO 5 STEP 1	Assigns −5 to X; increases value of X by 1 for each loop.
140 LET Y = (C − A * X)/B	Computes Y coordinate.
150 PRINT X; ","; Y	Displays ordered pair (X, Y).
160 NEXT X	Goes back to line 130 until X > 5.
200 PRINT "MORE? (1 = YES, 0 = NO)"	
210 INPUT Z	Waits for input (entry) of 1 or 0.
220 IF Z = 1 THEN 110	If 1 is input, returns to line 110.
900 END	

```
RUN
ENTER A, B, C
? 3, 2, 6
-5, 10.5
-4, 9
```

This is the beginning of the sample run for the equation 3x + 2y = 6.

Only the first two ordered pairs (−5, 10.5) and (−4, 9) are shown here.

In line 150 the comma is in quotation marks so that it will be displayed between the values of *X* and *Y*.

To determine different coordinates, change line 130. For x = 1, 1.5, 2, 2.5, and 3, use: 130 FOR X = 1 TO 3 STEP .5

1. When the original program is run, how many pairs are displayed? Eleven pairs are displayed.

List the ordered pairs that will be displayed when the input is

2. 3, 2, 6. **3.** 3, −4, 18. **4.** −13, 20, 18.

What values should be input for each of the following equations? List the ordered pairs that will be displayed for each.

5. $5x + 4y = 20$ **6.** $3x + 8y = 11$ **7.** $7x − 4y = 8$

8. $9x = 7 + 10y$ **9.** $2y = 7x − 5$ **10.** $6x + 25y + 1 = 0$

For more information about BASIC, see the Computer Handbook at the back of the book.

Computer Activity

You may wish to remind the students that a FOR . . . NEXT . . . statement is one way to avoid an infinite loop. There is a discussion of FOR . . . NEXT . . . statements on page 539 in the Computer Handbook.

ADDITIONAL ANSWERS

Computer Activity

2.		3.	
−5,	10.5	−5,	−8.25
−4,	9	−4,	−7.5
−3,	7.5	−3,	−6.75
−2,	6	−2,	−6
−1,	4.5	−1,	−5.25
0,	3	0,	−4.5
1,	1.5	1,	−3.75
2,	0	2,	−3
3,	−1.5	3,	−2.25
4,	−3	4,	−1.5
5,	−4.5	5,	−.75

4.		5.	
−5,	−2.35	5, 4, 20	
−4,	−1.7	−5,	11.25
−3,	−1.05	−4,	10
−2,	−.4	−3,	8.75
−1,	.25	−2,	7.5
0,	.9	−1,	6.25
1,	1.55	0,	5
2,	2.2	1,	3.75
3,	2.85	2,	2.5
4,	3.5	3,	1.25
5,	4.15	4,	0
		5,	−1.25

6.		7.	
3, 8, 11		7, −4, 8	
−5,	3.25	−5,	−10.75
−4,	2.875	−4,	−9
−3,	2.5	−3,	−7.25
−2,	2.125	−2,	−5.5
−1,	1.75	−1,	−3.75
0,	1.375	0,	−2
1,	1	1,	−.25
2,	.625	2,	1.5
3,	.25	3,	3.25
4,	−.125	4,	5
5,	−.5	5,	6.75

[*Answers continue on page A4.*]

163

This chapter develops addition, subtraction, and multiplication of polynomials (division of polynomials is included in Chapter 8).

Work with exponents is included in the material that deals with multiplication of polynomials. The use of exponents is a thread that runs through much of the book. Thus, the students learn to use exponents in a variety of situations, and the concept of an exponent is extended as the students work with various sets of numbers.

The chapter closes with a lesson that involves applying polynomials in the solution of equations and in problem solving.

CHAPTER 5

Formal gardens are designed using various geometric shapes. The perimeters and areas of the flower beds can be expressed as polynomials, using variables to represent one or more dimensions of the beds and walks.

POLYNOMIALS

PREREQUISITE SKILLS REVIEW

For students who need additional practice with the algebraic skills in this Prerequisite Skills Review, you may assign Follow-Up exercises on page 502 in the students' books.

An item-by-item error analysis of the Prerequisite Skills Review appears on page T23.

Prerequisite Skills Review

Write the letter for the correct answer.

1. $(-2)^5 =$ _?_   d
   a. 10   b. -10 c. 32   d. -32

2. $-5(-3)^2 =$ _?_   b
   a. 45   b. -45 c. 30   d. -30

3. $(0.1)^3 =$ _?_   c
   a. 0.3   b. 0.01   c. 0.001   d. 0.0001

4. $[4(-2)]^2 + 4(-2) =$ _?_   c
   a. 8   b. -24 c. 56   d. -72

5. $\frac{1}{5}(-5)^3 =$ _?_   c
   a. -1 b. -3 c. -25 d. 25

6. $12\left(8 + \frac{1}{3}\right) - \frac{1}{3} =$ _?_   d
   a. 20   b. 86   c. 96   d. $99\frac{2}{3}$

7. $3 - 3(3)^2 =$ _?_   b
   a. -78 b. -24 c. -15 d. 0

8. Simplify $3x + 4x$.   b
   a. $12x$ b. $7x$ c. $7x^2$ d. $12x^2$

9. Which expression is equivalent to $5 \cdot x \cdot x \cdot x + 3 \cdot x \cdot x + 7 \cdot x \cdot x$?   a
   a. $5x^3 + 10x^2$ b. $8x^3 + 7x^2$ c. $15x^2$ d. $15x^7$

10. Simplify $5x^2 + 2(x^2 - 4x)$.   d
    a. $10x^2 - 8x$ b. $10x^2 - 4x$ c. $7x^2 - 4x$ d. $7x^2 - 8x$

11. The expression $5ab - 10a$ is equivalent to _?_ .   d
    a. $-5b$ b. $-5ab$ c. $-50a^2b$ d. $5a(b - 2)$

12. Simplify $5xy - 7xy + 4y$.   d
    a. $-2 + 4y$ b. $2y$ c. $2(-xy + y)$ d. $-2xy + 4y$

13. The length of a rectangle is 5 more than twice its width x. The area is _?_ .   b
    a. $10x^2$ b. $x(2x + 5)$ c. $x(2x - 5)$ d. $2x^2 + 5$

<table>
</table>

WARM-UP EXERCISES

Simplify.

1. $7x + 2x$ $9x$
2. $5x^2 - 3x^2$ $2x^2$
3. $8x^4 + 7x^3 - 8x^4$ $7x^3$

LESSON NOTES

Notice that this lesson defines the degree of any monomial (whether it has one variable, more than one variable, or no variable). The text also defines the degree of any polynomial in *one variable*. For a polynomial in more than one variable, the degree is the highest degree of any of its terms (assuming the polynomial is in simplified form). Thus, the degree of $x^3y^2 - xy - 2y$ is 5.

As you discuss monomials and other polynomials, be sure the students realize that an expression such as $3x$ means $3x^1$ (degree 1); also, a constant such as 8 can be thought of as $8x^0$ (degree 0).

ALTERNATE EXAMPLES

1. Identify each polynomial as a monomial, a binomial, or a trinomial.

   a. $\frac{1}{5}x^3$ Monomial: There is just one term.

   b. $x^2 - 3x + 1$ Trinomial: The terms are x^2, $-3x$, and 1.

   c. $x^3 + 5x$ Binomial: The terms are x^3 and $5x$.

2. Give the degree of each monomial.

   a. $5x^4$ b. $-2x^7$
   Degree 4   Degree 7

   c. $3y$ d. 25
   Degree 1   Degree 0

5-1   Kinds of Polynomials

OBJECTIVES

To tell whether a polynomial is a monomial, binomial, or trinomial.
To simplify a polynomial and state its degree.

Each expression below is a monomial.

$$4 \qquad y \qquad 5x^3 \qquad -x^4 \qquad 2x^4y^2$$

A **monomial** is a constant, a variable, or the product of a constant and variables. The exponents of the variables must be positive integers.

A **polynomial** is a monomial or the sum of terms, each of which is a monomial. A polynomial such as $4x^3 + (-3x^2) + (-2x) + 5$ may be written as $4x^3 - 3x^2 - 2x + 5$.

Special names are given to polynomials with one, two, or three terms.

$5x^3$ is a **monomial.**   It has just one term.

$2x + 7$ is a **binomial.**   It has two terms, $2x$ and 7.

$8x^3 - 3x + 6$ is a **trinomial.**   It has three terms, $8x^2$, $-3x$, and 6.

EXAMPLE 1   Identify each polynomial as a monomial, a binomial, or a trinomial.

a. $\frac{1}{3}x + 4$ Binomial: The terms are $\frac{1}{3}x$ and 4.

b. $-5x^4$ Monomial: There is just one term.

c. $2x^2 - 7x - 3$ Trinomial: The terms are $2x^2$, $-7x$, and -3.

Each polynomial in Example 1 is a polynomial in x, since the only variable that appears is x. The polynomial $3a^2 - 2ab + b^2$ is a polynomial in a and b.

The **degree of a monomial** is the sum of the exponents of the variables. Each monomial below has degree 4. The sum of the exponents of the variables is 4.

$$7x^4 \qquad 2n^4 \qquad -x^2y^2 \qquad 6abc^2$$

For a monomial in one variable, the exponent is its degree. When there is no variable, the degree is zero. Every nonzero constant is regarded as a polynomial of degree 0.

EXAMPLE 2   Give the degree of each monomial.

a. $2x^3$ b. $5xy$ c. $-3n^5$ d. 8

degree 3   degree 2   degree 5   degree 0

Recall that the numerical factor of a monomial is called its *coefficient*. The coefficients of $7xy^2$ and $-x^3$ are 7 and -1. Monomials that have the same variables with the same exponents are *like terms*, regardless of their coefficients. The following are examples of like terms.

$$8x^2y^3 \qquad -3x^2y^3 \qquad y^3x^2 \qquad -\frac{1}{2}y^3x^2$$

A polynomial is *simplified* when all of its like terms have been combined. The **degree of a polynomial in one variable** is the greatest exponent of the variable that appears in the simplified form. The terms are usually arranged in decreasing degree for a particular variable.

EXAMPLE 3 Give the degree of each polynomial. Simplify first, if necessary.

a. $3x^5 - 2x^3 + x^2 + 6$

This is already in simplest form. The degree is 5.

b. $2x^6 - 3x^4 + 7x^2 + x^4 - 2x^6 + 5 = (2-2)x^6 + (-3+1)x^4 + 7x^2 + 5$

$$= 0x^6 - 2x^4 + 7x^2 + 5$$
$$= -2x^4 + 7x^2 + 5$$

Note that when the *like terms* $2x^6$ and $-2x^6$ are combined, the sum is 0. The degree of the polynomial is 4.

Polynomials with one or more variables represent numbers, since variables themselves represent numbers.

EXAMPLE 4 Evaluate $2x^2 + 3x + 5$ **a.** when $x = 10$.   **b.** when $x = -2$.

a.	$2x^2 + 3x + 5$	**b.**	$2x^2 + 3x + 5$
	$= 2(10)^2 + 3(10) + 5$		$= 2(-2)^2 + 3(-2) + 5$
	$= 2(100) + 3(10) + 5$		$= 2(4) + (-6) + 5$
	$= 200 + 30 + 5$		$= 8 - 6 + 5$
	$= 235$		$= 7$

EXAMPLE 5 Evaluate $a^2 - b^2$ when $a = 8$ and $b = 3$.

$$a^2 - b^2 = 8^2 - 3^2 = 64 - 9 = 55$$

CLASS EXERCISES

*Classify each polynomial as a **monomial, binomial, trinomial,** or **none of these.***

1. $x^2 + 7x$ Binomial   **2.** $-163x$ Monomial   **3.** x^3 Monomial

4. $1 - x - x^2 + x^3$ None of these   **5.** $y - y^2 + y^3$ Trinomial   **6.** $100h^8 + 10h^7$ Binomial

POLYNOMIALS   167

ALTERNATE EXAMPLES

3. Give the degree of each polynomial. Simplify it first, if necessary.
   a. $2x^6 - 1$ This is already in simplest form. The degree is 6.
   b. $5x^3 + 3x^2 - 5x^3 + x^2 - x$
   The simplified form is $4x^2 - x$. The degree is 2.

4. Evaluate $x^2 + 2x - 5$
   a. when $x = 5$. 30 **b.** when $x = -3$. -2

5. Evaluate $a^3 - b^3$ when $a = 3$ and $b = 2$. 19

DAILY QUIZ

Simplify each polynomial. Then give the degree.
1. $7x + 3 - 5x$ $2x + 3$; 1
2. $9x + 2 - 9x$ 2; 0
3. $-x^4 + 6x^4 - 7x^2 + x^2$
   $5x^4 - 6x^2$; 4

Evaluate $x^2 - 2x + \frac{1}{2}$
4. when $x = \frac{1}{2}$. $-\frac{1}{4}$
5. when $x = -\frac{1}{2}$. $1\frac{3}{4}$

Simplify each polynomial. Then give the degree.

7. $a^2 + 5a - 2a$ $a^2 + 3a$; 2   8. $3x^2 - 2x^2 + 4x$ 9. $x + 5 + 3x + 4$ $4x + 9$; 1
                                            $x^2 + 4x$; 2
10. $1 + h + h + h$ $3h + 1$; 1   11. $2 - t^2 - 3t - 6$ 12. $x + 2x - 3x - 6$ -6; 0
                                    $-t^2 - 3t - 4$; 2
13. $y^3 + 7y^2 + y^2 + 7y^2$ $y^3 + 15y^2$; 3   14. $-x^3 + 6x^3 + 7x - 9x$ $5x^3 - 2x$; 3
15. $2b^4 - 5b^4 - 6b + 10b$ $-3b^4 + 4b$; 4   16. $-20x + 8x^2 + 6x^3 - 15x^2$
                                         $6x^3 - 7x^2 - 20x$; 3
17. Evaluate $3x^2 - 5x + 4$ when $x = 2$.   6

EXERCISES

A   *Classify each polynomial as a **monomial, binomial, trinomial,** or **none of these.***

1. $1 + 3x$ Binomial   2. $17x^3 - 4 - 3x^2$ Trinomial   3. $8 + n + n^2 + n^5$ None of these

4. $3a^2 + 2a - 4$ Trinomial   5. 2   Monomial   6. $5x^7 + x^6$ Binomial

Simplify each polynomial. Then give the degree.

7. $6x + 2 - 4x$ $2x + 2$; 1   8. $a^2 - 7a + 2a^2$ 9. $x^2 - 3x + x$ $x^2 - 2x$; 2
                                      $3a^2 - 7a$; 2
10. $6x + 1 - 6x$ 1; 0   11. $y^3 + 6y^2 - y^3$ $6y^2$; 2   12. $3 - h + h^4 - 2h$
                                          $h^4 - 3h + 3$; 4
13. $-x^3 + 5x^3 - 7x + x$ $4x^3 - 6x$; 3   14. $14y + 3y - 4y^2 + y^2$ $-3y^2 + 17y$; 2
15. $-2y + 3y^2 + 6y - y^2$ $2y^2 + 4y$; 2   16. $a^3 + 2 - 7 + 3a^3 + 9a$ $4a^3 + 9a - 5$; 3
17. $-1 + x + x^3 - x^2$ $x^3 - x^2 + x - 1$; 3   18. $-3h^2 + 3h + h^3 - 1$ $h^3 - 3h^2 + 3h - 1$; 3
19. $3x^5 + x^3 - x^5 - x^3$ $2x^5$; 5   20. $2t - t^2 + t^3 - 2t$ $t^3 - t^2$; 3

Evaluate each polynomial when $x = 3$, $a = 4$, and $b = -5$.

21. $x + a$ 7   22. $2b + x$ -7 23. $2x^2 - a^2$ 2   24. $2x^2ab$ -360

B   *Evaluate $x^2 - x + \frac{1}{4}$ for each value of x.*

25. $x = -\frac{1}{2}$ 1   26. $x = \frac{1}{2}$ 0   27. $x = -1$ $2\frac{1}{4}$ 28. $x = 1$ $\frac{1}{4}$

Simplify each polynomial. Then give the degree.

29. $x^3 - 3x^2 + 2x - 5x^2 + 15x - 10$ 30. $5x^2 + 15x - 10 + x^3 + 3x^2 - 10$
31. $a^4 - a^3 + 2a^2 + a^3 + 2a - 1$ 32. $5.4x - 2.8x^2 - 7.9x$

33. $-\frac{3}{4}x - 2x + \frac{1}{4}x + 3$ 34. $x^2 - \frac{1}{2}x + \frac{1}{4}x - \frac{1}{8}$

35. $x^3 + 3x^2 - 2x - 5x^2 + 15x + 10$ 36. $5x^2 + 15x - 10 + x^3 + 3x^2 - 2x$

37. $-4x^4 + 3x^3 + 24x^2 - 6x^3 - 18x - 2x^2 + 4x$

CHAPTER 5

EXTRA PRACTICE, page 515

Evaluate each polynomial.

38. $5x + 13$ when $x = 10$ 63

39. $-11 - 3y$ when $y = -4$ 1

40. $15 - y$ when $y = -1$ 16

41. $5n^2 + 3n + 25$ when $n = 0$ 25

42. $3x - x^2 + 19$ when $x = -2$ 9

43. $3n - 100$ when $n = 8$ -76

44. $6x + 3x^2 - 17$ when $x = 2$ 7

45. $2x^2 + 3x$ when $x = 4$ 44

46. $10 - 8a^2$ when $a = 3$ -62

47. $6x^3 + 2$ when $x = -1$ -4

48. $x^4 - 2x^3$ when $x = 2$ 0

49. $3n^2 - 27$ when $n = 0$ -27

50. $x^3 + 4x^2$ when $x = \frac{1}{2}$ $1\frac{1}{8}$

51. $24 - 6a^2$ when $a = \frac{1}{4}$ $23\frac{5}{8}$

C

*Simplify each polynomial. Arrange terms in decreasing degree of the variable **x**.*

Sample: $x^2 + y^2 + 3xy + 2y^2 = x^2 + 3xy + 3y^2$

52. $10x^2 - 15xy + 21y^2 - 14xy$

53. $3x^4 + 9x^2y - 20y^2 - 3x^2y - 7y^2$

54. $8x^2y + 4x^2y + 10xy^2 - 6x^2y - 5x^3 + 5xy^2$

*Write as a polynomial in simplified form. Then evaluate for **x = −3** and for **x = 0**.*

55. $2(3x + 1)$

56. $3(x - 4x^2)$

57. $3x + 3(2x + 1)$

58. $4(x^3 + x) + 3x$

59. $5x^2 + 2(2x + x^2)$

60. $-6(x - 2) + 6x$

61. $5(x^2 + 3x) - 2x^2 - 7x$

62. $2x^2 + 3(x^3 + x^2) - 3x^2$

Solve and check.

63. $2x + 3 + 5x - 15 = 21 - x + 11 + 4x$ $x = 11$

64. $x^2 - 15x - 36 = x^2 + x + 12$ $x = -3$

65. $51n - 5 - 27n + 19 = 11n - 11 + 12n - 39$ $n = -64$

66. $3(n + 8) = 4n + 19 - 3n + 89$ $n = 42$

Evaluate.

67. $x^2 - 2y^2$ when $x = 2$ and $y = -3$ -14

68. $3a^2 - 2ab + b^2$ when $a = -1$ and $b = 5$ 38

69. $x^3 + 3x^2y + 3xy^2 + y^3$ when $x = 2$ and $y = -2$ 0

***70.** Substitute $3x - \frac{1}{2}$ for x in the expression $\frac{1}{3}x + \frac{1}{6}$. Compare with the result when $\frac{1}{3}x + \frac{1}{6}$ is substituted for x in the expression $3x - \frac{1}{2}$.   The result is x in each case.

Using BASIC

To evaluate a polynomial such as $5x + 13$ for several values of *x*:

```
10 PRINT "ENTER X"
20 INPUT X
30 LET V = 5 * X + 13
40 PRINT "VALUE IS "; V
50 PRINT
60 GO TO 10
```

To evaluate a different polynomial, replace line 30 with the correct expression.

ADDITIONAL ANSWERS

Exercises

52. $10x^2 - 29xy + 21y^2$

53. $3x^4 + 6x^2y - 27y^2$

54. $-5x^3 + 6x^2y + 15xy^2$

55. $6x + 2$; -16; 2

56. $-12x^2 + 3x$; -117; 0

57. $9x + 3$; -24; 3

58. $4x^3 + 7x$; -129; 0

59. $7x^2 + 4x$; 51; 0

60. 12; 12; 12

61. $3x^2 + 8x$; 3; 0

62. $3x^3 + 2x^2$; -63; 0

Write the opposite of

1. -4 4 **2.** 1.5 -1.5

3. $-\frac{1}{2}$ $\frac{1}{2}$ **4.** $(x - 3)$ $-x + 3$

LESSON NOTES

You can use numbers to reinforce the work with polynomials. For example, you can use $x = 6$ and have the students evaluate:

a. the opposite of $-x^2 + 3x - 2$ 20
b. $x^2 - 3x + 2$ 20

The students will find that each expression has the same value;
$-1(-x^2 + 3x - 2) = x^2 - 3x + 2$.
   In subtracting polynomials in vertical form, students must think of the example as addition and mentally "change the sign" of each term in the second polynomial. Thus, in the subtraction example

$$7x^2 - 8x + 10$$
$$2x^2 + 10x - 3$$

students must mentally add $-2x^2 - 10x + 3$ to $7x^2 - 8x + 10$.

ALTERNATE EXAMPLES

1. Add $3x^2 - 2x + 7$ and $-x^2 + 5x$. $2x^2 + 3x + 7$

2. Find the opposite of each polynomial.
   a. polynomial: $2x - y - z$
      opposite: $-2x + y + z$
   b. polynomial: $a^2 - 1$
      opposite: $-a^2 + 1$, or $1 - a^2$

3. Subtract $5x - 4$ from $x + 2$.
   $-4x + 6$, or $6 - 4x$

5-2   Adding and Subtracting Polynomials

OBJECTIVES

To write the opposite of a polynomial.
To find sums and differences of polynomials.

To add two polynomials, write the sum and combine like terms.

EXAMPLE 1   Add $x^2 + 5x - 8$ and $-4x^2 + 6$.

$$(x^2 + 5x - 8) + (-4x^2 + 6) = x^2 + 5x - 8 - 4x^2 + 6$$
$$= x^2 - 4x^2 + 5x - 8 + 6$$
$$= -3x^2 + 5x - 2$$

You can also arrange like terms in columns and add vertically.

$$x^2 + 5x - 8$$
$$\underline{-4x^2 \qquad + 6}$$ Leave a space for the missing x-term.
$$-3x^2 + 5x - 2$$

Recall that polynomials represent numbers. To subtract a number, add its opposite. The same procedure holds for polynomials. The **opposite of a polynomial** is obtained by multiplying it by -1.

The opposite of $-x^2 + 3x - 2$ is
$$-1(-x^2 + 3x - 2) = x^2 - 3x + 2$$

EXAMPLE 2   Find the opposite of each polynomial.

   a. polynomial: $x + y - z$ **b. polynomial: $a - b$**
      opposite: $-x - y + z$ opposite: $-a + b$, or $b - a$

EXAMPLE 3   Subtract $3x - 1$ from $5x + 3$.

$$(5x + 3) - (3x - 1) = (5x + 3) + (-3x + 1)$$
$$= 5x + 3 - 3x + 1$$
$$= 2x + 4$$

Polynomials can also be subtracted by using a vertical scheme. To

170

subtract $2x^2 + 10x - 3$ from $7x^2 - 8x + 10$, write like terms in the same columns.

$$\begin{array}{r} 7x^2 - 8x + 10 \\ 2x^2 + 10x - 3 \\ \hline 5x^2 - 18x + 13 \end{array}$$

Add the opposite of $2x^2 + 10x - 3$.

$10 + (+3)$

$-8x + (-10x)$

$7x^2 + (-2x^2)$

You can check in the same way you check subtraction with numbers.

$$\left.\begin{array}{r} 7x^2 - 8x + 10 \\ 2x^2 + 10x - 3 \\ \hline 5x^2 - 18x + 13 \end{array}\right\} \text{ Add.}$$

$$7x^2 - 8x + 10 \qquad \text{This sum should be the first polynomial.}$$

An expression may include both sums and differences of polynomials.

EXAMPLE 4   Simplify $(9x + 5y) + (-3x + 2y) - (-2x + 12y)$.

$$(9x + 5y) + (-3x + 2y) - (-2x + 12y) = 9x + 5y - 3x + 2y + 2x - 12y$$
$$= 8x - 5y$$

CLASS EXERCISES

Add.

1. $4x + 5$
$\underline{3x + 9}$
$7x + 14$

2. $-2n + 3$
$\underline{-6n + 7}$
$-8n + 10$

3. $x^2 - 4x - 5$
$\underline{5x^2 + 7x}$
$6x^2 + 3x - 5$

Subtract.

4. $8x + 9$
$\underline{6x + 5}$
$2x + 4$

5. $14x + 6$
$\underline{-9x - 2}$
$23x + 8$

6. $2y - 7$
$\underline{8y - 2}$
$-6y - 5$

7. $-n^2 - 3n + 4$
$\underline{4n^2 - 1}$
$-5n^2 - 3n + 5$

8. $6x^2 + 3x$
$\underline{x^2 - 4x - 3}$
$5x^2 + 7x + 3$

9. $4x^2 + 2$
$\underline{-4x^2 + 5x + 2}$
$8x^2 - 5x$

Simplify.

10. $(6x - 5) + (2x + 7)$ $8x + 2$

11. $(8a + 1) + (7a - 3)$ $15a - 2$

12. $(10r + 5) - (2r + 1)$ $8r + 4$

13. $(a^2 - ab) - (b^2 - ab)$ $a^2 - b^2$

14. $(x^2 - x + 2) + (x + 3) - (x^2 + 5)$ 0

15. $(3x - 2y + 5z) - (-2x + 5y - z)$
$5x - 7y + 6z$

ALTERNATE EXAMPLE

4. Simplify: $(2x - 3y) + (8x + 5y) - (-2x - 5y)$ $12x + 7y$

DAILY QUIZ

Add.

1. $6x^2 + 5x$
$\underline{2x^2 - 6x}$
$8x^2 - x$

2. $4x^2 - 6x - 10$
$\underline{3x^2 - 9x + 8}$
$7x^2 - 15x - 2$

Subtract.

3. $5x + 6$
$\underline{3x - 3}$
$2x + 9$

4. $6x - 3y + 5$
$\underline{-8x + 2y - 3}$
$14x - 5y + 8$

Simplify.

5. $(4x + 10y - z) - (4x - 12y + 2z)$
$22y - 3z$

ASSIGNMENT GUIDE
(pages 172–173)
Minimum course: 1–35 odd, 45,
47, 49
Average course: 1–47 odd,
49–54
Maximum course: 1–47 odd,
48–50, 55–58

ENRICHMENT ACTIVITY

The Challenge at the end of this lesson deals with magic squares. Suggest that the students do research on the history of magic squares and write a report about what they find. Let them also report on the procedures for constructing magic squares of odd order: 3-by-3 and 5-by-5. A good reference book is *An Introduction to the History of Mathematics* by Howard Eves.

ADDITIONAL ANSWERS

Exercises

31. $21b$
32. $2y$
33. $-2x - 5y$
34. $3q - 7r + 3x$
35. $-8xy + 14x + 3$
36. $4x^2y - 5y$
37. $7x^2 + 7x + 4$
38. $x^2 - 9x + 8$
39. $-4a^3 + a^2 + a$
40. $-a - 5b$
41. $-2x - 2y$
42. $4x^2 + 5x - 16$
43. $-11a - 12$
44. $-7y^2 - 3y + 4$

EXERCISES

A *Add.*

1. $\begin{aligned} 5x^2 + 4x \\ \underline{x^2 + 5x} \\ 6x^2 + 9x \end{aligned}$

2. $\begin{aligned} -3a^3 + 2 \\ \underline{4a^3 - 3} \\ a^3 - 1 \end{aligned}$

3. $\begin{aligned} 6n + 10 \\ \underline{6n - 2} \\ 12n + 8 \end{aligned}$

4. $\begin{aligned} 3n^2 - 5n - 9 \\ \underline{2n^2 - 8n + 7} \\ 5n^2 - 13n - 2 \end{aligned}$

5. $\begin{aligned} 3x^2 + 5x + 7 \\ \underline{5x^2 - 2x - 9} \\ 8x^2 + 3x - 2 \end{aligned}$

6. $\begin{aligned} x^2 + 2x - 7y \\ \underline{-5x^2 - 3x - 6y} \\ -4x^2 - x - 13y \end{aligned}$

7. $\begin{aligned} 1.8a + 7b + 0.3 \\ \underline{-0.2a - 4b + 0.5} \\ 1.6a + 3b + 0.8 \end{aligned}$

8. $\begin{aligned} x + 2y + 3z \\ \underline{6x \qquad + 5z} \\ 7x + 2y + 8z \end{aligned}$

9. $\begin{aligned} 5x + 1\frac{1}{2}y + \frac{1}{4}z \\ \underline{2x \qquad - 7z} \\ 7x + 1\frac{1}{2}y - 6\frac{3}{4}z \end{aligned}$

Subtract.

10. $\begin{aligned} 4x + 5 \\ \underline{2x + 2} \\ 2x + 3 \end{aligned}$

11. $\begin{aligned} 6a + 7 \\ \underline{3a - 2} \\ 3a + 9 \end{aligned}$

12. $\begin{aligned} 5n^2 - 6 \\ \underline{-2n^2 + 3} \\ 7n^2 - 9 \end{aligned}$

13. $\begin{aligned} 7a^2 - 6a + 1 \\ \underline{2a^2 - 8a - 5} \\ 5a^2 + 2a + 6 \end{aligned}$

14. $\begin{aligned} 2a + b \\ \underline{a - b} \\ a + 2b \end{aligned}$

15. $\begin{aligned} 3x + 2y \\ \underline{x - y} \\ 2x + 3y \end{aligned}$

16. $\begin{aligned} 5x - 2y + 4 \\ \underline{2x + y + 2} \\ 3x - 3y + 2 \end{aligned}$

17. $\begin{aligned} n^2 \qquad + 8 \\ \underline{6n^2 + 5m} \\ -5n^2 - 5m + 8 \end{aligned}$

18. $\begin{aligned} -6x \qquad + 7z \\ \underline{4x + 9y + 5z} \\ -10x - 9y + 2z \end{aligned}$

Simplify.

19. $(x^2 - 2x + 1) - (x^2 - 4x + 3)$ $2x - 2$

20. $(5x + 3y - 2) + (-5x - 3y + 2)$ 0

21. $(7x - 4) + (3x + 2)$ $10x - 2$

22. $(-3x + 9) + (2x - 13)$ $-x - 4$

23. $(10r + 5) - (2r + 1)$ $8r + 4$

24. $(-n^2 - 2n + 3) - (n^2 - 3 + 2n)$ $-2n^2 - 4n + 6$

25. $(-y - 4) - (7y + 6)$ $-8y - 10$

26. $(3a - 2b) + (c + 2b) - (a + c)$ $2a$

27. $(a^2 - ab) + (ab - b^2)$ $a^2 - b^2$

28. $(6n^2 - 5n) + (4n^3 - 8n^2 + 2n)$ $4n^3 - 2n^2 - 3n$

29. $(3a + 9b - c) - (3a - 11b + c)$ $20b - 2c$

30. $(3a^7 - 8a^3 + 7) + (-5a^7 - 3a^3 - 8)$ $-2a^7 - 11a^3 - 1$

B **31.** $(5a + 9b - 2c) - (5a - 12b - 2c)$

32. $(4x - y) - (5x - 4y) + (x - y)$

33. $(-5x + 2y - z) + (3x - 7y + z)$

34. $(2q - 3r + 8x) - (4r - q + 5x)$

35. $(3xy + 5x) - (11xy - 9x - 3)$

36. $(3x^2y - 4y) - (-x^2y + y)$

37. $(4x^2 - x + 6) + (3x^2 + 8x - 2)$

38. $(4x^2 - x + 6) - (3x^2 + 8x - 2)$

39. $(a^3 - a^2 + a) + (-5a^3 + 2a^2)$

40. $(2a + b) + (4a - 5b) - (7a + b)$

41. $(4x - y) - (x + 2y) - (5x - y)$

42. $(5x^2 - 11) - (5 + 2x) - (x^2 - 7x)$

43. $(3a - 4) - (7a + 9) + (2a - 2) - (9a - 3)$

44. $(4y^2 - 2y) + (2y - 3y^2) - (8y^2 + 3y - 4)$

172

CHAPTER 5

EXTRA PRACTICE, pages 515–516

Add.

45.
$$6x^2 - 5x$$
$$x^3 - 8x^2 + 2x + 9$$
$$\underline{-5x^2 - 3x - 8}$$
$$x^3 - 7x^2 - 6x + 1$$

46.
$$-6a \qquad + 7c$$
$$4a + 9b + 5c$$
$$\underline{a + b - c}$$
$$-a + 10b + 11c$$

47.
$$x^2 + 2xy + y^2$$
$$x^2 - xy - y^2$$
$$\underline{3x^2 - 2xy - y^2}$$
$$5x^2 - xy - y^2$$

For each polygon, express the perimeter in terms of **x**. *Then find the perimeter when* **x** = 3.

48.

$3x^2 - 5$

$x^2 + 2$

$2x^2$

$6x^2 - 3$; 51

49.

$x + 2$

$3x - 1$ $3x - 1$

$x + 2$

$8x + 2$; 26

50.

$2x + 4$ $3x$

$x + 6$ $3x$

$4x - 1$

$13x + 9$; 48

C

51. Add $2x + 4y - z$, $2y + 3z + 2x$, and $z - 3x - 4y$. $x + 2y + 3z$

52. Add $\frac{1}{2}x - 6$, $-\frac{3}{2}x - 9$, and $2x - 3$. $x - 18$

53. Add $2x^3 + 14x^2 - 8$ and $x^4 + 7x^3 - 4x$. $x^4 + 9x^3 + 14x^2 - 4x - 8$

54. From the sum of $x + 3y$ and $-3x - y$, subtract $x - y$. $-3x + 3y$

55. Subtract $a^2 - b^2 - c^2$ from the sum of $4a^2 - 3b^2 + 5c^2$ and $2a^2 + 3b^2 - c^2$.
$5a^2 + b^2 + 5c^2$

56. Subtract the sum of $15n - n^3 + 2n^2$ and $4n^3 - n^2 - 5$ from $2n + 5n^3$.
$2n^3 - n^2 - 13n + 5$

57. From the sum of $a^2 - 2a + 3$ and $2a^2 - a + 5$, subtract $4a^2 - 4a + 7$. $-a^2 + a + 1$

58. The perimeter of this rectangle is $(12x - 8)$ cm.
Its length is $(2x + 6)$ cm.

$2x + 6$

   a. Express its width in terms of x. $(4x - 10)$ cm

   b. Find its width, length, and perimeter if $x = 4$.
     Width 6 cm; length 14 cm; perimeter 40 cm

CHALLENGE

Magic Squares

This is a 3-by-3 magic square. The sum of the numbers in any row, column, or diagonal is 15.

1. Form a 3-by-3 magic square using nine consecutive integers. Let n represent the first number. What is the *magic sum*?
$3n + 12$

2. Try forming a 3-by-3 magic square using nine consecutive even numbers. Let n represent the first even number. What is the *magic sum*? $3n + 24$

Write in factored form.
1. 10^3 $10 \times 10 \times 10$
2. 3^2 3×3
3. $(0.2)^4$ $0.2 \times 0.2 \times 0.2 \times 0.2$

LESSON NOTES

As you develop the material in this lesson, remind the students that when a variable is shown without an exponent, its exponent is understood to be 1. Thus,
$a \cdot a^2 = a^1 \cdot a^2 = a^{1+2} = a^3$.

In Example 1d, $7^3(-7) = 7^3(-7^1)$. Here the bases do not seem to be the same; but (-7^1) can be thought of as $(-1)7^1$. Then $7^3(-7) = (-1)(7^3)(7^1) = -1(7^{3+1}) = -(7^4)$, or -7^4.

In finding the product of $(2a^2b)$ and (a^3b^4) in Example 3a, $(2a^2b)$ can be thought of as $(2a^2b^1)$. Then the students can group powers with the same base together and add exponents:

$(2a^2b)(a^3b^4) = (2)(a^2b^1)(a^3b^4)$
$= (2)(a^2 \cdot a^3)(b^1 \cdot b^4)$
$= 2a^5b^5$

POSSIBLE ERROR

Students make frequent errors in working with exponents. Here are two common errors:

$3^2 \cdot 3^5 = 9^7$ (incorrect)
$3^2 \cdot 3^5 = 3^{10}$ (incorrect)

To help students avoid such errors, make frequent reference to the definition $x^a \cdot x^b = x^{a+b}$.

ALTERNATE EXAMPLES

1. Express each product, using a single exponent.
   a. $(5^3)(5^7)$
      5^{10}
   b. $(x^2)(x^4)$
      x^8
   c. $(-3)^2(-3)^5(-3)$
      $(-3)^8$
   d. $(8)^2(-8)$
      -8^3
2. Simplify: $(-3x^5)(-7x^2)$ $21x^7$

5-3 Multiplying Monomials

OBJECTIVE

To multiply monomials containing powers with the same base.

Recall that 2^5, the fifth power of 2, means the product of five 2's.
$$2^5 = 2 \cdot 2 \cdot 2 \cdot 2 \cdot 2$$
Look at these groupings of the five factors. Each product equal 2^5.

$(2)(2 \cdot 2 \cdot 2 \cdot 2) = 2^5$	$(2 \cdot 2)(2 \cdot 2 \cdot 2) = 2^5$
$(2^1)(2^4) = 2^{1+4} = 2^5$	$(2^2)(2^3) = 2^{2+3} = 2^5$

This suggests the following rule for multiplying powers with the same base when the exponents are positive integers.

Product of Powers with the Same Base

When you multiply two or more powers with the same base, add the exponents.

$$(x^a)(x^b) = x^{a+b}$$

EXAMPLE 1   Express each product, using a single exponent.

When the bases are the same, add the exponents.

a. $(3^2)(3^5) = 3^{2+5}$
   $= 3^7$

b. $(x^3)(x^8) = x^{3+8}$
   $= x^{11}$

c. $(-2)^7(-2)(-2)^4 = (-2)^{7+1+4}$
   $= (-2)^{12}$

d. $7^3(-7) = -(7^3 \cdot 7)$
   $= -(7^4)$, or -7^4

EXAMPLE 2   Simplify $(5x^4)(-7x^2)$.

$(5x^4)(-7x^2) = (5)(-7)(x^4 \cdot x^2)$
$= (-35)(x^{4+2})$
$= -35x^6$

When multiplying monomials, group powers together that have the same base, using the commutative and associative properties. To simplify the product, express each variable with just one exponent.

EXAMPLE 3   Simplify each product.

a. $(2a^2b)(a^3b^4) = (2)(a^2 \cdot a^3)(b \cdot b^4)$ Group powers with the
$= 2a^5b^5$ same base together.

b. $(-3x^4y)(4x^2z)(2xy^2z) = (-3 \cdot 4 \cdot 2)(x^4 \cdot x^2 \cdot x)(y \cdot y^2)(z \cdot z)$
$= -24x^7y^3z^2$

EXAMPLE 4   Write *true* or *false*. If the answer is false, give a reason.

a. $8^2 \cdot 8^3 = 8^6$ False. When multiplying powers with the same base, do not multiply the exponents. Add them. $8^2 \cdot 8^3 = 8^5$

b. $6^2 \cdot 6^7 = 6^9$ True.

c. $6^4 \cdot 2^3 = 12^7$ False. The bases are not the same. However, $12^4 \cdot 12^3 = 12^7$.

d. $4^3 \cdot 4^2 = 16^5$ False. Do not multiply the bases. $4^3 \cdot 4^2 = 4^5$

ALTERNATE EXAMPLES

3. Simplify each product.
   a. $(5ab^5)(-6a^2b)$ $-30a^3b^6$
   b. $(-xy^2)(-3x^3y)(9x^5y)$ $27x^9y^4$

4. Write true or false. If the answer is false, give a reason.
   a. $2^2 \cdot 3^5 = 6^7$ False. The bases are not the same.
   b. $7 \cdot 7^5 = 7^6$ True.
   c. $2^5 \cdot 2^2 = 2^{10}$ False. Do not multiply the exponents.
   d. $3^4 \cdot 3^2 = 9^6$ False. Do not multiply the bases.

DAILY QUIZ

Express each product in exponential form with just one exponent.
   1. $3^3 \cdot 3^4$ 3^7 **2.** $(-3)^6(-3)^3$ $(-3)^9$
Simplify.
   3. $(-3xy^2)(3x^3y)$ $-9x^4y^3$
   4. $(-2x^5)(4x^2)(6x^3)$ $-48x^{10}$
   5. $(-5x)(-2xy)(-8xyz)$ $-80x^3y^2z$

CLASS EXERCISES

Express each product in exponential form with just one exponent.

1. $5^2 \cdot 5^3$ 5^5 **2.** $5 \cdot 5^4$ 5^5 **3.** $(-4)^3(-4)^4$ $(-4)^7$ **4.** $10^3 \cdot 10^3$ 10^6

5. $(b^6)(b^{16})$ b^{22} **6.** $(c)(c^5)$ c^6 **7.** $(0.4)(0.4)^5$ $(0.4)^6$ **8.** $(-4)^6(-4)$ $(-4)^7$

Simplify.

9. $2y(-3y)$ $-6y^2$ **10.** $(-2x)(x^3)$ $-2x^4$ **11.** $x(3x)$ $3x^2$ **12.** $(-n^3)(3n^5)$ $-3n^8$

13. $(-4ab)(-b^2)$ $4ab^3$ **14.** $5(a^3x)(3a^2x^5)$ $15a^5x^6$ **15.** $(ab)(-3ab^2)(-b)$ $3a^2b^4$

*Classify each statement as **true** or **false**.*

16. $5^2 \cdot 5^4 = 5^6$ True   **17.** $4^2 \cdot 7^3 = 28^5$ False   **18.** $2^3 \cdot 2^{11} = 4^{14}$ False

19. $(2^2)^2 = 2^4$ True   **20.** $-2^2 = (-2)^2$ False   **21.** $2^2(-2)^2 = -2^4$ False

EXERCISES

A

Express each product in exponential form with just one exponent.

1. $2^5 \cdot 2^2$ 2^7 **2.** $(-2)^8(-2)^3$ $(-2)^{11}$ **3.** $2 \cdot 2^6$ 2^7 **4.** $a \cdot a^6$ a^7

5. $b^4 \cdot b^5$ b^9 **6.** $x^2 \cdot x^4$ x^6 **7.** $x^2 \cdot x^3$ x^5 **8.** $m^3 \cdot m^4$ m^7

9. $y^2 \cdot y^3$ y^5 **10.** $d^3 \cdot d$ d^4 **11.** $\left(\frac{2}{3}\right)^2\left(\frac{2}{3}\right)^3$ $\left(\frac{2}{3}\right)^5$ **12.** $\frac{1}{10}\left(\frac{1}{10}\right)^2$ $\left(\frac{1}{10}\right)^3$

ASSIGNMENT GUIDE
(pages 175–177)

Minimum course: 1–41 odd,
            59–63 odd
Average course: 9–71 odd,
            72
Maximum course: 13–87 odd
All courses: *Checkpoint*
            review
            exercises

POLYNOMIALS

175

EXTRA PRACTICE, page 516

B

Classify each statement as **true** or **false**.

13. $8^3 \cdot 8^2 = 64^5$ False   14. $2^5 \cdot 2^4 \cdot 2^6 = 2^{15}$ True

15. $(-7)^2(-7)^6 = (-7)^{12}$ False   16. $(0.3)(0.3)^5(0.3)^2 = (0.3)^8$ True

Simplify.

17. $(d)(-d)$ $-d^2$ 18. $(-q^5)(q^2)$ $-q^7$ 19. $(x)(-x^2)$ $-x^3$ 20. $(-a^2)(a^2)$ $-a^4$

21. $(-t^3)(-t^3)$ t^6 22. $(-n)(-n^2)$ n^3 23. $(-x^2)(-x^2)$ x^4 24. $(2y)(3y^2)$ $6y^3$

25. $(3x^2)(x)$ $3x^3$ 26. $(5a^2)(7a^4)$ $35a^6$ 27. $(-x^5)(3x^3)$ $-3x^8$ 28. $(ab)(3b^2)$ $3ab^3$

29. $(3ab)(2a)$ $6a^2b$ 30. $(-2n^4)(-3n^2)$ $6n^6$ 31. $(-4b^2)(2b^2)$ $-8b^4$

32. $(-4b^2)\left(-\dfrac{1}{2}ab\right)$ $2ab^3$ 33. $(3x^3y)\left(\dfrac{1}{3}x^2y^5\right)$ x^5y^6 34. $\left(\dfrac{1}{4}xy^2\right)(2x^2y)$ $\dfrac{1}{2}x^3y^3$

35. $(-2xy^2)(2x^3y)$ $-4x^4y^3$ 36. $(-4a^2b)(-5ab)$ $20a^3b^2$ 37. $(4xy)(-x^2y^3)$ $-4x^3y^4$

38. $(8xy^2)(-3x^2y^4)(x)$ $-24x^4y^6$ 39. $(-a^5)(3a^2)(7a^3)$ $-21a^{10}$ 40. $(2x)(-6x^5)(3x^3)$ $-36x^9$

41. $(5xy)(4x^2y)(xy^2)$ $20x^4y^4$ 42. $(-a^2b)(5ab^2)(9ab)$ $-45a^4b^4$ 43. $-1(n^5)(-n)$ n^6

44. $x(3xy)(2y)$ $6x^2y^2$ 45. $(3a)(2a^2b)(4b^2)$ $24a^3b^3$ 46. $2x(-xy)(-y^3)$ $2x^2y^4$

47. $-t^3(-3tu)(t^4u^2)$ $3t^8u^3$ 48. $(5ab)(-b)(3a^5b)$ $-15a^6b^3$ 49. $a^3(-3ab)(5c^3)$ $-15a^4bc^3$

50. $(-x^2)(-3xy)(-y^2)$ $-3x^3y^3$ 51. $(x^2yz^2)(xy^2z)$ $x^3y^3z^3$ 52. $(2.1)^3(2.1)^4$ $(2.1)^7$

53. $(0.5)^2(0.5)^2(0.5)^3$ $(0.5)^7$ 54. $(0.1)^3(0.1)^3(0.1)^3$ $(0.1)^9$

55. $(-4a)(-2ab)(-3abc)$ $-24a^3b^2c$ 56. $(4a^5)(-2a^2b)(-ab^2)$ $8a^8b^3$

57. $(4xy^2z^3)(0.25y^2z)$ xy^4z^4 58. $(-0.3x^2y)(0.7xy^3)$ $-0.21x^3y^4$

Simplify. Express the powers of 10 in exponential form and then convert to decimal form.

   Sample $(2 \times 10^3)(4 \times 10^2) = (2 \times 4)(10^3 \times 10^2) = 8 \times 10^5 = 800,000$

59. $(2 \times 10^5)(3 \times 10^2)$ 60. $(2.1 \times 10)(10^3 \times 10^2)$

61. $(2.5 \times 10^3)(1.2 \times 10^6)$ 62. $(5.4 \times 10^7)(9.3 \times 10)$

63. $(8.2 \times 10^9)(1.1 \times 10^2)$ 64. $(5.3 \times 10^3)(3.5 \times 10^5)$

Simplify each product. Then combine like terms.

65. $(3x)(2x^4) + (3x^2)(x^3)$ $9x^5$ 66. $(y^3)(5y^3) + (-y^3)(2y^3)$ $3y^6$

67. $(2a)(a^2)(-a) + (3a^2)(2a^2)$ $4a^4$ 68. $(n^2)(-3n^2)(-5n) + (6n^2)(-2n^3)$ $3n^5$

69. $(x^2y)(2x^2y^3) - (x^2y^2)(-5x^2y^2)$ $7x^4y^4$ 70. $(a^2b)(2ab^2)(a^2b^2) - (a^4b^4)(ab)$ a^5b^5

71. $\left(\dfrac{1}{3}x^2y\right)\left(\dfrac{2}{3}xy^3\right)(9x^3) - \left(\dfrac{4}{3}x^3y^3\right)(6x^3y) + \left(\dfrac{2}{3}xy^3\right)(9x^5y)$ 0

176

C Rewrite each expression using only one exponent.

72. $a^x \cdot a^2$ a^{x+2} **73.** $x^a \cdot x$ x^{a+1} **74.** $x^2 \cdot x^b$ x^{2+b}

75. $x^a \cdot x^b$ x^{a+b} **76.** $y^{2a} \cdot y^{3a}$ y^{5a} **77.** $x^n \cdot x^n$ x^{2n}

78. $(a^x)(a^x)(a^x)$ a^{3x} **79.** $(3^{5x})(3^{2x})$ 3^{7x} **80.** $(a^n)(a^{2n})(a^{3n})$ a^{6n}

81. $(x^{m-3})(x^3)$ x^m **82.** $(x^{2a+1})(-x^{2a-1})$ $-x^{4a}$

83. $(a^{3m+5})(a^{4m-4})$ a^{7m+1} **84.** $(a+1)^3(a+1)^4$ $(a+1)^7$

85. $(a+1)^n(a+1)^2$ $(a+1)^{n+2}$ **86.** $(a+1)^{3n}(a+1)^{m-n}$ $(a+1)^{2n+m}$

Express the area of each figure in terms of the variables and simplify.
Then use the result to find the area if $x = 2$, $y = 10$, and $z = 1$.

87.

$5xy$

$3x^2y$

area = length × width

88.

$15x^3y^2$;
12,000 sq. units

$3x^3z$

$6x^2z^6$

area = $\frac{1}{2}$base × height

$9x^5z^7$;
288 sq. units

*89. Find two unequal positive integers a and b such that $a^b = b^a$.
$a = 2, b = 4$

CHECKPOINT

Simplify. Then give the degree of the polynomial.

1. $2x + 3x$ $5x$; 1   **2.** $-11x + 1x$ $-10x$; 1   **3.** $8(3x - x^3) + 3x^3 + x$
                                                       $-5x^3 + 25x$; 3

4. $5x + 3(1 + x) - x$ **5.** $4(2x^5 - x^4) - 8x^5$ $-4x^4$; 4   **6.** $2x - 2(x + 1)$ -2; 0
      $7x + 3$; 1

7. Evaluate $3x^2 - 2x + 5$ when $x = -1$.   10

Simplify.

8. $(9x + 6y + 7) - (-4x + 7y + 9)$ **9.** $(3x + 4y) + (-2y + 7z - 4x)$
    $13x - y - 2$ $-x + 2y + 7z$

10. $(x^2 - 3xy) - (y^2 - 3xy)$ $x^2 - y^2$ **11.** $(2x^2 - 17) - (13 - 2x) - (x^2 + 3x)$
                                                $x^2 - x - 30$

12. $(5a^2)(7a^4)$ $35a^6$ **13.** $(-x^5)(3x^3)$ $-3x^8$ **14.** $(3ab)(2a)$ $6a^2b$

15. $(-4b^2)(-ab)$ $4ab^3$ **16.** $(3x^3y)(x^2y^5)$ $3x^5y^6$ **17.** $(4xy)(2x^2y)$ $8x^3y^2$

Express each product in exponential form with just one exponent.

18. $x^3 \cdot x^5$ x^8 **19.** $x^4 \cdot x$ x^5 **20.** $7^2 \cdot 7^9$ 7^{11} **21.** $a^x \cdot a^y$ a^{x+y}

POLYNOMIALS

LESSON NOTES

The opening paragraphs of this lesson contrast two concepts: the product of powers (with the same base) and the power of a power. It may be helpful to contrast the two generalizations: $(x^a)(x^b) = x^{a+b}$ and $(x^a)^b = x^{ab}$.

In considering the power-of-a-product rule, $(x \cdot y)^a = x^a y^a$ and the model examples that follow it, do not hesitate to show the expansion of an expression such as $(-2y)^3$ in detail:

$$(-2y)^3 = (-2y)(-2y)(-2y)$$
$$= (-2)(-2)(-2)\,(y)(y)(y)$$
$$= (-2)^3 y^3$$
$$= -8y^3$$

[*Lesson notes continue on page 179.*]

POSSIBLE ERROR

Students often confuse the rules for working with exponents and may add when they are finding the power of a power. Thus, they may write $(3^4)^3 = 3^7$, which is incorrect.

Correct such errors by referring to the definition $(x^a)^b = x^{ab}$ and by showing the appropriate expansion. For example:

$$(3^4)^3 = (3^4)(3^4)(3^4) = 3^{4+4+4}$$
$$= 3^{12}$$

ALTERNATE EXAMPLE

1. Rewrite using only one exponent.
   a. $(5^3)^4$ b. $\left(\left(\dfrac{3}{4}\right)^2\right)^3$ c. $(y^3)^6$

      5^{12} $\left(\dfrac{3}{4}\right)^6$ y^{18}

5-4 Powers of Monomials

OBJECTIVE

To apply the power-of-a-power and the power-of-a-product rules of exponents.

The first rule for exponents concerned the *product of powers* with the same base. To simplify such a product, you add the exponents.

$$(7^2)(7^3) = 7^{2+3} = 7^5$$

Now consider a *power of a power*, such as the cube of 4^2, or $(4^2)^3$. The base 4 is a factor $2 \cdot 3$, or 6 times.

$$(4^2)^3 = (4^2)(4^2)(4^2) = 4^{2+2+2} = 4^{2 \cdot 3} = 4^6$$

Note that $(4^2)^3 = 16^3 = 4096$ and that $4^6 = 4096$. This suggests the following rule for simplifying a power of a power when the exponents are positive integers.

> **Power of a Power**
>
> **To find the power of a power, multiply the exponents.**
>
> $$(x^a)^b = x^{ab}$$

EXAMPLE 1   Rewrite using only one exponent.

a. $(3^4)^3 = 3^{4 \cdot 3}$ b. $\left(\left(\dfrac{2}{3}\right)^7\right)^2 = \left(\dfrac{2}{3}\right)^{7 \cdot 2}$ c. $(x^2)^5 = x^{2 \cdot 5}$
$\quad\;\; = 3^{12}$ $\qquad\qquad\quad = \left(\dfrac{2}{3}\right)^{14}$ $\qquad = x^{10}$

Another rule for exponents involves the *power of a product* such as $(2 \cdot 10)^3$.

$$(2 \cdot 10)^3 = (2 \cdot 10)(2 \cdot 10)(2 \cdot 10)$$
$$= (2 \cdot 2 \cdot 2)(10 \cdot 10 \cdot 10)$$
$$= 2^3 \cdot 10^3$$

Note that $(2 \cdot 10)^3 = 20^3 = 8000$ and that $2^3 \cdot 10^3 = 8 \cdot 1000 = 8000$. In general, for a positive integer exponent, the following rule applies.

> **Power of a Product**
>
> **To find the power of a product, multiply the factors raised to the given power.**
>
> $$(x \cdot y)^a = x^a \cdot y^a$$

EXAMPLE 2   Simplify.

a. $(3x)^2 = 3^2x^2$ **b.** $(-2y)^3 = (-2)^3y^3$ **c.** $(2xy)^4 = 2^4x^4y^4$
$\quad\quad\quad\quad = 9x^2$ $\quad\quad\quad\quad\quad = -8y^3$ $\quad\quad\quad\quad\quad = 16x^4y^4$

EXAMPLE 3   Simplify.

a. $(2r^3s^2)^4 = 2^4(r^3)^4(s^2)^4$ **b.** $(-3x)^2(2y^3)^5 = (-3)^2(x)^2(2^5)(y^3)^5$
$\quad\quad\quad\quad\quad = 2^4(r^{3\cdot4})(s^{2\cdot4})$ $\quad\quad\quad\quad\quad\quad\quad = (-3)^2(2^5)(x^2)(y^{3\cdot5})$
$\quad\quad\quad\quad\quad = 16r^{12}s^8$ $\quad\quad\quad\quad\quad\quad\quad = (9)(32)(x^2)(y^{15})$
$\quad\quad\quad\quad\quad\quad\quad\quad\quad\quad\quad\quad\quad = 288x^2y^{15}$

The power-of-a-product rule can also be used to find a product of powers that have the same exponent. For example, you can simplify $12^2(\frac{1}{6})^2$ in two ways.

Square, then multiply.   Multiply the bases, then square.

$$12^2\left(\frac{1}{6}\right)^2 = (144)\left(\frac{1}{36}\right) \quad\quad 12^2\left(\frac{1}{6}\right)^2 = \left(12\cdot\frac{1}{6}\right)^2$$
$$= 4 \quad\quad\quad\quad\quad\quad\quad\quad = 2^2, \text{ or } 4$$

CLASS EXERCISES

Simplify. Give each answer as a power of 10.

1. $(10^3)^2$ 10^6 **2.** $(10^5)^2$ 10^{10} **3.** $(10^7)^2$ 10^{14} **4.** $(10^2)^7$ 10^{14}

Simplify.

5. $(3a)^2$ $9a^2$ **6.** $(4x)^2$ $16x^2$ **7.** $(-3)^3$ -27 **8.** $(-2m)^4$ $16m^4$

9. $(-2n)^5$ $-32n^5$ **10.** $(x^2y)^3$ x^6y^3 **11.** $(a^2b^3)^4$ a^8b^{12} **12.** $(3x^5y^2)^2$ $9x^{10}y^4$

EXERCISES

A   *Simplify. Give each answer as a power of 5.*

1. $(5^3)^2$ 5^6 **2.** $(5^2)^3$ 5^6 **3.** $(5^4)^5$ 5^{20} **4.** $(5^5)^3$ 5^{15}

Simplify.

5. $(4a)^2$ $16a^2$ **6.** $(2x)^3$ $8x^3$ **7.** $(-4n)^2$ $16n^2$ **8.** $(-2b)^3$ $-8b^3$

9. $(5x)^2$ $25x^2$ **10.** $(2x)^5$ $32x^5$ **11.** $(2y)^2$ $4y^2$ **12.** $(-2y)^2$ $4y^2$

13. $(-t^2)^2$ t^4 **14.** $(t^2)^2$ t^4 **15.** $(-t^2)^3$ $-t^6$ **16.** $(t^2)^6$ t^{12}

17. $(ab)^2$ a^2b^2 **18.** $(2a)^2$ $4a^2$ **19.** $(5a)^2$ $25a^2$ **20.** $(2ab)^2$ $4a^2b^2$

21. $(abc)^3$ $a^3b^3c^3$ **22.** $(3b)^3$ $27b^3$ **23.** $(-xy)^3$ $-x^3y^3$ **24.** $(4x^2y)^2$ $16x^4y^2$

In the material that precedes the Class Exercises, the text shows two ways of simplifying $(12)^2\left(\frac{1}{6}\right)^2$. The second approach involves using the power-of-a-product rule "in reverse"; that is, the expression a^2b^2 is interpreted as $(a\cdot b)^2$. In this case, the computation is simpler than in the first approach, since $a\cdot b$ is 2, and $2^2 = 4$. Whenever $a\cdot b$ can be simplified, the second approach is simpler.

ALTERNATE EXAMPLES

2. Simplify.
    a. $(7x)^2$ **b.** $(-5y)^2$ **c.** $(4xy)^3$
    $49x^2$ $25y^2$ $64x^3y^3$
3. Simplify.
    a. $(3a^3b)^2$ **b.** $(-2x^2y^3)^2(-xy^2)^4$
    $9a^6b^2$ $4x^8y^{14}$

DAILY QUIZ

Simplify.
    1. $(3x)^2$ $9x^2$
    2. $(-2x^2)^2$ $4x^4$
    3. $(8x^2y^3)^2$ $64x^4y^6$
    4. $-3x(2xy)^3$ $-24x^4y^3$
    5. $(xy)^2(x^2y)^3$ x^8y^5

ASSIGNMENT GUIDE
(pages 179–181)
Minimum course: 1–4, 5–55 odd
second day: 6–50 even
Average course: 1–61 odd
second day: 26–62 even
Maximum course: 1–63 odd
second day: 44–72 even
All courses: *Strategies for Problem Solving*

EXTRA PRACTICE, page 516

25. $(5x^2)^3$ $125x^6$ 26. $(-4a)^2$ $16a^2$ 27. $(-3a)^3$ $-27a^3$ 28. $(5x^4)^2$ $25x^8$

29. $(a^2b)^4$ a^8b^4 30. $(3x^3y)^3$ $27x^9y^3$ 31. $(5x^4y^3)^3$ $125x^{12}y^9$ 32. $(9a^2b^3)^2$ $81a^4b^6$

33. $(2a^3b^2)^5$ $32a^{15}b^{10}$ 34. $\left(\frac{1}{2}x^3y^4\right)^2$ $\frac{1}{4}x^6y^8$ 35. $\left(-\frac{3}{5}a^5h^3\right)^2$ $\frac{9}{25}a^{10}b^6$ 36. $\left(-\frac{2}{3}xy^4\right)^3$ $\frac{8}{27}x^3y^{12}$

B   Write **true** or **false**. If false, correct the right side to make a true statement.

37. $(3^4)^5 = 3^9$ False; 3^{20} 38. $8^4 \cdot 8^3 = 8^7$ True   39. $\left(\left(\frac{2}{3}\right)^2\right)^6 = \left(\frac{2}{3}\right)^{12}$ True

40. $\left(\frac{1}{2}\right)^3\left(\frac{1}{2}\right)^5 = \left(\frac{1}{4}\right)^8$ 41. $(-5)^2(-6)^2 = 30^4$ 42. $(6)^3\left(\frac{1}{2}\right)^3 = 3^3$ True

     False; $\left(\frac{1}{2}\right)^8$ False; 30^2

Simplify.

43. $-2x(3xy)^3$ $-54x^4y^3$ 44. $x^2(xy^2)^2$ x^4y^4 45. $a^4(a^2b)^4$ $a^{12}b^4$

46. $(-3a)(-a^3b)^2$ $-3a^7b^2$ 47. $(3n)^3(3w^2)^2$ $243n^3w^4$ 48. $(-b)^3(-2b^2)^2$ $-4b^7$

49. $(x^2y)^2(-xy^3)^3$ $-x^7y^{11}$ 50. $(-xy^2)^3(-2x^2y)^2$ $-4x^7y^8$ 51. $(xy)^3(x^2y)^2(xy^2)$ x^8y^7

Simplify. First write each expression in the form $a \cdot 10^n$. Then convert to decimal form.

52. $(2 \times 10^3)^2$ 53. $(2.5 \times 10^3)^2$ 54. $(3.1 \times 10^5)^2$ 55. $(1.2 \times 10^2)^6$

Simplify powers and products. Then combine like terms.

56. $(2x^2)^3 + x^6$ $9x^6$ 57. $(xy)^3 + (3x)^3y^3$ $28x^3y^3$ 58. $(2a^2b)^3 - (a^3)^2b^3$ $7a^6b^3$

59. $(-x)^4y - (x^2)^2y$ 0 60. $(x^2y)^4 + (4x^4y^2)^2$ $17x^8y^4$ 61. $8(x^2y)^3 - 2y(2x^3y)^2$ 0

C   Evaluate each expression in two ways.

     Sample   Evaluate $2x(-3x^2)\left(\frac{1}{2}x^3\right)$ for $x = 2$ in two ways.

$$2x(-3x^2)\left(\frac{1}{2}x^3\right) = 2 \cdot 2(-3 \cdot 2^2)\left(\frac{1}{2} \cdot 2^3\right) = 4(-12)(4) = -192$$

$$2x(-3x^2)\left(\frac{1}{2}x^3\right) = -3x^6 = -3 \cdot 2^6 = -3 \cdot 64 = -192$$

62. $10x^2\left(\frac{1}{5}x\right)\left(\frac{1}{2}x^3\right)$ 63. $(-2x^2y)(4xy^2)(-3y^3)$ 64. $(-3ab^2c)(-2a^2b^3c^2)(-5a^3bc^5)$

     for $x = 10$ for $x = \frac{1}{2}$ and $y = 2$ for $a = 2$, $b = \frac{1}{2}$, $c = -1$

     x^6; 1,000,000 $24x^3y^6$; 192 $-30a^6b^6c^8$; -30

Simplify.

65. $(a^n)^n$ a^{n^2} 66. $(ab^x)^y$ a^yb^{xy} 67. $(-2a^x)^3$ $-8a^{3x}$ 68. $(2a^x)^3$ $8a^{3x}$

69. $((2^3)^2)^2$ 70. $(((-1)^3)^3)^3$ 71. $[(x^2)^3y]^4$ $x^{24}y^4$ 72. $\left[\left(-\frac{1}{2}a^5b^5\right)^2\right]^2$

     $2^{12} = 4096$ $-1^{27} = -1$ $\frac{1}{16}a^{20}b^{20}$

73. Show that raising a power to a power is not an associative operation. Find numbers a, b, and c for which $(a^b)^c \neq a^{(bc)}$.

Guessing and Testing

Strategies for Problem Solving

The problem-solving technique of guessing and testing is used widely in mathematics, in science, and in the social sciences. Usually, the guess is an "educated guess" based on some data, some analyses, or other types of evidence.

Recently, the square of a man's age was the same number as the year he was born. How old is he now?

One way to find an answer is to **make some guesses and test them.**

Step 1 Try some ages and find their squares.

age 25	$25^2 = 625$	too young
age 35	$35^2 = 1225$	too young
age 45	$45^2 = 2025$	too old

Step 2 Try to improve your guess. Choose ages close to 45, the best of your first guesses.

age 42	$42^2 = 1764$
age 43	$43^2 = 1849$
age 44	$44^2 = 1936$ ←This is the only possibility for someone living now.

Step 3 You now know that the man was born in 1936. He was 44 in 1980. How old is he now?

Practice this strategy on some other problems.

1. A woman was living at the time Columbus was born. Later, the square of her age was the year of her birth. How old was she in 1492? 48

2. A certain year during Albert Einstein's life was equal to the square of the number that was 13 less than his age at that time. When was he born? 1879

3. There was a year during George Washington's life that was the square of 10 more than his age then. When was George Washington born? 1732

4. Leonhard Euler was a great mathematician who lived in Switzerland during the 18th century. The year that was 19 years before he died was equal to the square of the quantity that was 15 less than his age then. In what year was he born, and in what year did he die? 1707; 1783

POLYNOMIALS

Multiply.
1. $(3x)(x)$ $3x^2$
2. $(-2y)(y)$ $-2y^2$
3. $(y)(-5)$ $5y$
4. $(-7)(x)$ $-7x$

LESSON NOTES

Recall the distributive property and the fact that it applies not only to addition but also to subtraction as well:

$$a(b + c) = ab + ac$$
$$a(b - c) = ab - ac$$

Point out, too, that it does not matter if the binomial appears first: $(b + c)a = ba + ca$, and $(b - c)a = ba - ca$. This idea is used in $(x^3 - 1)6x^2$, the fourth model illustration that follows the opening paragraph on the text page.

   Discuss Examples 1 and 2 thoroughly. In Example 2a, be sure the students see that, initially, the multiplication produces two x^2-terms ($3x^2$ and $5x^2$) and two x-terms ($-4x$ and $10x$). You can show the combining of like terms as an intermediate step to help students see how $5x^3 + 8x^2 + 6x$ is obtained as an answer.

   Similarly, in Example 2b, you can show why the xy-terms disappear:

$$xy - yx = 1xy - 1xy$$
$$= (1 - 1)xy = 0xy$$

ALTERNATE EXAMPLES

1. Multiply: $-3x$ and
   $-2x^3 + 3x^2 - x - 1$
   $6x^4 - 9x^3 + 3x^2 + 3x$
2. Simplify each expression.
   a. $2x(x - 3) - x(x^2 - x - 3)$
      $-x^3 + 3x^2 - 3x$
   b. $a(a - b) - b(b - a)$
      $a^2 - b^2$

DAILY QUIZ

Multiply.
1. $2x(2x + 3)$ $4x^2 + 6x$
2. $-3x(6x - 1)$ $-18x^2 + 3x$
3. $-y(y^2 + 2)$ $-y^3 - 2y$
4. $x(2x^2 + 5x - 3)$
   $2x^3 + 5x^2 - 3x$
5. $-x^2y(x^2y^3 - 3xy^2)$
   $-x^4y^4 + 3x^3y^3$

5-5   Multiplying a Monomial and a Polynomial

OBJECTIVE

To multiply a monomial and a polynomial by using the distributive property.

Remember the rules for working with exponents as you use the distributive property to multiply a monomial and a polynomial.

$$x(\overset{\frown}{3x + 5}) \qquad 2h(h^2 - 3h) \qquad -3ab^2(a - b) \qquad (\overset{\frown}{x^3 - 1})6x^2$$
$$3x^2 + 5x \qquad 2h^3 - 6h^2 \qquad -3a^2b^2 + 3ab^3 \qquad 6x^5 - 6x^2$$

The distributive property can be used when the polynomial has more than two terms. The multiplication can be arranged horizontally or vertically.

EXAMPLE 1   Multiply $-2n$ and $n^3 - 3n^2 - 5n + 6$.

Method I $-2n(n^3 - 3n^2 - 5n + 6) = -2n^4 + 6n^3 + 10n^2 - 12n$

Method II

$$\begin{array}{r} n^3 - 3n^2 - 5n + 6 \\ -2n \\ \hline -2n^4 + 6n^3 + 10n^2 - 12n \end{array}$$

To simplify some expressions, it is necessary to multiply more than once and then combine like terms.

EXAMPLE 2   Simplify each expression.

a. $x(3x - 4) + 5x(x^2 + x + 2) = 3x^2 - 4x + 5x^3 + 5x^2 + 10x$
   $\qquad\qquad\qquad\qquad\qquad\qquad\qquad = 5x^3 + 8x^2 + 6x$

b. $x(x + y) - y(x + y) = x^2 + xy - yx - y^2 = x^2 - y^2$

CLASS EXERCISES

Multiply.

1. $x(6x + 4)$ $6x^2 + 4x$ 2. $x(2x + 9)$ $2x^2 + 9x$ 3. $(x^2 + x)3x$ $3x^3 + 3x^2$
4. $(y^3 + y^2)5y$ $5y^4 + 5y^3$ 5. $2t(t - 2)$ $2t^2 - 4t$ 6. $t^2(8t - 9)$ $8t^3 - 9t^2$
7. $(x + y)(-2x)$ $-2x^2 - 2xy$ 8. $(x^3 + y^3)x^2$ $x^5 + x^2y^3$ 9. $x^3y(x - y)$ $x^4y - x^3y^2$
10. $a(a^3 - a + 1)$ $a^4 - a^2 + a$ 11. $(1 - x^3)x^5$ $x^5 - x^8$ 12. $3b^2(4b^3 + b^2 - 2)$ $12b^5 + 3b^4 - 6b^2$

EXERCISES

A

Multiply.

1. $x(3x + 2)$ **2.** $3x(x + 1)$ **3.** $5x(3x + 4)$ **4.** $(2y + 3)5y$

5. $4y(y - 8)$ **6.** $(3y + 4)y^2$ **7.** $(4y - 3)7y$ **8.** $(y + 6)2y$

9. $-3n(n + 9)$ **10.** $-n(2n - 5)$ **11.** $n(n^2 - 3)$ **12.** $(8n - 7)n$

13. $(5x - 3y)(-4x)$ **14.** $2x^2(x^7 - 5x)$ **15.** $2x(x^2 - 4x + 3)$

16. $x(x^2 - 2x + 1)$ **17.** $2(r^2 - rt + 3t^2)$ **18.** $3(2a^2 - ab + b^2)$

19. $n(n^2 + 5n + 2)$ **20.** $-3(2 - n - n^2)$ **21.** $-1(3 + n - n^2)$

22. $c^2(c^2 - 6c + 3)$ **23.** $2ab(a^2 - b^2)$ **24.** $3y^2(y^2 - 2y - 1)$

B

25. $(6x^2 - 4xy + 5y^2)(-2x)$ **26.** $(-y^4 - 4y^2z + 5yz^2)4z$

27. $-a^2b(a^2b^3 + 2ab^2 - b)$ **28.** $(x^2y - 2xy + y^3 + y^2)(-y^2)$

29. $-3a^2b(a - 2ab^2 + 3a^2b^3)$ **30.** $-2x^2y^3(x^4y^3 + 3x^2y - 3x)$

31. $-6x^2y^2(2x - 3y + 4xy - x^2y^2)$ **32.** $(n^3 - 2n^2t - 3nt^2 + 4n^2)5nt^3$

33. $4h\left(h^4 - \frac{1}{4}h^3 + \frac{1}{16}h^2 - 4h + 1\right)$ **34.** $-5t^2\left(\frac{1}{125}t^2 - \frac{1}{25}t + \frac{1}{5}\right)$

Simplify. Remember to combine like terms.

35. $5(y + 7) + y$ $\quad 6y + 35$ **36.** $x - 6(2x + 8)$ $\quad -11x - 48$

37. $2(2a - 1) + 2(4 - a)$ $\quad 2a + 6$ **38.** $-2(r - 1) - r(r + 2)$ $\quad -r^2 - 4r + 2$

39. $t(2t - 3) - 2t(t - 2)$ $\quad t$ **40.** $x^2(x - 1) - x^3(2x + 1)$ $\quad -2x^4 - x^2$

41. $-3y(2y + 5) + y(7y - 1)$ $\quad y^2 - 16y$ **42.** $a(a^2 - 1) + 6a(5a^2 + 2)$ $\quad 31a^3 + 11a$

43. $xy(x - y) + xy(x + y)$ $\quad 2x^2y$ **44.** $r^2(3rs - s) - s(r^3 + r^2)$ $\quad 2r^3s - 2r^2s$

C

45. $2x^2(x^2 + 3x + 4) + x(x^2 + 3x + 4) - 9(x^2 + 3x + 4)$ $\quad 2x^4 + 7x^3 + 2x^2 - 23x - 36$

46. $5(4[3(2 + x)]) - 5(-4[-3(2 - x)])$ $\quad 120x$

47. $x^2 - x(x + y[z(x - y) + x(y - z) + y(z - x)])$ $\quad 0$

Solve for **x** and check.

48. $3(x + 2) = x + 4$ $\quad -1$ **49.** $3(3x - 2) = 10 + x$ $\quad 2$ **50.** $3(x + 1) + 2x = 1 - x$ $\quad -\frac{1}{3}$

Find the area in terms of **x,** or in terms of **x** and π.

51.

2x

3x − 7

$6x^2 + \pi x^2 - 14x$, or
$(6 + \pi)x^2 - 14x$

52.

3

5x

2x

$5x^2 + 7\frac{1}{2}x$

53.

x

$\frac{x + 1}{2}$

$\frac{1}{2}x^2 + \frac{5}{3}x$

POLYNOMIALS

183

EXTRA PRACTICE, page 516

ASSIGNMENT GUIDE
(page 183)

Minimum course: 1–12,
13–37 odd
Average course: 1–45 odd,
49, 51
Maximum course: 1–53 odd

ENRICHMENT ACTIVITY

Challenge the students to solve this problem.

Let n represent the smallest of three consecutive integers. Show that if 1 is added to the product of the smallest integer and the largest integer, the result is equal to the sum of *the smallest integer times the middle integer* and *1 times the middle integer.*
$n(n + 2) + 1 \overset{?}{=} n(n + 1) + 1(n + 1)$
$n^2 + 2n + 1 \overset{?}{=} (n^2 + n) + (n + 1)$
$n^2 + 2n + 1 = n^2 + 2n + 1$ ✔

ADDITIONAL ANSWERS

Exercises

1. $3x^2 + 2x$ **2.** $3x^2 + 3x$
3. $15x^2 + 20x$ **4.** $10y^2 + 15y$
5. $4y^2 - 32y$ **6.** $3y^3 + 4y^2$
7. $28y^2 - 21y$ **8.** $2y^2 + 12y$
9. $-3n^2 - 27n$ **10.** $-2n^2 + 5n$
11. $n^3 - 3n$ **12.** $8n^2 - 7n$
13. $-20x^2 + 12xy$
14. $2x^9 - 10x^3$
15. $2x^3 - 8x^2 + 6x$
16. $x^3 - 2x^2 + x$
17. $2r^2 - 2rt + 6t^2$
18. $6a^2 - 3ab + 3b^2$
19. $n^3 + 5n^2 + 2n$
20. $-6 + 3n + 3n^2$

[Answers continue on page A4.]

LESSON NOTES

Numbers can be used to reinforce the work with multiplication of polynomials. For example, $(x + 4)(2x + 3)$ can be interpreted as $(10 + 4)(2 \cdot 10 + 3)$.

$$
\begin{array}{rcl}
2 \cdot 10 + 3 & \longrightarrow & 23 \\
10 + 4 & \longrightarrow & 14 \\
\hline
8 \cdot 10 + 12 & \longrightarrow & 92 \\
2 \cdot 10^2 + 3 \cdot 10 & \longrightarrow & 230 \\
\hline
2 \cdot 10^2 + 11 \cdot 10 + 12 & & 322
\end{array}
$$

Notice that use of 10 as the value for x results in a highlighting of place-value ideas in the decimal system.

ALTERNATE EXAMPLES

1. Multiply: $(5x - 3)$ and $(x^2 - 2x + 7)$
$$5x^3 - 13x^2 + 41x - 21$$

2. Multiply.
a. $(3x - y)(x + y)$
$$3x^2 + 2xy - y^2$$
b. $(x^2 - y^2)(3x^2 + y^2)$
$$3x^4 - 2x^2y^2 - y^4$$

5-6 Multiplying Polynomials

OBJECTIVE

To use the distributive property in multiplying polynomials.

You can use the distributive property to multiply two binomials. To multiply $(x + 4)$ and $(2x + 3)$, start by thinking of one binomial as a single quantity.

$$
\begin{array}{rcll}
(a + b) \cdot c & = & a \cdot c \ + \ b \cdot c & \text{Distributive property} \\
(x + 4)(2x + 3) & = & x(2x + 3) \ + \ 4(2x + 3) & \text{Replace } c \text{ with } (2x + 3). \\
& = & 2x^2 + 3x \ + \ 8x + 12 & \\
& = & 2x^2 + 11x + 12 & \text{Combine like terms.}
\end{array}
$$

The same result is obtained by multiplying vertically.

$$
\begin{array}{l}
2x + 3 \\
\underline{x + 4} \\
8x + 12 \quad \longleftarrow 4(2x + 3) \\
\underline{2x^2 + \ 3x} \quad \longleftarrow x(2x + 3) \\
2x^2 + 11x + 12
\end{array}
$$

Place like terms, such as $8x$ and $3x$, in the same column.

Use either procedure when you multiply polynomials. Just be sure to multiply each term in one polynomial by each term in the other polynomial. Then combine like terms.

EXAMPLE 1 Multiply $(3x - 1)$ and $(x^2 + 5x - 4)$.

Method I

$(3x - 1)(x^2 + 5x - 4)$
$3x(x^2 + 5x - 4) - 1(x^2 + 5x - 4)$
$3x^3 + 15x^2 - 12x - x^2 - 5x + 4$
$3x^3 + 14x^2 - 17x + 4$

Method II

$$
\begin{array}{l}
x^2 + 5x - 4 \\
\underline{3x - 1} \\
-x^2 - 5x + 4 \\
\underline{3x^3 + 15x^2 - 12x} \\
3x^3 + 14x^2 - 17x + 4
\end{array}
$$

EXAMPLE 2 Multiply.

a. $(x - 2y)(x - y) = x(x - y) - 2y(x - y)$
$$= x^2 - xy - 2yx + 2y^2$$
$$= x^2 - 3xy + 2y^2$$

b. $(x^2 + y^2)(2x^2 + 3y^2) = x^2(2x^2 + 3y^2) + y^2(2x^2 + 3y^2)$
$$= 2x^4 + 3x^2y^2 + 2x^2y^2 + 3y^4$$
$$= 2x^4 + 5x^2y^2 + 3y^4$$

CHAPTER 5

Before multiplying polynomials, it is helpful to arrange terms in decreasing degree of a variable.

EXAMPLE 3   Multiply $x - x^2 + 5$ by $1 + x$.

$$
\begin{array}{r}
x - x^2 + 5 \longrightarrow \quad -x^2 + x + 5 \\
\underline{1 + x \longrightarrow \qquad\quad x + 1} \\
-x^2 + x + 5 \\
\underline{-x^3 + x^2 + 5x \qquad\quad} \\
-x^3 \qquad\quad + 6x + 5
\end{array}
$$

CLASS EXERCISES

Complete.

1. $(x + 5)(x + 9) = x(x + 9) + 5(\underline{\,?\,})$ $x + 9$

2. $(n + 2)(n - 7) = n(n - 7) + 2(\underline{\,?\,})$ $n - 7$

3. $(3y - 2)(y + 4) = 3y(y + 4) - \underline{\,?\,}(y + 4)$ 2

4. $(2x + 7)(3x - 4) = 2x(\underline{\,?\,}) + 7(3x - 4)$ $3x - 4$

Multiply.

5. $(x + 3)(x + 5)$ $x^2 + 8x + 15$
6. $(b + 2)(b - 3)$ $b^2 - b - 6$
7. $(n - 4)(n - 1)$ $n^2 - 5n + 4$
8. $(2x + 1)(x + 1)$ $2x^2 + 3x + 1$
9. $(2x - 5)(x - 5)$ $2x^2 - 15x + 25$
10. $(q - 2)(a + 3)$ $a^2 + a - 6$
11. $(3x + 4)(2x + 5)$ $6x^2 + 23x + 20$
12. $(2x + 3)(3x - 2)$ $6x^2 + 5x - 6$
13. $(3x - 4)(3x - 2)$ $9x^2 - 18x + 8$

EXERCISES

A   *Multiply.*

1. $(x + 2)(x + 4)$
2. $(x + 3)(x + 4)$
3. $(x + 7)(x + 3)$
4. $(y + 9)(y + 5)$
5. $(y + 2)(y + 1)$
6. $(y - 3)(y + 2)$
7. $(r + 3)(r + 2)$
8. $(x - 12)(x + 3)$
9. $(x - 2)(x + 4)$
10. $(x + 3)(x + 3)$
11. $(x + 8)(2x - 3)$
12. $(2x + 4)(x - 5)$
13. $(x + 2)(2x - 1)$
14. $(5x + 1)(x - 2)$
15. $(2x - 5)(3x - 2)$
16. $(2x + 1)(3x + 2)$
17. $(4x - 5)(2x - 3)$
18. $(3a - 1)(3a + 1)$
19. $(5x - 2)(2x + 5)$
20. $(2y - 3)(3y - 4)$
21. $(3x - 2)(3x - 2)$
22. $(2x - 3)(3x - 2)$
23. $(2x + 5)(3x - 1)$
24. $(3x + 6)(x - 9)$
25. $(x + 2)(6x^2 + 3x + 2)$
26. $(x + 1)(x^2 + 2x + 1)$
27. $(x - 1)(x^2 + 3x + 1)$
28. $(x - 1)(x^2 + 2x + 1)$

POLYNOMIALS

185

186

ENRICHMENT ACTIVITY

Have the students find the products for the following:

$(a - 1)(a + 1) =$? $a^2 - 1$
$(a - 1)(a^2 + a + 1) =$? $a^3 - 1$
$(a - 1)(a^3 + a^2 + a + 1) =$?
$a^4 - 1$

Then ask them to predict the form of the next example in the pattern.

$(a - 1)(a^4 + a^3 + a^2 + a + 1)$
$=$? $a^5 - 1$

Finally, ask them to try to write the general case—that is, the equation that describes all the examples in the pattern.

$(a - 1)(a^n + a^{n-1} + \ldots$
$+ a + 1) = a^{n+1} - 1$

ADDITIONAL ANSWERS
(continued)

25. $6x^3 + 15x^2 + 8x + 4$
26. $x^3 + 3x^2 + 3x + 1$
27. $x^3 + 2x^2 - 2x - 1$
28. $x^3 + x^2 - x - 1$
29. $2a^2 - 11ab + 15b^2$
30. $3a^2 + 5ab + 2b^2$
31. $c^2 + 3cd + 2d^2$
32. $2x^2 + 5xy + 2y^2$
33. $4a^2 - b^2$ 34. $x^2 - 9y^2$
35. $ac + bc + ad + bd$
36. $ac + bc - ad - bd$
37. $ac - bc + ad - bd$
38. $ac - bc - ad + bd$
39. $ab - 2b - 2a + 4$
40. $a^2b^2 - 2b^2 - 2a^2 + 4$
41. $a^4 - 36$ 42. $x^4 - 1$
43. $n^4 + 8n^2 + 16$
44. $t^4 - 9$ 45. $a^4 - b^4$
46. $n^4 - 18n^2 + 81$

68. $9x^3 + 6x^2 - 23x + 10$
69. $x^3 + 8$
70. $a^3 + 7a^2 + 16a + 12$
71. $-4s^3 - 4s^2t + st^2 + t^3$
72. $x^4 - 1$ 73. $-x^8 + 1$
74. $x^6 - 64y^6$

B

Multiply. Combine like terms when possible.

29. $(a - 3b)(2a - 5b)$
30. $(3a + 2b)(a + b)$
31. $(c + d)(c + 2d)$
32. $(2x + y)(x + 2y)$
33. $(2a - b)(2a + h)$
34. $(x + 3y)(x - 3y)$
35. $(a + b)(c + d)$
36. $(a + b)(c - d)$
37. $(a - b)(c + d)$
38. $(a - b)(c - d)$
39. $(a - 2)(b - 2)$
40. $(a^2 - 2)(b^2 - 2)$
41. $(a^2 + 6)(a^2 - 6)$
42. $(x^2 + 1)(x^2 - 1)$
43. $(n^2 + 4)(n^2 + 4)$
44. $(t^2 + 3)(t^2 - 3)$
45. $(a^2 - b^2)(a^2 + b^2)$
46. $(n^2 - 9)(n^2 - 9)$
47. $(a^2 - 2b^2)(a^2 - 2b^2)$ $a^4 - 4a^2b^2 + 4b^4$
48. $(x^2 - 2y^2)(x^2 + 2y^2)$ $x^4 - 4y^4$
49. $(3x^2 - 2y^2)(3x^2 + 2y^2)$ $9x^4 - 4y^4$
50. $(2a^2 + 3b^2)(3a^2 + 2b^2)$ $6a^4 + 13a^2b^2 + 6b^4$
51. $\left(\dfrac{3}{4}x + 2\right)\left(\dfrac{1}{2}x + 16\right)$ $\dfrac{3}{8}x^2 + 13x + 32$
52. $\left(\dfrac{1}{2}x + y\right)\left(\dfrac{1}{2}y + x\right)$ $\dfrac{1}{2}y^2 + 1\dfrac{1}{4}xy + \dfrac{1}{2}x^2$
53. $(3x - 0.1)(x + 0.1)$ $3x^2 + 0.2x - 0.01$
54. $(0.5y + 2)(0.3y + 6)$ $0.15y^2 + 3.6y + 12$
55. $(a - 3b)(a^2 - 6ab + 9b^2)$
$a^3 - 9a^2b + 27ab^2 - 27b^3$
56. $(x + y)(x^2 - 2xy + 3y^2)$
$x^3 - x^2y + xy^2 + 3y^3$
57. $(x + y)(x^2 - xy + y^2)$ $x^3 + y^3$
58. $(x - y)(x^2 + xy + y^2)$ $x^3 - y^3$

C

Perform the indicated operations.

Sample $(2x - 3)(x + 7) - (6x + 5)(3x - 4)$
$[2x(x + 7) - 3(x + 7)] - [6x(3x - 4) + 5(3x - 4)]$
$[2x^2 + 14x - 3x - 21] - [18x^2 - 24x + 15x - 20]$
$[2x^2 + 11x - 21] - [18x^2 - 9x - 20]$
$2x^2 + 11x - 21 - 18x^2 + 9x + 20$
$-16x^2 + 20x - 1$

59. $(x + 1)(x + 2) - (x + 3)(x + 4)$
$-4x - 10$
60. $(a + b)(a - b) + (a + b)(a + b)$ $2a^2 + 2ab$
61. $(x + 2)(2x - 1) + (x - 1)(x + 3)$
$3x^2 + 5x - 5$
62. $(2x - 3)(x - 1) + x(2x + 1)$ $4x^2 - 4x + 3$
63. $(3a - 1)(3a + 1) - (3a - 1)(3a - 1)$ $6a - 2$

Multiply.

64. $(x + 1)(x + 2)(x + 3)$
$x^3 + 6x^2 + 11x + 6$
65. $(2a - 1)(3a - 2)(4a - 3)$
$24a^3 - 46a^2 + 29a - 6$
66. $(x + 2)(x + 2)(x + 2)$
$x^3 + 6x^2 + 12x + 8$
67. $(a - b)(a - b)(a - b)$
$a^3 - 3a^2b + 3ab^2 - b^3$

Arrange terms in decreasing degree of a variable. Then multiply vertically.

68. $(4x + 3x^2 - 5)(3x - 2)$
69. $(4 + x^2 - 2x)(2 + x)$
70. $(5a + 6 + a^2)(a + 2)$
71. $(2s^2 + 3st + t^2)(t - 2s)$
72. $(x - 1 - x^2 + x^3)(x + 1)$
73. $(x^4 - x^6 + 1 - x^2)(1 + x^2)$
*74. $(8x^2y^3 + 16xy^4 + 4x^3y^2 + 2x^4y + x^5 + 32y^5)(x - 2y)$

5-7 Multiplying Binomials: A Shortcut

OBJECTIVE

To find the product of two binomials by inspection.

You have used the distributive property to multiply binomials.

$$(x + 3)(x + 5) = x(x + 5) + 3(x + 5)$$
$$= x^2 + 5x + 3x + 15$$
$$= x^2 + 8x + 15$$

With practice, you can apply the following steps to find the product more directly.

Step 1 Multiply the *first* terms.

Step 2 Multiply the *outer* terms: 5x. Then multiply the *inner* terms: 3x. These products are often like terms: 5x + 3x = 8x.

Step 3 Multiply the *last terms*.

Here are these three steps shown in a more concise form.

$$(x + 3)\ (x + 5) = x^2 + (5x + 3x) + 15 = x^2 + 8x + 15$$

Notice that each term of the first binomial is multiplied by each term of the second binomial.

EXAMPLE 1 Multiply by inspection. **a.** $(2x + 1)(3x - 7)$ **b.** $(x - 8)(x - 5)$

a. $(2x + 1)\ (3x - 7)$

$$= 6x^2 - 11x - 7$$

b. $(x - 8)\ (x - 5)$

$$= x^2 - 13x + 40$$

POLYNOMIALS

187

WARM-UP EXERCISES

Simplify.
1. $3x + 5x$ $8x$
2. $-2x + 7x$ $5x$
3. $-8y + (-4y)$ $-12y$
4. $6y + (-6y)$ $0y$, or 0

LESSON NOTES

This lesson develops the traditional FOIL technique for multiplying binomials. The mnemonic FOIL is purposely not introduced at this point, since an early mention of it might lead the students to do their work by rote. Feel free to introduce the mnemonic *after* the students have shown understanding of the method.

F	O	I	L
Mult. the first terms.	Mult. the outer terms.	Mult. the inner terms.	Mult. the last terms.

Example 3 applies the FOIL technique to the special case of squaring a binomial—in this instance, $(x - 3)^2$. You can follow this example by considering $(x + 3)^2$:

$$(x + 3)^2 = (x + 3)(x + 3)$$
$$= x^2 + 6x + 9$$

Point out that in squaring a binomial the middle term is 2(first term × second term) and has the same sign as the sign that separates the terms of the original binomial. In variables:

$$(a + b)^2 = a^2 + 2ab + b^2$$
$$(a - b)^2 = a^2 - 2ab + b^2$$

ALTERNATE EXAMPLE

1. Multiply by inspection.
   a. $(2x + 4)(3x - 2)$
   $6x^2 + 8x - 8$
   b. $(x - 2)(x - 3)$
   $x^2 - 5x + 6$

EXAMPLE 2   Multiply $(2x - 3)(x + 4)$.

$$(2x - 3)(x + 4) = 2x^2 + 5x - 12$$

Squaring a binomial is a special case of multiplying two binomials. For this case, the instruction *expand* is sometimes used.

EXAMPLE 3   Expand $(x - 3)^2$.

$$(x - 3)^2 = (x - 3)(x - 3) = x^2 - 6x + 9$$

EXAMPLE 4   Expand.

a. $(3p + 4)^2 = (3p)^2 + 2(3p)(4) + 4^2$ **b.** $(3q - 4)^2 = (3q)^2 - 2(3q)(4) + 4^2$
$= 9p^2 + 24p + 16$ $= 9q^2 - 24q + 16$

CLASS EXERCISES

Complete.

1. $(x + 8)(x + 2) = x^2 + 10x +$? 16   **2.** $(y + 5)(y + 6) = y^2 +$? $+ 30$ 11y
3. $(3x + 1)(2x - 5) =$? $- 13x - 5$ 6x²   **4.** $(2x + 3)(x - 6) = 2x^2 -$? $- 18$ 9x
5. $(x - 5)^2 = x^2 - 10x +$?   25   **6.** $(x + 4)^2 = x^2 +$? $+ 16$ 8x

Multiply.

7. $(x + 3)(x + 2)$ **8.** $(x + 5)(x + 4)$ **9.** $(x - 4)(x - 2)$
$x^2 + 5x + 6$ $x^2 + 9x + 20$ $x^2 - 6x + 8$
10. $(x - 2)(x - 9)$ **11.** $(x - 3)(x + 7)$ **12.** $(x + 5)(x - 1)$
$x^2 - 11x + 18$ $x^2 + 4x - 21$ $x^2 + 4x - 5$

EXERCISES

A   Complete.

1. $(x + 8)(x + 1) = x^2 +$? $+ 8$ 9x   **2.** $(x + 4)(x - 2) = x^2 +$? $- 8$ 2x
3. $(x - 3)(x + 5) = x^2 + 2x -$?   15   **4.** $(x - 3)(x - 7) = x^2 -$? $+ 21$ 10x
5. $(x - 10)^2 = x^2 - 20x +$?   100   **6.** $(x + 9)^2 = x^2 +$? $+ 81$ 18x

Multiply.

7. $(x + 5)(x + 3)$ **8.** $(x + 5)(x - 3)$ **9.** $(x + 5)(x + 7)$
10. $(y - 2)(y + 3)$ **11.** $(y - 2)(y - 3)$ **12.** $(y + 9)(y - 3)$
13. $(y - 6)(y + 1)$ **14.** $(y - 5)(y - 7)$ **15.** $(y + 2)(y - 2)$

EXTRA PRACTICE, page 517

16. $(x - 8)(x + 3)$ $x^2 - 5x - 24$ **17.** $(x - 5)(x + 1)$ $x^2 - 4x - 5$ **18.** $(x + 5)(x - 1)$ $x^2 + 4x - 5$

19. $(x + 7)(x + 3)$ $x^2 + 10x + 21$ **20.** $(x - 7)(x + 3)$ $x^2 - 4x - 21$ **21.** $(x + 7)(x - 3)$ $x^2 + 4x - 21$

22. $(x - 7)(x - 3)$ $x^2 - 10x + 21$ **23.** $(y + 4)(y - 5)$ $y^2 - y - 20$ **24.** $(y + 4)(y + 5)$ $y^2 + 9y + 20$

25. $(x - 8)(x + 8)$ $x^2 - 64$ **26.** $(x - 7)(x + 7)$ $x^2 - 49$ **27.** $(3x - 4)(3x + 4)$ $9x^2 - 16$

28. $(4x - 3)(4x - 3)$ $16x^2 - 24x + 9$ **29.** $(4y - 9)(y + 3)$ $4y^2 + 3y - 27$ **30.** $(2x + 3)(4x - 7)$ $8x^2 - 2x - 21$

31. $(a - 9b)(a + 9b)$ $a^2 - 81b^2$ **32.** $(4x + y)(4x + y)$ $16x^2 + 8xy + y^2$ **33.** $(4x - y)(4x + y)$ $16x^2 - y^2$

Expand.

34. $(x + 2)^2$ $x^2 + 4x + 4$ **35.** $(x + 3)^2$ $x^2 + 6x + 9$ **36.** $(n - 2)^2$ $n^2 - 4n + 4$ **37.** $(n + 5)^2$ $n^2 + 10n + 25$

38. $(n - 5)^2$ $n^2 - 10n + 25$ **39.** $(x - 6)^2$ $x^2 - 12x + 36$ **40.** $(x + 6)^2$ $x^2 + 12x + 36$ **41.** $(n + 10)^2$ $n^2 + 20n + 100$

42. $(2x + 1)^2$ $4x^2 + 4x + 1$ **43.** $(3x + 2)^2$ $9x^2 + 12x + 4$ **44.** $(3x - 2)^2$ $9x^2 - 12x + 4$ **45.** $(9x - 2)^2$ $81x^2 - 36x + 4$

B

Multiply.

46. $(3x - y)(3x + y)$ **47.** $(a + 2b)(a + 2b)$ **48.** $(6r - s)(3r + 4s)$

49. $(15x - 1)(4x + 3)$ **50.** $(12y + 5)(9y - 4)$ **51.** $(x^2 + 2)(x^2 + 3)$

52. $(x^2 - 4)(x^2 + 6)$ **53.** $(n + 7)(7 - n)$ **54.** $(n - 2)(5 + n)$

55. $\left(n + \frac{1}{2}\right)\left(n - \frac{1}{2}\right)$ **56.** $\left(\frac{1}{3} - 3a\right)\left(\frac{1}{3} + 3a\right)$ **57.** $\left(\frac{1}{3} + 3a\right)\left(\frac{1}{3} + 3a\right)$

Use the forms $(a \pm b)^2 = a^2 \pm 2ab + b^2$ to evaluate each expression.

Samples $23^2 = (20 + 3)^2 = 20^2 + 2(20)(3) + 3^2 = 400 + 120 + 9 = 529$

$18^2 = (20 - 2)^2 = 20^2 - 2(20)(2) + 2^2 = 400 - 80 + 4 = 324$

58. 32^2 $(30 + 2)^2 = 1024$ **59.** 41^2 $(40 + 1)^2 = 1681$ **60.** 58^2 $(60 - 2)^2 = 3364$ **61.** 89^2 $(90 - 1)^2 = 7921$ **62.** 27^2 $(30 - 3)^2 = 729$

C

Multiply.

63. $\left(\frac{1}{2}x + 1\right)\left(\frac{1}{2}x - 1\right)$ **64.** $\left(\frac{1}{2}x + \frac{1}{4}\right)\left(\frac{1}{4}x - \frac{1}{2}\right)$ **65.** $\left(x - \frac{1}{6}\right)\left(x - \frac{1}{6}\right)$

66. $(a^2 - 2b)(a^2 - 3b)$ $a^4 - 5a^2b + 6b^2$ **67.** $(2x^2 - 5)(3x^2 + 7)$ $6x^4 - x^2 - 35$

68. $(x^2 - y^2)(x^2 + y^2)$ $x^4 - y^4$ **69.** $(ax^2 + b)(ax^2 - b)$ $a^2x^4 - b^2$

70. $(x^3 + y^2)(x^3 + y^2)$ $x^6 + 2x^3y^2 + y^4$ **71.** $(x^3 + y^2)(x^3 - y^2)$ $x^6 - y^4$

72. $(-3x + 1)(-5x - 6)$ $15x^2 + 13x - 6$ **73.** $(-3x + 1)(5x + 6)$ $-15x^2 - 13x + 6$

Expand.

74. $(n^2 - 3)^2$ $n^4 - 6n^2 + 9$ **75.** $(2a^3 + 3)^2$ $4a^6 + 12a^3 + 9$ **76.** $(a^2b - 4)^2$ $a^4b^2 - 8a^2b + 16$ **77.** $(x - 0.1)^2$ $x^2 - 0.2x + 0.01$

POLYNOMIALS

189

Multiply. Then simplify.
1. $3(x - 7) - 2x$ $x - 21$
2. $x(x + 6) - x^2$ $6x$

LESSON NOTES

This lesson continues the students' work with equation solving. Multiplication with polynomials is used and x^2-terms appear initially in the products; however, the equations are structured so that the x^2-terms disappear as the equations are simplified. Thus, the students solve linear equations rather than quadratic equations. (Quadratic equations are solved in Chapter 6.)

Give special attention to the introduction of the term *identity*. Point out to the students that they have already had experiences with many identities—for instance, $x + 3 = 3 + x$.

ALTERNATE EXAMPLES

1. Solve and check:
   $(5x + 2)(3x - 1)$
   $= 15x^2 + 8$ $x = 10$

2. Solve: $3(x - 5) = 3x + 15$
   The resulting equation is $3x - 15 = 3x + 15$, or $15 = -15$, which is false. Therefore, $3(x - 5) = 3x + 15$ has no solution.

5-8 More Equation Solving

OBJECTIVES

To solve equations when various operations on polynomials are required.
To determine whether an equation has no solution.
To determine whether an equation is an identity.

Now that you can add, subtract, and multiply polynomials, you can solve more complicated equations.

EXAMPLE 1 Solve and check: $(6x + 5)(2x + 3) = 12x^2 + 29$

$$(6x + 5)(2x + 3) = 12x^2 + 29 \qquad \text{First simplify this equation.}$$
$$12x^2 + 28x + 15 = 12x^2 + 29 \qquad \text{Add } -12x^2 \text{ to each side.}$$
$$28x + 15 = 29 \qquad \text{Add } -15 \text{ to each side.}$$
$$28x = 14 \qquad \text{Divide each side by 28.}$$
$$x = \frac{1}{2}$$

Check
$$\left(6 \cdot \frac{1}{2} + 5\right)\left(2 \cdot \frac{1}{2} + 3\right) \stackrel{?}{=} 12\left(\frac{1}{2}\right)^2 + 29$$

$$(3 + 5)(1 + 3) \stackrel{?}{=} 12\left(\frac{1}{4}\right) + 29$$

$$(8)(4) \stackrel{?}{=} 3 + 29$$

$$32 = 32 \; ✔$$

The solution is $\frac{1}{2}$.

It is possible to have an equation that has *no* solution. When solving an equation leads to a statement that is known to be *false*, there is no solution. The solution set is the empty set.

EXAMPLE 2 Solve $2(x + 4) = 2x + 6$.

$$2(x + 4) = 2x + 6 \qquad \text{Simplify.}$$
$$2x + 8 = 2x + 6 \qquad \text{Add } -2x \text{ to each side.}$$
$$8 = 6 \qquad \text{This equation is false.}$$

Therefore, $2(x + 4) = 2x + 6$ has *no* solution.

190   CHAPTER 5

An **identity** is an equation that is true no matter what number is substituted for the variable. The solution set is {all numbers}. For example,

$$2x + 5 = 5 + 2x$$

is an identity since all values of x make it a true statement. When solving such an equation, you will obtain a statement that is *always* true.

EXAMPLE 3   Solve $3(x + 4) - 8 = 4 + 3x$.

$3(x + 4) - 8 = 4 + 3x$	Simplify.
$3x + 12 - 8 = 4 + 3x$	
$3x + 4 = 4 + 3x$	Add $-3x$ to each side.
$4 = 4$	This equation is always true.

$3(x + 4) - 8 = 4 + 3x$ is an identity, and every number is a solution.

CLASS EXERCISES

*Solve for **x**. If no solution exists, write **no solution**. If the equation is an identity, write **identity**.*

1. $6x + (5 - 2x) = 33$ 7   **2.** $(8x - 1) - 5x = -4$ -1

3. $3x + 5(x - 6) = 2$ 4   **4.** $3(1 - 5x) + 10x = 13$ -2

5. $(x - 3)(x + 3) = x^2 - 9x$ 1   **6.** $(x + 3)^2 = x^2 + 3$ -1

7. $2x + 1 = 2x$ No solution   **8.** $1 + 3x = 3x + 1$ Identity

9. $(x + 1)3 - 2x = x + 3$ Identity   **10.** $x - 1 = -1 - x$ 0

EXERCISES

A   *Solve for **x** and check.*

1. $3(x + 5) - 6 = 18$ 3   **2.** $7(x - 2) + 8 = 15$ 3

3. $2x - 7(x - 1) = -3$ 2   **4.** $-5x + 4(2x + 6) = -3$ -9

5. $x^2 - x(x + 4) = 16$ -4 **6.** $3x(x - 5) - 3x^2 = -30$ 2

7. $8x - 11 = 3(x + 4) + 2$ 5   **8.** $10 - 9(x - 2) = 32 - 5x$ -1

9. $3(x - 5) + x = 7(x + 2) - 2$ -9 **10.** $20 - 9(x + 6) = 10(2 - x) - 2x$ 18

11. $x + 2 + 2(x + 2) = 3(2x - 5)$ 7   **12.** $6x - 5(3x + 4) - 7 = 9(x - 5)$ 1

Show that each equation has no solution, or else that it is an identity.

13. $3(x + 4) - 7 = 3x + 9$ No solution   **14.** $2(2 + x) = 6x - 4x + 4$ Identity

15. $3(x + 2) - 2(x - 2) = 10 + x$ Identity   **16.** $4(2x + 1) = -2(3 - 4x)$ No solution

POLYNOMIALS

191

ALTERNATE EXAMPLE

3. Solve: $2(x + 4) - 1 = 7 + 2x$
The resulting equation is $2x + 7 = 7 + 2x$, which is always true. Therefore, $2(x + 4) - 1 = 7 + 2x$ is an identity, and every number is a solution.

DAILY QUIZ

Solve.
1. $2(x + 4) - 5 = 17$ 7
2. $7x - 9 = 2(x + 3)$ 3
3. $(x + 2)^2 = x^2 + 3x$ -4
Solve for x. If no solution exists, write *no solution*. If the equation is an identity, write *identity*.
4. $3(4x + 2) = 10x + 6 + 2x$
Identity
5. $5(x^2 - 2) = -9 + 5x^2$
No solution

ASSIGNMENT GUIDE
(pages 191–192)

Minimum course: 1–16,
17–21 odd
Average course: 1–15 odd,
17–27
Maximum course: 1–25 odd,
27–34
All courses: *Checkpoint*
review
exercises

EXTRA PRACTICE, page 517

B

Solve for **x** and check. If no solution exists, write **no solution**. If the equation is an identity, write **identity**.

17. $(x + 1)^2 = (x + 2)^2$ $\quad -\frac{3}{2}$ 18. $1 + x(x - 5) = (x + 8)(x - 8)$ $\quad 13$

19. $(x + 3)^2 = x(x - 3) + 9(x + 1)$ Identity 20. $x^2 - 3x(x + 4) = 27 - 2x^2 - 3x$ $\quad -3$

21. $(2x - 2)^2 = 6x^2 - x(2x + 8)$ $\quad$ No solution 22. $(x + 3)^2 + 6 = (x + 5)(x - 1)$ $\quad -10$

23. $2(x + 1) - 8 = 6x - 2(2x + 3)$ Identity 24. $(2x + 1)^2 = (4x - 3)(x + 3)$ $\quad 2$

25. $4(3x - 2) = 7(x - 1)$ $\quad \frac{1}{5}$ 26. $x(x - 9) + 5 = (x + 4)(x - 13)$
$\quad$ No solution

C

27. $\frac{1}{3}(5x - 2) = \frac{5}{6}(x - 1)$ $\quad -\frac{1}{5}$ 28. $\frac{1}{2}(4x - 5) = \frac{1}{4}(2x + 6)$ $\quad \frac{8}{3}$

29. $(6x - 5)(3x + 4) + 2 = (2x + 7)(9x - 8)$ $\quad 1$

30. $3x(3x - 10) + 25 = (3x - 5)(3x) - 5(3x - 4)$ $\quad$ No solution

31. $x(x - 2) + 2(2x - 1) = x^2 + (1 - x)(-2)$ $\quad$ Identity

32. $x + (3x - 6)(x - 6) = (2x - 1)(x - 11) + x^2 + 29$ $\quad$ No solution

33. $(x + 3)^2 - (x + 5)^2 = 10 - 2(13 + 2x)$ $\quad$ Identity

34. $(x^2 - 4x + 4)(x - 2) = x^2(x - 6) - 4(3 - x)$ $\quad -\frac{1}{2}$

CHECKPOINT

Write as a polynomial in simplified form. Then evaluate for **x** = −2.

1. $4(x - 2) + 3x - 3$ 2. $3x^2 - 3(x^2 + x - 1)$ 3. $5 - 2(2x + 3)$
$\quad 7x - 11; -25$ $\quad -3x + 3; 9$ $\quad -4x - 1; 7$

Simplify.

4. $(2a + 1) + (3a - 5) - (7a + 2)$ $-2a - 6$ 5. $(4x - y) - (3x + 2y) - (5x - 4y)$ $-4x + y$

6. $(ab)^2(ab)^3$ $\quad a^5b^5$ 7. $ab^2(ab^3)$ $\quad a^2b^5$ 8. $(-x^5)(3x^3)(8x^2)$ $\quad -24x^{10}$

9. $(x^3y^2)^3(xy)^2(xy^3)$ $x^{12}y^{11}$ 10. $5 - 2(8x + 3)$ $-16x - 1$ 11. $(ab)^3 - a^3b^3$ $\quad 0$

Multiply.

12. $(x + 2)(2x - 1)$ 13. $(2x - 3)(x - 1)$ 14. $(3x - 1)(3x - 1)$
$\quad 2x^2 + 3x - 2$ $\quad 2x^2 - 5x + 3$ $\quad 9x^2 - 6x + 1$

15. $(2x - 3)(3x - 4)$ 16. $(3x + 2)(2x + 2)$ 17. $(4x - 3)(4x + 3)$
$\quad 6x^2 - 17x + 12$ $\quad 6x^2 + 10x + 4$ $\quad 16x^2 - 9$

Solve for **x** and check.

18. $2(x - 3) + 1 = 7$ $\quad 6$ 19. $5x + 3(3 - x) = 10$ $\quad \frac{1}{2}$

20. $(x + 1)(x + 2) = x^2$ $\quad -\frac{2}{3}$ 21. $(x - 1)(x + 4) = x^2 - x$ $\quad 1$

192

5-9 Problem Solving: Using Polynomials

OBJECTIVE

To solve problems by using more complicated equations in one variable.

The new skills you have learned in working with polynomials can be used in problem solving.

EXAMPLE 1

A rectangle with a perimeter of 44 centimeters is 8 centimeters longer than it is wide. What is the area of the rectangle?

Strategy: Draw a figure. Use the perimeter to find the length and width.

Read the problem to find the key ideas.

The given information can be used to find the length and width, then the area.

Use a variable.

Let x = the width. Then $x + 8$ = the length.

x

$x + 8$

Write an equation.

$2(x + x + 8) = 44$ $2(\text{width} + \text{length}) = \text{perimeter}$

Find the solution.

$$2(2x + 8) = 44$$
$$4x + 16 = 44$$
$$4x = 28$$
$$x = 7 \text{ and } x + 8 = 15$$

Check. Does $2(\text{width} + \text{length}) = 44$? $2(7 + 15) = 2(22) = 44$ ✔

Answer the question.

The area is 105 cm^2, since width × length = $7 \cdot 15 = 105$.

EXAMPLE 2

Find five consecutive integers if the square of the fifth less the square of the first is equal to the sum of the other three integers.

Use a variable.

Let the integers be x, $x + 1$, $x + 2$, $x + 3$, and $x + 4$.

Write an equation.

$(x + 4)^2 - x^2 = (x + 1) + (x + 2) + (x + 3)$

Find the solution.

$$x^2 + 8x + 16 - x^2 = 3x + 6$$
$$8x + 16 = 3x + 6$$
$$5x + 16 = 6$$
$$5x = -10$$
$$x = -2$$

The next four integers are -1, 0, 1, and 2.

Check. Does $2^2 - (-2)^2$ equal $-1 + 0 + 1$?

Answer the question.

The five consecutive integers are -2, -1, 0, 1, and 2.

POLYNOMIALS

193

If n represents a number, how would you represent the number that is

1. 1 more than twice n $2n + 1$
2. 3 less than n $n - 3$
3. 4 less than half n $\dfrac{n}{2} - 4$

LESSON NOTES

If a problem involves a geometric figure, students are apt to find that a drawing is helpful in visualizing the problem and in writing an appropriate equation for the problem. However, even if a problem does not involve a geometric figure, a drawing can sometimes be helpful in visualizing and solving the problem.

As you discuss the model examples, be sure to emphasize the importance of checking the solution of the equation. The students should always ask themselves: Does the solution fit the conditions of the problem? Does my answer make sense in the given situation?

Note that the last line of Exercise 21 reminds students of an important idea: often, a problem can be solved in more than one way.

ALTERNATE EXAMPLES

1. A rectangle has a perimeter of 28 centimeters. The width of the rectangle is 2 centimeters less than the length. What is the area of the rectangle?   The area is 48 cm^2.

2. Find five consecutive integers if the square of the first less the square of the third is 5 less than the sum of the fourth and the fifth integers.   The integers are -1, 0, 1, 2, 3.

Solve.

1. The width of a rectangle is 3 cm less than the length. The perimeter is 42 cm. What is the area of the rectangle?   The area is 108 cm²

2. The square of a number equals the square of 6 more than the number. What is the number? The number is −3.

3. The square of a certain positive integer is 23 less than the square of the next positive integer. What is the smaller integer?   The smaller integer is 11.

4. Find four consecutive integers if the product of the two smaller integers is 30 less than the product of the two larger integers.   The integers are 6, 7, 8, 9.

5. The altitude of a triangle is 2 cm shorter than its base. If the altitude is increased by 4 cm, the area of the resulting triangle is 20 cm² more than the area of the original triangle. Find the altitude of the original triangle. The altitude is 8 cm.

ASSIGNMENT GUIDE
(pages 194–196)

Minimum course: 1–10
        second day: 11–18
Average course: 1–12
        second day: 13–19
Maximum course: 1–13
        second day: 14–22

CLASS EXERCISES

Read the problem carefully. Then answer the questions that follow.

The perimeter of a rectangle is 32 centimeters. The length is 1 centimeter more than twice the width. Find the area of the rectangle.

1. Let x be the width of the rectangle. Then the length is _?_. $2x + 1$

2. Express the perimeter in terms of x. $2(2x + 1 + x)$ or $6x + 2$

3. Write an equation using two equal expressions for the perimeter. $6x + 2 = 32$

4. Solve the equation for x. $x = 5$

5. What is the width of the rectangle? What is the length?   5 cm; 11 cm

6. What is the area of the rectangle?   55 cm²

EXERCISES

A   *Read the problem and then answer the questions that follow.*

A rectangle is 10 inches longer than it is wide. If the width is increased by 2 inches and the length is decreased by 3 inches, the area is unchanged. What is the length of the original rectangle?

1. Let x be the width of the original rectangle. Then the length is _?_. $x + 10$

2. Write an expression for the area of the original rectangle. $x(x + 10)$

3. The second rectangle has a width of _?_ and a length of _?_. $x + 2; x + 7$

4. Write an expression for the area of the second rectangle. $(x + 2)(x + 7)$

5. Write an equation which states that the two areas are equal. $x(x + 10) = (x + 2)(x + 7)$

6. Solve the equation for x. $x = 14$

7. What is the length of the original rectangle?   24 in.

Solve.

8. The width of a rectangle is 3 meters less than the length. The perimeter is 34 meters. What is the area of the rectangle?   70 m²

9. Some notepaper is $3x$ in. wide and $5x$ in. long. If the width is increased by 4 in. and the length is decreased by 1 in., the paper would be a square.
   a. Find x.   **b.** Find the length of a side of the square. $2\frac{1}{2}$; $11\frac{1}{2}$ in.

194

EXTRA PRACTICE, pages 517–518

10. The squares at the right have sides
x in., 8 in., and (x + 4) in. If the sum
of the areas of the first two squares
equals the area of the third, find the
area of each square. 36 in.²; 64 in.²; 100 in.²

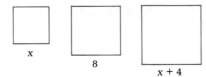

x

8

x + 4

11. The square of a certain number equals the square of 4 more than
the number. What is the number?   −2

12. The square of 9 more than a number is equal to 9 more than the
square of the number. What is the number?   −4

13. Mr. Red Eagle flew from Birmingham to Miami, and from there to
San Francisco, a total of 3250 miles. If the second part of his trip
was 4 times as long as the first, how many miles was the flight from
Birmingham to Miami?   650 mi

B

14. The altitude of a triangle is 2 cm longer than its base. If the altitude
is decreased by 7 cm, the area of the resulting triangle is 42 cm²
less than the area of the original triangle. Find the altitude of the
original triangle. *Hint:* Use the formula $A = \frac{1}{2}bh$.   14 cm

15. Find four consecutive odd integers if the product of the two smaller
integers is 80 less than the product of the two larger integers.   7, 9, 11, 13

16. Find three consecutive even integers if the square of the third less
the square of the first is equal to 128.   14, 16, 18

17. Kim's hourly pay rate is based on a 40-hour week. For overtime, he
is paid $1\frac{1}{2}$ times as much. If he earned $312 for 48 hours, what is
his regular rate? $6 per hr.

18. Kara bought $150 worth of equipment when she started a small
business making pottery bowls. It will cost her $2.50 for each bowl
that she makes. If she can sell each bowl for $3.25, how many
bowls must she make to "break even," that is, to earn as much
money as she has paid out?   200

C

19. Refer to the shaded regions in the
figure below. Find the area of the
rectangular region in the center if it
equals the sum of the areas of the
four square regions in the corners.
144 sq. units

x	4x − 6	x

x

x + 2

x

20. A rectangular swimming pool is 15
feet longer than it is wide. A con-
crete walk 2.5 feet wide surrounds
the pool. If the area of the walk is
350 square feet, what are the dimensions of the pool?   25 ft by 40 ft

2.5 ft

21. *Read this conversation. Then solve the equation and answer the questions that follow.*

Salesperson: I'll sell you the washing machine for $410. Or, if you want to save money, you can buy both the washer and the dryer for $740.

Customer: You probably want to sell both because of the extra profit.

Salesperson: Not really. Actually, it's a special deal—this week only. The profit on the $410 sale is exactly the same as on the $740 sale.

Customer: How can that be? How much did the machines cost the store?

Salesperson: I'm not allowed to tell you that. However, I can say that the cost of each machine was the same.

Customer: You've told me enough. I can tell how much each machine cost and what the profit is.

Salesperson: How can you figure that out?

Customer: With algebra. I'll show you.

This is what the customer wrote.

Let x = cost of one machine.
Then $410 - x$ = profit on the washer.
Also $2x$ = cost of the two machines
and $740 - 2x$ = profit on the two machines.

profit on washer →$410 - x = 740 - 2x$← profit on the two machines

What is the solution of the equation? How much did each machine cost? What is the profit? Can you find the answer by any other method?

22. A door-to-door salesperson sells a deluxe dictionary for $48, and sells the standard edition at two for $85. The salesperson makes the same profit on either sale. If the cost to the salesperson is the same for either edition, find this cost and profit per sale. 　Cost is $37; profit is $11.

CHALLENGE

Algebraic Magic Square

Find a value for x so that the numbers in every row, column, and diagonal have the same sum, as in a "magic square."

$2(x + 1)$	$x - 5$	$3(x - 3)$
$3(x - 5)$	$5(x - 5)$	$x(x - 5)$
$2(x - 3)$	$(x + 2)(x - 5)$	$(x - 3)$

Balancing a Checkbook

Applications

This Applications page requires the students to process data that involves a balance, deposits, checks, and service charges.

Note that algebraic skills are utilized in Exercises 3 and 4.

Balancing a checkbook involves making your records agree with those sent in a statement from the bank. These are the steps to follow.

Step 1 Start with the balance shown on the bank statement.

Step 2 Add all deposits not credited on the statement.

Step 3 Subtract all outstanding checks not yet charged to the account.

Step 4 Compare this result with the balance in your checkbook, after subtracting the service charge. If they agree, your checkbook is balanced.

Example A statement balance is $543.36, including a service charge of $4.60. Two deposits of $200 and $225 have not yet been credited, and checks totaling $133.87 are outstanding. Before the service charge is subtracted, your checkbook balance is $839.09. Does it agree with the bank statement?

$$543.36 + 200.00 + 225.00 - 133.87 \overset{?}{=} 839.09 - 4.60$$
$$834.49 = 834.49$$

Yes, the checkbook agrees with the bank statement. Your actual present balance is $834.49.

Suppose a bank determines its service charge by the following method.

$2.00 flat charge per month, plus
$.20 per check processed

1. Find the service charge for a month if 24 checks are processed. $6.80

2. Find the number of checks processed if the service charge is $4.20. 11

3. Write an expression for the service charge if n checks are processed. $(2 + 0.2n)$

4. Write an expression for the number of checks processed if the service charge is S dollars. $\frac{S-2}{0.2}$

A bank statement lists 23 processed checks and a present balance of $297.03. A $120 deposit is not yet credited, and checks totaling $160.14 are outstanding.

5. Find the service charge. $6.60

6. What amount should your checkbook show before subtracting the service charge? $263.49

7. What is your actual present balance? $256.89

These exercises review basic algebraic skills.

Simplify.

1. $24 - 6 \times 2 \div 3$ 20

2. $|-8| \cdot |\frac{1}{2}|$ 4

3. $-14 + 21 - 19 - 12 - 27$
   -51

4. $6x - 9 + 5x$ $11x - 9$

5. $5x^2z + 2x - 4x^2z$ $x^2z + 2x$

Evaluate when $a = 8$, $b = -4$, and $c = -2$.

6. $7b - 2c$ -24

7. $\dfrac{c^2 - b^2}{a}$ $-\dfrac{3}{2}$

8. $b - 3(a - b)$ -40

Solve for x.

9. $x - (-3.5) = 4.2$ 0.7

10. $-28 = 67 + x$ -95

11. $-\dfrac{2}{3}x = 8$ -12

12. $\dfrac{4x}{9} - 3 = 5$ 18

13. $1.2x - 2.7 = -2.1$ 0.5

14. $4\left(x - \dfrac{1}{2}\right) = 10$ 3

15. Find the slope of the line through $(-6, 0)$ and $(0, -3)$. $-\dfrac{1}{2}$

16. Find the x-intercept and the y-intercept of the line $y - 3x = 5$.
    x-int., $-\dfrac{5}{3}$; y-int., 5

17. Write the equation for the line that has a slope of -2 and contains $(4, 0)$. $y = -2x + 8$

18. Subtract $4x + 3y$ from $5x - y$.
    $x - 4y$

19. Multiply: $(3x - 5)(2x + 7)$
    $6x^2 + 11x - 35$

20. The length of a rectangle is 5 units longer than the width. The perimeter is 58 units. Find the length and the width.
    Length = 17 units;
    width = 12 units

CHAPTER 5 REVIEW

VOCABULARY

monomial (p. 166)
polynomial (p. 166)
binomial (p. 166)
trinomial (p. 166)
degree of a monomial (p. 166)

degree of a polynomial in one variable (p. 167)
opposite of a polynomial (p. 170)
product of powers (p. 174)
power of a power (p. 178)
identity (p. 191)

SUMMARY

After classifying various types of polynomials, the basic operations of addition, subtraction, and multiplication of polynomials are studied. The distributive property is used in the multiplication of polynomials, which also requires extensions of the properties of powers. A shortcut for multiplying binomials is presented after the general procedures for multiplying polynomials have been demonstrated. The new algebraic procedures with polynomials are applied to solving equations, and then are used in solving verbal problems.

REVIEW EXERCISES

5-1   *Classify each polynomial as a monomial, binomial, or trinomial.*

1. $3x + 8$ Binomial   2. $9x^2$ Monomial   3. $x^2 + 5 - 2x$ Trinomial   4. $-3x^2 + 5x - x^5$ Trinomial

Simplify each polynomial. Then give the degree.

5. $2x^2 + 5x - 3x$
   $2x^2 + 2x;\ 2$

6. $x^3 + 2x^4 - x - 2x^4$
   $x^3 - x;\ 3$

7. $-x^2 + x^4 + 9x^2$
   $x^4 + 8x^2;\ 4$

Evaluate $-3x^2 + x - 1$ for each value of x.

8. $x = -2$ -15 9. $x = 2$ -11 10. $x = \dfrac{2}{3}$ $-\dfrac{5}{3}$ 11. $x = 0$ -1

5-2   12. Add. $\begin{aligned} 2x^2 + 7x - 9 \\ -5x^2 + x + 4 \\ \hline -3x^2 + 8x - 5 \end{aligned}$

13. Subtract. $\begin{aligned} x^3 - 4x^2 + 7 \\ 2x^3 - 2x^2 + 5x - 6 \\ \hline -x^3 - 2x^2 - 5x + 13 \end{aligned}$

14. Subtract $(x^4 + x^3 - 3x^2 - 2)$ from the sum of $(3x^4 + x^3 - x)$ and $(2x^2 - 7x - 8)$. $2x^4 + 5x^2 - 8x - 6$

Simplify.

15. $(2x - 9) + (-x + 17)$ $x + 8$

16. $(n^3 + n + 4) - (4 - n^2 - n^3)$ $2n^3 + n^2 + n$

17. $(x^2 - 3x) + (5x^2 - 6x + 7) - (4x^2 + 8x - 10)$ $2x^2 - 17x + 17$

198   CHAPTER 5

5-3 *Express each product in exponential form with just one exponent.*

18. $5(5^2)(5^3)$ 5^6 **19.** $n \cdot n^6 \cdot n^2$ n^9 **20.** $(-1)^2(-1)^5(-1)$ $(-1)^8$

Simplify.

21. $(3x^2)(-7x^4)$ $-21x^6$ **22.** $x(2x)(6x^4)$ $12x^6$ **23.** $(-7x)(4x^3)(x^2)$ $-28x^6$

24. $3(-r^2s)(-rs^3)$ $3r^3s^4$ **25.** $(-2x^3)(-3)(-x^5)$ $-6x^8$ **26.** $-1(x^2y)(xy^2)(-xy)$ x^4y^4

5-4 **27.** $(x^3)^2$ x^6 **28.** $-5x^2(2x)^3$ $-40x^5$ **29.** $(-2ab^4)^3$ $-8a^3b^{12}$

30. $(2ab)^3(3a^2b)^2$ $72a^7b^5$ **31.** $(a^3b^2)^3(-ab^2)^2$ $a^{11}b^{10}$ **32.** $(-3a^2b^3c^4)^2$ $9a^4b^6c^8$

5-5 *Multiply.*

33. $2x(5x - 1)$ $10x^2 - 2x$ **34.** $-5x(-x + 7)$ $5x^2 - 35x$ **35.** $3x(x^2 - 2x + 3)$
$3x^3 - 6x^2 + 9x$

36. $x^2(1 - x + x^2)$ **37.** $(3y - 4x)2xy^2$ **38.** $ab(a^2 - ab + b^2)$
$x^2 - x^3 + x^4$ $6xy^3 - 8x^2y^2$ $a^3b - a^2b^2 + ab^3$

39. $3x^2(2x^2y - 3xy + 5)$ **40.** $y^2(1 - 2x + 3y)$
$6x^4y - 9x^3y + 15x^2$ $y^2 - 2xy^2 + 3y^3$

Simplify.

41. $2x + 4x(x - 2)$ $4x^2 - 6x$ **42.** $2(3x - x^2) + 2x^2$ $6x$ **43.** $5x(x + 1) - 7x^2$ $-2x^2 + 5x$

44. $x^3(x^4 - x^2 + 1) + x^5$ $x^7 + x^3$ **45.** $2t^2 - 3(t^2 - 6t^4) + 7t^4$ $25t^4 - t^2$

5-6 *Multiply.*

46. $(x + 2)(x + 11)$ **47.** $(x + 8)(x - 7)$ **48.** $(x - 9)(x - 3)$
$x^2 + 13x + 22$ $x^2 + x - 56$ $x^2 - 12x + 27$

49. $(x + 7)(x + 9)$ **50.** $(7x - 2)(x + 3)$ **51.** $(3x - 4)(5x - 1)$
$x^2 + 16x + 63$ $7x^2 + 19x - 6$ $15x^2 - 23x + 4$

52. $(2x + 3)(3x - 2)$ **53.** $(4 - 5x)(3 - 6x)$ **54.** $(a^2 - b)(3a + 2b)$
$6x^2 + 5x - 6$ $12 - 39x + 30x^2$ $3a^3 + 2a^2b - 3ab - 2b^2$

55. $(5x - 4y)(5x - 4y)$ **56.** $(4x^2 + 5)(4x^2 - 5)$ **57.** $(2x - 1)(2x - 1)$
$25x^2 - 40xy + 16y^2$ $16x^4 - 25$ $4x^2 - 4x + 1$

58. $(2x + 1)(x^2 - 3x + 2)$ **59.** $(3x - 1)(x^2 + 5x + 2)$
$2x^3 - 5x^2 + x + 2$ $3x^3 + 14x^2 + x - 2$

5-7 *Multiply by inspection.*

60. $(x + 7)(2x + 3)$ **61.** $(r + 2s)(r - 2s)$ **62.** $(a^2 + b^2)(a^2 - b^2)$
$2x^2 + 17x + 21$ $r^2 - 4s^2$ $a^4 - b^4$

Expand.

63. $(x + 5)^2$ $x^2 + 10x + 25$ **64.** $(x - 11)^2$ $x^2 - 22x + 121$ **65.** $(3x - 4)^2$ $9x^2 - 24x + 16$

5-8 *Solve for **x** and check. If no solution exists, write **no solution**. If the equation is an identity, write **identity**.*

66. $(2x - 1)^2 = 4x^2 + 13$ -3 **67.** $8 - x = 3x - 3(x + 1)$ 11

68. $6x^2 + x = (3x + 4)(2x - 7)$ -2 **69.** $x(x + 2) - 8 = (x + 4)(x - 2)$ Identity

70. $(x - 3)^2 = (x + 1)^2$ 1 **71.** $3(2x - 5) = 4(x + 1) - (7 - 2x)$
No solution

72. The sum of two consecutive integers minus the next consecutive integer is 18. Find the integers.   19, 20, 21

73. Nine more than the square of an integer is the same as the square of the next consecutive integer. Find the integer.   4

74. A rectangle with a perimeter of 60 meters is 12 meters longer than it is wide. What is the area of the rectangle?   189 sq. meters

75. The square of a number is 16 more than the square of 2 less than the number. Find the number.   5

CHAPTER 5
TEST

5-1   *Simplify each polynomial. Then evaluate when* $x = 2$.

1. $2x^2 + 5x - 6x^2 + x^3 + 4x^2$ $x^3 + 5x$; 18   **2.** $3x - 5x^4 + 6 + 2x^4 - x + 3x^4$ $2x + 6$; 10

5-2   **3.** Add. $-3x^2 - 5xy + y^2$
                    $-x^2 + 9xy + 4y^2$
               $\overline{-4x^2 + 4xy + 5y^2}$

                                  4. Subtract. $x^2 + 6x + 2$
                                               $x^2 - 3x + 5$
                                                $\overline{9x - 3}$

   5. Simplify $(x^3 + 3x^2 + 1) + (x^2 - 6x) - (2x^3 - 3x^2 + 5x - 2)$. $-x^3 + 7x^2 - 11x + 3$

5-3   *Simplify. Then evaluate when* $x = -1$.

6. $(3^2)(-2x)(4x^2)$ $-72x^3$; 72   **7.** $(2x^2)(5x)(x^3)$ $10x^6$; 10

Simplify.

5-4   **8.** $(-2a^2b)^3$ $-8a^6b^3$ **9.** $(-n)(-3n^4)^3$ $27n^{13}$

5-5   **10.** Multiply $(3x^2 - 2x + 4)$ and $(2x)$. $6x^3 - 4x^2 + 8x$

11. Simplify $5x - 3(x + 1)$. $2x - 3$

5-6   *Multiply.*

12. $(3x + 4)(6x - 5)$ $18x^2 + 9x - 20$ **13.** $(4a - 9b)(4a + 9b)$ $16a^2 - 81b^2$

14. $(2x - 3)(3x^2 + x - 1)$
      $6x^3 - 7x^2 - 5x + 3$ **15.** $(a + 3)(6a^2 + 11a - 10)$
                                             $6a^3 + 29a^2 + 23a - 30$

5-7   *Expand.*

16. $(x + 7)^2$ $x^2 + 14x + 49$ **17.** $(2x - y)^2$ $4x^2 - 4xy + y^2$

5-8   *Solve for* x.

18. $(x + 3)(x - 1) = 5 + x^2$ 4   **19.** $-(x - 2) - (2x - 1) = 1$ $\frac{2}{3}$

5-9   **20.** The length of a rectangle is 7 cm more than its width. The perimeter is 34 cm. Find the area.   60 cm²

200

Ulam's Conjecture

A famous mathematician, Stanislaw Ulam, has noticed a pattern that appears to be true for all natural numbers, $\{1, 2, 3, \ldots\}$.

- a. Start with any natural number.
- b. If the number is 1, stop. If not, go to steps c, d, and e.
- c. If the number is even, divide it by 2.
- d. If the number is odd, multiply it by 3 and add 1.
- e. Use the result as the new number and repeat step b.

For every number tested, Ulam found that the sequence reached 1 and stopped. Try several natural numbers yourself.

The program below permits you to test any number to see if the same pattern holds true. To perform steps c and d, the computer must determine whether the number is even or odd. This is done by using the *greatest integer function*, INT(X), which finds the greatest integer that is *not greater* than X. For a decimal, the number is rounded down. For example, INT(3) = 3 and INT(7.9) = 7. With the even number 8, $\text{INT}(8/2) = \frac{8}{2}$. But with the odd number 9, $\text{INT}(9/2) \neq \frac{9}{2}$. Note how this is used in line 140.

The Program	What It Does
`100 REM ULAM'S CONJECTURE`	
`110 PRINT "NATURAL NUMBER";`	
`120 INPUT N`	Performs step a, above.
`130 IF N = 1 THEN 900`	Performs step b.
`140 IF INT(N/2) = N/2 THEN 170`	If number is even, jumps to line 170.
`150 LET N = 3 * N + 1`	Performs step d.
`160 GO TO 180`	
`170 LET N = N/2`	Performs step c.
`180 PRINT N`	
`190 IF N > 1 THEN 140`	Performs step e.
`900 PRINT "REACHED ONE."`	
`990 END`	

Note how the GO TO statement in line 160 may be used to direct the computer to another line. Since GO TO statements can make a program difficult to follow, they should be used only when needed.

What numbers will be displayed for each of the following entries?

1. 24   **2.** 13   **3.** 80   **4.** 17   **5.** 192   **6.** 1024

7. Would the display be changed if line 190 were changed to GO TO 130? Enter the new line and test it.

8. Test the numbers from 95 to 100. Which reaches 1 in the fewest steps? Which takes the greatest number of steps?

For more information about BASIC, see the Computer Handbook at the back of the book.

Computer Activity

Notice that in Exercise 7 the students find that the program still runs correctly even when line 190 is changed as indicated. This should help students realize that there may be several ways of accomplishing the same thing in BASIC.

ADDITIONAL ANSWERS

Computer Activity

1. 12, 6, 3, 10, 5, 16, 8, 4, 2, 1
2. 40, 20, 10, 5, 16, 8, 4, 2, 1
3. 40, 20, 10, 5, 16, 8, 4, 2, 1
4. 52, 26, 13, 40, 20, 10, 5, 16, 8, 4, 2, 1
5. 96, 48, 24, 12, 6, 3, 10, 5, 16, 8, 4, 2, 1
6. 512, 256, 128, 64, 32, 16, 8, 4, 2, 1
7. The display is not changed. (The program runs correctly with either version of line 190.)
8. 96 takes 12 steps, the fewest. 97 takes 118 steps, the greatest.

In this chapter, the text presents many forms of factoring. The opening lesson deals with factoring positive integers; this provides a helpful basis for the work with factoring polynomials. Next, monomials are factored and divided. Common monomial factors are then used to factor polynomials that have more than one term. Step by step, the text then develops the other basic techniques for factoring polynomials, including factoring by grouping and the traditional methods of factoring trinomials of the form $ax^2 + bx + c$.

Following this work, there is a lesson devoted to solving equations by factoring. The students learn to make use of the zero-product rule: If $ab = 0$, then $a = 0$ or $b = 0$.

The chapter closes with a problem-solving lesson in which the students make use of what they have learned and solve a variety of problems involving quadratic equations.

CHAPTER 6

A baseball diamond is actually a square with sides 90 feet in length. The area of the diamond is 90×90, or 8100 square feet.

FACTORING

Prerequisite Skills Review

Write the letter for the correct answer.

1. $-18x = -2(\underline{\ ?\ })$ a
   a. $9x$ **b.** $-9x$ **c.** $36x$ **d.** $-16x$

2. $r^3t = (\underline{\ ?\ })rt$ b
   a. r **b.** r^2 **c.** 3 **d.** r^2t

3. $(6 + 3)^2 = 6^2 + 3^2 + \underline{\ ?\ }$ b
   a. 60 **b.** 36 **c.** 18 **d.** 0

4. $(9 - 1)^2 = \underline{\ ?\ }$ d
   a. $9^2 - 1^2$ **b.** $9^2 + 1^2$ **c.** $9^2 + 1^2 - 9$ **d.** $9^2 + 1^2 - 18$

5. $3x(5 - x) = \underline{\ ?\ }$ b
   a. $3x^2 + 15x$ **b.** $-3x^2 + 15x$ **c.** $8x - 3x^2$ **d.** $15x - x^2$

6. $-(x - y)$ is equivalent to $\underline{\ ?\ }$. c
   a. $y + x$ **b.** $-y + x$ **c.** $y - x$ **d.** $-x - y$

7. $5(x - y) - 2(x - y) = \underline{\ ?\ }$ d
   a. $3x - 7y$ **b.** $3x - 2y$ **c.** $3x$ **d.** $3(x - y)$

8. Evaluate $x(x - 2) - 2(x - 2)$ when $x = 14$. a
   a. 144 **b.** 164 **c.** 166 **d.** 168

9. Which product is equivalent to $9x^2 + 12x - 5$? a
   a. $(3x - 1)(3x + 5)$ **b.** $(3x + 1)(3x - 5)$
   c. $(9x + 1)(x - 5)$ **d.** $(9x - 5)(x + 1)$

10. Which product is equivalent to $2x^2 - 26x + 72$? c
    a. $(2x - 9)(x - 8)$ **b.** $(2x - 3)(x - 24)$
    c. $2(x - 4)(x - 9)$ **d.** $2(x - 12)(x - 3)$

11. Use substitution to find the solutions of $x^2 - 6x + 5 = 0$. a
    a. 1 and 5 **b.** -1 and 5 **c.** -1 and -5 **d.** 1 and -5

12. What are the solutions of $x^2 + 6x = 0$? d
    a. 0 and 6 **b.** -6 and 6 **c.** 0 only   **d.** 0 and -6

13. Simplify $2x(5x^3 - x^2)$. c
    a. $8x^2$ **b.** $10x^2$ **c.** $10x^4 - 2x^3$ **d.** $10x^4 - x^2$

PREREQUISITE SKILLS REVIEW

For students who need additional practice with the algebraic skills in this Prerequisite Skills Review, you may assign Follow-Up exercises on pages 502–503 in the students' books.

An item-by-item error analysis of the Prerequisite Skills Review appears on page T24.

Find the missing factor.
1. $55 = 5 \cdot n$ 11
2. $42 = 2 \cdot 3 \cdot y$ 7
3. $125 = x \cdot 5 \cdot 5$ 5

LESSON NOTES

Students should be familiar with prime numbers and prime factorizations. However, use Example 2 to emphasize: If a positive integer has exactly two different factors, it is a prime number. If a positive integer has more than two different factors, it is *not* prime; it is a composite number.

Notice that in finding factors of integers, we need to consider only the factors of positive integers; the factors of any negative integer such as −30 can be readily named after the positive factors of the corresponding positive integer (30) have been found.

In discussing prime factorization, be sure the students realize that the prime factorization of an integer is *unique* except for the order in which the factors are written.

[*Lesson Notes continue on page 205.*]

ALTERNATE EXAMPLES

1. Find all factors of 75.
   1, 3, 5, 15, 25, 75

2. List all the factors of each number. Then tell whether it is prime.

6	7	8	9
1,2,3,6	1,7	1,2,4,8	1,3,9
No	Yes	No	No

6-1 Factoring Positive Integers

OBJECTIVES

To factor a positive integer as a product of two positive integers in all possible ways.
To write the prime factorization of a positive integer.
To find the greatest common factor (GCF) of two or more integers.

There are three ways to express 12 as a product of two positive integers.

$$1 \cdot 12 \qquad 2 \cdot 6 \qquad 3 \cdot 4$$

Since $12 = 3 \cdot 4$, we say that 3 and 4 are *factors* of 12, and that $3 \cdot 4$ is a **factored form** of 12. Unless otherwise indicated, only positive integer factors will be considered here.

Division can be used to find factors of an integer. In the following division the remainder is 0, so both 9 and 3 are factors of 27. We also say that 27 **is divisible by** 9 and by 3.

$$\text{divisor} \longrightarrow 9\overline{)27} \quad \begin{array}{c} 3 \longleftarrow \text{quotient} \end{array}$$

EXAMPLE 1   Find all factors of 36.

Divide 36 by 1, 2, 3, and so on. Consider only numbers by which 36 is divisible, with a remainder of 0.

$$1\overline{)36}^{\,36} \qquad 2\overline{)36}^{\,18} \qquad 3\overline{)36}^{\,12} \qquad 4\overline{)36}^{\,9} \qquad 6\overline{)36}^{\,6}$$

Since the next divisor would be 9, there is no need to continue dividing. The factors of 36 are 1, 2, 3, 4, 6, 9, 12, 18, and 36.

A positive integer that has exactly two different factors, itself and 1, is a **prime number.** The number 1 is not prime since it has only one factor.

EXAMPLE 2   List the factors of each number. Then tell whether it is prime.

n	2	3	4	5
factors of n	1, 2	1, 3	1, 2, 4	1, 5
Is n prime?	Yes	Yes	No	Yes

The first ten prime numbers are 2, 3, 5, 7, 11, 13, 17, 19, 23, and 29.

204

To *factor a positive integer completely*, write it as the product of primes. This product is called the **prime factorization** of the number.

An integer has only one prime factorization. For example, to factor 280 completely, start with any two factors. Then continue factoring until all factors are prime. Two possibilities are shown here. The prime factorization is the same.

$$280$$
$$28 \cdot 10$$
$$2 \cdot 14 \cdot 2 \cdot 5$$
$$2 \cdot 2 \cdot 7 \cdot 2 \cdot 5$$
$$2^3 \cdot 5 \cdot 7$$

$$280$$
$$2 \cdot 140$$
$$2 \cdot 2 \cdot 70$$
$$2 \cdot 2 \cdot 2 \cdot 35$$
$$2 \cdot 2 \cdot 2 \cdot 5 \cdot 7$$
$$2^3 \cdot 5 \cdot 7$$

The **greatest common factor** (GCF) of two or more positive integers is the greatest factor that is common to each of the integers.

EXAMPLE 3   Write the prime factorization of each number.

$$12 = 2 \cdot 6 \qquad 36 = 2 \cdot 18 \qquad 77 = 7 \cdot 11$$
$$= 2 \cdot 2 \cdot 3 \qquad\quad = 2 \cdot 2 \cdot 9$$
$$= 2^2 \cdot 3 \qquad\quad\ = 2 \cdot 2 \cdot 3 \cdot 3$$
$$= 2^2 \cdot 3^2$$

EXAMPLE 4   Find the GCF of 24 and 36.

First write the prime factorization of each number.

$$24 = \boxed{2 \cdot 2} \cdot 2 \cdot \boxed{3}$$
$$36 = \boxed{2 \cdot 2} \cdot 3 \cdot \boxed{3}$$

The factored forms contain two 2's and one 3 in common. Multiply these common factors.

The GCF of 24 and 36 is $(2)(2)(3) = 12$.

CLASS EXERCISES

Express as the product of two positive integers in all possible ways.

1. 6 $1 \cdot 6, 2 \cdot 3$ **2.** 7 $1 \cdot 7$ **3.** 10 $1 \cdot 10, 2 \cdot 5$ **4.** 18 $1 \cdot 18, 2 \cdot 9, 3 \cdot 6$ **5.** 21 $1 \cdot 21, 3 \cdot 7$

Write all positive factors of each integer.

6. 9   1, 3, 9   **7.** 14   1, 2, 7, 14   **8.** 15   1, 3, 5, 15   **9.** 20   1, 2, 4, 5, 10, 20   **10.** 41   1, 41

Determine which of the following numbers are prime.

11. 31   Prime   **12.** 51   Not prime   **13.** 79   Prime   **14.** 90   Not prime   **15.** 111   Not prime

FACTORING

Example 4 shows how prime factorizations are used to find the GCF of two numbers. Another method of finding the GCF is the Euclidean algorithm. Divide the smaller integer into the greater integer. Then divide the remainder into the preceding divisor. Continue the process until the remainder is 0. The last divisor is the GCF.

$$\begin{array}{r} 1 \\ 24\overline{)36} \\ 24 \\ \hline 12 \end{array} \quad \begin{array}{r} 2 \\ 12\overline{)24} \\ 24 \\ \hline 0 \end{array}$$

GCF

ALTERNATE EXAMPLES

3. Write the prime factorization of each number.
54   $2 \cdot 3^3$ 42 $2 \cdot 3 \cdot 7$

4. Find the GCF of 45 and 60.
The GCF is $(3)(5) = 15$.

POSSIBLE ERROR

When classifying positive integers as prime or not prime, some students incorrectly identify 1 as a prime number. Stress the fact that a prime number is a positive integer that has exactly two different factors, but 1 has only one factor. Thus, 1 is not a prime number.

1 is not a composite number either, since a composite number has more than two factors.

DAILY QUIZ

Write the prime factorization of each integer.
1. 32 2^5 **2.** 52 $2^2 \cdot 13$
3. 330 $2 \cdot 3 \cdot 5 \cdot 11$
Find the greatest common factor (GCF) of each set of integers.
4. 18, 48, 60   6   **5.** 45, 60, 105   15

205

ENRICHMENT ACTIVITY

No one has ever devised a formula that will generate only prime numbers; in fact, it has been proven that no polynomial function can produce only primes. In 1772, Euler suggested this formula:

$$n^2 - n + 41$$

Have students investigate this formula, substituting values for n beginning with $n = 1$. The formula gives prime numbers from $n = 1$ through $n = 40$ and fails for $n = 41$. ($41^2 - 41 + 41 = 41^2$, and 41^2 is not prime.)

You might also suggest that they test this formula developed by Escott in 1879:

$$n^2 - 79n + 1601$$

(This is a good activity to try on a computer, if the students have access to computers.)

ADDITIONAL ANSWERS

Exercises
49. $1 \cdot 169, 13 \cdot 13$
50. $1 \cdot 210, 2 \cdot 105, 3 \cdot 70, 5 \cdot 42,$
$6 \cdot 35, 7 \cdot 30, 10 \cdot 21, 14 \cdot 15$
51. $1 \cdot 211$
52. $1 \cdot 363, 3 \cdot 121, 11 \cdot 33$
53. $1 \cdot 455, 5 \cdot 91, 7 \cdot 65, 13 \cdot 35$

Write the prime factorization of each integer.

16. 30 $2 \cdot 3 \cdot 5$ **17.** 33 $3 \cdot 11$ **18.** 44 $2^2 \cdot 11$ **19.** 64 2^6 **20.** 150 $2 \cdot 3 \cdot 5^2$

Find the greatest common factor (GCF) for each pair of integers.

21. 10, 12   2   **22.** 35, 50   5   **23.** 28, 35   7   **24.** 25, 75   25

25. 88, 121   11   **26.** 16, 48   16   **27.** 24, 54   6   **28.** 56, 72   8

EXERCISES

A   *Express as the product of two positive integers in all possible ways.*

1. 7 $1 \cdot 7$ **2.** 9 $1 \cdot 9, 3 \cdot 3$ **3.** 14 $1 \cdot 14, 2 \cdot 7$ **4.** 15 $1 \cdot 15, 3 \cdot 5$ **5.** 19 $1 \cdot 19$

6. 20 $1 \cdot 20, 4 \cdot 5,$ **7.** 26 $1 \cdot 26, 2 \cdot 13$ **8.** 39 $1 \cdot 39, 3 \cdot 13$ **9.** 43 $1 \cdot 43$ **10.** 45 $1 \cdot 45, 3 \cdot 15,$
        $2 \cdot 10$ $5 \cdot 9$
11. 62 $1 \cdot 62, 2 \cdot 31$ **12.** 67 $1 \cdot 67$ **13.** 74 $1 \cdot 74, 2 \cdot 37$ **14.** 95 $1 \cdot 95, 5 \cdot 19$ **15.** 48 $1 \cdot 48, 2 \cdot 24,$
                                                                                              $3 \cdot 16, 4 \cdot 12, 6 \cdot 8$

Write all positive factors of each integer.

16. 6   1, 2, 3, 6   **17.** 4   1, 2, 4   **18.** 91   1, 7, 13, 91   **19.** 10   1, 2, 5, 10   **20.** 23   1, 23

21. 31   1, 31   **22.** 1   1   **23.** 25   1, 5, 25   **24.** 14   1, 2, 7, 14   **25.** 21   1, 3, 7, 21

Determine which of the following numbers are prime.

26. 39   Not prime   **27.** 41   Prime   **28.** 2   Prime   **29.** 67   Prime   **30.** 91   Not Prime

Write the prime factorization of each integer.

31. 15 $3 \cdot 5$ **32.** 51 $3 \cdot 17$ **33.** 32 2^5 **34.** 48 $2^4 \cdot 3$ **35.** 95 $5 \cdot 19$

36. 39 $3 \cdot 13$ **37.** 81 3^4 **38.** 82 $2 \cdot 41$ **39.** 128 2^7 **40.** 129 $3 \cdot 43$

Find the greatest common factor (GCF) of each pair of integers.

41. 21, 30   3   **42.** 15, 32   1   **43.** 72, 80   8   **44.** 28, 35   7

45. 18, 30   6   **46.** 45, 60   15   **47.** 24, 60   12   **48.** 34, 51   17

B   *Write as the product of two positive integers in all possible ways.*

49. 169   **50.** 210   **51.** 211   **52.** 363   **53.** 455

54. List all the prime numbers between 1 and 75.
       2, 3, 5, 7, 11, 13, 17, 19, 23, 29, 31, 37, 41, 43, 47, 53, 59, 61, 67, 71, 73

Write the prime factorization of each integer.

55. 420 $2^2 \cdot 3 \cdot 5 \cdot 7$ **56.** 450 $2 \cdot 3^2 \cdot 5^2$ **57.** 900 $2^2 \cdot 3^2 \cdot 5^2$ **58.** 715 $5 \cdot 11 \cdot 13$

59. 2662 $2 \cdot 11^3$ **60.** 4147 $11 \cdot 13 \cdot 29$ **61.** 1210 $2 \cdot 5 \cdot 11^2$ **62.** 10,000 $2^4 \cdot 5^4$

CHAPTER 6

Find the greatest common factor (GCF) of each set of integers.

63. 12, 42, 60   6   **64.** 42, 56, 70   14   **65.** 48, 64, 80   16   **66.** 42, 63, 84   21

67. 45, 63, 108, 126, 180   9   **68.** 78, 104, 130, 156, 208   26

C *Factor as the product of two integers, positive or negative, in all possible ways.*

69. 15   **70.** 105   **71.** −99   **72.** −165

*Write each integer in the form 15,873n, where **n** is written in completely factored form.*

73. 111,111   **74.** 222,222   **75.** 555,555

From your answers to the preceding exercises, try to predict the following products. Then check by computation or with a calculator.

76. 15,873 × 21   333,333   **77.** 15,873 × 28   444,444   **78.** 15,873 × 42   666,666

79. 15,873 × 49   777,777   **80.** 15,873 × 56   888,888   **81.** 15,873 × 63   999,999

USING THE CALCULATOR

Prime Numbers

To test whether a number n is prime, it isn't necessary to divide by any number greater than $\sqrt{n}$, the square root of n.

Sample   Is 523 prime?

Press 523, then press $\boxed{\sqrt{x}}$.

$\sqrt{523} = 22.869193$

Since $\sqrt{523}$ is less then 23, you need only divide by prime numbers less than 23. These are 2, 3, 5, 7, 11, 13, 17, and 19. None of these primes is a divisor of 523. Therefore 523 is a prime number.

Use your calculator to tell which of these numbers are prime.

1. 527   Not prime   **2.** 659   Prime   **3.** 1001   Not prime   **4.** 403   Not prime

5. 773   Prime   **6.** 1351   Not prime   **7.** 847   Not prime   **8.** 1111   Not prime

9. 2087   Prime   **10.** 4441   Prime   **11.** 10,001   Not prime   **12.** 36,617   Not prime

WARM-UP EXERCISES

Simplify each fraction.

1. $\dfrac{4\cdot 2}{5\cdot 2}$ $\dfrac{4}{5}$ 2. $\dfrac{7\cdot 3}{10\cdot 3}$ $\dfrac{7}{10}$

3. $\dfrac{8\cdot 4}{9\cdot 4}$ $\dfrac{8}{9}$ 4. $\dfrac{6\cdot 5}{5\cdot 5\cdot 5}$ $\dfrac{1}{5}$

LESSON NOTES

The product rule $\dfrac{a}{b}\cdot\dfrac{c}{d}=\dfrac{ac}{bd}$ is important; it is used extensively in Chapter 8. In this lesson, we use it to obtain the cancellation rule.

On the chalkboard, show the students the restatement of the product rule using $c = d$.

$$\frac{a}{b}\cdot\frac{d}{d}=\frac{ad}{bd}$$

When this restatement is shown, let the students substitute appropriate values in the equation and then simplify. For example, use $a = 3$, $b = 4$, and $d = 5$.

$$\frac{3}{4}\cdot\frac{5}{5}=\frac{3\cdot 5}{4\cdot 5}=\frac{3}{4}$$

Point out that, for any nonzero number d, $\dfrac{d}{d}=1$, the identity element for multiplication. The cancellation rule makes it possible to divide a numerator and denominator by the same quantity (not zero).

Discuss Example 1 thoroughly and then devote careful attention to the quotient-of-powers rule. Use numerical examples if you think it will make the ideas clearer. For example:

$$\frac{2^5}{2^3}=\frac{\overset{1}{\cancel{2}}\cdot\overset{1}{\cancel{2}}\cdot\overset{1}{\cancel{2}}\cdot 2\cdot 2}{\underset{1}{\cancel{2}}\cdot\underset{1}{\cancel{2}}\cdot\underset{1}{\cancel{2}}}=\frac{2\cdot 2}{1}=2^2$$

ALTERNATE EXAMPLE

1. Simplify.

a. $\dfrac{12xy}{3y}$ $4x$ b. $\dfrac{8b}{12ab}$ $\dfrac{2}{3a}$

c. $\dfrac{n^8}{n^5}$ n^3 d. $\dfrac{n^2}{n^5}$ $\dfrac{1}{n^3}$

6-2 Factoring and Dividing Monomials

OBJECTIVES

To divide monomials.
To find the missing factor, given one factor of a monomial.

When you multiply fractions $\frac{a}{b}$ and $\frac{c}{d}$, you use the rule $\frac{a}{b}\cdot\frac{c}{d}=\frac{ac}{bd}$. Reversing this product rule and letting $c = d$ results in the *cancellation rule*.

> **Cancellation Rule**
>
> $$\frac{ad}{bd}=\frac{a}{b}\text{ when } b\neq 0 \text{ and } d\neq 0$$

The cancellation rule says that a fraction can be simplified by dividing the numerator and denominator by the same quantity.

EXAMPLE 1 Simplify.

a. $\dfrac{6xy}{3x}=\dfrac{2\cdot\cancel{3x}\cdot y}{\cancel{3x}}=2y$ b. $\dfrac{10a}{15ab}=\dfrac{2\cdot\cancel{5a}}{3\cdot\cancel{5a}\cdot b}=\dfrac{2}{3b}$

c. $\dfrac{n^5}{n^2}=\dfrac{\cancel{n^2}\cdot n^3}{\cancel{n^2}}=n^3$ d. $\dfrac{n^3}{n^8}=\dfrac{\cancel{n^3}\cdot 1}{\cancel{n^3}\cdot n^5}=\dfrac{1}{n^5}$

The preceding example suggests a rule for dividing powers that have the same base. Note that the exponents are positive integers, and that the base cannot be 0.

> **Quotient of Powers Rule**
>
> **To divide powers that have the same base, subtract the exponents.**
>
> $$\frac{x^a}{x^b}=x^{a-b}\text{ if }a>b \qquad \frac{x^a}{x^b}=\frac{1}{x^{b-a}}\text{ if }b>a$$

If *both* the exponents and the bases are the same, the quotient equals 1. For example, $\frac{x^3}{x^3}=1$, providing $x\neq 0$.

The cancellation rule and the quotient of powers rule provide alternative ways of simplifying a quotient of monomials.

208

EXAMPLE 2   First simplify by using the cancellation rule, then by using the quotient of powers rule.

a. $\dfrac{12x^6y^5z}{-3y^3x} = \dfrac{4\cdot 3\cdot x^5\cdot x\cdot y^3\cdot y^2\cdot z}{-1\cdot 3\cdot x\cdot y^3} = -4x^5y^2z$ Cancellation rule

$\dfrac{12x^6y^5z}{-3y^3x} = -4\cdot x^{6-1}\cdot y^{5-3}\cdot z = -4x^5y^2z$ Quotient of powers rule

b. $\dfrac{20a^2b^3}{16a^4bc} = \dfrac{5\cdot 4\cdot a^2\cdot b^2\cdot b}{4\cdot 4\cdot a^2\cdot a^2\cdot b\cdot c} = \dfrac{5b^2}{4a^2c}$ Cancellation rule

$\dfrac{20a^2b^3}{16a^4bc} = \dfrac{5}{4}\cdot \dfrac{1}{a^{4-2}}\cdot b^{3-1}\cdot \dfrac{1}{c} = \dfrac{5b^2}{4a^2c}$ Quotient of powers rule

EXAMPLE 3   Find the missing factor: $9x^{10}y^3 = (x^2y^2)(\underline{\ ?\ })$

Divide the product $9x^{10}y^3$ by the given factor x^2y^2.

$$\dfrac{9x^{10}y^3}{x^2y^2} = 9\cdot \dfrac{x^{10}}{x^2}\cdot \dfrac{y^3}{y^2} = 9\cdot x^{10-2}\cdot y^{3-2} = 9x^8y$$

Thus, $9x^{10}y^3 = (x^2y^2)(9x^8y)$ The missing factor is $9x^8y$.

CLASS EXERCISES

Simplify each expression. Assume that no denominator is 0.

1. $\dfrac{6x}{x}$ 6   2. $\dfrac{4ab}{2a}$ 2b   3. $\dfrac{10xy}{2y}$ 5x   4. $\dfrac{-12xy}{6xy}$ -2

5. $\dfrac{n^7}{n}$ n^6 6. $\dfrac{x^8}{x^5}$ x^3 7. $\dfrac{10x^8}{-5x^9}$ $-\dfrac{2}{x}$ 8. $\dfrac{-16a^3b^2c}{-4abc^3}$ $\dfrac{4a^2b}{c^2}$

Find the missing factors.

9. $6x^2 = (2x)(\underline{\ ?\ })$ 3x   10. $5b^4 = 5b(\underline{\ ?\ })$ b^3 11. $-24a^2b = -12a(\underline{\ ?\ })$ 2ab

EXERCISES

Find the missing factors.

1. $4a^2 = 2a(\underline{\ ?\ })$ 2a   2. $3b^2 = 3b(\underline{\ ?\ })$ b   3. $6xy = (\underline{\ ?\ })(2y)$ 3x

4. $16x^2 = 2x(\underline{\ ?\ })$ 8x   5. $-49xy = (-7x)(\underline{\ ?\ })$ 7y   6. $-2a^2b = a(\underline{\ ?\ })$ -2ab

7. $12a^3 = 4a(\underline{\ ?\ })$ $3a^2$ 8. $x^{12} = (\underline{\ ?\ })x^4$ x^8 9. $-y^{10} = (\underline{\ ?\ })y^5$ $-y^5$

10. $-6n^8 = n(\underline{\ ?\ })$ $-6n^7$ 11. $9x^4 = 3x^3(\underline{\ ?\ })$ 3x   12. $21a^4b^2 = 7ab(\underline{\ ?\ })$ $3a^3b$

13. $18x^6y^4 = x^5(\underline{\ ?\ })$ $18xy^4$ 14. $11x^5y^6 = (\underline{\ ?\ })x^2y^2$ $11x^3y^4$ 15. $a^4bc = ac(\underline{\ ?\ })$ a^3b

FACTORING

209

2. First simplify by using the cancellation rule, then by using the quotient of powers rule.

a. $\dfrac{15x^5y^4z}{-5yx^2}$ $-3x^3y^3z$

b. $\dfrac{27a^3b^2}{18a^4bc}$ $\dfrac{3b}{2ac}$

3. Find the missing factor:
$15x^7y^5 = (5x^4y)(?)$ $3x^3y^4$

POSSIBLE ERROR

When finding the quotient of powers of the same base, students may divide exponents instead of subtracting exponents. For example, they may write:

$$\dfrac{n^6}{n^2} = n^3 \quad \text{(incorrect)}$$

To help them avoid such errors, refer frequently to the definitions. Also, show them that

$$\dfrac{n^6}{n^2} = \dfrac{\cancel{n}\cdot\cancel{n}\cdot n\cdot n\cdot n\cdot n}{\cancel{n}\cdot\cancel{n}} = \dfrac{n\cdot n\cdot n\cdot n}{1} = n^4$$

DAILY QUIZ

Simplify each expression. Assume that no denominator is 0.

1. $\dfrac{4x}{x}$ 4   2. $\dfrac{12bc}{4c}$ 3b

3. $\dfrac{8x}{-32xy}$ $-\dfrac{1}{4y}$ 4. $\dfrac{x^9}{x^4}$ x^5

5. $\dfrac{-4xz^4}{-48xy^2z^3}$ $\dfrac{z}{12y^2}$

ASSIGNMENT GUIDE
(pages 209–212)

Minimum course: 1–47 odd, 55, 57
Average course: 1–57 odd
Maximum course: 7–57 odd, 59–64
second day: *Extra Topic*

EXTRA PRACTICE, page 518

Simplify each expression. Assume that no denominator is 0.

16. $\dfrac{3a}{a}$ 3 17. $\dfrac{5xy}{x}$ $5y$ 18. $\dfrac{8cd}{4d}$ $2c$ 19. $\dfrac{-9xy}{3xy}$ -3

20. $\dfrac{14sl}{-7t}$ $2s$ 21. $\dfrac{16ab}{-4a}$ $-4b$ 22. $\dfrac{a^b}{a}$ a^5 23. $\dfrac{n^2}{2n^5}$ $\dfrac{1}{2n^3}$

24. $\dfrac{x^8}{x^3}$ x^5 25. $\dfrac{12x^5}{3x^2}$ $4x^3$ 26. $\dfrac{18r^4}{-3r}$ $-6r^3$ 27. $\dfrac{-x^9}{2x^4}$ $-\dfrac{x^5}{2}$

28. $\dfrac{xy^3}{xy}$ y^2 29. $\dfrac{a^3b^2}{ab}$ a^2b 30. $\dfrac{c^4d^5}{c^2d^7}$ $\dfrac{c^2}{d^2}$ 31. $\dfrac{8x^5y^7}{4x^3y}$ $2x^2y^6$

32. $\dfrac{-24a^2b^8}{8ab^5}$ $-3ab^3$ 33. $\dfrac{14a^9b^3}{-2a^5b}$ $-7a^4b^2$ 34. $\dfrac{-25x^4y^6}{-5xy}$ $5x^3y^5$ 35. $\dfrac{22a^3b^2c}{11abc}$ $2a^2b$

B

36. $\dfrac{-42ab^2c^3}{-3ac^2}$ $14b^2c$ 37. $\dfrac{5a^3x^2y^5}{3ax^2y^5}$ $\dfrac{5a^2}{3}$ 38. $\dfrac{-12ab^2c^3}{6abc^2}$ $-2bc$ 39. $\dfrac{5x^2y^3z^3}{40xz^3}$ $\dfrac{xy^3}{8}$

40. $\dfrac{6a^5x^2y^4z^3}{2a^2x^2y^6z^3}$ $\dfrac{3a^3}{y^2}$ 41. $\dfrac{-28a^4b^2c^3}{-14a^3b^2c^2}$ $2ac$ 42. $\dfrac{-20x^3y^5}{10xy^4}$ $-2x^2y$ 43. $\dfrac{-21h^3k^2r^2}{7h^2k^2r}$ $-3hr$

44. $\dfrac{-12a^2b^2}{4a^5b^2}$ $\dfrac{-3}{a^3}$ 45. $\dfrac{-8a^2b^2}{16a^2b^2}$ $-\dfrac{1}{2}$ 46. $\dfrac{20a^3bc^4}{10ab^2c^2}$ $\dfrac{2a^2c^2}{b}$ 47. $\dfrac{35xy^4z^9}{5xy^4z^3}$ $7z^6$

Complete.

48. $10a^4b \div 5ab = \underline{\ ?\ }$ $2a^3$ 49. $21xy^5 \div 7xy^4 = \underline{\ ?\ }$ $3y$ 50. $30p^2q^4r \div 6pqr = \underline{\ ?\ }$ $5pq^3$

51. $5a^4bc \div 5ab = \underline{\ ?\ }$ a^3c 52. $8x^4y^5 \div \underline{\ ?\ } = 2x^2y^3$ 53. $9x^5yz \div \underline{\ ?\ } = 9xy$ x^4z

                                     $4x^2y^2$

Find the missing factors.

54. $x^2 + 2x = x(\underline{\ ?\ }) + 2(\underline{\ ?\ })$ $x; x$

55. $6a^2b + 2ab^2 = (\underline{\ ?\ })(3a) + (\underline{\ ?\ })(b)$ $2ab; 2ab$

56. $12x^3y^3 - 8x^6y^2 = (\underline{\ ?\ })(3y) - (\underline{\ ?\ })(2x^3)$ $4x^3y^2; 4x^3y^2$

57. $18x^2y^5 - 32xy^2 = 2xy^2(\underline{\ ?\ }) - 2xy^2(\underline{\ ?\ })$ $9xy^3; 16$

58. $20a^2b^2 + 15a^3b^4 = 5a^2b^2(\underline{\ ?\ }) + 5a^2b^2(\underline{\ ?\ })$ $4; 3ab^2$

C

59. $6x^4y + 15x^3y^2 - 3x^2y^4 = (\underline{\ ?\ })(2x^2) + (\underline{\ ?\ })(5xy) - (\underline{\ ?\ })(y^3)$ $3x^2y; 3x^2y; 3x^2y$

60. $21a^2b^7 - 42a^6b^3 - 3a^2b^2 = (\underline{\ ?\ })(7b^5) - (\underline{\ ?\ })(14a^4b) - (\underline{\ ?\ })(3a^2b^2)$ $3a^2b^2; 3a^2b^2; 1$

61. $(x^2 - 3x) + (4x - 12) = (\underline{\ ?\ })(x - 3) + (\underline{\ ?\ })(x - 3)$ $x; 4$

62. $(x^2 + 5x) - (2x + 10) = x(\underline{\ ?\ }) - 2(\underline{\ ?\ })$ $x + 5; x + 5$

63. $(10x + 15) - (6x + 9) = 5(\underline{\ ?\ }) - 3(\underline{\ ?\ })$ $2x + 3; 2x + 3$

64. $(2x^2 - 2xy) + (5xy - 5y^2) = 2x(\underline{\ ?\ }) + 5y(\underline{\ ?\ })$ $x - y; x - y$

Integers as Exponents

What is the smallest positive number you can express with these three cards?

-32 and -23 are both negative. -2^3 and -3^2 are also negative since the minus sign is not part of the base. The expression $3 - 2$ is positive, but that is not the answer. Can you express a smaller positive number? If not, try again later.

You have already worked with exponents that are positive integers. It is also possible to use 0 and negative integers as exponents. To do this we will require that the rule $\frac{x^a}{x^b} = x^{a-b}$ apply for any integral exponents, not just when a is greater than b.

Then $\frac{x^3}{x^3} = x^{3-3} = x^0$, but $\frac{x^3}{x^3} = 1$.   So x^0 should equal 1.

Also $\frac{x^3}{x^5} = x^{3-5} = x^{-2}$,   but $\frac{x^3}{x^5} = \frac{x^3}{x^3 \cdot x^2} = \frac{1}{x^2}$.   So x^{-2} should equal $\frac{1}{x^2}$.

Therefore we have the following definitions for any integer n, when $b \neq 0$.

$$b^0 = 1 \quad \text{and} \quad b^{-n} = \frac{1}{b^n}$$

With these new definitions, all our rules for positive integral exponents now apply to *any* integral exponents.

Example 1 Write each number without using exponents.

 a. $29^0 = 1$ b. $4^{-3} = \frac{1}{4^3} = \frac{1}{64}$ c. $\left(-\frac{1}{2}\right)^{-3} = \frac{1}{\left(-\frac{1}{2}\right)^3} = \frac{1}{-\frac{1}{8}} = -8$

Example 2 Simplify. Write the answer without using exponents.

 a. $(5^{-2})(5^3) = 5^{-2+3} = 5^1 = 5$ b. $\frac{5^{-2}}{5^3} = 5^{-2-3} = 5^{-5} = \frac{1}{5^5} = \frac{1}{3125}$

Example 3 Simplify. Use positive exponents only.

 a. $x \cdot x^{-3} = x^{-2}$ b. $\frac{x^5}{x^{-2}} = x^{5-(-2)}$ c. $(a^2 b^{-3})^{-2} = (a^2)^{-2}(b^{-3})^{-2}$

   $= \frac{1}{x^2}$ $= x^7$ $= a^{-4}b^6$

   $= \frac{b^6}{a^4}$

Extra Topic
The opening question may serve to spark interest on the part of the students. It is a "puzzle" to be solved. The solution, of course, is 3^{-2}, which equals $\frac{1}{3^2}$, or $\frac{1}{9}$. As the text implies, the students may be able to answer the question *after* they have worked through the Extra Topic.

When the students have completed pages 211–212, you may wish to note that negative exponents are used in scientific notation, where the calculations involve numbers less than 1.

EXERCISES

Write each number without using exponents.

1. 2^{-3} $\frac{1}{8}$ **2.** 3^{-2} $\frac{1}{9}$ **3.** 2^{-1} $\frac{1}{2}$ **4.** 6^{-2} $\frac{1}{36}$ **5.** 4^{-4} $\frac{1}{256}$

6. 3^{-3} $\frac{1}{27}$ **7.** $(-2)^{-3}$ $-\frac{1}{8}$ **8.** $(-3)^{-2}$ $\frac{1}{9}$ **9.** $(-1)^0$ 1 **10.** $\left(\frac{1}{2}\right)^{-4}$ 16

11. $\left(\frac{1}{6}\right)^0$ 1 **12.** $(3^{-1})^2$ $\frac{1}{9}$ **13.** $(3^{-1})^{-2}$ 9 **14.** $(4^2)^0$ 1 **15.** $(3^4)^{-1}$ $\frac{1}{81}$

Simplify. Write the answer without using exponents.

16. $2^{-4} \cdot 2^2$ $\frac{1}{4}$ **17.** $3^5 \cdot 3^{-1}$ 81 **18.** $5^0 \cdot 5^3$ 125 **19.** $8^2 \cdot 8^{-3}$ $\frac{1}{8}$

20. $\dfrac{6^{-4}}{6^{-2}}$ $\frac{1}{36}$ **21.** $\dfrac{10^2}{10^{-4}}$ $1{,}000{,}000$ **22.** $\dfrac{10^{-2}}{10^4}$ $\frac{1}{1{,}000{,}000}$ or 0.000001 **23.** $\dfrac{3^{-3}}{3^0}$ $\frac{1}{27}$

24. $\dfrac{2^3 \cdot 2^2}{2^6}$ $\frac{1}{2}$ **25.** $\dfrac{3^{-7} \cdot 3^4}{3}$ $\frac{1}{81}$ **26.** $\dfrac{5^2 \cdot 5^{-6}}{5^{-3}}$ $\frac{1}{5}$ **27.** $\dfrac{6^{-2}}{6^4 \cdot 6^{-7}}$ 6

Simplify. Use positive exponents only.

28. $x^{-3} \cdot x^5$ x^2 **29.** $x^3 \cdot x^{-5}$ $\frac{1}{x^2}$ **30.** $x^{-3} \cdot x^{-5}$ $\frac{1}{x^8}$ **31.** $\dfrac{x^3}{x^5}$ $\frac{1}{x^2}$

32. $\dfrac{x^{-3}}{x^{-5}}$ x^2 **33.** $\dfrac{x^{-3}}{x^5}$ $\frac{1}{x^8}$ **34.** $\dfrac{x^3}{x^{-5}}$ x^8 **35.** $\dfrac{x^0}{x^{-5}}$ x^5

36. $a^0(a^2b)$ a^2b **37.** $(a^{-2}b^2)^{-1}$ $\frac{a^2}{b^2}$ **38.** $(5ab^{-2})^{-3}$ $\frac{b^6}{125a^3}$ **39.** $(2x^{-2})^4$ $\frac{16}{x^8}$

Write each power of 2 in the form 2^n.
   Sample $16 = 2^4$

40. 32 2^5 **41.** 128 2^7 **42.** $\dfrac{1}{8}$ 2^{-3} **43.** $\dfrac{1}{256}$ 2^{-8} **44.** $\dfrac{64}{1024}$ 2^{-4}

Write each power of 3 in the form 3^n.
   Sample $243 = 3^5$

45. 81 3^4 **46.** $\dfrac{1}{27}$ 3^{-3} **47.** 729 3^6 **48.** $\dfrac{1}{9^{-1}}$ 3^2 **49.** $\dfrac{3}{27^{-2}}$ 3^7

Write each power of 10 in the form 10^n.
   Sample $10{,}000 = 10^4$

50. 1000 10^3 **51.** 0.1 10^{-1} **52.** 0.001 10^{-3} **53.** 1 10^0 **54.** 0.01 10^{-2}

Determine the value of **n**.

55. $\dfrac{1}{2} = 2^n$ -1 **56.** $27^{-1} = 3^n$ -3 **57.** $5^{n+1} = 125$ 2 **58.** $3^n + 4 = 5$ 0

6-3 Common Monomial Factors

OBJECTIVE

To factor the greatest common factor from the terms of a polynomial.

You can factor a polynomial if all of its terms have a common factor. For example, both terms of $6x + 12y$ have 6 as a factor.

$$6x + 12y = 6(x) + 6(2y) \qquad \text{Use the distributive property to factor 6}$$
$$\text{from each term.}$$
$$6x + 12y = 6(x + 2y) \longleftarrow \textbf{factored form}$$

Now consider the common monomial factors of the terms in $4a^3b + 6a^2b^4$.

2 is the greatest common factor (GCF) of the coefficients.

a^2 is the highest power of a common to the two terms.

b^1 is the highest power of b common to the two terms.

The product of 2, a^2, and b^1 is $2a^2b$. This is called the *greatest common factor* (GCF) of the terms of the polynomial $4a^3b + 6a^2b^4$.

Example 1 shows the **greatest common factor** (GCF) of the terms of a polynomial. It is the product of the GCF of the coefficients times the highest powers of the variables common to all terms.

EXAMPLE 1   Find the greatest common factor of the terms of each polynomial.

$8x + 2xy$	$3xy + 5x$	$2x^4 + 6x^3$	$34x^3y + 51x^2y^2$
GCF: $2x$	x	$2x^3$	$17x^2y$

To factor a polynomial completely, be sure to factor the greatest common factor from its terms.

EXAMPLE 2   Factor $10x^2 + 5x$ completely, and check.

The greatest common factor is $5x$.

$$10x^2 + 5x = 5x(2x + 1)$$

Check $5x(2x + 1) = 10x^2 + 5x$ ✔

EXAMPLE 3   Factor $15a^3 + 10a^2b^2 - 5a^2b$.

The greatest common factor is $5a^2$.

$$15a^3 + 10a^2b^2 - 5a^2b = (5a^2)(3a) + (5a^2)(2b^2) - (5a^2)(b)$$
$$= 5a^2(3a + 2b^2 - b)$$

FACTORING

213

WARM-UP EXERCISES

Find the positive integer that is the GCF of
1. 4 and 6   2
2. 10 and 30   10
3. 12 and 54   6
Find the variable that is a common factor of
4. xz and xy x
5. ab and bc b

LESSON NOTES

In this lesson, the concept of the greatest common factor is extended to polynomials in one or more variables. Be sure the students understand that to find the GCF of a polynomial, they must find the GCF of the coefficients of all the terms and also the highest powers of the variables common to all terms; then the GCF of the polynomial is the product of these common monomial factors.

[*Lesson Notes continue on page 214.*]

ALTERNATE EXAMPLES

1. Find the greatest common factor of the terms of each polynomial.
   $6x + 3xy$ $3x$ $4xy - y$ y
   $x^5 + 3x^3$ x^3
                 $24x^2y + 16x^2y^2$ $8x^2y$

2. Factor $15x^3 + 5x^2$ completely, and check. $5x^2(3x + 1)$

3. Factor $8a^4b + 4a^3b - 2a^3b^2$
   $2a^3b(4a + 2 - b)$

The common factor may have a negative coefficient.

EXAMPLE 4   Factor $-6x^2 + 4x + 2$.

$$-6x^2 + 4x + 2 = 2(-3x^2 + 2x + 1)$$
$$\text{or}$$
$$-6x^2 + 4x + 2 = -2(3x^2 - 2x - 1)$$

The answer may be written with the coefficient of x^2 positive.

CLASS EXERCISES

Find the greatest common factor of the terms of each polynomial.

1. $5ax - a$ a
2. $2x^4 + 4x^3 + 6x^2$ $2x^2$
3. $30x^3y + 10x^2y^2 + 15xy$ $5xy$

Factor completely.

4. $2x + 4$ $2(x + 2)$
5. $4y + 6$ $2(2y + 3)$
6. $12a^2 + 30$
$6(2a^2 + 5)$
7. $x^2 + 2x$ $x(x + 2)$
8. $10x^2 - 15x$
$5x(2x - 3)$
9. $6rs^2 - 9rs$
$3rs(2s - 3)$
10. $3t^2 + 3t$
$3t(t + 1)$
11. $b^2x + b^2$
$b^2(x + 1)$

EXERCISES

A   Find the greatest common factor of the terms in each polynomial.

1. $42n^3 + 28n^2$
$14n^2$
2. $18ab^3c - 36a^2bc^2$
$18abc$
3. $a^2x^3y^2 - 6axy$
axy

Factor completely, and check.

4. $5x + 15$ $5(x + 3)$
5. $6x + 12$ $6(x + 2)$
6. $8x - 2$ $2(4x - 1)$
7. $7y - 28$ $7(y - 4)$
8. $9y + 6$ $3(3y + 2)$
9. $10y + 25$
$5(2y + 5)$
10. $18h^2 - 24h$
$6h(3h - 4)$
11. $8x^2 - 20x$
$4x(2x - 5)$
12. $15n - 10$
$5(3n - 2)$
13. $24a - 12$
$12(2a - 1)$
14. $x^2 - 5x$
$x(x - 5)$
15. $x^2 + 6x$
$x(x + 6)$
16. $4x^2 + 2x$
$2x(2x + 1)$
17. $8ab + a$
$a(8b + 1)$
18. $3xy - y$
$y(3x - 1)$
19. $21ab + 7a$
$7a(3b + 1)$
20. $2x^2 - 2x$
$2x(x - 1)$
21. $10t^2 - 5t$
$5t(2t - 1)$
22. $9ax - 36a$
$9a(x - 4)$
23. $40ax + 30a$
$10a(4x + 3)$
24. $x^4 + x^2$
25. $3x^3 - 6x^2$
26. $45h^2 + 60h$
27. $39a + 65a^2$

28. $42n^3 + 28n^2$
29. $54hx^2 - 36h$
30. $42xy^2 - 70x^2y$

31. $3x^2 - 6x + 9$
32. $5h^2 - 10h + 20$
33. $6x^3 - 8x^2 + 4x$

34. $21a^3 - 7a^2 + 14a$
35. $60 + 45b + 30b^3$
36. $39a^3 + 65ac^2$

B   Factor. Write each answer in two ways, using both positive and negative signs with the GCF.

37. $-6x + 3$
38. $-9n + 9$
39. $-a + 3a^2$
40. $-n^2 + 4n$

41. $-6x - 2$
42. $-12x^2 + 9x$
43. $-y^2 + y$
44. $-5x^3 + 5x^2$

214

Factor each polynomial completely, and check.

45. $60t^4 - 4at^2 + 12t$

46. $30x^2y^2 + 45x^2y - 75y^2$

47. $9x^4 - 18x^3 + 12x^2 - 30x$

48. $120h^5 + 100h^4 + 50h^3 + 10h$

49. $6x^5y - 15x^4y^2 + 20x^3y^3 + 6xy^5$

50. $7a^6b + 21a^5b^2 + 21a^2b^5 + 7ab^6$

51. $84x^8y^5 + 105x^3y^2 - 63x^2y^3$

52. $63x^6y^5z^4 - 105x^5y^4z^3 + 21x^4y^3$

C

Simplify each fraction. Assume that no denominator is 0.

Sample $\dfrac{6x^2 + 4x}{2x} = \dfrac{2x(3x + 2)}{2x} = 3x + 2$

53. $\dfrac{5y^4 + 5y^3}{5y}$ $y^2(y + 1)$ **54.** $\dfrac{2x^3 - 4x^2 + 6x}{2x}$ $x^2 - 2x + 3$ **55.** $\dfrac{12b^5 + 3b^4 - 6b^2}{3b^2}$ $4b^3 + b^2 - 2$

56. $\dfrac{2a^2b + 4a^2b^2 + 2ab^2}{2ab}$ $a + 2ab + b$ **57.** $\dfrac{-3n^3 - 15n^2 - 6n}{-3n}$ $n^2 + 5n + 2$

58. The length of a rectangle is 6x. The area is $18x^2 + 12x$. Find the width. $3x + 2$

59. Find the cost of an item if the cost per dozen is $(36a - 24b)$ dollars. $\$(3a - 2b)$

Write a factored form to represent the area of each shaded region. Begin by adding or subtracting areas. Recall that for a circle, $A = \pi r^2$.

60.

Semicircles on a square $r^2(4 + \pi)$

61.

4k

Semicircle in a rectangle $8k^2(4 - \pi)$

62.

Quarter circles in a square $r^2(4 - \pi)$

These problems are from the annual American High School Mathematics Examination (M.A.A. Contest Problem Book).

*63. If the length of a diagonal of a square is $a + b$, then the area of the square is: *(B)*

(A) $(a + b)^2$ (B) $\dfrac{1}{2}(a + b)^2$ (C) $a^2 + b^2$ (D) $\dfrac{1}{2}(a^2 + b^2)$

(E) none of these

*64. The bottom, side, and front areas of a rectangular box are known. The product of these areas is equal to: *(D)*

(A) the volume of the box.

(B) the square root of the volume.

(C) twice the volume.

(D) the square of the volume.

(E) the cube of the volume.

FACTORING   215

Simplify.
1. $2x + 3x$ $5x$
2. $4(a + b) + 3(a + b)$ $7(a + b)$
3. $1(x + y) - 1(x + y)$ 0

LESSON NOTES

As you discuss factoring by grouping, numbers can be used to help students "see" the equivalence of the expressions. For example:

$(6 + 3)5 + (6 + 3)2 \stackrel{?}{=} (6 + 3)(5 + 2)$

$\downarrow$ $\downarrow$

$9 \cdot 5 + 9 \cdot 2$ $9(5 + 2)$

$\downarrow$

$9(5 + 2)$

In the work with polynomials that have four terms, emphasize that we group the terms into pairs in such a way that both pairs have the same binomial factor. Example 3 shows the necessity of rearranging terms in order to obtain a common binomial factor for both pairs.

In the C exercises, the sample that precedes Exercises 47–52 shows how a trinomial such as $x^2 + 6x + 5$ can be factored by grouping. The procedure involves expressing the middle term as a binomial that can then be "split apart" to furnish terms that can be combined advantageously with the other two terms. These exercises anticipate an Extra Topic, "Factoring $ax^2 + bx + c$: An Alternate Method," which follows Lesson 6-8.

ALTERNATE EXAMPLES

1. Factor: $a(b + c) + b + c$
          $(a + 1)(b + c)$
2. Factor: $x(x - 2) + (2 - x)$
          $(x - 1)(x - 2)$

6-4   Factoring by Grouping

OBJECTIVES

To factor a common binomial factor from the terms of a polynomial.
To factor polynomials that have four terms, by grouping into pairs.

A common factor of the terms of a polynomial may be a monomial, such as x.

$$xy + xz = x(y + z)$$

A common factor may be a binomial, such as $(a + 3)$.

$$(a + 3)y + (a + 3)z = (a + 3)(y + z)$$

Note that a common binomial factor may appear on the right.

$$2x(x - 3) + 5y(x - 3) = (2x + 5y)(x - 3)$$

Sometimes you use 1 as a factor of a binomial.

EXAMPLE 1   Factor $n(a + b) + a + b$.

$$n(a + b) + a + b = n(a + b) + 1(a + b)$$
$$= (n + 1)(a + b)$$

You may use -1 as a factor to obtain the opposite of a binomial.

EXAMPLE 2   Factor $x(x - 4) + (4 - x)$. $4 - x = -1(x - 4)$

$$x(x - 4) + (4 - x) = x(x - 4) - 1(x - 4)$$
$$= (x - 1)(x - 4)$$

Treating a binomial as a factor is a way of factoring some polynomials that, at first, do not look as though they can be factored.

Consider the polynomial $xy + 2y + 3x + 6$. There is no factor common to all four terms. However, the factor y is common to the first two terms, and the factor 3 is common to the last two terms.

$(xy + 2y) + (3x + 6)$ Group into binomials.

$(x + 2)y + (x + 2)3$ $(x + 2)$ is a common binomial factor.

$(x + 2)(y + 3)$

This is an example of *factoring by grouping*. The terms of the polynomial $xy + 2y + 3x + 6$ could have been grouped in a different way.

$(xy + 3x) + (2y + 6)$ Rearrange the terms and group.

$x(y + 3) + 2(y + 3)$ Now $(y + 3)$ is the common factor.

$(x + 2)(y + 3)$ The factored forms are the same.

CHAPTER 6

In some problems you *must* rearrange terms before you factor by grouping.

EXAMPLE 3   Factor $x^2 - 5y + 5x - xy$.

The last two terms have a common factor x, but the first two terms have no common factor. Try rearranging the terms.

$$x^2 - 5y + 5x - xy = x^2 + 5x - xy - 5y$$
$$= (x + 5)x - (x + 5)y$$
$$= (x + 5)(x - y)$$

If the binomial factors are opposites in your first factoring step, you can still obtain common binomial factors, as shown in the next example.

EXAMPLE 4   Factor $x^2 - ax - bx + ab$.

Suppose you factor b from the last two terms.
$$x^2 - ax - bx + ab = x(x - a) + b(-x + a) \quad \longleftarrow \text{Binomials are}$$
$$\text{opposites.}$$
Now try factoring $-b$ from the last two terms.
$$x^2 - ax - bx + ab = x(x - a) - b(x - a) \quad \longleftarrow (x - a) \text{ is a}$$
$$= (x - b)(x - a) \quad\quad\quad\quad \text{common factor.}$$

To check the factoring, multiply $(x - b)$ by $(x - a)$.

CLASS EXERCISES

Factor.

1. $x(x + 4) + 3(x + 4)$ $(x + 3)(x + 4)$ 2. $2(x - 5) + x(x - 5)$ $(2 + x)(x - 5)$

3. $2x(x + 7) - 5(x + 7)$ $(2x - 5)(x + 7)$ 4. $4(x - 6) - 3x(x - 6)$ $(4 - 3x)(x - 6)$

5. $x^2(y + 9) + 2(y + 9)$ $(x^2 + 2)(y + 9)$ 6. $y^2(x - 3) + 6(x - 3)$ $(y^2 + 6)(x - 3)$

7. $(x + y)x - (x + y)y$ $(x + y)(x - y)$ 8. $(x + 3)x + (x + 3)$ $(x + 1)(x + 3)$

9. $3x - 12 + ax - 4a$ $(3 + a)(x - 4)$ 10. $2a + 10 + ab + 5b$ $(2 + b)(a + 5)$

11. $x^2 - 3y + 3x - xy$ $(x - y)(x + 3)$ 12. $4b + 2a + 2bn + an$ $(2 + n)(2b + a)$

EXERCISES

A   *Factor.*

1. $x(y + 2) + 3(y + 2)$ $(x + 3)(y + 2)$ 2. $3x(y - 5) + 4(y - 5)$ $(3x + 4)(y - 5)$

3. $x(2y + 1) - 6(2y + 1)$ $(x - 6)(2y + 1)$ 4. $y(x^2 + 1) - 7(x^2 + 1)$ $(y - 7)(x^2 + 1)$

5. $y(x + 5) - 4(x + 5)$ $(y - 4)(x + 5)$ 6. $a(a + b) + 3(a + b)$ $(a + 3)(a + b)$

7. $(a + b)a^2 + (a + b)4$ $(a^2 + 4)(a + b)$ 8. $b(a^2 + 1) - 3(a^2 + 1)$ $(b - 3)(a^2 + 1)$

EXTRA PRACTICE, page 519

3. Factor: $x^2 + 3y + 3x + xy$
   $(x + y)(x + 3)$

4. Factor: $y^2 - cy - dy + cd$
   $(y - d)(y - c)$

POSSIBLE ERROR

Students frequently make errors of this type when they factor by grouping:

$(x + 2)3 + (x + 2)y = (x + 2)3y$
                   (incorrect)

Help the students correct such errors by using *a* to represent the binomial $x + 2$. Then:

$$a \cdot 3 + a \cdot y = a(3 + y)$$

Next substitute $x + 2$ for *a*:

$(x + 2)3 + (x + 2)y =$
                  $(x + 2)(3 + y)$

DAILY QUIZ

Factor.
1. $x(y - 2) + 4(y - 2)$
   $(x + 4)(y - 2)$
2. $(x + 5)x - (x + 5)$
   $(x + 5)(x - 1)$
3. $4xy + 6y + 6x + 9$
   $(2y + 3)(2x + 3)$
4. $ab + b + a + 1$
   $(b + 1)(a + 1)$
5. $y^2 - 2x + 2y - xy$
   $(y - x)(y + 2)$

ASSIGNMENT GUIDE
(pages 217–218)

Minimum course: 1–8, 9–39 odd
Average course: 1–43 odd
Maximum course: 1–51 odd

Suggest that the students solve these problems:

The area of a rectangle is given by the polynomial $6xy - 4x + 15y - 10$. The length can be represented by $ax + b$; the width can be represented by $cy + d$. What is a? b? c? d?
$a = 2$; $b = 5$; $c = 3$; $d = -2$

The area of a triangle is given by the polynomial $16xy - 24y + 4x - 6$. The base can be represented by $ex + f$; the height can be represented by $gy + h$. What is e? f? g? h?
$e = 4$; $f = -6$; $g = 8$; $h = 2$
or $e = 2$; $f = -3$; $g = 16$; $h = 4$
or $e = 8$; $f = -12$; $g = 4$; $h = 1$

ADDITIONAL ANSWERS

Exercises

30. $(1 - a)(1 - b)$ or $(a - 1)(b - 1)$
31. $(x^2 + r)(y - s)$
32. $(a - 5)(x^2 + y^2)$
33. $(a + b)(p - q)$
34. $(a - k)(7 - y)$ or $(k - a)(y - 7)$
35. $(5 - x)(3 - y)$ or $(x - 5)(y - 3)$
36. $(3 + a)(2 - b)$
37. $(4 - 3y)(1 - x)$ or $(3y - 4)(x - 1)$
38. $(x - 2b)(x + a)$
39. $(ab + c)(a + bc)$
40. $(x - 2y)(x + 3y)$

B

9. $(x - y)x + (x - y)$ $(x - y)(x + 1)$
10. $y(x^3 + 1) - (x^3 + 1)$ $(y - 1)(x^3 + 1)$
11. $xy + 3y + 2x + 6$ $(y + 2)(x + 3)$
12. $ab + 7a + 5b + 35$ $(a + 5)(b + 7)$
13. $2xy + 12x + y + 6$ $(2x + 1)(y + 6)$
14. $6xy + 4y + 15x + 10$ $(2y + 5)(3x + 2)$
15. $a^2 + ab + 3a + 3b$ $(a + 3)(a + b)$
16. $ab + b^2 + 7a + 7b$ $(b + 7)(a + b)$
17. $3xy + 5y + 6x + 10$ $(y + 2)(3x + 5)$
18. $15xy + 6y + 20x + 8$ $(3y + 4)(5x + 2)$
19. $x^2 + 3xy + 5x + 15y$ $(x + 5)(x + 3y)$
20. $2xy + y^2 + 12x + 6y$ $(2x + y)(y + 6)$
21. $y + 1 + xy + x$ $(1 + x)(y + 1)$
22. $xy + y + x + 1$ $(y + 1)(x + 1)$

23. $x^2 - 2y + 2x - xy$ $(x - y)(x + 2)$
24. $x^2 - 21y - 7x + 3xy$ $(x + 3y)(x - 7)$
25. $2ab - 7a + a^2 - 14b$ $(a - 7)(a + 2b)$
26. $8u - 5v^2 + uv - 40v$ $(u - 5v)(8 + v)$
27. $x^2y + y - 9x^2 - 9$ $(x^2 + 1)(y - 9)$
28. $a^2b - 15 + 3b - 5a^2$ $(b - 5)(a^2 + 3)$
29. $xy - ab + ay - bx$ $(y - b)(x + a)$
30. $-b - a + 1 + ab$
31. $x^2y - rs - x^2s + ry$
32. $ax^2 - 5y^2 + ay^2 - 5x^2$
33. $ap + bp - aq - bq$
34. $7a - ay + ky - 7k$
35. $15 - 5y - 3x + xy$
36. $6 + 2a - 3b - ab$
37. $4 + 3xy - 3y - 4x$
38. $x^2 + ax - 2bx - 2ab$
39. $a^2b + ab^2c + ca + bc^2$
40. $x^2 + 3xy - 2xy - 6y^2$

C

Factor completely. First factor the GCF from the terms of the polynomial.

Sample
$$3x^2y - 12x^2 + 9xy - 36x = 3x[xy - 4x + 3y - 12]$$
$$= 3x[(y - 4)x + (y - 4)3]$$
$$= 3x[(y - 4)(x + 3)]$$
$$= 3x(y - 4)(x + 3)$$

41. $ab^3 + b^4 + 6ab^2 + 6b^3$ $b^2(6 + b)(a + b)$
42. $10xy^2 - 5y^2 + 30xy - 15y$ $5y(y + 3)(2x - 1)$
43. $3x^2y - 12x^2 - 12x^3 + 3xy$ $3x(x + 1)(y - 4x)$
44. $x^3y^2 - x^3y - 3xy^2 + 3xy$ $xy(x^2 - 3)(y - 1)$
45. $8 - 4y^2 + 8x - 4xy^2$ $4(2 - y^2)(1 + x)$
46. $10x^2y^2 - 10y^3 + 15x^2y - 15y^2$ $5y(2y + 3)(x^2 - y)$

Factor the following trinomials by grouping.

Sample
$$x^2 + 6x + 5 = x^2 + (x + 5x) + 5$$
$$= (x^2 + x) + (5x + 5)$$
$$= x(x + 1) + 5(x + 1)$$
$$= (x + 5)(x + 1)$$

47. $x^2 + 7x + 12$ $(x + 3)(x + 4)$
48. $n^2 + 10n + 21$ $(n + 3)(n + 7)$
49. $x^2 - x - 6$ $(x + 2)(x - 3)$
50. $a^2 - 8a + 15$ $(a - 3)(a - 5)$
51. $x^2 - 10x + 21$ $(x - 3)(x - 7)$
52. $n^2 + 5n + 6$ $(n + 2)(n + 3)$

6-5   Difference of Two Squares

OBJECTIVE

To recognize a binomial that is a difference of two squares, and then factor.

In certain cases, the product of two binomials is another binomial. When you multiply $(a + b)$ and $(a - b)$, the product is $a^2 - b^2$. Note that $a^2 - b^2$ is the difference of two squares.

$$(a + b)\ (a - b) = a^2 - ab + ab - b^2 = a^2 - b^2$$

If you reverse the steps above, you have a formula for factoring the difference of two squares.

> **Factoring the Difference of Two Squares**
>
> $$a^2 - b^2 = (a + b)(a - b)$$
>
> opposite signs

EXAMPLE 1   Factor $x^2 - 25$.

$x^2 - 25$ is the difference of two squares because the first term, x^2 is the square of x, the second term 25 is the square of 5, and the two terms are separated by a minus sign.

Therefore, $x^2 - 25 = x^2 - 5^2 = (x + 5)(x - 5)$.

EXAMPLE 2   Factor $9x^2 - 1$.

$$9x^2 - 1 = (3x)^2 - 1^2$$
$$= (3x + 1)(3x - 1)$$

With practice, you will be able to recognize the difference of two squares by inspection. Then the solution in the preceding example can be written briefly as $9x^2 - 1 = (3x + 1)(3x - 1)$.

FACTORING   **219**

Find the products.
 1. $(x + 3)(x + 3)$ $x^2 + 6x + 9$
 2. $(x + 3)(x - 3)$ $x^2 - 9$
 3. $(2x + 5)(2x - 5)$ $4x^2 - 25$

LESSON NOTES

You can begin this lesson by reminding students that the product of two binomials may have four terms, three terms, or two terms.

$(a + b)(c + d) = ac + ad + bc + bd$

$(n - 3)(n + 1) = n^2 - 3n + 1n - 3$
$\qquad\qquad\quad = n^2 - 2n - 3$

$(x + 6)(x - 6) = x^2 + 6x - 6x - 36$
$\qquad\qquad\quad = x^2 - 36$

Tell the students that in this lesson they will learn how to factor binomials such as $x^2 - 36$, $a^2 - b^2$, and $4y^2 - 9$, each of which is the difference of two squares.

The introductory material on page 219 uses the product of $(a + b)$ and $(a - b)$ to lead to the generalization about factoring the difference of two squares. Be sure to discuss each of the model examples carefully, pointing out how each term in the given binomial is a square.

In Example 4, explain that $-x^2 + 1$ may not look like the difference of two squares, but rearranging its terms produces $1 - x^2$, which is clearly the difference of two squares (1^2 and x^2).

After you discuss Example 4, you may wish to note that an alternate procedure for factoring $-x^2 + 1$ begins with factoring -1 from the two terms.

$-x^2 + 1 = -1(x^2 - 1)$
$\qquad\quad = -1(x + 1)(x - 1)$
$\qquad$ or $-(x + 1)(x - 1)$

ALTERNATE EXAMPLES

 1. Factor: $x^2 - 64$ $(x + 8)(x - 8)$
 2. Factor: $25x^2 - 1$
    $(5x + 1)(5x - 1)$

3. Factor: $9x^2 - 4y^2$
  $(3x + 2y)(3x - 2y)$

4. Factor: $-x^2 + 4$
  $(2 + x)(2 - x)$

5. Factor $4a - ay^2$ completely.
  $a(2 + y)(2 - y)$

DAILY QUIZ

Factor.
1. $x^2 - 81$ $(x + 9)(x - 9)$
2. $4y^2 - 25$ $(2y + 5)(2y - 5)$
3. $36 - x^2$ $(6 + x)(6 - x)$
4. $3x^2 - 12$ $3(x + 2)(x - 2)$
5. $2xy^2 - 2x^3$ $2x(y + x)(y - x)$

ASSIGNMENT GUIDE
(pages 220–222)

Minimum course: 1–39 odd,
49, 51
Average course: 1–47 odd,
49, 51, 55
Maximum course: 7–65 odd,
66–69
All courses: *Checkpoint*
review
exercises

ADDITIONAL ANSWERS

Class Exercises

5. $(x + 4)(x - 4)$
6. $(x + 7)(x - 7)$
7. $(x + h)(x - h)$
8. $(h + x)(h - x)$
9. $(8 + b)(8 - b)$
10. $(4x + 1)(4x - 1)$
11. $(9a + 2)(9a - 2)$
12. $(3x + 5y)(3x - 5y)$
13. $(11p + 12q)(11p - 12q)$
14. $(11a + 6b)(11a - 6b)$
15. $(x + 100)(x - 100)$

EXAMPLE 3 Factor $4x^2 - 9y^2$.

$$4x^2 - 9y^2 = (2x + 3y)(2x - 3y)$$

EXAMPLE 4 Factor $-x^2 + 1$.

$$-x^2 + 1 = 1 - x^2 \qquad \text{Rearrange the terms.}$$
$$= (1 + x)(1 - x)$$

To check the factoring, multiply $(1 + x)(1 - x)$.

$$(1 + x)(1 - x) = 1 - x + x - x^2 = 1 - x^2, \text{ or } -x^2 + 1 \; ✔$$

Sometimes you must factor a polynomial more than once to factor it completely. The binomial $2x^3 - 18x$ is not the difference of two squares, since neither term is a square. But there is a common factor of $2x$.

$$2x^3 - 18x = 2x(x^2 - 9)$$
$$= 2x(x + 3)(x - 3)$$

EXAMPLE 5 Factor $a - 4ay^2$ completely.

$$a - 4ay^2 = a(1 - 4y^2)$$
$$= a(1 + 2y)(1 - 2y)$$

CLASS EXERCISES

Complete.

1. $x^2 - y^2 = (x + \underline{?})(x - \underline{?})$ y, y **2.** $4x^2 - 49 = (2x + \underline{?})(2x - \underline{?})$ $7, 7$

3. $25b^2 - 1 = (\underline{?} + 1)(\underline{?} - 1)$ $5b, 5b$ **4.** $s^2 - 100 = (\underline{?} + \underline{?})(\underline{?} - \underline{?})$ $s, 10, s, 10$

Factor.

5. $x^2 - 16$ **6.** $x^2 - 49$ **7.** $x^2 - h^2$ **8.** $h^2 - x^2$

9. $64 - b^2$ **10.** $16x^2 - 1$ **11.** $81a^2 - 4$ **12.** $9x^2 - 25y^2$

13. $121p^2 - 144q^2$ **14.** $121a^2 - 36b^2$ **15.** $x^2 - 10,000$

EXERCISES

A Complete.

1. $n^2 - 9 = (n + 3)(\underline{?})$ $n - 3$ **2.** $a^2 - 4 = (\underline{?})(a - 2)$ $a + 2$

3. $4p^2 - 25 = (2p + 5)(\underline{?})$ $2p - 5$ **4.** $100 - a^2 = (\underline{?})(10 - a)$ $10 + a$

5. $16 - y^2 = (\underline{?})(4 - y)$ $4 + y$ **6.** $25x^2 - 16y^2 = (5x + 4y)(\underline{?})$ $5x - 4y$

7. $64x^2 - \underline{?} = (8x + 1)(8x - 1)$ 1 **8.** $81 - 4x^2 = (9 + 2x)(\underline{?})$ $9 - 2x$

9. $\underline{?} - 81 = (7a + 9)(7a - 9)$ $49a^2$ **10.** $a^2 - \underline{?} = (a + 2b)(a - 2b)$ $4b^2$

EXTRA PRACTICE, page 519

Factor.

11. $x^2 - 4$ **12.** $x^2 - 9$ **13.** $x^2 - 36$ **14.** $a^2 - 64$

15. $h^2 - 100$ **16.** $25 - b^2$ **17.** $121 - t^2$ **18.** $x^2 - 4y^2$

19. $9a^2 - b^2$ **20.** $25x^2 - y^2$ **21.** $9h^2 - 1$ **22.** $4a^2 - 9$

23. $25 - 64t^2$ **24.** $4 - 169b^2$ **25.** $x^2 - 196b^2$ **26.** $225h^2 - 1$

27. $p^2 - 144q^2$ **28.** $1 - 25t^2$ **29.** $9a^2 - 4$ **30.** $49u^2 - 25$

31. $25u^2 - 16t^2$ **32.** $49x^2 - 100y^2$ **33.** $121x^2 - 900y^2$

B

Factor completely.

34. $x^3 - 9x$ **35.** $y^3 - 25y$ **36.** $2x^2 - 8$

37. $3a^2 - 27$ **38.** $5x^3 - 125x$ **39.** $7h^3 - 28h$

40. $3x^3 - 12xy^2$ **41.** $7ab^2 - 63a^3$ **42.** $5x^3 - 125h^2x$

43. $16a - a^3b^2$ **44.** $16x^2 - 4c^2d^2$ **45.** $27a^3 - 363ab^2$

46. $x^3y - xy^3$ **47.** $2a^3bc^2 - 32ab^3$ **48.** $24a^2b - 54b^3$

Go over

C

Use factors to calculate the value of each numerical expression.

Sample $52^2 - 48^2 = (52 + 48)(52 - 48) = 100 \cdot 4 = 400$

49. $21^2 - 19^2$ **50.** $98^2 - 2^2$ **51.** $9999^2 - 1^2$ **52.** $3^2 - 97^2$

53. $1.5^2 - 0.5^2$ ***54.** $10^2 - 9^2 + 8^2 - 7^2 + 6^2 - 5^2 + 4^2 - 3^2 + 2^2 - 1^2$

Factor completely.

Sample $x^4 - y^4 = (x^2)^2 - (y^2)^2 = (x^2 + y^2)(x^2 - y^2)$
$$= (x^2 + y^2)(x + y)(x - y)$$

55. $x^4 - 16$ **56.** $h^4 - 1$ **57.** $1 - 81h^4$ **58.** $16x^4 - y^4$

59. $(x + 3)^2 - 9$ **60.** $(a - 5)^2 - 25$ **61.** $x^8 - 256$

Factor as the difference of two squares by using rational numbers.

Sample $x^2 - \dfrac{1}{4} = x^2 - \left(\dfrac{1}{2}\right)^2 = \left(x + \dfrac{1}{2}\right)\left(x - \dfrac{1}{2}\right)$

62. $x^2 - \dfrac{1}{9}$ **63.** $\dfrac{1}{4}y^2 - 9$ **64.** $\dfrac{1}{9}x^2 - 2\dfrac{1}{4}$ **65.** $x^2 - 0.01$

66. Factor completely $\dfrac{1}{5}hx^2 - \dfrac{1}{5}hy^2$. Then evaluate the expression when $h = 15$, $x = 57$, and $y = 43$.

FACTORING   **221**

67. Write in factored form the area of the shaded portion that remains when one square is cut from the other. Use the result to find the area when
$(x + y)(x - y)$
a. $x = 8.5$ and $y = 1.5$ 70 cm²

b. $x = 26.2$ and $y = 3.8$ 672 cm²

x cm

68. Factor $\pi R^2 - \pi r^2$ completely. Use the result to calculate the area of the shaded portion when
$\pi(R + r)(R - r)$
a. $R = 7.5$ and $r = 0.5$ 176

b. $R = 26.2$ and $r = 3.8$ 2112

Use $\frac{22}{7}$ for π.

69. A circular disc of radius R cm has 25 holes drilled in it, each of radius r cm. Write a formula for the area that remains in the disc. Find this area when $R = 68$ and $r = 6.4$. Use 3.14 as an approximation for π. $\pi(R + 5r)(R - 5r)$; 11,304

CHECKPOINT

Find the greatest common factor (GCF) of each set of integers.

1. 45, 108   9   **2.** 104, 156   52   **3.** 38, 57   19   **4.** 12, 30, 42   6

Simplify each expression. Assume that no denominator is 0.

5. $\frac{6xy}{y}$ 6x   **6.** $\frac{-12xy}{4xy}$ −3   **7.** $\frac{40xy^5z^8}{8xy^5z^3}$ $5z^5$ **8.** $\frac{-32x^4y^2z^3}{-16x^3y^2z^2}$ $2xz$

Factor completely.

9. $6x + 18$ $6(x + 3)$ **10.** $5x + 10$ $5(x + 2)$ **11.** $10x - 5$ $5(2x - 1)$ **12.** $9x^2 - 27x$ $9x(x - 3)$

13. $-3x^3 + 3x^2$ **14.** $39x^4 + 26x^2$ **15.** $-14x^2 + 7x$ **16.** $28x^3 - 14x$
$-3x^2(x - 1)$, or $3x^2(-x + 1)$ $13x^2(3x^2 + 2)$ $7x(-2x + 1)$ $14x(2x^2 - 1)$
17. $9x^3 - 6x^2 + 3x$ **18.** $x^2 - 49$ $(x - 7)(x + 7)$ **19.** $7x^2 - 5y^2 + 7y^2 - 5x^2$
$3x(3x^2 - 2x + 1)$ $2(x^2 + y^2)$
20. $2x(y - 3) + 5(y - 3)$ **21.** $y - 1 + xy - x$ **22.** $3y + xy + 2x + 6$
$(2x + 5)(y - 3)$ $(y - 1)(1 + x)$ $(y + 2)(x + 3)$
23. $4 - x^2$ **24.** $9x^2 - 16$ **25.** $16x^2 - 9y^2$ **26.** $100x^2 - 1$
$(2 - x)(2 + x)$ $(3x - 4)(3x + 4)$ $(4x - 3y)(4x + 3y)$ $(10x - 1)(10x + 1)$
27. $x^3 - 81x$ **28.** $3x^3 - 27x$ **29.** $242 - 2x^2$ **30.** $5x^2y - 125y^3$
$x(x - 9)(x + 9)$ $3x(x - 3)(x + 3)$ $2(11 - x)(11 + x)$ $5y(x - 5y)(x + 5y)$

CHAPTER 6

6-6 Trinomial Squares

OBJECTIVES

To identify a trinomial square.
To factor a trinomial square as the square of a binomial.

If you square a binomial, you get a trinomial. Such a trinomial is called a *trinomial square*.

$$(x + 7)^2 = (x + 7)(x + 7) = x^2 + 14x + 49 \longleftarrow$$
$$(x - 7)^2 = (x - 7)(x - 7) = x^2 - 14x + 49 \longleftarrow$$

trinomial squares

There are two basic patterns—one for squaring a sum, one for squaring a difference.

same sign
$$(a + b)^2 = a^2 + 2ab + b^2$$

same sign
$$(a - b)^2 = a^2 - 2ab + b^2$$

Trinomial squares can be factored by reversing the process of squaring the binomials.

Factoring Trinomial Squares

$$a^2 + 2ab + b^2 = (a + b)^2$$
$$a^2 - 2ab + b^2 = (a - b)^2$$

EXAMPLE 1 Factor $x^2 + 6x + 9$.

This is a trinomial square of the form $a^2 + 2ab + b^2$, with $a = x$ and $b = 3$.

$$x^2 + 6x + 9 = x^2 + 2(x)(3) + 3^2 = (x + 3)^2$$
$$ a^2 \quad + \quad 2ab \quad + \quad b^2$$

EXAMPLE 2 Factor $4x^2 - 4x + 1$.

$$4x^2 - 4x + 1 = (2x)^2 - 2(2x)(1) + 1^2 = (2x - 1)^2$$

Learn to recognize a trinomial square. If the end terms have the form a^2 and b^2, the middle term must have the form $\pm 2ab$.

FACTORING

LESSON NOTES

As you discuss the patterns for $(a + b)^2$ and $(a - b)^2$, it will be worthwhile to show the complete multiplication process:

$$(a + b)^2 = (a + b)(a + b)$$
$$a^2 + ab + ba + b^2$$
$$a^2 + 2ab + b^2$$
$$(a - b)^2 = (a - b)(a - b)$$
$$a^2 - ab - ba + b^2$$
$$a^2 - 2ab + b^2$$

Emphasize that the middle term is *twice* the product ab and is preceded by the same sign as the one that separates the terms of the original binomial. Also note that b^2 is always preceded by a plus sign.

Following Example 2, the text cautions the students that they should learn to recognize a trinomial square. If the end terms have the form a^2 and b^2, then the middle term must have the form $\pm 2ab$. After the students work Example 3, you may wish to reinforce their understanding of the pattern for a trinomial square by having them explain why certain trinomials are *not* trinomial squares. For example:

$x^2 + 7x + 49$ $4x^2 - 8x + 1$
Not a trinomial   Not a trinomial
square since   square since
$7x \neq 2(x)7$ $-8x \neq -2(2x)1$

In the exercises, the samples that precede Exercises 32–40, 41–44, 45–47, and 48–53 extend the students' abilities to factor.

ALTERNATE EXAMPLES

1. Factor: $x^2 + 8x + 16$ $(x + 4)^2$
2. Factor: $9x^2 - 12x + 4$ $(3x - 2)^2$

223

223

EXAMPLE 3   Find the middle term for each trinomial square. Then factor.

a. $x^2 + \underline{?} + 36$
      ↓   ↓
    $(x)^{\square}$ $(6)^{\square}$

middle term → $2(x)(6)$

$x^2 + 12x + 36 = (x + 6)^2$

b. $9y^2 - \underline{?} + k^2$
      ↓   ↓
   $(3y)^{\square}$ $(k)^{\square}$

$2(3y)(k)$ ← middle term

$9y^2 - 6yk + k^2 = (3y - k)^2$

CLASS EXERCISES

Expand.

1. $(x + 8)^2$
   $x^2 + 16x + 64$
2. $(x - 11)^2$
   $x^2 - 22x + 121$
3. $(2x - 3)^2$
   $4x^2 - 12x + 9$
4. $(3x + 5)^2$
   $9x^2 + 30x + 25$

Factor.

5. $y^2 - 6y + 9$ $(y - 3)^2$
6. $x^2 - 8x + 16$ $(x - 4)^2$
7. $n^2 + 12n + 36$ $(n + 6)^2$

Find the middle term for each trinomial square. Then factor.

8. $x^2 + \underline{?} + 25$
9. $n^2 + \underline{?} + 1$
10. $x^2 + \underline{?} + 4$
11. $n^2 - \underline{?} + 49$ 10x; $(x + 5)^2$
12. $y^2 + \underline{?} + 100$ 2n; $(n + 1)^2$
13. $y^2 - \underline{?} + 81$ 4x; $(x + 2)^2$

14n; $(n - 7)^2$ 20y; $(y + 10)^2$ 18y; $(y - 9)^2$

EXERCISES

A   Expand.

1. $(x + 6)^2$
   $x^2 + 12x + 36$
2. $(n + 12)^2$
   $n^2 + 24n + 144$
3. $(9x - 2)^2$
   $81x^2 - 36x + 4$
4. $(2x - 5)^2$
   $4x^2 - 20x + 25$

Factor.

5. $x^2 + 4x + 4$ $(x + 2)^2$
6. $h^2 + 14h + 49$ $(h + 7)^2$
7. $9x^2 - 6x + 1$ $(3x - 1)^2$

8. $25t^2 - 30t + 9$ $(5t - 3)^2$
9. $x^2 + 30x + 225$ $(x + 15)^2$
10. $y^2 - 20y + 100$ $(y - 10)^2$

11. $a^2 - 24a + 144$
12. $9h^2 - 24h + 16$
13. $49x^2 + 42x + 9$
14. $x^2 + 2xy + y^2$ $(a - 12)^2$
15. $4x^2 - 20xy + 25y^2$ $(3h - 4)^2$
16. $4y^2 - 28yt + 49t^2$ $(7x + 3)^2$
    $(x + y)^2$ $(2x - 5y)^2$ $(2y - 7t)^2$

Find the missing term for each trinomial square. Then factor.

17. $x^2 + \underline{?} + 81$
18. $n^2 - \underline{?} + 144$
19. $4y^2 + \underline{?} + 1$ 4y; $(2y + 1)^2$
    18x; $(x + 9)^2$ 24n; $(n - 12)^2$
20. $36y^2 - \underline{?} + 1$
21. $9x^2 + \underline{?} + 25$
22. $64n^2 - \underline{?} + 25t^2$
    12y; $(6y - 1)^2$ 30x; $(3x + 5)^2$ 80nt; $(8n - 5t)^2$

B   23. $x^2 - 10x + \underline{?}$
      24. $x^2 + 6xy + \underline{?}$
      25. $x^2 - 6x + \underline{?}$

26. $c^2 - 14cd + \underline{?}$
27. $9x^2 + 30xy + \underline{?}$
28. $25t^2 - 60tq + \underline{?}$

29. $\underline{?} + 42x + 9$
30. $\underline{?} + 24ab + 9b^2$
31. $81n^2 + 18nt + \underline{?}$

EXTRA PRACTICE, page 519

Factor completely.

Sample $4x^3 + 8x^2 + 4x = 4x(x^2 + 2x + 1) = 4x(x + 1)^2$

32. $x^3 - 6x^2 + 9x$ **33.** $h^3 + 10h^2 + 25h$ **34.** $a^3 - 2a^2 + a$

35. $18x^3 - 12x^2 + 2x$ **36.** $-36x^2 + 24x - 4$ **37.** $-9x^3 - 18x^2 - 9x$

38. $12a^3 + 36a^2b + 27ab^2$ **39.** $x^4y^6 - 22x^3y^4z + 121x^2y^2z^2$

40. If the area of a square is $4x^2 + 12x + 9$, how long is each side? $2x + 3$

C

Factor.

Sample $x^2 + 2x + 1 - y^2 = (x + 1)^2 - y^2 = (x + 1 + y)(x + 1 - y)$

41. $x^2 - 2x + 1 - a^2$ $(x - 1 + a)(x - 1 - a)$ **42.** $x^2 + 6x + 9 - y^2$ $(x + 3 + y)(x + 3 - y)$

43. $n^2 + 14n + 49 - x^2$
$(n + 7 + x)(n + 7 - x)$

44. $25x^2 - 36y^2 + 4 + 20x$
$(5x + 2 + 6y)(5x + 2 - 6y)$

Rewrite as the difference of two squares and factor.

Sample
$$x^2 - 16x - 57 = x^2 - 16x + 64 - 64 - 57$$
$$= (x - 8)^2 - 121$$
$$= (x - 8 + 11)(x - 8 - 11) = (x + 3)(x - 19)$$

45. $x^2 + 10x - 56$
$(x + 14)(x - 4)$

46. $x^2 - 16x + 63$
$(x - 9)(x - 7)$

47. $9x^2 + 6x - 8$
$(3x + 4)(3x - 2)$

Factor using rational numbers.

Sample $x^2 + \frac{2}{3}x + \frac{1}{9} = \left(x + \frac{1}{3}\right)^2$

48. $h^2 + \frac{2}{5}h + \frac{1}{25}$ $\left(h + \frac{1}{5}\right)^2$ **49.** $4x^2 - x + \frac{1}{16}$ $\left(2x - \frac{1}{4}\right)^2$ **50.** $x^2 + x + 0.25$ $(x + 0.5)^2$

51. $4x^2 - 2x + 0.25$
$(2x - 0.5)^2$
52. $x^2 + \frac{5}{3}x + \frac{25}{36}$ $\left(x + \frac{5}{6}\right)^2$ **53.** $9x^2 - 4x + \frac{4}{9}$ $\left(3x - \frac{2}{3}\right)^2$

Each square is separated into four regions. Find the areas of these regions in terms of *a* and *b* in order to demonstrate each formula.

***54.** $(a + b)^2 = a^2 + 2ab + b^2$

***55.** $(a - b)^2 = a^2 - 2ab + b^2$

Show that the form
$(a + b)^2 = a^2 + 2ab + b^2$ can be applied to enhance skill in mental computation. For example, show that to find 23^2 mentally, we can think:

$$(20 + 3)^2 = 20^2 + 2 \cdot 3 \cdot 20 + 3^2$$
$$= 400 + 120 + 9 = 529$$

In a similar manner, to find 59^2, we can think of 59 as $60 - 1$ and mentally compute $(60 - 1)^2$:

$$(60 - 1)^2 = 60^2 - 2 \cdot 60 + 1$$
$$= 3600 - 120 + 1 = 3481$$

Suggest that the students practice such shortcuts until they become proficient at their use.

ADDITIONAL ANSWERS
(continued)

26. $49d^2$; $(c - 7d)^2$
27. $25y^2$; $(3x + 5y)^2$
28. $36q^2$; $(5t - 6q)^2$
29. $49x^2$; $(7x + 3)^2$
30. $16a^2$; $(4a + 3b)^2$
31. t^2; $(9n + t)^2$
32. $x(x - 3)^2$ **33.** $h(h + 5)^2$
34. $a(a - 1)^2$ **35.** $2x(3x - 1)^2$
36. $-4(3x - 1)^2$ **37.** $-9x(x + 1)^2$
38. $3a(2a + 3b)^2$
39. $x^2y^2(xy^2 - 11z)^2$

54. $(a + b)^2$
  $= I + II + III + IV$
  $= b^2 + ab + a^2 + ab$
  $= a^2 + 2ab + b^2$
55. $(a - b)^2$
  $= I$
  $= (I + II + III + IV) - II - III - IV$
  $= a^2 - b(a - b) - b^2 - b(a - b)$
  $= a^2 - ab + b^2 - b^2 - ab + b^2$
  $= a^2 - 2ab + b^2$

Multiply.
1. $(x + 5)(x + 4)$ $x^2 + 9x + 20$
2. $(x - 5)(x - 4)$ $x^2 - 9x + 20$
3. $(x + 5)(x - 4)$ $x^2 + x - 20$
4. $(x - 5)(x + 4)$ $x^2 - x - 20$

LESSON NOTES

One of the key ideas in this lesson is stated in the paragraph preceding Example 1. To factor a trinomial of the form $x^2 + bx + c$, we try to find two numbers with a product of c and a sum or a difference of b. In the case of $x^2 + 9x + 18$ or $x^2 - 6x + 8$, the sign of the third term is positive, so the two factors of c must have the same sign, and their sum must equal b. In the case of $x^2 + 2x - 15$ (Example 4), the last term is negative, so the two factors must have different signs, and the difference between the two factors must equal b (disregarding signs).

As you discuss the model examples, stress the importance of checking the factoring by multiplying.

After you finish discussing the model examples, you may wish to show that a binomial such as $x^2 - 64$ may be thought of as $x^2 + 0x - 64$ and then factored by using the approach in this lesson.

ALTERNATE EXAMPLES

1. Factor: $x^2 + 11x + 30$.
   $(x + 5)(x + 6)$
2. Factor: $x^2 - 8x + 15$.
   $(x - 3)(x - 5)$

6-7   Factoring $x^2 + bx + c$

OBJECTIVE _____

To find binomial factors of $x^2 + bx + c$ when b and c are integers.

_____

The product of the binomials $(x + 2)$ and $(x + 3)$ is a trinomial.

$$(x + 2)(x + 3) = x^2 + 5x + 6$$

Therefore, if you start with the trinomial $x^2 + 5x + 6$, you should be able to find its binomial factors. Here is a useful hint about how to begin.

The last term is the product $2 \cdot 3$.
$$x^2 + 5x + 6 = (x + 2)(x + 3)$$
The coefficient of the middle term is the sum $2 + 3$.

Many, but not all, trinomials can be factored. To factor a trinomial of the form $x^2 + bx + c$, try to find two numbers with a product of c and a sum or difference of b.

Consider first a case where b and c are positive.

EXAMPLE 1   Factor $x^2 + 9x + 18$.

Step 1   Set up the factors in the form $x^2 + 9x + 18 = (x +\ \ )(x +\ \ )$.

Step 2   Find two integers whose product is 18 and whose sum is 9.

Factors of 18	Product	Sum	Both conditions satisfied
1 and 18	$1 \times 18 = 18$	$1 + 18 = 19$	No
2 and 9	$2 \times 9 = 18$	$2 + 9 = 11$	No
3 and 6	$3 \times 6 = 18$	$3 + 6 = 9$	Yes

Step 3   Use 3 and 6 to complete the factors.
$x^2 + 9x + 18 = (x + 3)(x + 6)$

Step 4   Multiply to check: $(x + 3)(x + 6) = x^2 + 3x + 6x + 18 = x^2 + 9x + 18$

In the next example the coefficient of the second term is negative.

EXAMPLE 2   Factor $x^2 - 6x + 8$.

Step 1   Set up the factors in the form $x^2 - 6x + 8 = (x -\ \ )(x -\ \ )$.

Step 2   Find two factors of 8 with a sum of 6.
The numbers are 2 and 4 since $(2)(4) = 8$ and $2 + 4 = 6$.

Step 3   Complete the factoring: $x^2 - 6x + 8 = (x - 2)(x - 4)$

Step 4   Multiply to check: $(x - 2)(x - 4) = x^2 - 4x - 2x + 8 = x^2 - 6x + 8$

EXAMPLE 3   Factor each trinomial.

a. $x^2 + 7x + 10 = (x + 5)(x + 2)$ b. $x^2 - 7x + 10 = (x - 5)(x - 2)$

Finally, consider a trinomial in which the third term is negative.

EXAMPLE 4   Factor $x^2 + 2x - 15$.

Step 1   The last term is negative, so the signs in the factors are opposite. Set up the factors in the form $x^2 + 2x - 15 = (x + \ )(x - \ )$.

Step 2   Find two factors of 15 with a *difference* of 2, without regard to sign. The numbers are 5 and 3: $(5)(3) = 15$; $5 - 3 = 2$

Step 3   Test 5 and 3 in the factors to obtain the correct middle term.

$(x + 3)(x - 5) = x^2 - 2x - 15$ Incorrect middle term
$(x + 5)(x - 3) = x^2 + 2x - 15$ Correct middle term

Therefore $x^2 + 2x - 15 = (x + 5)(x - 3)$.

CLASS EXERCISES

*Write the values of **p** and **q**, given their product and their sum or difference.*

1. $pq = 7$, $p + q = 8$ 1; 7   **2.** $pq = 12$, $p + q = 7$ 3; 4   **3.** $pq = 40$, $p + q = 13$ 5; 8

4. $pq = 3$, $p - q = 2$ 3; 1   **5.** $pq = 6$, $p - q = 5$ 6; 1   **6.** $pq = 6$, $p - q = 1$ 3; 2

Factor.

7. $x^2 + 3x + 2$ **8.** $a^2 + 7a + 6$ **9.** $x^2 - 4x + 3$ $(x - 1)(x - 3)$
   $(x + 1)(x + 2)$ $(a + 1)(a + 6)$
10. $a^2 - 8a + 7$ **11.** $x^2 + x - 12$ **12.** $x^2 - 4x - 12$
   $(a - 1)(a - 7)$ $(x - 3)(x + 4)$ $(x + 2)(x - 6)$

EXERCISES

A   *Find values for **r** and **s**, given their product and their sum or difference.*

1. $rs = 8$, $r + s = 6$ 2; 4   **2.** $rs = 8$, $r + s = 9$ 1; 8   **3.** $rs = 24$, $r - s = 10$ 12; 2

4. $rs = 24$, $r - s = 5$ 8; 3   **5.** $rs = 42$, $r - s = 1$ 7; 6   **6.** $rs = 36$, $r + s = 13$ 9; 4

Factor. Check by multiplying.

7. $x^2 + 6x + 8$ **8.** $x^2 + 12x + 27$ **9.** $x^2 + 10x + 9$ $(x + 1)(x + 9)$
   $(x + 2)(x + 4)$ $(x + 3)(x + 9)$
10. $x^2 + 2x + 1$ **11.** $x^2 - 10x + 9$ **12.** $x^2 - 8x + 16$ $(x - 4)(x - 4)$
   $(x + 1)(x + 1)$ $(x - 1)(x - 9)$
13. $x^2 - 23x + 102$ **14.** $x^2 - 9x + 14$ **15.** $x^2 + 4x - 45$ $(x - 5)(x + 9)$
   $(x - 6)(x - 17)$ $(x - 2)(x - 7)$

FACTORING   **227**

EXTRA PRACTICE, page 519

227

16. $x^2 - 10x - 39$
$(x + 3)(x - 13)$

17. $x^2 - 18x - 19$
$(x + 1)(x - 19)$

18. $x^2 - 15x - 16$
$(x + 1)(x - 16)$

19. $y^2 - 24y + 95$
$(y - 5)(y - 19)$

20. $a^2 + 26a + 133$
$(a + 7)(a + 19)$

21. $w^2 + 51w + 144$
$(w + 3)(w + 48)$

22. $y^2 + 17y + 16$
$(y + 1)(y + 16)$

23. $r^2 + 15r + 26$
$(r + 2)(r + 13)$

24. $a^2 - 16a + 28$
$(a - 2)(a - 14)$

25. $t^2 - 44t + 43$
$(t - 1)(t - 43)$

26. $a^2 + 29a - 62$
$(a - 2)(a + 31)$

27. $b^2 + 11b + 18$
$(b + 2)(b + 9)$

28. $c^2 - 3c + 2$
$(c - 1)(c - 2)$

29. $h^2 - 6h + 9$
$(h - 3)(h - 3)$

30. $k^2 - 10k + 25$
$(k - 5)(k - 5)$

B

31. The area of a rectangle is $x^2 - 3x - 28$. If the length is $x + 4$, find the width. $(x - 7)$

32. An auditorium has a total of $n^2 + 12n + 32$ seats. There are $n + 4$ rows, all with the same number of seats. How many seats are in each row? $n + 8$

Factor. Check by multiplying.

Sample $x^2 + 3xy + 2y^2 = (x + 2y)(x + y)$

33. $x^2 + xy - 2y^2$

34. $x^2 - xy - 2y^2$

35. $a^2 + 5ab + 6b^2$

36. $a^2 + ab - 6b^2$

37. $a^2 - ab - 6b^2$

38. $a^2 - 5ab + 6b^2$

39. $x^2 - 3nx - 4n^2$

40. $x^2 + 3nx - 4n^2$

41. $y^2 - 11by + 24b^2$

C

Factor completely.

Sample $x^3 - 8x^2 + 15x = x(x^2 - 8x + 15) = x(x - 5)(x - 3)$

42. $x^3 + 8x^2 + 15x$
$x(x + 3)(x + 5)$

43. $x^3 - 18x^2 + 17x$
$x(x - 1)(x - 17)$

44. $-x^3 + 4x^2 - 3x$
$-x(x - 1)(x - 3)$

45. $3a^2 - 33a + 54$
$3(a - 2)(a - 9)$

46. $-2x^2 - 4x + 70$
$-2(x - 5)(x + 7)$

47. $28x^3 - 35x^2 + 7x^4$
$7x^2(x - 1)(x + 5)$

CHALLENGE

Special Squares

Here is a shortcut for **squaring a number when the units digit is 5.**

$15^2 = 225$	$(1 \times 2 = 2)$	$45^2 = 2025$	$(4 \times 5 = 20)$
$25^2 = 625$	$(2 \times 3 = 6)$	$55^2 = 3025$	$(5 \times 6 = 30)$
$35^2 = 1225$	$(3 \times 4 = 12)$	$65^2 = 4225$	$(6 \times 7 = 42)$

Do you see the pattern? Multiply the tens digit by its successor—the next greater integer. The number will end with 25.

Now use the pattern to find 75^2, 85^2, 95^2. Then check by computation. You can use algebra to see why this shortcut works. $75^2 = 5625$; $85^2 = 7225$; $95^2 = 9025$

Let $10n + 5$ represent the number you are squaring.

Show that $(10n + 5)^2$ is equal to $n(n + 1)100 + 25$.

Test this result by substituting different values for n. Let $n = 7, 8, 9$.

CHAPTER 6

6-8 Factoring $ax^2 + bx + c$

OBJECTIVE

To factor trinomials of the form $ax^2 + bx + c$.

So far you have factored trinomials of the form $ax^2 + bx + c$, where $a = 1$. When $a > 1$, you may need to try several combinations of binomial factors before you find the correct pair. With practice, you will be able to shorten the process.

EXAMPLE 1   Factor $6x^2 + 13x + 5$.

The product of the first terms must be $6x^2$.

The product of the last terms must be 5.

$$(\ \ +\ \ )(\ \ +\ \ )$$

$$(\ \ +\ \ )(\ \ +\ \ )$$

There are two possibilities.

$(6x +\ \ )(x +\ \ )$
or $(3x +\ \ )(2x +\ \ )$

The only factors of 5 are 1 and 5.

$(\ \ + 1)(\ \ + 5)$
or $(\ \ + 5)(\ \ + 1)$

Try the four combinations. Check to see if the middle term is 13x.

$(6x + 1)(x + 5) = 6x^2 + 31x + 5$
$(6x + 5)(x + 1) = 6x^2 + 11x + 5$
$(3x + 1)(2x + 5) = 6x^2 + 17x + 5$
$(3x + 5)(2x + 1) = 6x^2 + 13x + 5$ Correct middle term

Therefore, $6x^2 + 13x + 5 = (3x + 5)(2x + 1)$.

EXAMPLE 2   Factor $2x^2 - 15x + 25$.

$(2x -\ \ )(x -\ \ )$ Start with this form. Insert two minus signs since the middle term is negative and the constant, 25, is positive.

The pairs of factors of 25 are 1 and 25 or 5 and 5. Try all combinations.

$(2x - 1)(x - 25) = 2x^2 - 51x + 25$
$(2x - 25)(x - 1) = 2x^2 - 27x + 25$
$(2x - 5)(x - 5) = 2x^2 - 15x + 25$ Correct middle term

Therefore, $2x^2 - 15x + 25 = (2x - 5)(x - 5)$.

FACTORING

229

When the third term of a trinomial is negative, there may be many combinations of factors to consider. To shorten the number of trials, we list forms for the factors without the signs. Then we determine the *difference of outer and inner products* without regard to sign.

EXAMPLE 3 Factor $4x^2 - 5x - 6$.

The pairs of factors of $4x^2$: $4x$ and x; $2x$ and $2x$
The pairs of factors of 6:   6 and 1; 3 and 2

Forms for Binomial Factors	Outer Product	Inner Product	Difference
$(2x \quad 1)(2x \quad 6)$	$12x$	$2x$	$10x$
$(2x \quad 3)(2x \quad 2)$	$4x$	$6x$	$2x$
$(4x \quad 1)(x \quad 6)$	$24x$	x	$23x$
$(4x \quad 6)(x \quad 1)$	$4x$	$6x$	$2x$
$(4x \quad 2)(x \quad 3)$	$12x$	$2x$	$10x$
$(4x \quad 3)(x \quad 2)$	$8x$	$3x$	$5x$

Since the difference in the last case is 5x, insert signs in the factors so that the middle term is $-5x$.

$(4x - 3)(x + 2) = 4x^2 + 5x - 6$ Incorrect middle term, $5x$
$(4x + 3)(x - 2) = 4x^2 - 5x - 6$ Correct middle term, $-5x$

Therefore $4x^2 - 5x - 6 = (4x + 3)(x - 2)$.

Many trinomials cannot be factored. If you check all combinations and do not get the correct middle term, then the trinomial is not factorable. For example, try to factor $2x^2 + 3x + 5$. There are only two possible combinations.

$$(2x + 1)(x + 5) = 2x^2 + 11x + 5$$
$$(2x + 5)(x + 1) = 2x^2 + 7x + 5$$

Neither middle term is 3x, so $2x^2 + 3x + 5$ is not factorable over the integers.

CLASS EXERCISES

Factor and check.

1. $2x^2 + 7x + 3$
  $(2x + 1)(x + 3)$
2. $6x^2 + 17x + 5$
  $(3x + 1)(2x + 5)$
3. $3x^2 - 7x + 2$
  $(3x - 1)(x - 2)$
4. $6x^2 - 13x + 5$
  $(3x - 5)(2x - 1)$
5. $2x^2 - 5x - 3$
  $(2x + 1)(x - 3)$
6. $2x^2 + x - 3$
  $(2x + 3)(x - 1)$

EXERCISES

A

Complete.

1. $2x^2 + 9x + 7 = (\underline{?} + 7)(\underline{?} + 1)$ $2x, x$ 2. $7x^2 - 23x + 6 = (\underline{?} - 2)(\underline{?} - 3)$ $7x, x$

3. $5x^2 - 14x - 3 = (\underline{?} + 1)(\underline{?} - 3)$ $5x, x$ 4. $4x^2 - 5x - 6 = (4x + \underline{?})(x - \underline{?})$ $3, 2$

5. $2x^2 + x - 28 = (\underline{?} - 7)(\underline{?} + 4)$ $2x, x$ 6. $9x^2 - 15x + 4 = (\underline{?} - 1)(\underline{?} - 4)$ $3x, 3x$

7. $10x^2 + 21x + 9 = (2x + \underline{?})(5x + \underline{?})$ $3, 3$

Factor and check.

8. $2x^2 + 5x + 3$
$(2x + 3)(x + 1)$

9. $3x^2 + 8x + 4$
$(3x + 2)(x + 2)$

10. $3x^2 + 13x + 4$
$(3x + 1)(x + 4)$

11. $3x^2 - 5x + 2$
$(3x - 2)(x - 1)$

12. $5x^2 - 23x + 12$
$(5x - 3)(x - 4)$

13. $5x^2 - 7x - 12$
$(5x - 12)(x + 1)$

14. $6x^2 + 5x - 1$
$(6x - 1)(x + 1)$

15. $5x^2 + 19x + 12$
$(5x + 4)(x + 3)$

16. $5x^2 + 32x + 12$
$(5x + 2)(x + 6)$

17. $3x^2 - 5x - 2$
$(3x + 1)(x - 2)$

18. $5x^2 + 13x - 6$
$(5x - 2)(x + 3)$

19. $6x^2 - 7x - 5$
$(2x + 1)(3x - 5)$

B

20. $10x^2 + x - 9$
$(10x - 9)(x + 1)$

21. $6x^2 + 19x + 10$
$(3x + 2)(2x + 5)$

22. $6x^2 + 17x + 10$
$(6x + 5)(x + 2)$

23. $16x^2 + 24x + 9$
$(4x + 3)(4x + 3)$

24. $8x^2 - 22x + 9$
$(2x - 1)(4x - 9)$

25. $8x^2 - 27x + 9$
$(x - 3)(8x - 3)$

26. $20x^2 - 23x + 6$
$(4x - 3)(5x - 2)$

27. $6x^2 - 23x + 10$
$(3x - 10)(2x - 1)$

28. $12x^2 - 40x + 25$
$(2x - 5)(6x - 5)$

29. $6x^2 - 5x - 6$
$(3x + 2)(2x - 3)$

30. $9x^2 + 9x - 10$
$(3x - 2)(3x + 5)$

31. $21x^2 - 17x - 8$
$(7x - 8)(3x + 1)$

*Factor, if it is possible. Otherwise write **not factorable**.*

32. $15x^2 + 8x - 12$
$(5x + 6)(3x - 2)$

33. $4x^2 + 7x + 3$
$(x + 1)(4x + 3)$

34. $26x^2 + 5x - 9$
$(13x + 9)(2x - 1)$

35. $28x^2 + 9x - 4$
$(7x + 4)(4x - 1)$

36. $6x^2 - 9x - 10$
Not factorable

37. $8x^2 + 36x - 21$
Not factorable

38. $25x^2 - 25x - 24$
$(5x + 3)(5x - 8)$

39. $6x^2 + 21x - 4$
Not factorable

40. $15x^2 - 2x - 24$
$(5x + 6)(3x - 4)$

C

Factor completely.

Sample $12x^3 + 10x^2 - 12x = 2x(6x^2 + 5x - 6) = 2x(2x + 3)(3x - 2)$

41. $6x^2 + 16x + 10$ 42. $24x^3 - 6x^2 - 3x$ 43. $9x^3 + 18x^2 + 9x$

44. $-7x^2 + 31x + 20$ 45. $28x^2y + 2xy - 8y$ 46. $8x^3 + 11x^2 - 10x$

47. $12x^3 + 6x^2 - 18x$ 48. $-8x^2 + 27xy - 9y^2$ 49. $14x^2 - 8y^2 - 6xy$

50. $18x^3y - 9x^2y^2 - 9xy^3$ 51. $16x^2y^3 + 25x^4y + 40x^3y^2$

52. Find the greatest common factor of $10a^2 - 35ab + 15b^2$ and $5a^2 - 30ab + 45b^2$ $5(a - 3b)$

53. A plane flies at a cruising speed of $(4n + 1)$ miles per hour. At this rate, how long will it take to fly $(12n^2 - 17n - 5)$ miles? $(3n - 5)$ hours

54. If $(x - 5)$ tapes cost $(x^2 - 3x - 10)$ dollars, what will $5x$ tapes cost? $[5x(x + 2)]$ or $(5x^2 + 10x)$ dollars

FACTORING   **231**

Extra Topic

In this consideration of factoring $ax^2 + bx + c$, we have limited the work to cases in which $a > 0$. If $a < 0$, we could begin by factoring -1 from the polynomial; then the discussion would apply to the new polynomial (the opposite of the given polynomial).

Factoring $ax^2 + bx + c$: An Alternate Method

The following method of factoring trinomials eliminates some of the guesswork. First consider the product of $(a + b)$ and $(c + d)$.

$$(a + b)(c + d) = ac + ad + bc + bd$$

$(ad)(bc) = abcd$

$(ac)(bd) = abcd$

Notice that the two inner terms have the same product as the two outer terms. The same pattern can be found in the following special case.

$$(2x - 5)(3x + 4) = 6x^2 + 8x - 15x - 20 = 6x^2 - 7x - 20$$

$(8x)(-15x) = -120x^2$

$(6x^2)(-20) = -120x^2$

The alternative method of factoring $ax^2 + bx + c$ reverses the steps above.

To factor a trinomial such as $8x^2 + 10x + 3$, first notice that the product of the outer terms is $(8x^2)(3) = 24x^2$. We then separate the $10x$ into the sum of two terms whose product is $24x^2$. Two such terms are $6x$ and $4x$.

$$8x^2 + 10x + 3 = 8x^2 + 6x + 4x + 3$$
$$= 2x(4x + 3) + 1(4x + 3)$$
$$= (2x + 1)(4x + 3)$$

We can now factor in two steps by grouping pairs of terms.

In the following example, we again "split" the middle term and then factor by grouping.

Example   Factor $6n^2 + 5n - 6$ by the alternate method.

Since $(6n^2)(-6) = -36n^2$, we look for two terms that have a product of $-36n^2$ and a sum of $5n$. By testing combinations of factors of $-36n^2$, we find the required ones are $9n$ and $-4n$.

$$6n^2 + 5n - 6 = 6n^2 + 9n - 4n - 6$$
$$= 3n(2n + 3) - 2(2n + 3)$$
$$= (3n - 2)(2n + 3)$$

Note that the signs of the two terms formed from the "split" middle term are the same or opposite, depending on whether the sign of the last term is plus or minus.

Use this method to factor the following polynomials.

1. $x^2 + 10x + 21$
$(x + 7)(x + 3)$

2. $x^2 - 11x + 18$
$(x - 9)(x - 2)$

3. $18x^2 + 9x + 1$
$(6x + 1)(3x + 1)$

4. $6x^2 - 23x + 20$
$(3x - 4)(2x - 5)$

5. $10x^2 - 11x - 6$
$(5x + 2)(2x - 3)$

6. $12x^2 + 29x - 8$
$(4x - 1)(3x + 8)$

CHAPTER 6

C

Sample $4x^2 + 28x + 49 - 9y^2 = (4x^2 + 28x + 49) - 9y^2$
$$= (2x + 7)^2 - (3y)^2$$
$$= (2x + 7 + 3y)(2x + 7 - 3y)$$

49. $9a^2 - 6ab + b^2 - 256$
   $(3a - b + 16)(3a - b - 16)$
50. $81y^2 - 16x^2 + 24x - 9$
   $(9y + 4x - 3)(9y - 4x + 3)$
51. $x^2 + 6xy + 9y^2 - 9a^2 - 6ab - b^2$
   $(x + 3y + 3a + b)(x + 3y - 3a - b)$
52. $5(t + r)^2 - 5(2t - r)^2$
   $-15t(t - 2r)$
53. $2a^2 + 4ab + 2b^2 - 2c^2 + 4cd - 2d^2$
   $2(a + b + c - d)(a + b - c + d)$
54. $(x^4 - 1)^2 - (x^2 - 1)^2$
   $x^2(x^2 + 2)(x + 1)^2(x - 1)^2$

Factor as a trinomial.

Sample Factor $(x + 1)^2 + 3(x + 1) + 2$.

Let $a = x + 1$ and factor $a^2 + 3a + 2$.

$$a^2 + 3a + 2 = (a + 2)(a + 1)$$

Then replace a by $x + 1$.

$$(x + 1)^2 + 3(x + 1) + 2 = (x + 1 + 2)(x + 1 + 1)$$
$$= (x + 3)(x + 2)$$

55. $(x + 3)^2 - 7(x + 3) + 10$
   $(x + 1)(x - 2)$
56. $(x - 2)^2 + 16(x - 2) + 63$
   $(x + 7)(x + 5)$
57. $3(2x + 5)^2 + 5(2x + 5) - 2$
   $2(3x + 7)(2x + 7)$
58. $16(x - 1)^2 + 8(x - 1) + 1$
   $(4x - 3)^2$

CHECKPOINT

Simplify each expression. Assume that no denominator is 0.

1. $\dfrac{-36xy^2z^3}{-4xy^2}$ $9z^3$
2. $\dfrac{7x^3y^2z^5}{4xy^2z^5}$ $\frac{7x^2}{4}$
3. $\dfrac{-14xy^2z^3}{7xyz^2}$ $-2yz$
4. $\dfrac{6x^2y^3z^3}{42xy^3}$ $\frac{xz^3}{7}$

5. $\dfrac{12x^5y^2z^4w^3}{3x^2y^2z^2w^2}$ $4x^3z^2w$
6. $\dfrac{-30x^4y^2z^3}{-15x^3y^2z^2}$ $2xz$
7. $\dfrac{-33x^3y^5}{11xy^4}$ $-3x^2y$
8. $\dfrac{-24x^3y^2z^2}{8x^2yz}$ $-3xyz$

Factor completely.

9. $6x^2 + 3x$
   $3x(2x + 1)$
10. $x^6 + x^4$
   $x^4(x^2 + 1)$
11. $48x^3 - 18x^2$
   $6x^2(8x - 3)$
12. $4x^2 - 8x$
   $4x(x - 2)$
13. $x^2 + 2xy + 2x + 4y$
   $(x + 2)(x + 2y)$
14. $x^2 - abx - acx + a^2bc$
   $(x - ac)(x - ab)$
15. $25x^2 - y^2$
   $(5x - y)(5x + y)$
16. $36 - 16x^2$
   $4(3 - 2x)(3 + 2x)$
17. $x^3 - 16x$
   $x(x - 4)(x + 4)$
18. $4x^2 - 100$
   $4(x - 5)(x + 5)$
19. $16x^4 - 81$
   $(4x^2 + 9)(2x - 3)(2x + 3)$
20. $625x^4 - y^4$
   $(5x - y)(5x + y)(25x^2 + y^2)$
21. $x^2 + 16x + 64$
   $(x + 8)^2$
22. $16x^2 - 24x + 9$
   $(4x - 3)^2$
23. $8x^3 - 24x^2 + 18x$
   $2x(2x - 3)^2$
24. $x^2 - 4x - 21$
   $(x - 7)(x + 3)$
25. $x^2 + 5x - 24$
   $(x + 8)(x - 3)$
26. $3x^2 - 5x + 2$
   $(3x - 2)(x - 1)$
27. $9x^2 + 27x + 8$
   $(3x + 1)(3x + 8)$

FACTORING

235

ENRICHMENT ACTIVITY

Let the students find these products:

$(a - b)(a^2 + ab + b^2)$ $a^3 - b^3$
$(a + b)(a^2 - ab + b^2)$ $a^3 + b^3$

Then ask them to show the factors of the following:

$x^3 - y^3$ $(x - y)(x^2 + xy + y^2)$
$x^3 + y^3$ $(x + y)(x^2 - xy + y^2)$
$8x^3 - 343$ $(2x - 7)(4x^2 + 14x + 49)$
$125n^3 + 27$ $(5n + 3)(25n^2 - 15n + 9)$

Checkpoint

Students may check their answers with those given in the back of their books.

ADDITIONAL ANSWERS
(continued)

9. $5(5n + 11)(5n - 11)$
10. $(x^2 + 4)(x + 2)(x - 2)$
11. $2ab(a^2 + b^2)(a + b)(a - b)$
12. $a^2(1 + 9b)(1 - 9b)$

26. $-(y - 4)(y - 1)$
27. $2(3x + 4)^2$
28. $(9 - 2x)^2$
29. $-1(5x - y)^2$
30. $3x(x + 2)(x - 6)$
31. $-2(x + 17)(x - 5)$
32. $2y(2x + 3)(x + 9)$
33. $x^2(3x + 5)(x + 11)$
34. $2(5y - 2x)(y - 3x)$
35. $5x(2x - 3)^2$
36. $(x + 1)^2(x - 1)^2$
37. $(x + 1)(x + 2)$

44. $(n + t + 3)(n - t + 5)$
45. $(4 + x - y)(4 - x + y)$
46. $4xy$
47. $(2x + y + 2)(2x - y)$
48. $4(5x - 9y)(-3x + 7y)$

Solve for x.
1. $3 \cdot x = 0$ 0   2. $x \cdot 7 = 0$ 0
3. $5(x - 1) = 0$ 1
4. $-6(x - 5) = 0$ 5

LESSON NOTES

The zero-product rule has two parts:
(1) If $ab = 0$, then $a = 0$ or $b = 0$.
(2) If $a = 0$ or $b = 0$, then $ab = 0$.

At more advanced levels of mathematics, the two parts are often combined in a *biconditional*: $ab = 0$ if and only if $a = 0$ or $b = 0$. For students in a beginning course in algebra, the zero-product rule is clearer when given in two separate if-then statements.

POSSIBLE ERROR

Students sometimes mistakenly apply the zero-product rule to situations in which the product is not 0. For example, in Exercise 62 they may incorrectly state:

If $(x + 4)(x - 4) = 9$,
   then $x + 4 = 9$ or $x - 4 = 9$.
                  (incorrect)

Emphasize that only if a product is 0 do we know that at least one of the factors must be 0. Point out that if $a \cdot b = 9$, then it is not true that a or b must be 9. (Both a and b may be 3; a may be 18 and b may be $\frac{1}{2}$; and so on.)

ALTERNATE EXAMPLE

1. Solve $x^2 + 7x = 0$ and check.
   0 and -7

6-10 Solving Equations by Factoring

OBJECTIVE

To solve equations by using the zero-product rule.

The second degree equation $x^2 - 5x + 6 = 0$ may be written in factored form.

$$(x - 2)(x - 3) = 0$$

If $x = 2$, one factor is 0.
If $x = 3$, the other factor is 0.

Therefore if $x = 2$ or $x = 3$, the product $(x - 2)(x - 3)$ equals 0, and the equation $(x - 2)(x - 3) = 0$ has solutions 2 and 3. Check that 2 and 3 are both solutions of the given equation $x^2 - 5x + 6 = 0$.

In solving this equation we have used the *zero-product* rule. You know that a product is equal to 0 if any factor equals 0. The reverse statement is also true. If a product equals 0, then at least one factor must be 0. These statements are combined in the following rule.

$$(6)(0) = 0$$
$$(0)(-3) = 0$$
$$(0)(0) = 0$$

Zero Product Rule

If $ab = 0$, then $a = 0$ or $b = 0$.
If $a = 0$ or $b = 0$, then $ab = 0$.

The zero-product rule can be used to solve an equation when one side is 0 and the other side is in factored form.

EXAMPLE 1   Solve the equation $x^2 + 3x = 0$ and check.

$x^2 + 3x = 0$	Factor the left side.
$x(x + 3) = 0$	Use the zero-product rule.
	Let each factor equal 0.

$$x = 0 \text{ or } x + 3 = 0$$
$$x = 0 \qquad\quad x = -3$$

Check   For $x = 0$: $x^2 + 3x = 0$ For $x = -3$: $x^2 + 3x = 0$

$$0^2 + 3(0) \stackrel{?}{=} 0 \qquad\qquad (-3)^2 + 3(-3) \stackrel{?}{=} 0$$
$$0 = 0 \;\checkmark \qquad\qquad\qquad\qquad 9 - 9 \stackrel{?}{=} 0$$
$$0 = 0 \;\checkmark$$

Therefore 0 and -3 are the solutions.

236

EXAMPLE 2

Solve each equation.

a. $x^2 - 25 = 0$

$(x + 5)(x - 5) = 0$

$x + 5 = 0$ or $x - 5 = 0$

$x = -5$ $x = 5$

b. $x^3 - 3x^2 - 28x = 0$

$x(x^2 - 3x - 28) = 0$

$x(x + 4)(x - 7) = 0$

$x = 0$ or $x + 4 = 0$ or $x - 7 = 0$

$x = 0$ $x = -4$ $x = 7$

Check   Are -5 and 5 solutions?   Are 0, -4, and 7 solutions?

EXAMPLE 3

Solve for x: $2x^2 - 4 = -7x$

$2x^2 - 4 = -7x$ Add $7x$ to each side to get 0 on one side.

$2x^2 + 7x - 4 = 0$ Factor.

$(2x - 1)(x + 4) = 0$ Now use the zero product rule.

$2x - 1 = 0$ or $x + 4 = 0$

$2x = 1$ $x = -4$

$x = \dfrac{1}{2}$

Check   Are the solutions $\dfrac{1}{2}$ and -4?

EXAMPLE 4

Solve for x: $x^2 + 10x + 25 = 0$

$x^2 + 10x + 25 = 0$

$(x + 5)(x + 5) = 0$ The two factors are the same.

$x + 5 = 0$

$x = -5$ There is only one possible solution.

Check $(-5)^2 + 10(-5) + 25 \stackrel{?}{=} 0$

$25 - 50 + 25 \stackrel{?}{=} 0$

$0 = 0$ ✔

The solution is -5. This is sometimes called a *double root*.

CLASS EXERCISES

Find the solutions of each equation.

1. $(x + 5)(x + 3) = 0$ $-3; -5$ **2.** $(x + 1)(x - 4) = 0$ $-1; 4$

3. $x(x - 7) = 0$ $7; 0$ **4.** $2x(x + 2) = 0$ $-2; 0$ **5.** $x(3x - 1) = 0$ $\frac{1}{3}; 0$

Solve by factoring and check.

6. $x^2 - 8x = 0$ $8; 0$ **7.** $2x^2 + 6x = 0$ $-3; 0$ **8.** $x^2 + 6x + 8 = 0$ $-4; -2$

9. $x^2 - 4x + 3 = 0$ $1; 3$ **10.** $x^2 + x - 6 = 0$ $2; -3$ **11.** $x^2 - 25 = 0$ $5; -5$

12. $x^2 - 100 = 0$ $10; -10$ **13.** $x^2 - 3x = 10$ $5; -2$ **14.** $x^2 + 1 = 2x$ 1

A *Find the solutions of each equation.*

1. $(x - 3)(x - 7) = 0$ 3; 7   **2.** $(x + 2)(x + 6) = 0$ −2; −6

3. $(x - 4)(x - 4) = 0$ 4   **4.** $x(x - 10)(x + 10) = 0$ 0; 10; −10

5. $x(x - 4) = 0$ 4; 0   **6.** $x(2x - 1) = 0$ 0; $\frac{1}{2}$ **7.** $(x - 7)x = 0$ 7; 0

8. $(x - 1)^2 = 0$ 1   **9.** $3x(2x + 3) = 0$ 0; $-\frac{3}{2}$ **10.** $2x(x + 7) = 0$ −7; 0

*Solve by factoring, and check. Be sure that one side of the equation is 0
before you factor.*

11. $x^2 - 9x = 0$ 9; 0   **12.** $x^2 + 12x = 0$ −12; 0   **13.** $x^2 - 4x = 0$ 4; 0

14. $x^2 + 6x = 0$ −6; 0   **15.** $2x^2 - 6x = 0$ 3; 0   **16.** $x^2 - 81x = 0$ 81; 0

17. $x^2 + 3x - 4 = 0$ 1; −4   **18.** $2x^2 - 128 = 0$ 8; −8   **19.** $x^2 - 3x - 10 = 0$ 5; −2

20. $x^2 - 9x + 14 = 0$ 2; 7   **21.** $x^2 - 6x - 27 = 0$ 9; −3   **22.** $x^2 + 11x + 10 = 0$ −1; −10

23. $x^2 = 7x$ 7; 0   **24.** $x^2 = -9x$ −9; 0   **25.** $x^2 - 2x = 3$ 3; −1

26. $5x^2 = -30x$ −6; 0   **27.** $y^2 + 8 = 6y$ 2; 4   **28.** $x^2 + 15 = -8x$ −3; −5

29. $5x^2 = 30x$ 6; 0   **30.** $2n^2 - 5n = 3$ 3; $-\frac{1}{2}$ **31.** $x^2 - 5x = 36$ 9; −4

32. $x^2 - 20 = 8x$ 10; −2   **33.** $3x^2 = 3$ 1; −1   **34.** $3n^2 - 9n = 0$ 3; 0

35. $x^2 - 16 = 0$ 4; −4   **36.** $3x^2 + 5x = 2$ $\frac{1}{3}$; −2   **37.** $x^2 + 6x + 9 = 0$ −3

38. $x^2 - 8x + 16 = 0$ 4   **39.** $x^2 + 2x = -1$ −1   **40.** $x^2 = 24 - 10x$ 2; −12

41. $x^2 = 10x + 11$ 11; −1   **42.** $3n^2 + 4 = 13n$ $\frac{1}{3}$; 4   **43.** $2x^2 - 7x + 3 = 0$ 3; $\frac{1}{2}$

B **44.** $2p^2 + 2p - 84 = 0$ **45.** $n^3 + 2n^2 + n = 0$ −1; 0 **46.** $x^3 - 4x^2 + 4x = 0$ 2; 0
                 6; −7
47. $x^3 - 36x = 0$ 6; −6; 0   **48.** $2x^2 - 32x = 0$ 16; 0   **49.** $x^3 + 3x^2 + 2x = 0$
                                                                         −2; −1; 0
50. $x^3 - 5x^2 + 6x = 0$ **51.** $a^3 + 9a = 6a^2$ 3; 0 **52.** $4x^3 = 4x^2 - x$ $\frac{1}{2}$; 0
            2; 3; 0
53. $3x^3 = 90x - 3x^2$ **54.** $12b^2 = 2b + 2$ $\frac{1}{2}$; $-\frac{1}{3}$ **55.** $2y^2 - 1 = y^2 + 3$ 2; −2
            5; −6; 0
56. $x^3 + 2x^2 - 35x = 0$ 5; −7; 0   **57.** $2x + 15 = 5 - x + x^2$ 5; −2

58. The product of two consecutive whole numbers is 56. Let x = the
lesser number. Then write and solve an equation to find the numbers.   7 and 8

59. The product of two consecutive integers is 132. Find two pairs of
numbers that satisfy this condition.   11, 12 or −11, −12

60. The length of a rectangle is 5 cm more than the width.
The area is 84 cm². Find the width.   7 cm

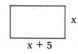

CHAPTER 6

EXTRA PRACTICE, page 520

61. A square 3-by-3 cm is removed from the corner of a larger square. The area that remains in the larger square is 55 cm². Find the dimensions of the larger square. **8 by 8 cm**

Solve for **x**.

Samples	$(x - 3)(x + 2) = 6$	$x^3 + 3x^2 - 4x - 12 = 0$
	$x^2 - x - 6 = 6$	$x^2(x + 3) - 4(x + 3) = 0$
	$x^2 - x - 12 = 0$	$(x^2 - 4)(x + 3) = 0$
	$(x - 4)(x + 3) = 0$	$(x + 2)(x - 2)(x + 3) = 0$
	$x = 4$ or $x = -3$	$x = -2$ or $x = 2$ or $x = -3$

62. $(x + 4)(x - 4) = 9$ **5; −5**

63. $(x + 4)(x - 2) = -9$ **−1**

64. $(x - 5)(x - 4) = 12$ **8; 1**

65. $x(x - 8) = 20$ **10; −2**

66. $2x(6x - 1) - 2 = 0$ $-\frac{1}{3}, \frac{1}{2}$

67. $2x(x + 1) = 84$ **−7, 6**

68. $x(x^2 + 4) = 4x^2$ **0, 2**

69. $x(x + 12) = x^3$ **0, 4, −3**

C

70. $x^3 - x + 7x^2 - 7 = 0$ **−7, 1, −1**

71. $x^3 - 9x = 36 - 4x^2$ **3, −3, −4**

72. $x^2(x + 1) = 16x + 16$ **4, −4, −1**

73. $2x^3 - 147 = 49x - 3x^2 + x^3$ **7, −7, −3**

74. $(2x + 3)(3x - 4) = (5x + 4)(x - 1)$ **2, −4**

75. $(5x - 3)(x + 2) = (2x + 1)^2 - 3$ **1, −4**

76. A long sheet of aluminum with a 14-inch edge has to be bent to form a gutter of rectangular cross-section.

a. The length of each short edge that is at right angles with the base is x inches. Write a formula for the area A of the cross section. $A = x(14 - 2x)$

b. If the area of the cross section must be 24 in.², what is the greatest possible depth of the gutter? **4 in.**

*77. Solve for x: $a^2x^2 - 2abx^2 + ax + b^2x^2 - bx = 0$. Assume $a \neq b$. $\frac{1}{b - a}$

This page serves to remind students that numbers and algebraic relationships can often be visualized through geometric models (or other types of models). The ability to make an abstract idea clearer—through a model—is an important problem-solving skill.

Some students will find that geometric factoring is an enjoyable game. You may wish to point out, however, that geometric factoring is not intended as a substitute for regular factoring skills. In many cases, geometric factoring of a polynomial would be cumbersome and time-consuming.

STRATEGIES for PROBLEM SOLVING

Using Models

Have you ever thought of factoring geometrically? Here's one way it can be done. Terms are thought of as areas of squares and rectangles.

Let this represent 1. $1 \cdot 1 = 1$

Let this represent x. $1 \cdot x = x$

Let this represent x^2. $x \cdot x = x^2$

$x^2 + 4x + 3$ can be factored if the pieces representing **one x^2**, **four x's**, and **three 1's**, can be arranged into a rectangular array. If they can, the dimensions of the rectangle give the factors of the trinomial.

These pieces represent the terms.

This arrangement shows the factors.

Thus $x^2 + 4x + 3$ can be factored as $(x + 3)(x + 1)$.

If the pieces cannot be arranged into a rectangular array, the trinomial cannot be factored.

Try to find the geometric factoring for the trinomial without doing it algebraically.

1. $x^2 + 3x + 2$
   $(x + 1)(x + 2)$
4. $3x^2 + 4x + 2$
   Cannot be factored

2. $x^2 + 2x + 1$
   $(x + 1)(x + 1)$
5. $4x^2 + 4x + 1$
   $(2x + 1)(2x + 1)$

3. $2x^2 + 3x + 1$
   $(x + 1)(2x + 1)$
6. $2x^2 + 5x + 2$
   $(x + 2)(2x + 1)$

CHAPTER 6

6-11 Problem Solving: Using Factoring

OBJECTIVE ————————————————————————

To solve problems by using equations that require factoring.

————————————————————————

Equations that can be solved by factoring are useful in problem solving.

EXAMPLE 1

The length of a rectangle is 3 centimeters more than its width. If the width is doubled and the length is decreased by 2 centimeters, then the area is increased by 6 square centimeters. Find the length and width of the original rectangle.

Strategy:
Draw a figure. Relate the new area to the original area.

Read the problem to find the key idea.
 The relationship between areas of two rectangles can be used to find the required length and width.

Use a variable.

Let x = the width of the original rectangle
and $x + 3$ = the length of the original rectangle

Then $2x$ = the width of the new rectangle
and $x + 3 - 2$, or $x + 1$, = the length of the new rectangle

Write an equation.

$x(x + 3) + 6 = 2x(x + 1)$ Original area + 6 = new area

Find the solution.

$$x^2 + 3x + 6 = 2x^2 + 2x$$
$$x^2 - 2x^2 + 3x - 2x + 6 = 0 \qquad \text{Rewrite with 0 on one side.}$$
$$-x^2 + x + 6 = 0$$
$$x^2 - x - 6 = 0 \qquad \text{Multiply each side by } -1.$$
$$(x - 3)(x + 2) = 0$$
$$x - 3 = 0 \quad \text{or} \quad x + 2 = 0$$
$$x = 3 \qquad \qquad x = -2 \qquad \begin{array}{l}\text{The equation has two solutions, but}\\ \text{a length is positive. Reject } -2.\end{array}$$

If $x = 3$, then $x + 3 = 6$.

Check

If the original rectangle is 3 cm by 6 cm and the new rectangle is 6 cm by 4 cm, has the area increased by 6 cm²?

$3 \times 6 = 18; \quad 6 \times 4 = 24; \quad 18 + 6 = 24$ ✔

Answer the question.

The width is 3 cm and the length is 6 cm.

FACTORING   **241**

ALTERNATE EXAMPLE

2. If 3 times some number is added to its square, the result is 88. Find the number.   −11 or 8

DAILY QUIZ

Solve. Show all solutions if more than one is possible.
  1. If 5 is added to the square of a number, the result is 86. Find the number.   9 or −9
  2. The larger of two positive numbers is 7 more than the smaller. If their product is 228, what are the numbers?   12 and 19
  3. The product of two consecutive integers is 132. Find the integers.   11 and 12, or −12 and −11
  4. Two positive integers differ by 6. Their product is 91. Find the integers.   7 and 13
  5. If the product of two consecutive even integers is added to their sum, the result is 62. Find the integers.   6 and 8, or −10 and −8

ASSIGNMENT GUIDE
(pages 242–244)

Minimum course: 1–15 odd
       second day: 2–20 even
Average course: 1–21 odd
       second day: 2–24 even
Maximum course: 1–29 odd
       second day: 2–30 even

EXAMPLE 2   If 5 times some number is added to its square, the result is 36. Find the number.

Use a variable.   Let x = the number.
  $5x$ = 5 times the number.
  x^2 = the square of the number.

Write an equation. $x^2 + 5x = 36$ If $5x$ is added to x^2, the result is 36.
Solve the equation.
$$x^2 + 5x - 36 = 0$$
$$(x + 9)(x - 4) = 0$$
$$x + 9 = 0 \quad \text{or} \quad x - 4 = 0$$
$$x = -9 \qquad\qquad x = 4$$

Check each of the possible solutions.

The square of the number plus 5 times the number equals 36.
$$(-9)^2 + 5(-9) \overset{?}{=} 36 \qquad 4^2 + 5(4) \overset{?}{=} 36$$
$$81 - 45 = 36 \qquad\qquad 16 + 20 = 36$$

Answer the question.   Both −9 and 4 are solutions. The number is −9 or 4.

CLASS EXERCISES

Read the problem. Then answer the questions that follow.

Find two positive integers that differ by 4 and whose product is 60.

1. Let the smaller positive integer be n. Then the larger is $n +$ _?_.   4

2. The product of these two integers, $n(n + 4)$, equals what number?   60

3. Rewrite the equation $n(n + 4) = 60$ with 0 on one side. Then solve for n. $n(n + 4) - 60 = 0$; $n = 6$ or $n = -10$

4. Of the two solutions to the equation, you must reject −10. Why?
   The integer must be positive.
5. What two positive integers differ by 4 and have a product of 60?   6 and 10

EXERCISES

A   *Solve. Show all solutions if more than one is possible.*

1. If 6 is subtracted from the square of a number, the result is 30. Find the number.   6 or −6

2. If 16 is added to the square of a number, the result is 25. What is the number?   3 or −3

3. The sum of a positive number and its square is 72. Find the number.   8

4. Find two positive integers if their difference is 4 and their product is 96.   8 and 12

5. The larger of two positive numbers is 5 more than the smaller. If their product is 84, what are the numbers? 7 and 12

CHAPTER 6

EXTRA PRACTICE, page 520

6. The product of two integers that differ by 7 is 78. Find the integers.
6 and 13, or −13 and −6

7. The product of two consecutive even integers is 360. Find the integers. 18 and 20, or −20 and −18

8. If 43 is subtracted from the product of two consecutive odd integers, the result is 100. Find the integers. 11 and 13, or −13 and −11

9. Twice the square of a number equals the number. What is the number? 0 or $\frac{1}{2}$

10. A number is 2 less than 3 times its square. Find the number. 1 or $-\frac{2}{3}$

11. Fourteen times a number is 49 more than the square of the number. Find the number. 7

12. The length of a rectangle is 5 cm more than the width. The area is 24 cm². Find the length and width. Length is 8 cm; width is 3 cm.

13. The length of a rectangular lawn is twice the width. If the area is 98 yd², find the length and width. Length is 14 yd; width is 7 yd.

B

14. If the sides of a square are doubled, the new area is 75 in.² greater than the original area. Find the length of a side of the original square. 5

15. The area of the rectangle is 14 ft² more than the area of the square. Find x. 1 ft

16. The two rectangular rugs below have the same area. Find the number of square units in the area of each rug. 96

17. If the product of two consecutive odd integers is added to their sum, the result is 119. Find the integers. 9 and 11, or −13 and −11

18. Twice the square of a number is 5 less than 11 times the number. Find the number. $\frac{1}{2}$ or 5

19. The sum of 9 times a number and 1 is the same as the square of 1 more than the number. What is the number? 7 or 0

20. The sum of the squares of two consecutive positive integers is 85. Find the integers. 6 and 7

21. Find three consecutive even integers if twice the product of the two smaller integers is 4 less than the square of the third. 6, 8, and 10, or −2, 0, and 2

As an extension to Exercise 29 on page 244, have students consider this problem:
Suppose you begin with a square piece of cardboard 12 cm on each side. You cut out squares of side x cm on each corner, and fold up the remaining piece to form a box without a top. Write an expression that represents the volume of the box (in terms of x).
$$V = (12 - 2x)(12 - 2x)x$$
$$= 4x^3 - 48x^2 + 144x$$
Which value for x will give the greatest volume for the box? (Test various values until you believe you have found a good approximation of x.) x = 2

In order to limit the trials, the students should be encouraged to analyze the equation
$V = (12 - 2x)(12 - 2x)x$ and determine the allowable values of x.
$0 < x < 6$

22. Find four consecutive integers if the sum of the squares of the first and fourth is equal to 5 times the sum of the second and third. *3, 4, 5, and 6, or −1, 0, 1, and 2*

23. A margin x in. wide is drawn on a book cover measuring 12 in. by 14 in. If the area of the margin is 88 in.², find x. *2*

24. A rectangular garden is 20 m by 30 m. The garden is surrounded by a path of uniform width. If the total area of the garden and the path is 936 m², how wide is the path? *3m*

25. A square screen is $2x + 1$ ft on a side. A rectangular one is $x + 2$ ft by $x + 6$ ft. If the area of the square screen is 4 ft² more than the area of the rectangular one, find the dimensions of each screen.

Square is 7 ft on a side.
Rectangle is 9 ft by 5 ft.

C

26. The sum of a number cubed and 3 times the square of the number is 75 more than 25 times the number. Find the number. *−3, −5, or 5*

27. John is 2 years older than Maria. The product of their ages in 5 years will be 26 more than twice the product of their ages now. How old are they? *Maria is 9. John is 11.*

28. Find x, if the shaded areas below are equal. Use $A = \pi r^2$ for the area of a circle. *4*

Half-ring between semicircles of radii 18 cm and 14 cm

Ring between circles of radii $(x + 6)$ cm and 6 cm

29. A square piece of cardboard is 13 cm on a side. Squares of side x cm are cut out of the four corners, leaving an area of 144 cm² of cardboard. Find x. $\frac{5}{2}$

30. The length of a rectangular shaped box is 12 cm more than its height, and the width is 3 cm less than the height. The volume is 324 cm³. Find the length, width, and height.
Length = 18 cm; width = 3 cm; height = 6 cm

Bank Interest

Bankers use many different formulas in computing the interest they pay on deposits and earn on loans. Books of tables list amounts under various payment plans. Other important figures can be found quickly at the computer terminal.

Example   Regular monthly deposits of $100 each are made. What will be the total amount at the end of 10 years if interest is 8%, compounded monthly? Below is part of a table that gives the needed information at the rate of 8%, compounded monthly.

Year	Yearly Deposits	New Interest Added	Total Amount in Account
1	1200.00	44.99	1244.99
2	1200.00	148.33	2593.32
3	1200.00	260.24	4053.56
4	1200.00	381.43	5634.99
5	1200.00	512.70	7347.69
6	1200.00	654.84	9202.53
7	1200.00	808.80	11211.33
8	1200.00	975.53	13386.86
9	1200.00	1156.09	15742.95
10	1200.00	1351.65	18294.60
11	1200.00	1563.44	21058.04
12	1200.00	1792.80	24050.84
13	1200.00	2041.20	27292.04
14	1200.00	2310.22	30802.26
15	1200.00	2601.56	34603.82
16	1200.00	2917.10	38720.92
17	1200.00	3258.81	43179.73
18	1200.00	3628.89	48008.62
19	1200.00	4029.68	53238.30
20	1200.00	4463.75	58902.05

The amount at the end of 10 years is $18,294.60. → 10

Of that amount, note that only $12,000.00 was deposited. The difference, $6294.60, is the total interest earned.

Use the table to answer these questions.

1. Find the amount at the end of 15 years. $34,603.82
2. Find the interest earned during the 15th year. $2601.56
3. Find the total interest earned during 15 years. $16,603.82
4. At what point is the yearly interest greater than the year's deposits?   In the 10th year
5. After how many years will the amount be more than double the total deposits?   After 16 years

FACTORING

245

Applications

This Applications page provides students with valuable experience in the use of a mathematical table. Many businesses rely on such tables.

The interest table on this page also reveals how a regular savings plan makes money "grow." Notice that the interest earned in the first year is only $44.99. In contrast, the interest earned in the 20th year is $4,463,75. A total input of $24,000 (20 × $1200) has grown into almost $60,000.

These exercises review basic algebraic skills.

Simplify.

1. $6 - 5 \cdot 3 + 4 \cdot 2$ -1
2. $(-3x^2y^3)(-6xy^2)^2$ $-108x^4y^7$
3. $x^2(x - 1) - x(x^2 - x - 3)$ $3x$

Evaluate when $a = 4$, $b = -5$, and $c = 3$.

4. $-2(a^2bc)$ 480
5. $2a^2 - 3b + c$ 50
6. $\dfrac{ab - bc}{abc}$ $\dfrac{1}{12}$

Solve for x.

7. $x - 3.5 = 0.5 - x$ 2
8. $\dfrac{3x}{2} + 1 = \dfrac{x}{5}$ $-\dfrac{10}{13}$
9. $6(x - 3) = 3 - 3(x + 1)$ 2
10. The length of a rectangle is 15 cm less than 3 times the width. The perimeter is 50 cm. Find the length and the width.   Length = 15 cm, width = 10 cm
11. Paul's age is 5 years less than half the age of his father. If the total of their ages is 58, how old is each?   The father is 42. Paul is 16.
12. Find the slope of the line $14x - 7y = 0$. 2
13. Find the equation of the line that has no slope and that contains the point $(-11, 4)$. $x = -11$
14. Graph the equation $x + y = -3$.

15. Subtract $5 - 2x + x^2$ from $3x^2 - 7$. $2x^2 + 2x - 12$
16. Multiply: $(7x - 8)(3x + 4)$ $21x^2 + 4x - 32$

Factor completely.

17. $x^2 - 12x + 36$ $(x - 6)^2$
18. $x^4 - 81$ $(x^2 + 9)(x + 3)(x - 3)$

[Maintaining Skills continues on page 247.]

CHAPTER 6 REVIEW

VOCABULARY

prime number (p. 204)
prime factorization (p. 205)
greatest common factor (GCF) of two or more positive integers (p. 205)
greatest common factor (GCF) of the terms of a polynomial (p. 213)

factored form of a polynomial (p. 213)
factoring by grouping (p. 216)
difference of two squares (p. 219)
trinomial square (p. 223)
zero-product rule (p. 236)
double root (p. 237)

SUMMARY

In this chapter various techniques for factoring polynomials are developed and illustrated through numerous examples. Included in these techniques are factoring out common factors, factoring by grouping, factoring the difference of squares, factoring trinomial squares, and factoring trinomials. With the aid of the zero-product rule, the factoring methods are applied in solving polynomial equations and word problems.

REVIEW EXERCISES

6-1   1. Express 84 as the product of two positive integers in all possible ways.
$1 \cdot 84$; $2 \cdot 42$; $3 \cdot 28$; $4 \cdot 21$; $6 \cdot 14$; $7 \cdot 12$

2. Write all positive factors of 84. $1, 2, 3, 4, 6, 7, 12, 14, 21, 28, 42, 84$

3. Write the prime factorization of 84. $2^2 \cdot 3 \cdot 7$

4. Write the prime factorization of 108. $2^2 \cdot 3^3$

5. Find the greatest common factor (GCF) of 84 and 108. 12

6-2   *Find the missing factors.*

6. $5y^3 = 5y(\underline{\ ?\ })$ y^2 7. $12x^2y = 6x(\underline{\ ?\ })$ $2xy$ 8. $-3a^3b = ab(\underline{\ ?\ })$ $-3a^2$

Simplify each expression. Assume that no denominator is 0.

9. $\dfrac{x^8}{-2x}$ $-\dfrac{x^7}{2}$ 10. $\dfrac{51x^3y}{3xy}$ $17x^2$ 11. $\dfrac{18a^4b^2}{27a^5b^5}$ $\dfrac{2}{3ab^3}$

12. $\dfrac{-4ab^2}{-12b^3}$ $\dfrac{a}{3b}$ 13. $\dfrac{36x^2y^3}{9x^2y}$ $4y^2$ 14. $\dfrac{-96x^4y^2z^3}{32xy^2z^2}$ $-3x^3z$

6-3   *Factor completely.*

15. $8a - 4b$ $4(2a - b)$ 16. $16x^2 - 6x$ $2x(8x - 3)$ 17. $12x^2 - 8xy$ $4x(3x - 2y)$

18. $2x^2 - 6x + 2$ $2(x^2 - 3x + 1)$ 19. $9x^3 - 9x^2 - 9x$ $9x(x^2 - x - 1)$ 20. $4x^5 - 10x^4 - 18x^3$ $2x^3(2x^2 - 5x - 9)$

Simplify each fraction. Assume that no denominator is 0.

21. $\dfrac{4 + 2x}{2}$ $2 + x$ **22.** $\dfrac{ax^2 + ax}{a}$ $x(x + 1)$ **23.** $\dfrac{9x^3y^2 - 18x^2y^2}{-9xy^2}$ $x(2 - x)$

6-4   Factor.

24. $x(x + 2) + 7(x + 2)$ $(x + 2)(x + 7)$ **25.** $3x(3x + 5) - 2(3x + 5)$ $(3x + 5)(3x - 2)$

26. $xy + x + 2y + 2$ $(y + 1)(x + 2)$ **27.** $x^2 - 2xy - 10y + 5x$ $(x - 2y)(x + 5)$

6-5   Factor as the difference of two squares.

28. $a^2 - 144$
$(a - 12)(a + 12)$

29. $y^2 - 100$
$(y - 10)(y + 10)$

30. $4x^2 - 9$
$(2x - 3)(2x + 3)$

31. $25x^2 - 49$
$(5x - 7)(5x + 7)$

32. $9x^2 - \dfrac{1}{9}$ $\left(3x - \dfrac{1}{3}\right)\left(3x + \dfrac{1}{3}\right)$

33. $x^2 - 81y^2$
$(x - 9y)(x + 9y)$

34. $a^2 - 225b^2$
$(a - 15b)(a + 15b)$

35. $400a^2 - 1$
$(20a - 1)(20a + 1)$

36. $121a^2 - 144b^2$
$(11a - 12b)(11a + 12b)$

6-6   Find the missing term for each trinomial square. Then factor.

37. $x^2 - \underline{?} + 49$
$14x; (x - 7)^2$

38. $x^2 + \underline{?} + 4y^2$
$4xy; (x + 2y)^2$

39. $81x^2 + 18x + \underline{?}$
$1; (9x + 1)^2$

Factor completely.

40. $x^2 - 12x + 36$ $(x - 6)^2$ **41.** $4x^2 - 28x + 49$ $(2x - 7)^2$ **42.** $9x^2 + 6xy + y^2$ $(3x + y)^2$

43. $4x^2 + 32x + 64$
$4(x + 4)^2$

44. $3x^2 + 6xy + 3y^2$
$3(x + y)^2$

45. $4x^2 - 12xy + 9y^2$
$(2x - 3y)^2$

6-7   **46.** $x^2 - 2x - 48$
$(x - 8)(x + 6)$

47. $x^2 + 12x + 32$
$(x + 4)(x + 8)$

48. $x^2 - 15x + 54$
$(x - 6)(x - 9)$

49. $x^2 - 4x - 21$
$(x - 7)(x + 3)$

50. $y^2 - 16y + 15$
$(y - 15)(y - 1)$

51. $y^2 - 19y + 90$
$(y - 9)(y - 10)$

52. $x^2 + 30x + 81$
$(x + 3)(x + 27)$

53. $x^2 + 8x + 15$
$(x + 3)(x + 5)$

54. $x^2 - 14xy + 24y^2$
$(x - 2y)(x - 12y)$

6-8   **55.** $2x^2 - 5x - 7$
$(2x - 7)(x + 1)$

56. $3x^2 + 5x + 2$
$(3x + 2)(x + 1)$

57. $5x^2 + 2x - 3$
$(5x - 3)(x + 1)$

58. $5x^2 - 26x + 5$
$(5x - 1)(x - 5)$

59. $3x^2 + 19x + 28$
$(3x + 7)(x + 4)$

60. $12x^2 + 17x - 5$
$(3x + 5)(4x - 1)$

61. $9x^2 - 7x - 2$
$(9x + 2)(x - 1)$

62. $6x^2 - 25x + 4$
$(6x - 1)(x - 4)$

63. $4x^2 + 11x + 6$
$(4x + 3)(x + 2)$

6-9   **64.** $32x^3 - 8x$
$8x(2x - 1)(2x + 1)$

65. $2x^4 + 6x^3 + 2x^2 + 6x$
$2x(x^2 + 1)(x + 3)$

66. $-x^2 + 8x - 12$
$-(x - 2)(x - 6)$

6-10   Solve by factoring, and check.

67. $x^2 + x - 12 = 0$ **68.** $x^2 + 15x + 54 = 0$ **69.** $x^3 - 4x = 0$

70. $2x^2 - 6x = 0$ **71.** $6x^2 + 11x = 10$ **72.** $(x + 7)(x - 4) = 4x + 2$

6-11   Solve. Show all solutions if more than one is possible.

73. The larger of two numbers is 6 more than the smaller. Their product is 135. Find the two numbers.   9 and 15, or -15 and -9

19. Solve by factoring:
$x^2 + x = 56$ $7; -8$

20. The width of a rectangle is 3 cm less than the length. The area of the rectangle is 40 cm². Find the length and the width.
Length = 8 cm, width = 5 cm

ADDITIONAL ANSWERS

Review Exercises

67. -4 or 3 **68.** -6 or -9

69. 0 or 2 or -2 **70.** 0 or 3

71. $\dfrac{2}{3}$ or $-\dfrac{5}{2}$ **72.** 6 or -5

74. The length of a square is increased by 2 cm and the width is decreased by 3 cm. The area of the square is 17 cm² larger than the area of the resulting rectangle. Find the length of a side of the square. **11 cm**

75. Find three consecutive even integers if the square of the largest is 12 more than the sum of the squares of the two smaller integers. **0, 2, and 4, or 4, 6, and 8**

≡ CHAPTER 6 ≡
TEST

6-1   **1.** Which of the following numbers are prime?

1, 2, 7, 21, 33, 39, 41, 51, 93   **2, 7, 41**

2. Find the GCF of 20 and 28. **4**

6-2   *Simplify.*

3. $\dfrac{8a^3b^3}{-2ab^2}$ **$-4a^2b$**   **4.** $\dfrac{x^4y^2}{3x^3y^3}$ **$\dfrac{x}{3y}$**   **5.** $\dfrac{-45x^3y^2z^2}{15xy^2z}$ **$-3x^2z$**

Factor completely.

6-3   **6.** $24x^3 + 30x^4$ **$6x^3(4 + 5x)$**   **7.** $4y^2 - 8y + 44$ **$4(y^2 - 2y + 11)$**

6-4   **8.** $x^2 - 5x + x - 5$ **$(x - 5)(x + 1)$**   **9.** $xy - 3y + 6x - 18$ **$(y + 6)(x - 3)$**

6-5   **10.** $x^2 - 81$ **$(x - 9)(x + 9)$**   **11.** $4y^2 - 25x^2$ **$(2y - 5x)(2y + 5x)$**

6-6   **12.** $x^2 + 8x + 16$ **$(x + 4)^2$**   **13.** $4x^2 - 28x + 49$ **$(2x - 7)^2$**

6-7   **14.** $x^2 + x - 30$ **$(x + 6)(x - 5)$**   **15.** $x^2 - 11x + 18$ **$(x - 2)(x - 9)$**

6-8   **16.** $3x^2 - 8x + 5$ **$(3x - 5)(x - 1)$**   **17.** $8x^2 + 19x - 15$ **$(8x - 5)(x + 3)$**

6-9   **18.** $2x^3 - 14x^2 - 16x$ **$2x(x - 8)(x + 1)$**   **19.** $2x^4 - 162$ **$2(x^2 + 9)(x - 3)(x + 3)$**

6-10   *Solve for x.*

20. $x(x - 4) = 0$ **0, 4**   **21.** $x^2 - 100 = 0$ **10, −10**

22. $5x^2 + 13x - 6 = 0$ **$\frac{2}{5}$, −3**   **23.** $x(5x - 12) = (x + 3)(x - 3)$ **$\frac{3}{2}$**

6-11   **24.** The sum of the squares of three consecutive positive integers is 110. Find the integers. **5, 6, 7**

25. The length of a rectangle exceeds the width by 4 cm. The area of the rectangle is 96 cm². Find the length and the width. **12 cm, 8 cm**

248

Factoring a Number

To determine whether one number is a factor of another number, we use the *greatest integer function*. Note the relationships.

When the divisor *is a factor*:
15/5 = 3   INT(15/5) = 3
So   15/5 = INT(15/5)

When the divisor is *not a factor*:
15/6 = 2.5   INT(15/6) = 2
So   15/6 ≠ INT(15/6)

Also note that when 15/5 = 3, both 5 and 3 are factors of 15.

The Program	What It Does
100 REM FACTORS	
110 PRINT "ENTER NUMBER";	
120 INPUT N	Waits for you to enter (input) the number to be factored.
130 PRINT "ITS FACTORS ARE:"	Tells computer to test each integer from 1 through the number itself.
140 FOR D = 1 TO N	
160 IF N/D < > INT(N/D) THEN 180	If not a factor, jumps to line 180.
170 PRINT D, N/D	Displays a pair of factors.
180 NEXT D	Returns to line 140 and continues.
900 PRINT "THAT'S ALL."	Signals that all factors are displayed.
990 END	

```
RUN
ENTER NUMBER? 6
ITS FACTORS ARE:
1        6
2        3
3        2
6        1
THAT'S ALL.
```

This sample run displays the factors of 6.

The comma in line 170 causes the factors to be displayed in two columns.

Since all factors have been displayed once the factor in the first column exceeds the factor in the second column, we can insert the following line to reduce the number of values to be tested.

150   IF D > N/D THEN 900

Use line 150 to find what factors are displayed for each of the following.

1. 24   **2.** 91   **3.** 625   **4.** 171   **5.** 507   **6.** 2001

7. When the number 2500 is input, how many divisors are tested
   a. with line 150 in the program?   50   **b.** without line 150 in the program?   2500

Use the program FACTORS to determine which of these are prime.
8. 9753 Not prime **9.** 4013   Prime **10.** 7201 Not prime **11.** 8513   Prime **12.** 17,803 Not prime

13. How many factors does the number 420,876 have?   36

For more information about BASIC, see the Computer Handbook at the back of the book.

PART I

Write the letter for the correct answer.

Chap. 1   **1.** Which number is an integer but not a whole number? a

    a. -1 **b.** 0   **c.** 2   **d.** $\frac{1}{2}$ **e.** -0.2

  2. The phrase "5 less than twice a certain number" is represented by ? . e

    a. $2(x - 5)$ **b.** $5 - 2x$ **c.** $5x - 2$ **d.** $5(x - 2)$ **e.** $2x - 5$

Chap. 2   **3.** Simplify: $7 - 8 - (3 - 1)$ b

    a. -5 **b.** -3 **c.** 1   **d.** 3   **e.** 13

  4. Simplify: $3a - 4 - 5a + 5 + a$ b

    a. $1 + a$ **b.** $1 - a$ **c.** 1   **d.** $a - 1$ **e.** $2a - 1$

  5. Evaluate: $2|x| - x - |-3|$ if $x = -4$ d

    a. -7 **b.** -6 **c.** 1   **d.** 9   **e.** 15

Chap. 4   **6.** Which point is *not* on the graph of $y = 3x - 4$? b

    a. $(0, -4)$ **b.** $(-1, -1)$ **c.** $(3, 5)$ **d.** $(-2, -10)$ **e.** $(2, 2)$

  7. Find the slope of the line whose equation is $5x - y = 3$. e

    a. -5 **b.** -3 **c.** -1 **d.** 3   **e.** 5

  8. What is the slope of the line with equation $y = -1$? b

    a. -1 **b.** 0   **c.** 1   **d.** 2   **e.** undefined

Chap. 5   **9.** What is the degree of the polynomial $8x^3 - 4$? c

    a. 1   **b.** 2   **c.** 3   **d.** 4   **e.** 8

  10. Subtract $3n - 4$ from $2n - 1$. b

    a. $n - 3$ **b.** $-n + 3$ **c.** $-n - 5$ **d.** $5n + 3$ **e.** $5n - 5$

  11. Simplify: $(2n^3)(3n^2)$ d

    a. $5n^6$ **b.** $5n^9$ **c.** $5n^5$ **d.** $6n^5$ **e.** $6n^6$

  12. Simplify: $(-2x^3y)^2$ e

    a. $-4x^9y^2$ **b.** $4x^5y^2$ **c.** $4x^9y^2$ **d.** $-4x^6y^2$ **e.** $4x^6y^2$

Chap. 6   **13.** Which expression is *not* a factor of $9x^3y^4$? c

    a. xy **b.** $3x^3$ **c.** $6x^3y^2$ **d.** $9x^2y$ **e.** x^3y^3

  14. Solve for x: $2x^2 = x$ e

    a. 0 only   **b.** $\frac{1}{2}$ only   **c.** 1 only   **d.** $-\frac{1}{2}$ or 0   **e.** $\frac{1}{2}$ or 0

PART II

Simplify.

Chap. 1   **15.** $19 - 14 + 13$ 18   **16.** $17 - 3 \times 2$ 11   **17.** $36 \div (18 \div 2)$ 4

Chap. 2   **18.** $(-18) + (-19) + 25 + (-33)$ −45 **19.** $-18 + 17 + 26 - 15 - 17$ −7

        20. $10y + 12y - 13$ **21.** $-25x - 16x - 21x$ **22.** $x^2y + 9xy^2 - 5x^2y$
            $22y - 13$ $-62x$ $9xy^2 - 4x^2y$

        23. $-\dfrac{18x}{12}$ $-\frac{3x}{2}$ **24.** $\dfrac{(3x)^2}{9}$ x^2 **25.** $\dfrac{24xy^2}{-4y}$ −6xy **26.** $\dfrac{-300y}{-60y^3}$ $\frac{5}{y^2}$

        Evaluate when $x = 3$ and $y = -5$.

        27. $8x + 2y$ 14   **28.** y^x −125   **29.** $xy - y^2$ −40   **30.** $(xy)^2 - y^2$ 200

Chap. 3   *Solve for x.*

        31. $-33 = 77 + x$ −110 **32.** $-2.6 + x = 3$ 5.6 **33.** $-1.6x = 9.6$ −6

        34. $\dfrac{3x}{5} - 6 = 0$ 10 **35.** $6(x + 10) = 30$ −5 **36.** $8\left(x - \dfrac{1}{4}\right) = 14$ 2

Chap. 4   *Find the slope of the line through the two given points.*

        37. $(0, 5), (-2, -1)$ 3 **38.** $(1, 3), (2, 3)$ 0 **39.** $(-2, -3), (-5, -2)$ $-\frac{1}{3}$

        40. Find the x-intercept and the y-intercept of the line $y - 4x = 3$.   x-intercept is $-\frac{3}{4}$;   y-intercept is 3.

        41. Write the equation $2y - x = 2$ in slope-intercept form. $y = \frac{1}{2}x + 1$

        42. Write the equation, in standard form, of the line containing the points $(3, 6)$ and $(-2, -4)$. $2x - y = 0$

        Write an equation for each line and then draw its graph.

        43. $m = -1$; containing $(0, 1)$ $y = -x + 1$ **44.** vertical; containing $(3, 2)$ $x = 3$

        45. parallel to $y = \frac{3}{2}x - 1$, with the same y-intercept as $y = 2x - 3$ $y = \frac{3}{2}x - 3$

Chap. 5   *Simplify.*

        46. $(4x + 10y) - (4x + 8y)$ 2y **47.** $-3x(2xy)^3$ $-24x^4y^3$ **48.** $6(y + 8) + 2y$ 8y + 48

        49. $(2x - 1)(4x + 7)$ **50.** $(2x + 3y)(x + y)$ **51.** $(2x + 3)^2$
           $8x^2 + 10x - 7$ $2x^2 + 5xy + 3y^2$ $4x^2 + 12x + 9$
        52. Solve for x: $(x + 1)^2 = (x - 4)(x + 3) + 52$ 13

Chap. 6   *Factor completely.*

        53. $n^2 + 14n + 49$ $(n + 7)^2$ **54.** $12x^2 - 27$ **55.** $3x^2 + 10x - 8$
                                      $3(2x + 3)(2x - 3)$ $(3x - 2)(x + 4)$

Chap. 2   **56.** A freely falling body, starting at rest, falls s feet in t seconds, where $s = 16t^2$. How far will a body fall in $\frac{1}{2}$ minute?   14,400 ft

43.

44.

45.

In this chapter the text focuses on systems of linear equations. First the graphic method of solution is taught. Then algebraic methods are developed in detail, including solutions by substitution, by addition or subtraction, and by multiplication with addition or subtraction.

The students also learn to classify systems as consistent or inconsistent, and independent or dependent. Both the algebraic and the graphic interpretations are discussed, so that the students gain a better understanding of the classifications.

The chapter closes with two lessons devoted to problem solving using systems of equations. A variety of applications are presented, including age, coin, and digit problems.

CHAPTER 7

Systems of equations can be used to obtain information that will help improve the timing of traffic signals at busy intersections.

SYSTEMS OF LINEAR EQUATIONS

Prerequisite Skills Review

Prerequisite Skills Review

For students who need additional practice with the algebraic skills in this Prerequisite Skills Review, you may assign Follow-Up exercises on page 503 in the students' books.

An item-by-item error analysis of the Prerequisite Skills Review appears on page T24.

Write the letter for the correct answer.

1. In the coordinate plane, which point lies on the x-axis? d
   a. $(4, -2)$ **b.** $(-7, -1)$ **c.** $(0, 5)$ **d.** $(-6, 0)$

2. Which point is in Quadrant III? b
   a. $(-1, 0)$ **b.** $(-6, -1)$ **c.** $(2, -5)$ **d.** $(-5, 1)$

3. Which line is parallel to the x-axis? c
   a. $y = x + 5$ **b.** $y = -2x$ **c.** $y = 7$ **d.** $x = 4$

4. Which line is parallel to the y-axis? d
   a. $x + y = 1$ **b.** $y = -2$ **c.** $y = x$ **d.** $x = 7$

5. The slope of the line through $(-3, 2)$ and $(1, 10)$ is __?__ . a
   a. 2 **b.** -2 **c.** 4 **d.** -4

6. Which line has a slope of -3? c
   a. $y = 3x + 1$ **b.** $2y + 3x = 6$ **c.** $y + 3x = 6$ **d.** $y = -3$

7. Which line has a y-intercept of 2? a
   a. $y = x + 2$ **b.** $y = 2x + 3$ **c.** $3y = x + 2$ **d.** $-y = 2$

8. Which line has a slope of -1 and a y-intercept of 5? d
   a. $y = x + 5$ **b.** $y - x = 5$ **c.** $y = 5x - 1$ **d.** $x + y = 5$

9. Which point does *not* lie on the line $y = 3x - 4$? b
   a. $(1, -1)$ **b.** $(0, 4)$ **c.** $\left(\frac{4}{3}, 0\right)$ **d.** $(2, 2)$

10. The point $(3, -4)$ lies on which line? c
    a. $y - x = 1$ **b.** $y = x - 1$ **c.** $y = x - 7$ **d.** $3x + 4y = 0$

11. Which line does *not* contain the point $(-1, 4)$? a
    a. $y = x - 5$ **b.** $y + 4x = 0$ **c.** $y = -2x + 2$ **d.** $y = 4$

12. Refer to the line at the right. Which statement is incorrect? d
    a. The slope is $\frac{1}{3}$.
    b. The y-intercept is 2.
    c. An equation of the line is $y = \frac{1}{3}x + 2$.
    d. An equation of the line is $3y - x = 2$.

Determine whether (3, −2) is a
solution for each equation.
  1. $x + y = 1$ Yes
  2. $y = x − 5$ Yes
Determine whether (−1, 2) is a
solution for each equation.
  3. $y = 2x + 5$ No
  4. $x + 4y = 7$ Yes

LESSON NOTES

Remind the students that in each ordered pair, the x-value is given first.
Thus, when we substitute the numbers from (1, 2) in $x + y = 3$ or
$y = x − 1$, we substitute 1 for x and
2 for y (regardless of the positions
of x and y in the equations).
  The material at the bottom of
page 254 recalls two ways of graphing linear equations. Once the equation has been written in $y = mx + b$
form, the students can: (a) assign
values to x and compute the corresponding y-values; (b) use the slope
and the y-intercept. Notice that this
reminder of graphing procedures
leads into Example 2 and its use of
the slope-intercept approach.
  You may wish to remind the students that an equation can also be
graphed by using the x- and y-
intercepts as the determining points
for the line. Some of the exercises,
such as Class Exercises 1 and 2,
are easily graphed using the x- and
y-intercepts.

ALTERNATE EXAMPLE

  1. Is the given ordered pair a solution of the system of equations?
    a. (3, 2) $x + 2y = 7$
         $y = −x + 5$ Yes
    b. (−3, 1) $y = x + 4$
         $y = 2x + 5$ No

7-1   Solving Systems by Graphing

OBJECTIVES

To tell whether a given ordered pair is a solution of a system of equations.
To solve systems of linear equations by graphing.
To tell whether a system represents parallel or intersecting lines.

The graphs of $x + y = 3$ and $y = x + 1$ are
shown on the same set of axes. The lines intersect at the point (1, 2). Since this point is on
both lines, the ordered pair (1, 2) is the common
solution to both equations, $x + y = 3$ *and*
$y = x + 1$.

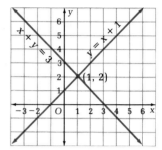

Check $x + y = 3$ $y = x + 1$
         $1 + 2 \underset{?}{=} 3$ $2 \underset{?}{=} 1 + 1$
             $3 = 3$ ✔ $2 = 2$ ✔

  Two equations in x and y make up a **system of equations**. A **solution**
of the system is an ordered pair (x, y) that satisfies both equations.
Thus (1, 2) is a solution of the system:

$$x + y = 3$$
$$y = x + 1$$

EXAMPLE 1   Is the given ordered pair a solution of the system of equations?

  a. (4, 1); $x + 3y = 7$ **b.** (−2, 3); $y = 2x + 7$
         $y = −x + 5$ $y = x + 1$

  Check (4, 1) in both equations.   Check (−2, 3) in both equations.

  $x + 3y = 7$ $y = −x + 5$ $y = 2x + 7$ $y = x + 1$
  $4 + 3(1) \underset{?}{=} 7$ $1 \underset{?}{=} −(4) + 5$ $3 \underset{?}{=} 2(−2) + 7$ $3 \underset{?}{=} −2 + 1$
  $4 + 3 \underset{?}{=} 7$ $1 \underset{?}{=} −4 + 5$ $3 \underset{?}{=} −4 + 7$ $3 \underset{?}{=} −1$ False
      $7 = 7$ ✔ $1 = 1$ ✔ $3 = 3$ ✔

  Thus (4, 1) is a solution of the   (−2, 3) is not a solution of
  system. $y = x + 1$. Thus (−2, 3) is *not* a
                                        solution of the system.

  To graph a linear equation, solve for y in terms of x. You can then
select values for x and compute corresponding y-values for points on
the line. You can also use the slope and the y-intercept to graph the
line.

CHAPTER 7

EXAMPLE 2   Solve the system by graphing: $2x + y = 9$
$4y = x$

$2x + y = 9$
$\quad y = -2x + 9$

Slope: -2

y-intercept: 9

$4y = x$
$\quad y = \frac{1}{4}x$

Slope: $\frac{1}{4}$

y-intercept: 0

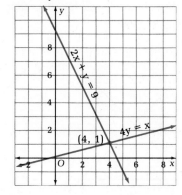

You can find from a carefully drawn graph that the lines appear to intersect at (4, 1). Check this point in the *original* equations, $2x + y = 9$ and $4y = x$. Since it checks, (4, 1) is the solution of the system.

When two lines have different slopes, they intersect in exactly one point and the system has a unique solution. But when two different lines have the same slope, they are parallel and the system has *no* solution.

These two lines have the same slope, 2, but different y-intercepts.

$$y = 2x + 1$$
$$y = 2x - 4$$

Hence we know, even without drawing the graph, that the lines are parallel and the system has no solution.

CLASS EXERCISES

Find the solution for each system from the graphs. Check by substituting in both equations.

1. $y - x = 3$
$2y + x = 0$ $(-2, 1)$

2. $x + y = 0$
$y = x - 2$ $(1, -1)$

3. $2y + 3x = 3$
$2y + x = 1$ $(1, 0)$

2. Solve the system by graphing.
$x + 2y = 4$
$2y = x$

POSSIBLE ERROR

Students sometimes locate or draw the graphs incorrectly, thus obtaining an incorrect answer. Be sure the students always check the possible solution in *both* of the original equations; in that way, they will discover whether they have made an error in the graphing process.

DAILY QUIZ

Solve each system by graphing.
1. $y = -x + 6$
$y = x - 6$ (6, 0)
2. $y = 2x + 3$
$y = -x$ $(-1, 1)$
3. $y = -2x + 3$
$y = 3x - 7$ $(2, -1)$
4. $y = -3x - 5$
$y = 4x + 9$ $(-2, 1)$
5. $2y - 4x = -12$
$3y + 6x = 21$ $\left(3\frac{1}{4}, \frac{1}{2}\right)$

EXERCISES

A *Find the solution for each system from the graphs. Check by substituting in both equations.*

1. $y = x + 2$
$y = -x + 6$ (2, 4)

2. $y = -x + 8$
$y = x + 4$ (2, 6)

3. $y = 2x$
$y = -2x + 8$ (2, 4)

Solve each system by graphing.

4. $y = -x + 8$
$y = x - 4$ (6, 2)

5. $y = -2x + 5$
$y = 3x - 5$ (2, 1)

6. $y = -3x + 9$
$y = 4x + 2$ (1, 6)

7. $y = -x + 3$
$y = x - 1$ (2, 1)

8. $y = 2x + 5$
$y = -x + 2$ (-1, 3)

9. $y = -x + 10$
$y = x - 2$ (6, 4)

10. $y = -x - 4$
$y = x - 8$ (2, -6)

11. $y = -x + 1$
$y = x$ $\left(\frac{1}{2}, \frac{1}{2}\right)$

Determine whether the given pair is a solution of the system of equations.

12. (4, 3); $x + y = 7$
$x - 2y = 4$ No

13. (6, 4); $x - 2y = -2$
$3x - 2y = 10$ Yes

14. (1, -1); $2x - 3y = 5$
$x + 2y = -1$ Yes

15. (3, 2); $3x + 4y = 17$
$2x - 3y = 0$ Yes

16. (0, -2); $x - 2y = 4$
$x + 3y = -6$ Yes

17. (0, 0); $y = 3x - 7$
$y = 3x + 13$ No

Determine whether the system has a solution or not. Find the solution, if it exists, by graphing.

18. $y = 3x + 1$
$y = 3x - 4$
No solution

19. $y = -2x + 3$
$y = 2x - 1$ (1, 1)

20. $y - 4x = 3$
$y + 3 = 4x$
No solution

21. $y = 2$
$x = 2$ (2, 2)

22. $y = 3x$
$y - 3x = 1$
No solution

23. $x - y = 1$
$y - x = 1$
No solution

24. $y + x = 8$
$x - y = 2$ (5, 3)

25. $2y + 4x = 4$
$y + 2x = -3$
No solution

26. $x + 2y = 8$
$2x - y = 1$ (2, 3)

27. $3x + 9y = 9$
$2x - 3y = 6$ (3, 0)

28. $x + 2y = 0$
$x + y = 1$ (2, -1)

29. $x + y = 3$
$x + y = -2$
No solution

30. $y = 3$
$x + y = 5$ (2, 3)

31. $x - y = 1$
$y = 2$ (3, 2)

32. $x = 2$
$x + y = 5$ (2, 3)

33. $x + 3y = 0$
$2x - y = 7$ (3, -1)

CHAPTER 7

EXTRA PRACTICE, pages 520–521

34. $3y + 15 = 6x$ $\left(3\frac{1}{2}, 2\right)$
$2y + 4x = 18$

35. $3x - 5y = 6$ No
$6x - 10y = 10$ solution

36. $6x - 3y = 9$
$6x + 3y = 15$ (2, 1)

37. $2x + 2y = -2$
$3x - 2y = 12$ (2, −3)

38. $2x - 4y = -4$
$3x - 2y = -6$ (−2, 0)

39. $3x - 2y = -1$
$2x - 4y = 2$ (−1, −1)

40. $3x + 3y = 21$
$3x + 4y = 24$ (4, 3)

41. $4x + y = 10$
$3x + 2y = 10$ (2, 2)

42. $3y - 15 = -x$
$2y = x + 5$ (3, 4)

43. The sum of two numbers is 12. The first number is 4 more than the second. Let x be the first number, and let y be the second number. Write a system of equations and solve by graphing. What are the two numbers? $x + y = 12$ Numbers are 8 and 4.
$x = y + 4$

44. Write an equation of the line parallel to $y = 2x - 5$ with y-intercept 2. $y = 2x + 2$

45. For what value of k will this system have no solution? $2y + 6x = -4$
$3y + kx = 8$ 9

46. The solution of the system below is (2, −5). Find the values of A and B.
$Ax + 2y = 8$ $A = 9$
$x + By = 12$ $B = -2$

USING THE CALCULATOR

A Pattern with Slopes

Find these slopes. Write the first six decimal places and do not round.

x	slope = $\dfrac{1}{x}$		
1000	0.001000		
1001	0._____?		0.000999
1002	0._____?		0.000998
1003	0._____?		0.000997

Study the answers.

What kind of pattern do you see?   As x increases by 1, $\frac{1}{x}$ decreases by 0.000001.

What would you predict for the slope if x = 1004?   if x = 999?   0.000996; 0.001001
Check your answers.

Look for an extension of the pattern. Find the first six decimal places in the slope for the following x-values.

1. a. 10,001   0.000099   **b.** 10,002   0.000099   **c.** 10,003   0.000099

2. a. 100,001   0.000009   **b.** 100,002   0.000009   **c.** 100,003   0.000009

3. a. 1,000,001   0.000000   **b.** 1,000,002   0.000000   **c.** 1,000,003   0.000000

Try to generalize the results. As x becomes larger, what happens to the slope?
The slope becomes smaller—closer and closer to zero.

7-2   Solving Systems by Substitution

OBJECTIVE

To solve systems of linear equations by the substitution method.

The graphs of the two equations in a system are shown. What is the ordered pair of numbers that is the solution of the system?
   The y-coordinate of the point where the lines meet appears to be 1. But what is the x-coordinate? You cannot tell exactly by looking at the graph. However, the system can be solved by the *substitution method*.

EXAMPLE 1   Solve by substitution: $\begin{array}{l} y = 6x - 1 \\ 3x - 3y = -2 \end{array}$

The first equation says that y is equal to $6x - 1$.
So substitute $6x - 1$ for y in the second equation. Then solve for x.

$$3x - 3y = -2$$
$$3x - 3(6x - 1) = -2$$
$$3x - 18x + 3 = -2$$
$$-15x = -5$$
$$x = \frac{1}{3}$$

To find the corresponding value for y, substitute $\frac{1}{3}$ for x in either of the two equations. Both will give the same y-value.

First equation	Second equation
$y = 6x - 1$	$3x - 3y = -2$
$y = 6\left(\dfrac{1}{3}\right) - 1$	$3\left(\dfrac{1}{3}\right) - 3y = -2$
$y = 2 - 1$	$1 - 3y = -2$
$y = 1$	$-3y = -3$
	$y = 1$

The solution of the system of equations is $\left(\frac{1}{3}, 1\right)$.

It is often necessary to rewrite an equation in order to express one variable in terms of the other.

EXAMPLE 2 Solve by substitution: $\begin{array}{l} 3x + y = 5 \\ 4x - 2y = 10 \end{array}$

Solve the first equation for y, since the coefficient of y is 1.

$3x + y = 5$
$\quad y = 5 - 3x$

Now substitute $5 - 3x$ for y in the second equation and solve for x.

$4x - 2(5 - 3x) = 10$
$\quad 4x - 10 + 6x = 10$
$\qquad\qquad 10x = 20$
$\qquad\qquad\ \ x = 2$

Substitute 2 for x in either equation and solve for y.

$3(2) + y = 5$ Substitute in the first equation.
$\ \ 6 + y = 5$
$\qquad\ y = -1$

Check the values $x = 2$ and $y = -1$ in both of the given equations.
The solution of the system of equations is $(2, -1)$.

Sometimes you may get a numerical equation that is false. This means that there is *no solution* and the graphs of the equations are parallel lines. Suppose you solve the system $y = 3x - 5$ *and* $6x - 2y = 1$.

$6x - 2(3x - 5) = 1$ Substitute $3x - 5$ for y in the second
$6x - 6x + 10 = 1$ equation and solve for x.
$\qquad\qquad 10 = 1$ False

The false statement means that the system has no solution.

CLASS EXERCISES

Start with the system: $\begin{array}{l} 3x + y = 4 \\ x - y = 8 \end{array}$

1. Solve the second equation for x. $x = y + 8$

2. Substitute for x in the first equation. Solve for y. $3(y + 8) + y = 4; y = -5$

3. Substitute the y-value in one of the equations. Solve for x. $x = 3$

4. Check the values for x and y in both equations. $3(3) - 5 = 4; 3 + 5 = 8$

5. What is the solution of the system of equations? $(3, -5)$

Consider solving by substitution the system: $\begin{array}{l} 2y + 5x = 3 \\ 3y - x = -4 \end{array}$

6. Which variable would it be more convenient to solve for first, and in which equation? x; second

7. What expression would you substitute for that variable in the other equation? $3y + 4$

8. What is the solution of the system? $(1, -1)$

ALTERNATE EXAMPLE

2. Solve by substitution.
$2x + y = 5$
$3x - 2y = 11$ $(3, -1)$

POSSIBLE ERROR

Students are often confused by the results they obtain when they use substitution with a system such as $4y = x + 3$ and $x - 4y = -2$ (Exercise 27). They may rewrite $4y = x + 3$ as $x = 4y - 3$ and then substitute and simplify as follows:

$(4y - 3) - 4y = -2$
$\qquad\qquad -3 = -2$

The false equality may puzzle them; they may believe that it indicates they have made a mistake. Remind them that the false numerical equality does *not* indicate a mistake; rather, it indicates that the system has no solution. You might also point out that the equations, expressed in $y = mx + b$ form, are

$$y = \frac{1}{4}x + \frac{3}{4}$$
$$y = \frac{1}{4}x + \frac{1}{2}$$

Thus, they have the same slope and their graphs are parallel lines. Since parallel lines do not intersect, the equations have no common solution.

DAILY QUIZ

Solve each system of equations by the substitution method.

1. $x = 5$
$\ \ x - y = 3$
$\ \ (5, 2)$

2. $y = 3$
$\ \ x + y = 2$
$\ \ (-1, 3)$

3. $y = 2x$
$\ \ x + 3y = 14$
$\ \ (2, 4)$

4. $2y - x = 3$
$\ \ 3y + 5x = 24$
$\ \ (3, 3)$

5. $x + y = 3$
$\ \ 2x - 3y = 5$ $\left(2\frac{4}{5}, \frac{1}{5}\right)$

ENRICHMENT ACTIVITY

Have the students tell whether the graphs are perpendicular to each other.

$y = 4x$ $\qquad$ $y = 3x$

$y = \frac{1}{4}x$ No $\qquad$ $y = -\frac{1}{3}x$ Yes

$y = 5x - 1$

$y = -\frac{1}{5}x + 2$ Yes

$y = -\frac{1}{2}x + 3$

$y = 2x - 4$ Yes

Have the students experiment with other pairs of equations such as these and try to generalize. (Two lines are perpendicular if they have slopes whose product is -1. After the students discover this fact, you may wish to note that two numbers whose product is -1 are called *negative reciprocals* of each other.)

EXERCISES

A Solve each system of equations by the substitution method. If no solution exists, write **no solution**.

1. $y = 2$ $\left(4\frac{1}{2}, 2\right)$
$\quad 2x - 4y = 1$

2. $x = 3$ $\quad(3, 2)$
$\quad x - y = 1$

3. $y = 3x$ $\quad(2, 6)$
$\quad x + y = 8$

4. $x - y = -4$ $\quad(4, 8)$
$\quad y = 2x$

5. $x = 5y$ $(-5, -1)$
$\quad y = 3x + 14$

6. $x - y = 0$ $\quad(0, 0)$
$\quad 2x - y = 0$

7. $x + y = 5$ $\left(2\frac{1}{2}, 2\frac{1}{2}\right)$
$\quad x - y = 0$

8. $2x + y = 1$ $(-1, 3)$
$\quad x = 8 - 3y$

9. $x + y = 2$ $\quad(2, 0)$
$\quad 3x - 2y = 6$

10. $y = 2x$ $\quad(1, 2)$
$\quad 2x - 4y = -6$

11. $2x + 5y = 14$
$\quad x = y$ $\quad(2, 2)$

12. $x = -4y$ $\quad(4, -1)$
$\quad 5x - 3y = 23$

13. $x + y = 1$ $\quad(0, 1)$
$\quad 2x - 4y = -4$

14. $x + y = 16$
$\quad y = 2x + 1$ $(5, 11)$

15. $x + y = 16$
$\quad 2y = -2x + 2$
No solution

16. $x + y = 7$
$\quad x - 2y = 4$ $\quad(6, 1)$

17. $x + 2y = -8$
$\quad 2x + 4y = 24$
No solution

18. $x - 2y = -2$
$\quad 3x - 2y = 10$ $(6, 4)$

19. $2x - 3y = 5$
$\quad x + 2y = -1$ $(1, -1)$

20. $3x + 4y = 17$
$\quad 2x - y = 4$ $\quad(3, 2)$

B

21. $x - 2y = 4$
$\quad x + 3y = -6$ $(0, -2)$

22. $y - 2x = -3$
$\quad 3x + 5y = 24$ $(3, 3)$

23. $2x = 4y + 10$
$\quad 5x - 2y = 17$ $(3, -1)$

24. $4y + 3x = 20$
$\quad 3y = 15 - 6x$ $(0, 5)$

25. $6y - 3x = -8$
$\quad 3x = 4 - 6y$ $\left(2, -\frac{1}{3}\right)$

26. $3x + 4y = 6$
$\quad 5y + 3x = 0$ $(10, -6)$

27. $4y = x + 3$
$\quad x - 4y = -2$
No solution

28. $2x - y = 3$
$\quad x = \frac{1}{2}y + 2$
No solution

29. Find the coordinates of the point that is on the graph of both
$y = 7x - 20$ and $2x - y = 7$. $\left(\frac{13}{5}, -\frac{9}{5}\right)$

30. What is the solution (x, y) of the system consisting of the equations
$y + 3x = t$ and $3y - x = 2t$? $\left(\frac{t}{10}, \frac{7t}{10}\right)$

C

31. $(2, 1)$ is a solution of the system $2y + x = 4$ and $6y + 3x = 12$. The
ordered pair $(8, -2)$ is also a solution. Explain how a system of two
linear equations can have more than one solution. The equations are equivalent.
$\qquad\qquad\qquad\qquad$ Any solution of one equation is a solution of the other.

32. The sum of twice a number and 4 times another number is equal to
20. The sum of the first number and half the second number is 40.
Let x be the first number and y be the second number. Write a system of equations and solve by substitution. What are the two numbers? 50 and -20

33. One number is 5 less than 3 times a second number. The sum of
the first number and 4 times the second number is 5. Find the two
numbers. $\left(-\frac{5}{7}, \frac{10}{7}\right)$

Solve the system of three equations for the ordered number triple (x, y, z).

34. $x = 4$ $\left(4, 6\frac{1}{2}, 3\frac{1}{2}\right)$
$\quad x + y - z = 7$
$\quad 2x - y + 3z = 12$

35. $x + 3y - z = 2$
$\quad x + y + z = 70$
$\quad z + 7 = 0$ $(118, -41, -7)$

*36. $2x + y - 3z = 12$
$\quad 3x + 3y + z = -1$
$\quad 4y + z = 4$ $(-1, 2, -4)$

CHAPTER 7

EXTRA PRACTICE, page 521

7-3 Using Addition or Subtraction

OBJECTIVE

To solve systems of equations by adding or subtracting like terms.

The addition property of equality can be stated in the following way.

$$\text{If } a = b \text{ and } c = d, \quad \text{then } a + c = b + d.$$

This property can be used to solve systems of equations by adding similar terms. It is especially useful when the terms in one variable are opposites of each other.

EXAMPLE 1   Solve by addition: $\begin{array}{l} x - y = 1 \\ x + y = 5 \end{array}$

$$\begin{array}{ll} x - y = 1 & \text{Add similar terms on each side of the two equations.} \\ x + y = 5 & \\ \hline 2x \quad\;\; = 6 & \text{The resulting equation has only one variable, } x. \\ \quad\; x = 3 & \text{Solve for } x. \end{array}$$

To find y, substitute 3 for x in either equation in the system. Both give the same y-value.

$$\begin{array}{l} x + y = 5 \\ 3 + y = 5 \\ \quad\;\; y = 2 \end{array}$$

Check by substituting $x = 3$ and $y = 2$ in both of the equations.

The solution is (3, 2).

EXAMPLE 2   Solve by addition: $\begin{array}{l} y = 5x + 11 \\ 5x + 2y = 7 \end{array}$

Express both equations in the form $ax + by = c$.
Write $y = 5x + 11$ as $-5x + y = 11$. Then align and add similar terms.

$$\begin{array}{ll} -5x + \;\; y = 11 & \\ \underline{5x + 2y = \;\; 7} & \\ \quad\quad\;\; 3y = 18 & \text{Adding eliminates the variable } x. \\ \quad\quad\;\;\; y = 6 & \end{array}$$

Substitute 6 for y in either of the original equations.

$$\begin{array}{l} y = 5x + 11 \\ 6 = 5x + 11 \\ -5 = 5x \\ -1 = x \end{array}$$

Thus $(-1, 6)$ is the solution of the system. The check is left to you.

WARM-UP EXERCISES

Add these polynomials.
1. $x + 2y$
$\underline{x - 2y}$ $2x$

2. $-3x + 4y$ $9y$
$\underline{\;\;3x + 5y}$

LESSON NOTES

Examples 1–2 illustrate how to solve a system of equations by addition. Example 3 (page 262) illustrates solving a system of equations by using subtraction. Contrast the two methods, discussing the way in which we decide whether to use addition or to use subtraction. Point out: When the terms in one variable are opposites of each other, it is convenient to add. When the terms in one variable are the same, it is convenient to subtract.

$$\begin{array}{ll} x + 2y = 3 & x\text{-terms are} \\ -x + 5y = 4 & \text{opposites;} \\ & \text{add.} \\[6pt] 2x + y = 6 & y\text{-terms are} \\ x + y = 3 & \text{the same;} \\ & \text{subtract.} \end{array}$$

ALTERNATE EXAMPLES

1. Solve by addition.
   $2x - y = 5$
   $x + y = 4$ (3, 1)
2. Solve by addition.
   $y = 3x + 10$
   $3x + 2y = 2$ $(-2, 4)$

3. Solve by subtraction.

$x + 3y = 3$

$x - 2y = -7$ $(-3, 2)$

** For an example in which one of the equations does not have both variables on the same side of the equal sign, use

$2x + 3y = 5$

$2x = 5y - 3$

(See B Exercises 21–24.)

Rewrite $2x = 5y - 3$ as $2x - 5y = -3$.

Then subtract and solve by the usual procedure.

The solution is $(1, 1)$.

POSSIBLE ERROR

$4x + 2y = 20$

$4x = 5y + 6$

In solving a system such as the one in Exercise 21, students sometimes fail to notice that the second equation does not have both variables on the left side. Students may subtract unthinkingly and write $-3y = 14$, which is incorrect.

Stress the need to read the equations carefully and to *think* about an appropriate approach before performing any operations.

DAILY QUIZ

Solve each system by addition or subtraction. Then check.

1. $x + y = -1$ **2.** $3x + 3y = -3$

$x - y = -3$ $2x - 3y = 13$

$(-2, 1)$ $(2, -3)$

3. $2x + 2y = 14$ **4.** $x - y = 0$

$2x + 3y = 12$ $3x + y = 0$

$(9, -2)$ $(0, 0)$

5. $5x - 3y = 8$

$5x - 2y = 5$ $\left(-\frac{1}{5}, -3\right)$

When the terms in one variable are the same, use subtraction to eliminate that variable.

EXAMPLE 3   Solve by subtraction: $\begin{array}{l} x + 2y = 7 \\ x - y = -5 \end{array}$

$\begin{array}{rl} x + 2y = & 7 \\ x - y = & -5 \end{array}$ Subtract similar terms on each side of the two equations.

$3y = 12$ Subtracting eliminates the variable x.

$y = 4$

Substitute 4 for y in either of the given equations and solve for x.

$x - y = -5$

$x - 4 = -5$

$x = -1$

Check to see that the solution is $(-1, 4)$.

CLASS EXERCISES

Solve each system and check. Use addition or subtraction.

1. $x + 2y = 3$ **2.** $3x - y = 1$ **3.** $-3x - y = 3$

$-x + 5y = 4$ $(1, 1)$ $-x + y = -9$ $(-4, -13)$ $3x + 4y = 6$ $(-2, 3)$

4. $5x + y = 12$ **5.** $-2x + 5y = -3$ **6.** $x + y = 1$

$2x + y = 3$ $(3, -3)$ $-6x + 5y = 1$ $(-1, -1)$ $-x + 3y = 1$ $\left(\frac{1}{2}, \frac{1}{2}\right)$

7. $x + y = 5$ **8.** $2x - y = -1$ **9.** $3x + 3y = 3$

$x + 4y = 11$ $(3, 2)$ $7x + y = 19$ $(2, 5)$ $2x + 3y = 1$ $(2, -1)$

EXERCISES

A   *Solve each system by addition. Then check.*

1. $x + y = 2$ **2.** $x + y = 1$ **3.** $2x + y = 2$

$x - y = 0$ $(1, 1)$ $x - y = -3$ $(-1, 2)$ $-2x + 2y = 4$ $(0, 2)$

Solve each system by subtraction. Then check.

4. $x + 3y = 3$ **5.** $2x + y = 6$ **6.** $x - 2y = 0$

$-2x + 3y = 6$ $\left(-1, \frac{4}{3}\right)$ $x + y = 3$ $(3, 0)$ $x - y = 1$ $(2, 1)$

Solve each system by addition or subtraction. Then check.

7. $2x + 2y = -2$ **8.** $x + 2y = 0$ **9.** $x - y = 0$

$3x - 2y = 12$ $(2, -3)$ $x + y = 1$ $(2, -1)$ $2x + y = 0$ $(0, 0)$

10. $3x + 3y = 21$ **11.** $x - y = 2$ **12.** $y = 3$

$3x + 4y = 24$ $(4, 3)$ $x + y = -3$ $\left(-\frac{1}{2}, -\frac{5}{2}\right)$ $x - y = 5$ $(8, 3)$

EXTRA PRACTICE, page 521

B Solve and check each system. Use addition, subtraction, or substitution.

13. $x + y = -6$
$x = -3$ $(-3, -3)$

14. $-2x + 3y = 6$
$2x + 3y = -12$ $\left(-4\frac{1}{2}, -1\right)$

15. $x - y = 1$
$y = 2$ $(3, 2)$

16. $x - 2y = -2$
$3x - 2y = -6$ $(-2, 0)$

17. $x + y = 8$
$x - y = 5$ $\left(6\frac{1}{2}, 1\frac{1}{2}\right)$

18. $3x - 2y = 11$
$6x + 2y = -8$ $\left(\frac{1}{3}, -5\right)$

19. $-4x + y = -10$
$-4x - 3y = 22$ $\left(\frac{1}{2}, -8\right)$

20. $7x - 2y = 9$
$7x - 3y = 3$ $(3, 6)$

21. $4x + 2y = 20$
$4x = 5y + 6$ $(4, 2)$

22. $5x + 2y = 61$
$3x = 2y + 43$ $(13, -2)$

23. $3x - 5y = 8$
$4x = 5y + 12$ $\left(4, \frac{4}{5}\right)$

24. $0.1x + 0.3y = 0.9$
$0.1x = 0.4y + 0.2$ $(6, 1)$

C
25. $\frac{1}{2}x + \frac{1}{4}y = 18$
$\frac{1}{2}x + \frac{1}{8}y = 14$ $(20, 32)$

26. $y + \frac{1}{2}x = 7$
$2y - \frac{1}{2}x = 8$ $(4, 5)$

27. $\frac{1}{3}x + \frac{1}{6}y = 2$
$\frac{2}{3}x + \frac{1}{6}y = 5$ $(9, -6)$

Here is another problem from the annual American High School Mathematics Examination (***M.A.A. Contest Problem Book***).

*28. Ann and Sue bought identical boxes of stationery. Ann used hers to write 1-sheet letters and Sue used hers to write 3-sheet letters. Ann used all the envelopes and had 50 sheets of paper left, while Sue used all of the sheets of paper and had 50 envelopes left. The number of sheets of paper in each box was

(A) 150   (B) 125   (C) 120   (D) 100   (E) 80   (A)

CHECKPOINT

Solve each system by graphing. Then check.

1. $y = 2x - 5$
$y = -x + 4$ $(3, 1)$

2. $2x + y = 1$
$3x - y = 4$ $(1, -1)$

3. $y = 2x + 4$
$y = 4x + 2$ $(1, 6)$

Solve each system by the substitution method. Then check.

4. $x = 4y$
$5x + 3y = -23$ $(-4, -1)$

5. $x + y = 1$
$y = 2x + 1$ $(0, 1)$

6. $x - 4y = 0$
$3x - 2y = 10$ $(4, 1)$

Solve each system by addition or subtraction. Then check.

7. $2x + y = 2$
$x - y = 4$ $(2, -2)$

8. $-x + y = 1$
$-x + 3y = 1$ $(-1, 0)$

9. $2x + y = -1$
$7x + y = 9$ $(2, -5)$

10. At what point do the lines $x + 10y = 6$ and $2x + y = 12$ intersect? $(6, 0)$

ENRICHMENT ACTIVITY

Have the students solve and check each of these systems.

$4x + y = b$
$3x + y = d$ $(b - d, 4d - 3b)$

$ax + by = c$
$ax - by = \frac{1}{2}c$ $\left(\frac{3c}{4a}, \frac{c}{4b}\right)$

Checkpoint

Students may check their answers with those given in the back of their books.

ADDITIONAL ANSWERS

Checkpoint

1.

2.

3.

LESSON NOTES

Discuss each of the model examples in detail, since some students have difficulty when both multiplication and addition are involved in the solution of a system of equations.

After Examples 1 and 2 have been discussed, point out the difference between the two situations. In Example 1, we need only multiply *one* of the equations because the coefficient of one variable is a factor of the coefficient of the same variable in the other equation. (That is, the coefficient of *x* is 1, which is a factor of the coefficient of 3*x*.) However, in Example 2, no coefficient of one variable is a factor of the coefficient of the same variable in the other equation. (That is, the coefficient of 2*x* is not a factor of the coefficient of 5*x*; and the coefficient of 2*y* is not a factor of the coefficient of 3*y*.) As you recognize, in situations such as the one in Example 2, we make use of the concept of common multiples.

Notice that in B Exercises 28–32, there are decimal coefficients for most of the variables. These equations can be simplified by first multiplying each equation by 10. However, the systems can be solved *without* multiplying by 10; the students might use a procedure similar to the one in Example 2. For instance, in Exercise 29, they can multiply the second equation by −2 and then use addition.

ALTERNATE EXAMPLE

1. Solve by eliminating *x*.
   $2x + y = 0$
   $x - 2y = 15$ $(3, -6)$

7-4 Using Multiplication with Addition

OBJECTIVE

To solve systems of equations by using multiplication together with addition.

The system below cannot be solved directly by addition or subtraction.

$$3x - y = 2$$
$$x + 2y = 3$$

But you can use multiplication to obtain a new equivalent system that *can* be solved by addition. Multiply each side of the first equation by 2.

$$2(3x - y) = 2(2)$$
$$x + 2y = 3$$
$$\longrightarrow$$

$$\begin{array}{l} 6x - 2y = 4 \\ \underline{x + 2y = 3} \\ 7x \quad\quad = 7 \\ \quad\quad x = 1 \end{array}$$

Now add, to eliminate *y*.

Substitute 1 for *x* in either equation and solve for *y*.

$$x + 2y = 3$$
$$1 + 2y = 3$$
$$2y = 2$$
$$y = 1$$

Check $x = 1$ and $y = 1$ in the original equations.

$$\begin{array}{cc} 3x - y = 2 & x + 2y = 3 \\ 3(1) - 1 \stackrel{?}{=} 2 & 1 + 2(1) \stackrel{?}{=} 3 \\ 2 = 2 \; \checkmark & 3 = 3 \; \checkmark \end{array}$$

The solution is (1, 1).

EXAMPLE 1   Solve by eliminating *x*: $\begin{array}{l} 3x + 2y = 0 \\ x - 5y = 17 \end{array}$

You can eliminate *x* by addition if you first multiply each side of the second equation by −3.

$$3x + 2y = 0$$
$$-3(x - 5y) = -3(17)$$
$$\longrightarrow$$

$$\begin{array}{l} 3x + 2y = 0 \\ \underline{-3x + 15y = -51} \\ 17y = -51 \\ y = -3 \end{array}$$

Now add.

Solve for *y*.

$$3x + 2(-3) = 0$$ Substitute −3 for *y* in the first equation.
$$3x - 6 = 0$$ Solve for *x*.
$$3x - 6$$
$$x = 2$$

To check, substitute $x = 2$ and $y = -3$ in the original equations.

The solution is (2, −3).

CHAPTER 7

Sometimes you need to use the multiplication property of equality with *each* equation. You can eliminate either variable this way.

EXAMPLE 2 Solve the system: $\begin{array}{l} 2x - 3y = -8 \\ 5x + 2y = -1 \end{array}$

Method I Eliminate y first. Multiply the first equation by 2 and the second by 3. Then add.

$$2(2x - 3y) = 2(-8)$$
$$3(5x + 2y) = 3(-1)$$

$\longrightarrow$

$$\begin{array}{r} 4x - 6y = -16 \\ 15x + 6y = -3 \\ \hline 19x = -19 \\ x = -1 \end{array}$$

Now find y by substituting -1 for x.

$$\begin{array}{r} 2x - 3y = -8 \\ 2(-1) - 3y = -8 \\ -3y = -6 \\ y = 2 \end{array}$$

The solution is $(-1, 2)$.

Method II Eliminate x first. Multiply the first equation by 5 and the second by -2. Then add.

$$5(2x - 3y) = 5(-8)$$
$$-2(5x + 2y) = -2(-1)$$

$\longrightarrow$

$$\begin{array}{r} 10x - 15y = -40 \\ -10x - 4y = 2 \\ \hline -19y = -38 \\ y = 2 \end{array}$$

Show by substitution that $x = -1$. The solution is $(-1, 2)$.

CLASS EXERCISES

Tell what steps you would take to eliminate **x** *by addition. Then solve the system.*
Steps may vary.

1. $-3x + y = -7$
$x - 4y = -5$
Mult. (2) by 3; (3, 2)

2. $x - y = 2$
$4x + 2y = -28$
Mult. (1) by -4; $(-4, -6)$

3. $5x + 2y = 17$
$3x - 7y = 2$
Mult. (1) by 3; Mult. (2) by -5; (3, 1)

Tell what steps you would take to eliminate **y** *by addition. Then solve the system.*

4. $3x - 2y = 2$
$2x + y = 6$
Mult. (2) by 2; (2, 2)

5. $2x + 4y = -2$
$-3x - 5y = 4$
Mult. (1) by 5; Mult. (2) by 4;
$(-3, 1)$

6. $5x - 6y = 32$
$2x - 5y = 18$
Mult. (1) by 5; Mult (2) by -6;
$(4, -2)$

EXERCISES

A Solve each system, using multiplication with addition. Then check.

1. $x + y = 0$
$9x - 5y = 42$ $(3, -3)$

2. $-5x + 8y = 18$
$x - y = 0$ $(6, 6)$

3. $x - y = 1$
$9x + 8y = 77$ $(5, 4)$

4. $3x - 2y = 10$
$x - y = 1$ $(8, 7)$

5. $8x - 5y = 58$
$x + y = 4$ $(6, -2)$

6. $6x - 10y = 4$
$x + y = 14$ $(9, 5)$

2. Solve the system by two methods.
$3x - 2y = -12$
$4x + y = -5$ $(-2, 3)$

POSSIBLE ERROR

In using multiplication with addition to solve a system of equations, students sometimes forget to multiply *both* sides of an equation. For instance, in solving Class Exercise 1, students may incorrectly multiply as shown below.

$$-3x + y = -7$$
$$3(x - 4y) = -5$$
$$\downarrow$$
$$-3x + y = -7$$
$$3x - 12y = -5$$

This error leads to the answer $\left(\dfrac{89}{33}, \dfrac{12}{11}\right)$, which is incorrect.

Again emphasize the importance of checking the possible answer in both of the original equations.

Also, it will be worthwhile to provide practice in multiplying equations. For instance:

Multiply $4x - 2y = 3$ by 5.
$20x - 10y = 15$

DAILY QUIZ

Solve each system, using multiplication with addition. Then check.

1. $x + y = 0$
$3x - 2y = 15$
$(3, -3)$

2. $2x - 3y = 9$
$x - y = 3$
$(0, -3)$

3. $8x - 2y = 52$
$6x + 3y = 48$
$(7, 2)$

4. $4x + 3y = 6$
$x - 2y = -4$
$(0, 2)$

5. $4x + 5y = 25$
$3x + 7y = 61$ $(-10, 13)$

EXTRA PRACTICE, page 521

ENRICHMENT ACTIVITY

Challenge the students to solve this problem:

A rectangle has two of its sides on the coordinate axes and one of its vertices at the intersection of these lines:

$$2x + 3y = 7$$
$$4x - 2y = 5$$

Find the area of the rectangle.

$2\dfrac{5}{128}$ sq. units

Using BASIC

The solution for Exercise 50 can be used to write a program for solving a system of equations in the form:

$$ax + by = c$$
$$dx + ey = f$$

```
10  PRINT "ENTER A, B, C"
20  INPUT A, B, C
30  PRINT "ENTER D, E, F"
40  INPUT D, E, F
50  LET K = A * E - B * D
60  LET X = (C * E - B * F) / K
70  PRINT "X = "; X
80  LET Y = (A * F - C * D) / K
90  PRINT "Y = "; Y
99  END
```

---

7. $7x - 5y = 161$
 $x - 4y = 0$ (28, 7)

8. $2x + y = 5$
 $x + 2y = 19$ (−3, 11)

9. $4x + 5y = 30$
 $6x + y = 19$ $\left(\frac{5}{2}, 4\right)$

10. $x + y = 13$
 $x - y = 5$ (9, 4)

11. $5x + 2y = 61$
 $3x - 2y = 43$ (13, −2)

12. $11x - 4y = 41$
 $7x + 2y = 42$ $\left(5, \frac{7}{2}\right)$

13. $5x + 6y = 17$
 $3x - 2y = 27$ (7, −3)

14. $2x + 3y = 8$
 $3x + y = 5$ (1, 2)

15. $x + 2y = 3$
 $-4x + 7y = 18$ (−1, 2)

16. $2x - 3y = -5$
 $3x - 2y = -5$ (−1, 1)

17. $4x + 3y = 1$
 $3x + 4y = -1$ (1, −1)

18. $5x + 6y = 11$
 $2x - 4y = -2$ (1, 1)

19. $x - 2y = 7$
 $5x - 2y = -5$ (−3, −5)

20. $6x + 3y = 48$
 $4x - y = 26$ (7, 2)

21. $8x + 6y = 5$
 $2x + y = 1$ $\left(\frac{1}{4}, \frac{1}{2}\right)$

22. $6x - 5y = -5$
 $4x + 2y = 2$ (0, 1)

23. $-6x + 7y = -2$
 $9x - 5y = -8$ (−2, −2)

24. $2x + 5y = 26$
 $-3x - 4y = -25$ (3, 4)

B

25. $11x - 3y + 34 = 0$
 $8x + 10y - 24 = 0$ (−2, 4)

26. $5x - 4y - 16 = 0$
 $4x - 5y - 11 = 0$ (4, 1)

27. $5x + 4y = 24$
 $7x + 3y = 57$ (12, −9)

28. $2x - 1.5y = 10$
 $3x - 0.5y = 8$ (2, −4)

29. $0.4x - 0.2y = 0.4$
 $0.2x - 0.3y = 0.6$ (0, −2)

30. $0.5x + 0.2y = 0.8$
 $0.2x - 0.3y = 0.7$ (2, −1)

31. $0.7x - 0.5y = 9.4$
 $0.9x + 0.7y = 0$ (7, −9)

32. $0.3x + 0.4y = 5$
 $0.4x + 0.3y = 5.5$ (10, 5)

33. $x = 2 - y$
 $y = x$ (1, 1)

34. $6x + 10y = 10$
 $9x = 4y + 53$ (5, −2)

35. $2y + x = 0$
 $x + y - 1 = 0$ (2, −1)

36. $y = 1 - x$
 $x = y - 3$ (−1, 2)

37. $3x + 1 = 2y$
 $-4y + 2x = 2$ (−1, −1)

38. $5x = 7y - 92$
 $9x + 4y = 17$ (−3, 11)

39. $3x = 9 - 9y$
 $-3y = 6 - 2x$ (3, 0)

40. $\dfrac{1}{2}x + \dfrac{1}{2}y = 2$

 $4x + 7y = 10$ (6, −2)

41. $\dfrac{1}{2}x + \dfrac{2}{3}y = 4$

 $x + y = 8$ (8, 0)

42. $\dfrac{x}{3} - 4y = 7$

 $\dfrac{x}{9} + 3y = -2$ (9, −1)

C

43. $2(y - 2) + x = 0$
 $2(x - 1) + y = 0$ (0, 2)

44. $x + 2(y + 4) = 21$
 $2x - (y + 1) = 0$ (3, 5)

45. $3(3x + 1) = 13y$
 $3(2x - 1) = 7y$ (4, 3)

Solve for x and y. First let $a = \frac{1}{x}$ and $b = \frac{1}{y}$. Solve for a and b. Then find x and y.

46. $\dfrac{3}{x} - \dfrac{2}{y} = 10$

 $\dfrac{4}{x} + \dfrac{1}{y} = 28$ $\left(\frac{1}{6}, \frac{1}{4}\right)$

47. $\dfrac{10}{x} + \dfrac{6}{y} = 7$

 $\dfrac{14}{x} - \dfrac{9}{y} = 4$ (2, 3)

48. $\dfrac{1}{2x} + \dfrac{1}{3y} = 12$

 $\dfrac{1}{4x} + \dfrac{1}{9y} = 5$ $\left(\frac{1}{12}, \frac{1}{18}\right)$

49. $\dfrac{1}{2x} - \dfrac{3}{8y} = 2$

 $\dfrac{5}{3x} - \dfrac{5}{6y} = 8\frac{1}{3}$ $\left(\frac{1}{7}, \frac{1}{4}\right)$

*50. Solve the following system for x and y. Assume that $ae - bd \neq 0$.
 $ax + by = c$
 $dx + ey = f$ $x = \dfrac{ce - bf}{ae - bd}, \; y = \dfrac{af - cd}{ae - bd}$

Generalizing from the Specific

1. Choose a two-digit number with the tens digit greater than the units (ones) digit.

   Example   Start with 75.

   tens digit ⤴
   units digit ⤴

   Subtract 9 times the positive difference of the digits from the number.

   $75 - 9(7 - 5) = 57$

   $\underbrace{\qquad\qquad}_{?}$

   How is the result related to the original number?   The digits are reversed.

   Try some examples of your own. Do you still get a similar result?   Yes

2. Choose a two-digit number with the tens digit less than the units (ones) digit.

   Example   Start with 48.

   tens digit
   units digit

   Add 9 times the positive difference of the digits to the number.

   $48 + 9(8 - 4) = 84$

   $\underbrace{\qquad\qquad}_{?}$

   How is the result related to the original number?   The digits are reversed.

   Again, try some other examples of your own. Do you get a similar result?   Yes

3. Try to prove algebraically why these results occur, using the number $10t + u$. Here t is the tens digit and u is the units digit. If $t = 4$ and $u = 8$, then $10(4) + 8 = 48$.

   Consider both the cases, where $t > u$ and where $t < u$.

   Case 1 $t > u$, so that $t - u$ is positive.
   - Express 9 times the difference of the digits. $9(t - u)$
   - Subtract 9 times the difference of the digits from the number $10t + u$. Then simplify. $10t + u - 9(t - u) = t + 10u$
   - How is the result related to the original number, $10t + u$?
     t and u are reversed.

   Case 2 $t < u$, so that $u - t$ is positive.
   - Express 9 times the difference of the digits. $9(u - t)$
   - Add 9 times the difference of the digits to the number $10t + u$. Then simplify. $10t + u + 9(u - t) = t + 10u$
   - How is the result related to the original number? t and u are reversed.

Strategies for Problem Solving
The puzzle aspect of this situation should appeal to many students. However, there is an important point to be made. After doing Exercises 1–2, we know only that the specified manipulations of such two-digit numbers result in a two-digit number with the digits reversed. Will this always happen? If so, why? In Exercise 3, we prove algebraically that *it will always happen*. The power of algebra is revealed in a single experience in this lesson.

LESSON NOTES

In this lesson, the text examines and summarizes the three distinct types of results that can occur when a system of linear equations is solved algebraically. These results are

(a) We obtain a single unique solution such as $x = 3$ and $y = 4$. (The system is consistent and independent.)
(b) We obtain a false equality such as $-1 = 2$. (The system is inconsistent and independent.)
(c) We obtain a true equality such as $-3 = -3$. (The system is consistent and dependent.)

The students have worked mostly with consistent, independent systems in preceding lessons. In Lesson 7-2, they also worked with pairs of equations whose graphs were parallel lines; thus, those systems were inconsistent and independent. Example 1 shows what happens when such a system is solved algebraically. Then, on page 269, the text considers a dependent system—that is, a system which consists of a pair of equivalent equations. Example 2 shows what happens when such a system is solved algebraically. Emphasize to the students: Before classifying a system as inconsistent or dependent, they should check the numerical equality that they obtained to see whether it is true or false.

ALTERNATE EXAMPLE

1. Solve the system.
   $y = 7x - 3$
   $y = 7x + 5$ No solution

7-5 Classifying Systems of Equations

OBJECTIVES

To determine whether a system of linear equations has no solution, one solution, or many solutions.
To identify a system of equations as consistent or inconsistent, dependent or independent.

A system is **consistent** if it has at least one solution.

A system is **independent** if its equations have different graphs.

The system of equations shown here has just one solution, $\left(\frac{1}{2}, \frac{1}{2}\right)$. It is a consistent and independent system.

$y = 3x - 1$
$y = -3x + 2$
consistent
independent

Other systems of equations have *no* solutions. Their graphs are parallel lines. Such systems are **inconsistent** and independent.

EXAMPLE 1 Solve the system: $\begin{aligned} y &= 3x - 1 \\ y &= 3x + 2 \end{aligned}$

Method I Substitution

Substitute $3x - 1$ for y in the second equation.

$3x - 1 = 3x + 2$

$\qquad -1 = 2$ False; no solution

Method II Addition or subtraction

Subtract similar terms.

$y = 3x - 1$
$\underline{y = 3x + 2}$
$0 = 0 \ - 3$
$0 = -3$ False; no solution

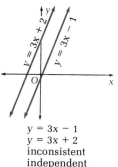

$y = 3x - 1$
$y = 3x + 2$
inconsistent
independent

Either method shows that the system is inconsistent and independent. There is no solution since the lines are parallel.

268

A system of equivalent equations has graphs that are identical lines. It is a consistent system because it has infinitely many solutions. But it is a **dependent** system because its equations have identical, not distinct, graphs.

Example 2 shows what happens when you try to solve a dependent system.

EXAMPLE 2   Solve the system: $\begin{array}{l} 3x - y = 1 \\ -9x + 3y = -3 \end{array}$

$$3x - y = 1$$
$$-9x + 3y = -3$$
consistent
dependent

Method I   Substitution

Solve the first equation for y.

$$y = 3x - 1$$

Substitute $3x - 1$ for y in the second equation.

$$-9x + 3(3x - 1) = -3$$
$$-9x + 9x - 3 = -3$$
$$-3 = -3 \qquad \text{True}$$

Method II   Multiplication and addition

Multiply the first equation by 3 and add.

$$\begin{array}{ll} 3(3x - y) = 3(1) & \longrightarrow \qquad 9x - 3y = 3 \\ -9x + 3y = -3 & \qquad\qquad\quad \underline{-9x + 3y = -3} \\ & \qquad\qquad\qquad\qquad 0 = 0 \qquad \text{True} \end{array}$$

Since the resulting equation is true by either method, *every* point (x, y) on the single line graph is a solution. The system is consistent and dependent.

Dependent systems can be identified without first trying to solve them. Express each equation in slope-intercept form, $y = mx + b$.

$$3x - y = 1 \qquad \longrightarrow \qquad y = 3x - 1$$
$$-9x + 3y = -3 \qquad \longrightarrow \qquad y = 3x - 1$$

Here is a summary of the classifications for systems of linear equations.

Classification	Graph	Number of Solutions
Consistent and independent	Lines that intersect in exactly one point	Exactly one
Inconsistent and independent	Parallel lines, which never intersect	None
Consistent and dependent	Identical lines, which intersect at every point	Infinitely many

ALTERNATE EXAMPLE

2. Solve the system.
$3x - 2y = 5$
$-6x + 4y = -10$
Every point on the single line is a solution. The system is consistent and dependent.

POSSIBLE ERROR

Some students may not understand the distinction between a system that is inconsistent and a system that is dependent.

Stress that an inconsistent system has no solution. On the other hand, a dependent system has an infinite number of solutions. Point out that in a dependent system, any ordered pair (x, y) that is a solution of one equation is a solution of the other equation. To help students understand dependent systems, have them substitute values such as $(0, -1)$, $(1, 2)$, and $(2, 5)$ in both equations in Example 2. They will find that each of the ordered pairs is a solution for both equations.

Solve each system if a unique solution exists. Then classify the system.

1. $x + y = 6$
$x - y = 4$ (5, 1)
Consist.; indep.

2. $4x - 3y = 7$
$8x - 6y = 10$ Inconsist.; indep.

For each system, write *no solution, one solution,* or *infinitely many solutions.*

3. $x + 2y = 5$
$3x + 6y = 15$ Inf. many sol.

4. $3x - 5y = 6$
$5y - 3x = 4$ No sol.

5. $x - 4y = 16$
$x + 4y = 0$ One sol.

ASSIGNMENT GUIDE
(pages 270–271)

Minimum course: omit
Average course: 1–33 odd
Maximum course: 1–33 odd,
34–38
Average and
maximum courses: *Checkpoint*
review
exercises

ADDITIONAL ANSWERS

Exercises

1. (5, 3); consist.; indep.
2. Inconsist.; indep.
3. Inconsist.; indep.
4. Consist.; dep.
5. (−1, 2); consist.; indep.
6. Inconsist.; indep.
7. (2, 3); consist.; indep.
8. (8, 5); consist.; indep.
9. Inconsist.; indep.
10. Inconsist.; indep.
11. Inconsist.; indep.
12. Inconsist.; indep.

CLASS EXERCISES

A system of two equations has the given graph. Classify the system as consistent or inconsistent, and as dependent or independent.

1. **2.** **3.**

Inconsistent; independent   Consistent; independent   Consistent; dependent

Classify each system as consistent or inconsistent, and as dependent or independent.

4. $y = 3x + 4$ Consistent; independent
$y = 2x + 4$

5. $y = 3x + 1$ Inconsistent; independent
$y = 3x + 2$

6. $y = 2x + 4$ Consistent; dependent
$2x - y = -4$

7. $x + y = 5$ Consistent; dependent
$2x + 2y = 10$

8. $y = x + 4$ Inconsistent; independent
$2y = 2x + 4$

9. $y = x - 3$ Consistent; independent
$y = 3x - 1$

Solve each system for which exactly one solution exists.

10. $x + 3y = 7$
$-x + 3y = 5$ (1, 2)

11. $y = x - 8$
$x + 5y = 2$ (7, −1)

12. $y = -5x$
$3y + 15x = 6$ No solution

EXERCISES

A   Solve each system if a unique solution exists. Then classify the system.

1. $x + y = 8$
$x - y = 2$

2. $x + y = -4$
$-x - y = 8$

3. $2x - y = 3$
$6x - 3y = 11$

4. $3x - y = 4$
$2y - 6x = -8$

5. $2x + 5y = 8$
$3x - 2y = -7$

6. $4x - 6y = 8$
$6x - 9y = 14$

7. $3x + 2y = 12$
$3y - 2x = 5$

8. $5x - 8y = 0$
$7y - 4x = 3$

9. $2x - 2y = 5$
$-x + y = 2$

10. $y - 2x = -8$
$2x - y = 10$

11. $x + y = 4$
$28 - 2x = 2y$

12. $y + 4x = 10$
$8x = 10 - 2y$

For each system, write **no solution, one solution,** or **infinitely many solutions.**

13. $3x - y = 4$
$6x + 2y = 8$ One sol.

14. $3x - 4y = 1$
$-9x + 12y = -3$ Inf. many sol.

15. $5x - 10y = 15$
$x - y = 15$ One sol.

16. $-2x - 3y = 5$
$4x + 6y = -10$ Inf. many sol.

17. $-4x + 12y = 20$
$-x + 3y = 5$ Inf. many sol.

18. $x - y = 3$
$y - x = 0$ No sol.

19. $2x - 5y = 1$
$4x - 10y + 1 = 0$ No sol.

20. $x + 3y - 4 = 0$
$4x = 1 - 3y$ One sol.

21. $2x - y + 1 = 0$
$y = 2x + 1$ Inf. many sol.

EXTRA PRACTICE, page 521

B

Solve each system if a unique solution exists. Then classify the system.

22. $9 = x + y$
$2y + 2x = 10$

23. $6x + 3y = 6$
$3x + y = 2$

24. $2x - 3 = 4y$
$2y - 6 = x$

25. $3x - 2 = 4y$
$3x - 4y = 1$

26. $3x - 5 = y$
$4x + y = 5$

27. $0.5x + 0.3y = 0.4$
$0.3x + 0.2y = 0.5$

28. $0.4x + 0.3y = 1.6$
$9 = 8x + 6y$

29. $x - 4 = 0.5y$
$0.5x + y = -3$

30. $0.8x - 1.2y = 1$
$1.8y - 1.2x = 1.5$

31. $6y = 2(4x - 5)$
$4x - 3y = 10$

32. $2x - 7y = 0$
$2(3x - 8) = 5y$

33. $0.3(x - 1) = 2y$
$7y = x$

34. If the sum of two numbers, x and y, is 13 and the difference is 5, what are the numbers?   9 and 4

C

35. Two numbers, s and t, have a sum of 10. The first number decreased by 5 is equal to the opposite of the second number. How many pairs of numbers satisfy these conditions?   None

Determine whether each system of equations in **x** and **y** has **no solution, one solution,** or **infinitely many solutions.** The coefficients, **a, b,** and **n,** are all nonzero, and **c ≠ d.**

36. $ax + by = c$
$ax + by = d$
No solution

37. $ax + by = d$
$nax + nby = nd$
Infinitely many solutions

38. $ax + by = d$
$nax - nby = nc$
One solution

CHECKPOINT

Solve each system by graphing. Then check.

1. $x + y = 1$
$x - y = 5$ (3, −2)

2. $x + y = 0$
$2x + y = 4$ (4, −4)

3. $y = 3$
$y - x = 5$ (−2, 3)

Solve each system, if a unique solution exists. Then classify the system as **consistent** or **inconsistent** and as **dependent** or **independent.**

4. $x + 3y = 9$
$x = 4y + 2$ (6, 1);
consistent; independent

5. $y - 8x = 4$
$y + 5 = 8x$
Inconsistent; independent

6. $8x + 6y = 5$
$2x + y = 1$ $\left(\frac{1}{4}, \frac{1}{2}\right)$;
consistent; independent

7. $-8x - 3y = 23$
$2x - 5y = -23$ (−4, 3);
consistent; independent

8. $8x - 6y = 0$
$-4x + 3y = 0$
consistent; dependent

9. $-2x + \frac{1}{2}y = 4\frac{1}{2}$
$-4x - 3y = 1$ $\left(-\frac{7}{4}, 2\right)$;
consistent; independent

10. The sum of two numbers, x and y, is 17. Three times the smaller number x is 1 more than twice the larger number y. Find x and y. $x = 7; y = 10$

Let l be the length of a rectangle. Let w be the width. Write an equation that indicates:

1. The length is 3 less than twice the width. $l = 2w - 3$
2. The perimeter of the rectangle is 42 cm. $2(l + w) = 42$ or $2l + 2w = 42$

LESSON NOTES

As you develop this lesson, some students may suggest that a situation such as the one in Example 1 or 2 can be solved by using an equation in one variable. For instance, in Example 1:

Let x = Ken's age.
Then $x + 8$ = Rema's age.
$x + (x + 8) = 60$
$\quad 2x + 8 = 60$
$\quad\quad 2x = 52$
$\quad\quad\quad x = 26$ and $x + 8 = 34$
Ken is 26 and Rema is 34.

Commend any student who can demonstrate the solution using just one equation in one variable. However, encourage the students to use the system-of-equations approach, since it is more useful in a number of the exercises. The equations that are written using the system approach are generally simpler than those equations that use just one variable.

ALTERNATE EXAMPLES

1. Carlos is 4 years older than his sister, Maria. The sum of their ages is 28. Find the age of each. Carlos is 16 and Maria is 12.
2. The length of a rectangle is 1 less than 3 times its width. The perimeter is 22 cm. What is the length? The length is 8 cm.

7-6 Problem Solving: Using Two Variables

OBJECTIVE

To solve word problems by using systems of equations.

Systems of two equations with two variables are used to solve many kinds of problems.

EXAMPLE 1

Rema is older than Ken. The difference of their ages is 8, and the sum of their ages is 60. Find the age of each.

Strategy: Write and solve two equations in two unknowns.

Read the problem to find the key ideas.

Two ages differ by 8 and have a sum of 60.

Use two variables.

Let x be Rema's age and let y be Ken's age.

Write two equations.

$x - y = 8$ — Rema's age is 8 more than Ken's age.
$x + y = 60$ — The sum of their ages is 60.

Find the solution.

$$\begin{aligned} x - y &= 8 \\ x + y &= 60 \end{aligned}$$ — Add the two equations and solve for x.

$$\begin{aligned} 2x &= 68 \\ x &= 34 \end{aligned}$$

$34 + y = 60$ — Substitute 34 for x in the second equation and solve for y.
$\quad\quad y = 26$

Check that the ages differ by 8 and have a sum of 60.

Answer the question.

Rema is 34 and Ken is 26 years old.

EXAMPLE 2

The length of a rectangle is 1 cm more than twice the width. The perimeter is 32 cm. What is the width?

Use two variables.

Let l be the length; let w be the width.

Write two equations.

$l = 2w + 1$ — l is 1 more than twice w.
$2(l + w) = 32$ — The perimeter is 32.

Find the solution.

$2(2w + 1 + w) = 32$ — In the second equation, substitute
$4w + 2 + 2w = 32$ — $2w + 1$ for l and solve for w.
$\quad\quad 6w = 30$
$\quad\quad\; w = 5$

To check, find the length and show that the perimeter is 32 cm.

Answer the question. The width is 5 cm.

272

EXAMPLE 3

Large boxes of cereal cost $1.29 each and small boxes cost $.83 each. Brook spent $6.82 for some of both sizes. He spent $3.50 more on the larger size. How many of each size did he buy?

Let x = number of larger size.

Let y = number of smaller size.

$$1.29x + 0.83y = 6.82$$
$$\underline{1.29x - 0.83y = 3.50}$$
$$2.58x \qquad\quad = 10.32$$
$$x = 4$$

$$1.29(4) + 0.83y = 6.82$$
$$5.16 + 0.83y = 6.82$$
$$0.83y = 1.66$$
$$y = 2$$

Check with the conditions of the problem.

Four large boxes cost $5.16, and two small boxes cost $1.66.
Total cost: $5.16 + $1.66 = $6.82 ✔
Difference in costs, larger size less smaller: $5.16 − $1.66 = $3.50 ✔

Answer   Brook bought 4 large boxes and 2 small boxes of cereal.

CLASS EXERCISES

*Solve a system of equations to find the two numbers. Let **x** represent the smaller number and **y** the larger.*

1. The sum of two numbers is 23. Their difference is 9. 7 and 16

2. The sum of two numbers is 25. One number is 4 times the other number. 5 and 20

3. One number exceeds another by 36. Together their sum is 116. 40 and 76

4. The smaller of two numbers is 9 less than the larger. The larger number is 1 less than twice the smaller. 10 and 19

Solve, using two equations in two variables.

5. Amy is 13 years older than Andy. The sum of their ages is 27. How old are they? Andy, 7; Amy, 20

6. The length of a rectangle is 2 cm less than 3 times the width. The perimeter is 52 cm. What is the width? 7 cm

7. Six grapefruits and 10 oranges cost $3.00. The oranges cost 60¢ less than the grapefruits. Find the price of one orange and the price of one grapefruit. One orange costs 12¢; one grapefruit costs 30¢

SYSTEMS OF LINEAR EQUATIONS

273

ALTERNATE EXAMPLE

3. Large pads cost $1.25 and small pads cost $.75. Greg spent $9.75 for some of both sizes. He spent $5.25 more on the large pads. How many of each size did he buy? Greg bought 6 large pads and 3 small pads.

POSSIBLE ERROR

In solving a word problem by using a system of equations, students may automatically give the solution of the system as the answer to the problem. Yet the solution of the system is not always the answer to the problem. For instance, in Example 2, some students might solve for l as well as for w and give $w = 5$, $l = 11$ as the answer. Point out that the problem asks only for the width, and emphasize the need to read problems carefully.

To further emphasize this point, show how the solution of the system would remain the same but the answer to the problem would change if the question were "What is the area of the rectangle?" The solution of the system would still be $w = 5$, $l = 11$, but the answer to the problem would be 55 cm².

DAILY QUIZ

Solve by using two equations in two variables.

1. The sum of two numbers is 63. Their difference is 13. Find the two numbers. 38 and 25

2. The difference between two numbers is 18. The larger is three times the smaller. Find the numbers. 27 and 9

3. Adam is twice as old as Beth. The sum of their ages is 54. Find the age of each. Adam is 36; Beth is 18.

[Daily Quiz continues on page 274.]

4. The length of a rectangle is 3 inches more than four times its width. The perimeter is 106 inches. Find the dimensions. The width is 10 inches; the length is 43 inches.

5. The sum of two numbers is 81. Three times the first is 9 more than the second number. What are the numbers? The first number is $22\frac{1}{2}$; the second number is $58\frac{1}{2}$.

ASSIGNMENT GUIDE
(pages 274–275)

Minimum course: 1–8
    second day: 9–16
Average course: 1–23 odd
    second day: 12–26 even
Maximum course: 1–27 odd

EXERCISES

A *Solve, using two equations in two variables.*

1. The sum of two numbers is 65; their difference is 11. Find the numbers. 38 and 27

2. The sum of two numbers is 73; their difference is 37. Find the numbers. 18 and 55

3. The difference between two numbers is 15. The larger is four times the smaller. Find the numbers. 5 and 20

4. The larger of two numbers exceeds the smaller by 3. If you double the smaller number, the result is 4 more than the larger. 7 and 10

5. Derek is three times as old as Denise. The difference between their ages is 16. Find the age of each. Denise is 8. Derek is 24.

6. Fred is 3 years more than twice as old as Jan. The sum of their ages is 48. How old is each? Jan is 15. Fred is 33.

7. A board 20 feet long is cut into two pieces. The difference between the lengths of the two pieces is 3 feet. How long is each piece? $8\frac{1}{2}$ ft.; $11\frac{1}{2}$ ft.

8. The length of a rectangle is 6 inches more than twice its width. The perimeter is 72 inches. Find the length and width. Width is 10″. Length is 26″.

9. The length of a rectangle is 5 inches less than three times its width. The perimeter is 86 inches. Find the length and width. Width is 12″. Length is 31″.

10. Large cans of soup cost 74¢ and small cans cost 52¢. Tony bought several cans for $4.30. He spent 14¢ more for the large cans than for the small ones. How many cans of each size did he buy? 3 large, 4 small

B

11. The sum of two numbers is 135. Twice the first number equals 280 minus 3 times the second number. What are the numbers? 125 and 10

12. The sum of two numbers is 100. Twice the first number is 5 more than the second number. What are the numbers? 35 and 65

13. The difference between two numbers is 9. Twice the larger number is equal to 5 times the smaller number. Find the numbers. 6 and 15

14. The sum of two numbers is 68. Their difference is twice the smaller number. Find the numbers. 17 and 51

15. Peter is 6 years older than Ben. In 5 years Peter will be twice as old as Ben. How old are they now? Peter is 7. Ben is 1.

	Ages now	Ages in 5 years
Peter	p	$p + 5$
Ben	b	$b + 5$

16. Frieda is 5 years older than her brother, Gene. Three years ago she was twice as old as her brother. How old is each now? Frieda is 13. Gene is 8.

17. Lana bought 17¢ and 20¢ stamps. She bought 5 more of the 20¢ stamps and spent $1.39 more on them. How many of each did she buy?
13 of the 17¢ stamps, 18 of the 20¢ stamps

CHAPTER 7

EXTRA PRACTICE, pages 521–522

18. Mark is 1 year older than Fran. Last year their ages added to 49. How old is each now? *Mark is 26. Fran is 25.*

19. Two years ago Cary was twice as old as Dan. In 4 years the sum of their ages will be 30. How old are they now? *Dan is 8. Cary is 14.*

	Ages now	Ages 2 years ago	Ages in 4 years
Cary	c	$c - 2$	$c + 4$
Dan	d	$d - 2$	$d + 4$

20. Last year Lily was 3 times as old as Lyle. In 3 years she will be 1 year more than twice as old as Lyle. How old are they now? *Lyle is 6. Lily is 16.*

21. A rectangle has a perimeter of 30 inches. If the length were increased an amount equal to the width, the perimeter would be 42. Find the length and width. *Length is 9 in. Width is 6 in.*

22. The length of a rectangle is 2 inches more than twice its width. If its length is increased by 5 inches, the rectangle would be 3 times as long as it is wide. Find the dimensions of the rectangle. *Length is 16 in. Width is 7 in*

23. The sum of two numbers is 68. Their difference exceeds twice the smaller number by 4. Find the numbers. *16 and 52*

24. An isosceles triangle has two sides each 3 inches longer than the third side. The perimeter of the triangle is 48 inches. Find the lengths of the three sides. *14", 17", 17"*

C

25. One square has a perimeter twice that of another square. If the perimeter of the smaller square is increased by 16 inches, it would have the same perimeter as the larger square. How long are the sides of each square? *Smaller 4"; larger 8"*

26. The manager of Kep's Deli has $520 in $1 and $5 bills. She has 5 times as many $1 bills as $5 bills. How many of each kind does she have? *Two hundred sixty $1 bills; fifty-two $5 bills*

27. The sum of the ages of Amy and her dog is now 18 years. In 4 years, the dog will be $\frac{1}{5}$ as old as Amy. How old is each now? *Dog is $\frac{1}{3}$ yr old. Amy is $17\frac{2}{3}$ yr old.*

28. Linda's age plus Al's age is 32 years. The difference between twice Al's age and $\frac{1}{2}$ Linda's age is 29 years. How old is each? *Al is 18. Linda is 14.*

CHALLENGE

Three-Coin Puzzle

Three coins are placed on a table as shown, two "heads" and one "tails."

Can you turn the coins, two at a time, so the result is two "tails" and one "heads"?

Write an algebraic expression to
represent the value in cents of each
of the following:
1. n quarters $25n$
2. x dimes $10x$
3. y pennies y
4. d dimes and n nickels
$10d + 5n$

LESSON NOTES

Coin and digit problems provide interesting situations in which to apply
the work with systems of equations.

As you discuss Example 1, you
may wish to note that the system
can also be solved by using multiplication and addition. For instance:

$$d + q = 50 \quad \rightarrow -10d - 10q = -500$$
$$10d + 25q = 1100 \rightarrow \underline{10d + 25q = 1100}$$
$$15q = 600$$
$$q = 40$$
$$d + 40 = 50$$
$$d = 10$$

In Example 2, a few students may
be puzzled by the term "units digit."
If so, use the term "ones digit,"
which may be more familiar to them.

ALTERNATE EXAMPLE

1. 21 coins in dimes and quarters
have a value of $3.45. How
many dimes and how many
quarters are there? There are
12 dimes and 9 quarters.

7-7 Problem Solving: Coin and Digit Problems

OBJECTIVE _____

To use systems of equations in solving coin and digit problems.

When solving coin problems, the total value of certain numbers of
coins needs to be computed. This is done by finding the product of the
value of each coin times the number of such coins.

EXAMPLE 1

50 coins in dimes and quarters have a total value of $11.00. How
many dimes and how many quarters are there?

**Strategy: Use two
equations in two
unknowns, one for
the total number of
coins and one for
the total value.**

Read the problem to find the key ideas.

The number of coins is 50. The value of the coins is $11.00.

Use two variables.

	Number	Value in Cents
dimes	d	$10d$
quarters	q	$25q$

Write two equations.

$$d + q = 50 \qquad \text{Total number of coins}$$
$$10d + 25q = 1100 \qquad \text{Total value in cents}$$

Solve the system.

Use substitution. Solve the first equation for d.
$$d + q = 50$$
$$d = 50 - q$$

Substitute $50 - q$ for d in the second equation.
$$10d + 25q = 1100$$
$$10(50 - q) + 25q = 1100$$
$$500 - 10q + 25q = 1100$$
$$15q = 600$$
$$q = 40$$

Solve for d.
$$d + q = 50$$
$$d + 40 = 50$$
$$d = 10$$

Check the solutions with the conditions of the problem.

Is 50 the sum of 10 and 40?
Is $11.00 the value of 10 dimes and 40 quarters?

Answer the question.

There are 10 dimes and 40 quarters.

Coin problems must have answers that are positive integers. Otherwise, a coin problem has no solution.

Every two-digit number can be expressed as $10t + u$, where t is the tens digit and u is the units digit. If $t = 8$ and $u = 9$, the number is $10(8) + 9$, or 89. Sometimes the digits t and u can be found by solving two equations in two variables, t and u.

EXAMPLE 2   The sum of the digits in a two-digit number is 9. The number is 12 times the tens digit. Find the number.

Use two variables.

Let $t =$ the tens digit
Let $u =$ the units digit

Write two equations.

$t + u = 9$ The sum of the digits is 9.

$10t + u = 12t$ The number is 12 times the tens digit.

Solve the system.

$u = 9 - t$ Solve the first equation for u and
$10t + (9 - t) = 12t$ substitute in the second equation.
$9t + 9 = 12t$
$9 = 3t$
$3 = t$

$3 + u = 9$ Substitute 3 for t in the first
$u = 6$ equation.

Answer the question.   The number is 36. Check 36 with the given conditions.

In a digit problem, the values for the digits must be integers 0 through 9. Otherwise, the problem has no solution.

CLASS EXERCISES

Solve each problem, using two equations in two variables.

1. The tens digit of a two-digit number is 2 less than the units digit. The number is equal to 4 times the sum of the digits. Find the number.   24

2. Jewel has 24 coins in nickels and dimes. Their total value is $1.65. How many of each are there?   15 nickels; 9 dimes

EXERCISES

A   *Solve each problem, using a system of equations.*

1. The units digit of a two-digit number is 2 more than the tens digit. If the sum of the digits is 12, find the number.   57

2. A two-digit number is equal to 14 times its tens digit. The sum of the digits is 10. Find the two-digit number.   28

3. In a two-digit number, the tens digit is 3 more than the units digit. Twice the units digit is 2 more than the tens digit. Find the number.   85

SYSTEMS OF LINEAR EQUATIONS

277

EXTRA PRACTICE, page 522

Challenge the students to try to solve this problem:

I am thinking of a four-digit number. The sum of the digits is 14. The product of the digits is 0. The tens digit is 2 less than the units digit. If the thousands and units digits of the number are reversed and this number is added to the original number, the sum is 9109. What is the original number? 2057

Note: The problem can be represented by a system of four equations (in four variables). This system cannot be solved directly using the methods of this chapter. However, if the product of the digits is 0, then the hundreds digit or the tens digit or the units digit must be zero. Also, we know that the units digit is 2 more than the tens digit, so the units digit cannot be zero. Thus, the possibilities are

    (a) the tens digit is 0
    (b) the hundreds digit is 0

By trying each of these possibilities in turn, the students will obtain systems of three equations in three variables. Only possibility (b) leads to the solution.

4. Find a two-digit number if the sum of the digits is 11 and if 6 times the units digit is 5 less than the number. 47

5. A collection of nickels and quarters contains 25 coins. If there are 3 more nickels than quarters, what is the total value of the coins? $3.45

6. Norma saved nickels and dimes. The first 50 coins she saved were worth $3.90. How many of each type had she saved? 22 nickels, 28 dimes

7. Ada has $2.05 in nickels and dimes. The number of dimes is 4 more than the number of nickels. How many dimes has she? How many nickels? 15; 11

8. Max has $2.15 in dimes and quarters. The number of dimes is 2 more than 4 times the number of quarters. How many quarters has he? 3 quarters

9. Sixty quarters and dimes were emptied from a candy machine. Their total value was $9.75. How many of each type were there? 25 quarters, 35 dimes

B

10. The sum of the digits of a two-digit number is 9. When 63 is subtracted from the number, the new number is the same as the original with the digits reversed. Find the original number. 81
Hint: Let $10u + t$ represent the original number *with digits reversed.*

11. The sum of the digits of a two-digit number is 12. If the digits are interchanged, the number is decreased by 54. Find the number. 93

12. Find a three-digit number if its value is 51 times the units digit, the sum of the digits is 12, and the tens digit is zero. 408

13. Sam has some nickels and quarters. There are 33 coins in all, with $3.75 more in quarters than in nickels. How many of each are there? 18 quarters, 15 nickels

14. In a walkathon, Mary collected $9 in quarters and half-dollars. If all the coins had been half-dollars, she would have earned $4 more. How many quarters did she collect? How many half-dollars? 16 quarters, 10 half-dollars

C

15. The value of some dimes and quarters is $4.00. If each dime were replaced by a quarter and each quarter replaced by a dime, the value would be $5.80. How many of each are there? 8 quarters, 20 dimes

16. The sum of the digits of a two-digit number is 15. The tens digit is one-half of 3 times the units digit. What is the two-digit number? 96

17. The tens digit of a three-digit number is 6. The sum of the three digits is 14. When the digits are reversed, the new number is 198 more than the original number. Find the original number. 365

18. Rita counted her change and found she had $1.10 in nickels, dimes, and pennies. Of the 23 coins, there were four more pennies than nickels. Determine the number of each type of coin. Solve a system of three equations, with variables p, n, and d. 10 pennies, 6 nickels, 7 dimes

Break-Even Point

Many businesses have what is called a *"break-even point."* That is the number of items they need to sell so that *expenses* just equal *revenues*. If more items are sold, there is a *profit*. If fewer items are sold, there is a *loss*.

A weekly magazine has regular expenses of $20,000 per week and printing expenses of $.25 per copy. It receives $5000 per week in advertising revenues and charges $1.00 per copy. Find the number of copies that must be sold to reach the break-even point.

We will show a graphical solution. *Expense* and *revenue lines* are drawn on the same set of axes. The break-even point occurs where these lines meet. That is the point where expenses and revenues are the same.

Expenses = 20,000 + 0.25n
Revenues = 5000 + 1.00n

(n = number sold)

To simplify the graphing, the numbers are expressed in thousands.

$$y = 20 + 0.25x$$

$$y = 5 + x$$

(x = number sold in thousands)
(y = dollars in thousands)

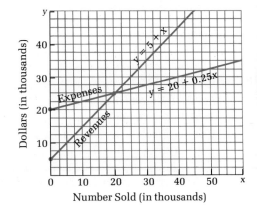

1. At what value of x does the break-even point occur? **20**

2. How many magazines need to be sold to break even? **20,000**

3. What are the expenses and revenues at the break-even point?
Expenses: $25,000, Revenues: $25,000

4. Use the graph to find the profit if 30,000 magazines are sold. **Profit: $7500**
Hint: Profit = Revenues − Expenses

5. If only 15,000 magazines are sold, what would be the loss? **Loss: $3750**

6. Suppose regular weekly expenses are $15,000 and printing expenses $.50 per copy. Advertising brings in $9000 weekly and the magazine sells for $2.00 per copy. Find the break-even point.
Hint: A graph is not required! **Break-even point: 4000 copies**

MAINTAINING SKILLS

These exercises review basic algebraic skills.

Simplify.

1. $5 - 10 \cdot 3 + 6 \div \frac{1}{2} - 7$ -20

2. $\dfrac{x^2 + 14x + 49}{x + 7}$ $x + 7$

3. $(x - 3)(x - 7) + (x + 2)(x - 3)$
$2x^2 - 11x + 15$

Evaluate when $a = 3$, $b = -6$, and $c = -2$.

4. $2a - 2b - c$ 20

5. $a^2b - b^2c$ 18

Solve for x.

6. $4(x - 5) - 3x = 5(2 - x)$ 5

7. $\dfrac{1}{x} = \dfrac{2}{x^2 + 1}$ 1

8. $(x - 3)^2 + 2 = 2x - 1$ 2 or 6

[*Maintaining Skills continues on page 281.*]

ADDITIONAL ANSWERS

Review Exercises

4.

5.

6.

CHAPTER 7 REVIEW

VOCABULARY

system of equations (p. 254)
solution of a system of
 equations (p. 254)
consistent system (p. 268)

independent system (p. 268)
inconsistent system (p. 268)
dependent system (p. 269)

SUMMARY

In this chapter, three methods of solving linear systems of equations are studied. They are solution by graphing, solution by substitution, and solution by addition or subtraction combined with multiplication. These methods are applied to solve verbal problems involving systems of linear equations. Systems of two linear equations are also classified, and through this classification it becomes possible to determine the number of solutions of a system, if any, without actually finding the solutions.

REVIEW EXERCISES

7-1   *Find the solution for each system from the graphs. Check by substituting in both equations.*

1. $y = -x - 1$
 $x - 2y = 5$ $(1, -2)$

2. $3y - x = 3$
 $y = x - 1$ $(3, 2)$

3. $2x - y = 3$
 $x + 2y = -11$ $(-1, -5)$

      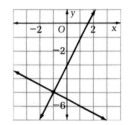

Solve each system by graphing.

4. $x + 2y = 0$
 $y = 2x + 5$ $(-2, 1)$

5. $3x + 2y = 6$
 $2x - 3y = -9$ $(0, 3)$

6. $x = -3$
 $y = 3$ $(-3, 3)$

Determine whether the given point is a solution of the system of equations.

7. $(2, 14)$; $y - 3x = 8$ No
 $x - y = 12$

8. $(3, -5)$; $2x + y = 1$ Yes
 $2x - y = 11$

9. $(1, -6)$; $3x - y = 9$ Yes
        $6x + y = 0$

10. $(0, 2)$; $y = 3x + 2$ Yes
        $y = 5x + 2$

7-2   *Solve each system of equations by the substitution method.*

11. $y = 3x - 2$ $\left(\frac{1}{2}, -\frac{1}{2}\right)$ **12.** $x = 1 + y$ $(2, 1)$ **13.** $3x + 5y = 31$ $(2, 5)$
     $3x + y = 1$ $2x - 3y = 1$ $y = 3x - 1$

7-3   *Solve each system by addition or subtraction.*

14. $3x + y = 2$ $(1, -1)$ **15.** $x + y = 1$ $(-2, 3)$ **16.** $y = 3x - 7$ $(4, 5)$
     $x - y = 2$ $4x + y = -5$ $3x - 2y = 2$

7-4   *Solve each system, using multiplication with addition. Write **no solution** if none exists.*

17. $3x + 2y = 10$ $(2, 2)$ **18.** $x - 3y = 0$ $(3, 1)$ **19.** $4x - 2y = -14$ $(-2, 3)$
     $2x + y = 6$ $3x + 4y = 13$ $3x + 3y = 3$

20. $-2x - 3y = -7$ **21.** $x - y = 1$ $(-1, -2)$ **22.** $y - 3x = 4$ Many solutions
     $6x + 9y = 0$ No solution $2x + 3y = -8$ $y - 3x - 4 = 0$

7-5   **23.** Classify each system in problems **17–22** as dependent or independent.
       Ind.: 17, 18, 19, 20, 21. Dep.: 22
       24. Classify each system in problems **17–22** as consistent or inconsistent.
       Consist.: 17, 18, 19, 21, 22. Inconsist.: 20

A system of two equations has the given graph. Classify the system as consistent or inconsistent, and dependent or independent.

25.

26.

27.

Consistent, independent   Consistent, dependent   Inconsistent, independent

Solve each problem, using a system of equations.

7-6   **28.** The sum of two numbers is 12. If twice the larger number is added to 3 times the smaller number, the result is 16. Find the two numbers.   20 and −8

      29. The length of a rectangle exceeds its width by 4. The perimeter is 48. Find the dimensions of the rectangle.   length 14; width 10

REVIEW

9. Find the equation, in standard form, of the line that has a slope of $\frac{2}{3}$ and that contains the point $(0, 5)$. $2x - 3y = -15$

10. What is the value of *a* if the line $ax - 3y = 6$ is parallel to the line $8x - y = 2$?   24

11. Add:
     $(x^3 - x^2 + x) + (5x^2 - 3x - 1)$
     $x^3 + 4x^2 - 2x - 1$

12. Subtract:
     $(6x^2 - x + 4) - (x^2 - 6x - 3)$
     $5x^2 + 5x + 7$

13. Find three consecutive integers such that 4 times the first is 7 more than 3 times the third.   13, 14, 15

Factor completely.

14. $x^2y - 13xy + 30y$
     $y(x - 3)(x - 10)$

15. $6x^2 - 19x + 3$
     $(6x - 1)(x - 3)$

16. $xy - 5x + 7y - 35$
     $(x + 7)(y - 5)$

17. Solve by factoring:
     $8x^2 - 6x + 1 = 0$ $\frac{1}{2}$ or $\frac{1}{4}$

Determine whether the following systems of equations are consistent or inconsistent, dependent or independent. (Do not solve.)

18. $x - 3y = 5$ Inconsistent and
     $-2x + 6y = 10$ independent

19. $2x - y = 3$ Consistent and
     $x - 2y = 5$ independent

20. Solve the system of equations.
     $y - x = 7$
     $3x - y = 1$ (4, 11)

1.

2.

3.

7-7 **30.** The ones, or units, digit of a two-digit number is one more than twice the tens digit. If 4 were added to the tens digit, it would equal the units digit. Find the number.   37

31. A collection of 23 coins contains nickels and dimes. If the number of dimes exceeds the number of nickels by 5, what is the total value of the coins? $1.85 (9 nickels, 14 dimes)

CHAPTER 7 TEST

7-1 Solve each system by graphing.

1. $y = x - 2$ $(1, -1)$
$y = -3x + 2$

2. $3y - 2x = 0$ $(-3, -2)$
$y = -2$

3. $2x + y = 1$ $(1, -1)$
$-x + 2y = -3$

Solve each system.

7-2 **4.** $y = 5x - 2$ $(1, 3)$
$2x + y = 5$

5. $2x + y = 11$ $(4, 3)$
$y = x - 1$

6. $x = 2y - 7$ $(-3, 2)$
$3x - y = -11$

7-3 **7.** $x - 2y = 3$ $(7, 2)$
$3x + 2y = 25$

8. $5x - y = -10$ $(-1, 5)$
$2x + y = 3$

9. $2x + 3y = 4$ $\left(\frac{1}{2}, 1\right)$
$-2x + y = 0$

7-4 **10.** $-4y + 4x = -4$ $(4, 5)$
$3y - 2x = 7$

11. $2x - 3y = -3$ $\left(-\frac{9}{4}, -\frac{1}{2}\right)$
$4x + 2y = -10$

12. $2y = 3x - 9$ $\left(4, \frac{3}{2}\right)$
$4x - 8y = 4$

7-5 Classify each system as **consistent** or **inconsistent**.

13. $x - y = 4$ I
$x - y = 5$

14. $3x - 4y = 1$ C
$9x - 12y = 3$

15. $2x - y = 5$ C
$2x + y = 5$

Select the correct answer.

16. If two lines have the same slope and y-intercept, then is their system of equations dependent or independent?   Dependent

17. If two lines are parallel, then is their system of equations consistent or inconsistent?   Inconsistent

Solve, using two equations in two variables.

7-6 **18.** An isosceles triangle has a perimeter of 40 meters. One of the equal sides is 5 meters longer than the base. Find the dimensions of the triangle.   15 m, 15 m, 10 m

7-7 **19.** Fifty coins in quarters and dimes have a total value of $7.55. How many coins of each type are there?   17 quarters, 33 dimes

20. The sum of the digits of a two-digit number is equal to 5 times the difference of the two digits. If the units digit is 2 less than the tens digit, find the number.   64

Using Formulas

A computer rejects invalid input only if it is programmed to do so. To check the input, we can use IF . . . THEN . . . statements.

In Chapter 1 we saw these formulas:

The sum of the first n counting numbers is	The sum of the squares of the first n counting numbers is
$$\frac{n(n + 1)}{2}$$	$$\frac{n(n + 1)(2n + 1)}{6}$$

These formulas give invalid results when negative numbers or decimals are used for n. Such numbers are excluded from lines 130 and 140.

The Program	What It Does
| ```
100 REM SUMS
110 PRINT "ENTER N";
120 INPUT N
130 IF N < 0 THEN 110
140 IF N <> INT(N) THEN 110
150 LET A = N * (N + 1)/2
160 PRINT "SUM OF NUMBERS IS "; A
170 LET B = N * (N + 1) * (2 * N + 1)/6
180 PRINT "SUM OF SQUARES IS "; B
300 PRINT "ANOTHER? (1 = YES, 0 = NO)"
310 INPUT Z
320 IF Z = 1 THEN 110
900 END
``` | Rejects negative input.<br>Rejects decimal numerals.<br>Computes sum of first $n$ numbers.<br>Displays this sum.<br>Computes sum of their squares.<br>Displays sum of squares. |

```
RUN
ENTER N ? 9
SUM OF NUMBERS IS 45
SUM OF SQUARES IS 285
```
This is a sample run when $n = 9$.

What will the computer display when each of the following is input?

1. 5   **2.** 7   **3.** 13   **4.** 24   **5.** 65   **6.** 100

7. What is the purpose of the semicolons in lines 160 and 180?

8. Would the program function correctly if line 130 were changed to IF N < 1? What additional input will be excluded?

9. What will happen if you input −3.75 when the computer displays ANOTHER? (1 = YES, 0 = NO)? Why?

10. Modify the program so it also finds the sum of the cubes of the first n counting numbers, using $\frac{n^2(n + 1)^2}{4}$.

For more information about BASIC, see the Computer Handbook at the back of the book.

Computer Activity

You may wish to discuss line 140 with the students.

Basic Expression N<>INT(N)

Meaning N is less than or greater than the greatest integer function for N

This is true when N is between two integers. So line 140 rejects decimal values such as 6.2 or 0.8 as inputs.

$$6.2 > 6$$
$$0.8 < 1$$

ADDITIONAL ANSWERS

Computer Activity

1. SUM OF NUMBERS IS 15
   SUM OF SQUARES IS 55
2. SUM OF NUMBERS IS 28
   SUM OF SQUARES IS 140
3. SUM OF NUMBERS IS 91
   SUM OF SQUARES IS 819
4. SUM OF NUMBERS IS 300
   SUM OF SQUARES IS 4900
5. SUM OF NUMBERS IS 2145
   SUM OF SQUARES IS 93665
6. SUM OF NUMBERS IS 5050
   SUM OF SQUARES IS 338350
7. The semicolon causes the value of the variable to be printed on the same line as, and close to, the preceding message. If the display does not fit on one line, replace the semicolon with a comma.
8. The program functions properly, but the entry of a zero is rejected.
9. The program ends. Line 320 sends the computer to the next line (line 900) for all values of Z except 1.
10. Insert these two lines into the program:
    190 LET C = N*N*(N + 1)* (N + 1)/4
    200 PRINT "SUM OF CUBES IS "; C
```

This chapter provides a systematic development of skills with algebraic fractions. First, the students learn to simplify rational expressions. Then they learn how to multiply, divide, add, or subtract rational expressions. Division with polynomials is included as a natural part of the work with division, thus completing the operations with polynomials that were taught earlier in the course.

The chapter ends with a lesson devoted to complex fractions. This lesson uses many of the skills developed throughout the chapter.

CHAPTER 8

In banking, computers are used to find average rates of interest. Such rates can be written as rational expressions.

RATIONAL EXPRESSIONS

Prerequisite Skills Review

PREREQUISITE SKILLS REVIEW

For students who need additional practice with the algebraic skills in this Prerequisite Skills Review, you may assign Follow-Up exercises on pages 503–504 in the students' books.

An item-by-item error analysis of the Prerequisite Skills Review appears on page T25.

Write the letter for the correct answer.

1. Which statement is false?　a

   a. $6\left(\dfrac{2}{5}\right) = \dfrac{12}{30}$　　**b.** $\dfrac{4}{3}(3) = 4$　　**c.** $8\left(\dfrac{3}{4}\right) = 2(3)$　　**d.** $4\left(\dfrac{a}{b}\right) = \dfrac{4a}{b}$

2. Which fraction is equal to -1?　c

   a. $\dfrac{9-6}{2-(-1)}$　　**b.** $\dfrac{6-1}{6}$　　**c.** $\dfrac{3-7}{7-3}$　　**d.** $\dfrac{5(-2)}{2(-5)}$

3. Which fraction is *not* equal to $\dfrac{4}{5}$?　d

   a. $\dfrac{16}{20}$　　**b.** $\dfrac{1.6}{2}$　　**c.** $\dfrac{4\left(\frac{1}{2}\right)}{5\left(\frac{1}{2}\right)}$　　**d.** $\dfrac{4\frac{1}{2}}{5\frac{1}{2}}$

4. When $x = \dfrac{1}{2}$, which fraction is undefined?　c

   a. $\dfrac{1}{2x}$　　**b.** $\dfrac{2x-1}{x}$　　**c.** $\dfrac{x}{2x-1}$　　**d.** $\dfrac{x}{x-1}$

5. Which polynomial cannot be factored?　c

   a. $x^2 + x$　　**b.** $x^2 - 1$　　**c.** $x^2 + 1$　　**d.** $3x - 15$

6. Factor $x^2 + 2x - 15$.　b

   a. $x(x + 2) - 15$　　　　**b.** $(x - 3)(x + 5)$
   c. $(x + 3)(x + 5)$　　　　**d.** $(x + 3)(x - 5)$

7. When -2 is factored from the terms of $-2x^2 + 12x - 18$, the remaining factor is __?__.　c

   a. $x^2 - 6x - 9$　　　　**b.** $x^2 + 12x - 18$
   c. $x^2 - 6x + 9$　　　　**d.** $x^2 + 6x - 9$

8. Which expression does *not* represent the opposite of $x - 5$?　c

   a. $-x + 5$　　**b.** $5 - x$　　**c.** $x + 5$　　**d.** $-(x - 5)$

9. Multiply $(3x - 2)(3x - 2)$.　d

   a. $3x^2 - 4$　　**b.** $9x^2 + 4$　　**c.** $9x^2 - 6x + 4$　　**d.** $9x^2 - 12x + 4$

1. $\frac{2}{3} \cdot \frac{3}{5}$ $\frac{2}{5}$ 2. $\frac{4}{5} \cdot \frac{1}{4}$ $\frac{1}{5}$

3. $\frac{a}{b} \cdot \frac{b}{a}$ 1 4. $\frac{2a}{3} \cdot \frac{1}{a}$ $\frac{2}{3}$

LESSON NOTES

Rational expressions in algebra are the equivalent of fractions in arithmetic; the rational expression $\frac{a}{b}$ indicates $a \div b$.

Whenever a variable appears in the denominator of a rational expression, students should investigate the possibility that certain values of the variable might make the denominator equal to 0, thus making the expression undefined. This is illustrated in Example 1, Class Exercises 3–6, and Exercises 1–8.

ALTERNATE EXAMPLE

1. State all values of x for which $\dfrac{5x}{2x(x-3)}$ is undefined.
$x = 0$ or $x = 3$

8-1   Simplifying Rational Expressions

OBJECTIVE

To simplify rational expressions and to state when they are undefined.

The numerical fractions $\frac{3}{5}$, $\frac{-5}{4}$, and $\frac{9}{1}$ name rational numbers. Each has the form $\frac{a}{b}$, where a and b are integers, with $b \neq 0$. A **rational expression** has the form $\frac{a}{b}$ where a and b are *polynomials*. Rational expressions like the following have the same properties as numerical fractions, since variables stand for numbers.

$$\frac{3}{x} \qquad \frac{x+1}{x} \qquad \frac{a+b}{4} \qquad \frac{1}{n-1} \qquad \frac{x^2-1}{x+2}$$

First note that *a rational expression is undefined when the denominator is 0.*

$\dfrac{x+1}{x}$ is undefined when $x = 0$.

$\dfrac{5}{x-y}$ is undefined when $x - y = 0$, that is, when $x = y$.

$\dfrac{a+b}{4}$ is defined for all values of a and b. The denominator is a nonzero constant.

$\dfrac{x-1}{x^2+1}$ is defined for all real numbers x, since $x^2 + 1$ is always positive.

EXAMPLE 1   State all values of x for which $\dfrac{3}{x(x-5)}$ is undefined.

Set the denominator equal to 0.

$x(x - 5) = 0$
$x = 0$ or $x = 5$ If $ab = 0$, then $a = 0$ or $b = 0$.

Therefore $\dfrac{3x}{x(x-5)}$ is undefined when $x = 0$ or $x = 5$.

To simplify a fraction, you may use the *cancellation rule*. Remember that when applying this rule, you are really dividing the numerator and denominator by the same number. Thus,

$$\frac{12}{15} = \frac{\overset{1}{\cancel{3}}(4)}{\underset{1}{\cancel{3}}(5)} = \frac{4}{5}$$

Use the same procedure to simplify a rational expression. The expression is simplified when numerator and denominator have no common factor except 1 or -1.

EXAMPLE 2   Simplify each expression. Assume no denominator has a 0 value.

a. $\dfrac{6x}{8x^5} = \dfrac{(2x)(3)}{(2x)(4x^4)}$

$= \dfrac{3}{4x^4}$

b. $\dfrac{(2x-1)^2}{5(2x-1)} = \dfrac{(2x-1)(2x-1)}{5(2x-1)}$

$= \dfrac{2x-1}{5}$

You may need to factor polynomials before simplifying a rational expression.

EXAMPLE 3   Simplify $\dfrac{x+5}{x^2-25}$.

$\dfrac{x+5}{x^2-25} = \dfrac{x+5}{(x+5)(x-5)}$ Factor the difference of two squares.

$= \dfrac{1(x+5)}{(x+5)(x-5)}$ Remember the factor 1 in the numerator.

$= \dfrac{1}{x-5}$

Therefore $\dfrac{x+5}{x^2-25} = \dfrac{1}{x-5}$ except for $x = 5$ and $x = -5$.

EXAMPLE 4   Simplify each expression.

a. $\dfrac{2x^2-6x}{x} = \dfrac{2x(x-3)}{x}$

$= 2(x-3),$

Thus $\dfrac{2x^2-6x}{x} = 2(x-3)$

$x \neq 0$

b. $\dfrac{2x^2-11x-6}{x^2-9x+18} = \dfrac{(2x+1)(x-6)}{(x-3)(x-6)}$

$= \dfrac{2x+1}{x-3}$

Thus $\dfrac{2x^2-11x-6}{x^2-9x+18} = \dfrac{2x+1}{x-3}$

$x \neq 3, x \neq 6$

Restrictions on the variable will not be stated in most cases, but you should be aware that such restrictions exist.

EXAMPLE 5   Let $x = 4$ and evaluate $\dfrac{5x+15}{2x^2+6x}$ twice, before and after simplifying.

Before   When $x = 4$, $\dfrac{5x+15}{2x^2+6x} = \dfrac{5(4)+15}{2(4)^2+6(4)} = \dfrac{35}{32+24} = \dfrac{35}{56} = \dfrac{5}{8}$

After $\dfrac{5x+15}{2x^2+6x} = \dfrac{5(x+3)}{2x(x+3)} = \dfrac{5}{2x}$ When $x = 4$, $\dfrac{5}{2x} = \dfrac{5}{2(4)} = \dfrac{5}{8}$

To tell whether a rational expression is in simplest form, look for common factors of the numerator and denominator. For instance, $\dfrac{3x}{x+3}$ is in simplest form because neither 3 nor x is a factor of the denominator.

RATIONAL EXPRESSIONS   **287**

Simplify.

1. $\dfrac{x^5}{3x^7}$ $\dfrac{1}{3x^2}$

2. $\dfrac{y^2(x^2 - 1)}{y^2(x^2 + 1)}$ $\dfrac{x^2 - 1}{x^2 + 1}$

3. $\dfrac{15}{5x + 10}$ $\dfrac{3}{x + 2}$

4. $\dfrac{x^2 + 4x + 4}{x^2 - 4}$ $\dfrac{x + 2}{x - 2}$

5. $\dfrac{9x^2 - 4}{6x^2 - 5x - 6}$ $\dfrac{3x - 2}{2x - 3}$

ENRICHMENT ACTIVITY

Mathematicians in ancient Egypt tried to write all fractions as the sum of fractions with unit numerators. The Rhind papyrus, for example, shows $\frac{2}{7}$ expressed as the sum $\frac{1}{4} + \frac{1}{28}$.

Suggest that students refer to a book that deals with the history of mathematics and prepare a report on *unit fractions*. One reference could be *An Introduction to the History of Mathematics* by Howard Eves (Holt, Rinehart and Winston © 1976).

Some students may enjoy making up unit-fraction examples of their own.

CLASS EXERCISES

1. Why is it not always correct to say that $\frac{x}{x}$ equals 1?   It is undefined when $x = 0$.

2. Is $\frac{a + 2}{a + 3}$ defined when $a = -2$? when $a = -3$?   Yes; no

For what values of **x** *is each expression undefined?*

3. $\dfrac{x + 5}{x - 8}$ 8

4. $\dfrac{1}{x(x + 3)}$ 0; −3

5. $\dfrac{x}{7 - x}$ 7

6. $\dfrac{(x - 1)(x + 2)}{(x + 3)(x - 4)}$ −3; 4

Find the greatest common factor of the numerator and denominator.
Then simplify.

7. $\dfrac{21}{35}$ $7; \frac{3}{5}$

8. $\dfrac{3a + 3b}{3x}$ $3; \frac{a + b}{x}$

9. $\dfrac{4x - 4y}{3x - 3y}$ $x - y; \frac{4}{3}$

10. $\dfrac{x - 2}{x^2 - 4}$ $x - 2; \frac{1}{x + 2}$

EXERCISES

A   *For what values of* **x** *is each expression undefined?*

1. $\dfrac{5}{x}$ 0

2. $\dfrac{1}{x - 5}$ 5

3. $\dfrac{x}{x + 6}$ −6

4. $\dfrac{x - 7}{3}$ None

5. $\dfrac{-3}{(x + 4)(x - 5)}$ −4; 5

6. $\dfrac{x - 3}{2x(x + 4)}$ 0; −4

7. $\dfrac{x - 2}{x^2 - 9}$ 3; −3

8. $\dfrac{x + 2}{x^2 + 9}$ None

Find the greatest common factor of the numerator and denominator.
Then simplify.

9. $\dfrac{a^3}{4a^6}$ $a^3; \frac{1}{4a^3}$

10. $\dfrac{abc}{2abc}$ $abc; \frac{1}{2}$

11. $\dfrac{7n^3}{21n^8}$ $7n^3; \frac{1}{3n^5}$

12. $\dfrac{x^2 y}{xy^2}$ $xy; \frac{x}{y}$

13. $\dfrac{x(a - 1)}{x(a - 2)}$ $x; \frac{a - 1}{a - 2}$

14. $\dfrac{a(x + 3)}{b(x + 3)}$ $x + 3; \frac{a}{b}$

15. $\dfrac{2(c - 1)}{a(c - 1)}$ $c - 1; \frac{2}{a}$

16. $\dfrac{2b(x + 1)}{4b(x - 1)}$ $2b; \frac{x + 1}{2(x - 1)}$

17. $\dfrac{6}{2x + 4}$ $2; \frac{3}{x + 2}$

18. $\dfrac{4a + 4b}{8x}$ $4; \frac{a + b}{2x}$

19. $\dfrac{3a - 6b}{9x - 12}$ $3; \frac{a - 2b}{3x - 4}$

20. $\dfrac{4x - 4}{7x - 7}$ $x - 1; \frac{4}{7}$

21. $\dfrac{x^2 + 5x + 6}{x + 3}$ $x + 3; x + 2$

22. $\dfrac{n^2 - n - 2}{n + 1}$ $n + 1; n - 2$

23. $\dfrac{a^2 - 7a + 12}{a^2 - 16}$ $a - 4; \frac{a - 3}{a + 4}$

24. $\dfrac{x^2 - 2x - 3}{x^2 - 1}$ $x + 1; \frac{x - 3}{x - 1}$

25. $\dfrac{n - 4}{n^2 - 9n + 20}$ $n - 4; \frac{1}{n - 5}$

26. $\dfrac{x + 8}{x^2 + 11x + 24}$ $x + 8; \frac{1}{x + 3}$

27. $\dfrac{3a - 3}{a^2 + 6a - 7}$ $a - 1; \frac{3}{a + 7}$

28. $\dfrac{4x + 20}{x^2 + 2x - 15}$ $x + 5; \frac{4}{x - 3}$

29. $\dfrac{a^2 - 25}{a^2 + 13a + 40}$ $a + 5; \frac{a - 5}{a + 8}$

B   *Evaluate each expression twice—before simplifying the expression,*
then after simplifying it. Use the value given for the variable.

30. $\dfrac{5x^2 - 10x + 5}{15x^2 - 15x}$, when $x = 4$ $\frac{x - 1}{3x}; \frac{1}{4}$

31. $\dfrac{2x^2 - 10x}{x^2 - 2x - 15}$, when $x = -1$ $\frac{2x}{x + 3}; -1$

CHAPTER 8

EXTRA PRACTICE, page 522

32. $\dfrac{a^2 + 5a + 4}{a^2 + 8a + 16}$, when $a = 11$ $\quad \dfrac{a+1}{a+4};\dfrac{4}{5}$ **33.** $\dfrac{3x^2 + 9x + 6}{x^2 - 4}$, when $x = -1$ $\quad \dfrac{3(x+1)}{x-2};0$

Simplify. State all restrictions on the variables.

34. $\dfrac{xy^5}{-x^3} \cdot -\dfrac{y^5}{x^2}; x \neq 0$ **35.** $\dfrac{3a^5b^2}{6a^5b^3}$ $\dfrac{1}{2b}, \begin{matrix} a \neq 0 \\ b \neq 0 \end{matrix}$ **36.** $\dfrac{-8a^2b^2}{-12a^5b}$ $\dfrac{2b}{3a^3}, \begin{matrix} a \neq 0 \\ b \neq 0 \end{matrix}$ **37.** $\dfrac{2x^2 - 2}{x - 1}$

$\qquad\qquad\qquad\qquad\qquad\qquad\qquad\qquad\qquad\qquad\qquad\qquad\qquad\qquad\qquad\qquad\qquad 2(x + 1); x \neq 1$

38. $\dfrac{7n^2 + 14n - 21}{n^2 + 10n + 21}$ **39.** $\dfrac{x^2 + 11x + 30}{3ax^2 + 15ax}$ **40.** $\dfrac{n^2 - n - 20}{5n^2 + 20n}$

41. $\dfrac{4x^2 - 1}{2x^2 - 5x - 3}$ **42.** $\dfrac{6x^2 + 7x + 2}{4x^2 - 1}$ **43.** $\dfrac{an^2 + 6an + 9a}{n^2 + 2n - 3}$

44. $\dfrac{2x^3 - 18x}{x^2 + 3x}$ **45.** $\dfrac{5x + 20}{15x^2 + 60x}$ **46.** $\dfrac{x - 1}{x^2 - 2x + 1}$

47. $\dfrac{x + 1}{x^3 - x}$ **48.** $\dfrac{x^2 - x}{x^3 + x^2 - 2x}$ **49.** $\dfrac{6x - 30}{x^2 - 7x + 10}$

*Simplify. If the expression cannot be simplified, write **in simplest form**.*

50. $\dfrac{3x + 1}{x + 3}$ In simplest form **51.** $\dfrac{x^2 - 1}{x^2 - 4}$ In simplest form **52.** $\dfrac{x^2 + 6x + 5}{2x + 2}$ $\dfrac{x+5}{2}$ **53.** $\dfrac{x^2 + 2x + 3}{x^2 + 2x + 2}$

$\qquad\qquad\qquad\qquad\qquad\qquad\qquad\qquad\qquad\qquad\qquad\qquad\qquad\qquad\qquad\qquad\qquad\qquad$ In simplest form

54. $\dfrac{6x^2 + 5x - 4}{2x^2 + 11x - 6}$ $\dfrac{3x+4}{x+6}$ **55.** $\dfrac{3x + 6}{xy + 2y - 3x - 6}$ $\dfrac{3}{y-3}$ **56.** $\dfrac{x^2 + 1}{x^3 + 4x^2 + x + 4}$ $\dfrac{1}{x+4}$

57. $\dfrac{5a^2 - 46a + 9}{25a^2 - 10a + 1}$ $\dfrac{a-9}{5a-1}$ **58.** $\dfrac{x^2 - x - 6}{15x - 5x^2}$ $-\dfrac{x+2}{5x}$ ***59.** $\dfrac{x^3 - 9x + 2x^2 - 18}{x^3 - x^2 - 6x}$ $\dfrac{x+3}{x}$

*Use factoring by grouping to find any restrictions on **x** or on **y**.*

60. $\dfrac{1}{x^3 - 9x^2 + x - 9}$ **61.** $\dfrac{x}{3x^3 - 2x^2 + 6x - 4}$ **62.** $\dfrac{2x + 1}{y^3 - 5y^2 + 3y - 15}$

*Express each fraction in terms of **x**. Then state any restrictions on **x**.*

Sample The denominator of a fraction is 1 more than twice the numerator.
Let x represent the numerator.

$$\dfrac{x}{2x + 1}; x \neq -\dfrac{1}{2}$$

63. The denominator of a fraction is 3 less then twice the numerator. Let x represent the numerator. $\quad \dfrac{x}{2x-3}; x \neq \dfrac{3}{2}$

64. The numerator of a fraction is 5 more than 3 times the denominator. Let x represent the denominator. $\quad \dfrac{3x+5}{x}; x \neq 0$

65. The denominator of a fraction is the square of 1 more than the numerator. $\dfrac{x}{(x+1)^2};$

66. The numerator of a fraction is 1 more than the square of the denominator. $x \neq -1$

$\qquad\qquad\qquad\qquad\qquad\qquad\qquad\qquad\qquad\qquad\qquad\qquad\qquad\qquad\qquad \dfrac{x^2 + 1}{x}; x \neq 0$

Using BASIC

The computer can be used to help emphasize the fact that division by zero is not permitted. This program attempts to evaluate $\dfrac{1}{x - 5}$ for each value of x from -10 to 10. When it reaches $x = 5$, the computer stops and displays an error message.

```
10   FOR X = -10 TO 10
20   PRINT "WHEN X IS"; X
30   LET Y = 1/(X - 5)
40   PRINT "1/(X - 5) IS"; Y
50   FOR J = 1 TO 1500
60   NEXT J
70   PRINT
80   NEXT X
90   END
```

Lines 50 and 60 slow down the display. The values may be changed to slow down or speed up the display.

ADDITIONAL ANSWERS

Exercises

38. $\dfrac{7(n - 1)}{n + 7}; n \neq -3, n \neq -7$

39. $\dfrac{x + 6}{3ax}; a \neq 0, x \neq 0, x \neq -5$

40. $\dfrac{n - 5}{5n}; n \neq 0, n \neq -4$

41. $\dfrac{2x - 1}{x - 3}; x \neq 3, x \neq -\dfrac{1}{2}$

42. $\dfrac{3x + 2}{2x - 1}; x \neq \dfrac{1}{2}; x \neq -\dfrac{1}{2}$

43. $\dfrac{a(n + 3)}{n - 1}; n \neq 1, n \neq -3$

44. $2(x - 3); x \neq 0, x \neq -3$

45. $\dfrac{1}{3x}; x \neq 0, x \neq -4$

46. $\dfrac{1}{x - 1}; x \neq 1$

47. $\dfrac{1}{x(x - 1)}; x \neq 0, x \neq 1, x \neq -1$

48. $\dfrac{1}{x + 2}; x \neq 0, x \neq 1, x \neq -2$

49. $\dfrac{6}{x - 2}; x \neq 2, x \neq 5$

60. $\dfrac{1}{(x^2 + 1)(x - 9)}; x \neq 9$

61. $\dfrac{x}{(x^2 + 2)(3x - 2)}; x \neq \dfrac{2}{3}$

62. $\dfrac{2x + 1}{(y^2 + 3)(y - 5)}; y \neq 5$

Write the opposite of each expression.

1. $a + b$ **2.** $a - b$
    $-a - b$ $b - a$
3. $-a - b$ **4.** $a - 3$
    $a + b$ $3 - a$

LESSON NOTES

If a polynomial of two or more terms appears in parentheses and is preceded by a negative sign, the expression can be rewritten using -1 in place of the negative sign, and the distributive property can be applied:

$$-(x - 3) = -1(x - 3) = -x + 3$$

Be sure that the students realize that the sign of each term in the parenthetical expression has changed.

We can also apply the process in reverse. All the signs of a polynomial can be changed if we place the polynomial inside parentheses and prefix a negative sign:

$$x - y + z = -(x + y - z)$$

Point out that a fraction or a rational expression has three signs:

$$\frac{1}{2} = +\frac{+1}{+2}$$

We can change any two of these signs and have an equivalent expression. To illustrate this, you may wish to discuss carefully a problem such as Class Exercise 12. $x - 2$ and $2 - x$ are opposites of each other, so we can proceed as shown below.

$$\frac{x - 2}{2 - x} = \frac{-1(2 - x)}{(2 - x)} = -1$$

ALTERNATE EXAMPLE

1. Simplify: $\dfrac{x - 6}{36 - x^2}$

$-\dfrac{1}{6 + x}$; $x \neq 6$, $x \neq -6$

8-2   Using −1 as a Factor

OBJECTIVE

To use -1 as a factor in simplifying rational expressions.

Can you simplify $\dfrac{x - 1}{2(1 - x)}$? It appears that the numerator and denominator have no common factor. But $x - 1$ is the *opposite* of $1 - x$. So you can rewrite the numerator as $-1(1 - x)$.

$$\frac{x - 1}{2(1 - x)} = \frac{-1(1 - x)}{2(1 - x)} = \frac{-1}{2}, \text{ or } -\frac{1}{2}$$

Note that $\dfrac{-1}{2}$, $\dfrac{1}{-2}$, and $-\dfrac{1}{2}$ are equal. They all name the opposite of $\dfrac{1}{2}$. This property of fractions applies to any rational expression:

$$\frac{-a}{b} = \frac{a}{-b} = -\frac{a}{b}$$

EXAMPLE 1   Simplify $\dfrac{x - 3}{9 - x^2}$.

$$\frac{x - 3}{9 - x^2} = \frac{x - 3}{(3 + x)(3 - x)} \qquad \text{The numerator, } x - 3, \text{ is the opposite}$$
$$\qquad\qquad\qquad\qquad\qquad\qquad \text{of the factor } 3 - x \text{ in the denominator.}$$
$$= \frac{-1(3 - x)}{(3 + x)(3 - x)}$$
$$= \frac{-1}{3 + x}$$
$$= -\frac{1}{3 + x} \qquad \frac{-a}{b} = -\frac{a}{b}$$

There is another way to simplify $\dfrac{x - 3}{9 - x^2}$ in Example 1. It is based on the observation that when $a - b$ is divided by its opposite, $b - a$, the quotient is -1.

$$\frac{a - b}{b - a} = \frac{-1}{1} = -1$$

Thus $\dfrac{x - 3}{9 - x^2}$ can be simplified as follows:

$$\frac{x - 3}{9 - x^2} = \frac{x - 3}{(3 + x)(3 - x)} = \frac{\overset{-1}{\cancel{x - 3}}}{(3 + x)\underset{1}{\cancel{(3 - x)}}} = \frac{-1}{3 + x} = -\frac{1}{3 + x}$$

Before you factor a polynomial, it is usually easier to make the *leading coefficient* positive. The leading coefficient is the coefficient of the highest power of the variable.

EXAMPLE 2   Simplify $\dfrac{-n^2 - n + 6}{n^2 - 4n + 4}$.

$$\dfrac{-n^2 - n + 6}{n^2 - 4n + 4} = \dfrac{-1(n^2 + n - 6)}{n^2 - 4n + 4} \qquad \text{Factor } -1 \text{ out of the numerator.}$$

$$= \dfrac{-1(n + 3)(n - 2)}{(n - 2)(n - 2)}$$

$$= \dfrac{-(n + 3)}{n - 2}$$

$$= -\dfrac{n + 3}{n - 2}$$

This answer can also be written in the form $\dfrac{n + 3}{2 - n}$. Do you see why?

EXAMPLE 3   Simplify $-\dfrac{-5x + 20}{2x - 8}$.

$$-\dfrac{-5x + 20}{2x - 8} = -\dfrac{-5(x - 4)}{2(x - 4)} \qquad \begin{array}{l}\text{Factor } -5 \text{ out of the numerator.}\\ \text{Factor } 2 \text{ out of the denominator.}\end{array}$$

$$= -\dfrac{-5}{2}$$

$$= \dfrac{5}{2} \qquad\qquad -\dfrac{-a}{b} = -\left(-\dfrac{a}{b}\right) = \dfrac{a}{b}$$

What are the restrictions on x, if any? $x \neq 4$

CLASS EXERCISES

Complete.

1. $\dfrac{-2}{5} = -\dfrac{2}{?}$ 5   **2.** $\dfrac{3}{-4} = -\dfrac{?}{4}$ 3   **3.** $-\dfrac{3}{-10} = \dfrac{3}{?}$ 10   **4.** $\dfrac{a}{-b} = -\dfrac{a}{?}$ b

5. $1 - x = -(\underline{\ ?\ })(x - 1)$ **6.** $2(a - b) = \underline{\ ?\ }(b - a)$ -2 **7.** $-2x^2 + 4x = -2x(\underline{\ ?\ })$ $(x - 2)$

8. $\dfrac{-1}{a + b} = -\dfrac{?}{a + b}$ 1   **9.** $\dfrac{-2}{x - y} = \dfrac{?}{y - x}$ 2   **10.** $\dfrac{x - 1}{2 - x} = -\dfrac{x - 1}{?}$ $x - 2$

Simplify.

11. $-\dfrac{x - 1}{x - 1}$ -1 **12.** $\dfrac{x - 2}{2 - x}$ -1 **13.** $\dfrac{2x - 4}{2 - x}$ -2

EXERCISES

A   *Complete.*

1. $\dfrac{-3}{x + 1} = \dfrac{3}{?}$ $-x - 1$ **2.** $\dfrac{x}{-4} = \dfrac{?}{4}$ $-x$ **3.** $\dfrac{2 - x}{a + b} = \dfrac{-1(\ ?\ )}{a + b}$ $(x - 2)$

4. $\dfrac{-3}{5} = -\dfrac{3}{?}$ 5   **5.** $\dfrac{-2xy}{-3} = \dfrac{?}{3}$ $2xy$ **6.** $\dfrac{-3}{1 - x} = \dfrac{3}{?}$ $x - 1$

RATIONAL EXPRESSIONS

291

EXTRA PRACTICE, page 523

---

2. Simplify: $\dfrac{-n^2 + n + 6}{n^2 + 5n + 6}$

$-\dfrac{n - 3}{n + 3}$ or $\dfrac{3 - n}{n + 3}$;

$n \neq -2, n \neq -3$

3. Simplify: $\dfrac{-4x + 24}{2x - 12}$

$-2; x \neq 6$

POSSIBLE ERROR

The -1 factor frequently confuses students. Here are two common errors:

$$\dfrac{x - 3}{x + 3} = -1 \quad \text{(incorrect)}$$

$$\dfrac{-x + 3}{5} = -\dfrac{x + 3}{5} \quad \text{(incorrect)}$$

To help students recognize this type of error, continue to use simple numerical counter-examples.

$$\dfrac{5 - 3}{5 + 3} \overset{?}{=} -1 \qquad \dfrac{-1 + 3}{5} \overset{?}{=} -\dfrac{1 + 3}{5}$$

$$\dfrac{2}{8} \neq -1 \qquad \dfrac{2}{5} \neq -\dfrac{4}{5}$$

Also stress the fact that when the -1 factor is factored from a polynomial, the sign of each term in the polynomial is changed. Thus, $-x + y - 2$ is equivalent to $-1(x - y + 2)$.

DAILY QUIZ

Simplify.

1. $\dfrac{x - 7}{x - 7}$ -1

2. $\dfrac{x^2 - 5x + 6}{-6 + 5x - x^2}$ -1

3. $\dfrac{x - 3}{12 - 4x}$ $-\dfrac{1}{4}$

4. $\dfrac{3 - x}{x^2 - 2x - 3}$ $\dfrac{-1}{x + 1}$ or $-\dfrac{1}{x + 1}$

5. $\dfrac{(x - 4)^2}{(4 - x)^2}$ 1

291

ENRICHMENT ACTIVITY

Write these expressions on the
board.

$$x \qquad -x \qquad -(x + y) \qquad |x|$$

Ask students to decide which of
the expressions always represent
negative values, and which always
represent positive values.
Answer: None of the expressions always represents a positive value,
and none of the expressions always
represents a negative value. The
first three expressions may be positive, negative, or 0, depending on
the values that we use for x and y.
The fourth expression may be positive or it may be 0 (it is never negative).

ADDITIONAL ANSWERS

Using the Calculator

3. In Exercise 2, the first expression

can be simplified to $-\dfrac{x + 3}{x - 2}$.

$$\dfrac{-x^2 - x + 6}{x^2 - 4x + 4} = \dfrac{-(x^2 + x - 6)}{x^2 - 4x + 4}$$

$$= \dfrac{-(x + 3)(x - 2)}{(x - 2)(x - 2)}$$

$$= -\dfrac{x + 3}{x - 2}$$

Thus, the two expressions are
equivalent.

Simplify.

7. $-\dfrac{x + 4}{x + 4}$ \qquad -1 \quad **8.** $\dfrac{x - 4}{4 - x}$ \qquad -1 \quad **9.** $\dfrac{-(x + 4)}{x + 4}$ \qquad -1 \quad **10.** $\dfrac{-(x - 4)}{-(x - 4)}$ \qquad 1

11. $\dfrac{n - 2}{4 - 2n}$ \quad $-\frac{1}{2}$ \quad **12.** $\dfrac{n + 2}{-n - 2}$ \quad -1 \quad **13.** $\dfrac{-a + 3}{2a - 6}$ \quad $-\frac{1}{2}$ \quad **14.** $\dfrac{x - 14}{-3x + 42}$ \quad $-\frac{1}{3}$

15. $\dfrac{x^2 - 1}{1 + x}$ \quad $x - 1$ \quad **16.** $\dfrac{x^2 - 1}{1 - x}$ \quad $-x - 1$ \quad **17.** $\dfrac{-x + 1}{3 - 3x^2}$ \quad $\frac{1}{3(1 + x)}$ \quad **18.** $\dfrac{b - a}{-(b^2 - a^2)}$ \quad $\frac{-1}{b + a}$

19. $\dfrac{a^2 + 2a + 1}{-a - 1}$ \quad $\substack{-a - 1,\text{ or} \\ -1(a + 1)}$ \quad **20.** $\dfrac{x^2 + 2x - 3}{1 - x}$ \quad $-x - 3$ \quad **21.** $\dfrac{-(n^2 - 5n + 6)}{-n + 2}$ \quad $n - 3$

B

22. $\dfrac{-x^2 - 2x + 15}{x^2 + 2x - 15}$ \quad -1 \quad **23.** $\dfrac{1 - x}{x^2 - 3x + 2}$ \quad $\frac{-1}{x - 2}$ \quad **24.** $\dfrac{4a - an}{n^2 - n - 12}$ \quad $\frac{-a}{n + 3}$

25. $\dfrac{a^2 - 2a + 1}{2a^2 + 6a - 8}$ \quad $\frac{a - 1}{2(a + 4)}$ \quad **26.** $\dfrac{2x^2 + 7x - 4}{1 - 3x + 2x^2}$ \quad $\frac{x + 4}{x - 1}$ \quad **27.** $-\dfrac{(h - 3)^2}{-(h^2 - 9)}$ \quad $\frac{h - 3}{h + 3}$

28. $\dfrac{4 - x^2}{(x - 2)^2}$ \quad $\frac{-(2 + x)}{x - 2}$ \quad **29.** $\dfrac{(x - 3)^3}{(3 - x)^3}$ \quad -1 \quad **30.** $\dfrac{(x - 5)^2}{(5 - x)^2}$ \quad 1 \quad **31.** $\dfrac{(x + 7)^2}{-x - 7}$ \quad $-x - 7$

\qquad or $\frac{-x - 2}{x - 2}$

C

32. $\dfrac{32 - 2x^2}{x^4 - 256}$ \quad $\frac{-2}{x^2 + 16}$ \quad **33.** $\dfrac{16 - 4a^2}{a^3 + 2a^2 + 4a + 8}$ \quad $\frac{4(2 - a)}{a^2 + 4}$ \quad **34.** $\dfrac{u^3 + 16u - 2u^2 - 32}{-u^2 - 16}$ \quad $-u + 2$

35. $\dfrac{x^4 - 81}{27 - 9x + 3x^2 - x^3}$ \quad $-(x + 3)$ \quad **36.** $\dfrac{12x^2 - 36x - x^3}{5x^2 - 60x + 180}$ \quad $-\frac{x}{5}$ \quad **37.** $\dfrac{y^5 - y}{y - y^2 + y^3 - y^4}$ \quad $-y - 1$

⌨ USING THE CALCULATOR

Rational Expressions—Equivalent or Not?

You can prove that two rational expressions are *not* equivalent if you show
that they are unequal for only one value of the variable. Thus, $\frac{1}{x} \neq \frac{1}{x^2}$ since
for $x = 2$, $\frac{1}{2} \neq \frac{1}{4}$.

Which expressions are not equal for the given value of x?

1. $\dfrac{x^2 + 2x - 3}{x^2 + 6x + 9} ; \dfrac{2x + 6}{x^2 + x - 6}$ \quad Use $x = 22$. \quad **2.** $\dfrac{-x^2 - x + 6}{x^2 - 4x + 4} ; -\dfrac{x + 3}{x - 2}$ \quad Use $x = 4.5$.

\qquad 0.84 \qquad 0.1 \qquad Not equal \qquad\qquad -3 \qquad -3 \qquad Equal

3. For those that are equal for the given x-value, either prove that the
expressions are equivalent by simplifying them or show that they are
unequal for some *other* value of x.

CHAPTER 8

8-3 Multiplying Rational Expressions

OBJECTIVE

To multiply two or more rational expressions, and to simplify the product.

This is how fractions are multiplied in arithmetic.

$$\frac{1}{2} \cdot \frac{4}{5} = \frac{1 \cdot 4}{2 \cdot 5} = \frac{1 \cdot \overset{2}{\cancel{4}}}{\underset{1}{\cancel{2}} \cdot 5} = \frac{2}{5}$$

To multiply two fractions, multiply their numerators and multiply their denominators.

Rule for Multiplying Fractions

If $b \neq 0$ and $d \neq 0$, then $\dfrac{a}{b} \cdot \dfrac{c}{d} = \dfrac{ac}{bd}$.

This rule applies to numerical fractions or to any rational expressions.

EXAMPLE 1   Multiply.

a. $4 \cdot \dfrac{3}{7} = \dfrac{4}{1} \cdot \dfrac{3}{7} = \dfrac{4 \cdot 3}{1 \cdot 7} = \dfrac{12}{7}$ **b.** $1\dfrac{1}{2} \cdot \dfrac{5}{8} = \dfrac{3}{2} \cdot \dfrac{5}{8} = \dfrac{15}{16}$

c. $\dfrac{2x}{3} \cdot \dfrac{5}{7y} = \dfrac{2x \cdot 5}{3 \cdot 7y} = \dfrac{10x}{21y}$ **d.** $\dfrac{3}{x-1} \cdot \dfrac{x+5}{x-1} = \dfrac{3(x+5)}{(x-1)^2}$

EXAMPLE 2   Multiply $\dfrac{15}{2y^2}$ and $\dfrac{y^4}{20}$.

Method I   Multiply first, then simplify.

$$\frac{15}{2y^2} \cdot \frac{y^4}{20} = \frac{15y^4}{40y^2} = \frac{\cancel{5y^2} \cdot 3y^2}{\cancel{5y^2} \cdot 8} = \frac{3y^2}{8}$$

Method II   Simplify first, then multiply.

$$\frac{15}{2y^2} \cdot \frac{y^4}{20} = \frac{\overset{3}{\cancel{15}}}{\underset{2}{\cancel{2y^2}}} \cdot \frac{\overset{y^2}{\cancel{y^4}}}{\underset{4}{\cancel{20}}} = \frac{3y^2}{8}$$

3. Multiply: $\dfrac{x^2 + x - 2}{5x} \cdot \dfrac{25}{x^2 + 5x + 6}$

$\dfrac{5(x - 1)}{x(x + 3)}$

POSSIBLE ERROR

Students sometimes make errors when multiplying a fraction by a whole number. For example, they may write:

$$5 \cdot \dfrac{(x - 1)}{(x + 1)} = \dfrac{5x - 5}{5x + 5}$$
(incorrect)

To help students avoid this type of error, you can encourage them to express the whole number as a fraction with a denominator of 1.:

$$5 \cdot \dfrac{(x - 1)}{(x + 1)} = \dfrac{5}{1} \cdot \dfrac{(x - 1)}{(x + 1)}$$
$$= \dfrac{5x - 5}{x + 1}$$

DAILY QUIZ

Multiply and simplify.

1. $\dfrac{2}{3} \cdot \dfrac{5}{8}$ $\dfrac{5}{12}$

2. $\dfrac{x^2}{y^3} \cdot \dfrac{y^3}{x^2}$ 1

3. $\dfrac{x^2 + 3x}{x - 3} \cdot \dfrac{x - 3}{x^2}$ $\dfrac{x + 3}{x}$

4. $\dfrac{x^2 - 4x + 4}{x^2 - 4} \cdot \dfrac{x^2 - 2x - 8}{x^2 - 2x}$ $\dfrac{x - 4}{x}$

5. $\dfrac{x}{2} \cdot \dfrac{4xy}{x^2 - y^2} \cdot \dfrac{x + y}{x^2 y}$ $\dfrac{2}{x - y}$

ASSIGNMENT GUIDE
(pages 294–295)

Minimum course: 1–12, 13–37 odd
Average: 1–45 odd, 51
Maximum course: 1–49 odd, 51, 52

EXAMPLE 3   Multiply $\dfrac{x^2 - x - 2}{2x} \cdot \dfrac{6}{x^2 + 2x + 1}$.

$$\dfrac{x^2 - x - 2}{2x} \cdot \dfrac{6}{x^2 + 2x + 1} = \dfrac{6(x^2 - x - 2)}{2x(x^2 + 2x + 1)}$$

$$= \dfrac{\overset{3}{\cancel{6}}(x - 2)\cancel{(x + 1)}}{\underset{1}{\cancel{2}}x \,\cancel{(x + 1)}(x + 1)}$$ Factor the numerator and denominator. Then simplify.

$$= \dfrac{3(x - 2)}{x(x + 1)}$$

The product may also be written as $\dfrac{3x - 6}{x^2 + x}$, but the factored form is usually preferred.

CLASS EXERCISES

Multiply. Simplify your answers.

1. $5 \cdot \dfrac{1}{2}$ $\dfrac{5}{2}$ 2. $\dfrac{4}{5} \cdot \dfrac{2}{3}$ $\dfrac{8}{15}$ 3. $2\dfrac{1}{3} \cdot \dfrac{1}{14}$ $\dfrac{1}{6}$ 4. $3 \cdot 3\dfrac{2}{3}$ 11

5. $\dfrac{x}{y} \cdot \dfrac{x}{y^2}$ $\dfrac{x^2}{y^3}$ 6. $\dfrac{a}{3x} \cdot \dfrac{2b}{5y}$ $\dfrac{2ab}{15xy}$ 7. $\dfrac{x^2 - 9}{x + 3} \cdot \dfrac{1}{6}$ $\dfrac{x - 3}{6}$ 8. $(x - 1)\left(\dfrac{2}{x}\right)$ $\dfrac{2(x - 1)}{x}$

9. $\dfrac{x - 1}{a^2} \cdot \dfrac{2ab}{(x - 1)^2}$ $\dfrac{2b}{a(x - 1)}$ 10. $\dfrac{15x}{x - 9} \cdot \dfrac{x - 9}{5x^2}$ $\dfrac{3}{x}$ 11. $\dfrac{a^2 + ab}{a - b} \cdot \dfrac{1}{a + b}$ $\dfrac{a}{a - b}$

EXERCISES

A   *Multiply. Simplify your answers.*

1. $\dfrac{1}{3} \cdot \dfrac{1}{4}$ $\dfrac{1}{12}$ 2. $\dfrac{2}{3} \cdot \dfrac{1}{4}$ $\dfrac{1}{6}$ 3. $\dfrac{2}{5} \cdot \dfrac{3}{4}$ $\dfrac{3}{10}$ 4. $\dfrac{3}{10} \cdot \dfrac{9}{5}$ $\dfrac{27}{50}$

5. $\dfrac{-1}{5} \cdot \dfrac{2}{9}$ $-\dfrac{2}{45}$ 6. $\dfrac{3}{8} \cdot 1\dfrac{1}{3}$ $\dfrac{1}{2}$ 7. $\dfrac{-1}{2} \cdot \dfrac{-1}{2}$ $\dfrac{1}{4}$ 8. $-\dfrac{4}{7} \cdot \dfrac{2}{3}$ $-\dfrac{8}{21}$

9. $\dfrac{10}{5} \cdot \dfrac{16}{9}$ $\dfrac{32}{9}$ 10. $-2 \cdot \dfrac{15}{8}$ $-\dfrac{15}{4}$ 11. $\dfrac{2x}{3} \cdot \dfrac{4x}{5}$ $\dfrac{8x^2}{15}$ 12. $\dfrac{5x}{7y} \cdot \dfrac{3x}{2y}$ $\dfrac{15x^2}{14y^2}$

13. $\dfrac{a}{b} \cdot \dfrac{b}{a}$ 1   14. $\dfrac{3a^2}{b} \cdot \dfrac{b^2}{a^3}$ $\dfrac{3b}{a}$ 15. $\dfrac{-14xy}{z} \cdot \dfrac{z^3}{7x^3}$ $-\dfrac{2yz^2}{x^2}$ 16. $\dfrac{6xy^3}{4x^2} \cdot \dfrac{12x^2}{9xy^2}$ $2y$

17. $\dfrac{3}{7} \cdot \dfrac{5}{8} \cdot \dfrac{1}{2}$ $\dfrac{15}{112}$ 18. $\dfrac{7}{8} \cdot \dfrac{6}{5} \cdot \dfrac{10}{3}$ $\dfrac{7}{2}$ 19. $\dfrac{-9}{5} \cdot \dfrac{1}{3} \cdot \dfrac{15}{-6}$ $\dfrac{3}{2}$ 20. $\dfrac{x}{2} \cdot \dfrac{y}{3} \cdot \dfrac{6}{7}$ $\dfrac{xy}{7}$

21. $\dfrac{x}{2} \cdot \dfrac{3}{x^2} \cdot \dfrac{8x}{5}$ $\dfrac{12}{5}$ 22. $\dfrac{a}{b^2} \cdot \dfrac{ab}{6} \cdot \dfrac{3b^2}{4a}$ $\dfrac{ab}{8}$ 23. $\dfrac{a}{b} \cdot \dfrac{c}{d} \cdot \dfrac{b}{a}$ $\dfrac{c}{d}$ 24. $\dfrac{1}{2} \cdot \dfrac{1}{3} \cdot \dfrac{1}{4} \cdot \dfrac{1}{5}$ $\dfrac{1}{120}$

25. $\dfrac{2}{x} \cdot \dfrac{x^2}{3} \cdot \dfrac{4}{x^3} \cdot \dfrac{x^4}{5}$ $\dfrac{8x^2}{15}$ 26. $\dfrac{x + 1}{5} \cdot \dfrac{10}{(x + 1)^2}$ $\dfrac{2}{x + 1}$ 27. $\dfrac{x - 2}{x + 3} \cdot \dfrac{x + 3}{5(x - 2)}$ $\dfrac{1}{5}$

EXTRA PRACTICE, page 523

28. $\dfrac{x(x + 2)}{x - 4} \cdot \dfrac{x - 4}{x^2}$ $\dfrac{x + 2}{x}$ **29.** $\dfrac{x^2 + x}{5} \cdot \dfrac{30}{x + 1}$ $6x$ **30.** $\dfrac{2x + 8}{x - 3} \cdot \dfrac{x^2 - 9}{2(x + 4)}$ $x + 3$

31. $\dfrac{4}{(x - 5)^2} \cdot \dfrac{x^2 - 5x}{2x^2}$ $\dfrac{2}{x(x - 5)}$ **32.** $(x + 3)\left(\dfrac{5x - 5}{x^2 - 9}\right)$ $\dfrac{5(x - 1)}{x - 3}$ **33.** $\left(\dfrac{x^2}{x - 4}\right)(x^2 - 16)$ $x^2(x + 4)$

B

34. $\dfrac{x^2 - x - 12}{5x} \cdot \dfrac{x^2 - 5x}{2x^2}$ $\dfrac{(x + 3)(x - 4)(x - 5)}{10x^2}$ **35.** $\dfrac{12x}{x^2 - 2x + 1} \cdot \dfrac{1 - x^2}{24x^2}$ $\dfrac{-(1 + x)}{2x(x - 1)}$

36. $\dfrac{x^2 - 5x + 6}{3x} \cdot \dfrac{x^2}{x - 2}$ $\dfrac{x(x - 3)}{3}$ **37.** $\dfrac{y^2 - 6y + 9}{y^2 - 9} \cdot \dfrac{y^2 + 4y + 3}{y^2 - 3y}$ $\dfrac{y + 1}{y}$

38. $\dfrac{4x^2 + 4x + 1}{2x^2 + x} \cdot \dfrac{x}{2x^2 - x - 1}$ $\dfrac{1}{x - 1}$ **39.** $\dfrac{x^2 - 1}{x^2 + x - 12} \cdot \dfrac{3x^2 - 27}{2x^2 + 6x + 4}$ $\dfrac{3(x - 1)(x + 3)}{2(x + 2)(x + 4)}$

40. $\dfrac{n^2 - 3n + 2}{2n^2 + 3n + 1} \cdot \dfrac{n^2 + 2n + 1}{1 - n^2}$ $\dfrac{-(n - 2)}{2n + 1}$ **41.** $\dfrac{a^2 - b^2}{3a^2 - 21a + 30} \cdot \dfrac{75 - 3a^2}{a^2 - 2ab + b^2}$ $\dfrac{-(a + b)(a + 5)}{(a - b)(a - 2)}$

42. $\dfrac{2x^2 - 7x - 4}{x^2 + 2x + 1} \cdot \dfrac{-(x + 1)^2}{4 + 7x - 2x^2}$ 1 **43.** $\dfrac{2x - x^2}{x^2 - 4} \cdot \dfrac{x^2 - 3x - 10}{x^3} \cdot \dfrac{x}{2}$ $-\dfrac{(x - 5)}{2x}$

44. $\dfrac{x^2 - 25}{x^2 - 2x - 24} \cdot \dfrac{x^2 + 4x}{2x^2 - 10x} \cdot \dfrac{4}{x + 5}$ $\dfrac{2}{x - 6}$ **45.** $\dfrac{x^2 - 2xy + y^2}{x^2 - y^2} \cdot \dfrac{x^2 + y^2}{2xy} \cdot \dfrac{x + y}{x - y}$ $\dfrac{x^2 + y^2}{2xy}$

C

46. $\dfrac{x^2 - 3x + 2}{x^2 - 4} \cdot \dfrac{x + 3}{x^2 + 3x} \cdot \dfrac{x^2 + 2x}{x^2 - 2x + 1}$ $\dfrac{1}{x - 1}$

47. $\dfrac{a^2 - 4b^2}{2a^2 + 5ab - 3b^2} \cdot \dfrac{2a^2 + ab - b^2}{2a^2 + 3ab + b^2} \cdot \dfrac{a^2 + 2ab - 3b^2}{a^2 - 3ab + 2b^2}$ $\dfrac{a + 2b}{2a + b}$

48. $\dfrac{t^2 + t}{2t^2 - 5t - 3} \cdot \dfrac{4t^2 - 4t + 1}{2t^2 + 7t - 4} \cdot \dfrac{2t^2 + 5t - 12}{t^2 - 2t^3}$ $-\dfrac{(t + 1)(2t - 3)}{t(t - 3)(2t + 1)}$

49. $\dfrac{x^3 + 3x^2 - 4x - 12}{x^3 - 6x^2 + x - 6} \cdot \dfrac{3x^3 + 3x}{x^3 + 5x^2 + 6x}$ $\dfrac{3(x - 2)}{x - 6}$

50. $\dfrac{x^4 - 1}{1 - a^2} \cdot \dfrac{a^2 - 8a + 7}{2x^2 + 6x + 4} \cdot \dfrac{ax + x + 2a + 2}{x^2 + 1}$ $-\dfrac{(x - 1)(a - 7)}{2}$

51. The width w of the rectangular box is $(x + 10)$ cm and the area of the base is $100x$ cm^2. If the height h is $\frac{4}{5}$ of the length l, what is the volume of the box in terms of x? $\dfrac{8000x^2}{x + 10}$ cm^3

52. The lateral surface area A of a right circular cylinder is $A = 2\pi rh$, and its volume V is $V = \pi r^2 h$. If $A = 100$ in.^{2}, find V in terms of h. $V = \dfrac{2500}{\pi h}$ in.^{3}

lateral surface
(Think of the
cylinder unrolled.)
$2\pi r$

RATIONAL EXPRESSIONS

LESSON NOTES

This lesson explains that the rule for dividing rational expressions is the same as the rule for dividing fractions. To find $\dfrac{a}{b} \div \dfrac{c}{d}$, we multiply $\dfrac{a}{b}$ by the reciprocal of $\dfrac{c}{d}$.

Informally, we get the reciprocal of $\dfrac{c}{d}$ by interchanging the numerator and denominator. Remind students that whole numbers also have reciprocals; for example, the reciprocal of 2 is $\dfrac{1}{2}$.

Students are frequently tempted to invert the divisor as they copy the original problem. If this is done, they do not have the original problem on their paper for checking purposes.

In Exercises 42–48 you may wish to point out that once the division examples have been changed to multiplication examples, the problems are similar to those in Lesson 8-3.

ALTERNATE EXAMPLES

1. Divide $\dfrac{3}{7}$ by 5. $\dfrac{3}{35}$

2. Divide.

   a. $2\dfrac{1}{4} \div \left(-\dfrac{1}{3}\right)$ $-\dfrac{27}{4}$

   b. $\dfrac{5x}{3y} \div \dfrac{3}{2x}$ $\dfrac{10x^2}{9y}$

8-4 Dividing Rational Expressions

OBJECTIVE

To apply the rule for dividing fractions to dividing rational expressions.

Recall that $24 \div 6 = \dfrac{24}{6}$, and that $\dfrac{24}{6} = 24 \cdot \dfrac{1}{6}$. So $24 \div 6 = 24 \cdot \dfrac{1}{6}$. To divide by 6 is the same as to multiply by its reciprocal, $\dfrac{1}{6}$.

To divide fractions, multiply by the reciprocal of the divisor.

Rule for Dividing Fractions

If $b \neq 0$, $c \neq 0$, and $d \neq 0$, then $\dfrac{a}{b} \div \dfrac{c}{d} = \dfrac{a}{b} \cdot \dfrac{d}{c}$.

This rule for dividing fractions applies to any rational expressions.

EXAMPLE 1   Divide $\dfrac{5}{12}$ by 3.

Change the operation.

$$\dfrac{5}{12} \div 3 = \dfrac{5}{12} \cdot \dfrac{1}{3} = \dfrac{5}{36} \qquad \text{The reciprocal of 3 is } \dfrac{1}{3}.$$

Use the reciprocal.

EXAMPLE 2   Divide.

a. $1\dfrac{1}{3} \div \left(-\dfrac{2}{5}\right) = \dfrac{4}{3} \div \left(-\dfrac{2}{5}\right)$ The divisor is $\left(-\dfrac{2}{5}\right)$.

$\qquad\qquad\quad = \dfrac{4}{3} \cdot \left(-\dfrac{5}{2}\right)$ Multiply by $\left(-\dfrac{5}{2}\right)$.

$\qquad\qquad\quad = -\dfrac{20}{6}$

$\qquad\qquad\quad = -\dfrac{10}{3}$

b. $\dfrac{2x}{3y} \div \dfrac{5}{4x} = \dfrac{2x}{3y} \cdot \dfrac{4x}{5}$ The divisor is $\dfrac{5}{4x}$, so multiply by $\dfrac{4x}{5}$.

$\qquad\qquad\quad = \dfrac{8x^2}{15y}$

EXAMPLE 3

Divide and simplify.

a. $\dfrac{12x^2b}{5y^2} \div \dfrac{12x^2}{b} = \dfrac{12x^2b}{5y^2} \cdot \dfrac{b}{12x^2} = \dfrac{b^2}{5y^2}$

b. $\dfrac{x^2 + 2x + 1}{18y^2} \div \dfrac{x + 1}{6y} = \dfrac{x^2 + 2x + 1}{18y^2} \cdot \dfrac{6y}{x + 1}$

$\qquad\qquad = \dfrac{(x + 1)(x + 1)}{18y^2} \cdot \dfrac{6y}{x + 1}$ Factor, then simplify.

$\qquad\qquad = \dfrac{\cancel{(x + 1)}(x + 1)\cancel{6y}}{\underset{3y}{\cancel{18y^2}}\cancel{(x + 1)}}$

$\qquad\qquad = \dfrac{x + 1}{3y}$

CLASS EXERCISES

Divide and simplify.

1. $2 \div \dfrac{1}{2}$ $\quad$ 4 $\qquad$ 2. $\dfrac{1}{2} \div 2$ $\quad$ $\dfrac{1}{4}$ $\qquad$ 3. $\dfrac{4}{3} \div \dfrac{1}{3}$ $\quad$ 4 $\qquad$ 4. $1 \div \dfrac{1}{3}$ $\quad$ 3

5. $\dfrac{2x}{3} \div \dfrac{7x^2}{5}$ $\quad$ $\dfrac{10}{21x}$ $\qquad$ 6. $\dfrac{3x}{y} \div \dfrac{2y}{x}$ $\quad$ $\dfrac{3x^2}{2y^2}$ $\qquad$ 7. $\dfrac{10r}{x} \div \dfrac{2r}{5x}$ $\quad$ 25 $\qquad$ 8. $\dfrac{4x}{3} \div 6x$ $\quad$ $\dfrac{2}{9}$

9. $1 \div \dfrac{1}{x + 1}$ $\;$ $x + 1$ $\quad$ 10. $1 \div \dfrac{2}{x + 3}$ $\;$ $\dfrac{x + 3}{2}$ $\;\checkmark$ 11. $\dfrac{3x + 6}{x} \div \dfrac{3}{x}$ $\;$ $x + 2$ $\;$ 12. $\dfrac{x^2}{5} \div \dfrac{x^2 + x}{10}$ $\;$ $\dfrac{2x}{x + 1}$

13. $\dfrac{x - 1}{a} \div \dfrac{2 - 2x}{a}$ $\;$ $-\dfrac{1}{2}$ $\quad$ 14. $\dfrac{x(n - 1)}{3} \div \dfrac{x^3}{6}$ $\;$ $\dfrac{2(n - 1)}{x^2}$ $\quad$ 15. $\dfrac{a + b}{a - b} \div (a^2 + 2ab + b^2)$ $\;$ $\dfrac{1}{(a + b)(a - b)}$

EXERCISES

A *Divide and simplify.*

1. $\dfrac{3}{4} \div 6$ $\;$ $\dfrac{1}{8}$ $\quad$ 2. $\dfrac{2}{5} \div \dfrac{1}{10}$ $\;$ 4 $\quad$ 3. $6 \div \dfrac{2}{3}$ $\;$ 9 $\quad$ 4. $2 \div 1\dfrac{1}{2}$ $\;$ $\dfrac{4}{3}$

5. $3\dfrac{1}{5} \div \left(-\dfrac{4}{5}\right)$ $\;$ -4 $\quad$ 6. $-\dfrac{3}{7} \div \dfrac{6}{7}$ $\;$ $-\dfrac{1}{2}$ $\quad$ 7. $\dfrac{3x^2}{5} \div \dfrac{2x}{3}$ $\;$ $\dfrac{9x}{10}$ $\quad$ 8. $\dfrac{2x}{3y^2} \div \dfrac{8x^3}{15y}$ $\;$ $\dfrac{5}{4x^2y}$

*Given the two expressions, **a.** multiply them, **b.** divide the first by the second.*

9. $6x, \dfrac{1}{2x}$ $\;$ **a.** 3 $\;$ **b.** $12x^2$ $\qquad$ 10. $\dfrac{1}{2x}, 6x$ $\;$ **a.** 3 $\;$ **b.** $\dfrac{1}{12x^2}$ $\qquad$ 11. $\dfrac{a^2b}{c}, \dfrac{ab^2}{c}$ $\;$ **a.** $\dfrac{a^3b^3}{c^2}$ $\;$ **b.** $\dfrac{a}{b}$ $\qquad$ 12. $\dfrac{x}{y}, \dfrac{x}{y}$ $\;$ **a.** $\dfrac{x^2}{y^2}$ $\;$ **b.** 1

13. $\dfrac{x}{y}, \dfrac{y}{x}$ $\;$ **a.** 1 $\;$ **b.** $\dfrac{x^2}{y^2}$ $\qquad$ 14. $\dfrac{x}{y}, z$ $\;$ **a.** $\dfrac{xz}{y}$ $\;$ **b.** $\dfrac{x}{yz}$ $\qquad$ 15. $x, \dfrac{y}{z}$ $\;$ **a.** $\dfrac{xy}{z}$ $\;$ **b.** $\dfrac{xz}{y}$ $\qquad$ 16. $\dfrac{x}{y}, \dfrac{r}{s}$ $\;$ **a.** $\dfrac{xr}{ys}$ $\;$ **b.** $\dfrac{xs}{yr}$

RATIONAL EXPRESSIONS

297

ENRICHMENT ACTIVITY

To test the associative property for multiplication and division of fractions, have students test each pair of operations to see if the operations in the expression on the left yield the same result as the operations in the expression on the right.

1. $\dfrac{a}{b} \cdot \left(\dfrac{c}{d} \cdot \dfrac{e}{f}\right); \left(\dfrac{a}{b} \cdot \dfrac{c}{d}\right) \cdot \dfrac{e}{f}$

2. $\dfrac{a}{b} \div \left(\dfrac{c}{d} \div \dfrac{e}{f}\right); \left(\dfrac{a}{b} \div \dfrac{c}{d}\right) \div \dfrac{e}{f}$

1. Both expressions result in $\dfrac{ace}{bdf}$.

2. The left expression results in $\dfrac{ade}{bcf}$, whereas the right expression results in $\dfrac{adf}{bce}$.

Multiplication is associative, but division is not.

Divide and simplify.

17. $\dfrac{x+1}{3} \div \dfrac{2(x+1)}{9}$ $\quad \frac{3}{2}$ **18.** $\dfrac{4}{x-2} \div \dfrac{16}{x}$ $\quad \frac{x}{4(x-2)}$ **19.** $\dfrac{4}{x-2} \div \dfrac{16}{(x-2)^2}$ $\quad \frac{x-2}{4}$

20. $\dfrac{4}{x-2} \div \dfrac{16}{x^2-4}$ $\quad \frac{x+2}{4}$ **21.** $\dfrac{2x-6}{5x} \div \dfrac{x-3}{10}$ $\quad \frac{4}{x}$ **22.** $\dfrac{3}{x^2-x} \div \dfrac{9}{x^2}$ $\quad \frac{x}{3(x-1)}$

23. $\dfrac{3}{x^2+x} \div \dfrac{2}{x+1}$ $\quad \frac{3}{2x}$ **24.** $\dfrac{n+1}{n^2-n} \div \dfrac{n+1}{n^2-2n}$ $\quad \frac{n-2}{n-1}$ **25.** $\dfrac{a-3}{a+2} \div \dfrac{a^2-9}{a+3}$ $\quad \frac{1}{a+2}$

26. $\dfrac{a}{b} \div \dfrac{a^2-ab}{ab+b^2}$ $\quad \frac{a+b}{a-b}$ **27.** $\dfrac{x+y}{x-y} \div \dfrac{x^2-y^2}{(x-y)^2}$ $\quad 1$ **28.** $\dfrac{x-y}{y-x} \div \dfrac{x}{y}$ $\quad -\frac{y}{x}$

29. $\dfrac{5}{x^2-4} \div \dfrac{10}{x+2}$ $\quad \frac{1}{2(x-2)}$ **30.** $\dfrac{x^2-4}{x-y} \div \dfrac{x-2}{y-x}$ $\quad \begin{matrix}-x-2 \\ \text{or} \\ -(x+2)\end{matrix}$ **31.** $\dfrac{x^2-3x}{x^2-x-6} \div \dfrac{x^2}{x+2}$ $\quad \frac{1}{x}$

B

32. $\dfrac{x^2-5x+6}{5} \div \dfrac{x-3}{15}$ $\quad 3(x-2)$ **33.** $\dfrac{x^2-2x-8}{x(x+2)^2} \div \dfrac{x-4}{x+2}$ $\quad \frac{1}{x}$

34. $\dfrac{y^2+3y-4}{y^3+4y^2} \div \dfrac{y^2-2y+1}{5y}$ $\quad \frac{5}{y(y-1)}$ **35.** $\dfrac{2t^2-3t-2}{t^2-4t-12} \div \dfrac{2t^2-7t-4}{5t^2-30t}$ $\quad \frac{5t(t-2)}{(t+2)(t-4)}$

36. $\dfrac{3a^2-7a-6}{a^2-9} \div \dfrac{9a^2-4}{3a^2+7a-6}$ $\quad 1$ **37.** $\dfrac{xy-y^2}{2x^2+xy-3y^2} \div \dfrac{x^2y+y^3}{2x^2+5xy+3y^2}$ $\quad \frac{x+y}{x^2+y^2}$

38. $\dfrac{2x}{3x^2+6x+3} \div \dfrac{6x-6}{x^2-1}$ $\quad \frac{x}{9(x+1)}$ **39.** $\dfrac{4x^2-20x+25}{6x^2-15x} \div \dfrac{25-4x^2}{x}$ $\quad \frac{-1}{3(5+2x)}$

40. $\dfrac{x^2-2x}{x+1} \div \dfrac{x^2+3x}{x^2+4x+3}$ $\quad x-2$ **41.** $\dfrac{x^2-y^2}{x^2+2xy+y^2} \div \dfrac{x^2-3xy+2y^2}{x^2+3xy+2y^2}$ $\quad \frac{x+2y}{x-2y}$

C

Simplify. Perform the multiplications and divisions from left to right unless parentheses indicate a different order.

Sample $\dfrac{a}{b} \div \dfrac{c}{d} \div \dfrac{e}{f} \cdot \dfrac{g}{h} = \dfrac{a}{b} \cdot \dfrac{d}{c} \cdot \dfrac{f}{e} \cdot \dfrac{g}{h} = \dfrac{adfg}{bceh}$

42. $\dfrac{a}{b} \cdot \dfrac{c}{d} \div \dfrac{e}{f} \cdot \dfrac{g}{h}$ $\quad \frac{acfg}{bdeh}$ **43.** $\dfrac{1}{a} \cdot \dfrac{1}{a^2} \div \dfrac{1}{a^3}$ $\quad 1$ **44.** $\dfrac{a}{b} \div \left(\dfrac{c}{d} \div \dfrac{d}{c}\right)$ $\quad \frac{ad^2}{bc^2}$

45. $\dfrac{x^2-16}{x^2+x} \div \dfrac{x+4}{x^2} \cdot \dfrac{x+1}{x^3}$ $\quad \frac{x-4}{x^2}$ **46.** $\dfrac{10r-10s}{r^2-s^2} \div \left(\dfrac{8r+8s}{r+3} \cdot \dfrac{5r+15}{r+s}\right)$ $\quad \frac{1}{4(r+s)}$

47. $\dfrac{x+3}{x^2-4} \div \dfrac{x^2+3x}{x^2-3x+2} \cdot \dfrac{x^3+4x^2+4x}{x-x^2}$ $\quad \frac{-x-2}{x} \text{ or } \frac{-(x+2)}{x}$

48. $\dfrac{x^2+x-6}{2x^2-3x-2} \cdot \dfrac{2x^2+9x+4}{x^2+7x+12} \div \dfrac{x^2+4x}{x+7}$ $\quad \frac{x+7}{x(x+4)}$

*49. $\dfrac{12x^2+11x-5}{x^4-16} \div \dfrac{x-3x^2}{x^3+4x-2x^2-8} \div \dfrac{4x+5}{x^2}$ $\quad \frac{-x}{x+2}$

8-5 Dividing Polynomials

OBJECTIVES

To divide a polynomial by a monomial.
To divide polynomials, using a long-division method.

Division by a monomial can be distributed over the terms of the numerator, or the *dividend*. For example, divide $6x^3 - 8x^2 + 10x$ by $2x$.

$$\underbrace{\frac{6x^3 - 8x^2 + 10x}{\underset{\uparrow}{2x}}}_{\text{dividend}} = \frac{6x^3}{2x} - \frac{8x^2}{2x} + \frac{10x}{2x} = \overbrace{3x^2 - 4x + 5}^{\text{quotient}}$$

divisor

You can also use factoring, if the divisor is a factor of the dividend.

$$\frac{6x^3 - 8x^2 + 10x}{2x} = \frac{2x(3x^2 - 4x + 5)}{2x} = 3x^2 - 4x + 5$$

A process of long division can be used when the divisor is not a monomial. It is similar to long division in arithmetic.

EXAMPLE 1   Divide $x^2 - 5x + 9$ by $x - 3$.

$$\begin{array}{r} x \\ x-3\overline{)x^2 - 5x + 9} \\ \underline{x^2 - 3x} \\ -2x \end{array}$$

Divide x into x^2. The quotient is x.
Multiply x by $x - 3$.
Subtract.

$$\begin{array}{r} x \\ x-3\overline{)x^2 - 5x + 9} \\ \underline{x^2 - 3x} \\ -2x + 9 \end{array}$$

Bring down 9, the next term of the dividend.

$$\begin{array}{r} x - 2 \\ x-3\overline{)x^2 - 5x + 9} \\ \underline{x^2 - 3x} \\ -2x + 9 \\ \underline{-2x + 6} \\ 3 \end{array}$$

Divide x into $-2x$. Write the quotient, -2, above.
Multiply -2 by $x - 3$. Subtract.
Stop dividing, since 3 is a constant.

quotient × divisor + remainder = dividend

Check as in arithmetic. $(x - 2)(x - 3) + 3 = x^2 - 5x + 6 + 3$
$ = x^2 - 5x + 9$

Answer $x - 2 + \dfrac{3}{x - 3}$ ←remainder
$\phantom{Answer   x - 2 + \dfrac{3}{x - 3}}$ ←divisor

RATIONAL EXPRESSIONS

299

LESSON NOTES

Division of a polynomial by a monomial can be accomplished by either of the two procedures illustrated in the opening of this lesson.

More challenging is the division of one polynomial by another. The steps in Example 1 can be shown at the chalkboard alongside comparable steps of an example of long division from arithmetic:

$$\begin{array}{r} 21 \\ 23\overline{)489} \\ \underline{46} \\ 29 \\ \underline{23} \\ 6 \end{array}$$

Check:
$(21)(23) + 6 = 489$

Notice that Example 1 involves division in which the remainder is *not* 0. In contrast, Example 2 involves division in which the remainder *is* 0; thus, the divisor $x - 2$ and the quotient $x^2 + 2x + 4$ are factors of the dividend, $x^3 - 8$.

ALTERNATE EXAMPLE

1. Divide $x^2 + 2x - 25$ by $x + 6$.
$$x - 4 + \frac{-1}{x + 6}$$
or $x - 4 - \dfrac{1}{x + 6}$

299

POSSIBLE ERROR

When dividing an expression such as $x^3 - 1$ by $x + 1$ (Exercise 27), some students neglect to write the necessary zero terms in the $x^3 - 1$. That is, they neglect to express $x^3 - 1$ as $x^3 + 0x^2 + 0x - 1$. Consequently, their work is confused and incorrect.

Help them avoid this type of error by stressing the need for the dividend to have its terms in decreasing order of degree and with *no* missing terms involving the variable.

DAILY QUIZ

Divide.

1. $\dfrac{18x^2 - 12x}{6x}$ $3x - 2$

2. $\dfrac{x^2 - 16}{x + 4}$ $x - 4$

Use long division to find the quotient and remainder.

3. $\dfrac{x^2 + 5x + 7}{x + 1}$ $x + 4 + \dfrac{3}{x + 1}$

4. $\dfrac{3x^2 - 7x + 8}{x - 3}$ $3x + 2 + \dfrac{14}{x - 3}$

5. $(6x^3 - 9x^2 + 4x - 4) \div (2x + 1)$
$3x^2 - 6x + 5 + \dfrac{-9}{2x + 1}$

ASSIGNMENT GUIDE
(page 301)

Minimum course: 1–23 odd
 second day: 10–30 even
Average course: 1–33 odd
Maximum course: 1–35 odd,
 36–38

EXAMPLE 2   Divide $x^3 - 8$ by $x - 2$.

Write the terms of the dividend in decreasing order of degree. Insert the two zero terms.

$$
\begin{array}{r}
x^2 + 2x\ + 4 \\
x - 2\overline{)x^3 + 0x^2 + 0x - 8} \\
\end{array}
$$

$x^3 - 2x^2$	Divide. Multiply x^2 by $x - 2$.
$2x^2 + 0x$	Subtract. Bring down $0x$.
$2x^2 - 4x$	Divide. Multiply $2x$ by $x - 2$.
$4x - 8$	Subtract. Bring down -8.
$4x - 8$	Divide. Multiply 4 by $x - 2$.
0	Subtract.

Check
$$
\begin{array}{r}
x^2 + 2x + 4 \\
x - 2 \\
\hline
-2x^2 - 4x - 8 \\
x^3 + 2x^2 + 4x \\
\hline
x^3 \qquad\qquad - 8
\end{array}
$$
Multiply the quotient and divisor.

The result is the dividend.

Therefore the quotient is $x^2 + 2x + 4$ and the remainder is 0.

The answer to Example 2 can be expressed another way.
$$
\begin{aligned}
x^3 - 8 &= (x - 2)(x^2 + 2x + 4) + 0 \\
&= (x - 2)(x^2 + 2x + 4)
\end{aligned}
$$

This shows that when the remainder in a division problem is 0, *then the divisor and quotient are factors of the dividend.*

CLASS EXERCISES

Divide.

1. $\dfrac{21x^2 - 14x}{7x}$ $3x - 2$ 2. $\dfrac{x^5 + 3x^2 + 2x}{x}$ $x^4 + 3x + 2$ 3. $\dfrac{6x^3 - 2x}{2x}$ $3x^2 - 1$

4. $\dfrac{12x^3 + 6x^2}{3x^2}$ $4x + 2$ 5. $\dfrac{x^3y - 3x^2y^2}{x^2y}$ $x - 3y$ 6. $\dfrac{x^2 - 8x + 15}{x - 5}$ $x - 3$

7. $\dfrac{x^2 - 25}{x + 5}$ $x - 5$ 8. $\dfrac{x^2 - 8x + 16}{x - 4}$ $x - 4$ 9. $\dfrac{x^2 + 10x - 24}{x + 12}$ $x - 2$

Check the long division shown at the right.
Then complete Exercises *10* and *11*.

10. Is $x + 3$ a factor of $x^2 + 9$?   No

11. $(x^2 + 9)$ divided by $(x + 3)$ is equal to $x - 3 + \dfrac{18}{?}$. $x + 3$

$$
\begin{array}{r}
x\ - 3 \\
x + 3\overline{)x^2 + 0x + 9} \\
x^2 + 3x \\
\hline
-3x + 9 \\
-3x - 9 \\
\hline
18
\end{array}
$$

CHAPTER 8

EXERCISES

Divide and check. Each divisor is a factor of the dividend.

1. $\dfrac{x^8 + 10x^6}{x^6}$ $x^2 + 10$

2. $\dfrac{9x^5 + 15x^4 - 6x^3}{3x^2}$ $3x^3 + 5x^2 - 2x$

3. $\dfrac{-10x^4 - 5x^3 + 15x^2}{5x^2}$ $-2x^2 - x + 3$

4. $\dfrac{6x^2 - 12x^4}{3x^2}$ $2 - 4x^2$

5. $\dfrac{-7x + 7x^2 + 21x^3}{7x}$ $-1 + x + 3x^2$

6. $\dfrac{x^2 + 2x - 15}{x - 3}$ $x + 5$

7. $\dfrac{x^2 - 10x + 25}{x - 5}$ $x - 5$

8. $\dfrac{x^2 - 10x - 24}{x + 2}$ $x - 12$

9. $\dfrac{2x^2 + 13x - 7}{2x - 1}$ $x + 7$

Use long division to find the quotient and the remainder. Check.

10. $\dfrac{x^2 + 2x + 2}{x + 1}$ $x + 1 + \dfrac{1}{x + 1}$

11. $\dfrac{x^2 - 2x - 1}{x - 1}$ $x - 1 - \dfrac{2}{x - 1}$

12. $\dfrac{x^2 - 2x - 1}{x - 3}$ $x + 1 + \dfrac{2}{x - 3}$

13. $\dfrac{x^2 + 2x + 2}{x + 4}$ $x - 2 + \dfrac{10}{x + 4}$

14. $\dfrac{x^2 + 6x - 9}{x - 4}$ $x + 10 + \dfrac{31}{x - 4}$

15. $\dfrac{x^2 - 10x - 8}{x + 6}$ $x - 16 + \dfrac{88}{x + 6}$

16. $\dfrac{2x^2 - 5x + 6}{x - 6}$ $2x + 7 + \dfrac{48}{x - 6}$

17. $\dfrac{3x^2 + 5x + 10}{x + 5}$ $3x - 10 + \dfrac{60}{x + 5}$

18. $\dfrac{x^3 - 3x^2 + 3x - 1}{x - 1}$ $x^2 - 2x + 1$

19. $(x^3 - 3x^2 + 3x - 1) \div (x + 2)$

20. $(x^3 + 5x^2 - 7x + 3) \div (x - 2)$

21. $(x^3 + 6x^2 + 12x + 8) \div (x + 2)$

22. $(x^3 + 6x^2 + 12x + 8) \div (x - 3)$

23. $\dfrac{2x^2 - 7x - 8}{2x + 1}$

24. $\dfrac{6x^2 - 10x + 5}{3x - 2}$

25. $\dfrac{4x^4 - 5x^2 + 7}{2x - 3}$

26. $\dfrac{9x^3 + 5x + 2}{3x + 2}$

27. $\dfrac{x^3 - 1}{x + 1}$

28. $\dfrac{8x^2 - 1}{2x - 1}$

29. $(8x^3 - 12x^2 + 6x - 1) \div (2x - 1)$

30. $(8x^3 - 12x^2 + 6x - 1) \div (2x + 1)$

In Exercises **31–35** the divisors are of degree 2. This means that the remainders may be constants or polynomials of degree 1.

31. $(x^4 + x^3 - 3) \div (x^2 + 1)$

32. $(x^3 - 1) \div (x^2 + x + 1)$

33. $(2x^5 - 7x^3 + 8) \div (x^2 - 2x)$

34. $(x^6 - 64) \div (x^2 - 4)$

35. $(x^4 - 4x^3 + 6x^2 - 4x + 3) \div (x^2 - 2x + 1)$ $x^2 - 2x + 1 + \dfrac{2}{x^2 - 2x + 1}$

36. Show that $x + 2$ is one factor of $x^3 - x^2 - 4x + 4$. Then find two other factors. $(x + 2)(x^2 - 3x + 2) = x^3 - x^2 - 4x + 4; (x - 1), (x - 2)$

37. Given that x and $x - 1$ are factors of $x^4 + 2x^3 - x^2 - 2x$, find two other factors of this polynomial. $(x + 1)(x + 2)$

38. Given that $2x^3 - 3x^2 - 32x - 15 = (\underline{\ ?\ })(x + 3)(x - 5)$, find the missing factor. $(2x + 1)$

*39. Find k so that $(x - 3)$ is a factor of $x^3 + 3x^2 - 13x + k$. $k = -15$

RATIONAL EXPRESSIONS

ENRICHMENT ACTIVITY

Refer to Example 1 (page 299) and have students use substitution as an alternate method of checking polynomial division. For instance, let $x = 5$.

$$x^2 - 5x + 9 = 9$$
$$x - 3 = 2$$

$$\dfrac{x^2 - 5x + 9}{x - 3} = \dfrac{9}{2} = 4\dfrac{1}{2}$$

Then evaluate the quotient:

$$x - 2 + \dfrac{3}{x - 3} = 3 + \dfrac{3}{2} = 4\dfrac{1}{2}$$

Finally, have students check again by using a different value for the variable.

ADDITIONAL ANSWERS

Exercises

19. $x^2 - 5x + 13 - \dfrac{27}{x + 2}$

20. $x^2 + 7x + 7 + \dfrac{17}{x - 2}$

21. $x^2 + 4x + 4$

22. $x^2 + 9x + 39 + \dfrac{125}{x - 3}$

23. $x - 4 - \dfrac{4}{2x + 1}$

24. $2x - 2 + \dfrac{1}{3x - 2}$

25. $2x^3 + 3x^2 + 2x + 3 + \dfrac{16}{2x - 3}$

26. $3x^2 - 2x + 3 - \dfrac{4}{3x + 2}$

27. $x^2 - x + 1 - \dfrac{2}{x + 1}$

28. $4x + 2 + \dfrac{1}{2x - 1}$

29. $4x^2 - 4x + 1$

30. $4x^2 - 8x + 7 - \dfrac{8}{2x + 1}$

31. $x^2 + x - 1 - \dfrac{x + 2}{x^2 + 1}$

32. $x - 1$

33. $2x^3 + 4x^2 + x + 2 + \dfrac{4x + 8}{x^2 - 2x}$

34. $x^4 + 4x^2 + 16$

EXTRA PRACTICE, page 523

LESSON NOTES

In this lesson we deal with adding and subtracting rational expressions which have common denominators. The rule, as with arithmetic fractions, is to retain the denominator and to add or subtract the numerators.

In discussing Examples 2 and 3, point out that answers must be simplified when factorization and cancellation are possible.

ALTERNATE EXAMPLES

1. Add or subtract as indicated.

   a. $\frac{3x}{10} + \frac{4x}{10}$ $\frac{7x}{10}$

   b. $\frac{2x}{3x} + \frac{5}{3x}$ $\frac{2x + 5}{3x}$

   c. $\frac{3}{20x} - \frac{5}{20x}$ $-\frac{1}{10x}$

2. Combine and simplify:
   $\frac{x^2 + 2x}{x - 7} - \frac{12x - 21}{x - 7}$ $x - 3$

8-6 Combining Rational Expressions: Same Denominators

OBJECTIVE

To add or subtract rational expressions that have the same denominator.

Adding and subtracting fractions is easy when the denominators are the same. Just show the sum or difference of the numerators over the common denominator.

$$\frac{2}{5} + \frac{1}{5} = \frac{2 + 1}{5} = \frac{3}{5} \qquad \frac{5}{7} - \frac{2}{7} = \frac{5 - 2}{7} = \frac{3}{7}$$

Rules for Adding and Subtracting Fractions

If $d \neq 0$, $\quad \dfrac{a}{d} + \dfrac{b}{d} = \dfrac{a + b}{d} \quad$ and $\quad \dfrac{a}{d} - \dfrac{b}{d} = \dfrac{a - b}{d}$.

The same rules apply to all rational expressions.

EXAMPLE 1   Add or subtract as indicated.

a. $\dfrac{x}{4} + \dfrac{2x}{4} = \dfrac{x + 2x}{4}$ b. $\dfrac{x}{8x} + \dfrac{6}{8x} = \dfrac{x + 6}{8x}$ c. $\dfrac{3}{12x} - \dfrac{5}{12x} = \dfrac{3 - 5}{12x}$

$\qquad\qquad\quad = \dfrac{3x}{4}$ $\qquad\qquad\qquad\qquad\qquad\qquad\qquad\qquad = \dfrac{-2}{12x}$

$\qquad\qquad\qquad\qquad\qquad\qquad\qquad\qquad\qquad\qquad\qquad\qquad\qquad = -\dfrac{1}{6x}$

EXAMPLE 2   Combine and simplify $\dfrac{x^2 + 2x}{x - 2} - \dfrac{2x + 4}{x - 2}$.

$\dfrac{x^2 + 2x}{x - 2} - \dfrac{2x + 4}{x - 2} = \dfrac{x^2 + 2x - (2x + 4)}{x - 2}$ Parentheses are needed here.

$\qquad\qquad\qquad\qquad = \dfrac{x^2 + 2x - 2x - 4}{x - 2}$

$\qquad\qquad\qquad\qquad = \dfrac{x^2 - 4}{x - 2}$ Simplify the numerator.

$\qquad\qquad\qquad\qquad = \dfrac{(x + 2)(x - 2)}{x - 2}$ Then factor.

$\qquad\qquad\qquad\qquad = x + 2$

302

EXAMPLE 3   Combine and simplify $\dfrac{a - 5b}{a^2 - b^2} + \dfrac{6b - 2a}{a^2 - b^2}$.

$$\dfrac{a - 5b}{a^2 - b^2} + \dfrac{6b - 2a}{a^2 - b^2} = \dfrac{a - 5b + 6b - 2a}{a^2 - b^2}$$

$$= \dfrac{b - a}{(a - b)(a + b)} \qquad \text{Simplify the numerator.}$$
Factor the denominator.

$$= -\dfrac{1}{a + b}$$

ATERNATE EXAMPLE

3. Combine and simplify:

$\dfrac{a - 4b}{a^2 - b^2} + \dfrac{3b - 2a}{a^2 - b^2} - \dfrac{1}{a - b}$

POSSIBLE ERROR

Some students might make the mistake of adding both the numerators and denominators when adding rational expressions. They might write

$$\dfrac{3a}{x} + \dfrac{2a}{x} = \dfrac{5a}{2x} \text{ (incorrect)}$$

Emphasize the basic rules; add or subtract the numerators and keep the common denominator.

CLASS EXERCISES

Add or subtract. Write answers in simplest form.

1. $\dfrac{2}{4} + \dfrac{3}{4}$ $\frac{5}{4}$ **2.** $\dfrac{3}{5} - \dfrac{2}{5}$ $\frac{1}{5}$ **3.** $\dfrac{4}{5} - \dfrac{4}{5}$ 0 **4.** $\dfrac{5}{40} + \dfrac{5}{40}$ $\frac{1}{4}$

5. $\dfrac{a}{5} + \dfrac{2a}{5}$ $\frac{3a}{5}$ **6.** $\dfrac{2y}{3} - \dfrac{x}{3}$ $\frac{2y-x}{3}$ **7.** $\dfrac{1}{x} + \dfrac{5}{x}$ $\frac{6}{x}$ **8.** $\dfrac{3}{x} - \dfrac{8}{x}$ $-\frac{5}{x}$

9. $\dfrac{5}{6} + \dfrac{-2}{6} + \dfrac{-1}{6}$ $\frac{1}{3}$ **10.** $\dfrac{7x}{9} + \dfrac{6x}{9} + \dfrac{5x}{9}$ $2x$ **11.** $\dfrac{a + b}{a^2 + 1} - \dfrac{b}{a^2 + 1}$ $\frac{a}{a^2 + 1}$

12. $\dfrac{x}{x + 1} + \dfrac{1}{x + 1}$ 1 **13.** $\dfrac{2a}{a + x} - \dfrac{a - x}{a + x}$ 1 **14.** $\dfrac{1 - 2x}{3x^2} + \dfrac{2 + 5x}{3x^2}$ $\frac{1+x}{x^2}$

EXERCISES

A   Add or subtract. Write answers in simplest form.

1. $\dfrac{6}{7} + \dfrac{1}{7}$ 1 **2.** $\dfrac{5}{8} + \dfrac{1}{8}$ $\frac{3}{4}$ **3.** $\dfrac{1}{5} - \dfrac{6}{5}$ -1 **4.** $\dfrac{5}{8} - \dfrac{1}{8}$ $\frac{1}{2}$

5. $\dfrac{3a}{7} + \dfrac{2a}{7}$ $\frac{5a}{7}$ **6.** $\dfrac{5x}{9} - \dfrac{2x}{9}$ $\frac{x}{3}$ **7.** $\dfrac{a}{9} - \dfrac{3a}{9}$ $\frac{-2a}{9}$ **8.** $\dfrac{6b}{5} - \dfrac{b}{5}$ b

9. $\dfrac{14x}{15} - \dfrac{17x}{15}$ $-\frac{x}{5}$ **10.** $\dfrac{x}{6} + \dfrac{4x}{6}$ $\frac{5x}{6}$ **11.** $\dfrac{3y}{10} - \dfrac{2y}{10}$ $\frac{y}{10}$ **12.** $\dfrac{5}{x} - \dfrac{4}{x}$ $\frac{1}{x}$

13. $\dfrac{-12}{5x} + \dfrac{7}{5x}$ $-\frac{1}{x}$ **14.** $\dfrac{a}{x} + \dfrac{b}{x}$ $\frac{a + b}{x}$ **15.** $\dfrac{2h}{15} - \dfrac{7h}{15}$ $-\frac{h}{3}$ **16.** $\dfrac{a}{3b} - \dfrac{2a}{3b}$ $-\frac{a}{3b}$

17. $\dfrac{4}{3} + \dfrac{4}{3} + \dfrac{4}{3}$ 4 **18.** $\dfrac{9x}{5} + \dfrac{6x}{5} - \dfrac{5x}{5}$ $2x$ **19.** $\dfrac{17}{y} - \dfrac{7}{y} - \dfrac{3}{y}$ $\frac{7}{y}$

20. $\dfrac{2}{x + 1} + \dfrac{-1}{x + 1}$ $\frac{1}{x + 1}$ **21.** $\dfrac{5}{x - 1} + \dfrac{x}{x - 1}$ $\frac{5 + x}{x - 1}$ **22.** $\dfrac{2t}{t + 2} + \dfrac{t}{t + 2}$ $\frac{3t}{t + 2}$

23. $\dfrac{2n + 5}{n + 1} - \dfrac{n + 4}{n + 1}$ 1 **24.** $\dfrac{1}{3x - 1} - \dfrac{3x}{3x - 1}$ -1 **25.** $\dfrac{h + 3}{h^2 - 1} - \dfrac{4}{h^2 - 1}$ $\frac{1}{h + 1}$

DAILY QUIZ

Add or subtract, then simplify.

1. $\dfrac{5}{8} - \dfrac{3}{8}$ $\frac{1}{4}$

2. $\dfrac{3x}{7} - \dfrac{5x}{7}$ $\frac{-2x}{7}$

3. $\dfrac{5y}{x} + \dfrac{y}{x}$ $\frac{6y}{x}$

4. $\dfrac{x}{x^2 - 9} + \dfrac{3}{x^2 - 9}$ $\frac{1}{x - 3}$

5. $\dfrac{6x^2}{3x - 2} - \dfrac{6 - 5x}{3x - 2}$ $2x + 3$

ASSIGNMENT GUIDE

(pages 303—304)

Minimum course: 1–33 odd
Average course: 1–41 odd
46
Maximum course: 1–45 odd, 46, 47
All courses: *Checkpoint* review exercises

RATIONAL EXPRESSIONS

EXTRA PRACTICE, page 523

B

26. $\dfrac{x}{x^2-4} + \dfrac{2}{x^2-4}$ $\quad \frac{1}{x-2}$ 27. $\dfrac{x}{x^2-4} - \dfrac{2}{x^2-4}$ $\quad \frac{1}{x+2}$ 28. $\dfrac{c^2}{c+2} - \dfrac{4}{c+2}$ $\quad c-2$

29. $\dfrac{x^2}{x-2} - \dfrac{4}{x-2}$ $\quad x+2$ 30. $\dfrac{x^2}{x+1} + \dfrac{2x+1}{x+1}$ $\quad x+1$ 31. $\dfrac{a^2}{u-2} - \dfrac{4a-4}{u-2}$ $\quad a-2$

32. $\dfrac{9}{3-y} - \dfrac{y^2}{3-y}$ $\quad 3+y$ 33. $\dfrac{-2x}{x+5} + \dfrac{-10}{x+5}$ $\quad -2$ 34. $\dfrac{7x}{3-x} - \dfrac{21}{3-x}$ $\quad -7$

35. $\dfrac{4a}{x-4} - \dfrac{ax}{x-4}$ $\quad -a$ 36. $\dfrac{2x^2}{x+3} + \dfrac{6x}{x+3}$ $\quad 2x$ 37. $\dfrac{a+2b}{3ab} + \dfrac{2a+b}{3ab}$ $\quad \frac{a+b}{ab}$

38. $\dfrac{5x+3}{x+1} - \dfrac{3x+1}{x+1}$ $\quad 2$ 39. $\dfrac{4x^2}{2x-1} - \dfrac{4x-1}{2x-1}$ $\quad 2x-1$ 40. $\dfrac{x^2+x}{x-2} - \dfrac{6}{x-2}$ $\quad x+3$

C

41. $\dfrac{2x^2}{2x-1} - \dfrac{11x-5}{2x-1}$ $\quad x-5$ 42. $\dfrac{x^3}{x-2} - \dfrac{4x^2-4x}{x-2}$ $\quad x(x-2)$ 43. $\dfrac{xy+2x}{x+1} + \dfrac{y+2}{x+1}$ $\quad y+2$

44. $\dfrac{2x}{2x^2+3x-5} + \dfrac{5}{2x^2+3x-5}$ $\quad \frac{1}{x-1}$ 45. $\dfrac{-(3-x^3)}{x+3} - \dfrac{x}{x+3} + \dfrac{3x^2}{x+3}$ $\quad x^2-1$

46. The sides of a trapezoid are $\dfrac{x^2}{x+3}$, $\dfrac{2x+3}{x+3}$, $\dfrac{2x+1}{x+3}$, and $\dfrac{x+2}{x+3}$. Find the perimeter in terms of x and simplify. $\quad x+2$

trapezoid

47. This cross section of a tunnel has walls $\frac{1}{2x}$ units high and a base $\frac{2}{x}$ units across. The roof is semicircular. Find the perimeter of the cross section in terms of x and π and simplify. Use the formula for the circumference of a circle, $C = 2\pi r$. $\quad \frac{3+\pi}{x}$

CHECKPOINT

Complete the indicated operations. Simplify your answers.

1. $\dfrac{5}{6} \cdot \dfrac{2}{7}$ $\quad \frac{5}{21}$ 2. $-\dfrac{3}{8} \cdot \dfrac{2}{9}$ $\quad -\frac{1}{12}$ 3. $\dfrac{x^2}{y} \cdot \dfrac{y^2}{x}$ $\quad xy$ 4. $\dfrac{x^2-4}{x+2} \cdot \dfrac{3}{2-x}$ $\quad -3$

5. $\dfrac{5}{8} \div 2$ $\quad \frac{5}{16}$ 6. $\dfrac{3}{4} \div \dfrac{3}{2}$ $\quad \frac{1}{2}$ 7. $\dfrac{3x}{2y^2} \div \dfrac{15x^3}{8y}$ $\quad \frac{4}{5x^2y}$ 8. $\dfrac{x^2-8x+12}{x^2+8x+12} \div \dfrac{x^2-4}{x^2-36}$ $\quad \frac{(x-6)^2}{(x+2)^2}$

9. $\dfrac{5x}{8} - \dfrac{3x}{8}$ $\quad \frac{x}{4}$ 10. $\dfrac{x}{x^2-9} + \dfrac{3}{x^2-9}$ $\quad \frac{1}{x-3}$ 11. $\dfrac{x^2}{x+3} - \dfrac{9}{x+3}$ $\quad x-3$

Use long division to find the quotient and remainder.

12. $\dfrac{x^2+2x+2}{x-1}$ $\quad x+3+\frac{5}{x-1}$ 13. $\dfrac{x^2+6x-9}{x+4}$ $\quad x+2-\frac{17}{x+4}$ 14. $\dfrac{6x^2-11x+5}{3x+2}$ $\quad 2x-5+\frac{15}{3x+2}$

8-7 Combining Rational Expressions: Different Denominators

OBJECTIVE

To add or subtract rational expressions that have different denominators.

To add or subtract fractions that have different denominators, first rewrite the fractions so that they have the same denominator.

If one denominator is a multiple of the other, rewrite the fraction with the lesser denominator. For example, in $\frac{7}{12} + \frac{1}{2}$ the denominator 12 is a multiple of the denominator 2. So rewrite $\frac{1}{2}$ with denominator 12.

$$\frac{7}{12} + \frac{1}{2} = \frac{7}{12} + \frac{1 \cdot 6}{2 \cdot 6}$$

Multiplying the numerator and denominator by the same number does not change the value of the fraction.

$$= \frac{7}{12} + \frac{6}{12}$$

$$= \frac{7 + 6}{12}$$

$$= \frac{13}{12}, \text{ or } 1\frac{1}{12}$$

EXAMPLE 1 Add or subtract, and simplify.

a. $\dfrac{1}{x} + \dfrac{7}{3x} = \dfrac{3 \cdot 1}{3 \cdot x} + \dfrac{7}{3x}$

$= \dfrac{3}{3x} + \dfrac{7}{3x}$

$= \dfrac{10}{3x}$

b. $\dfrac{4}{x - 1} - \dfrac{4}{x(x - 1)} = \dfrac{(x)(4)}{x(x - 1)} - \dfrac{4}{x(x - 1)}$

$= \dfrac{4x - 4}{x(x - 1)}$

$= \dfrac{4(x - 1)}{x(x - 1)}$

$= \dfrac{4}{x}$

EXAMPLE 2 Combine, and simplify.

a. $\dfrac{2}{3x^2} + \dfrac{7}{3x} - \dfrac{1}{x} = \dfrac{2}{3x^2} + \dfrac{7(x)}{3x(x)} - \dfrac{1(3x)}{x(3x)}$

$= \dfrac{2}{3x^2} + \dfrac{7x}{3x^2} - \dfrac{3x}{3x^2}$

$= \dfrac{2 + 7x - 3x}{3x^2}$

$= \dfrac{2 + 4x}{3x^2}, \text{ or } \dfrac{2(1 + 2x)}{3x^2}$

b. $\dfrac{x}{y} + 3 = \dfrac{x}{y} + \dfrac{3}{1}$

$= \dfrac{x}{y} + \dfrac{3(y)}{1(y)}$

$= \dfrac{x}{y} + \dfrac{3y}{y}$

$= \dfrac{x + 3y}{y}$

4. Combine: $\dfrac{2}{x-2} - \dfrac{1}{x+2}$

$$\dfrac{x+6}{(x-2)(x+2)}$$

POSSIBLE ERROR

When adding a whole number to a fraction, students often make careless mistakes such as this:

$$\dfrac{x}{y} + 3 = \dfrac{x+3}{y} \text{ (incorrect)}$$

This error shows a lack of understanding regarding the need for a common denominator in the addition and subtraction of fractions.

Point out that before adding 3 to $\dfrac{x}{y}$, 3 should be expressed as $\dfrac{3}{1} = \dfrac{3y}{y}$. Thus, $\dfrac{x}{y} + 3$ becomes $\dfrac{x}{y} + \dfrac{3y}{y}$, resulting in the sum $\dfrac{x+3y}{y}$.

DAILY QUIZ

Add or subtract, then simplify.

1. $\dfrac{5}{8} - \dfrac{3}{4}$ $-\dfrac{1}{8}$

2. $\dfrac{2}{xy} + \dfrac{3}{y}$ $\dfrac{2 + 3x}{xy}$

3. $8 - \dfrac{3x}{y^2}$ $\dfrac{8y^2 - 3x}{y^2}$

4. $\dfrac{x}{x-2} - \dfrac{2}{x+2}$ $\dfrac{x^2 + 4}{(x-2)(x+2)}$

5. $\dfrac{3}{x-1} + \dfrac{2}{x+1} - \dfrac{x}{x^2-1}$ $\dfrac{4x+1}{(x-1)(x+1)}$

If neither denominator is a multiple of the other, you can find a common denominator by multiplying the given denominators.

EXAMPLE 3   Add $\dfrac{1}{6x} + \dfrac{3}{8}$.

$$\dfrac{1}{6x} + \dfrac{3}{8} = \dfrac{1(8)}{6x(8)} + \dfrac{3(6x)}{8(6x)} \qquad \text{A common denominator is } (6x)(8), \text{ or } 48x.$$

$$= \dfrac{8}{48x} + \dfrac{18x}{48x}$$

$$= \dfrac{8 + 18x}{48x}$$

$$= \dfrac{2(4 + 9x)}{48x} \qquad \text{Factor the numerator.}$$

$$= \dfrac{4 + 9x}{24x} \qquad \text{Divide numerator and denominator by 2.}$$

In Example 3, 48x was used as the common denominator. But it wasn't the *least* common denominator. You could have used 24x just as well. In the next lesson you will practice using the least common denominator.

EXAMPLE 4   Combine $\dfrac{1}{x-1} - \dfrac{6}{x+1}$.

$$\dfrac{1}{x-1} - \dfrac{6}{x+1} = \dfrac{1(x+1)}{(x-1)(x+1)} - \dfrac{6(x-1)}{(x+1)(x-1)} \qquad \text{The common denominator is } (x-1)(x+1).$$

$$= \dfrac{(x+1) - 6(x-1)}{(x-1)(x+1)}$$

$$= \dfrac{x+1 - 6x + 6}{(x-1)(x+1)} \qquad \text{Remove parentheses in the numerator.}$$

$$= \dfrac{-5x + 7}{(x-1)(x+1)} \qquad \text{Simplify.}$$

CLASS EXERCISES

Rewrite each fraction with denominator 12.

1. $\dfrac{1}{6}$ $\dfrac{2}{12}$
2. $\dfrac{x}{2}$ $\dfrac{6x}{12}$
3. $\dfrac{5x}{4}$ $\dfrac{15x}{12}$
4. $\dfrac{5}{1}$ $\dfrac{60}{12}$
5. $\dfrac{n+1}{3}$ $\dfrac{4n+4}{12}$

Add or subtract. Simplify your answers.

6. $\dfrac{3}{4} + \dfrac{7}{12}$ $\dfrac{4}{3}$
7. $1 - \dfrac{7}{15}$ $\dfrac{8}{15}$
8. $\dfrac{1}{2} + \dfrac{1}{3}$ $\dfrac{5}{6}$
9. $\dfrac{7}{8} - \dfrac{5}{6}$ $\dfrac{1}{24}$

10. $\dfrac{3}{2x} + \dfrac{1}{2}$ $\dfrac{3+x}{2x}$
11. $\dfrac{2}{3} - \dfrac{5}{a}$ $\dfrac{2a-15}{3a}$
12. $\dfrac{3}{5} + \dfrac{1}{n+1}$ $\dfrac{3n+8}{5(n+1)}$
13. $\dfrac{x+2}{2} - \dfrac{1}{x}$ $\dfrac{x^2+2x-2}{2x}$

306

EXERCISES

ASSIGNMENT GUIDE
(pages 307–308)

Minimum course: 1–29 odd
second day: 10–30 even
Average course: 1–37 odd
second day: 22–40 even,
45
Maximum course: 1–41 odd
second day: 26–40 even,
44,45
All courses: *Strategies for
Problem
Solving*

A

Rewrite each fraction with denominator 27x.

1. $\dfrac{12}{27}$ $\;\frac{12x}{27x}$ **2.** $\dfrac{-4}{9}$ $\;\frac{-12x}{27x}$ **3.** $\dfrac{2}{x}$ $\;\frac{54}{27x}$ **4.** $\dfrac{x}{9}$ $\;\frac{3x^2}{27x}$ **5.** $\dfrac{7}{9x}$ $\;\frac{21}{27x}$

Add or subtract. Simplify your answers.

6. $\dfrac{3}{7} - \dfrac{7}{3}$ $\;-\frac{40}{21}$ **7.** $1 + \dfrac{5}{8}$ $\;\frac{13}{8}$ **8.** $\dfrac{1}{8} - \dfrac{1}{9}$ $\;\frac{1}{72}$ **9.** $\dfrac{1}{9} - \dfrac{1}{8}$ $\;-\frac{1}{72}$

10. $6\dfrac{3}{4} + \dfrac{5}{8}$ $\;\frac{59}{8}$ or $7\frac{3}{8}$ **11.** $5\dfrac{7}{8} - \dfrac{2}{3}$ $\;\frac{125}{24}$ or $5\frac{5}{24}$ **12.** $2\dfrac{1}{2} + 3\dfrac{1}{3}$ $\;\frac{35}{6}$ or $5\frac{5}{6}$ **13.** $\dfrac{1}{5} + 2\dfrac{3}{10}$ $\;\frac{5}{2}$ or $2\frac{1}{2}$

14. $\dfrac{x}{2} + \dfrac{x}{10}$ $\;\frac{3x}{5}$ **15.** $\dfrac{x}{2} + \dfrac{5}{x}$ $\;\frac{x^2+10}{2x}$ **16.** $\dfrac{5}{x} - \dfrac{x}{2}$ $\;\frac{10-x^2}{2x}$ **17.** $\dfrac{2}{3x} + \dfrac{3}{4x}$ $\;\frac{17}{12x}$

18. $\dfrac{2}{y} + \dfrac{3}{xy}$ $\;\frac{2x+3}{xy}$ **19.** $\dfrac{1}{x} + 5$ $\;\frac{1+5x}{x}$ **20.** $\dfrac{a}{b} + 2$ $\;\frac{a+2b}{b}$ **21.** $4 - \dfrac{x}{y}$ $\;\frac{4y-x}{y}$

22. $\dfrac{1}{x} + \dfrac{1}{2x}$ $\;\frac{3}{2x}$ **23.** $x + \dfrac{1}{2x}$ $\;\frac{2x^2+1}{2x}$ **24.** $\dfrac{9}{5} - \dfrac{4}{3} + \dfrac{1}{15}$ $\;\frac{8}{15}$ **25.** $\dfrac{1}{x} + \dfrac{2}{x^2} + \dfrac{3}{x^3}$ $\;\frac{x^2+2x+3}{x^3}$

B

Combine and simplify.

26. $\dfrac{x}{x-3} - \dfrac{3}{x+3}$ $\;\frac{x^2+9}{(x-3)(x+3)}$ **27.** $\dfrac{4}{h+1} + \dfrac{2}{h+2}$ $\;\frac{6h+10}{(h+1)(h+2)}$ or **28.** $\dfrac{5}{b-2} + \dfrac{3}{b+1}$ $\;\frac{8b-1}{(b-2)(b+1)}$

29. $\dfrac{x}{6x+6} - \dfrac{1}{x+1}$ $\;\frac{x-6}{6(x+1)}$ **30.** $2 + \dfrac{2x+1}{6x}$ $\;\frac{2(3h+5)}{(h+1)(h+2)}$ $\;\frac{14x+1}{6x}$ **31.** $\dfrac{5x+6}{x^2+3x} + \dfrac{x}{x+3}$ $\;\frac{x+2}{x}$

32. $\dfrac{x^2+5x+6}{x^2+2x} - 1$ $\;\frac{3}{x}$ **33.** $\dfrac{5t+30}{t^2+6t} + 1$ $\;\frac{t+5}{t}$ **34.** $\dfrac{t-3}{t+3} + \dfrac{t-3}{t^2-9}$ $\;\frac{t-2}{t+3}$

35. $\dfrac{8}{h-1} + \dfrac{2h}{h^2-2h+1}$ $\;\frac{2(5h-4)}{(h-1)^2}$ **36.** $\dfrac{x}{x-7} - \dfrac{x+3}{x^2-4x-21}$ $\;\frac{x-1}{x-7}$

C

37. $\dfrac{1}{x+5} + \dfrac{2}{x-5} + \dfrac{4}{x^2-25}$ $\;\frac{3(x+3)}{(x-5)(x+5)}$ **38.** $\dfrac{3}{x+1} - \dfrac{1}{1-x} + \dfrac{x}{x^2-1}$ $\;\frac{5x-2}{(x-1)(x+1)}$

39. $\dfrac{a}{a+2} + \dfrac{4}{a-2} - \dfrac{8}{a^2-4}$ $\;\frac{a}{a-2}$ **40.** $\dfrac{2c}{c-2} + \dfrac{2}{c-3} + \dfrac{4}{c^2-5c+6}$ $\;\frac{2c}{c-3}$

41. $1 - \dfrac{2}{x+1} - \dfrac{1}{(x+1)^2}$ $\;\frac{x^2-2}{(x+1)^2}$ ***42.** $\dfrac{1}{x^2-9} - \dfrac{1}{x^2-4x+3}$ $\;\frac{-4}{(x-1)(x-3)(x+3)}$

*43. $\dfrac{1}{h-2} - \dfrac{h}{h^2+1} - \dfrac{h+3}{h^3-2h^2+h-2}$ $\;\frac{1}{h^2+1}$

44. Find the perimeter of a rectangle with length $\dfrac{3}{2x+2}$ and width $\dfrac{1}{x+1}$. $\;\frac{5}{x+1}$

45. The perimeter of a triangle is $\dfrac{11}{4n}$. Two sides have lengths $\dfrac{2}{3n}$ and $\dfrac{1}{n}$. Find the length of the third side. $\;\frac{13}{12n}$

RATIONAL EXPRESSIONS

307

ENRICHMENT ACTIVITY

Use the Strategies for Problem Solving (page 308) to stimulate discussion of the importance of estimation. Provide a number of challenging examples that will allow students to estimate the answer before they attempt any computation or experimentation.

Here are a few such examples: How many ping-pong balls will fit into the classroom? How high is a pile of a million pennies? How far would one million dollar bills extend if placed end to end?

Strategies for Problem Solving

Estimating is a key mathematical skill because often we need only an approximate answer. Also, sometimes it is impossible to arrive at the exact answer to a problem.

Note that the choices for the exercises do not include the exact answers, but they are reasonably close to the answers. For example, in Exercise 1, $\frac{3}{5} + \left(\frac{3}{5}\right)^2 = \frac{15}{25} + \frac{9}{25} = \frac{24}{25}$, and the result is very close to 1.

Some students might initially reject the answer to Exercise 10, arguing that the average of 40 and 50 is exactly 45. Explain that it takes longer to go out at 40 mph than to come back at 45 mph. Since more time is spent traveling at the lesser rate, the average speed for the entire trip is less than 45 mph.

It is frequently helpful to estimate answers. These exercises will give you some practice in this very important problem-solving skill. In the following, make the best estimate by selecting one of the given choices without doing detailed calculations.

Estimate the number.

1. The sum of a number and its square is 1.   b   **a.** $\frac{2}{5}$ **b.** $\frac{3}{5}$ **c.** $\frac{4}{5}$

2. The sum of a number and its reciprocal is 3. a   **a.** $2\frac{1}{2}$ **b.** 2   **c.** $\frac{4}{5}$

3. Two times the square of a number is 40.   c   **a.** $3\frac{1}{2}$ **b.** 4   **c.** $4\frac{1}{2}$

Estimate the cost.

4. 10 cans at 79¢ each   b
   a. $7   **b.** $8   **c.** $9

5. n boxes at 98¢ each   a
   a. n dollars   **b.** 9n dollars   **c.** 10n dollars

6. n pounds at $1.03 per pound   c
   a. n cents   **b.** 10n cents   **c.** 100n cents

Estimate the average speed.

7. 485 miles in 8 hours   b
   a. 50 mph   **b.** 60 mph
   c. 70 mph

8. 300 miles in 2 minutes   b
   a. 900 mph   **b.** 9000 mph
   c. 90,000 mph

9. n miles in 2 hours 53 minutes   c
   a. less than $\frac{n}{3}$ mph   **b.** $\frac{n}{3}$ mph
   c. more than $\frac{n}{3}$ mph

10. 40 mph going out and 50 mph coming back   a
   a. less than 45 mph   **b.** 45 mph
   c. more than 45 mph

8-8 Combining Rational Expressions: Least Common Denominator

OBJECTIVE

To add or subtract rational expressions, using the LCD.

The multiples of 6 are   6, 12, 18, 24, 30, 36, 42, 48, 54, . . .
The multiples of 8 are   8, 16, 24, 32, 40, 48, 56, 64, 72, . . .

Some *common multiples* of 6 and 8 are 24, 48, and 72. The **least common multiple (LCM)** is 24.

To find the least common multiple of two positive integers, you can use their prime factors. Multiply each factor the greatest number of times it occurs in either integer. For example:

$$6 = 2 \cdot 3 \quad \text{and} \quad 8 = 2 \cdot 2 \cdot 2$$

The required factors are three 2's and one 3: $2 \cdot 2 \cdot 2 \cdot 3 = 24$

Therefore the least common multiple of 6 and 8 is 24. A similar procedure is used to find the least common multiple for algebraic expressions.

EXAMPLE 1   Find the least common multiple of $2x^3y$ and x^2y^2.

$$2x^3y = (2)(x)(x)(x)(y) \quad \text{and} \quad x^2y^2 = (x)(x)(y)(y)$$

The required factors are one 2, three x's, and two y's.
The least common multiple is $2x^3y^2$.

To add or subtract fractions, it is often simpler if you use the **least common denominator (LCD),** which is the least common multiple of the denominators.

EXAMPLE 2   Combine $\dfrac{2x + 1}{9x} - \dfrac{5}{3x^2}$. Use the LCD.

$$9x = (3)(3)(x) \quad \text{and} \quad 3x^2 = (3)(x)(x)$$

The required factors are two 3's and two x's.
The LCD is $9x^2$.

$$\frac{2x + 1}{9x} - \frac{5}{3x^2} = \frac{(2x + 1)(x)}{9x(x)} - \frac{5(3)}{3x^2(3)}$$
$$= \frac{2x^2 + x}{9x^2} - \frac{15}{9x^2}$$
$$= \frac{2x^2 + x - 15}{9x^2}, \text{ or } \frac{(2x - 5)(x + 3)}{9x^2}$$

RATIONAL EXPRESSIONS

309

3. Combine: $\dfrac{8x}{x^2 - x - 6} + \dfrac{x}{2x - 6}$

$\dfrac{x(x + 18)}{2(x - 3)(x + 2)}$

Combine and simplify.

1. $\dfrac{3}{x^2} + \dfrac{5}{2x}$ $\dfrac{6 + 5x}{2x^2}$

2. $\dfrac{x^2 - 5x}{x^2 - 25} - \dfrac{2}{x + 5}$ $\dfrac{x - 2}{x + 5}$

3. $\dfrac{4}{3(x - 1)} + \dfrac{4}{x^2 - 5x + 4}$ $\dfrac{4}{3(x - 4)}$

4. $\dfrac{6}{2x + 8} + \dfrac{2}{x^2 - 16}$ $\dfrac{3x - 10}{(x - 4)(x + 4)}$

5. $\dfrac{5}{x - 3} - \dfrac{3}{3 - x}$ $\dfrac{8}{x - 3}$

EXAMPLE 3   Combine $\dfrac{10x}{x^2 - 2x - 3} + \dfrac{5x}{2x + 2}$.

Find the least common multiple of the denominators.

$x^2 - 2x - 3 = (x + 1)(x - 3)$ and $2x + 2 = 2(x + 1)$

The LCD is $2(x + 1)(x - 3)$.

$$\dfrac{10x}{x^2 - 2x - 3} + \dfrac{5x}{2x + 2} = \dfrac{10x}{(x + 1)(x - 3)} + \dfrac{5x}{2(x + 1)}$$

$$= \dfrac{20x}{2(x + 1)(x - 3)} + \dfrac{5x(x - 3)}{2(x + 1)(x - 3)}$$

$$= \dfrac{20x + 5x(x - 3)}{2(x + 1)(x - 3)}$$

$$= \dfrac{20x + 5x^2 - 15x}{2(x + 1)(x - 3)}$$

$$= \dfrac{5x^2 + 5x}{2(x + 1)(x - 3)}$$

$$= \dfrac{5x(x + 1)}{2(x + 1)(x - 3)}$$

$$= \dfrac{5x}{2(x - 3)}$$

CLASS EXERCISES

Find the least common multiple for each pair of expressions.

1. 10, 14   70
2. 21, 63   63
3. 8x, 6x   24x

4. $6a^3b, 4a^2c$ $12a^3bc$
5. $3xy^2, 5x^3$ $15x^3y^2$
6. $3, 4(x - 1)$ $12(x - 1)$

Find the LCD. Then combine and simplify.

7. $\dfrac{3}{8} - \dfrac{1}{6}$ $24; \frac{5}{24}$
8. $\dfrac{11}{12} - \dfrac{5}{8}$ $24; \frac{7}{24}$
9. $\dfrac{y}{4} + \dfrac{y}{3}$ $12; \frac{7y}{12}$

10. $\dfrac{5x}{8} + \dfrac{x}{10}$ $40; \frac{29x}{40}$
11. $\dfrac{1}{x} + \dfrac{1}{y}$ $xy; \frac{y + x}{xy}$
12. $\dfrac{5}{3x} - \dfrac{5}{6x}$ $6x; \frac{5}{6x}$

13. $\dfrac{a}{a + b} - \dfrac{ab}{(a + b)^2}$ $(a + b)^2; \frac{a^2}{(a + b)^2}$
14. $\dfrac{4x}{x^2 - y^2} - \dfrac{2}{x + y}$ $(x - y)(x + y); \frac{2}{x - y}$
15. $\dfrac{x - 3}{3x} + \dfrac{x + 5}{5x}$ $15x; \frac{8}{15}$

EXERCISES

A   *Find the least common multiple for each pair of expressions.*

1. 8, 12   24
2. 15, 25   75
3. 21x, 35x   105x

4. 4x, 6xy   12xy
5. $5ab, 5a^2$ $5a^2b$
6. $2x, 2x^2 + x$ $2x(2x + 1)$

Find the LCD. Then combine and simplify.

7. $\dfrac{3}{8} - \dfrac{1}{10}$ $40; \frac{11}{40}$ 8. $2\dfrac{1}{5} + 1\dfrac{1}{4}$ $20; \frac{69}{20}$ or $3\frac{9}{20}$ 9. $\dfrac{3}{5} + 6\dfrac{1}{2}$ $10; \frac{71}{10}$ or $7\frac{1}{10}$ 10. $7 - 1\dfrac{1}{2}$ $2; \frac{11}{2}$ or $5\frac{1}{2}$

11. $\dfrac{n}{2} + \dfrac{n}{4}$ $4; \frac{3n}{4}$ 12. $\dfrac{5x}{8} + \dfrac{x}{6}$ $24; \frac{19x}{24}$ 13. $\dfrac{2a}{7} - \dfrac{a}{14}$ $14; \frac{3a}{14}$ 14. $\dfrac{1}{x} + \dfrac{2}{3x}$ $3x; \frac{5}{3x}$

15. $\dfrac{4}{ab} + \dfrac{1}{a}$ $ab; \frac{4+b}{ab}$ 16. $\dfrac{7}{x^2} + \dfrac{5}{2x}$ $2x^2; \frac{14+5x}{2x^2}$ 17. $\dfrac{5}{2n} - \dfrac{6}{3n}$ $6n; \frac{1}{2n}$ 18. $\dfrac{3}{5x} - \dfrac{2}{10x}$ $10x; \frac{2}{5x}$

19. $\dfrac{3}{8} + \dfrac{1}{2} + \dfrac{1}{3}$ $24; \frac{29}{24}$ or $1\frac{5}{24}$ 20. $\dfrac{4x}{9} + \dfrac{x}{3} + \dfrac{1}{12}$ $36; \frac{43x}{36}$ 21. $\dfrac{4}{2a^2} - \dfrac{1}{3a}$ $6a^2; \frac{6-a}{3a^2}$ 22. $\dfrac{x+1}{x-1} + \dfrac{4}{x}$ $x(x-1); \frac{x^2+5x-4}{x(x-1)}$

23. $\dfrac{4}{a+1} + \dfrac{a+9}{a^2-1}$ $(a-1)(a+1); \frac{5}{a-1}$ 24. $\dfrac{6}{4x^2-9} - \dfrac{1}{2x-3}$ $(2x-3)(2x+3); \frac{-1}{2x+3}$ 25. $\dfrac{1}{4(x-1)} - \dfrac{1}{(x+3)(x-1)}$ $4(x-1)(x+3); \frac{1}{4(x+3)}$

B Combine and simplify.

26. $\dfrac{3}{2x+10} + \dfrac{15}{x^2-25}$ 27. $\dfrac{a+b}{a+2b} + \dfrac{a-4b}{4a+8b}$ 28. $\dfrac{6x+9}{x^2+3x} + \dfrac{x}{x+3}$

29. $\dfrac{t+3}{t+6} - \dfrac{t+24}{t^2+6t}$ 30. $\dfrac{a+2}{a-2} - \dfrac{a-2}{a+2}$ 31. $\dfrac{2+4x}{4-x^2} + \dfrac{3}{4+2x}$

32. $\dfrac{x}{x^2-6x+8} - \dfrac{2}{x-4}$ $\frac{-1}{x-2}$ 33. $\dfrac{x+3}{x^2+6x+9} - \dfrac{7}{2x+6}$ $\frac{-5}{2(x+3)}$

34. $\dfrac{x}{2x-14} - \dfrac{5x}{x^2-4x-21}$ $\frac{x}{2(x+3)}$ 35. $\dfrac{h}{h-1} + \dfrac{2h}{h^2-2h+1}$ $\frac{h(h+1)}{(h-1)^2}$

C 36. $\dfrac{3b+15}{b^2-25} - \dfrac{b-4}{b^2-9b+20}$ $\frac{2}{b-5}$ 37. $\dfrac{1}{n} + \dfrac{1}{n+1} + \dfrac{n+3}{n^2-1}$ $\frac{3n-1}{n(n-1)}$

38. $\dfrac{6}{x^2-4} - \dfrac{1}{x+2} - \dfrac{5x}{4-x^2}$ $\frac{4}{x-2}$ 39. $\dfrac{2x}{2x+5} + \dfrac{1}{x-2} - \dfrac{5-7x}{2x^2+x-10}$ $\frac{x}{x-2}$

CHECKPOINT

Complete the indicated operations. Simplify your answers.

1. $\dfrac{3x}{5y} \cdot \dfrac{10y^2}{9x^3}$ $\frac{2y}{3x^2}$ 2. $\dfrac{3x-6y}{x+y} \cdot \dfrac{x+y}{3}$ $x-2y$ 3. $\dfrac{x^2-6x+5}{x^2-1} \cdot \dfrac{x-1}{x-5}$ $\frac{x-1}{x+1}$

4. $\dfrac{x-1}{4} \div \dfrac{x^2-1}{8}$ $\frac{2}{x+1}$ 5. $\dfrac{5}{x^2+x} \div \dfrac{15}{x^3}$ $\frac{x^2}{3(x+1)}$ 6. $\dfrac{16-x^2}{9-x^2} \div \dfrac{x^2-7x+12}{x+3}$ $\frac{x+4}{(x-3)^2}$

7. $\dfrac{x^2}{x-1} - \dfrac{2x-1}{x-1}$ $x-1$ 8. $\dfrac{4}{2x-6} + \dfrac{3}{x^2-9}$ $\frac{2x+9}{(x-3)(x+3)}$ 9. $\dfrac{5}{2x+6} + \dfrac{5}{x^2+4x+3}$ $\frac{5}{2(x+1)}$

RATIONAL EXPRESSIONS

ENRICHMENT ACTIVITY

Have students verify the following rule for finding the sum of any two fractions $\dfrac{a}{b}$ and $\dfrac{c}{d}$.

$$\dfrac{a}{b} + \dfrac{c}{d} = \dfrac{ad+bc}{bd}$$

Suggest that students use the rule in adding pairs of fractions. For example, to find the sum $\dfrac{2}{3} + \dfrac{3}{5}$, they can compute as indicated:

$$\dfrac{2}{3} + \dfrac{3}{5} = \dfrac{(2)(5) + (3)(3)}{(3)(5)} = \dfrac{19}{15}$$

With practice, this work can be done mentally. Have students develop a similar rule for the difference, $\dfrac{a}{b} - \dfrac{c}{d}$.

ADDITIONAL ANSWERS

Exercises

26. $\dfrac{3}{2(x-5)}$

27. $\dfrac{5a}{4(a+2b)}$

28. $\dfrac{x+3}{x}$

29. $\dfrac{t-4}{t}$

30. $\dfrac{8a}{(a+2)(a-2)}$

31. $\dfrac{5}{2(2-x)}$

Checkpoint

Students may check their answers with those given in the back of their books.

Find the following products and quotients.

1. $\frac{1}{3} \div \frac{2}{3}$ $\frac{1}{2}$ **2.** $6 \div \frac{2}{3}$ 9

3. $2\left(\frac{1}{2} - 1\right)$ -1 **4.** $8\left(\frac{1}{4} - \frac{1}{8}\right)$ 1

5. $x\left(2x - 1\right)$ $2x^2 - x$

6. $3x\left(\frac{1}{3} - \frac{1}{x}\right)$ $x - 3$

LESSON NOTES

In this lesson, two methods of simplifying complex fractions are explained. Once the methods are understood, each student can use the method that seems easier to him or her.

Both methods require a careful, step-by-step procedure, as illustrated in the model examples. Insist that each step be shown. Too often, shortcuts produce careless mistakes.

Many students will be surprised to learn that some very involved complex fractions reduce to very simple expressions. This is particularly true in the C Exercises.

Students can use substitution as a limited "check" on the answers they have obtained. For example, in Exercise 35, let $x = 2$.

$$\frac{\dfrac{x^2}{x^2 + x}}{1 - \dfrac{x}{x^2 + x}} = \frac{\dfrac{4}{6}}{1 - \dfrac{2}{6}} = \frac{\dfrac{4}{6}}{\dfrac{4}{6}} = 1$$

Of course, even if one (or more than one) number seems to verify the answer, that does not *prove* the answer is correct.

ALTERNATE EXAMPLES

1. Simplify: $\dfrac{\dfrac{3}{5}}{\dfrac{6}{7}}$ $\dfrac{7}{10}$

2. Simplify: $\dfrac{2 + \dfrac{1}{x}}{x + \dfrac{2}{x}}$ by using each method.

$\dfrac{2x + 1}{x^2 + 2}$

8-9   Complex Fractions

OBJECTIVE

To simplify complex fractions.

A fraction is called a **complex fraction** if the numerator or denominator contains a fraction. Two methods of simplifying a complex fraction are shown in Example 1.

EXAMPLE 1   Simplify $\dfrac{\dfrac{2}{3}}{\dfrac{6}{5}}$.

Method I   Divide the numerator by the denominator.

$$\frac{\dfrac{2}{3}}{\dfrac{6}{5}} = \frac{2}{3} \div \frac{6}{5} = \frac{2}{3} \cdot \frac{5}{6} = \frac{10}{18} = \frac{5}{9}$$

Method II   Find the least common multiple of the denominators of the separate fractions. Then multiply numerator and denominator of the complex fraction by this number.

$$\frac{\dfrac{2}{3}}{\dfrac{6}{5}} = \frac{\dfrac{2}{3} \cdot 15}{\dfrac{6}{5} \cdot 15} = \frac{10}{18} = \frac{5}{9} \qquad \text{15 is the LCM of 3 and 5.}$$

EXAMPLE 2   Simplify $\dfrac{x - \dfrac{1}{x}}{1 + \dfrac{1}{x}}$ using each method.

Method I

First combine terms in the numerator and denominator.

$$\frac{x - \dfrac{1}{x}}{1 + \dfrac{1}{x}} = \frac{\dfrac{x^2 - 1}{x}}{\dfrac{x + 1}{x}}$$

$$= \frac{x^2 - 1}{x} \div \frac{x + 1}{x}$$

$$= \frac{x^2 - 1}{x} \cdot \frac{x}{x + 1}$$

$$= \frac{(x + 1)(x - 1)}{x} \cdot \frac{x}{x + 1}$$

$$= x - 1$$

Method II

Multiply the numerator and the denominator by x.

$$\frac{x - \dfrac{1}{x}}{1 + \dfrac{1}{x}} = \frac{\left(x - \dfrac{1}{x}\right) \cdot x}{\left(1 + \dfrac{1}{x}\right) \cdot x}$$

$$= \frac{x^2 - 1}{x + 1}$$

$$= \frac{(x + 1)(x - 1)}{x + 1}$$

$$= x - 1$$

312   CHAPTER 8

EXAMPLE 3   Simplify $\dfrac{\dfrac{2a^3}{a^2 - b^2}}{\dfrac{6a^2}{a + b}}$.

Method I	**Method II**

Method I

$$\frac{\dfrac{2a^3}{a^2 - b^2}}{\dfrac{6a^2}{a + b}} = \frac{2a^3}{a^2 - b^2} \div \frac{6a^2}{a + b}$$

$$= \frac{2a^3}{a^2 - b^2} \cdot \frac{a + b}{6a^2}$$

$$= \frac{2a^3}{(a + b)(a - b)} \cdot \frac{a + b}{6a^2}$$

$$= \frac{a}{3(a - b)}$$

Method II

$$\frac{\dfrac{2a^3}{a^2 - b^2}}{\dfrac{6a^2}{a + b}} = \frac{\dfrac{2a^3}{(a + b)(a - b)} \cdot (a + b)(a - b)}{\dfrac{6a^2}{(a + b)} \cdot (a + b)(a - b)}$$

$$= \frac{2a^3}{6a^2(a - b)}$$

$$= \frac{a}{3(a - b)}$$

CLASS EXERCISES

Use Method I to simplify. Divide the numerator by the denominator.

1. $\dfrac{\dfrac{3}{4}}{\dfrac{4}{2}}$ $\dfrac{3}{8}$

2. $\dfrac{\dfrac{7}{2}}{\dfrac{21}{1}}$ $\dfrac{1}{6}$

3. $\dfrac{\dfrac{a}{b}}{\dfrac{c}{1}}$ $\dfrac{a}{bc}$

4. $\dfrac{1}{\dfrac{2}{3}}$ $\dfrac{3}{2}$

Use Method II to simplify. Use the LCD of the separate fractions.

5. $\dfrac{\dfrac{3}{10}}{\dfrac{7}{10}}$ $\dfrac{3}{7}$

6. $\dfrac{1 + \dfrac{1}{2}}{1 - \dfrac{1}{5}}$ $\dfrac{15}{8}$

7. $\dfrac{\dfrac{1}{3} + \dfrac{1}{4}}{12}$ $\dfrac{7}{144}$

8. $\dfrac{\dfrac{x}{2} + \dfrac{x}{3}}{\dfrac{x}{6}}$ 5

EXERCISES

A   *Simplify. Use Method I.*

1. $\dfrac{\dfrac{2}{5}}{\dfrac{3}{5}}$ $\dfrac{2}{3}$

2. $\dfrac{\dfrac{6}{11}}{\dfrac{3}{22}}$ 4

3. $\dfrac{\dfrac{8}{15}}{\dfrac{10}{9}}$ $\dfrac{12}{25}$

4. $\dfrac{14}{\dfrac{7}{3}}$ 6

5. $\dfrac{\dfrac{a}{b}}{\dfrac{c}{d}}$ $\dfrac{ad}{bc}$

6. $\dfrac{\dfrac{x}{2y^2}}{\dfrac{3x^3}{y}}$ $\dfrac{1}{6x^2 y}$

7. $\dfrac{\dfrac{1}{x - 3}}{\dfrac{2}{x^2 - 9}}$ $\dfrac{x + 3}{2}$

8. $\dfrac{\dfrac{a}{a^2 - b^2}}{\dfrac{b}{a + b}}$ $\dfrac{a}{b(a - b)}$

RATIONAL EXPRESSIONS   **313**

Simplify. Use Method II.

9. $\dfrac{\frac{12}{5}}{\frac{9}{5}}$ $\frac{4}{3}$
10. $\dfrac{\frac{x}{2}}{\frac{x^2}{6}}$ $\frac{3}{x}$
11. $\dfrac{\frac{1}{a}+\frac{1}{b}}{\frac{1}{ab}}$ $b+a$
12. $\dfrac{\frac{2x+6}{y}}{\frac{x+3}{3y}}$ 6

13. $\dfrac{\frac{x+y}{xy}}{\frac{x-y}{xy}}$ $\frac{x+y}{x-y}$
14. $\dfrac{1-\frac{1}{4}}{12}$ $\frac{1}{16}$
15. $\dfrac{1}{\frac{1}{2}-\frac{1}{4}}$ 4
16. $\dfrac{\frac{1}{2}-\frac{1}{3}}{\frac{1}{2}+\frac{1}{3}}$ $\frac{1}{5}$

Simplify by either method.

17. $\dfrac{1-\frac{1}{x}}{1-\frac{1}{x^2}}$ $\frac{x}{x+1}$
18. $\dfrac{\frac{3}{2x}}{\frac{9}{8x^2}}$ $\frac{4x}{3}$
19. $\dfrac{1-\frac{n}{2}}{8}$ $\frac{2-n}{16}$
20. $\dfrac{\frac{x}{2}+\frac{x}{3}+\frac{x}{4}}{3}$ $\frac{13x}{36}$

B

21. $\dfrac{\frac{4}{3}}{\frac{4}{9}+\frac{10}{3}+6}$ $\frac{3}{22}$
22. $\dfrac{6-\frac{2}{7}}{\frac{11}{14}-1}$ $-\frac{80}{3}$
23. $\dfrac{\frac{2}{5}+\frac{3}{10}}{1-\frac{7}{15}}$ $\frac{21}{16}$
24. $\dfrac{\frac{2x+6}{3y}}{\frac{x+3}{y}}$ $\frac{2}{3}$

25. $\dfrac{\frac{x}{y-x}}{\frac{x^2}{y^2-x^2}}$ $\frac{y+x}{x}$
26. $\dfrac{\frac{x^2+5x}{y}}{\frac{x^2-25}{2y}}$ $\frac{2x}{x-5}$
27. $\dfrac{1-\frac{2}{x}}{1-\frac{4}{x^2}}$ $\frac{x}{x+2}$
28. $\dfrac{x-\frac{3}{4}}{\frac{1}{2}-x}$ $\frac{4x-3}{2-4x}$

29. $\dfrac{\frac{1}{x}-\frac{1}{3}}{x-3}$ $\frac{-1}{3x}$
30. $\dfrac{\frac{x^2-25}{y}}{5x^2-x^3}$ $-\frac{(x+5)}{x^2 y}$
31. $\dfrac{\frac{1}{a}+\frac{1}{b}}{\frac{1}{a^2}-\frac{1}{b^2}}$ $\frac{ab}{b-a}$
32. $\dfrac{\frac{1}{x}+\frac{1}{y}}{\frac{x}{y}-\frac{y}{x}}$ $\frac{1}{x-y}$

C

33. $\dfrac{\frac{x^2-9}{5x}}{\frac{x^2+6x+9}{10}}$ $\frac{2(x-3)}{x(x+3)}$
34. $\dfrac{\frac{x+3}{2x^2+9x-5}}{\frac{x^2+3x}{2x-1}}$ $\frac{1}{x(x+5)}$
35. $\dfrac{\frac{x^2}{x^2+x}}{1-\frac{x}{x^2+x}}$ 1

36. $\dfrac{1+\frac{2}{x}+\frac{1}{x^2}}{1-\frac{1}{x^2}}$ $\frac{x+1}{x-1}$
37. $\dfrac{2+\frac{1}{x}}{2+\frac{3}{x}+\frac{1}{x^2}}$ $\frac{x}{x+1}$
38. $\dfrac{\frac{1}{x}+\frac{2}{x^2}}{1+\frac{1}{x}-\frac{2}{x^2}}$ $\frac{1}{x-1}$

39. $\dfrac{\frac{x^2-3x+xy-3y}{x+y}}{\frac{(x-3)^2}{5}}$ $\frac{5}{x-3}$
*40. $1-\dfrac{1}{1-\frac{1}{1-\frac{1}{a}}}$ a

*41. The scores for three tests are x, y, and z. What is the average of z and the average of the first two scores? $\frac{x+y+2z}{4}$

CHAPTER 8

Drafting

Drafters must be able to draw figures so that other people can visualize them accurately. All necessary dimensions must be given so that any needed computation can be performed.

Applications

This Applications page tests the ability of students to interpret a three-dimensional object drawn on a two-dimensional page. The cylinder of metal cut from the block must be visualized, because it is not shown as a cylinder in the drawing.

Some students might be inclined to stop working after they determine the total volume of the drilled block. Point out the need to multiply the volume by 0.28, the weight of steel per cubic inch.

In the exercises, students must realize that the removed section of the block can be thought of as a rectangular solid united at one end with half a cylinder.

Example A block of steel has a round hole cut through it, as shown. All dimensions are in inches. Find the weight of the block if steel weighs 0.28 pounds per cubic inch.

Find the volume of the block alone. Subtract from it the volume of the cylindrical hole. Then multiply the difference by the weight of steel per cubic inch.

Volume of block alone:

$$V = lwh$$
$$= 5(3)\left(1\frac{1}{2}\right)$$
$$= 22\frac{1}{2}$$

Volume of cylindrical hole:

$$V = \pi r^2 h$$
$$= 3.14(1)^2\left(1\frac{1}{2}\right)$$
$$= 4.71$$

Total volume: $22.5 - 4.71 = 17.79$

Total weight: $17.79 \times 0.28 \approx 4.98$

The total weight of the block with the hole in it is about 4.98, or very nearly 5 pounds.

Now try these. Read the problem and plan a strategy before you begin.

A steel bracket has the size and shape shown. Dimensions are given in inches.

1. Find the volume in cubic inches.
   About 0.86 cubic inch
2. Find the weight in pounds.

   About 0.24 pound, or about $\frac{1}{4}$ pound

These exercises review basic algebraic skills.

Simplify.

1. $-3(x^2y)^3 \cdot 5x(xy^2)^3$ $-15x^{10}y^9$

2. $5(x-1)^2 - 3(x-5)$
$5x^2 - 13x + 20$

3. $\dfrac{2x^2 - 2x - 24}{x + 3}$ $2(x-4)$

4. $\dfrac{x - \frac{1}{x}}{\frac{x}{2} - 1}$ $\dfrac{2(x+1)(x-1)}{x(x-2)}$

Evaluate when $a = -3$, $b = -1$, and $c = 2$.

5. $-a^2bc$ 18

6. $(a+b)(a-b)$ 8

7. $\dfrac{a+b+c}{abc}$ $-\dfrac{1}{3}$

Solve for x.

8. $3(6-x) + 5x = 5(6+x)$ -4

9. $\dfrac{2}{x} = x - 1$ $-1, 2$

10. Solve the system:
$3x + y = -15$
$x = 4y - 5$ $(-5, 0)$

11. Subtract $(x^2 - 7 + 3x)$ from $(2 - x - x^2)$. $-2x^2 - 4x + 9$

12. Find the slope of the line $3x - 5y = 11$. $\dfrac{3}{5}$

13. Find the x- and y-intercepts of the line $3x - 5y = 11$.
x-int.: $\dfrac{11}{3}$
y-int.: $-\dfrac{11}{5}$

Factor completely.

14. $xy - 3x + 5y - 15$ $(x+5)(y-3)$

15. $5x^3 - 5x$ $5x(x+1)(x-1)$

16. $6x^2 - 30x + 6$ $6(x^2 - 5x + 1)$

17. Multiply. Simplify your answer.
$\dfrac{x-7}{x^2 + 10x + 21} \cdot \dfrac{x^2 + 14x + 49}{x^2 - 49}$
$\dfrac{1}{x+3}$

18. Combine. Write the denominator in factored form.
$\dfrac{1}{x+1} + \dfrac{1}{x-1} + \dfrac{1}{x}$
$\dfrac{3x^2 - 1}{x(x+1)(x-1)}$

[Maintaining Skills continues on page 317.]

316

CHAPTER 8 REVIEW

VOCABULARY

rational expression (p. 286)
least common multiple (p. 309)
least common denominator (p. 309)
complex fraction (p. 312)

SUMMARY

This chapter serves as an introduction to rational expressions, or fractions, as used in algebra. Work with algebraic rational expressions is very much like operating with fractions in arithmetic. The basic operations of addition, subtraction, multiplication, and division for both types of fractions are the same. Simplifying, multiplying, and dividing rational expressions are studied first. Then long division of polynomials is introduced, and is followed by the addition and subtraction of rational expressions. The chapter concludes with a section about complex fractions.

REVIEW EXERCISES

8-1   *For what values of x is each expression undefined?*

1. $\dfrac{x^5}{2x^2}$ 0 **2.** $\dfrac{x}{x+5}$ -5 **3.** $\dfrac{1}{x^2+4}$ None   **4.** $\dfrac{x-5}{3x^2 + 18x}$ $0, -6$

8-2   *Simplify.*

5. $\dfrac{x-2}{2-x}$ -1 **6.** $\dfrac{x^2 - x - 2}{8 - 2x - x^2}$ $-\frac{x+1}{x+4}$ **7.** $\dfrac{5-x}{x^2 - 8x + 15}$ $-\frac{1}{x-3}$ **8.** $\dfrac{x^4 - 256}{4x - x^2}$ $-\frac{(x^2+16)(x+4)}{x}$

8-3   *Multiply. Simplify your answers.*

9. $\dfrac{-12}{15} \cdot \dfrac{35}{28}$ -1 **10.** $\dfrac{27x}{-y} \cdot \dfrac{y^2}{15x^2}$ $-\frac{9y}{5x}$ **11.** $\dfrac{3}{x} \cdot \dfrac{x^2}{9} \cdot \dfrac{27}{x^3}$ $\frac{9}{x^2}$

12. $\dfrac{x^2 - 4}{5} \cdot \dfrac{10}{x+2}$ $2(x-2)$ **13.** $\dfrac{ab^2}{(b+3)^2} \cdot \dfrac{b^2 + 3b}{a^2b^3}$ $\frac{1}{a(b+3)}$

14. $\dfrac{2x^2 - 6x}{x^2 + 1} \cdot \dfrac{x^4 + x^2}{3 - x}$ $-2x^3$ **15.** $\dfrac{x^2 + 7x + 10}{x^2 - 4} \cdot \dfrac{x^2 - 7x + 10}{x^2 - 25}$ 1

16. $\dfrac{4y^2 - 4y + 1}{2y^2 + 7y - 4} \cdot \dfrac{y^2 + y}{2y^2 - y - 3}$ $\frac{y(2y-1)}{(y+4)(2y-3)}$ **17.** $\dfrac{(x-3)^2}{x^4 - 16} \cdot \dfrac{(x+2)^2}{x^2 - 9}$ $\frac{(x-3)(x+2)}{(x^2+4)(x-2)(x+3)}$

8-4   *Divide and simplify.*

18. $\dfrac{3x^3}{y} \div \dfrac{3x^2}{2y^2}$ $2xy$ **19.** $\dfrac{3x - 6}{7x} \div \dfrac{x-2}{14}$ $\frac{6}{x}$ **20.** $\dfrac{x^3 - x}{1 - x^2} \div \dfrac{x-2}{x^2 - x - 2}$ $-x(x+1)$

21. $\dfrac{x^2 + 5x + 6}{x^2 - 4} \div \dfrac{5x + 15}{6x - 12}$ $\quad \frac{6}{5}$

22. $\dfrac{15x + 10}{9x^2 - 4} \div \dfrac{5x}{3x - 2}$ $\quad \frac{1}{x}$

8-5 *Use long division to find the quotient and the remainder. Check.*

23. $\dfrac{x^2 - 2x - 1}{x + 3}$ $\quad x - 5 + \frac{14}{x+3}$
24. $\dfrac{x^2 + 2x + 2}{x - 4}$ $\quad x + 6 + \frac{26}{x-4}$
25. $\dfrac{2x^2 - 5x + 6}{x + 6}$ $\quad 2x - 17 + \frac{108}{x+6}$

26. $\dfrac{2x^2 - 7x - 8}{2x - 1}$

27. $\dfrac{3x^2 + 5x + 10}{x - 5}$

28. $\dfrac{8x^3 - 27}{2x - 3}$ $\quad 8$

29. $\dfrac{x^3 - 3x^2 + 3x - 1}{x + 1}$

30. $\dfrac{3x^3 + 4x^2 - 13x + 6}{x^2 + 2x - 3}$

Add or subtract. Write answers in simplest form.

8-6 **31.** $\dfrac{x}{7} - \dfrac{3x}{7}$ $\quad -\frac{2x}{7}$
32. $\dfrac{8x}{5} - \dfrac{3x}{5}$ $\quad x$
33. $\dfrac{x^2}{x - 3} - \dfrac{9}{x - 3}$ $\quad x + 3$
34. $\dfrac{x^2}{x + 2} + \dfrac{4x + 4}{x + 2}$ $\quad x + 2$

$\quad 7$

35. $\dfrac{x^2}{x^2 + 2x} - \dfrac{4}{x^2 + 2x}$
36. $\dfrac{2x}{3y} - \dfrac{4x}{3y} - \dfrac{x}{3y}$
37. $\dfrac{x + 5}{x^2 - 9} - \dfrac{2}{x^2 - 9}$

8-7 **38.** $3 + \dfrac{5}{7}$
39. $\dfrac{1}{9} - \dfrac{1}{4}$
40. $\dfrac{14}{x} - \dfrac{7}{y}$
41. $\dfrac{3}{x} + \dfrac{4}{xy}$
42. $x + \dfrac{x}{5}$

43. $\dfrac{y}{x + y} - \dfrac{x}{x - y}$
44. $\dfrac{2x}{x + 1} + \dfrac{3x}{x - 2}$
45. $\dfrac{5x}{x + 2} - \dfrac{3x}{x - 1}$

8-8 *Find the LCD. Then combine and simplify.*

46. $\dfrac{5}{6} - \dfrac{2}{8}$ $\quad 24; \frac{7}{12}$
47. $\dfrac{2}{3} + \dfrac{5}{3x}$ $\quad 3x; \frac{2x + 5}{3x}$
48. $\dfrac{3a}{8b} - \dfrac{5}{6a}$ $\quad 24ab; \frac{9a^2 - 20b}{24ab}$

49. $\dfrac{3}{x + 2} + \dfrac{x + 7}{x^2 - 4}$
50. $\dfrac{2x}{35} + \dfrac{3 - x}{7x}$
51. $\dfrac{x}{x - 2} + \dfrac{2x}{x^2 - 4x + 4}$

52. $\dfrac{3x}{x^2 - 6x + 8} - \dfrac{1}{x - 4}$
53. $\dfrac{1}{2} - \dfrac{6}{x + 1} + \dfrac{x}{x - 1}$

8-9 *Simplify.*

54. $\dfrac{3\frac{3}{4}}{\frac{9}{8}}$ $\quad \frac{10}{3}$
55. $\dfrac{\frac{y}{3x^3}}{\frac{2y^2}{x}}$ $\quad \frac{1}{6x^2 y}$
56. $\dfrac{\frac{x^2 - 9}{2}}{\frac{x - 3}{4}}$ $\quad 2(x + 3)$

57. $\dfrac{\frac{x}{x + 2}}{\frac{3x}{x^2 - 4}}$ $\quad \frac{x - 2}{3}$
58. $\dfrac{\frac{xy}{x - y}}{\frac{xy}{x + y}}$ $\quad \frac{x + y}{x - y}$
59. $\dfrac{\frac{x + y}{y}}{\frac{x^2 - y^2}{x}}$ $\quad \frac{x}{y(x - y)}$

REVIEW

317

MAINTAINING SKILLS
(continued)

19. In a collection of coins, there are ten more dimes than quarters. Find the number of each type of coin if together they have a total value of $3.80.

18 dimes, 8 quarters

20. Sherri is 3 years younger than Beth. Five years ago, Sherri was $\frac{3}{4}$ as old as Beth. How old is each girl now?

Sherri is 14. Beth is 17.

ADDITIONAL ANSWERS

Review Exercises

26. $x - 3 - \dfrac{11}{2x - 1}$

27. $3x + 20 + \dfrac{110}{x - 5}$

28. $4x^2 + 6x + 9$

29. $x^2 - 4x + 7 - \dfrac{8}{x + 1}$

30. $3x - 2$

35. $\dfrac{x - 2}{x}$

36. $-\dfrac{x}{y}$

37. $\dfrac{1}{x - 3}$

38. $\dfrac{26}{7}$

39. $\dfrac{-5}{36}$

40. $\dfrac{7(2y - x)}{xy}$

41. $\dfrac{3y + 4}{xy}$

42. $\dfrac{6x}{5}$

43. $\dfrac{-(x^2 + y^2)}{(x + y)(x - y)}$

44. $\dfrac{x(5x - 1)}{(x + 1)(x - 2)}$

45. $\dfrac{x(2x - 11)}{(x + 2)(x - 1)}$

49. $(x + 2)(x - 2);\ \dfrac{4x + 1}{(x + 2)(x - 2)}$

50. $35x;\ \dfrac{2x^2 - 5x + 15}{35x}$

[*Answers continue on page 318.*]

51. $(x - 2)^2$; $\dfrac{x^2}{(x - 2)^2}$

52. $(x - 4)(x - 2)$; $\dfrac{2x + 2}{(x - 4)(x - 2)}$

53. $2(x + 1)(x - 1)$;
$\dfrac{3x^2 - 10x + 11}{2(x + 1)(x - 1)}$

60. $\dfrac{\dfrac{x + 2}{3x^2 - 7x + 2}}{\dfrac{x^2 + 2x}{3x - 1}}$ $\quad \dfrac{1}{x(x - 2)}$ **61.** $\dfrac{\dfrac{2}{(x + 3)^2}}{4x^2 + 24x + 96}$ $\quad \dfrac{1}{2(x + 3)^2(x^2 + 6x + 24)}$ **62.** $\dfrac{\dfrac{x^3 - 2x^2}{(2 - x)^2}}{\dfrac{2x^2 + 18x}{x^2 + 7x - 18}}$ $\quad \dfrac{x}{2}$

CHAPTER 8 TEST

8-1 For what values of **x** is each expression undefined?

1. $\dfrac{x - 3}{x(x + 5)}$ $\quad 0, -5$ **2.** $\dfrac{x^2 + 4}{x^2 - 2x - 8}$ $\quad 4, -2$ **3.** $\dfrac{x + 3}{x^2 - 16}$ $\quad 4, -4$

8-2 Simplify.

4. $\dfrac{3x - x^2}{x^2 - 9}$ $\quad -\dfrac{x}{x + 3}$ **5.** $\dfrac{x^3 - 3x^2 + 2x}{x^3 - x}$ $\quad \dfrac{x - 2}{x + 1}$

8-3 Multiply. Simplify your answers.

6. $\dfrac{18b}{45a} \cdot \dfrac{a^2}{b^3}$ $\quad \dfrac{2a}{5b^2}$ **7.** $\dfrac{3x - x^2}{x^2 - 9} \cdot \dfrac{x + 3}{x}$ $\quad -1$ **8.** $\dfrac{x + 4}{x - 4} \cdot \dfrac{x^2 - 16}{x^2 + 16}$ $\quad \dfrac{(x + 4)^2}{x^2 + 16}$

8-4 Divide and simplify.

9. $\dfrac{24a^2b^2}{27ab^3} \div \dfrac{8ab^3}{9a^3b}$ $\quad \dfrac{a^3}{b^3}$ **10.** $\dfrac{3xy^2}{10z^3} \div \dfrac{6x^2y^2}{5z^2}$ $\quad \dfrac{1}{4xz}$ **11.** $\dfrac{16x^2 - 1}{4x^3 + x^2} \div \dfrac{1 - 4x}{3x}$ $\quad -\dfrac{3}{x}$

8-5 **12.** Divide: $(x^3 - 6x^2 + 4x - 3) \div (x - 2)$ $\quad x^2 - 4x - 4 - \dfrac{11}{x - 2}$

Add or subtract. Write answers in simplest form.

8-6 **13.** $\dfrac{x^2}{x + 2} + \dfrac{4x + 4}{x + 2}$ $\quad x + 2$ **14.** $\dfrac{2x}{4x^2 - 1} - \dfrac{1}{4x^2 - 1}$ $\quad \dfrac{1}{2x + 1}$

Combine and simplify. Where appropriate, write denominators in factored form.

8-7 **15.** $3x + \dfrac{x}{2}$ $\quad \dfrac{7x}{2}$ **16.** $\dfrac{3}{x - 2} - \dfrac{2}{x}$ $\quad \dfrac{x + 4}{x(x - 2)}$

8-8 **17.** $\dfrac{5}{9x^2 - 4} - \dfrac{2}{3x - 2}$ $\quad \dfrac{1 - 6x}{(3x - 2)(3x + 2)}$ **18.** $\dfrac{x}{2x^2 - 9x + 9} - \dfrac{3}{x^2 - 3x}$ $\quad \dfrac{x - 3}{x(2x - 3)}$

8-9 Simplify.

19. $\dfrac{\dfrac{3}{10}}{\dfrac{9}{25}}$ $\quad \dfrac{5}{6}$ **20.** $\dfrac{\dfrac{10}{x - 2}}{\dfrac{-5}{x^2 - 4}}$ $\quad -2(x + 2), \text{ or } -2x - 4$

Calculating Earnings

Because computers can store large amounts of data and recall them quickly when needed, they are frequently used to prepare payrolls.

Here is a simplified program for an industry in which employees are paid time and a half for work over 35 hours per week. There are no deductions for such items as Social Security and income taxes.

Since an employee cannot be paid a fraction of a cent, line 190 rounds the amount earned to the nearest cent. To see how this functions, consider these three typical computations.

Number to be rounded:	93.802	84.125	76.439
Multiply by 100.	9380.2	8412.5	7643.9
Add 0.5.	9380.7	8413.0	7644.4
Take greatest integer.	9380	8413	7644
Divide by 100.	93.80	84.13	76.44

The Program	What It Does
| ```
100 REM PAYROLL
110 PRINT "HOURLY RATE";
120 INPUT R
130 PRINT "NUMBER OF HOURS";
140 INPUT T
150 LET S = R * T
160 IF T < = 35 THEN 190
170 LET X = .5 * R * (T - 35)
180 LET S = S + X
190 LET S = INT(S * 100 + .5)/100
200 PRINT "EARNED: $"; S
900 END
``` | The computer will reject the input if it is preceded by a dollar sign.<br><br>The computer accepts fractions of an hour only in decimal form.<br><br>Computes regular wages.<br>If there is no overtime, jumps to line 190.<br>Computes overtime earnings.<br>Adds overtime to regular wages.<br>Rounds earnings to nearest cent.<br>Displays total earnings. |

1. Enter the hourly rate of $9.75, using a dollar sign. What error message did you receive? Why?

What will be displayed for the following entries?

	Hourly Rate	Number of Hours			Hourly Rate	Number of Hours	
2.	$6.00	35	$210	3.	$8.75	40	$371.88
4.	$13.50	43	$634.50	5.	$9.35	39.5	$390.36
6.	$10.24	34.25	$350.72	7.	$11.88	42.6	$551.23

8. Will the computer display the correct result for all problems if line 160 is entered as IF T < 35 THEN 190? Why?

9. What earnings will be displayed for entries of $10 and 10 hours if line 160 is entered incorrectly as IF T = 35 THEN 190? Why?

For more information about BASIC, see the Computer Handbook at the back of the book.

Computer Activity

This Computer Activity page can be used to remind students of the importance of the computer in data processing throughout our society. Let students suggest other, similar ways in which the computer is used.

ADDITIONAL ANSWERS

Computer Activity

1. Error messages will vary from computer to computer. (For a discussiong of string variables, see the manual for your computer.)

8. Yes. When T = 35, line 170 calculates T − 35 or 0 hours overtime.

9. $−25. Line 170 will calculate 10 − 35 or −25 hours overtime. This results in a computed overtime pay of $−125. When added to the regular earnings we obtain $−25, an incorrect result.
```

This chapter is devoted primarily to problem solving and applications. It is carefully structured so that it makes extensive use of skills developed in Chapter 8.

The chapter begins with several lessons that develop the basic procedures for solving equations that involve fractions. Then a lesson is devoted to problem solving in general. Thereafter, the chapter provides specific lessons dealing with work problems, problems involving interest and investment, mixture problems, and problems dealing with rate-time-distance relationships. As you will note, the chapter also includes special lessons that review ratio, proportion, and percent, so that students are better equipped to solve mixture problems and interest and investment problems.

CHAPTER 9

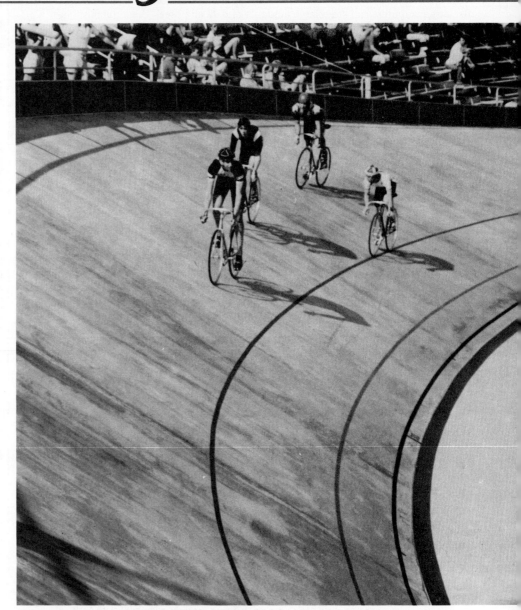

These bicycle racers are competing at the Velodrome in Los Angeles. Problems involving rates of speed are often solved by using fractional equations.

APPLYING FRACTIONS: SOLVING EQUATIONS AND PROBLEMS

PREREQUISITE SKILLS REVIEW

For students who need additional practice with the algebraic skills in this Prerequisite Skills Review, you may assign Follow-Up exercises on page 504 in the students' books.

An item-by-item error analysis of the Prerequisite Skills Review appears on page T26.

Prerequisite Skills Review

Write the letter for the correct answer.

1. If $x = -9$, then $\dfrac{6 - x}{3} = \underline{\ ?\ }$. c

   a. -7 **b.** -1 **c.** 5   **d.** 9

2. Simplify $-14x\left(\dfrac{1}{7}\right)$. b

   a. $2x$ **b.** $-2x$ **c.** $98x$ **d.** $-98x$

3. Which statement is false? d

   a. $45\left(\dfrac{2}{3}\right) = 15(2)$ **b.** $9\left(2 + \dfrac{1}{3}\right) = 18 + 3$

   c. $10\left(\dfrac{a}{2}\right) = 5a$ **d.** $12\left(\dfrac{3 - x}{4}\right) = 9 - 12x$

4. Simplify $2(x + 2)\left(\dfrac{3x}{x + 2}\right)$. b

   a. $3x$ **b.** $6x$ **c.** $3x^2 + 6x$ **d.** $3x^2$

5. The expression $6\left(\dfrac{5x - 2}{3}\right)$ is equivalent to $\underline{\ ?\ }$. a

   a. $10x - 4$ **b.** $10x - 2$ **c.** $10x - \dfrac{2}{3}$ **d.** $\dfrac{5x - 2}{2}$

6. Simplify $-\left[\dfrac{9 - 3\left(\frac{1}{3}\right)}{2}\right]$. d

   a. 1   **b.** -1 **c.** 4   **d.** -4

7. The least common multiple of 3, 4, and 8 is $\underline{\ ?\ }$. b

   a. 12   **b.** 24   **c.** 32   **d.** 96

8. The least common multiple of $(x + 3)^2$ and $2(x + 3)$ is $\underline{\ ?\ }$. c

   a. $(x + 3)$ **b.** $2(x + 3)$ **c.** $2(x + 3)^2$ **d.** $2(x + 3)(x + 3)^2$

9. The LCD of the fractions $\dfrac{x - 1}{x^2 - 4x + 4}$ and $\dfrac{5}{3x - 6}$ is $\underline{\ ?\ }$. a

   a. $3(x - 2)^2$ **b.** $3(x - 2)$ **c.** $5(x - 1)$ **d.** $x^2 - x - 2$

10. The equation $6\left(\dfrac{x - 1}{3}\right) = 6\left(\dfrac{1}{2}\right)$ is equivalent to $\underline{\ ?\ }$. a

    a. $2x - 2 = 3$ **b.** $2x - 1 = 3$ **c.** $6x - 1 = 3$ **d.** $6x - 3 = 3$

WARM-UP EXERCISES

WARM-UP EXERCISES

Find the LCD.

1. $\frac{1}{6}, \frac{5}{8}$ 24   **2.** $\frac{2}{5}, \frac{1}{3}$ 15

LESSON NOTES

In Example 1a, some students may suggest that $\frac{5}{4}n = 7\frac{1}{2}$ can be solved in one step by multiplying by the reciprocal of $\frac{5}{4}$. This would make use of a procedure developed in Chapter 3. Praise their alertness, but point out that the procedure would not be applicable in Example 1b or in Example 2.

ALTERNATE EXAMPLES

1. Solve each equation.

a. $\frac{7n}{6} = 9\frac{1}{3}$ **b.** $\frac{5}{9}x - 4 = \frac{1}{3}x$

   8   18

2. Solve:

$$\frac{7 - 4x}{2} - \frac{8x - 2}{4} = 2 + \frac{4}{3}x$$

$$\frac{3}{8}$$

POSSIBLE ERROR

Students often have difficulty when a negative sign precedes the factors to be multiplied. Thus, in Example 2, students might multiply by 6 and mistakenly simplify the left side of the equation as shown below:

$15 - 6x - 4x - 3 = 6 + 14x$
                (incorrect)

To help students avoid such errors, stress the need to use parentheses, as shown in the illustrated example.

OBJECTIVE

To solve equations that have fractional coefficients.

To solve an equation such as $\frac{5}{6}x = \frac{3}{4}x + \frac{1}{6}$, you could start by adding $-\frac{3}{4}x$ to each side. However, you can simplify your work by first clearing the equation of fractions. This is done by multiplying through by the least common denominator of the fractional coefficients.

$$\frac{5}{6}x = \frac{3}{4}x + \frac{1}{6}$$

Multiply each side by 12.

$$12\left(\frac{5}{6}x\right) = 12\left(\frac{3}{4}x + \frac{1}{6}\right)$$

$$10x = 9x + 2$$

$$x = 2$$

Check $\frac{5}{6}(2) \overset{?}{=} \frac{3}{4}(2) + \frac{1}{6}$

$\frac{10}{6} \overset{?}{=} \frac{6}{4} + \frac{1}{6}$

$\frac{10}{6} \overset{?}{=} \frac{9}{6} + \frac{1}{6}$

$\frac{10}{6} = \frac{10}{6}$ ✔ The solution is 2.

EXAMPLE 1   Solve each equation.

a. $\frac{5n}{4} = 7\frac{1}{2}$

$4\left(\frac{5}{4}n\right) = 4\left(\frac{15}{2}\right)$

$5n = 30$

$n = 6$

b. $\frac{3}{5}x - 7 = \frac{1}{4}x$

$20\left(\frac{3}{5}x - 7\right) = 20\left(\frac{1}{4}x\right)$

$12x - 140 = 5x$

$7x = 140$

$x = 20$

Check $\frac{5(6)}{4} \overset{?}{=} 7\frac{1}{2}$

$7\frac{1}{2} = 7\frac{1}{2}$ ✔

$\frac{3}{5}(20) - 7 \overset{?}{=} \frac{1}{4}(20)$

$5 = 5$ ✔

EXAMPLE 2   Solve $\frac{5 - 2x}{2} - \frac{4x - 3}{6} = 1 + \frac{7}{3}x$.

$6\left(\frac{5 - 2x}{2} - \frac{4x - 3}{6}\right) = 6\left(1 + \frac{7}{3}x\right)$ Multiply each side by 6, the least common multiple of 2, 6, and 3.

$3(5 - 2x) - (4x - 3) = 6 + 14x$

$15 - 6x - 4x + 3 = 6 + 14x$

$-24x = -12$

$x = \frac{1}{2}$ Check $x = \frac{1}{2}$ in the original equation.

CLASS EXERCISES

Rewrite each equation so that fractions are eliminated. Then solve.

1. $\frac{1}{3}x = \frac{5}{3}$ 5

2. $\frac{y}{2} = -\frac{11}{2}$ −11

3. $\frac{2x}{3} = \frac{1}{6}$ $\frac{1}{4}$

4. $\frac{4}{5}x = 80$ 100

5. $\frac{7y}{12} - \frac{1}{6} = 1$ 2

6. $\frac{2}{7}y - \frac{1}{2} = \frac{3}{2}$ 7

7. $\frac{5h}{4} - \frac{1}{2} = 4\frac{1}{2}$ 4

8. $\frac{4}{5}x = \frac{1}{2}x + \frac{3}{5}$ 2

EXERCISES

A *Solve and check.*

1. $\frac{2}{5}x = \frac{4}{5}$ 2

2. $\frac{1}{4}y = \frac{3}{2}$ 6

3. $\frac{3}{5}x = 3$ 5

4. $\frac{x}{2} + \frac{3x}{4} = 10$ 8

5. $2 + \frac{9n}{5} = \frac{1}{5}$ −1

6. $\frac{4x}{7} + 3 = \frac{1}{7}$ −5

7. $\frac{x}{10} - \frac{1}{10} = \frac{2}{5}$ 5

8. $\frac{2n}{3} - \frac{5}{6} = \frac{1}{2}$ 2

9. $\frac{5n}{8} + \frac{1}{6} = \frac{8}{3}$ 4

10. $\frac{3}{4}x - \frac{1}{2} = \frac{5}{2}$ 4

11. $\frac{2}{5}x + \frac{7}{2} = -\frac{5}{2}$ −15

12. $\frac{3}{2}x - \frac{1}{3}x + \frac{7}{3} = 0$ −2

B

13. $\frac{1}{2}x - \frac{1}{3}x + \frac{1}{4}x = \frac{5}{6}$ 2

14. $\frac{2}{3}x + \frac{3}{4}x - \frac{4}{5}x = \frac{37}{3}$ 20

15. $1 - \frac{7x + 7}{6} = 2x - \frac{15x + 3}{4}$ −1

16. $\frac{2}{3}(3x - 1) - \frac{x}{18} = \frac{1}{2}(2x + 10)$ 6

17. $\frac{3}{5}(2 - 4x) = \frac{9}{10}(x + 7) - \frac{8x}{5}$ −3

18. $\frac{3x - 12}{50} + \frac{x}{10} = \frac{x}{25} + \frac{x - 2}{100}$ 2

19. $\frac{7y + 1}{3} - 2y = \frac{2y + 7}{15} + \frac{y - 2}{9}$ −1

20. $\frac{5 - x}{4} - \frac{2x + 7}{14} = \frac{3x}{7} + \frac{13}{2}$ −7

21. Two-thirds of a number is 8 more than $\frac{1}{2}$ of the number. Find the number.   48

22. The width of a rectangle is one-third of the length. If the perimeter is 64 inches, find the dimensions.   l = 24 in., w = 8 in.

23. Alma, Ben, and Carol received a total of $275 in prize money. Ben won $\frac{1}{2}$ as much as Alma and Carol won $\frac{1}{3}$ as much as Alma. How much did each receive?   Alma $150, Ben $75, Carol $50

C

24. $\frac{x^2 - x}{4} = \frac{3 - x}{2}$ −3, 2

25. $\frac{x^2 - 5}{3} + \frac{x}{2} = \frac{x^2}{6} + \frac{x + 5}{2}$ 5, −5

26. $\frac{x^2}{2} - \frac{5 + 4x}{4} = \frac{7x - 1}{4} - x$ −$\frac{1}{2}$, 4

27. $2x^2 - \frac{18x + 1}{15} = \frac{x^2 - 1}{5} - \frac{1}{15}$ $\frac{1}{3}$

*First solve for **x** in terms of **y**, then for **y** in terms of **x**.*

28. $\frac{x}{3} - \frac{y}{2} = \frac{y}{3} - \frac{x}{6}$ $x = \frac{5}{3}y;\ y = \frac{3}{5}x$

29. $\frac{5x + y}{10} - \frac{y}{4} = \frac{x - 5y}{10}$ $x = -\frac{7}{8}y;\ y = -\frac{8}{7}x$

30. $\frac{5}{3}x + \frac{1}{6}(y + 3) = 3$ $x = \frac{15 - y}{10};\ y = 15 - 10x$

APPLYING FRACTIONS: SOLVING EQUATIONS AND PROBLEMS   **323**

DAILY QUIZ

Solve and check.

1. $\frac{2}{3}x = \frac{4}{3}$ 2

2. $\frac{1}{8}x = \frac{5}{4}$ 10

3. $\frac{1}{2}x + \frac{1}{3}x - \frac{1}{4}x = \frac{7}{2}$ 6

4. $1 - \frac{5x + 6}{6} = 2x$ 0

5. $\frac{3 - x}{2} - \frac{x + 5}{14} = \frac{2x}{7}$ $\frac{4}{3}$

ASSIGNMENT GUIDE
(page 323)

Minimum course: 1–19 odd,
21–23

Average course: 1–25 odd,
28

Maximum course: 1–19 odd,
21–30

ENRICHMENT ACTIVITY

Challenge the students to solve these problems:

Ann lived $\frac{1}{3}$ of her life in Oregon, $\frac{1}{4}$ of her life in Florida, $\frac{1}{24}$ of her life in Connecticut, and the remaining 27 years in Illinois. How long did Ann live?   72 years

The width of a rectangle is $\frac{1}{3}$ of its length. The number of units in its perimeter is $\frac{2}{3}$ of the number of square units in its area. What is its width and length?   Width = 4 units, length = 12 units

Have the students make up other, similar problems. Once they have solved the problems, let pairs of students exchange papers and each can solve the problems written by a classmate.

EXTRA PRACTICE, page 524

Find the LCD.

1. $\dfrac{1}{x}, \dfrac{3}{4x}$ $4x$

2. $\dfrac{x}{2}, \dfrac{3}{x-5}$ $2(x-5)$

3. $\dfrac{1}{x-1}, \dfrac{5}{x+1}, \dfrac{3}{x^2-1}$ x^2-1

LESSON NOTES

Discuss each model example carefully. Be sure the students understand the algebraic manipulations that are used in solving each example. For instance, in Example 3, multiplication by the LCD may seem complex or unclear to some students. You may wish to show the use of the distributive property and cancellation on the board:

$$(x+1)(x+2)\left(\dfrac{5}{x+1}\right)$$
$$- (x+1)(x+2)\left(\dfrac{x}{(x+1)(x+2)}\right)$$
$$= (x+1)(x+2)\left(\dfrac{2}{x+2}\right)$$

ALTERNATE EXAMPLES

1. Solve: $\dfrac{5}{x} - \dfrac{9}{2x} = \dfrac{1}{12}$ 6

2. Solve: $\dfrac{x}{4} + \dfrac{x}{x-4} = \dfrac{4}{x-4}$ -4

9-2 Rational Equations

OBJECTIVE

To solve equations that have variables in a denominator.

Equations involving rational expressions are called **rational equations.** Rational equations that have variables in a denominator can be solved in the same way as equations that have fractional coefficients. Multiply each side by the LCD (the least common multiple of the denominators).

EXAMPLE 1   Solve $\dfrac{2}{x} - \dfrac{3}{2x} = \dfrac{1}{10}$.

Multiply each side by the LCD, 10x.

$$10x\left(\dfrac{2}{x} - \dfrac{3}{2x}\right) = 10x\left(\dfrac{1}{10}\right)$$
$$20 - 15 = x$$
$$x = 5$$

Check $\dfrac{2}{5} - \dfrac{3}{2(5)} \overset{?}{=} \dfrac{1}{10}$

$$\dfrac{4}{10} - \dfrac{3}{10} \overset{?}{=} \dfrac{1}{10}$$
$$\dfrac{1}{10} = \dfrac{1}{10} \;✔$$

The solution is 5.

EXAMPLE 2   Solve $\dfrac{x}{3} + \dfrac{x}{x-3} = \dfrac{3}{x-3}$.

Multiply each side by the LCD, $3(x-3)$.

$$3(x-3)\left(\dfrac{x}{3} + \dfrac{x}{x-3}\right) = 3(x-3)\left(\dfrac{3}{x-3}\right)$$
$$(x-3)(x) + 3x = 9$$
$$x^2 - 3x + 3x = 9$$
$$x^2 = 9$$
$$x^2 - 9 = 0$$
$$(x+3)(x-3) = 0$$
$$x + 3 = 0 \quad \text{or} \quad x - 3 = 0$$
$$x = -3 \qquad\qquad x = 3$$

Check   Substitute -3 for x in the original equation.

$$\dfrac{-3}{3} + \dfrac{-3}{-3-3} \overset{?}{=} \dfrac{3}{-3-3}$$
$$-1 + \dfrac{1}{2} \overset{?}{=} -\dfrac{1}{2}$$
$$-\dfrac{1}{2} = -\dfrac{1}{2} \;✔$$

3 is not a solution of the original equation since the denominator $x - 3$ is 0 when $x = 3$, and division by 0 is undefined.

The original equation has one solution, -3.

In Example 2, the apparent solution $x = 3$ was introduced when both sides of the equation were multiplied by $x(x - 3)$. Such *extraneous roots* may occur when the LCD contains a variable. Therefore *it is necessary to check each solution of the new equation in the original equation.*

EXAMPLE 3   Solve $\dfrac{5}{x + 1} - \dfrac{x}{x^2 + 3x + 2} = \dfrac{2}{x + 2}$.

Factor the denominator $x^2 + 3x + 2$.

$$\frac{5}{x + 1} - \frac{x}{(x + 1)(x + 2)} = \frac{2}{x + 2}$$

Multiply each side by the LCD, $(x + 1)(x + 2)$.

$$(x + 1)(x + 2)\left(\frac{5}{x + 1} - \frac{x}{(x + 1)(x + 2)}\right) = (x + 1)(x + 2)\left(\frac{2}{x + 2}\right)$$

$$5(x + 2) - x = 2(x + 1)$$
$$5x + 10 - x = 2x + 2$$
$$2x = -8$$
$$x = -4$$

Check that -4 satisfies the original equation. The solution is -4.

EXAMPLE 4   Solve $\dfrac{5}{x - 5} = \dfrac{x}{x - 5} + 2$.

$$\frac{5}{x - 5} = \frac{x}{x - 5} + 2$$

$$(x - 5)\left(\frac{5}{x - 5}\right) = (x - 5)\left(\frac{x}{x - 5} + 2\right)$$

$$5 = x + 2x - 10$$
$$15 = 3x$$
$$5 = x$$

Since 5 is not a permissible value in the original equation, there is *no solution.*

CLASS EXERCISES

Write each equation without fractions. Then solve and check.
*Write **no solution** if none exists.*

1. $\dfrac{6}{x} = \dfrac{3}{5}$ 10

2. $\dfrac{3}{2x} = \dfrac{1}{6}$ 9

3. $\dfrac{9}{x - 1} = \dfrac{1}{2}$ 19

4. $\dfrac{x}{x + 2} = \dfrac{5}{7}$ 5

5. $\dfrac{x - 3}{2x} = \dfrac{7}{8}$ -4

6. $\dfrac{8}{3x} = \dfrac{-4}{x - 15}$ 6

7. $\dfrac{1}{x} + \dfrac{3}{2x} = \dfrac{5}{14}$ 7

8. $\dfrac{1}{2x} + \dfrac{2}{3x} = -\dfrac{7}{36}$ -6

9. $\dfrac{5}{2x - 1} = \dfrac{11}{4x + 1}$ 8

10. $\dfrac{x}{x + 3} = \dfrac{-3}{x + 3}$ No solution

11. $\dfrac{x - 5}{7 - 2x} = -\dfrac{4}{11}$ 9

12. $\dfrac{x + 2}{3} = \dfrac{3}{x + 2}$ $-5, 1$

APPLYING FRACTIONS: SOLVING EQUATIONS AND PROBLEMS   325

ALTERNATE EXAMPLES

3. Solve:
$$\frac{3}{x + 2} - \frac{x}{x^2 + 3x + 2} = \frac{3}{x + 1}$$
-3

4. Solve:
$$\frac{6}{x - 6} = \frac{x}{x - 6} + 3 \quad \text{No sol.}$$

POSSIBLE ERROR

In working with rational equations, students may neglect to check all of their possible solutions. Thus, in solving an equation such as $\dfrac{x}{3} + \dfrac{x}{x - 3} = \dfrac{3}{x - 3}$ (Example 2), they may clear the fractions, simplify, solve, and state the answer as $x = -3$ or $x = 3$, but fail to note that $x = 3$ is not a permissible solution.

To reduce the possibility of this type of error, emphasize the need to check all possible solutions. Another helpful technique is to examine the given equation at the outset and determine the restrictions on the variable. Thus, in Example 2, we note that there is a denominator of $x - 3$. Therefore, $x - 3 \neq 0$ and $x \neq 3$.

DAILY QUIZ

Solve and check. Write *no solution* if none exists.

1. $\dfrac{6}{x} + \dfrac{1}{4} = 1$ 8

2. $\dfrac{x + 4}{4} = \dfrac{4}{x + 4}$ 0 or -8

3. $\dfrac{1}{6} + \dfrac{1}{2x} = \dfrac{x + 4}{3x}$ -5

4. $\dfrac{5 + x}{x^2 - 1} = \dfrac{3}{x - 1} + \dfrac{2}{x + 1}$ No sol.

5. $\dfrac{2}{x^2 - 2x + 1} = \dfrac{1}{x - 1}$ 3

ASSIGNMENT GUIDE
(page 326)

Minimum course: 1–23 odd
second day: 2–22 even
Average course: 1–23 odd,
28, 29
Maximum course: 1–23 odd,
24–30

ENRICHMENT ACTIVITY

Have students explore inequalities that involve fractions. For example, have them try to solve inequalities such as the following:

$\dfrac{x}{2} < 5 \quad x < 10$

$\dfrac{x}{-3} < 4 \quad x > -12$

$\dfrac{-2}{5}x > 1 \quad x < -\dfrac{5}{2}$

$\dfrac{x}{3} - \dfrac{2x+1}{4} > 1 \quad x < -\dfrac{15}{2}$

Students will need to note that when both sides of an inequality are multiplied by a negative number, the direction of the inequality is reversed.

EXERCISES

A

*Solve and check. Write **no solution** if none exists.*

1. $\dfrac{5}{x} - \dfrac{1}{2} = 2$ 2   **2.** $1 - \dfrac{16}{x} = \dfrac{7}{3}$ −12   **3.** $\dfrac{y-1}{7-y} = 5$ 6

4. $\dfrac{3x-4}{5x} = \dfrac{4}{5}$ −4   **5.** $\dfrac{39}{n} + \dfrac{2}{3} = 5$ 9   **6.** $\dfrac{x+2}{2x-1} = \dfrac{7}{9}$ 5

7. $\dfrac{y+3}{4y} = \dfrac{1}{8} + \dfrac{1}{2y}$ −2   **8.** $\dfrac{20}{3x} + \dfrac{5}{2x} = \dfrac{5}{6}$ 11   **9.** $\dfrac{2x-3}{4x+5} + \dfrac{2}{7} = 0$ $\frac{1}{2}$

10. $\dfrac{2}{7y} - \dfrac{1}{2} = \dfrac{3}{14y}$ $\frac{1}{7}$ **11.** $\dfrac{8}{x-8} = \dfrac{x}{x-8}$ No solution   **12.** $\dfrac{x-2}{5} = \dfrac{1}{x+2}$ 3, −3

13. $\dfrac{1}{a-4} - \dfrac{4}{9} = \dfrac{a}{9}$ 5, −5   **14.** $\dfrac{3}{2a+3} = \dfrac{2a-3}{9}$ 3, −3   **15.** $\dfrac{1}{x^2-16} = \dfrac{1}{5(x-4)}$ 1

B

16. $\dfrac{3}{a+1} - \dfrac{1}{a+2} = -\dfrac{1}{2}$ −3, −4   **17.** $\dfrac{1}{x-3} + 1 = \dfrac{3}{x^2-3x}$ −1

18. $\dfrac{2}{x-1} = \dfrac{3}{x+1} + \dfrac{1}{15}$ 4, −19   **19.** $\dfrac{15+x}{x^2-1} = \dfrac{4}{x-1} - \dfrac{3}{x+1}$ No solution

20. $\dfrac{x+1}{x-1} = \dfrac{2}{x(x-1)} + \dfrac{4}{x}$ 2   **21.** $\dfrac{3}{x^2-3x-4} = \dfrac{1}{x+1}$ 7

22. $\dfrac{2}{3} + \dfrac{9}{b^2+4b+4} = \dfrac{b}{b+2}$ 7, −5   **23.** $\dfrac{5}{2x^2+x} - 1 = \dfrac{2}{2x+1}$ 1, $-\frac{5}{2}$

C

24. $\dfrac{x^2}{x^2-1} + \dfrac{1}{2(x+1)} + 1 = \dfrac{1}{2x-2}$ No solution

25. $\dfrac{3x}{2x^2+x} + \dfrac{x-7}{2x^2-7x-4} = \dfrac{9x}{x^2-4x}$ −2

26. $\dfrac{x+2}{x^2-5x+6} + \dfrac{2}{x^2-2x-3} + \dfrac{2x}{x^2-x-2} = 0$ 1, $-\frac{2}{3}$

27. $\dfrac{12}{x^3-3x^2-x+3} + \dfrac{6}{x^2-1} = \dfrac{1}{x-3}$ 5

28. The denominator of a fraction is 12 more than the numerator. Find this fraction if its value is equal to $\frac{3}{5}$. $\frac{18}{30}$

29. Two positive numbers differ by 6. Find the numbers if the sum of their reciprocals is $\frac{5}{8}$.   2 and 8

30. A rectangular vent is $\dfrac{5}{2x-10}$ cm wide and $\dfrac{15}{x-5}$ cm long. If its perimeter is 35 cm, find x.   6

EXTRA PRACTICE, page 524

9-3 Problem Solving: Number Problems with Fractions

OBJECTIVE

To use rational equations in solving problems.

A variable such as x may represent the numerator of a fraction, the denominator, or the fraction itself. How x is used depends upon the problem.

EXAMPLE 1

The numerator of a certain fraction is 3 less than the denominator. If the numerator is decreased by 1 and the denominator is increased by 2, then the new fraction equals $\frac{2}{5}$. Find the original fraction.

Strategy: Express the original fraction in terms of x. Modify this and set it equal to $\frac{2}{5}$.

Read the problem to find the key ideas.

Subtract 1 from the numerator. Add 2 to the denominator. The new fraction equals $\frac{2}{5}$.

Use a variable.

Let x be the denominator.
Then x − 3 is the numerator.

$$\frac{x - 3}{x}$$ The original fraction

$$\frac{(x - 3) - 1}{x + 2}$$ Decrease the numerator by 1.
Increase the denominator by 2.

Write an equation.

$$\frac{(x - 3) - 1}{x + 2} = \frac{2}{5}$$ The new fraction equals $\frac{2}{5}$.

Find the solution.

$$\frac{x - 4}{x + 2} = \frac{2}{5}$$

$5(x - 4) = 2(x + 2)$ Multiply each side by $5(x + 2)$.
$5x - 20 = 2x + 4$
$x = 8$ *and* $x - 3 = 5$

Check in the given statement of the problem that $\frac{5 - 1}{8 + 2}$ is equal to $\frac{2}{5}$.

Answer the question.

The original fraction is $\frac{5}{8}$.

In the preceding example, x was used as the denominator. In the next example, x represents the entire fraction.

If x is a number, how would you represent the following?
1. 4 more than x $x + 4$
2. 5 less than x $x - 5$
3. twice x $2x$
4. the reciprocal of x $\frac{1}{x}$
5. the reciprocal of $\frac{x}{2}$ $\frac{2}{x}$

LESSON NOTES

In discussing the model examples, contrast the circumstances in which we use a variable to represent the numerator (or denominator) of a fraction with those circumstances in which we use a variable to represent the entire fraction. If a problem provides details about the numerator and denominator—for instance, if we are told that the numerator is 3 less than the denominator—then we generally use a variable to represent one of the fraction's terms (the numerator or the denominator) and then write the other term as an expression involving the same variable (Example 1). On the other hand, if a problem refers to a fraction without giving details that relate the numerator and denominator, then we generally use a variable to represent the entire fraction (Example 2).

ALTERNATE EXAMPLE

1. The numerator of a certain fraction is 5 less than the denominator. If the numerator is increased by 1 and the denominator is decreased by 3, then the new fraction equals $\frac{5}{6}$. Find the original fraction. $\frac{4}{9}$

EXAMPLE 2   The sum of a fraction and its reciprocal is $\frac{13}{6}$. Find the fraction.

Use a variable.   Let x = the fraction.   Then $\frac{1}{x}$ = its reciprocal.

Write an equation.
$$x + \frac{1}{x} = \frac{13}{6}$$

Find the solution.
$$6x(x) + 6x\left(\frac{1}{x}\right) = 6x\left(\frac{13}{6}\right)$$
$$6x^2 + 6 = 13x$$
$$6x^2 - 13x + 6 = 0 \qquad \text{Solve for } x \text{ by first factoring.}$$
$$(3x - 2)(2x - 3) = 0$$
$$3x - 2 = 0 \quad \text{or} \quad 2x - 3 = 0$$
$$x = \frac{2}{3} \qquad\qquad x = \frac{3}{2}$$

Check that each fraction plus its reciprocal is $\frac{13}{6}$.

Answer the question.   There are two answers. The fraction is either $\frac{2}{3}$ or $\frac{3}{2}$.

CLASS EXERCISES

Complete the exercises for the following problem.

The denominator of a fraction is 2 more than the numerator. If you add 5 to both the numerator and the denominator, the resulting fraction equals $\frac{4}{5}$. Find the original fraction by answering these questions.

1. Let the numerator be x. Then the denominator is __?__ .   *x + 2*

2. Add 5 to both the numerator and denominator of $\frac{x}{x+2}$ and simplify. $\frac{x+5}{x+7}$

3. Multiply each side of $\frac{x+5}{x+7} = \frac{4}{5}$ by the LCD, and solve.   *x = 3*

4. What was the original fraction? Check your answer. $\frac{3}{5}$

EXERCISES

A

1. If a certain number is added to both the numerator and the denominator of $\frac{19}{37}$, the new fraction equals $\frac{4}{7}$. What is the number?   **5**

2. What number subtracted from both the numerator and the denominator of $\frac{34}{53}$ results in a new fraction that equals $\frac{1}{2}$?   **15**

3. The denominator of a fraction is 4 more than the numerator. If the numerator is multiplied by 3 and the denominator by 2, the resulting fraction is equal to $\frac{5}{6}$. Find the fraction. $\frac{5}{9}$

4. Find two consecutive even integers such that $\frac{2}{3}$ times the smaller is the same as $\frac{3}{5}$ times the larger.   **18, 20**

5. An integer minus 3 times its reciprocal equals $\frac{26}{3}$. Find the integer.   **9**

EXTRA PRACTICE, pages 524–525

B

6. The sum of the reciprocals of two consecutive integers is $\frac{13}{42}$. Find the integers. **6, 7**

7. The numerator of a fraction is 2 more than 3 times the denominator. If 1 is added to the denominator and 7 is subtracted from the numerator, the result is 2. Find the fraction. $\frac{23}{7}$

8. The sum of two fractions is $\frac{19}{8}$. If the smaller fraction is $\frac{7}{12}$ times the larger, find the two fractions. $\frac{3}{2}, \frac{7}{8}$

9. The reciprocal of twice an integer plus the reciprocal of 2 more than twice the integer equals $\frac{7}{24}$. Find the integer. **3**

10. The numerator of a fraction is 1 more than 3 times the denominator. If the denominator is multiplied by 3, and if 3 is added to the numerator, then the result is $\frac{4}{3}$. What is the original fraction? $\frac{13}{4}$

C

11. Twice the sum of a fraction and 1 is $\frac{2}{7}$ more than 5 times the fraction. Find the fraction if its denominator is 3 more than its numerator. $\frac{4}{7}$

12. The reciprocal of an integer minus the reciprocal of the next consecutive integer is divided by the sum of these reciprocals. If the quotient equals $\frac{1}{15}$, find the integer. **7**

13. The denominator of a fraction is 1 less than twice the numerator. If the fraction is divided by 3 more than itself, the quotient is equal to $\frac{5}{32}$. Find the fraction. $\frac{5}{9}$

CHECKPOINT

*Solve and check. Write **no solution** if none exists.*

1. $\frac{5x}{12} - \frac{1}{6} = \frac{1}{4}$ **1**   2. $\frac{3x}{10} - \frac{x}{5} = 10 - \frac{4x - 1}{2}$ **5**   3. $\frac{5x}{x - 2} = 2 + \frac{10}{x - 2}$

   No solution

4. $\frac{4x - 3}{3x} = \frac{1}{3}$ **1**   5. $\frac{6}{x} - \frac{1}{3} = 3$ **1.8, or $\frac{9}{5}$**   6. $\frac{3x - 2}{5x + 4} - \frac{2}{7} = 0$ **2**

7. $\frac{3}{2}(2x - 1) - \frac{7x}{8} = \frac{1}{4}(4x + 12)$ **4**   8. $\frac{2}{x + 1} - \frac{1}{x + 2} = \frac{-1}{x^2 + 3x + 2}$ **−4**

9. If a certain number is added to both the numerator and denominator of $\frac{11}{13}$, the new fraction is equal to $\frac{7}{8}$. What is the number? **3**

10. The denominator of a fraction is 5 more than the numerator. If the numerator is multiplied by 3 and the denominator by 2, the resulting fraction is equal to $\frac{12}{13}$. Find the fraction. $\frac{8}{13}$

APPLYING FRACTIONS: SOLVING EQUATIONS AND PROBLEMS   **329**

ENRICHMENT ACTIVITY

In the Enrichment Activity for Lesson 9-2, the students explored inequalities involving fractions. Have them continue the exploration using more challenging inequalities. For example:

$\frac{x + 1}{x} < 3$ $x < 0$ or $x > \frac{1}{2}$

$\frac{x}{x - 1} < 2$ $x < 1$ or $x > 2$

Students will need to note that two separate cases need to be considered for each example: (a) the denominator is greater than 0 (b) the denominator is less than 0

Checkpoint

Students may check their answers with those given in the back of their books.

By what expression would you multiply to clear the equation of fractions?

1. $\frac{3}{5} = \frac{1}{x}$ **2.** $\frac{1}{3} = \frac{1}{x} + \frac{1}{2x}$

   $5x$ $6x$

LESSON NOTES

As you discuss Example 1, be sure the students follow the basic reasoning. If Ann can do the job in 8 hours, then she can do $\frac{1}{8}$ of the job in 1 hour (assuming she works at a constant rate). Similarly, her older sister can do $\frac{1}{4}$ of the job in 1 hour. Working together, in 1 hour they can do $\frac{1}{8} + \frac{1}{4}$ of the job.

The equation $\frac{1}{8} + \frac{1}{4} = \frac{1}{x}$ may not be clear to some students. Remind them that if x is the time required for Ann and her sister to do the job when they are working together, then $\frac{1}{x}$ is the part of the job they do in 1 hour. Thus, $\frac{1}{8} + \frac{1}{4}$ must equal $\frac{1}{x}$, so the equation is $\frac{1}{8} + \frac{1}{4} = \frac{1}{x}$. In general, emphasize that the problem is solved by writing an equation that shows the facts relating to the fractional part of the job completed in one unit of time (1 hour in this case).

ALTERNATE EXAMPLE

1. It takes James 6 hours to paint the fence. His friend Steve can do the same job in 4 hours. How long does it take them to paint the fence working together? $2\frac{2}{5}$ hr, or 2 hr 24 min

9-4 Problem Solving: Work Problems

OBJECTIVE _____

To solve problems involving rates of work.

Suppose it will take you 8 hours to paint a garage. Then in 1 hour you will complete $\frac{1}{8}$ of the job, assuming that you work at a constant rate. In 2 hours you will complete $2(\frac{1}{8})$, or $\frac{1}{4}$, of the job. Likewise, if it takes you x hours to do the job, then the part of the job you will do in 1 hour is $\frac{1}{x}$.

In this section we will use fractions that represent the amount of work done in one unit of time. These fractions will be based on the assumption that work is done at a constant rate.

EXAMPLE 1

It takes Ann 8 hours to paint the porch of her house, and her older sister can do the same job in 4 hours. How long does it take them to paint the porch working together?

Strategy: Use the fractional amount of work done in 1 hour to form an equation.

Read the problem to find the key ideas.

In 1 hour Ann does $\frac{1}{8}$ of the job, and her sister does $\frac{1}{4}$ of it.

Use a variable.

Let x be the time required to paint the porch, working together.

Then $\frac{1}{x}$ = the part of the job done in 1 hour, working together

$\frac{1}{8}$ = the part of the job Ann does in 1 hour

$\frac{1}{4}$ = the part of the job her sister does in 1 hour

Write an equation.

$\frac{1}{8} + \frac{1}{4} = \frac{1}{x}$ In one hour, the part done by Ann alone plus the part done by her sister alone, equals the part done by both together.

Find the solution.

$$\frac{3}{8} = \frac{1}{x}$$

$$8x\left(\frac{3}{8}\right) = 8x\left(\frac{1}{x}\right) \quad \text{Multiply by the LCD, } 8x.$$

$$3x = 8$$

$$x = \frac{8}{3}, \text{ or } 2\frac{2}{3}$$

Check that Ann does $\frac{1}{3}$ of the work, and her sister does $\frac{2}{3}$.

$$2\frac{2}{3} \cdot \frac{1}{8} = \frac{8}{3} \cdot \frac{1}{8} = \frac{1}{3} \qquad 2\frac{2}{3} \cdot \frac{1}{4} = \frac{8}{3} \cdot \frac{1}{4} = \frac{2}{3}$$

The sum of the parts, $\frac{1}{3} + \frac{2}{3}$, equals 1, the complete job.

Answer the question.

Together they can paint the porch in $2\frac{2}{3}$ hr, or 2 hr 40 min.

It is often useful to estimate. In Example 1 consider these estimates of the hours needed to paint the porch if the sisters work together: more than 8? between 4 and 8? less than 4?

If the sisters work together, it is reasonable to expect them to do the job in less time than it would take either of them working alone, so less than 4 hours is the best estimate given.

EXAMPLE 2 When both inlet pipes to a swimming pool are open, it takes 6 hours to fill the pool. The larger pipe can fill the pool by itself in $\frac{1}{4}$ the time it takes the smaller pipe by itself. How long does it take each pipe alone to fill the pool?

Before reading the solution to this problem, make an estimate. Does one pipe alone take more or less than 6 hours to fill the pool?

Use a variable.   Let x = the number of hours for the larger pipe alone
Then 4x = the number of hours for the smaller pipe alone

$\frac{1}{x}$ = part of pool filled by larger pipe in 1 hour

$\frac{1}{4x}$ = part of pool filled by smaller pipe in 1 hour

Write an equation. $\frac{1}{6} = \frac{1}{x} + \frac{1}{4x}$ $\frac{1}{6}$ is the part of the pool filled in 1 hr when both pipes are open.

Find the solution. $12x\left(\frac{1}{6}\right) = 12x\left(\frac{1}{x}\right) + 12x\left(\frac{1}{4x}\right)$

$$2x = 12 + 3$$

$$x = \frac{15}{2}, \text{ or } 7\frac{1}{2}$$

$$\text{and } 4x = 4\left(\frac{15}{2}\right) = 30$$

Check that in 6 hours the parts of the pool filled by the larger and the smaller pipes have a sum of 1.

Larger pipe: $6\left(\frac{1}{x}\right) = 6\left(\frac{2}{15}\right) = \frac{12}{15} = \frac{4}{5}$

Smaller pipe: $6\left(\frac{1}{4x}\right) = 6\left(\frac{1}{30}\right) = \frac{6}{30} = \frac{1}{5}$ $\frac{4}{5} + \frac{1}{5} = 1$ ✔

Answer the question.   It takes the larger pipe $7\frac{1}{2}$ hours to fill the pool alone, and it takes the smaller pipe 30 hours.

2. When both inlet pipes to a water tank are open, it takes 5 hours to fill the tank. The larger pipe can fill the tank by itself in $\frac{1}{3}$ the time it takes the smaller pipe by itself. How long does it take each pipe alone to fill the tank?

Large pipe, $6\frac{2}{3}$ hr; small pipe, 20 hr

POSSIBLE ERROR

In solving work problems and other types of problems, students often obtain an answer that is not reasonable, but fail to recognize this fact because they have not estimated the answer in advance. For instance, in Example 1 the answer must be less than 4 hours because one sister can do the job alone in that period of time. An answer greater than 4 should be recognized as unreasonable.

Urge students to estimate answers to problems beforehand whenever possible. Class Exercise 5 and the A Exercises 1–6 are structured to encourage estimating.

Solve each problem.

1. José can spray-paint a car in 7 hours. Len can do the same job in 8 hours. If they work together, how long will it take them to complete the job? $3\frac{11}{15}$ hours, or 3 hours 44 minutes

2. Karen can wash the windows of her house in 4 hours. Selena can do the same job in 6 hours. If they work together, how long will it take them to do the job? $2\frac{2}{5}$ hours, or 2 hours 24 minutes

3. Two brothers can do a job in $3\frac{3}{5}$ days if they work together. The older brother can do the job alone in 6 days. How many days would it take the younger brother to do the job if he worked alone? 9 days

4. Two people, working together, can do a job in 5 hours. One of them, working alone, can do the job in 9 hours. How long would it take the other person to do the job if he worked alone? $11\frac{1}{4}$ hours

5. An inlet pipe can fill a tank in 3 hours and an outlet pipe can empty the same tank in 5 hours. How long will it take to fill the tank if both pipes are open? $7\frac{1}{2}$ hours

---

ASSIGNMENT GUIDE
(pages 332–334)

Minimum course: 1–6
    second day: 7–11
Average course: 1–8
    second day: 9–15
Maximum course: 1–11
    second day: 12–17
All courses: *Strategies for Problem Solving*

CLASS EXERCISES

1. It takes John 3 hours to mow the lawn. What part of the job can he do in 1 hour? $\frac{1}{3}$ in 2 hours? $\frac{2}{3}$ in x hours? $\frac{x}{3}$

2. It takes Sarah 45 minutes to do her math homework. What part of the homework can she do in 5 minutes? $\frac{1}{9}$ in 15 minutes? $\frac{1}{3}$ in a half hour? $\frac{2}{3}$ in t minutes? $\frac{t}{45}$

3. One pipe fills a tank in 5 hours and another can fill it in 4 hours. How much of the tank is filled in 1 hour if both pipes are open? $\frac{9}{20}$

4. One worker can complete a job in 3 hours, and another needs x hours. Write an expression for the part of the job they can do in 1 hour if they work together. $\frac{1}{3} + \frac{1}{x}$, or $\frac{x+3}{3x}$

5. In Exercise 4, assume that the workers take 2 hours to do the job working together. Estimate x. Is x more than 2 or less than 2? Then solve for x. 6

EXERCISES

A   *First estimate the solution, then solve the problem.*

1. Karin can paint her living room in 6 hours. If Mavis helps her, they can complete the job in 3 hours. How long would it take Mavis to complete the job working alone? 6 hours

2. David can load a truck in 5 hours. If Rao helps him, then together they can do the job in 3 hours. How long would it take Rao to load the truck by himself? $7\frac{1}{2}$ hours

3. Stan and Susan are going to decorate the gymnasium. Stan can do this by himself in 5 hours. How long would it take Susan alone if together they can complete the work in 2 hours? $3\frac{1}{3}$ hours, or 3 hr 20 min

4. Lou can paint a house in 5 days, and Bud can do it in 7 days. If they work together, how long does it take to paint the house? $2\frac{11}{12}$ days (appr. 3 days)

5. Kim can sand a floor in 4 hours. If Harry can sand it in 5 hours, how long will it take them to complete the job working together? $2\frac{2}{9}$ hours

6. The Acme Cleaning Service can clean a school in 8 hours. If the janitors take twice as long to clean the school, how long will it take to complete the job when the cleaning service and the janitors are working together? $5\frac{1}{3}$ hours

B   *Solve and check.*

7. Working together, two sisters can plant a garden in 3 hours. The older sister can do the job by herself in $\frac{1}{3}$ the time it would take the younger sister. How long would it take each of the sisters to plant the garden alone? Older sister, 4 hours; younger sister, 12 hours

CHAPTER 9

EXTRA PRACTICE, page 525

8. One pipe can fill a tank in 72 minutes, and a second pipe can fill it in 1 hour. How long does it take the two pipes to fill the tank? $\frac{6}{11}$ hours, or $32\frac{8}{11}$ min

9. If an inlet pipe can fill a tank in 90 minutes, and an outlet pipe can empty the tank in 135 minutes, how long does it take to fill the tank when both pipes are open? $4\frac{1}{2}$ hours

10. An inlet pipe can fill a swimming pool twice as fast as an outlet pipe can empty it. If both pipes are open, the pool is filled in $4\frac{1}{2}$ hours. How long does it take the inlet pipe to fill the pool if the outlet pipe is closed? $2\frac{1}{4}$ hours

11. A new mower can cut the grass on the fairways of a golf course in half the time it takes another mower to do the same job. If it takes 7 hours to finish the job when both mowers are working together, how long would it take each mower working alone?
Faster mower, $10\frac{1}{2}$ hours; slower mower, 21 hours

C

12. An earth-moving machine can level a hill 10 times as fast as a team of workers. Working together, the machine and the workers can do the job in 5 hours. How long would it take the workers alone? How long would it take the machine alone? 55 hours; $5\frac{1}{2}$ hours

13. The cold-water faucet fills a sink in 4 minutes less time than it takes the hot-water faucet. If both faucets are open, it takes $1\frac{1}{2}$ minutes. How long does it take each faucet to fill the sink?
Cold-water faucet, 2 minutes; hot-water faucet, 6 minutes

14. It takes two computers working together $4\frac{4}{5}$ minutes to do some calculations. If one can do the work in 4 minutes less than twice the time it takes the other, how long does it take each to do the work alone?
One computer, 12 minutes; other computer, 8 minutes

15. Jim and Ada work for an animal shelter. Jim can clean the cages alone in 2 hours, while it takes Ada 3 hours by herself. If they work together for $\frac{1}{3}$ hour before Jim stops, how long will it take Ada to finish the job? $2\frac{1}{6}$ hours

    Hint: The part of the job they do together is $\frac{1}{3}(\frac{1}{2}) + \frac{1}{3}(\frac{1}{3}) = \frac{5}{18}$.

16. Lee and Fran are printing name tags for a class reunion. Suppose that Lee can do this alone in 1 hour, and that it would take Fran $1\frac{1}{2}$ hours. If Lee works by himself for 20 minutes, and then Fran joins him, how long will they take to complete this work together? $\frac{2}{5}$ hour, or 24 min

17. A farmer can plow a field in 4 hours. After working alone for $1\frac{1}{2}$ hours, his son joins him. Together, they complete the work in 1 hour. How long would it take the son to plow the field by himself? $2\frac{2}{3}$ hours

*18. If 6 workers can assemble 6 machines in 6 hours, how long will it take 12 workers to assemble 12 machines? 6 hours

APPLYING FRACTIONS: SOLVING EQUATIONS AND PROBLEMS 333

Strategies for Problem Solving

The strategy explained on this page illustrates the usefulness of guessing the answers to some mathematical problems. *However,* stress that a guess is simply the first step in the process. A guess must be adjusted appropriately before we can obtain a correct answer.

STRATEGIES for PROBLEM SOLVING

Starting with a Guess

The ancient Egyptians had a clever way to solve certain problems by **starting with a guess.** Here is a translation of a problem that appeared in the *Rhind Papyrus,* written around 1650 B.C.

A quantity and one-seventh of it add to 19. Find the quantity.

Here is how they solved it, using 7 as a first guess.

Start with a convenient guess.	7
Take $\frac{1}{7}$ of it.	1
Find the sum.	8

With a guess of 7, the result is 8.

But the problem calls for a result of 19.

Find how many 8's are in 19. $\qquad 19 \div 8 = 2\frac{3}{8}$

Multiply the guess by this result. $\qquad 7 \times 2\frac{3}{8} = 16\frac{5}{8}$

The quantity is $16\frac{5}{8}$.

Check to see that $16\frac{5}{8}$ is the correct answer to the problem.

$$16\frac{5}{8} + \frac{1}{7}\left(16\frac{5}{8}\right) = 16\frac{5}{8} + \frac{19}{8}$$
$$= 16 + 3 = 19$$

Can you explain why this method, called **false position,** will always work for any first guess? Suppose you had started with 14 in the problem above, would your answer have been $16\frac{5}{8}$? Yes. The method is based on proportional quantities. $\frac{7}{8} = \frac{x}{19} \Rightarrow x = \frac{19}{8} \cdot 7$

Now try to solve these problems using the method of false position.

1. A quantity plus $\frac{1}{3}$ of it is equal to 22. Find the quantity by making a guess of 3, and then of 15. The quantity is $16\frac{1}{2}$.

2. A quantity less $\frac{1}{5}$ of it is 13. Find the quantity. $16\frac{1}{4}$

3. Solve $x + \frac{x}{9} = 23$. 20.7

4. Solve $x - \frac{x}{8} = 17$. $19\frac{3}{7}$

334

9-5 Ratio and Proportion

OBJECTIVE _____

To use proportions in solving problems.

The *ratio* of the length of the shorter pencil to the length of the longer pencil is 4 to 7, or $\frac{4}{7}$.

A **ratio** is a comparison of two numbers by division. The ratio of 4 to 7 can be written in several ways.

$$4 \text{ to } 7 \qquad \frac{4}{7} \qquad 4:7$$

EXAMPLE 1   Simplify each ratio.

  a. $\dfrac{15}{25}$ b. **4a to 8b**   c. **27:3**

  $\dfrac{15}{25} = \dfrac{3}{5}$ $\dfrac{4a}{8b} = \dfrac{a}{2b}$ $\dfrac{27}{3} = \dfrac{9}{1}$

Below are three ways to show that ratios such as 6:4 and 3:2 are equal.

$$\frac{6}{4} = \frac{3}{2} \qquad 6 \text{ is to } 4 \text{ as } 3 \text{ is to } 2. \qquad 6:4 = 3:2$$

An *equation* stating that two ratios are equal is called a **proportion.**

EXAMPLE 2   If 5 is to x as 20 is to 8, find x.

$$\frac{5}{x} = \frac{20}{8} \qquad \text{Write a proportion. Then solve for } x.$$

$$8x\left(\frac{5}{x}\right) = 8x\left(\frac{20}{8}\right) \qquad \text{Multiply each side by the LCD, } 8x.$$

$$40 = 20x$$

$$2 = x \qquad \text{Check that } \tfrac{5}{2} \text{ and } \tfrac{20}{8} \text{ are equal.}$$

In the proportion $a:b = c:d$, b and c are called the **means,** while a and d are called the **extremes.**

$$\overbrace{a:b}^{\text{means}} = \underbrace{c:d}_{\text{extremes}}$$

In any proportion, the product of the means is equal to the product of the extremes.

APPLYING FRACTIONS: SOLVING EQUATIONS AND PROBLEMS

335

LESSON NOTES

You may wish to point out that a proportion may be true, it may be false, or it may be neither true nor false.

$6:4 = 3:2$	True
$6:4 = 9:5$	False
$\dfrac{6}{4} = \dfrac{x}{10}$	Neither true nor false

When we *solve* a proportion such as $\dfrac{6}{4} = \dfrac{x}{10}$, we find the number that makes the equation true.

This lesson shows two ways to solve a proportion. In Example 2, the two sides of the equation are treated as fractions, and the LCD is used to multiply both sides. In Examples 3 and 4, the proportion property is used; that is, the students use cross products. Most students will be familiar with the cross-products technique from their work in earlier grades.

[*Lesson notes continue on page 336.*]

ALTERNATE EXAMPLES

1. Simplify each ratio.

  a. $\dfrac{12}{18}$ $\dfrac{2}{3}$

  b. 2a to 10b $\dfrac{a}{5b}$

  c. 24:4 $\dfrac{6}{1}$

2. If 3 is to x as 21 is to 35, find x.   5

In Example 5, the text considers a ratio situation in which we know the ratio of two numbers and we also know the sum of the numbers. The method of solution shown in the text uses the fact that the numbers can be represented as 5x and 6x; a simple equation such as 5x + 6x = 176 becomes the vehicle for solving the problem. Of course, an alternate method of solution is possible; we can let the numbers be represented by x and 176 − x; then the equation for the problem is $\frac{x}{176 - x} = \frac{5}{6}$. However, the method shown in the text is particularly useful for situations involving continued ratios (see C exercises 36–37).

ALTERNATE EXAMPLES

3. Solve the proportion: $\frac{4}{9} = \frac{8}{x + 2}$ 16

4. The ratio of girls to boys at a soccer game is 6 to 5. If there are 1800 girls, how many boys are there? 1500

5. Two numbers in the ratio 3 to 4 have a sum of 105. Find the numbers. 45 and 60

POSSIBLE ERROR

Students sometimes make careless errors in using the proportion property. For instance, in solving an equation such as the one in Example 3, they may multiply incorrectly.

$$\frac{3}{8} = \frac{6}{x \quad 1}$$

3x − 1 = 48 (incorrect)

To help them avoid such errors, emphasize the importance of using parentheses, as shown in Example 3. Students are less likely to make a mistake if the product of 3 and x − 1 is first shown as 3(x − 1).

The Proportion Property

If $\frac{a}{b} = \frac{c}{d}$, then $ad = bc.$

To verify this property, multiply each side of the proportion by bd.

$$\frac{a}{b} = \frac{c}{d}$$

$$bd\left(\frac{a}{b}\right) = bd\left(\frac{c}{d}\right)$$

$$da = bc \quad \text{or} \quad ad = bc$$

EXAMPLE 3 Solve the proportion: $\frac{3}{8} = \frac{6}{x - 1}$

$$\frac{3}{8} = \frac{6}{x - 1} \qquad \text{The means are 8 and 6. The extremes are 3 and } (x - 1).$$

$$3(x - 1) = (8)(6) \qquad \text{Use the proportion property.}$$
$$3x - 3 = 48$$
$$3x = 51$$
$$x = 17$$

Check $\frac{6}{17 - 1} = \frac{6}{16} = \frac{3}{8}$ ✔

EXAMPLE 4 The ratio of boys to girls in a school is 7 to 6. If there are 1400 boys, how many girls are there?

Let x = the number of girls.

$$\frac{7}{6} = \frac{1400}{x} \qquad \text{Write a proportion and solve for } x.$$

$$7x = 6 \cdot 1400 \qquad \text{Use the proportion property.}$$
$$x = 1200 \qquad \text{Check that } 1400 : 1200 = 7 : 6.$$

There are 1200 girls.

EXAMPLE 5 Two numbers in the ratio 5 to 6 have a sum of 176. Find the numbers.

Any two numbers in the ratio 5 : 6 can be represented by 5x and 6x, since $\frac{5x}{6x} = \frac{5}{6}$, x ≠ 0.

Then 5x + 6x = 176
$$x = 16$$

If x = 16, then 5x = 80 and 6x = 96.

Check $\frac{80}{96} = \frac{5}{6}$ and 80 + 96 = 176 ✔ The numbers are 80 and 96.

CHAPTER 9

CLASS EXERCISES

Simplify each ratio.

1. 35 to 15 $\frac{7}{3}$ **2.** $\frac{6ab}{12ab}$ $\frac{1}{2}$ **3.** $6x:x$ $\frac{6}{1}$ **4.** $38:2$ $\frac{19}{1}$

Identify the means and the extremes in each proportion.

5. $\frac{24}{3} = \frac{16}{2}$ m: 3, 16   **6.** $5:7 = 25:35$ **7.** $\frac{p}{q} = \frac{r}{s}$ m: q, r   **8.** $\frac{3}{6} = \frac{6}{x}$ m: 6, 6
           e: 24, 2   m: 7, 25; e: 5, 35   e: p, s   e: 3, x

Solve each proportion.

9. $\frac{1}{3} = \frac{x}{24}$ 8   **10.** $\frac{3}{4} = \frac{75}{x}$ 100   **11.** $\frac{5}{x} = \frac{1}{5}$ 25   **12.** $\frac{4}{x+1} = \frac{6}{15}$ 9

EXERCISES

A   *Solve each proportion.*

1. $\frac{3}{9} = \frac{x}{18}$ 6   **2.** $\frac{12}{6} = \frac{8}{x}$ 4   **3.** $\frac{x}{15} = \frac{15}{5}$ 45   **4.** $\frac{36}{x} = \frac{9}{12}$ 48

5. $\frac{14}{15} = \frac{x}{60}$ 56   **6.** $\frac{2}{3} = \frac{4x}{24}$ 4   **7.** $\frac{1}{3x} = \frac{6}{54}$ 3   **8.** $\frac{3}{4} = \frac{x+1}{12}$ 8

9. $\frac{x-1}{10} = \frac{3}{15}$ 3   **10.** $\frac{2x+3}{22} = \frac{1}{2}$ 4   **11.** $\frac{3}{11} = \frac{9}{5x-2}$ 7   **12.** $\frac{x-1}{20} = \frac{x+2}{32}$ 6

13. $\frac{x+3}{x-4} = \frac{12}{5}$ 9   **14.** $\frac{1}{2x-4} = \frac{7}{4x+2}$ 3   **15.** $\frac{4x}{26} = \frac{x-11}{7}$ −143

Express all ratios in simplest form.

16. A team won 12 games and lost 8. What is the ratio of wins to losses? $\frac{3}{2}$

17. There are 16 girls and 12 boys in a class. What is the ratio of girls to boys? $\frac{4}{3}$ of boys to girls? $\frac{3}{4}$

18. A farmer has 42 cows and 280 chickens. Find the ratio of cows to chickens. $\frac{3}{20}$

There are 42 marbles in a bag; 14 are red, and the rest are green. Find the ratio of the numbers indicated.

19. green marbles to red $\frac{2}{1}$ **20.** red marbles to green $\frac{1}{2}$

21. green marbles to total number $\frac{2}{3}$ **22.** total number to red marbles $\frac{3}{1}$

23. If the ratio of the number of tables to the number of chairs in a classroom is 3 to 8, and there are 6 tables, how many chairs are there?   16

24. The ratio of a father's weight to his daughter's weight is 11:7. How much does his daughter weigh if the father weighs 165 pounds?   105 lb

APPLYING FRACTIONS: SOLVING EQUATIONS AND PROBLEMS   **337**

EXTRA PRACTICE, page 525

ADDITIONAL ANSWERS

Exercises

41. $\dfrac{a}{b} = \dfrac{c}{d}$

$ad = bc$

$\dfrac{ad}{cd} = \dfrac{bc}{cd}$

$\dfrac{a}{c} = \dfrac{b}{d}$

42. $\dfrac{a}{b} = \dfrac{c}{d}$

$\dfrac{a}{b} + 1 = \dfrac{c}{d} + 1$

$\dfrac{a}{b} + \dfrac{b}{b} = \dfrac{c}{d} + \dfrac{d}{d}$

$\dfrac{a+b}{b} = \dfrac{c+d}{d}$

43. $\dfrac{a}{b} = \dfrac{c}{d}$

$ad = bc$

$\dfrac{ad}{cd} = \dfrac{bc}{cd}$

$\dfrac{a}{c} = \dfrac{b}{d}$

$\dfrac{a}{c} - 1 = \dfrac{b}{d} - 1$

$\dfrac{a}{c} - \dfrac{c}{c} = \dfrac{b}{d} - \dfrac{d}{d}$

$\dfrac{a-c}{c} = \dfrac{b-d}{d}$

25. The population of a town increased from 27,500 in 1970 to 33,000 in 1980. What is the ratio of the increase in population to the 1970 figure? $\frac{1}{5}$

26. A certain car can travel 120 miles on 4 gallons of gasoline. How far can the car travel on 14 gallons?   420 mi

27. According to the scale on a road map, 3 centimeters represent 10 kilometers. If two cities are 18 centimeters apart on the map, what is the distance between them in kilometers?   60 km

cm 0   1   2   3
km 0   5   10

28. Two numbers in the ratio 8:9 have a sum of 136. Find the numbers.   64, 72

B

29. The axle ratio of a truck is 4:1. This means that the drive shaft makes 4 revolutions for each complete revolution of the wheels. How many revolutions will the wheels make for 600 revolutions of the drive shaft?   150

30. Answer Exercise 29 for an axle ratio of $2\frac{1}{2}$ to 1.   240

31. A town has 3300 registered voters, all of them Democrats or Republicans. The ratio of Democrats to Republicans is 6:5. How many are in each party?   1800 Democrats, 1500 Republicans

32. There are 1232 students in a high school. The ratio of boys to girls is 9 to 7. Find the number of boys and the number of girls.   693 boys, 539 girls

33. The difference between two numbers is 15, and the ratio of the larger number to the smaller is 10:7. Find the numbers.   50, 35

34. Nine hundred dollars is one family's monthly budget for food and rent. The ratio of the amount for food to the amount for rent is 3:2. How much is spent on each? $540, food; $360, rent

35. Socks are on sale at 4 pairs for $6.20. What is the price for 10 pairs? $15.50

C

36. Prize money totaling $11,250 is to be distributed to the three top winners in the ratio 3:5:7. What is the amount of each prize? **Hint:** Let 3x, 5x, and 7x represent the amounts of the prizes.
$2250, $3750, $5250

37. A $75,000 inheritance is to be divided by three relatives in the ratio 6:8:11. What is each person's share? $18,000, $24,000, $33,000

38. A rectangular garden is 6 meters by 15 meters. The owner wants to use the space in the ratio of 4:5 for cucumbers and tomatoes respectively. How many square meters should be allotted to each type of vegetable?
Cucumbers, 40m²; tomatoes, 50m²

6 m
15 m

39. If $2a = b$, find the ratio $a:b$. $\frac{1}{2}$ **40.** If $7x = 3y$, find the ratio $x:y$. $\frac{3}{7}$

Given that $\dfrac{a}{b} = \dfrac{c}{d}$, show that each of the following is true.

41. $\dfrac{a}{c} = \dfrac{b}{d}$ **42.** $\dfrac{a+b}{b} = \dfrac{c+d}{d}$ **43.** $\dfrac{a-c}{c} = \dfrac{b-d}{d}$

338

9-6   Percent Problems

OBJECTIVE

To solve problems that involve a percent.

Percent means *per hundred*. Thus, 24 *percent* means 24 *hundredths*.

$$24\% = \frac{24}{100} = 0.24 \qquad 2\% = \frac{2}{100} = 0.02 \qquad 6.5\% = \frac{6.5}{100} = \frac{65}{1000} = 0.065$$

EXAMPLE 1   Write $\frac{3}{8}$ as a percent.

Method I	**Method II**
Solve a proportion.	Divide 3 by 8.

Method I

$$\frac{3}{8} = \frac{x}{100}$$

$$8x = 300$$

$$x = 37\frac{1}{2}$$

Thus, $\dfrac{3}{8} = \dfrac{37\frac{1}{2}}{100} = 37\frac{1}{2}\%$

Method II

$\frac{3}{8}$ means $3 \div 8$.

$$\begin{array}{r} 0.375 \\ 8\overline{)3.000} \end{array}$$

Thus, $\dfrac{3}{8} = 0.375$

$$\frac{3}{8} = 37.5\%$$

EXAMPLE 2   Find 45% of 200.

Write 45% as a decimal or as a fraction. The word *of* means *times*.

45% of 200 = x

$$0.45(200) = x \qquad \text{or} \qquad \frac{45}{100}(200) = x$$

$$90 = x \qquad\qquad\qquad 90 = x$$

Therefore 45% of 200 is 90.

EXAMPLE 3   15 is 30% of what number?

15 is 30% of x

$$15 = 0.30x \qquad \text{or} \qquad 15 = \frac{30}{100} \cdot x$$

$$\frac{15}{0.30} = x \qquad\qquad\qquad 1500 = 30x$$

$$x = 50 \qquad\qquad\qquad x = 50$$

Therefore 15 is 30% of 50.

APPLYING FRACTIONS: SOLVING EQUATIONS AND PROBLEMS   **339**

LESSON NOTES

This lesson reviews basic ideas of percent and provides experiences in solving problems involving percent.

Be sure the students understand that a percent such as 7% can be written as a decimal (0.07) or as a fraction $\left(\dfrac{7}{100}\right)$. The reverse is also true: a decimal or a fraction can be written as a percent.

Examples 2–4 review different types of percent problems—the three so-called cases of percent:

- finding a percent of a given number (Example 2)
- finding a number when a percent of it is known (Example 3)
- finding what percent one number is of another (Example 4)

The solutions of these model examples are shown using equations with fractions or decimals. If some students prefer to use proportions to solve such problems, they should be permitted to do so.

ALTERNATE EXAMPLES

1. Write $\frac{5}{8}$ as a percent.
   $62\frac{1}{2}\%$ or 62.5%

2. Find 35% of 400.   140

3. 24 is 60% of what number?   40

4. 12 is what percent of 75?   16%

5. A $58 jacket is on sale at a 25% discount. What is the sale price? $43.50

POSSIBLE ERROR

Some students have difficulty with percent. For example, they may misinterpret a problem such as "15 is 30% of what number?" (Example 3). Instead of writing the correct equation, they may write:

0.30 × 15 = x (incorrect)

With students who show evidence of this type of difficulty, spend extra time contrasting the various "cases" of percent, as illustrated in Examples 2, 3, and 4. Give special attention to the distinction between pairs of examples such as these:

25% of 60 is x   15
25% of x is 60   240

DAILY QUIZ

Write each decimal or fraction as a percent.

1. 0.65   65%   **2.** $\frac{9}{4}$ 225%

Solve.

3. 12 is 25% of what number?   48

4. 36 is what percent of 288? $12\frac{1}{2}\%$

5. A gallon of paint normally sells for $9.80. If the price is reduced 30%, how much is the discount price? $6.86

EXAMPLE 4   8 is what percent of 25?

Think   8 is x percent of 25.

$8 = \frac{x}{100} \cdot 25$

$8 = \frac{x}{4}$

$x = 32$

Therefore 8 is 32% of 25.

Check $8 \stackrel{?}{=} 32\%$ of 25

$8 \stackrel{?}{=} \frac{32}{100}(25)$

$8 = 8$ ✔

EXAMPLE 5   A $72 coat is on sale at a 20% discount. What is the sale price?

Method I
Let x = the sale price.
Form an equation.

sale price		original price		discount
↓		↓		↓
x	=	72	−	(20% of 72)
x	=	72	−	(0.20 × 72)
x	=	72	−	14.40
x	=	57.60.		

The sale price is $57.60.

Method II
The discount rate is 20%.
Since 100% − 20% = 80%, the sale price is 80% of $72.

0.80(72) = 57.60

The coat is on sale for $57.60.

CLASS EXERCISES

Complete the table. Write fractions in simplest form.

	Fraction	Decimal	Percent			Fraction	Decimal	Percent	
1.	$\frac{1}{4}$	?	?	0.25; 25%	**6.**	?	?	40%	$\frac{2}{5}$; 0.40
2.	?	0.70	?	$\frac{7}{10}$; 70%	**7.**	?	0.125	?	$\frac{1}{8}$; $12\frac{1}{2}\%$
3.	?	?	27%	$\frac{27}{100}$; 0.27	**8.**	$\frac{3}{1000}$	?	?	0.003; 0.3%
4.	?	0.12	?	$\frac{3}{25}$; 12%	**9.**	?	?	6%	$\frac{3}{50}$; 0.06
5.	$\frac{2}{3}$	?	?	$0.\overline{6}$ or $0.66\frac{2}{3}$; $66\frac{2}{3}\%$	**10.**	?	?	850%	$\frac{17}{2}$; 8.5

Find each of the following.

11. 20% of 42   8.4   **12.** 5% of 75   3.75   **13.** 11% of 11   1.21   **14.** 11% of 100   11

15. 21 is 70% of what number?   30   **16.** 15 is what percent of 60?   25%

EXERCISES

A Write each decimal or fraction as a percent.

1. 0.85 85% **2.** 0.015 1.5% **3.** 0.9 90% **4.** 0.15 15% **5.** 1.5 150%

6. 0.45 45% **7.** 0.06 6% **8.** 0.01 1% **9.** 0.8125 81.25% **10.** 0.007 0.7%

11. $\frac{4}{5}$ 80% **12.** $\frac{7}{8}$ 87.5% **13.** $\frac{17}{20}$ 85% **14.** $\frac{5}{4}$ 125% **15.** $\frac{33}{44}$ 75%

Find each of the following.

16. 25% of 4 1 **17.** 150% of 30 45 **18.** 37% of 60 22.2 **19.** 95% of 400 380

20. 8 is 25% of what number? 32 **21.** 2 is 1% of what number? 200

22. 54 is 120% of what number? 45 **23.** 45.6 is 5% of what number? 912

24. 60 is what percent of 80? 75% **25.** 8 is what percent of 320? 2.5%

26. 16 is what percent of 128? 12.5% **27.** 72 is what percent of 600? 12%

28. How much will you save on an $82 winter jacket if you wait to buy it at the spring sale when all prices are reduced 42%? $34.44

29. The price of $20 slacks is reduced 20%. Find the sale price. $16

B **30.** The price of a $9750 car is reduced 26%. What is the sale price? $7215

31. There is a 15% discount on a $6.98 album. Find the sale price. $5.94 (rounded up)

32. There is a 40% discount on the price of yesterday's bread that sold for $1.15. Find the sale price. 69¢

33. The price of a gallon of paint that normally sells for $9.80 is reduced 35%. How much is the discount? $3.43

34. You can get a 30% reduction on a lawn mower that costs $299.50 if you buy it in the winter. How much will you save? $89.85

35. A salesperson's commission is a percent of his sales. Mr. Waters received a 12% commission for selling furniture. If the commission was $150, what was the selling price of the furniture? $1250

36. A family's monthly rent is 18% of their monthly income. If the rent is $360, how much is the income? $2000

C **37.** Eldridge bought a calculator at a 30% discount for $42. What was the original price? $60

38. The commercials for a $\frac{1}{2}$-hour television program use 20% of the time. One of the sponsors gets $33\frac{1}{3}$% of the commercial time. How many minutes commercial time does this sponsor have? 2 minutes

APPLYING FRACTIONS: SOLVING EQUATIONS AND PROBLEMS

341

ENRICHMENT ACTIVITY

Suggest that students prepare a bulletin-board display showing various applications of percent. This can include percents used in ads for sales, interest rates offered by banks, graphs and charts that include percents, and news articles that discuss percents. Encourage them to identify misuses of percent wherever they occur. For instance, we cannot say that car A is 75% more attractive than car B, because attractiveness cannot be quantified or described in terms of percents.

Using BASIC

This program may be used to compute and display the percent of change.

```
10  PRINT "ENTER ORIGINAL
    VALUE"
20  INPUT A
30  PRINT "ENTER FINAL
    VALUE"
40  INPUT B
50  LET C = (B - A)/A
60  PRINT "PERCENT OF
    CHANGE IS"
70  PRINT C * 100; "%"
99  END
```

Checkpoint

Students may check their answers with those given in the back of their books.

39. The sticker price for a new car is $6696. This includes the optional items, which are 24% of the base price. If the customer pays cash, there will be a 15% reduction on the cost of the options and a 10% saving on the base price.
   a. Find the base price. $5400
   b. How much does the car sell for in a cash deal? $5961.60
   c. This cash price is what percent of the original sticker price? 89% appr.

When values change, the fraction $\dfrac{\textit{amount of change}}{\textit{original value}}$ can be expressed as a percent of increase or decrease.

Sample   A bus fare increased from $5 to $7. What was the percent of increase?

$$\text{Percent of increase} = \frac{\text{amount of increase}}{\text{original fare}} = \frac{7 - 5}{5} = \frac{2}{5} = 40\%$$

40. Video game sales in a department store increased from $2600 to $4550. What was the amount of increase? What was the percent of increase? $1950; 75%

41. After a family bought a compact car, its yearly gasoline costs decreased from $500 to $350. What was the percent of decrease? 30%

42. The price of an air conditioner was reduced from $315 to $252. Find the percent of discount. 20%

43. In 30 years, the value of a famous photograph rose from $250 to $4000. What was the percent of increase in value of the photograph? 1500%

CHECKPOINT

Solve and check.

1. $\dfrac{36}{x} = \dfrac{6}{9}$ 54   2. $\dfrac{3x + 2}{10} = \dfrac{1}{2}$ 1   3. $\dfrac{x - 1}{8} = \dfrac{4}{16}$ 3   4. $\dfrac{3}{4}x = \dfrac{5}{12}$ $\frac{5}{9}$

5. $\dfrac{x - 4}{x + 3} = \dfrac{5}{12}$ 9   6. $\dfrac{3x}{7} - \dfrac{11}{14} = 2x$ $-\frac{1}{2}$ 7. $\dfrac{x + 3}{x - 3} = \dfrac{-2}{x(x - 3)}$ $-1; -2$

8. 9 is what percent of 45? 20%   9. 44 is 110% of what number? 40

10. How much commission does a salesperson receive if she gets 15% on each sale, and she sells an item for $1670? $250.50

11. A gallon of paint normally selling for $14 is on sale for $12.46. What is the rate of discount? 11%

12. A television set is advertised at a sale price of $478.50, which is a $16\frac{1}{2}\%$ discount. What was the original price? $573.05

9-7 Interest and Investment Problems

OBJECTIVE _____

To use percents in solving interest and investment problems.

_____

A bank pays 6% interest per year on savings accounts. If you put $1000 in the bank, then the interest earned in 1 year will be $60.

$$6\% \text{ of } 1000 = 0.06 \times 1000 = 60$$

6% is the annual _rate of interest_, and $1000 is the _principal_.
In general, the following formula applies to _simple_ interest.

> **Interest = Principal × Rate × Time**
>
> $$I = prt$$

The variable t stands for the time the principal is on deposit. When the rate r is an _annual_ rate, then t must be expressed in _years_.

EXAMPLE 1 $500 is deposited at $6\frac{1}{2}\%$ interest per year. How much interest is earned in 3 months?

$p = 500, \quad r = 0.065, \quad t = \dfrac{1}{4}$ Since r is the interest per year,
                                                    t is expressed in years.

$I = prt$

$I = 500(0.065)\left(\dfrac{1}{4}\right)$

$\quad = 8.125$ The interest is $8.13.

In the next example, an interest rate _per month_ is given. So the time, t, is expressed in _months_.

EXAMPLE 2 $2000 is borrowed for 6 months at an interest rate of 1.5% per month. Find the interest.

$p = 2000, \quad r = 0.015, \quad t = 6$

$I = prt$

$I = 2000(0.015)(6)$

$\quad = 180$ The interest is $180.

APPLYING FRACTIONS: SOLVING EQUATIONS AND PROBLEMS   **343**

WARM-UP EXERCISES

Write as a decimal without the percent sign.

1. 9% 0.09   **2.** $1\frac{1}{2}\%$ 0.015

3. 2.5% 0.025   **4.** 3.4% 0.034

LESSON NOTES

This lesson uses the formula for simple interest; in the formula, the assumption is made that there is no compounding of interest. Devote special attention to Examples 3 and 4.

In Example 3, the values for I, p, and r are known; the correct value for t must be computed. After t has been found to be $3\frac{1}{8}$, have the students check the correctness of this possible solution by substituting $3\frac{1}{8}$ for t in the original equation.

In discussing Example 4, stress the importance of organizing the information. A table offers a convenient method of organization because it emphasizes that we are dealing with two parts of a $10,000 investment and that the interest for each is $p \times r$. (The sum of the two amounts of interest is $670.)

You may also wish to note that a situation such as the one in Example 4 can be solved by using a system of equations:

$$x + y = 10,000$$
$$0.075x + 0.065y = 670$$

ALTERNATE EXAMPLES

1. $600 is deposited at $5\frac{1}{4}\%$ interest per year. How much interest is earned in 6 months? $15.75

2. $3000 is borrowed for 4 months at an interest rate of 1.5% per month. Find the interest. $180

3. How long does it take a $4000 investment to earn $600 interest if the interest rate is 6% per year? $2\frac{1}{2}$ years

4. Part of a $12,000 investment earns $8\frac{1}{2}$% interest per year, and the rest earns $7\frac{1}{2}$% interest per year. How much is invested at each rate if the total interest for the year is $980? $8000 at $8\frac{1}{2}$%, $4000 at $7\frac{1}{2}$%

POSSIBLE ERROR

In using the formula $I = prt$, students often neglect to express t in an appropriate way. For instance, in a situation such as the one in Example 1, the students might write this equation:

$I = 500(0.065)(3)$
(incorrect)

Emphasize the fact that when the given rate is an annual rate, t must be expressed in years or parts of a year. Thus, in Example 1, t is expressed as $\frac{1}{4}$ (since 3 months is $\frac{3}{12}$ or $\frac{1}{4}$ of a year). If the time had been 18 months, then t would have to be expressed as $1\frac{1}{2}$ or 1.5.

DAILY QUIZ

Solve each problem.

1. Eight hundred dollars is borrowed at an interest rate of 1.5% per month. Find the interest paid over a period of 5 months. $60

2. How much money should be invested at an annual interest rate of 12% in order to earn $300 interest in a year? $2500

[Daily Quiz continues on page 345.]

EXAMPLE 3

How long does it take a $2000 investment to earn $500 interest if the interest rate is 8% per year?

$I = 500, \quad p = 2000, \quad r = 0.08$

$I = prt$

$500 = 2000(0.08)t$

$500 = 160t$

$t = 3\frac{1}{8}$ The time required is $3\frac{1}{8}$ years.

EXAMPLE 4

Part of a $10,000 investment earns $7\frac{1}{2}$% interest per year, and the rest earns $6\frac{1}{2}$% interest per year. How much is invested at each rate if the total interest for the year is $670?

Use a variable.

Let x = the amount invested at $7\frac{1}{2}$%.
Then $10,000 - x$ = the amount invested at $6\frac{1}{2}$%

The yearly interest at each rate can be shown in a table.

Principal	× Rate =	Interest
x	0.075	0.075x
10,000 − x	0.065	0.065(10,000 − x)

Write an equation.

The total interest is equal to the sum of the interests.

$0.075x + 0.065(10,000 - x) = 670$

Find the solution.

$75x + 65(10,000 - x) = 670,000$ Multiply each side by 10^3, or
$75x + 650,000 - 65x = 670,000$ 1000, in order to remove the
$10x = 20,000$ decimals.
$x = 2000$ and $10,000 - x = 8000$

Does the solution to the equation satisfy the problem?

$0.075(2000) + 0.065(8000) = 150 + 520 = 670$ ✔

Answer the question. $2000 was invested at $7\frac{1}{2}$% and $8000 was invested at $6\frac{1}{2}$%.

CLASS EXERCISES

Eighteen hundred dollars is invested in a savings account that pays 6% interest per year. Find the interest over each period of time.

1. 1 year $108   2. 4 years $432   3. 2 years $216   4. 18 months $162

5. How long will it take a $500 investment to earn $100 in interest at a rate of 10% per year?   2 years

6. A $2000 investment earns $180 interest in 1 year. Find the interest rate.   9%

7. Find the interest earned on $800 in 4 months if the rate is 1% per month. $32

344

EXERCISES

A

Six hundred dollars is borrowed at an interest rate of 1.4% per month.
Find the interest over each period of time.

1. 4 months $33.60   **2.** $\frac{3}{4}$ year $75.60   **3.** 27 months   **4.** 30 months $252
$226.80

How much money should be invested at an annual interest rate of 8%
in order to earn the given amounts of yearly interest?

5. $100 $1250   **6.** $200 $2500   **7.** $250 $3125   **8.** $275 $3437.50

9. How long will it take an $8000 investment to earn $200 interest at
a yearly interest rate of 7.5%? $\frac{1}{3}$ year, or 4 months

B

10. Harriet has $4000 invested in two savings accounts. One account
earns 6% interest per year, and the other pays 7% per year. If her
total interest for the year is $264, how much is invested at each rate?
$2400 at 7%; $1600 at 6%

11. Part of Miss Lincoln's $5200 is invested at 7% interest per year,
and the remainder is invested in an $8\frac{1}{4}$% bond. If the total annual $3600 at $8\frac{1}{4}$%;
income on both investments is $409, how much is invested at each rate? $1600 at 7%

12. One thousand dollars in a savings account pays 7% interest per
year. The interest earned after the first year is added to the account.
How much interest is earned on the new principal the following year? $74.90

13. Fifteen hundred dollars is left in a 12-month savings certificate that
earns 8.5% interest per year. The interest earned the first year is added
to the original $1500 investment.
a. At the same rate, how much interest will be earned the second year? $138.34
b. What is the total interest earned for the 2 years? $265.84

C

14. A sum of money invested at an annual interest rate of 9% earns $1080
interest for the year. Twice this sum invested at a yearly rate of $12,000 at 9%;
$9\frac{1}{2}$% earns $2280 for the year. How much is invested at each rate? $24,000 at $9\frac{1}{2}$%

15. Elliot has a sum of money that he has invested in two accounts.
Two-fifths of the sum is invested at 8% per year and the rest is invested at 7.6% per year. The total annual income is $620.80. How
much has he invested at each rate? $3200 at 8%; $4800 at 7.6%

16. The cost of two savings bonds is $12,000. One bond pays 6% inter-
est per year and the other pays 7%. The annual interest on the 7%
bond is $216 more than that on the 6% bond. How much does each
bond cost? $4800, 6% bond; $7200, 7% bond

17. A bank has a total of $42,000 invested in two small businesses. For
the year, the bank earned 12% interest on one business but lost
$10\frac{1}{2}$% on the second business. If the bank's net profit on these investments was $990, how much was invested at each rate?
$24,000 at 12%; $18,000 at $10\frac{1}{2}$%

APPLYING FRACTIONS: SOLVING EQUATIONS AND PROBLEMS   345

LESSON NOTES

The mixture formula is an application of the percent-of-a-number concept:

  Percent of an ingredient
          times
  Amount of the mixture
          equals
  Amount of the ingredient

However, since mixture problems often deal with different percents of different ingredients, the problems can be complicated. A table provides an effective way to organize the facts of the problem. A table can also help students to write an appropriate equation for the problem.

ALTERNATE EXAMPLE

  1. A solution of acid and water is 9% acid. How much water must be added to 5 gallons of the solution to obtain a new solution that is 6% acid?   2.5 gallons

9-8   Problem Solving: Mixture Problems

OBJECTIVE

To solve problems involving mixtures.

Forming mixtures by combining different ingredients is necessary in various branches of commerce and science. The formula below is basic to such problems.

  Percent of an ingredient $\times$ Amount of   =   Amount of
  in the mixture   the mixture   the ingredient

For instance, suppose 12 grams of an alloy is 5% gold. Then the *amount* of gold in the alloy is 0.6 gram.

$$5\% \text{ of } 12 = 0.05(12) = 0.6$$

EXAMPLE 1

A solution of oil and gasoline is 8% oil. How much gasoline must be added to 3 gallons of the solution to obtain a new solution that is 5% oil?

Strategy: Form a table and write an equation based on the fact that the amount of oil remains the same.

Read the problem to find the key ideas.

Adding only gasoline changes the *percent* of oil from 8% to 5%. The *amount* of oil doesn't change.

Use a variable and form a table.

Let x = the amount of gasoline to be added (gallons).

	Percent of oil	$\times$	Amount of mixture	=	Amount of oil
Original solution	8%		3		0.24
Gasoline added	0%		x		0
New solution	5%		3 + x		0.05(3 + x)

Write an equation, and solve.

  Amount of oil in   =   Amount of oil in
  original solution   new solution

$$0.24 = 0.05(3 + x)$$
$$24 = 5(3 + x) \qquad \text{Multiply each side by } 10^2, \text{ or } 100, \text{ in}$$
$$24 = 15 + 5x \qquad \qquad \text{order to remove the decimals.}$$
$$9 = 5x$$
$$x = \frac{9}{5} = 1.8$$

Check: $\dfrac{\text{amount of oil in solution}}{\text{total amount of solution}} = \dfrac{0.24}{3 + 1.8} = \dfrac{0.24}{4.8} = 0.05 = 5\%$ ✔

Answer the question.

1.8 gallons of gasoline must be added.

EXAMPLE 2   How many quarts of milk that has 1% butterfat must be added to 50 quarts that have 6% butterfat to obtain milk that has 2% butterfat?

Use a variable.   Let x = number of quarts of 1% butterfat milk to be added.

	Percent of butterfat	×	Amount of milk	=	Amount of butterfat
Original milk	6%		50		3
Milk added	1%		x		0.01x
New mixture	2%		50 + x		0.02(50 + x)

Write an equation.

$$\text{butterfat in 6\% mixture} + \text{butterfat in 1\% mixture} = \text{butterfat in new mixture}$$

$$3 + 0.01x = 0.02(50 + x)$$

Find the solution.

$$300 + x = 2(50 + x)$$
$$300 + x = 100 + 2x$$
$$300 = 100 + x$$
$$200 = x$$

Check: 1% of 200 = 2   There are 2 qt butterfat in 200 qt of milk.

$$\frac{\text{new amount of butterfat}}{\text{new amount of milk}} = \frac{3 + 2}{50 + 200} = \frac{5}{250} = 2\% \ ✔$$

Answer the question.   Add 200 quarts of milk that has 1% butterfat.

CLASS EXERCISES

A substance is 2% copper. Find the amount of copper in each of the following samples.

1. 25 grams   0.5 g   **2.** 50 grams   1 g   **3.** 80 grams   1.6 g   **4.** 100 grams   2 g

A saltwater solution weighs 8 ounces and is 18% salt.

5. How many ounces of salt are in the solution? 1.44

6. If x ounces of pure water are added, represent the total number of ounces in the new solution in terms of x.   x + 8

	Percent of salt	×	Number of ounces of solution	=	Number of ounces of salt
Salt water	18%		8		?
Pure water	0%		x		0
New solution	15%		?		?

7. If the new solution is to be 15% salt, represent the number of ounces of salt in the new solution.   0.15(x + 8)

8. How many ounces of pure water are added if the new solution is 15% salt? To find the answer, write and solve an equation.   0.15(x + 8) = 1.44   1.6 ounces

APPLYING FRACTIONS: SOLVING EQUATIONS AND PROBLEMS   **347**

ALTERNATE EXAMPLE

2. How many quarts of punch that are 3% orange juice must be added to 40 quarts that are 9% orange juice to obtain punch that is 5% orange juice?
80 quarts

POSSIBLE ERROR

Sometimes, in multiplying an equation such as 0.24 = 0.05(3 + x) by 100 to clear the decimals, the students may multiply every factor by 100 and obtain:

24 = 5(300 + 100x) (incorrect)

Point out that if we multiply both 0.05 and (3 + x) by 100, we are really multiplying the right side of the equation by 10,000. Explain that a = bc is *not* equivalent to 100a = 100b · 100c. A numerical example can be used to illustrate the idea: 20 = (4)(5); but 100 · 20 ≠ (100 · 4)(100 · 5).

DAILY QUIZ

Solve each problem.

1. A 30-gram solution of alcohol and water is 10% alcohol. How much water must be added to produce a 5% solution?   30 grams

2. How many ounces of salt must be added to 48 ounces of a 30% solution of saltwater to produce a 70% saltwater solution?   64 ounces

3. A chemist has 40 grams of an alcohol solution of which 15% is alcohol. How much pure alcohol must be added to obtain a 20% solution?   2.5 grams

4. A mixture of peanuts and cashews weighs 15 ounces. Forty percent of this weight is peanuts. If 3 ounces of cashews are eaten, then what percent of the remaining mixture is peanuts?   50%

5. How many quarts of pure antifreeze must be added to 8 quarts of a 40% antifreeze solution to obtain a 50% antifreeze solution?   1.6 quarts

ASSIGNMENT GUIDE
(page 348)
Minimum course: omit
Average course: 1–10
Maximum course: 1–12

ENRICHMENT ACTIVITY

Have each student choose two or three of the problems in the B and C Exercises and use them as models to write new problems of his/her own. Then each student can use the problems to challenge a classmate, Of course, before challenging a classmate, the student must have worked out the solution to each problem.

EXERCISES

A

1. A 20-gram solution of alcohol and water is 10% alcohol. How much water must be added to produce a 5% solution? 20 g

2. A chemist has 15 grams of an alcohol solution of which 12% is alcohol. How much *pure alcohol* must be *added* to obtain a 20% alcohol solution? 1.5 g

	Percent of alcohol	× Amount of mixture	= Amount of alcohol
Orig. solution	12%	15	?
Pure alcohol	100%	x	x
New solution	20%	?	?

3. How many ounces of salt must be added to 84 ounces of a 20% saltwater solution to produce a 50% saltwater solution? 50.4 oz

4. A mixture of peanuts and cashews weighs 12 ounces. Twenty-five percent of this weight is in cashews. If 2 ounces of peanuts are eaten, then what percent of the remaining mixture is cashews? 30%

B

5. A druggist has a 35% acid solution and a 45% acid solution. How many grams of each must be mixed to form 80 grams of solution that is 40% acid?
40 g of each solution

6. A milk plant has 26% butterfat-cream and 36% butterfat-cream. How many pounds of each must be mixed to produce 280 pounds of 30% butterfat-cream? 168 lb of 26%, 112 lb of 36% butterfat-cream

7. A farmer has two kinds of animal feed. One is 20% oats, and the other is 28% oats. How many pounds of each kind should be mixed to produce 50 pounds of feed that is 25% oats? $18\frac{3}{4}$ lb of 20% oats $31\frac{1}{4}$ lb of 28% oats

8. How many quarts of pure antifreeze must be added to 6 quarts of a 40% antifreeze solution to obtain a 50% antifreeze solution? 1.2 qt

9. How much water should be added to the 6 quarts of antifreeze solution in Exercise 8 to produce a 30% antifreeze solution? 2 qt

C

10. An auto mechanic has 35% antifreeze solution and 50% antifreeze solution. How many liters of each type should be mixed to produce 16 liters of a 45% antifreeze solution? $5\frac{1}{3}$ liters of 35% sol.; $10\frac{2}{3}$ liters of 50% sol.

11. A 6% copper alloy is to be melted with an 18% copper alloy to form a 10% copper alloy weighing 75 kilograms. How much of each type must be used? 50 kg of 6% copper alloy; 25 kg of 18% copper alloy

12. The candy counter in a department store has chocolates that sell for $1.65 a pound and caramels that sell for $1.25 a pound. A mixture of these candies is to sell for $1.49 a pound. How many pounds of each kind of candy should be used to make 10 pounds of the $1.49 mixture? 6 lb at $1.65; 4 lb at $1.25

CHAPTER 9

EXTRA PRACTICE, page 526

9-9 Problem Solving: Rate-Time-Distance Problems

OBJECTIVE

To solve problems involving uniform motion.

Kim drove her moped from the Southside High gym to Pete's Pizza Palace. She traveled 5 miles in 20 minutes ($\frac{1}{3}$ hour). To find her average speed, or rate, divide the distance by the time.

$$\text{Rate} = \frac{\text{Distance}}{\text{Time}}$$

Kim traveled at a rate equal to $5 \div \frac{1}{3}$, or 15 miles per hour.

The relationship between *rate r, time t,* and *distance d,* can be expressed in several ways.

$$d = rt \qquad r = \frac{d}{t} \qquad t = \frac{d}{r}$$

EXAMPLE 1

Mary and Nick were both driving east on Interstate 72. At noon, Nick was 5 miles east of Mary. Sometime later, Mary passed Nick. At what time did Mary pass Nick if Nick's speed was a constant 50 mph and Mary's was 55 mph?

Read the problem to find the key ideas.

The two cars traveled different distances in the same time.

Strategy: Draw a diagram. Write an equation on the basis that, since noon, Mary traveled 5 miles more than Nick.

Use a variable.

Let t = the number of hours Mary needed to pass Nick.

	r	$\times$ t	$=$ d
Nick	50	t	$50t$
Mary	55	t	$55t$

Write and solve an equation.

$55t = 5 + 50t$ Mary's distance is 5 miles more than Nick's.
$5t = 5$
$t = 1$

Check: In 1 hour Mary drove 5 miles more than Nick. $55 - 50 = 5$

Answer the question.

Mary passed Nick at 1 hour past noon, or at 1 P.M.

In Example 1, Mary and Nick were both traveling in the same direction. Some problems involve traveling in opposite directions.

EXAMPLE 2   Two motorboats start at the same time and travel toward each other from opposite ends of a large lake 96 kilometers long. One boat travels twice as fast as the other. Find the average speed of each boat if the boats meet in 2 hours.

Use a variable.   Let r = the speed of the slower boat (km per hr).
Then $2r$ = the speed of the faster boat.

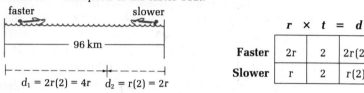

	r	$\times$ t	= d
Faster	$2r$	2	$2r(2)$
Slower	r	2	$r(2)$

$d_1 = 2r(2) = 4r$ $d_2 = r(2) = 2r$

Write an equation. $4r + 2r = 96$ The total distance traveled by the two boats
Find the solution. $6r = 96$ is 96 km.
$r = 16$

Check: If $r = 16$, the boats traveled at 16 km/h and 32 km/h. They traveled 32 km plus 64 km, or 96 km, in all. ✔

Answer the question.   The average speeds were 16 km/h and 32 km/h.

CLASS EXERCISES

A motorboat traveled upstream on a river at 15 mph and returned downstream at 20 mph. How far upstream did the boat travel if the round trip took $3\frac{1}{2}$ hours?

1. What does the problem ask for: time, rate, or distance?   distance

2. Let t be the time in hours used to travel upstream. Express the time used to travel downstream in terms of t. $3\frac{1}{2} - t$

3. Complete the table and write an equation. $15t = 20\left(3\frac{1}{2} - t\right)$

4. Solve the equation and answer the question. $t = 2$; 30 miles upstream

	r	$\times$ t	= d
Upstream	15	t	$15t$
Downstream	20	?	?

$3\frac{1}{2} - t$;
$20\left(3\frac{1}{2} - t\right)$

EXERCISES

A

1. Two cars pass each other along a straight highway and continue traveling in opposite directions. One car is traveling at 40 mph, and the other at 50 mph. How many hours does it take for the cars to be 225 miles apart? $2\frac{1}{2}$ hours

2. At noon, two airplanes leave an airport and travel in opposite directions at the same altitude. The slower plane is flying at 360 mph and the faster at 450 mph. When will they be 1350 miles apart?   1:40 P.M.

EXTRA PRACTICE, page 526

3. Two joggers start at the same time from opposite ends of a board-walk that is 12 kilometers long. One jogs twice as fast as the other. Find the rate in km/h of each jogger if they meet in 15 minutes.

   Hint: 15 minutes = $\frac{1}{4}$ hour   16 km/h, 32 km/h

4. A train that averages 100 km/h can travel from Gladstone to Wiscasset in 2 hours less time than a motorist driving at an average speed of 75 km/h. Find the distance from Gladstone to Wiscasset. 600 km

5. A round trip by bus between Pine Lake and Springfield took 3 hours. If the bus averaged 40 mph in one direction and 50 mph in the other, find the distance from Pine Lake to Springfield. $66\frac{2}{3}$ miles

6. Two jets leave New York at the same time, one flying due north at 900 km/h, and the other flying due south at 1050 km/h. After how many hours will the planes be 3900 km apart? 2 hours

7. How many hours would be required for the planes in Exercise 6 to be 6825 km apart? $3\frac{1}{2}$ hours

B

8. Mr. Santos lives 15 miles from the city in which he works. He walks for 15 minutes at 4 mph and then boards a bus that takes him to the city in 20 minutes. Find the speed of the bus. 42 mph

9. Joe and Amy were each bicycling from Morristown to Somerville. At 11 A.M. Amy was 3 miles ahead of Joe. Sometime later, Joe passed Amy. At what time did Joe pass Amy if Amy's speed was 15 mph and Joe's was 19 mph?   11:45 A.M.

10. A bicyclist left Rutherford at 10 A.M. and traveled due west at 17 mph. At 11 A.M. a motorist left Rutherford and traveled the same route as the bicyclist at 47 mph. At what time did the motorist overtake the bicyclist?   11:34 A.M.

11. A boat is traveling 30 kilometers per hour slower than a car. If the car travels 126 kilometers in the same time as the boat travels 56 kilometers, find the rate of each.   Car, 54 km/h; boat, 24 km/h

12. It takes a student 15 minutes to drive home from the school when there is heavy traffic. When there is very little traffic, the student can increase the rate by 16 km/h and make the trip in 12 minutes. How far does the student live from the school? 16 km

13. An airplane flying at the rate of 420 mph passed a mountaintop at noon. A faster plane, flying in the same direction but at a higher altitude, passed the same mountaintop at 1 P.M. At 2:30 P.M. the faster plane was directly over the first plane. What was the speed of the faster plane? 700 mph

APPLYING FRACTIONS: SOLVING EQUATIONS AND PROBLEMS

ENRICHMENT ACTIVITY

Ask students to find the average rate of speed if a person travels from town A to town B at 60 mph and returns at the rate of speed of 40 mph. Many students will incorrectly give the result as 50 mph. However, point out that the driver is going for a longer period of time at the slower rate. Let the students compute the answer by using a few specific values for the distance. For instance, let them compute the average rate if the distance from A to B is 120 miles. Then the trip takes 2 hours going and 3 hours returning, or 5 hours in all, to travel 240 miles. Therefore, the average rate is 240/5, or 48 mph. In a similar way, let the distance be 180 miles. Then the trip takes 3 hours going and $4\frac{1}{2}$ hours returning, or $7\frac{1}{2}$ hours to travel 360 miles. Therefore, the average rate is $\frac{360}{7\frac{1}{2}}$, or 48 mph. Challenge the students to generalize the results and show that if d is the distance one way, the rate is still 48 mph.   The time going is $d/60$ and the time returning is $d/40$. The average rate for the trip is

$$\frac{2d}{\frac{d}{60} + \frac{d}{40}} = \frac{2d}{\frac{2d+3d}{120}} = \frac{240d}{5d} = 48$$

C 14. A jogger travels 10 miles in an hour and 25 minutes. He averages 8 mph on level ground, and 6 mph over hilly ground. What part of the 10 miles is on level ground? 6 miles

15. A car averages 24 mph driving through a city and then 52 mph on the highway. The total distance traveled was 133 miles. Find the time it took to drive through the city if the entire trip took 2 hours and 55 minutes. 40 minutes

16. A motorboat takes 45 minutes to travel downstream with a 5 mph current. The return trip against the current takes 1 hour and 10 minutes. Find the rate of the motorboat in still water and the distance traveled one way.

Hint: Let x = rate of boat in still water.
    Add rates for the trip downstream.
Subtract rates for the trip upstream.
23 mph in still water, 21 miles

	r	$\times$	t	$=$	d
Downstream	$x + 5$		?		?
Upstream	$x - 5$		?		?

17. A plane, flying with the wind, travels between two cities in 2 hours. Returning against the wind, it travels only $\frac{2}{3}$ of this distance in 2 hours. If the speed of the plane in calm air is 250 mph, find the speed of the wind. 50 mph

CHALLENGE

River Currents

On a recent camping trip, Pete, Rich, Dennis, Ed, and Fred made separate camps along a river. Pete and Rich camped downstream from Fred. Dennis and Ed camped upstream from Fred. Dennis, Ed, Rich, and Pete each had a motorboat that would take its owner to Fred's camp in exactly 1 hour if there were no current in the river. However, there was a strong current in the river.

  The next morning Pete made the trip to Fred's camp in 75 minutes. Rich made it in 70 minutes. Dennis made it in 50 minutes, and Ed made it in 45 minutes. Each of the four then returned to his own camp. Which of the four completed the round trip between Fred's camp and his own in the shortest time? Rich

CHAPTER 9

Finance Charges

Many people shop with credit cards. The stores usually allow two different payment options.

1. Pay in full each month and avoid a finance charge.
2. Pay in installments and pay a finance charge.

Monthly statements contain the details about how finance charges are computed. Most compute charges using average daily balances as described in this statement.

Terms Disclosure

We figure the finance charge on your account by applying the periodic rate to the average daily balance of your account (including current transactions). To get the "average daily balance," we take the beginning balance of your account each day, add any new purchases, and subtract any payments. This gives us the daily balance. Then, we add all the daily balances for the billing cycle and divide the total by the number of days in the billing cycle. This gives us the "average daily balance."

The FINANCE CHARGE is computed on the Average Daily Balance at a Monthly Rate of 1.65%, which is equivalent to an ANNUAL PERCENTAGE RATE of 19.8%. (Minimum Charge, 50¢)

Example Assume a 30-day billing period beginning on October 15 with a $67.15 balance. New purchases totaling $38.50 are made on October 29. A $30.00 installment payment is received on November 8.

a. Find the average daily balance.

14 days with a $67.15 balance	$14 \times 67.15 = 940.10$	(10/15-10/28)
10 days with a $105.65 balance	$10 \times 105.65 = 1056.50$	(10/29-11/7)
6 days with a $75.65 balance	$6 \times 75.65 = \dfrac{453.90}{2450.50}$	(11/8-11/13)

$2450.50 \div 30 = 81.68 Average daily balance

b. Find the finance charge. $81.68 \times 0.0165 = 1.35 Finance charge

c. Find the new balance. $75.65 + $1.35 = 77.00 New balance

Assume that the next billing period is 31 days and ends December 14. The next installment payment of $30 is received on December 5. Find the new average daily balance, finance charge, and new balance for:

1. No new purchases   **2.** A $95.99 purchase on November 22

3. A $45.00 purchase on November 16 and a $125.05 purchase on December 1

APPLYING FRACTIONS: SOLVING EQUATIONS AND PROBLEMS

353

These exercises review basic algebraic skills.

Simplify.

1. $-3 - (-5) + (-2)(-3) - 8 \div (-4)$ 10

2. $\dfrac{x + 2}{x + 1} \cdot \dfrac{x^2 + x}{x^2 - 4} \cdot \dfrac{x - 2}{x}$ 1

3. $\dfrac{3a^2b}{5c} \div \dfrac{3ab}{c}$ $\dfrac{a}{5}$

Evaluate when $a = 5$, $b = -5$, and $c = 0$.

4. $\dfrac{b^2c}{a^2} - \dfrac{a^2}{b}$ 5

5. $\dfrac{-a^2 + (-b^2)}{ab + c}$ 2

Solve for x.

6. $x(3 - x) = 4 - x(x - 3)$ No sol.

7. $x^2 - 11x + 28 = 0$ 4 or 7

8. $\dfrac{3}{x + 1} = \dfrac{x}{x^2 - 1}$ $\dfrac{3}{2}$

9. Solve the system:
$x - 3y = 13$
$2x + y = 5$ $(4, -3)$

Factor completely.

10. $2x^2 - 11xy + 15y^2$ $(x - 3y)(2x - 5y)$

11. $5x^2 + 5$ $5(x^2 + 1)$

12. What value of n will make $x^2 + x + n$ a perfect-square trinomial? $\dfrac{1}{4}$

[*Maintaining Skills* continues on page 355.]

CHAPTER 9 REVIEW

VOCABULARY

rational equation (p. 324)
ratio (p. 335)
proportion (p. 335)
means (p. 335)

extremes (p. 335)
percent (p. 339)
rate of interest (p. 343)
principal (p. 343)

SUMMARY

This chapter presents a number of applications that involve rational equations. Among the topics covered are interest and investment problems, rate-time-distance problems, mixture problems, and work problems. The applications of these topics, along with ratio, proportion, and percent, make use of past work with decimal fractions, fractions, and percent. Together they indicate the powerful tool that algebra can be in the solution of practical problems.

REVIEW EXERCISES

9-1   *Solve and check.*

1. $\dfrac{1}{3}x = \dfrac{5}{6}$ $\dfrac{5}{2}$ **2.** $\dfrac{7}{8}x = 35$ 40   **3.** $\dfrac{9}{4}x = \dfrac{15}{8}$ $\dfrac{5}{6}$

4. $\dfrac{1}{2}x + \dfrac{1}{3}x = 10$ 12   **5.** $\dfrac{2}{3}x - \dfrac{1}{5}x = 7$ 15   **6.** $\dfrac{2}{3}x + \dfrac{1}{4}x + \dfrac{11}{2} = 0$ -6

7. $\dfrac{7x}{3} - 2x = \dfrac{40}{3}$ 40   **8.** $\dfrac{7x}{12} = \dfrac{11}{36}$ $\dfrac{11}{21}$ **9.** $\dfrac{2x}{5} - \dfrac{4x}{5} = 4$ -10

10. $\dfrac{3x}{4} + \dfrac{5}{6} = -\dfrac{2}{3}$ -2 **11.** $\dfrac{2x}{9} + \dfrac{x - 4}{12} = \dfrac{3}{2}$ 6   **12.** $\dfrac{5x}{4} - \dfrac{7}{8} = \dfrac{x}{12}$ $\dfrac{3}{4}$

9-2   **13.** $\dfrac{7}{2x - 10} = \dfrac{8}{x + 4}$ 12   **14.** $\dfrac{18}{x^2 - 16} - \dfrac{1}{x + 4} = \dfrac{1}{x - 4}$ 9

15. $\dfrac{1}{2} - \dfrac{6}{x + 1} = \dfrac{3}{x + 1}$ 17   **16.** $\dfrac{x}{35} - \dfrac{3 - x}{7x} = \dfrac{1}{5}$ $5, -3$

17. $\dfrac{5}{x + 3} + \dfrac{3}{x - 2} = \dfrac{2}{x^2 + x - 6}$ $\dfrac{3}{8}$ **18.** $\dfrac{x - 1}{x + 1} - \dfrac{x + 1}{x - 1} = \dfrac{8}{x^2 - 1}$ -2

9-3   **19.** Find two consecutive even integers such that $\dfrac{3}{4}$ of the smaller is equal to $\dfrac{2}{3}$ of the larger.   16, 18

20. The reciprocal of a number minus the reciprocal of 3 times the number is equal to $\dfrac{1}{15}$. Find the number.   10

9-4 **21.** Beth can mow the lawn in 3 hours. Her older sister can do the same job in 2 hours. How long will it take them working together? $\frac{6}{5}$ hr, or 1 hr 12 min

22. The hot and cold faucets working together can fill a tank in 15 minutes. A full tank can be emptied in 20 minutes. With both taps and drain open, how long will it take the tank to overflow? 1 hr

9-5 *Solve each proportion.*

23. $\dfrac{x+1}{6} = \dfrac{5}{9}$ $\frac{7}{3}$ **24.** $\dfrac{2}{x} = \dfrac{x}{8}$ 4, or −4   **25.** $\dfrac{3x}{5} = \dfrac{x-4}{7}$ $-\frac{5}{4}$ **26.** $\dfrac{2}{3x-2} = \dfrac{-4}{2x+3}$ $\frac{1}{8}$

27. If $\dfrac{w}{x} = \dfrac{y}{z}$, then what is the value of xy? *wz*

28. A 20-foot board is cut into two pieces with the ratio 2 : 3. How long is each piece? 8 ft, 12 ft

29. A car travels 156 miles on 6 gallons of gasoline. How far can the car travel on 16 gallons? 416 miles

9-6 **30.** What is 15% of 48?   7.2   **31.** 17 is what percent of 272? 6.25%

32. 30 is $12\frac{1}{2}$% of what number? 240   **33.** What is 0.1% of $500.00?   50¢

9-7 *Solve and check.*

34. How long will it take a $6000 investment to earn $340 interest at an annual rate of 8.5%? $\frac{2}{3}$ year, or 8 months

35. Part of $7200 is invested at 11% per year. The rest is put into a savings account at 6% per year. If the total interest derived from these two accounts in 1 year is $682, how much is invested at each rate?
$5000 @ 11%; $2200 @ 6%

9-8 **36.** A 12-quart solution of water and alcohol contains 30% alcohol. How much water must be added to obtain a solution that is 24% alcohol?
3 qt

37. Cashew nuts sell for $7.00 per pound, and salted peanuts sell for $2.85 per pound. A 10-pound mixture is to be made which will sell for $4.51 per pound. How many pounds of each type of nut should be used?
4 lb cashews; 6 lb peanuts

9-9 **38.** A train traveling at 45 mph leaves a depot at 12:00 noon. A second train going in the same direction and traveling at 65 mph leaves the same depot 1 hour later. What time will it be when the second train overtakes the first? 3:15 P.M.

39. Two ships leave the same port at the same time. One travels due east at 30 knots while the other travels due west at 42 knots. How long will it take for the two ships to be 360 nautical miles apart? (1 knot is 1 nautical mile per hour.) 5 hr

13. Write the equation, in slope-intercept form, of the line that is parallel to $y = 5 - x$ and contains the point $(4, 0)$.
$y = -x + 4$

14. Write the equation, in standard form, of the line that has a slope of $\frac{1}{2}$ and a y-intercept of 2.
$x - 2y = -4$

15. Multiply: $(8x - 3)(3x + 2)$
$24x^2 + 7x - 6$

16. Subtract $\dfrac{3}{1-x}$ from $\dfrac{1}{x-1}$.
$\dfrac{4}{x-1}$

17. For what value(s) of x is $\dfrac{x^2 + 5}{x^3 - 9x}$ undefined?
0, 3, and −3

18. Find three consecutive even integers such that the square of the first added to the square of the third results in a sum which is 8 greater than the second.
−2, 0, and 2

19. 21 is 3% of what number? 700

20. How much water must be added to 12 gallons of a 40% salt solution in order to obtain a 25% salt solution? $7\frac{1}{5}$ gallons

*Solve and check. Write **no solution** if none exists.*

9-1   **1.** $\dfrac{5x}{16} + \dfrac{3}{4} = 2$ 4   **2.** $\dfrac{3x}{5} - \dfrac{x}{4} = \dfrac{7}{4}$ 5

3. $\dfrac{1}{3}x - \dfrac{3}{2} = \dfrac{3}{4}x + \dfrac{1}{6}$ −4   **4.** $\dfrac{3x - 1}{4} - \dfrac{x - 1}{2} = 1$ 3

9-2   **5.** $\dfrac{1}{x} + \dfrac{1}{3x} = \dfrac{8}{3}$ $\dfrac{1}{2}$ **6.** $\dfrac{66}{x} - \dfrac{3}{5} = 6$ 10

7. $\dfrac{x}{6 - x} - 3 = \dfrac{6}{6 - x}$ No solution   **8.** $\dfrac{4}{x} = 3 + \dfrac{10}{x^2 + 3x}$ $\dfrac{1}{3}, -2$

9. $\dfrac{-x + 4}{x - 4} = \dfrac{x}{3}$ −3   **10.** $\dfrac{3}{x + 3} = \dfrac{2}{x^2 - 9} + \dfrac{1}{x + 3}$ 4

11. $\dfrac{x + 2}{x - 2} - \dfrac{2}{x + 4} = \dfrac{44}{x^2 + 2x - 8}$ −8, 4   **12.** $\dfrac{x}{3} + \dfrac{2}{x^2} - \dfrac{x - 3}{3x} = \dfrac{x - 1}{3}$ −2

9-5   *Solve each proportion.*

13. $\dfrac{2x}{9} = \dfrac{10}{15}$ 3   **14.** $\dfrac{7}{4} = \dfrac{x + 2}{8}$ 12   **15.** $\dfrac{x + 2}{2x} = \dfrac{2}{3}$ 6

9-6   **16.** 6 is 30% of what number?   20   **17.** 34 is what percent of 85?   40%

18. Find 2% of 15,500.   310   **19.** Find 110% of 320.   352

9-3   **20.** The denominator of a fraction is 2 more than 3 times the numerator. If the numerator is increased by 5, and the denominator is decreased by 8, then the resulting fraction is $\dfrac{10}{9}$. Find the fraction. $\dfrac{5}{17}$

9-4   **21.** It takes 3 days for a house painter and her assistant to paint a house. Working alone, it takes the painter 5 days. How long would it take the assistant alone to paint the house? $7\dfrac{1}{2}$ days

9-5   **22.** There are 132 employees working for a company. The number of full-time employees, to the number of part-time employees, is in the ratio of 9:2. How many full-time employees work for the company?
108 full-time; 24 part-time

9-6   **23.** After two weeks on a special diet, a man weighed 185 pounds. He lost 7.5% of his original weight. What did he weigh before he began his special diet?   200 lb

9-7   **24.** $8000 is invested at 7% simple interest per year. Find the amount of interest earned in 18 months. $840

9-8   **25.** How many ounces of an alloy containing 20% silver needs to be mixed with an alloy containing 25% silver to obtain 50 ounces of a new alloy containing 22% silver?   30 ounces

Compound Interest

Interest paid on the principal plus the accumulated interest to date is called compound interest. If p dollars is the amount invested at the beginning of a period at r percent annually and compounded n times per year, then the amount at the end of each period will be $p\left(1 + \frac{r}{n}\right)$.

This program displays the amount after each period for one year.

The Program	What It Does
`100 REM COMPOUND INTEREST`	
`110 PRINT "PRINCIPAL";`	
`120 INPUT P`	Stops for entry of principal.
`130 PRINT "ANNUAL RATE AS DECIMAL";`	
`140 INPUT R`	Stops for entry of annual interest rate as decimal.
`150 PRINT "PERIODS IN ONE YEAR";`	
`160 INPUT N`	Stops for entry of number of interest periods per year.
`170 PRINT "PERIOD", "AMOUNT"`	Labels the output.
`180 FOR T = 1 TO N`	
`190 LET P = P * (1 + R/N)`	After each period the amount becomes the new principal.
`200 LET P = INT(P*100+.5)/100`	Rounds to the nearest cent.
`210 PRINT T, P`	Displays period number and the amount at its close.
`220 NEXT T`	
`900 END`	

```
RUN
PRINCIPAL? 1000
ANNUAL RATE AS DECIMAL? .12
PERIODS IN ONE YEAR? 4
PERIOD AMOUNT
1       1030
2       1060.9
3       1092.73
4       1125.51
```

Sample run for an investment of $1000, compounded quarterly, at annual rate of 12%.

Zero cents is not displayed. The amount is $1060.90.

The amount after one year

What will the program display for each set of entries?

1. $p = \$10,000$; $r = 6\%$; $n = 2$ **2.** $p = \$5,000$; $r = 8\%$; $n = 4$

3. $p = \$4,000$; $r = 12\%$; $n = 12$ **4.** $p = \$5,000$; $r = 16\%$; $n = 4$

To compute the amount after two years, change line 180 to:

`180 FOR T = 1 TO 2*N`   *What is the amount after two years for:*

5. $p = \$5,000$; $r = 8\%$; $n = 4$ **6.** $p = \$2,500$; $r = 15\%$; $n = 12$

7. Delete line 200. Run each exercise again. Why do the results differ?

For more information about BASIC, see the Computer Handbook at the back of the book.

Computer Activity

Compound interest—which is considered on this page—provides a significant contrast to simple interest (discussed in Lesson 9-7). You may wish to note that most banks pay compound interest, not simple interest, on bank accounts.

To emphasize the advantages of the computer program for calculating compound interest, challenge students to try to solve Exercise 6 *without* using a computer or calculator.

ADDITIONAL ANSWERS

Computer Activity

1.
PERIODS	AMOUNT
1	10300
2	10609

2.
PERIODS	AMOUNT
1	5100
2	5202
3	5306.04
4	5412.16

3.
PERIODS	AMOUNT
1	4040
2	4080.4
3	4121.2
4	4162.41
5	4204.03
6	4246.07
7	4288.53
8	4331.42
9	4374.73
10	4418.48
11	4462.66
12	4507.29

4.
PERIODS	AMOUNT
1	5200
2	5408
3	5624.32
4	5849.29

5. $5858.30
6. $3368.39
7. After deletion of line 200, the answers are not rounded off.

PART I

Write the letter for the correct answer.

Chap. 2   **1.** Evaluate $-4 - [-5 - (-x)] - 3$ for $x = -2$.   a

    a. 0   **b.** 4   **c.** -4 **d.** 2   **e.** -2

Chap. 4   **2.** Find the slope of the line through the points $(-5, -4)$ and $(-3, 6)$.   b

    a. $\dfrac{7}{11}$ **b.** 5   **c.** $-\dfrac{1}{4}$ **d.** $\dfrac{5}{4}$ **e.** $\dfrac{1}{5}$

Chap. 5   **3.** Simplify: $(6x - 3y + 5) + (8x + 2y - 3) - (5x + 6)$ d

    a. $19x - y + 8$ **b.** $11x - y - 8$ **c.** $9x + 5y - 4$

    d. $9x - y - 4$ **e.** $19x - 5y + 8$

   4. Simplify: $(-2x^3y^3)^2(2x^5y)^3(3xy^4)$ d

    a. $96x^{14}y^{12}$ **b.** $12x^9y^8$ **c.** $72x^{22}y^{13}$ **d.** $96x^{22}y^{13}$ **e.** $72x^{14}y^{12}$

   5. Multiply: $(3x - 2y)(x - 3y)$ e

    a. $3x^2 - 5xy + 6y^2$ **b.** $3x^2 + 7xy + 5y^2$ **c.** $3x^2 + 6y^2$

    d. $3x^2 - 7xy + 6y^2$ **e.** $3x^2 - 11xy + 6y^2$

Chap. 6   **6.** Simplify: $\dfrac{36x^{10}y^{12}}{9x^5y^4}$ d

    a. $27x^5y^8$ **b.** $4x^2y^3$ **c.** $27x^2y^3$ **d.** $4x^5y^8$ **e.** $6x^2y^8$

   7. Factor: $8x^4 - 20x^3 - 12x^2$ e

    a. $4x^2(2x^2 - 5x - 3)$ **b.** $(4x^2 + 2x)(2x^2 - 6x)$ **c.** $(7x^2 - 4)(x^2 + 3)$

    d. $2x^2(4x + 2)(x - 3)$ **e.** $4x^2(2x + 1)(x - 3)$

Chap. 9   **8.** Solve the proportion: $\dfrac{5}{7} = \dfrac{x+1}{2x-3}$ a

    a. $\dfrac{22}{3}$ **b.** $-\dfrac{22}{3}$ **c.** $\dfrac{8}{3}$ **d.** $\dfrac{4}{3}$ **e.** $-\dfrac{8}{3}$

   9. Solve: $\dfrac{x}{2} + \dfrac{x+1}{3} = 4$ a

    a. $\dfrac{22}{5}$ **b.** $\dfrac{2}{5}$ **c.** 1   **d.** 5   **e.** 2

   10. A beaker contains 200 milliliters of a mixture that is 70% alcohol and 30% water. How much water must be added to make the mixture 40% alcohol?   e

    a. 33 mL   **b.** 100 mL   **c.** 80 mL   **d.** 50 mL   **e.** 150 mL

PART II

Chap. 4   **11.** Find the slope of the line containing the points $(-2, 6)$ and $(-5, -2)$. $\frac{8}{3}$

12. Write the equation of the horizontal line passing through $(5, -3)$. $y = -3$

13. Write the equation of the line parallel to $x = -2$, and with the same x-intercept as $5x - 3y = 8$. $x = \frac{8}{5}$

Simplify.

Chap. 2
Chap. 8   **14.** $7 - 16 \div 2 + 3 \times 4$ 11 **15.** $\dfrac{12x^2y^3 + 3xy^3}{3xy^3}$ $4x + 1$ **16.** $\dfrac{x^2 + 7x + 12}{x^2 - 16}$ $\dfrac{x+3}{x-4}$

Chap. 8   **17.** $\dfrac{x^2 - 7x + 10}{x^2 - 5x + 6}$ $\dfrac{x-5}{x-3}$ **18.** $\dfrac{2 - 2x}{x^2 - 1}$ $\dfrac{-2}{x+1}$ **19.** $\dfrac{x^2 - x - 6}{x^2 - 5x + 6} \cdot \dfrac{x^2 - 4}{x^2 + 4x + 4}$ 1

20. $\dfrac{2x^2 - 3x - 2}{x^2 - 4x - 12} \div \dfrac{2x^2 - 7x - 4}{5x^2 - 30x}$ **21.** $(2x^2 + 13x - 7) \div (2x - 1)$

22. $\dfrac{4}{x+2} + \dfrac{3}{x-1}$ $\dfrac{7x+2}{(x+2)(x-1)}$ **23.** $5 + \dfrac{x+2}{3x}$ $\dfrac{16x+2}{3x}$ **24.** $\dfrac{x}{x+3} + \dfrac{4}{x-3} - \dfrac{18}{x^2 - 9}$ $\dfrac{x-2}{x-3}$

25. $\dfrac{\frac{x}{3} + \frac{x}{4}}{\frac{x}{6}}$ $\dfrac{7}{2}$ **26.** $\dfrac{2 + \frac{1}{x}}{2 - \frac{1}{x}}$ $\dfrac{2x+1}{2x-1}$ **27.** $\left(1 - \dfrac{1}{x}\right) \div \left(1 - \dfrac{1}{x^2}\right)$ $\dfrac{x}{x+1}$

Factor completely.

Chap. 6   **28.** $45x^2 - 125y^2$ $5(3x - 5y)(3x + 5y)$ **29.** $3x^2 - 14x - 5$ $(3x + 1)(x - 5)$ **30.** $3xz - 2y + 2xy - 3z$ $(3z + 2y)(x - 1)$

Chap. 7   **31.** Solve by substitution: $\begin{aligned}4y &= 2x + 2 \\ y &= x + \frac{1}{4}\end{aligned}$ $\left(\frac{1}{2}, \frac{3}{4}\right)$ **32.** Solve: $\begin{aligned}5x + 2y &= 61 \\ 2x + 7y &= 12\end{aligned}$ $(13, -2)$

33. The value of a bag filled with quarters and dimes is $27.80. If each quarter were replaced by a dime and each dime were replaced by a quarter, the value of the coins would be $31.70. How many of each type of coin is in the bag?   72 quarters, 98 dimes

34. Two kinds of chocolate, one selling for $2.80 per pound and the other for $1.60 per pound, are to be made into a 50-pound mixture selling for $2.00 per pound. How many pounds of each kind of chocolate should be used? $16\frac{2}{3}$ lb @ $2.80, $33\frac{1}{3}$ @ $1.60

Solve for x.

Chap. 5
Chap. 6   **35.** $(x - 1)^2 = x(x + 8) - 9$ 1 **36.** $2x^3 + 14x^2 + 20x = 0$ $0; -2; -5$

Chap. 9   **37.** $\dfrac{3x}{4} - \dfrac{5}{8} = \dfrac{x}{2}$ $\dfrac{5}{2}$ **38.** $\dfrac{6}{x^2 - 4x - 5} = \dfrac{3}{x + 1}$ 7 **39.** $\dfrac{1}{x + 1} - \dfrac{4}{x + 2} = -\dfrac{2}{3}$ $2; -\frac{1}{2}$

CUMULATIVE REVIEW

359

In this chapter the students learn to solve and graph inequalities. The work includes inequalities in one or two variables.

The opening lesson of the chapter deals with graphing a simple inequality (in one variable) on a number line. Number comparisons are reviewed and basic concepts of inequalities are extended in this lesson.

In the next two lessons, the chapter develops properties for solving inequalities. Both the addition property and the multiplication properties are carefully considered. Special attention is given to the fact that when an inequality is multiplied by a negative number, the resulting inequality has the opposite direction. (That is, the sense of the inequality is reversed.)

Applications of inequalities are presented in a subsequent lesson. Then the students learn to draw graphs of inequalities in the coordinate plane. Finally, building on this work, the text presents a lesson devoted to graphs of systems of inequalities.

In terms of actual applications, mathematical inequalities play an important role in our society. Therefore, this chapter is a significant one for students who will be using mathematics in their future lives.

CHAPTER 10

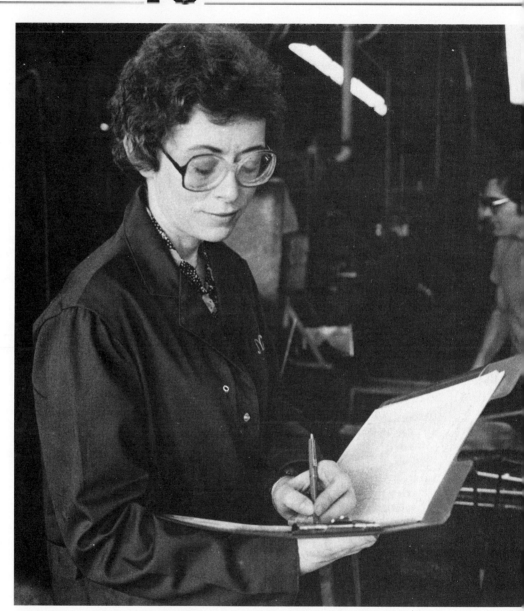

A manufacturer will show a profit only if the revenue from sales exceeds the cost of production. Mathematical inequalities are useful in expressing such relationships.

INEQUALITIES

Prerequisite Skills Review

Write the letter for the correct answer.

1. Which statement is incorrect? b

   a. $\dfrac{3}{8} < \dfrac{7}{8}$ **b.** $\dfrac{1}{3} < \dfrac{1}{7}$ **c.** $\dfrac{1}{2} > \dfrac{1}{5}$ **d.** $0.01 > 0.001$

2. In which arrangement are the numbers increasing from left to right? a
   a. 0.003; 0.025; 0.1 **b.** 0.1; 0.025; 0.003
   c. 0.025; 0.003; 0.1 **d.** 0.1; 0.003; 0.025

3. Which statement is *incorrect*? c

   a. $|6 - 2| = |-6 + 2|$ **b.** $\left|-\dfrac{1}{2} \cdot 8\right| > 1$ **c.** $-|4 - 9| = 5$ **d.** $\left|\dfrac{3}{4} - \dfrac{1}{2}\right| < \dfrac{1}{2}$

4. Simplify $|8 - 2| - |2 - 8|$. a
   a. 0 **b.** -4 **c.** 12 **d.** 16

5. Solve $|x| - 3 = 9$. d
   a. 6 or -6 **b.** 3 or -3 **c.** 12 only **d.** 12 or -12

6. If $10 - 5y = 3$, then $y = \underline{\ ?\ }$. c

   a. $\dfrac{3}{5}$ **b.** $-\dfrac{3}{5}$ **c.** $\dfrac{7}{5}$ **d.** $-\dfrac{7}{5}$

7. If $3 - \dfrac{1}{2}x = 5$, then $x = \underline{\ ?\ }$. b

   a. 4 **b.** -4 **c.** 16 **d.** -16

8. Express the equation $-y = 3x - 2$ in slope-intercept form. b
   a. $y = -3x - 2$ **b.** $y = -3x + 2$ **c.** $y = 3x + 2$ **d.** $y = 3x - 2$

9. Express the equation $4x - y = 2(3 + x)$ in slope-intercept form. c
   a. $y = -2x + 6$ **b.** $y = 2x + 6$ **c.** $y = 2x - 6$ **d.** $y = -2x - 6$

10. Which point does *not* lie on the line $x - 2y = 6$? d
    a. $(0, -3)$ **b.** $(6, 0)$ **c.** $(2, -2)$ **d.** $(4, 1)$

11. Which line has an x-intercept of -2 and a y-intercept of 1? c

    a. $\dfrac{x}{2} + y = 1$ **b.** $x + 2y = 2$ **c.** $y = \dfrac{1}{2}x + 1$ **d.** $2y + x = -2$

12. The lines $y = 2x - 1$ and $x + y = -4$ intersect in what point? b
    a. $(3, 5)$ **b.** $(-1, -3)$ **c.** $(2, 3)$ **d.** $(-3, -1)$

PREREQUISITE SKILLS REVIEW

For students who need additional practice with the algebraic skills in this Prerequisite Skills Review, you may assign Follow-Up exercises on pages 504-505 in the students' books.

An item-by-item error analysis of the Prerequisite Skills Review appears on page T27.

1. Which are solutions for $x < 2$?
   a. 4   b. -4 c. -2 d. 2
   b, c

2. Which are solutions for $x > -\frac{1}{2}$?

   a. $-\frac{1}{4}$ b. $-\frac{5}{6}$ c. $-\frac{1}{10}$ d. 0
   a, c, d

LESSON NOTES

This lesson considers inequalities and the way in which they are graphed on a number line. Have students recall the fundamental symbols of inequality. When analyzing specific graphs, stress the importance of solid and open dots. They indicate whether particular numbers belong to the solution sets.

Two important properties of inequalities are explained: the trichotomy property and the transitive property. These are illustrated in Examples 2 and 3.

Exercises 53–57 involve negations of familiar inequalities. The introductory material points out that by virtue of the trichotomy property, $a \not< b$ is equivalent to $a > b$. You may also wish to note that $x \not< 5$ is equivalent to $x \geq 5$, which can be expressed as the compound sentence $x > 5$ or $x = 5$. The topic of compound inequalities is considered in detail in Lessons 10-5 and 10-6.

ALTERNATE EXAMPLE

1. Graph each inequality.
   a. $x \geq 0$

   b. $x \leq -2$
   c. $x < -1$

10-1 Graphing Inequalities on a Line

OBJECTIVES

To graph inequalities on the number line.
To compare numbers using the trichotomy and transitive properties.

A sentence that contains either of the symbols $<$ or $>$ is an *inequality*.

| $a < b$ a is less than b. | $c > d$ c is greater than d. |

If $a < b$, then a is to the left of b on the number line.

If $c > d$, then c is to the right of d on the number line.

The inequality $a \leq b$ means $a < b$ or $a = b$, and $c \geq d$ means $c > d$ or $c = d$. For example, $2 \leq 7$ because $2 < 7$, and $3 \geq 3$ because $3 = 3$.

The inequality $x > 3$ is true for all x-values greater than 3. This set of numbers is called the **solution set,** or simply the *solution*. All solutions of $x > 3$ are shown to the right of 3 on the number line.

To graph the inequality $x > 3$, begin at 3 and draw a heavy arrow pointing to the right. The open circle at 3 means that 3 is not one of the solutions.

Numbers such as 8 and 9.5 are included even though they are not specifically marked on this graph.

Now compare the graphs of $x < 3$ and $x \leq 3$. They are the same except at 3.

The graph of an inequality with $\leq$ or $\geq$ shows a *solid* dot at the starting point. This means that the number is included in the solution set.

EXAMPLE 1   Graph each inequality.

a. $x \geq 2$ b. $x \leq 1$ c. $x < -3$

362

Any pair of real numbers may be compared according to the following fundamental property.

Trichotomy Property

For real numbers a and b, exactly one of the following is true.

$$a < b \qquad\qquad a = b \qquad\qquad a > b$$

When comparing rational numbers, it is sometimes helpful to use common denominators. With decimals, this means using the same number of decimal places.

EXAMPLE 2   Use $<$, $>$, or $=$ to complete each statement.

a. $2.8 \underset{\underline{}}{?} 2.08$

$2.8 > 2.08$

since $2.8 = 2.80$
and $2.80 > 2.08$

b. $2 - 5 \underset{\underline{}}{?} -2$

$2 - 5 < -2$

since $2 - 5 = -3$
and $-3 < -2$

c. $\dfrac{1}{3} \underset{\underline{}}{?} \dfrac{2}{5}$

$\dfrac{1}{3} < \dfrac{2}{5}$

since $\dfrac{1}{3} = \dfrac{5}{15}$, $\dfrac{2}{5} = \dfrac{6}{15}$,

and $\dfrac{5}{15} < \dfrac{6}{15}$

d. $\dfrac{2}{5} \underset{\underline{}}{?} 0.4$

$\dfrac{2}{5} = 0.4$

since $\dfrac{2}{5} = \dfrac{4}{10}$

and $\dfrac{4}{10} = 0.4$

ALTERNATE EXAMPLE

2. Use $<$, $>$, or $=$ to complete each statement.

a. $3.5 \underline{} 3.05$ $>$

b. $4 - 5 \underline{} 0$ $<$

c. $\dfrac{1}{4} \underline{} \dfrac{1}{2}$ $<$

d. $\dfrac{1}{8} \underline{} 0.125$ $=$

Suppose you know that $2 < x$ and that $x < y$. Can you compare 2 with y? This is easy to answer by looking at the number line. Since 2 must be to the left of y, $2 < y$.

This illustrates another property that is used to make comparisons.

Transitive Property of Inequalities

Let a, b, and c be any real numbers.
- **If $a < b$ and $b < c$, then $a < c$.**
- **If $a > b$ and $b > c$, then $a > c$.**

The transitive property also holds for inequalities with $\leq$ and $\geq$.

INEQUALITIES

ALTERNATE EXAMPLE

3. Use the transitive property to complete the following:
  a. If $x \le 5$ and $5 \le t$, then $x \underline{\;?\;} t$. $x \le t$
  b. If $x > y$ and $0 < y$, then $x \underline{\;?\;} 0$. $x > 0$

POSSIBLE ERROR

Students often make mistakes when interchanging the terms of an inequality. For example, they may incorrectly rewrite $2 < x$ as $x < 2$. Help them avoid this type of error by explaining that when the left and right members of an inequality are interchanged, the direction or sense of the inequality must be reversed. Thus, $2 < x$ is equivalent to $x > 2$.

DAILY QUIZ

Write the inequality for each graph.

1. $x < 1$
-1 1

2. $x \ge -1$
-1 1

3. $x > 3$
1 3

Graph each inequality.

4. $x \ge 5$
3 5

5. $x < -3$
-3 -1

ASSIGNMENT GUIDE
(pages 364–365)

Minimum course: 1–47 odd
     second day: 2–52 even
Average course: 1–57 odd
Maximum course: 1–63 odd

EXAMPLE 3   Use the transitive property to complete the following.

                                     Answers

a. If $x < 3$ and $3 < t$, then $x \underline{\;?\;} t$. $x < t$

b. If $x \ge y$ and $-1 \le y$, then $x \underline{\;?\;} 1$. $x \ge 1$
    Note that $-1 \le y$ can be rewritten as $y \ge -1$.

CLASS EXERCISES

Translate each inequality into words.

1. $h > 2$
  h is greater than 2

2. $5 < y$
  5 is less than y

3. $x \le 9$ x is less than or equal to 9

4. $z \ge -7$
  z is greater than or equal to -7

Write each sentence using an inequality symbol.

5. h is greater than -1. $h > -1$

6. x is less than or equal to 9. $x \le 9$

7. x is greater than or equal to 21. $x \ge 21$

8. 5 is greater than y. $5 > y$

Write true or false.

9. $7.5 < 7.05$ False
10. $-8 > -4$ False
11. $7 \le 7$ True
12. $-4.31 \ge -4.38$ True

Match each inequality with the correct graph.

13. $x > -1$ c
14. $x \le -1$ a
15. $x \ge -1$ b
16. $x < -1$ d

EXERCISES

A   *Use $<$, $>$, or $=$ to complete each statement.*

1. $-11 \underline{\;?\;} -9$ $<$

2. $-13 \underline{\;?\;} -20$ $>$

3. $1 \underline{\;?\;} -1$ $>$

4. $6.8 \underline{\;?\;} -4.1$ $>$

5. $5.37 \underline{\;?\;} 5.3$ $>$

6. $-2.4 \underline{\;?\;} -2.3$ $<$

7. $\frac{1}{2} \underline{\;?\;} -1\frac{1}{2}$ $>$

8. $-3\frac{3}{4} \underline{\;?\;} 0$ $<$

9. $\frac{1}{5} \underline{\;?\;} 0.2$ $=$

10. $\frac{3}{4} \underline{\;?\;} \frac{7}{8}$ $<$

11. $2.75 \underline{\;?\;} 2\frac{3}{4}$ $=$

12. $\frac{7}{10} \underline{\;?\;} 0.8$ $<$

13. $2 + 3 \underline{\;?\;} \frac{1}{2}(11)$ $<$

14. $3 - 5 \underline{\;?\;} -3$ $>$

15. $\left(\frac{1}{2}\right)^2 \underline{\;?\;} \frac{1}{2}$ $<$

16. If $p > q$ and $q > r$, then $p \underline{\;?\;} r$. $>$

17. If $x < t$ and $t < u$, then $x \underline{\;?\;} u$. $<$

18. If $w = x$ and $x > y$, then $w \underline{\;?\;} y$. $>$

19. If $b < f$ and $h > f$, then $b \underline{\;?\;} h$. $<$

EXTRA PRACTICE, page 527

Write **true** or **false**.

20. $8 \leq 8$ True   **21.** $-\frac{5}{2} \geq -\frac{5}{2}$ True   **22.** $7 \geq -10$ True   **23.** $-\frac{3}{4} \leq -\frac{4}{5}$ False

24. $3.5 > 3.05$ True   **25.** $10.8 \leq -12$ False   **26.** $0 \geq -8$ True

Write the inequality for each graph.

27.   **28.**   **29.**

30.   **31.**   **- 32.**

33.   **34.**

35.   **36.**

Graph each inequality.

37. $x > 3$ **38.** $x > 4$ **39.** $x < 5$ **40.** $x < -3$

41. $x < -2$ **42.** $x \geq -2$ **43.** $x \leq -3$ **44.** $x > 0$

45. $x \leq 0$ **46.** $x \geq 5$ **47.** $x \geq -2.5$ **48.** $x < 1.75$

B

49. $x \geq -\frac{3}{4}$ **50.** $x \leq \frac{7}{2}$ **51.** $x < \frac{9}{5}$ **52.** $x \leq -\frac{4}{3}$

Graph each inequality. The symbol $\nleq$ means **is not less than or equal to**.
If $a \nleq b$, then by the trichotomy property, $a > b$.

53. $x \nleq 2$ **54.** $x \nless 5$ **55.** $x \neq -4$ **56.** $x \ngtr 7$ **57.** $x \nless 2$

C

58. Explain why $x < x + 1$ and $x - 1 < x$ for any real number x. Refer
to the number line.   On the number line, $x + 1$ is one unit to the right of x, and x is one unit
to the right of $x - 1$.

Assume that $a < b$.   Use the transitive property to explain why each
inequality is true.

     Sample $a < b + 1$ Since $a < b$ and $b < b + 1$, then $a < b + 1$.
               $a < b$ $a < b$ $a < b$
59. $a - 1 < b$ $a - 1 < a$ **60.** $a < b + 2$ $b < b + 2$ **61.** $a - 3 < b$ $a - 3 < a$
           So $a - 1 < b$ So $a < b + 2$ So $a - 3 < b$
62. Suppose that $x > 0$ and $y > -2$, does it follow that $x > y$?
Explain your answer.   No. Example: $x = 6$, $y = 8$

63. If $x < 1$ and $y < 100$, does it follow that $x < y$? Explain.   No. Example: $x = 0$, $y = -1$
                                                   $x^2 - 2x + 1 = (x - 1)^2$
*64. Explain why $x^2 - 2x + 1 \geq 0$ for any real number x. $(x - 1)^2 \geq 0$
                                          So $x^2 - 2x + 1 \geq 0$

INEQUALITIES

365

Match the inequalities in the two columns. Which have the same solution set?

1. $x + 2 < 8$ **a.** $x > 6$
2. $x - 2 < 8$ **b.** $x < 6$
3. $x - 1 > 7$ **c.** $x < 10$
4. $x + 1 > 7$ **d.** $x > 8$
      1b, 2c, 3d, 4a

LESSON NOTES

Discuss each of the model examples carefully. In discussing Example 2, be sure the students understand how the addition property relates to the use of subtraction. For instance, instead of writing $x + 7 + (-7) \le 0 + (-7)$, write $x + 7 - 7 \le 0 - 7$, which produces the same result: $x \le -7$.

To check the solution for an inequality such as $x + 7 \le 0$, the students can first check to see that -7 satisfies the inequality; then they can use some other number such as -9 to see if it satisfies the inequality. (It may also be worthwhile to substitute a number that is outside the apparent range of solutions and see whether it makes the inequality false. For example, if -6.9 is used, the inequality becomes $-6.9 + 7 \le 0$, or $0.1 \le 0$, which is false.)

ALTERNATE EXAMPLES

1. Solve $x - 2 > 3$ and graph the solution set. $x > 5$

2. Solve $x + 3 \le 5$ and graph the solution set. $x \le 2$

10-2 Solving Inequalities: The Addition Property

OBJECTIVE

To solve inequalities by using the addition property.

What will happen if 3 pounds are added to each side of the scale? Adding the same amount to each side will not alter the scale setting. The left side was heavier to start with and it will still be heavier and by the same amount.

This suggests that when the same number is added to each side of an inequality, the resulting inequality will have the same *order*, or *direction*.

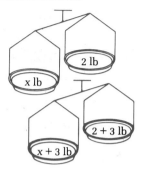

Addition Property of Inequalities

Let a, b, and c be any real numbers.
• If $a < b$, then $a + c < b + c$.
• If $a > b$, then $a + c > b + c$.

The addition property can also be stated using $\le$ and $\ge$ instead of $<$ and $>$. When this property is used to solve an inequality such as $x - 3 > 1$, an *equivalent* inequality is produced. That is, the two inequalities have the *same solution set*.

EXAMPLE 1   Solve $x - 3 > 1$ and graph the solution set.

Add 3 to each side.

$$x - 3 > 1$$
$$x - 3 + 3 > 1 + 3$$
$$x > 4$$

In Example 1, observe that the simplified inequality $x > 4$ is regarded as the solution of the given inequality. This solution may also be described in words as "the set of all numbers greater than 4."

EXAMPLE 2   Solve $x + 7 \le 0$ and graph the solution set.

$$x + 7 \le 0$$
$$x + 7 + (-7) \le 0 + (-7)$$
$$x \le -7$$

366

Since $a - c = a + (-c)$, the addition property allows you to add or subtract the same number from each side of an inequality.

EXAMPLE 3   Solve $7 + 2x \geq 9 + x$.

$$7 + 2x \geq 9 + x$$
$$7 + x \geq 9 \qquad \text{Subtract } x \text{ from each side.}$$
$$x \geq 2 \qquad \text{Subtract 7 from each side.}$$

CLASS EXERCISES

*Tell what you would do to each side to solve the inequality for **x**. Then solve.*

1. $x - 4 < 7$ **2.** $x + 8 > 5$ **3.** $x - 8 \geq -1$ **4.** $x + 5 \leq -5$

EXERCISES

A   *Solve each inequality. Then graph the solution set.*

1. $x + 3 > 5$ $x > 2$ **2.** $x + 4 > 7$ $x > 3$ **3.** $a + 5 < 4$ $a < -1$ **4.** $b + 3 < 1$ $b < -2$

5. $c + 2 \geq 4$ $c \geq 2$ **6.** $x + 5 \geq 8$ $x \geq 3$ **7.** $x - 1 \leq 6$ $x \leq 7$ **8.** $n - 2 \leq 9$ $n \leq 11$

9. $x - 2 > 2$ $x > 4$ **10.** $x - 3 > 5$ $x > 8$ **11.** $p - 7 < 12$ $p < 19$ **12.** $q - 2 < -2$ $q < 0$

Match each inequality with the correct graph.

13. $x - 6 > -5$ e   **a.** (arrow, filled at 3, line left)

14. $x - 1 \leq 2$ a   **b.** (filled at -2, line right)

15. $x + 12 < 9$ d   **c.** (open at 3, line left)   **d.** (open at -3, line left)

16. $4 + x \leq 6$ f

17. $x + 10 \geq 8$ b   **e.** (open at 1, line right)   **f.** (filled at 2, line right)

18. $13 > x + 10$ c

B   *Solve.*

19. $2x + 4 < x + 16$ $x < 12$ **20.** $7x - 8 \leq 6x + 7$ $x \leq 15$ **21.** $4x + 2 > 10 + 5x$ $x < -8$

22. $3(2 + x) \leq 9 + 4x$ $x \geq -3$ **23.** $2(y + 4) < 12 + 3y$ $y > -4$ **24.** $8(y - 4) > 9y + 8$ $y < -40$

25. $x - 3 \not< 8$ $x \geq 11$ **26.** $3x + 1 \not\leq 1 + 2x$ $x > 0$ **27.** $2(x - 1) \not\geq 3(x + 7)$ $x > -23$

28. If $2x < x$, show that $x < 0$.   **29.** If $5x > 4x$, show that $x > 0$.

C   *Suppose that **a** < **b**. State whether the following are **true** or **false**.*

30. $2a < a + b$ True   **31.** $a - b > 0$ False   **32.** $-b > -a$ False   **33.** $2b < 3b - a$ True

*34. Find values of a, b, c, and d, so that $a < b$ and $c < d$, but $a - c < b - d$ is false.
One possible answer: $a = 12$, $b = 15$, $c = 3$, $d = 10$

*35. Show that, if $a < b$ and $c < d$, then $a + c < b + d$.

INEQUALITIES   **367**

DAILY QUIZ

Solve each inequality. Then graph the solution set.

1. $x + 5 > 7$ $x > 2$
(number line, open at 2)

2. $x - 9 < 13$ $x < 22$
(number line, open at 22)

3. $x - 5 \leq -5$ $x \leq 0$
(number line, 0)

4. $4x + 8 < 3x + 20$ $x < 12$
(number line, open at 12)

5. $3(x + 1) \geq 2(x + 7)$ $x \geq 11$
(number line, filled at 11)

ASSIGNMENT GUIDE
(page 367)

Minimum course: 1–19 odd
second day: 2–20 even
Average course: 1–27 odd
second day: 2–28 even
Maximum course: 1–29 odd,
30–33

ENRICHMENT ACTIVITY

Have the students invent their own exercises similar to Exercises 30–33. Let pairs of students exchange papers and solve each other's exercises.

ADDITIONAL ANSWERS

Class Exercises

1. Add 4; $x < 11$
2. Subtract 8; $x > -3$
3. Add 8; $x \geq 7$
4. Subtract 5; $x \leq -10$

Exercises

See page A6.

EXTRA PRACTICE, page 527

Which inequalities have the same solution set?

1. $3x > 15$ **a.** $x < 20$
2. $\frac{1}{2}x < 10$ **b.** $x > 5$
3. $2x < 12$ **c.** $x > 0$
4. $5x > 0$ **d.** $x < 6$

    1*b*, 2*a*, 3*d*, 4*c*

LESSON NOTES

In this lesson the students use the multiplication property of inequalities. Discuss in detail the way in which this property differs from the multiplication property used in solving equations. The students must understand that when we multiply (or divide) both sides of an inequality by a negative number, we must reverse the direction of the symbol. Thus, when both sides of $-5x \geq 20$ are multiplied by $-\frac{1}{5}$, we obtain $x \leq -4$.

Example 3 and Exercises 33–42 call for special attention, since each problem requires the application of both the addition and multiplication properties of inequality.

ALTERNATE EXAMPLE

1. Solve each inequality.

   a. $\frac{1}{3}x < 2$ $x < 6$

   b. $4x > 28$ $x > 7$

10-3 Solving Inequalities: The Multiplication Property

OBJECTIVE

To solve inequalities by using the multiplication property.

You know that multiplying each side of an equation by the same number produces an equivalent equation. Let's see if this holds true for inequalities as well.

Compare the results of multiplying each side of the inequality $3 < 5$ by a positive number and by a negative number.

$$3 < 5 \qquad\qquad\qquad 3 < 5$$
$$2(3) \underset{?}{} 2(5) \quad \text{Multiply by 2.} \qquad -2(3) \underset{?}{} -2(5) \quad \text{Multiply by } -2.$$
$$6 < 10 \qquad\qquad\qquad -6 > -10$$

When each side of a given inequality is multiplied by the same *positive* number, the resulting inequality has the *same* direction as the given one. When each side of the given inequality is multiplied by the same *negative* number, the resulting inequality has the *reverse* direction.

Multiplication Property of Inequalities

When c is positive: If $a < b$,   then $ac < bc$.
                       If $a > b$,   then $ac > bc$.

When c is negative: If $a < b$,   then $ac > bc$.
                       If $a > b$,   then $ac < bc$.

You can use the multiplication property to solve inequalities. Dividing by a number—and multiplying by its reciprocal—give the same result.

EXAMPLE 1   Solve each inequality.

a. $\frac{1}{2}x < 4$

     $2\left(\frac{1}{2}x\right) < 2(4)$ Multiply each side by 2.

         $x < 8$

b. $3x > 15$

     $\frac{1}{3}(3x) > \frac{1}{3}(15)$ Multiply by $\frac{1}{3}$ or divide by 3.

         $x > 5$

In the next example, the inequality is multiplied by a negative number, so the direction of the inequality is reversed.

EXAMPLE 2   Solve $-5x \geq 20$. Then graph the solution set.

$$-5x \geq 20$$

$$-\frac{1}{5}(-5x) \leq -\frac{1}{5}(20)$$ Multiply by $-\frac{1}{5}$. Reverse the direction of the inequality.

$$x \leq -4$$

$$\overleftarrow{\underset{-7\,-6\,-5\,-4\,-3\,-2}{\rule{3cm}{0pt}}}$$

In Example 3, both the addition and multiplication properties are used.

EXAMPLE 3   Solve $2x + 7 < 5x - 2$.

$$2x + 7 < 5x - 2$$

$$-3x + 7 < -2$$ Add $-5x$ to each side.

$$-3x < -9$$ Add -7 to each side.

$$-\frac{1}{3}(-3x) > -\frac{1}{3}(-9)$$ Multiply each side by $-\frac{1}{3}$. Reverse the direction of the inequality.

$$x > 3$$

CLASS EXERCISES

Tell what you would do to each side of the inequality in order to solve for x. Will the direction of the inequality be changed?

1. $3x \geq -12$
Mult. by $\frac{1}{3}$; no

2. $-3x > -12$
Mult. by $-\frac{1}{3}$; yes

3. $\frac{2}{3}x < 4$
Mult. by $\frac{3}{2}$; no

4. $\frac{1}{2}x \leq -3$
Mult. by 2; no

5. $-3x > 12$
Mult. by $-\frac{1}{3}$; yes

6. $-3x \leq -12$
Mult. by $-\frac{1}{3}$; yes

7. $-x \leq -4$
Mult. by -1; yes

8. $-2x > 6$
Mult. by $-\frac{1}{2}$; yes

Complete.

9. If $7x \leq 35$, then $x \underline{\ ?\ }$.
≤ 5

10. If $\frac{1}{5}x < 12$, then $x \underline{\ ?\ }$.
< 60

11. If $-x \geq 7$, then $x \underline{\ ?\ }$.
≤ -7

EXERCISES

A   *Solve.*

1. $3x \geq 21$ $x \geq 7$ **2.** $\frac{1}{5}y \geq 1$ $y \geq 5$ **3.** $4b \leq 20$ $b \leq 5$ **4.** $3n \leq 9$ $n \leq 3$

5. $6y > 24$ $y > 4$ **6.** $5x < 0$ $x < 0$ **7.** $-7t < 14$ $t > -2$ **8.** $-11x \geq -33$ $x \leq 3$

9. $-8y \geq -32$ **10.** $-\frac{1}{3}x \leq 2$ **11.** $-\frac{1}{2}p \geq -3$ **12.** $-\frac{2}{3}y > 4$
    $y \leq 4$ $x \geq -6$ $p \leq 6$ $y < -6$

INEQUALITIES   **369**

EXTRA PRACTICE, page 527

ALTERNATE EXAMPLES

2. Solve $-4x \geq 12$. Then graph the solution set. $x \leq -3$

$$\overleftarrow{\underset{-3}{\rule{2.5cm}{0pt}}}$$

3. Solve: $3x + 5 < 6x - 1$ $x > 2$

POSSIBLE ERROR

In multiplying both sides of an inequality by a negative factor, students often multiply correctly on the left side and correctly reverse the direction of the symbol, but then become careless in multiplying the right side. For example, they may write

$$-5x \geq 20$$
$$x \leq 4 \text{ (incorrect)}$$

Here the students have multiplied the left side by $-\frac{1}{5}$, but multiplied the right side by $\frac{1}{5}$.

To help students see their mistake, review the multiplication property of inequalities and provide additional examples of its application.

DAILY QUIZ

Solve each inequality. Then graph the solution set.

1. $4x \geq 28$ $x \geq 7$

$$\underset{7}{\rule{2.5cm}{0pt}}$$

2. $7x < -21$ $x < -3$

$$\overleftarrow{\underset{-3}{\rule{2.5cm}{0pt}}}$$

3. $-\frac{1}{3}x \leq 3$ $x \geq -9$

$$\underset{-9}{\rule{2.5cm}{0pt}}$$

4. $5x > 6 - x$ $x > 1$

$$\underset{1}{\rule{2.5cm}{0pt}}$$

5. $-2(x - 4) > 3(x - 4)$ $x < 4$

$$\overleftarrow{\underset{4}{\rule{2.5cm}{0pt}}}$$

ENRICHMENT ACTIVITY

Have the students continue to explore inequalities that involve negations. Use inequalities in which the students must apply both the addition and multiplication properties. For example:

1. $3x - 2 \not> 10$ $x \le 4$
2. $5x + 3 \ne 18$ $x > 3$
3. $-10 \ne 2\frac{1}{2}(x - 2)$ $x > -2$

ADDITIONAL ANSWERS

Exercises

13.
  2

14.
  −2

[*Answers for the Exercises and for the Checkpoint continue on page A6.*]

Checkpoint

Students may check their answers with those given in the back of their books.

B

*Solve for **x** and graph the solution set.*

13. $-5x < -10$ $x > 2$
14. $5x < -10$ $x < -2$
15. $-5x > -10$ $x < 2$
16. $-5x > 10$ $x < -2$
17. $1 - x \le 2$ $x \ge -1$
18. $1 \ge 2 - x$ $x \ge 1$
19. $x - 1 \ge 2$ $x \ge 3$
20. $1 \le x - 2$ $x \ge 3$
21. $2x + 3 < 9$ $x < 3$
22. $3x - 2 < 28$ $x < 10$
23. $4x + 7 > 7$ $x > 0$
24. $6 - 4x \le 10$ $x \ge -1$

Solve.

25. $\frac{-x}{7} \le 1$ $x \ge -7$
26. $-\frac{x}{18} \ge -\frac{1}{3}$ $x \le 6$
27. $-\frac{3}{4}x \le -12$ $x \ge 16$
28. $4x > 5 - x$ $x > 1$
29. $3x + 2 < x$ $x < -1$
30. $4 + 2x \ge 6x$ $x \le 1$
31. $2 + 2x < x$ $x < -2$
32. $-2 - 5x \le 13$ $x \ge -3$
33. $7x + 4 > 2x + 19$ $x > 3$
34. $7x - 8 \le 2x + 7$ $x \le 3$
35. $2x + 3 \le 3x - 5$ $x \ge 8$
36. $3x - 5 \ne -3x + 7$ $x < 2$
37. $-6x - 4 \ne -16$ $x > 2$
38. $-9x + 3 \not< -33$ $x \le 4$

C

In **set-builder notation,** the solution set of the inequality $3(x - 2) < 4x + 3$ is $\{x \mid x > -9\}$, and is read "the set of numbers x such that x is greater than -9."

Write each solution set in set-builder notation.

39. $2x + 5 \le 5(x - 5)$ $\{x \mid x \ge 10\}$
40. $2(x + 3) \le 7x - 4$ $\{x \mid x \ge 2\}$
41. $8(x + 4) \ge 4(x - 7)$ $\{x \mid x \ge -15\}$
42. $-3(x - 4) > 5(x - 4)$ $\{x \mid x < 4\}$

*Since $3 < 4$, what type of real number **x** will make each inequality true? Choose **x** > 0 or **x** < 0 or **x** $\ne 0$.*

43. $3x < 4x$ $x > 0$
44. $3x > 4x$ $x < 0$
45. $\frac{3}{x} > \frac{4}{x}$ $x < 0$
46. $3x^2 < 4x^2$ $x \ne 0$

47. If $0 < a < 1$, then which of the following is true, $a^2 > a$ or $a^2 < a$? $a^2 < a$

*48. If $0 < a$ and $a < b$, explain why $\frac{1}{a} > \frac{1}{b}$.

*49. Suppose that a, b, c, and d are positive, such that $a > b$, and $c > d$. Explain why $ac > bd$.

CHECKPOINT

*Solve for **x** and graph the solution set.*

1. $x + 5 \ge 8$ $x \ge 3$
2. $x + 6 < 5$ $x < -1$
3. $x - 3 > 3$ $x > 6$
4. $-6x < -12$ $x > 2$
5. $6x < -12$ $x < -2$
6. $-6x > -12$ $x < 2$
7. $2 - x \le 3$ $x \ge -1$
8. $2 \le x - 3$ $x \ge 5$
9. $8x - 9 \le 7x + 8$ $x \le 17$
10. $5x + 3 > 11 + 6x$ $x < -8$
11. $8x + 5 > 3x + 20$ $x > 3$
12. $-4(x - 5) > 6(x - 5)$ $x < 5$
13. $-10x + 6 \not< -34$ $x \le 4$
14. $3(x - 2) \ne 4(x - 8)$ $x > 26$

CHAPTER 10

10-4 Problem Solving: Using Inequalities

OBJECTIVE _____

To use inequalities in solving problems.

_____

Problems involving inequalities often have key expressions that you
need to translate into mathematical expressions with inequality symbols.

Expression	Example	Translation
at least	The house is *at least* 50 feet high.	$h \geq 50$
no less than	The car will cost *no less than* $7000.	$c \geq 7000$
at most	Her weekly salary is *at most* $750.	$s \leq 750$
no more than	The world record for the long jump is *no more than* 30 feet.	$j \leq 30$

EXAMPLE 1

Two high-speed trains pass each other and continue in opposite directions. One train travels at 120 mph and the other at 135 mph. How
long must they travel to be at least 340 miles apart?

**Strategy: Form an
inequality by setting
the distance be-
tween the trains
greater than or
equal to 340.**

Read the problem to find the key ideas.

The trains travel in opposite directions. Add their distances to get
the total distance between them. This total must be at least 340
miles.

Use a variable.

Let t = the time they must travel (hours)
Then $120t$ = distance (miles) traveled for one train; $d = rt$
$\qquad 135t$ = distance traveled for the other train
$\qquad 120t + 135t$ = distance between trains

Write an inequality.

The *distance between* is *at least* 340.

$$120t + 135t \geq 340$$

Solve the inequality.

$$120t + 135t \geq 340$$
$$255t \geq 340$$
$$t \geq \frac{340}{255} \qquad \frac{340}{255} = \frac{85 \cdot 4}{85 \cdot 3} = \frac{4}{3}$$
$$t \geq \frac{4}{3}$$

INEQUALITIES

WARM-UP EXERCISES

1. If n is the smallest of three consecutive integers, what are the
other two integers? $n + 1$,
$n + 2$

2. If x is a number, what is three
less than twice the number?
$2x - 3$

3. If y is a number, what are two
ways of writing one-half y?
$\frac{1}{2}y, \frac{y}{2}$

LESSON NOTES

To solve problems involving inequalities, students must translate
sentences into inequalities. For
many students, this is more difficult
than translating words into equations. Expressions such as "no more
than," "at least," "no less than," and
"at most" are easy to misinterpret.
Therefore, it will be worthwhile to
give careful attention to each of the
model examples.

Example 1 lists steps that can be
helpful in solving a word problem
that involves an inequality.
1. Use a variable to represent the
unknown.
2. Write an inequality representing
the given information.
3. Solve the inequality.
4. Answer the question.
Students often forget step 4, a serious mistake. In Example 3, for instance, it would be wrong to end
with $n > 17$, since n is nowhere
mentioned in the problem. To give
an appropriate answer, we must interpret n in the context of the problem and identify the numbers that
answer the question that was asked.

ALTERNATE EXAMPLE

1. Two joggers pass each other
and continue in opposite directions. One jogger runs at 6 mph
and the other at 10 mph. How
long must they run to be at least
2 miles apart? The time must
be at least $\frac{1}{8}$ hour, or $7\frac{1}{2}$
minutes.

2. A roll of carpeting is $8\frac{1}{2}$ feet wide. Find the maximum length possible if the area is to be at most 100 square feet. The maximum length of the carpet is 16 feet.

3. The sum of three consecutive integers is greater than 63. Find the smallest integers for which this is possible. The integers are 21, 22, and 23.

POSSIBLE ERROR

Students often misinterpret phrases such as "at least," "no less than," "at most," and "no more than." To help them avoid confusion, you might use non-algebraic situations. For example, if Mary is at least 15 years old, she might be 15 *or* she might be older. If Jack is at most 16 years old, he could be 16, *or* he might be younger. Then you can translate these sentences as follows:

$$m \geq 15$$
$$j \leq 16$$

As a check, observe that if $t = \frac{4}{3}$, the distance between trains is $120(\frac{4}{3}) + 135(\frac{4}{3}) = 160 + 180 = 340$. If $t > \frac{4}{3}$, the distance is more than 340. If $t < \frac{4}{3}$, the distance is too small (less than 340).

Answer the question.

The time must be at least $1\frac{1}{3}$ hours, or 1 hour and 20 minutes.

EXAMPLE 2 A rectangular piece of cloth is $3\frac{1}{2}$ feet wide. Find the maximum length possible if the area is to be at most 42 square feet.

Use a variable. Let x = the length.

Then the area $= 3\frac{1}{2}x$.   Area = width × length.

Write an inequality. $3\frac{1}{2}x \leq 42$ The area is equal to or less than 42 ft².

Solve the inequality. $\frac{7}{2}x \leq 42$

$$\frac{2}{7} \cdot \frac{7}{2}x \leq \frac{2}{7} \cdot 42$$

$$x \leq 12$$

To check, observe that $\frac{7}{2}(12) = 42$. Also, note that if the length x were more than 12, the area would be too large.

Answer the question. The maximum length of the cloth is 12 feet.

EXAMPLE 3 The sum of three consecutive integers is greater than 54. Find the smallest integers for which this is possible.

Use a variable. Let n = the first integer.

Then n + 1 and n + 2 are the next two consecutive integers.

Write an inequality. The sum is greater than 54.

$$n + (n + 1) + (n + 2) > 54$$

Find the solution.

$$3n + 3 > 54$$
$$3n > 51$$
$$n > 17$$

Answer the question. Since $n > 17$ and n is an integer, then the smallest possible value for n is 18. The integers are 18, 19, 20.

To check, show that the sum is greater than 54. Also, note that if n = 17, the sum would not be greater than 54, but would equal 54.

The question in Example 3 could be rephrased to ask for *all* sets of three consecutive integers whose sums are greater than 54. In this case, the answer would consist of an infinite set of number triples:

$$\{(18, 19, 20), (19, 20, 21), (20, 21, 22), \ldots\}$$

CHAPTER 10

CLASS EXERCISES

*Use a variable and write an inequality for part **a**. Then answer parts **b** and **c**.*

1. **a.** Three added to a number is at least 17. $x + 3 \geq 17$
   b. Describe all numbers for which the statement in **a** is true. Numbers greater than or
   c. Find the smallest answer possible for part **a**. 14   equal to 14

2. **a.** Five subtracted from a number is no more than 23. $x - 5 \leq 23$
   b. Describe all numbers for which the statement in **a** is true.   Numbers less than or
   c. Find the largest answer possible for part **a**. 28   equal to 28

3. **a.** The sum of two consecutive odd positive integers is less than 32. $n + (n + 2) < 32$
   b. Find all pairs of integers for which **a** is true.   (13, 15), (11, 13), (9, 11), (7, 9),
   c. Find the largest pair of such integers possible. (13, 15)   (5, 7), (3, 5), (1, 3)

Write an inequality and answer the questions.

4. The sum of 3 and twice a number is at most 27. Find the largest
   such number possible. $3 + 2x \leq 27$; 12

5. Six less than 4 times a number is no less than 10. Find the smallest
   such number possible. $4x - 6 \geq 10$; 4

EXERCISES

A *Use a variable and write an inequality for part **a**. Then answer parts **b** and **c**.*

1. **a.** Two added to 3 times a positive number is at most 17. $3n + 2 \leq 17$
   b. Find all numbers for which part **a** is true. Numbers less than or equal to 5
   c. What is the largest possible answer for part **a**?   5

2. **a.** The sum of two consecutive integers is no less than 63. $n + (n + 1) \geq 63$
   b. Find all pairs of integers for which part **a** is true.   (31, 32), (32, 33), (33, 34), . . .
   c. What is the smallest pair of integers for which part **a** is true?   (31, 32)

3. **a.** Four times the sum of 5 and a number is at least 80. $4(5 + x) \geq 80$
   b. Describe all numbers for which part **a** is true. Numbers greater than or equal to 15
   c. What is the smallest such number possible?   15

4. **a.** The sum of two positive consecutive even integers is less than 48. $n + (n + 2) < 48$
   b. Find all pairs of integers for which part **a** is true. (22, 24), (20, 22), (18, 20), . . . , (2, 4)
   c. Find the pair with the largest sum.   (22, 24)

Use an inequality to solve each problem.

5. Four times the sum of 5 and twice a number is greater than or
   equal to 100. What is the smallest value possible for this number?   10

6. The sum of three consecutive integers is no more than 60. Find the
   largest integers for which this is possible.   19, 20, 21

7. If 3 is added to 4 times an integer, the sum is less than 15. What is
   the largest integer for which this is possible?   2

INEQUALITIES

DAILY QUIZ

Use an inequality to solve each problem.

1. Five added to 4 times a positive number is at most 17. What is the largest number for which this can be true?   3
2. The sum of three consecutive integers is no less than 81. What are the smallest integers for which this is true? 26, 27, 28
3. Three times the sum of 7 and a number is at least 39. What is the smallest such number possible?   6
4. Three times the sum of 6 and five times a number is greater than or equal to 93. What is the smallest possible value for this number?   5
5. The perimeter of an equilateral triangle is at least 147 mm. What is the smallest possible length of each side?   49 mm

ASSIGNMENT GUIDE
(pages 373–374)

Minimum course: omit
Average course: 1–4,
             5–13 odd
   second day: 6–14 even
Maximum course: 1–4,
             5–17 odd
   second day: 6–18 even

373

EXTRA PRACTICE, page 528

ENRICHMENT ACTIVITY

Challenge your students to prove that the largest rectangular garden area that can be enclosed with 100 foot of fencing is a square with sides measuring 25 feet.

Let w be the width of a rectangle that does *not* measure 25 feet by 25 feet. Then the length will be equal to $50 - w$, and the area will be $w(50 - w)$. The proof involves showing that:

$$25^2 > w(50 - w)$$

Rewrite the inequality as follows:

$$625 > 50w - w^2$$
$$w^2 - 50w + 625 > 0$$
$$(w - 25)^2 > 0$$

This last inequality is true for all w ($w \neq 25$). Since the steps are reversible, the first inequality is true for all w ($w \neq 25$). So the square has the greatest area.

8. The perimeter of an equilateral triangle is at least 18 centimeters. What is the shortest possible length of each side?   6 cm

9. Find the three smallest consecutive even integers such that the sum of the two larger integers is less than 3 times the first.   8, 10, 12

10. Adam is 2 years older than Beth. The sum of their ages is less than 20. What is the oldest that each could be?   Beth 8, Adam 10

11. Two jet aircraft take off from the same air base at the same time. One flies due north at 640 mph. The other jet flies due south at 580 mph. For how many hours will they be no more than 4880 miles apart?   4

12. Find all sets of four consecutive positive integers such that the largest integer in the set is greater than twice the smallest integer in the set.
    {1, 2, 3, 4}, {2, 3, 4, 5}

13. The average of six consecutive integers is less than 15. What are the largest values possible for the integers?   12, 13, 14, 15, 16, 17

14. Find the four greatest consecutive odd integers whose average is greater than their sum.   −5, −3, −1, 1

15. Ron received 78, 85, 70, and 83 on four tests. What is the lowest score he can make on the fifth test to average at least 80? at least 85?
    84; 109 (not possible if the highest possible test score is 100)

16. Rose and Ted will share prize money of at least $300. If Rose's prize is to be $50 more than Ted's, what is the minimum amount each will receive?
    Ted $125; Rose $175

17. A girl has saved 40 coins consisting only of nickels and quarters. The total value of the coins is less than $5.30. What is the least number of nickels she must have? 24

18. The sum of the digits of a two-digit number is 7. This number is greater than twice the number obtained by reversing the digits. Find the smallest possible value for the original number. 52

EXTRA TOPIC

The Language of Sets

The **union** (∪) of two sets is a set that contains the members *in one or the other or both* sets. The **intersection** (∩) contains *only those members common to both* sets. Thus if,

$$H = \{h, a, t\} \qquad C = \{c, o, a, t\} \quad \text{and} \quad S = \{s, o, c, k\},$$

then $H \cup C = \{a, c, h, o, t\}$ and $H \cap C = \{a, t\}$.

What are the members of $H \cup S$? of $H \cap S$? of $C \cap S$? of $C \cup S$?
$H \cup S = \{a, c, h, k, o, s, t\}$; $H \cap S = \emptyset$; $C \cap S = \{c, o\}$; $C \cup S = \{a, c, k, o, s, t\}$

374

10-5 Compound Inequalities

OBJECTIVE

To solve and graph conjunctions and disjunctions.

Two separate inequalities may be combined into one sentence, which is called a **compound inequality.**

When the inequality $x > 2$ is combined with $x < 4$ by the connective word **and,** the compound inequality is a **conjunction.** Thus

$$x > 2 \text{ and } x < 4$$

is a *conjunction*. This conjunction may also be written in the shortened form

$$2 < x < 4$$

Here are some ways that this conjunction can be read.

> x is greater than 2 *and* x is less than 4.
>
> 2 is less than x *and* x is less than 4.
>
> x is *between* 2 and 4.

A conjunction is true if *both of its parts are true.* To graph the solution set of $2 < x < 4$, we locate all points for which $x > 2$ and $x < 4$. That is, we graph the **intersection** of the individual solution sets.

Here are the graphs of some other conjuctions.

Conjunction	Short Form	Graph
$-6 \le x$ and $x \le 0$	$-6 \le x \le 0$	
$x > -1$ and $x \le 6$	$-1 < x \le 6$	
$x > 5$ and $x < 2$	none	no graph

There is no graph for the conjunction $x > 5$ and $x < 2$ because there is no solution. The *solution set* is the **empty set,** whose symbol is ∅.

The solution of a compound inequality may be stated as a simpler, equivalent inequality, as in Example 1 on page 376.

LESSON NOTES

In this lesson the students learn to solve compound inequalities. A conjunction is an *a and b* statement. The statement *a or b* is a disjunction. You may wish to use Venn diagrams to illustrate the difference between the two ideas. In these diagrams, *A* represents the set of values that make inequality *a* true; *B* represents the set of values that make inequality *b* true.

a and b   a or b

In the language of sets, a conjunction involves the intersection of two sets; a disjunction involves the union of two sets.

The text and the model examples illustrate the methods for graphing conjunctions and disjunctions. Use Example 4 to give careful attention to the distinction between graphing a conjunction and graphing a disjunction.

In Example 5a, note that there is a finite number of integers in the interval $-1 \le x < 3$. If non-integral numbers were permitted, there would be an infinite number of solutions to the inequality.

EXAMPLE 1   Solve the conjunction $3 < 2x + 4 < 7$.

Separate the conjunction into two parts and solve each part.

$3 < 2x + 4$ *and* $2x + 4 < 7$

$-1 < 2x$ *and* $2x < 3$ Subtract 4.

$-\frac{1}{2} < x$ *and* $x < \frac{3}{2}$ Divide by 2.

The solution consists of all x-values where $-\frac{1}{2} < x$ and $x < \frac{3}{2}$.

Thus the solution may be written as $-\frac{1}{2} < x < \frac{3}{2}$.

By not separating the parts, $3 < 2x + 4 < 7$ can be solved in a briefer way.

$3 < 2x + 4 < 7$

$3 - 4 < 2x + 4 - 4 < 7 - 4$ Subtract 4 from all three parts.

$-1 < 2x < 3$

$-\frac{1}{2} < x < \frac{3}{2}$ Divide all three parts by 2.

When two inequalities are combined with the connective word **or**, the resulting compound inequality is called a **disjunction.** Thus $x < -2$ or $x > 2$ is a *disjunction.* It is read:

x is less than -2 or x is greater than 2.

Note that there is no short way of writing a disjunction without using the connective word *or*.

A disjunction is true when *at least one of the individual inequalities is true.* Therefore the graph of $x < -2$ or $x > 2$ consists of all points in either individual graph, including any points common to both.

The graph of $x < -2$ or $x > 2$ is the **union** of the graphs of the individual solution sets.

EXAMPLE 2   Solve and graph the disjunction $x + 7 < 0$ or $x - 1 \geq 4$.

First solve and graph each separate inequality.

$x + 7 < 0$ $x - 1 \geq 4$
$x < -7$ $x \geq 5$

Write the solution. Form the union of the two graphs.

$x < -7$ or $x \geq 5$

376

EXAMPLE 3   Solve and describe the solution set of $x + 2 > 0$ or $2x - 1 < 5$.

$x + 2 > 0$ or $2x - 1 < 5$
$x > -2$ or $2x < 6$
$x > -2$ or $x < 3$

Since every real number is either greater than -2 or less than 3, the solution set consists of all real numbers.

Do not confuse conjunctions with disjunctions. The next example will help you to understand the difference.

EXAMPLE 4   Graph   **a.** the disjunction $x > -3$ or $x > 3$
              b. the conjunction $x > -3$ and $x > 3$

First graph the individual inequalities.

$x > -3$ $x > 3$

a. Form the union of the individual graphs. Note that all x-values that satisfy $x > 3$ also satisfy $x > -3$.

$x > -3$ or $x > 3$

b. Form the intersection of the individual graphs. Note that the common x-values satisfy $x > 3$.

$x > -3$ and $x > 3$

EXAMPLE 5   List all integers that satisfy each compound inequality. Use braces to show the solution set.

a. $-1 \leq x < 3$ **b.** $x > 3$ *or* $x \leq -5$

$\{-1, 0, 1, 2\}$ $\{\ldots, -7, -6, -5, 4, 5, 6, \ldots\}$

CLASS EXERCISES

*Write each conjunction in the short form that does not use **and**.*

1. $x > 6$ and $x < 10$
   $6 < x < 10$

2. $x \geq -3$ and $x \leq 5$
   $-3 \leq x \leq 5$

3. $0 < x$ and $x < 1.5$
   $0 < x < 1.5$

*Write each conjunction in the form that uses **and**.*

4. $0 \leq x \leq 1$
   $x \geq 0$ and $x \leq 1$

5. $-8 < y \leq 3$
   $y > -8$ and $y \leq 3$

6. $14 > x \geq -10$
   $x \geq -10$ and $x < 14$

Graph each compound inequality.

7. $-3 < x < 1$

8. $x \leq 7$ or $13 \leq x$

9. $x > 2$ or $x < -2$

10. $-5 \leq x \leq 5$

11. $x < -11$ or $x \geq 8$

12. $x > 2$ and $x > -2$

*Tell whether -3 is a solution of the compound inequality. Write **yes** or **no**.*

13. $x \geq 2$ or $x \leq -2$ Yes   **14.** $x < -3$ or $x > 3$ No   **15.** $x > -4$ and $x < -2$ Yes

INEQUALITIES   **377**

377

ENRICHMENT ACTIVITY

Have students explore unusual compound sentences such as the following.

1. $5 > 2$ or $x < 3$
   This is true for all numbers since 5 is always greater than 2. In a disjunction, p or q, if one part of the disjunction is true, the whole disjunction is true.
2. $2 > 5$ and $x < 3$
   The solution set is the empty set. For a conjunction, p and q, to be true, both parts of the conjunction must be true. Since the first part is false, the conjunction is false regardless of any value of x in the second part.

ADDITIONAL ANSWERS
Class Exercises

9. ←——○———○——→
       -2 2

10. ←——●———●——→
        -5 5

11. ←——○———●——→
        -11 8

12. ←———○———→
           2

Exercises

4. ←——○———○——→
       -4 1

5. ←——○———○——→
       -5 -1

6. ←——○———○——→
       -3 5

7. ←——●———●——→
       2 3

8. ←——●———●——→
       -5 -1

9. ←———○———→
          2

[Answers continue on page A7.]

EXERCISES

A *Which of the numbers $-6, 1, 10$ are in the solution set of the given inequality?*

1. $x > 9$ or $x < 1$ $\quad -6, 10$ **2.** $x \geq -6$ and $x > 0$ $\quad 1, 10$ **3.** $-5 \leq x \leq 8$ $\quad 1$

Graph each compound inequality.

4. $-4 < x < 1$ **5.** $-5 < x < -1$ **6.** $x \geq -3$ and $x < 5$

7. $x \geq 3$ or $x \leq 2$ **8.** $x \leq -5$ or $x \geq -1$ **9.** $x > 2$ or $x > 4$

Solve each compound inequality.

10. $3 < x + 2 < 5$ **11.** $2 < x + 1 < 6$ **12.** $-2 \leq x + 3 < 0$

13. $2x > 6$ or $3x < -9$ **14.** $4x \leq 12$ or $5x > 20$ **15.** $-4 \leq x - 2 < -1$

16. $7 < x - 5 \leq 10$ **17.** $4 < 2x$ and $2x < 8$ **18.** $9 > 3x$ and $3x > 6$

19. $x \geq 3$ or $x - 2 \leq 4$ **20.** $-1 < x - 4$ and $x - 4 < 0$

List all integers that satisfy each compound inequality.

21. $-9 < x \leq 0$ **22.** $-4 < x < -2$ $\quad \{-3\}$ **23.** $x > 5$ or $x \leq -5$
$\{-8, -7, -6, -5, -4, -3, -2, -1, 0\}$ $\qquad\qquad\qquad\qquad \{\ldots, -8, -7, -6, -5, 6, 7, 8, \ldots\}$

24. $-6 < x < 1$ **25.** $x > -4$ or $x < -1$ **26.** $x \geq 5$ or $x \leq -1$
$\{-5, -4, -3, -2, -1, 0\}$ $\qquad$ All integers $\qquad\qquad \{\ldots, -3, -2, -1, 5, 6, 7, \ldots\}$

B *Solve, and graph the solution set.*

27. $-9 \leq -3x \leq 12$ **28.** $4 < 2x + 6 < 10$ **29.** $-9 \leq 3x - 6 \leq 0$

30. $-8 < 6 - 2x < 8$ **31.** $2 < 4x + 10 < 14$ **32.** $-3 < 2x + 3 \leq 0$

33. $2x + 3 > 5$ or $x - 2 < -5$ **34.** $x + 4 \leq 1$ or $2x - 8 \geq 2$

35. $6x > 18$ or $4x + 3 < 15$ **36.** $8 - 7x \geq -13$ and $8 - 7x \leq 1$

Sample $x - 2 \neq 3 \longrightarrow x - 2 > 3$ or $x - 2 < 3$

$\qquad\qquad\qquad\qquad\qquad x > 5$ or $x < 5$ $\qquad$ ◄———⊕———► $\quad 5$

37. $x + 2 \neq 10$ **38.** $x - 1 \neq 4$ **39.** $x + 6 \neq -1$

40. $2x - 3 \neq 11$ **41.** $x \not\geq 3$ and $x \not< 1$ **42.** $x \not> -2$ or $x \not\leq 1$

C *Graph, or state that the solution is ∅, the empty set.*

43. $-3 < x < 2$ or $1 < x < 4$ **44.** $-3 < x < 2$ and $1 < x < 4$

45. $1 < x < 3$ or $3 < x < 5$ **46.** $1 < x < 3$ and $3 < x < 5$

Samples $x^2 > 9 \longrightarrow x > 3$ or $x < -3$ $\qquad x^2 \leq 36 \longrightarrow x \leq 6$ and $x \geq -6$

◄———⊕———⊕———► $\quad -3 \quad 3$ $\qquad\qquad$ ◄———●———●———► $\quad -6 \quad 6$

47. $x^2 \geq 4$ **48.** $x^2 \leq 4$ **49.** $(x - 1)^2 < 9$ **50.** $2y^2 + 1 < 9$

CHAPTER 10

EXTRA PRACTICE, page 527

10-6 Inequalities and Absolute Value

OBJECTIVE

To solve and graph inequalities involving absolute values.

Recall that the absolute value of a number is its distance from 0 on the number line.

$|x| = 4$ has two solutions.

$|x| = 4$ is equivalent to $x = 4$ or $x = -4$.

The inequality $|x| < 4$ is true for any number whose distance from the origin is *less* than 4.

$|x| < 4$ is equivalent to the *conjunction*

$$x > -4 \text{ and } x < 4$$
$$-4 < x < 4$$

Also, $|x| > 4$ is true for any number whose distance from the origin is *greater* than 4.

$|x| > 4$ is equivalent to the *disjunction*

$$x < -4 \text{ or } x > 4$$

EXAMPLE 1   Solve and graph $|t - 2| < 1$.

$$|t - 2| < 1$$
$$-1 < t - 2 < 1 \qquad \text{Write without absolute-value symbols.}$$
$$1 < t < 3 \qquad \text{Add 2 to each part.}$$

The solution set consists of all numbers between 1 and 3.

If the inequality in Example 1 were $|t - 2| \le 1$, then the compound inequality would be $1 \le t \le 3$, with 1 and 3 included in the solution set.

EXAMPLE 2   Solve and graph $|2x - 5| \ge 3$.

$$|2x - 5| \ge 3$$
$$2x - 5 \le -3 \quad \text{or} \quad 2x - 5 \ge 3 \qquad \text{Write without absolute-value symbols.}$$
$$2x \le 2 \quad \text{or} \quad 2x \ge 8$$
$$x \le 1 \quad \text{or} \quad x \ge 4$$

The solution set consists of all numbers less than 1 or greater than 4, as well as 1 and 4.

LESSON NOTES

In this lesson, students solve inequalities in which the variable appears within the absolute-value symbol. Such inequalities are equivalent to compound inequalities. For example:

$|x| > 3$ means that $x < -3$ or $x > 3$.
$|x| < 3$ means that $x > -3$ and $x < 3$.

(Point out to students that the second inequality can be stated in the shortened form, $-3 < x < 3$.)

To solve an absolute-value inequality, we can rewrite it as a compound inequality without absolute-value symbols and then solve this compound inequality. This procedure is illustrated in Examples 1 and 2.

Note that the exercises also require the students to reverse the process, rewriting compound inequalities as absolute-value inequalities.

ALTERNATE EXAMPLES

1. Solve and graph: $|t - 3| < 2$
   $1 < t < 5$

2. Solve and graph: $|4x - 10| \ge 6$
   $x \le 1$ or $x \ge 4$

DAILY QUIZ

Rewrite without using absolute-value symbols.

1. $|x| \leq 3$ $-3 \leq x \leq 3$
2. $|x| > 4$ $x > 4$ or $x < -4$
3. Rewrite $-2 < x < 2$ using absolute-value symbols. $|x| < 2$

Solve and graph.

4. $|x - 2| < 1$ $1 < x < 3$

5. $|4x - 3| \geq 5$

$x \geq 2$ or $x \leq -\frac{1}{2}$

ADDITIONAL ANSWERS

Exercises

13.

[Answers continue on page 381.]

380

CLASS EXERCISES

Rewrite each inequality without absolute-value symbols.

1. $|x| < 2$
$-2 < x < 2$

2. $|z| \leq 5$
$-5 \leq z \leq 5$

3. $|s| > 1$
$s > 1$ or $s < -1$

4. $|t| \geq 1$
$t \geq 1$ or $t \leq -1$

5. $|y - 1| < 2$
$-2 < y - 1 < 2$

For each graph, write an inequality with absolute-value symbols.

6. $|x| < 3$

7. $|x| \leq 2$

8. $|x| > 1$

9. $|x| \geq \frac{1}{2}$

EXERCISES

A   *Rewrite each inequality without absolute-value symbols.*

1. $|x| \leq 9$ $-9 \leq x \leq 9$
2. $|n| \geq 4$ $n \geq 4$ or $n \leq -4$
3. $|y| < 87$ $-87 < y < 87$

4. $|y + 3| < 1$
$-1 < y + 3 < 1$
5. $|y - 5| \geq 1$
$y - 5 \geq 1$ or $y - 5 \leq -1$
6. $|x - 2| \leq 31$
$-31 \leq x - 2 \leq 31$

Use absolute-value symbols to rewrite each inequality.

7. $-8 < x < 8$ $|x| < 8$
8. $x > 5$ or $x < -5$ $|x| > 5$
9. $x > 1.3$ or $x < -1.3$
$|x| > 1.3$

10. $x \geq \frac{3}{4}$ or $x \leq -\frac{3}{4}$
$|x| \geq \frac{3}{4}$
11. $x \geq -2$ and $x \leq 2$
$|x| \leq 2$
12. $-\frac{1}{3} < x < \frac{1}{3}$
$|x| < \frac{1}{3}$

Solve and graph.

13. $|y - 1| < 2$ $-1 < y < 3$
14. $|y - 1| > 2$
$y > 3$ or $y < -1$
15. $|x + 2| \leq 4$ $-6 \leq x \leq 2$

16. $|x + 2| \geq 4$
$x \geq 2$ or $x \leq -6$
17. $|x - 10| < 1$ $9 < x < 11$
18. $|t + 9| > 4$
$t > -5$ or $t < -13$

B   19. $|2x| < 2$ $-1 < x < 1$
20. $|3x| \leq 9$ $-3 \leq x \leq 3$
21. $\left|\frac{1}{2}x\right| < 1$ $-2 < x < 2$

22. $|4x| > 4$
$x > 1$ or $x < -1$
23. $|-x| \geq 3$
$x \geq 3$ or $x \leq -3$
24. $\left|\frac{1}{3}x\right| \geq 2$ $x \geq 6$ or $x \leq -6$

25. $|5 - x| < 2$ $3 < x < 7$
26. $|2 - x| \geq 1$
$x \geq 3$ or $x \leq 1$
27. $|2x - 1| < 3$ $-1 < x < 2$

28. $|1 - 2x| < 3$
$-1 < x < 2$
29. $|2x + 1| \geq 3$
$x \geq 1$ or $x \leq -2$
30. $\left|\frac{1}{2}x - 1\right| > 1$ $x > 4$ or $x < 0$

31. $\left|1 - \frac{1}{2}x\right| \leq 1$
$0 \leq x \leq 4$
32. $|3x - 4| < 1$ $1 < x < \frac{5}{3}$
33. $\left|x + \frac{1}{2}\right| > 4$
$x > 3\frac{1}{2}$ or $x < -4\frac{1}{2}$

C   *Solve each inequality.*

34. $|3x - 4| < \frac{1}{2}$ $\frac{7}{6} < x < \frac{3}{2}$
35. $|x| < 0$ $\emptyset$
36. $3|5x - 2| < 6$ $0 < x < \frac{4}{5}$

37. $|x| > 0$ $x > 0$ or $x < 0$
38. $\frac{1}{2}|3 - 2x| < \frac{1}{4}$ $\frac{5}{4} < x < \frac{7}{4}$
39. $3|x - 1| < |x - 1| + 2$
$0 < x < 2$

380

EXTRA PRACTICE, page 527

The inequality $2 < x < 4$ can be written as $|x - 3| < 1$. Every point on the graph is less than 1 unit from 3, the midpoint of the interval.

Use the observation above to write an inequality of the form $|x - m| < r$ for the given graph.

40. $|x - 2| < 1$ **41.** $|x - 5| < 3$

42. $|x - 2| < 3$ **43.** $|x + \frac{1}{2}| < 2\frac{1}{2}$

*44. Solve and graph the compound inequality $|x - 2| < 2$ *and* $|x - 1| > \frac{1}{2}$.
$0 < x < 4$ and $x > \frac{3}{2}$ or $x < \frac{1}{2}$; this can be simplified to $0 < x < \frac{1}{2}$ or $\frac{3}{2} < x < 4$

EXTRA TOPIC

Quadratic Inequalities

The following steps show how to solve a *second-degree*, or **quadratic inequality.** To illustrate, we will use $x^2 - 3x - 4 > 0$.

• Write the inequality in factored form: $(x + 1)(x - 4) > 0$.
• Since $(x + 1)(x - 4)$ is equal to 0 when $x = -1$ or $x = 4$, mark the points -1 and 4 on the number line. The line is now separated into three parts: $x < -1$, $-1 < x < 4$, and $x > 4$.
• Determine the sign of $(x + 1)(x - 4)$ for each part, as follows. For $x < -1$, use a convenient test value such as $x = -2$.

$$(x + 1) = -2 + 1 = -1 < 0 \qquad (x - 4) = -2 - 4 = -6 < 0$$

Since both factors are negative, their product $(x + 1)(x - 4)$ is positive. You can use the test value $x = 0$ for $-1 < x < 4$, and $x = 5$ for $x > 4$, to obtain the signs of $(x + 1)(x - 4)$ shown below.

Signs of the factors	$(x + 1)(x - 4)$	$(x + 1)(x - 4)$	$(x + 1)(x - 4)$
	$-\quad -$	$+\quad -$	$+\quad +$
	$x < -1$	$-1 < x < 4$	$x > 4$

Sign of product $(x + 1)(x - 4)$		-1		4	
	$+$		$-$		$+$

• Since the inequalities $(x + 1)(x - 4) > 0$ and $x^2 - 3x - 4 > 0$ are equivalent, the required solution is $x < -1$ *or* $x > 4$.

What is the solution of $x^2 - 3x - 4 \geq 0$? of $x^2 - 3x - 4 < 0$?
$x \leq -1$ or $x \geq 4$ $-1 < x < 4$
Use this method to solve these inequalities.

1. $x^2 - 5x + 4 > 0$
$x < 1$ or $x > 4$
2. $x^2 + 5x + 6 \leq 0$
$-3 \leq x \leq -2$
3. $2x^2 - 7x + 3 > 0$
$x < \frac{1}{2}$ or $x > 3$
4. $3x^2 + 5x \leq 2$
$-2 \leq x \leq \frac{1}{3}$
5. $x^2 \geq x + 30$
$x \leq -5$ or $x \geq 6$
6. $x^3 - 6x^2 + 8x < 0$
$x < 0$ or $2 < x < 4$

INEQUALITIES

381

Mathematical logic has a special language and symbolism. In this Strategies for Problem Solving, we show how variables are used to represent statements rather than numbers. Thus, $p \wedge q$ represents a compound statement which is true only when both p and q are true; similarly, $p \vee q$ represents a compound statement that is true if either or both of p and q are true.

Notice how the ideas of logic, the basic ideas of sets, and the number line combine in the demonstration that $\sim(p \wedge q)$ is equivalent to $\sim p \vee \sim q$.

The work provides students with introductory ideas and symbolism that they may encounter again at more advanced levels.

ADDITIONAL ANSWERS

Strategies for Problem Solving

1. All values of x; $x < 5$
2. Graphs suggest that $\sim(p \vee q)$ and $\sim p \wedge \sim q$ are equivalent.

$p \vee q$

$\sim(p \vee q)$

$\sim p \wedge \sim q$

The second and third graphs are the same; $\sim(p \vee q)$ and $\sim p \wedge \sim q$ are equivalent.

STRATEGIES for PROBLEM SOLVING

Using Logic

The logic used in mathematical reasoning can often be better understood by using appropriate symbolism.

Simple statements are statements that are either *true* or *false*. They can be expressed with variables such as p and q. If a statement p is true, then its *negation* $\sim p$ (not p) is false. If a statement q is false, then $\sim q$ is true.

Compound statements are formed by using connecting words between simple statements. The most common *connectives* are *and* and *or*.

| conjunction | $p \wedge q$ | "p and q" |
| disjunction | $p \vee q$ | "p or q" |

The conjunction $p \wedge q$ is true only when **both** p *and* q are true. The disjunction $p \vee q$ is true when **either** p or q or **both** are true.

For example, let p represent $2 + 3 = 5$, and q represent $x < 9$.

Then $p \wedge q$ is true only for $x < 9$, since both parts must be true. However, $p \vee q$ is true for all values of x since p is always true.

Now let us use an example which suggests that $\sim(p \wedge q)$ is *equivalent* to $\sim p \vee \sim q$. Define p and q as follows. $p: x > 2$ $q: x < 5$

Then $p \wedge q$ represents $x > 2$ *and* $x < 5$. This can be shown on a number line.

$p \wedge q$

The negation of $p \wedge q$ is represented by the set of points not included in the graph above. Thus $\sim(p \wedge q)$ is the set of points $x \le 2$ or $x \ge 5$.

Now consider the graph of $\sim p \vee \sim q$. If p represents $x > 2$, then $\sim p$ represents $x \le 2$. If q represents $x < 5$, then $\sim q$ represents $x \ge 5$. Thus we have the following.

Notice that the graphs for $\sim(p \wedge q)$ and for $\sim p \vee \sim q$ are the same. This demonstrates the equivalence of these two statements.

1. Let p be $x + 2 < 7$ and q be $3 - 7 = -4$. Find the values of x so that $p \vee q$ is true. For what values of x is $p \wedge q$ true?
2. Let p be $x < -1$ and q be $x > 2$. Show that $\sim(p \vee q)$ is equivalent to $\sim p \wedge \sim q$.

CHAPTER 10

10-7 Graphing Inequalities in the Plane

OBJECTIVE

To graph linear inequalities in two variables.

The linear equation $y = 3x - 2$ and the linear inequality $y < 3x - 2$ are both open sentences in two variables.

The graph of a linear equation is a line that separates the plane into two regions, or *half-planes*. The graph of the related inequality includes all points (x, y) on one side of the line.

To graph the inequality $y < 3x - 2$, follow these steps, beginning with the *boundary line*.

Step 1 Draw the graph of $y = 3x - 2$ as a dashed line. This is the boundary for the half-plane.

Step 2 To decide which half-plane is the graph of $y < 3x - 2$, test the coordinates of a point on each side of the boundary.

Test $(0, 1)$ above the line.	Test $(4, 0)$ below the line.
$y < 3x - 2$	$y < 3x - 2$
$1 < 3(0) - 2$	$0 < 3(4) - 2$
$1 < -2$ False	$0 < 10$ True

Step 3 Shade the half-plane that contains $(4, 0)$, since $(4, 0)$ is in the solution set of the inequality.

For inequalities with $\leq$ or $\geq$, the boundary line is included in the graph. Therefore the boundary for $y \leq 3x - 2$ would be drawn as a *solid* line.

EXAMPLE 1

Graph $y + x \geq 3$.

Step 1 Write $y + x \geq 3$ as $y \geq -x + 3$, and graph the boundary $y = -x + 3$.

Step 2 Test a point on each side of the boundary.

$(0, 5)$ is above the line.

$5 + 0 \geq 3$
$5 \geq 3$ True

$(0, 0)$ is below the line.

$0 + 0 \geq 3$
$0 \geq 3$ False

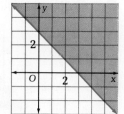

Step 3 Shade the half-plane that contains $(0, 5)$.

INEQUALITIES

383

WARM-UP EXERCISES

1. Which ordered pairs (x, y) make $y > x$ true?
   a. $(0, 1)$ **b.** $(4, 2)$
   c. $(-1, 0)$ **d.** $(-2, -2)$ *a, c*
2. Which ordered pairs (x, y) make $y + 2 < x$ true?
   a. $(0, 3)$ **b.** $(0, -3)$
   c. $(2, -1)$ **d.** $(-2, -2)$ *b, c*

LESSON NOTES

To graph an inequality in the coordinate plane, students should first graph a *boundary line*, and then shade correctly one of the regions determined by the boundary line. Each point in the shaded region should have coordinates that satisfy the inequality.

The boundary line is found by graphing the equation that results when we replace the inequality sign with an equal sign. If the inequality involves $\geq$ or $\leq$, the boundary line is drawn solid; the coordinates of points on the line satisfy the inequality. If the inequality involves $>$ or $<$, the boundary line is drawn dashed; the coordinates of points on the line do *not* satisfy the inequality.

As shown in the model examples, the decision as to which half-plane to shade can be made by using test points.

Exercises 44–52 involve absolute-value inequalities; each requires the graphing of a compound inequality. In Lesson 10-8, the students will work with systems of inequalities and will find that systems of inequalities involve conjunctions of two or more inequalities.

ALTERNATE EXAMPLE

1. Graph: $y + x \geq -3$

EXAMPLE 2   Graph $x > 3$.

Step 1   Graph the boundary $x = 3$ as a dashed line.

Step 2   Test $(0, 0)$ on the left of the boundary.
$0 > 3$ False

Test $(5, 0)$ on the right of the boundary.
$5 > 3$ True

Step 3   Shade the half-plane that contains $(5, 0)$.

CLASS EXERCISES

Write the equation of the boundary. Tell whether it should be drawn as a solid line or as a dashed line. Then draw the graph of the inequality.

1. $y < -x + 1$ **2.** $y \geq -x + 1$ **3.** $y < x - 1$ **4.** $y > x - 1$
$y = -x + 1$, dashed $y = -x + 1$, solid $y = x - 1$, dashed $y = x - 1$, dashed
5. $y \geq x$ **6.** $y \geq x + 3$ **7.** $y < x - 3$ **8.** $y \geq 2x - 3$
$y = x$, solid $y = x + 3$, solid $y = x - 3$, dashed $y = 2x - 3$, solid

Is the given point in the solution set of the inequality?

9. $(0, 0)$ **10.** $(4, 0)$ **11.** $(4, 0)$ **12.** $(0, 1)$
$y < -x + 1$ Yes $y \leq -x + 1$ No $y \geq -x + 1$ Yes $y \leq x + 1$ Yes

EXERCISES

A   Graph.

1. $y > x$ **2.** $y > 2x$ **3.** $y < -2x$ **4.** $y < -x$

5. $y > 3x$ **6.** $y > 4x$ **7.** $y < x + 1$ **8.** $y \leq x - 1$

9. $y < 2x - 3$ **10.** $y < 3x + 2$ **11.** $y > -x - 2$ **12.** $y > -x + 3$

13. $y \geq -2x + 3$ **14.** $y \leq -5x$ **15.** $y < 6x + 1$ **16.** $y > -3x - 2$

17. $y < -4x + 2$ **18.** $y \leq 5x - 3$ **19.** $y < x - 7$ **20.** $y > -x - 3$

21. $y < -x - 1$ **22.** $x > 1$ **23.** $x > -1$ **24.** $x < -2$

25. $x < 4$ **26.** $y > 2$ **27.** $y < -2$ **28.** $y \geq 3$

B   Write an inequality for each graph.

29.

$y < x$

30.

$y > 1$

31.

$x < -1$

384

CHAPTER 10

32.

$$y \le -x - 1$$

33.

$$y \ge x + 2$$

34.

$$y \le -\frac{1}{3}x + 1$$

Graph.

35. $4x + 2y - 6 > 0$　　**36.** $2x + 3y > 12$　　**37.** $3x + y - 6 < 0$

38. $y + 3x < 0$　　**39.** $2x - y > -4$　　**40.** $-3x + 2y \ge 12$

41. $-\frac{1}{4}x + y < -2$　　**42.** $\frac{1}{2}x - y \le 2$　　**43.** $\frac{x}{2} - \frac{y}{3} \ge 1$

C

Graph in the plane.

Samples　　$|x| > 1$　　　　$|x| \le 1$

$x > 1$ or $x < -1$　　$x \le 1$ and $x \ge -1$

44. $|x| \ge 3$　　**45.** $|x| < 4$　　**46.** $|y| = 2$

47. $|y| \le 3$　　**48.** $|x + 1| > 1$　　**49.** $|x - 2| < 3$

50. $|2y - 1| \le 5$　　**51.** $2(|y| - 1) < 3$　　***52.** $|x| \ge 2 - 2|x|$

CHECKPOINT

Solve for **x** and graph the solution set.

1. $4 < x + 3 < 6$　　**2.** $-1 \le x + 4 < 1$　　**3.** $5 < 2x + 7 < 11$

4. $3x + 4 > 10$ or $x - 1 < -4$　　**5.** $9 - 8x \ge -15$ and $9 - 8x \le 1$

6. $|x - 2| < 1$　　**7.** $|x - 2| > 1$　　**8.** $|3 - x| \ge 2$　　**9.** $|4x - 5| < 2$

INEQUALITIES

385

1. Does the ordered pair (3, 2) satisfy *both* inequalities? Yes

$y < x$

$x + y > 4$

2. Does the ordered pair (3, −2) satisfy *both* inequalities? No

$y < x + \frac{1}{2}$

$x - y < 0$

LESSON NOTES

In this lesson the students learn how to solve a system of linear inequalities by graphing. To find the graph of a system of inequalities in two variables, they graph each inequality on the same set of axes; then they identify the intersection of the solution sets. You may wish to point out that a system of inequalities involves the conjunction of two or more inequalities.

Example 2 illustrates a system of three inequalities. Here the graph of the solution set is the intersection of three half-planes. Exercises 18–26 provide additional practice with other systems consisting of three or more inequalities.

ALTERNATE EXAMPLES

1. Graph the system: $-2x + y > 1$
$2x + y < 3$

2. Graph the system: $y - x \geq 0$
$x + y \leq 1$
$y \geq -2$

10-8 Systems of Linear Inequalities

OBJECTIVE

To graph a system of linear inequalities in two variables.

When you graph a system of two equations, the solution shows all points (x, y) that satisfy both equations. Similarly, the graph of a system of two linear inequalities shows all points (x, y) that satisfy *both* inequalities.

EXAMPLE 1 Graph the system: $\begin{array}{c} -x + y > 2 \\ x + y < 1 \end{array}$

We want to find all points (x, y) such that $-x + y > 2$ *and* $x + y < 1$.

Step 1 Graph both inequalities on the same axes.

$-x + y > 2$ Draw the boundary $y = x + 2$.
$x + y < 1$ Draw the boundary $y = -x + 1$.

Both boundary lines are dashed.

Step 2 Shade the half-plane above the line $y = x + 2$.
Shade the half-plane below the line $y = -x + 1$.

The region with double shading is the required graph.

Step 3 Test a point in this region where the half-planes intersect. Does $(-3, 0)$ satisfy both inequalities, $-x + y > 2$ and $x + y < 1$?

Recall that for any inequality with $\geq$ or $\leq$, the boundary line is solid, since it is included in the graph of the inequality.

EXAMPLE 2 Graph the system: $\begin{array}{c} x - y \leq 2 \\ 2x + y \geq 0 \\ y \leq 1 \end{array}$

Step 1 All the boundary lines are solid.

$x - y \leq 2$ The boundary line is $x - y = 2$, or $y = x - 2$.

$2x + y \geq 0$ The boundary line is $2x + y = 0$, or $y = -2x$.

$y \leq 1$ The boundary line is $y = 1$.

Step 2 The half-planes above $2x + y = 0$, above $x - y = 2$, and below $y = 1$, intersect in a triangle and its interior. Shade this region.

Step 3 Show that the coordinates of a point in the shaded region, such as $(1, 0)$, satisfy all three given inequalities.

386

CLASS EXERCISES

Match each system of inequalities with the correct graph.

1. $y < x + 1$ **a.**
$\quad y \leq -x$ *b*

2. $y \geq 1 - x$
$\quad y < x$ *a*

3. $x < 2$
$\quad y \geq 1$ *c*

Graph each system of inequalities.

4. $y < 2x$
$\quad y < -x$

5. $y \leq x + 2$
$\quad y \geq -2x - 1$

6. $y > 2 - x$
$\quad y \leq 3$

7. $y \geq 1 + x$
$\quad x > -2$

EXERCISES

A *Graph each system of inequalities.*

1. $y > 2$
$\quad x < 2$

2. $y \leq -1$
$\quad y > 3x$

3. $x < 4$
$\quad y < \frac{1}{2}x$

4. $y < -x$
$\quad x > 2y$

5. $x \geq -3y$
$\quad y > 3x$

6. $x < 0$
$\quad x + y < 0$

7. $y \geq -x - 1$
$\quad y \leq -x + 3$

8. $y < -3x + 4$
$\quad y > -x + 1$

B

9. $3x + 2y > 6$
$\quad -2x + y > 3$

10. $5x - y \geq -4$
$\quad x < 4$

11. $x + y \leq 5$
$\quad 2x - y > 7$

12. $x + y > 4$
$\quad x - y > 2$

13. $3x + 2y > 5$
$\quad 2x + 3y > 1$

14. $x + 7y > 5$
$\quad 2x + y < 7$

Each shaded region is the solution of a system of linear inequalities.
Write the inequalities for each system.

15.

$y < 2; y > 2x - 2$

16.

$y \geq \frac{1}{3}x; y \geq -x$

17.

$y \geq 0; y \geq -x + 2$

INEQUALITIES

387

EXTRA PRACTICE, page 527

387

C

18.

$y < 1; y > -1; x > -1$

19.

$y \geq -2; y \leq -x + 1;$
$\qquad y \leq x + 1$

20.

$y \geq -3; x \leq 2; y \leq -\frac{1}{2}x + 2;$
$y \geq -3x - 3$

Graph each system of inequalities.

21. $2y + x \leq 6$
$\frac{1}{2}y + x \geq 0$
$4y \geq x$

22. $2y + x \leq 6$
$\frac{1}{2}y + x \leq 0$
$4y \geq x$

23. $x + y < 4$
$x - y > 2$
$2x + y > 4$

24. $x + y < 4$
$x - y < 2$
$2x + y > 4$

25. $2x + 3y > 6$
$x - y \geq 0$
$4x < 16$

26. $2x + 3y < 6$
$x - y \geq 0$
$4x < 16$
$y \geq -2$

*Graph each inequality.

27. $|2x - y| \leq x$

28. $|2x - y| < \frac{1}{2}$

29. $\left|\frac{1}{2}x - y\right| < 2$

ACTIVITY

Graphing Inequalities

For the inequalities below, find the point where each boundary line meets the next. Include the point (0, 0), which is on the first boundary, $y = -\frac{1}{3}x$, and on the last boundary, $y = x$. Graph these intersection points and the line segments connecting them. Then shade the region that satisfies all of the given inequalities.

1. $y \geq -\frac{1}{3}x$

2. $x \geq 3$

3. $y \leq x - 8$

4. $y \geq -2x - 2$

5. $y \geq \frac{1}{3}x - 9$

6. $x \geq 6$

7. $y \geq -11$

8. $x \leq 13$

9. $y \geq x - 15$

10. $x \leq 14$

11. $y \leq -x + 21$

12. $y \leq 10$

13. $y \leq x + 6$

14. $y \geq -5x + 18$

15. $y \leq x$

On the figure for Exercises 1–15, graph the following.

16. $y = -3$
for $3 \leq x \leq 5$

17. $y = -\frac{1}{2}x + 6$
for $4 \leq x \leq 6$

18. The point (5, 3)

Carpentry

Carpenters need to know many facts about lumber. For one thing, they must know the difference between nominal sizes and actual sizes. For example, 2 × 4's (two-by-four's) measure only about $1\frac{1}{2}'' \times 3\frac{1}{2}''$.

A carpenter is making a 10′ × 20′ deck out of 10′ redwood 2 × 4's. How many are needed to cover the 20′ length if $\frac{1}{4}''$ is allowed between boards?

For a good estimate, simply change 20 feet to inches and divide by 4.

$$\frac{20 \times 12}{4} = 60$$

However, an accurate answer would need more careful thinking.

Let n be the number of boards. Then $3\frac{1}{2}n$ is the total width of the boards placed together.

There will be $n - 1$ spaces between n boards. So $\frac{1}{4}(n - 1)$ is the total amount needed for the spaces.

The total width of the deck is to be 20′, or 240″. Hence we can write and solve the equation below.

$$3\frac{1}{2}n + \frac{1}{4}(n - 1) = 240$$

$$3\frac{1}{2}n + \frac{1}{4}n - \frac{1}{4} = 240$$

$$3\frac{3}{4}n = 240\frac{1}{4}$$

$$n = 64\frac{1}{15}$$

The solution $64\frac{1}{15}$ is not a meaningful answer. How can you use it to find the number of boards needed? How many boards would you use?   64

Absorb the extra $\frac{1}{15}$ of a board width in the spaces. They will be 0.254″ apart.

A 12′ × 24′ deck is to be made from pressure-treated 2 × 6's, which actually measure $1\frac{1}{2}'' \times 5\frac{1}{2}''$.

1. How many 12′ long 2 × 6's, using $\frac{3}{4}''$ spaces, are needed? Estimate first. Write an appropriate equation and use its solution to help find an answer.   Estimate: 48. Actual answer: 46 boards are needed.

2. If pressure-treated 2 × 6's cost 45¢ per running foot, what would be the cost of the 2 × 6's? Include a 6% sales tax. $263.30

Applications

The example on this Applications page will be easier to understand if students draw a picture of the problem.

They will *see* that n boards require $n - 1$ spaces between them.

When the answer turns out to be $64\frac{1}{15}$, some students might conclude that 65 boards are needed. Whereas this reasoning might be valid in many situations, it is not *realistic* in this case. A competent carpenter would buy only 64 boards, and increase the spaces separating them by an infinitesimal, undetectible amount.

These exercises review basic algebraic skills.

Simplify.

1. $x(x - 5) - 2(x^2 - 3)$
$- (x^2 + 2x - 1)$
$-2x^2 - 7x + 7$

2. $(-3x^2y)^3 \cdot (-xy^3)^2$ $-27x^8y^9$

Evaluate when $a = -5$, $b = -3$, and $c = -2$.

3. $a + (-b) - (-c) - ab$ -19

4. $\dfrac{abc}{a - b + c}$ $7\dfrac{1}{2}$

Solve each equation for x.

5. $x(x - 6) + 9 = (x - 3)^2$
Identity

6. $(x - 1)(x^2 - 25) = 0$ $1, 5, -5$

7. $|2x - 1| \geq 4$
$x \geq 2\dfrac{1}{2}$ or $x \leq -1\dfrac{1}{2}$

Solve each inequality for x, and graph the solution on a number line.

8. $5 - 2x > -5$ $x < 5$

9. $-5 \leq 1 - x < -1$ $2 < x \leq 6$

10. Is the following system of equations consistent or inconsistent, dependent or independent?

$5x - y = 3$ Independent
$y = 2 + 5x$ and inconsistent

[*Maintaining Skills continues on page 391.*]

ADDITIONAL ANSWERS

Review Exercises

9.
6

10.
15

11.
-8

12.
-2

13.
7

14.
-26

[*Answers continue on page 391.*]

390

CHAPTER 10 REVIEW

VOCABULARY

inequality (p. 362)
solution set (of an inequality) (p. 362)
trichotomy property (p. 363)
transitive property of inequalities (p. 363)
addition properties of inequalities (p. 366)
multiplication properties of inequalities (p. 368)

compound inequality (p. 375)
conjunction, *and* (p. 375)
intersection (p. 375)
disjunction, *or* (p. 376)
union (p. 376)
half-plane (p. 383)

SUMMARY

The major portion of this chapter deals with inequalities in one variable. Such inequalities are solved and graphed by using the addition and multiplication properties of inequalities. Then verbal problems are solved by making use of inequalities. Compound inequalities are considered next, which leads into the study of inequalities involving absolute values. The chapter concludes with graphing inequalities in two variables, and systems of such inequalities, in the coordinate plane.

REVIEW EXERCISES

10-1 *Use $<$, $>$, or $=$ to complete each statement.*

1. $-9 \underline{\ ?\ } -7$ $<$ **2.** $-11 \underline{\ ?\ } -13$ $>$ **3.** $\dfrac{3}{4} \underline{\ ?\ } \dfrac{3}{5}$ $>$

Write each sentence using an inequality symbol.

4. x is at most 7. $x \leq 7$ **5.** x is no less than 4. $x \geq 4$

Write the inequality for each graph.

6. $x < 1$ **7.** $x \geq 2$ **8.** $x < -3$

*Solve for **x** and graph the solution set.*

10-2 **9.** $4x + 13 < 3x + 19$ $x < 6$ **10.** $9x - 6 \leq 8x + 9$ $x \leq 15$ **11.** $6x + 4 > 12 + 7x$ $x < -8$

10-3 **12.** $5(4 + 2x) \geq 12 + 6x$ $x \geq -2$ **13.** $2x - 5 \not< 9$ $x \geq 7$ **14.** $4(2x - 3) \not= 5(2x + 8)$ $x > -26$

15. $5x + 4 < 2x$ $x < -\dfrac{4}{3}$ **16.** $6 + 4x \geq 8x$ $x \leq \dfrac{3}{2}$ **17.** $4 + 4x < 2x$ $x < -2$

18. $-\dfrac{x}{7} \leq 3$ $x \geq -21$ **19.** $\dfrac{x}{18} \geq -\dfrac{4}{3}$ $x \geq -24$ **20.** $-\dfrac{3}{4}x \leq -15$ $x \geq 20$

10-4 **21.** Write an inequality for part *a*. Then answer parts *b* and *c*.

a. Five times the sum of 6 and twice a number is at least 60. $5(6 + 2x) \geq 60$

b. Describe all numbers for which part **a** is true. Numbers greater than or equal to 3

c. What is the smallest such number possible? 3

390   CHAPTER 10

Solve each problem.

22. Three times the sum of 6 and twice a number is greater than or equal to 66. What is the smallest value possible for this number? 8

23. The perimeter of a square is at least 18 cm. What is the shortest possible length of each side? $4\frac{1}{2}$ cm

10-5 *Solve for* **x** *and graph the solution set of each compound inequality.*

24. $-7 \le -x \le 14$ **25.** $6 < 4x + 8 < 12$ **26.** $-9 \le 5x - 4 \le 1$

27. $-6 < 8 - x < 10$ **28.** $4 < 6x + 12 < 16$ **29.** $-1 \le 4x + 5 < 2$

30. $2x + 6 \le 2$ or $4x - 10 > 2$ **31.** $10 - 9x \ge -8$ and $10 - 9x \le 1$

10-6 *Solve for* **x** *and graph the solution set.*

32. $|4x| < 4$ **33.** $|5x| \le 15$ **34.** $\left|\frac{5}{2}x\right| < 10$

35. $|7 - 3x| < 4$ **36.** $|4 - 3x| \ge 3$ **37.** $|4x - 3| < 5$

38. $|3x + 2| > 8$ **39.** $\left|\frac{1}{2}x - 3\right| > 3$ **40.** $|4x + 3| \ge 5$

10-7 *Write an inequality for each graph.*

41.   **42.**   **43.**

$y > \frac{1}{2}x$ $y \le -1$ $y \le -x + 2$

Graph.

44. $6x - 2y - 8 > 2$ **45.** $4x + 5y > 20$ **46.** $5x + 3y - 6 < 0$

47. $y - 3x < 0$ **48.** $3x - y \le -5$ **49.** $-4x + 3y \ge 12$

10-8 *Graph each system of inequalities.*

50. $y > 3$
    $x < 3$

51. $y \le -2$
    $y \ge 2x$

52. $x < 3$
    $y < x$

53. $2x + 3y > 6$
    $-x + y > 3$

54. $4x - y \ge -4$
    $x < 2$

55. $x + y \le 4$
    $x - 2y > 4$

REVIEW

11. Write a second degree equation in the form $ax^2 + bx + c = 0$, if $a = 1$ and -3 and 2 are the roots of the equation.
$x^2 + x - 6 = 0$

12. If the line passing through the points $(8, -3)$ and $(5, n)$ has a slope of 0, what is the value of n? -3

13. Write the equation, in slope-intercept form, of the line that passes through the point $(-3, 7)$ and is parallel to the line $y = x$. $y = x + 10$

14. Express as a single fraction:
$\frac{1}{a} + \frac{1}{b} + \frac{1}{c}$ $\frac{bc + ac + ab}{abc}$

Factor completely.

15. $x^2y^2 - x^2 + 2y^2 - 2$
   $(x^2 + 2)(y + 1)(y - 1)$

16. $10x^2 - 35x + 15$
   $5(2x - 1)(x - 3)$

17. $25x^2 - \frac{1}{16}$ $\left(5x + \frac{1}{4}\right)\left(5x - \frac{1}{4}\right)$

18. What is 0.5% of 20? 0.1

19. 75 is what percent of 15? 500%

20. A fraction is equivalent to $\frac{3}{5}$. If 2 is added to both numerator and denominator, its value changes to $\frac{2}{3}$. Find the fraction. $\frac{6}{10}$

ADDITIONAL ANSWERS

Review Exercises

15.
$-\frac{4}{3}$

16.
$\frac{3}{2}$

17.
-2

18.
-21

19.
-24

20.
20

[Answers continue on page A11.]

6.
5

7.
17

8.
2

9.
8

12.
−3   1

13.
1   3

19.
1/2   1

20.
−8   −4

21.
3   5

24.

25.

CHAPTER 10 TEST

10-1 *Write each sentence using an inequality symbol.*

1. x is at least 5. $x \geq 5$

2. x is no more than 3. $x \leq 3$

Write the inequality for each graph.

3.
$x > -2$

4.
$x \geq 4$

5.
$x \leq 5$

Solve each inequality. Then graph the solution set.

10-2 **6.** $3x - 5 \leq 2x$ $x \leq 5$

7. $3(x - 1) \geq 2(x + 7)$ $x \geq 17$

10-3 **8.** $-6x + 14 < 2$ $x > 2$

9. $5(x + 6) \geq 9x - 2$ $x \leq 8$

10-4 **10.** The sum of three consecutive integers is greater than 132. Find the smallest set of integers for which this is possible.   44, 45, 46

11. Five times the sum of 7 and twice an integer is less than 105. What is the largest such integer?   6

10-5 *Graph each compound inequality.*

12. $x > -3$ and $x < 1$

13. $x < 1$ or $x \geq 3$

Solve each compound inequality.

14. $-10 \leq -5x \leq 15$
$-3 \leq x \leq 2$

15. $-5 < 3x + 1 < 0$
$-2 < x < -\frac{1}{3}$

16. $-12 \leq 3x - 6 < 3$
$-2 \leq x < 3$

17. $3x - 1 > 8$ or $2x + 1 < 5$
$x > 3$ or $x < 2$

18. $2 - 5x \geq -8$ and $3 - x \leq 5$
$x \leq 2$ and $x \geq -2$; $-2 \leq x \leq 2$

10-6 *Solve for **x** and graph the solution set.*

19. $|4x - 3| > 1$ $x > 1$ or $x < \frac{1}{2}$

20. $\left|\frac{1}{2}x + 3\right| < 1$
$-8 < x < -4$

21. $|8 - 2x| < 2$ $3 < x < 5$

10-7 *Write an inequality for each graph.*

22.

$y \leq \frac{1}{2}x - 1$

23.
$x > 1$

10-8 *Graph each system of inequalities.*

24. $y < 4$
$3x + 2y > 6$

25. $-x + 3y \geq 6$
$2x + y < 4$

CHAPTER 10

Ordering Numbers

To find the greatest number in a set, a computer must be programmed to compare each number with every other number.

In this program, numbers are entered by using READ-DATA statements. READ A, B, C instructs the computer to assign the first number in the DATA statement to A, the second number to B, and the third to C. At line 410, the computer loops back to line 110 and reads the next three values.

The Program	What It Does
100 REM GREATEST OF THREE	
110 READ A, B, C	Goes to DATA statement and reads three numbers in order.
120 PRINT A; B; C	Displays the three numbers.
200 IF A < = B THEN 300	Continues to next line if A > B.
210 IF A < = C THEN 350	Continues to next line if A > C.
220 PRINT A;	Displays A, since A > B and A > C.
230 GO TO 400	Skips next four lines because greatest number has been found.
300 IF B < = C THEN 350	Continues to next line if B > C.
310 PRINT B;	Displays B, the greatest number.
320 GO TO 400	
350 PRINT C;	Displays C, the greatest number.
400 PRINT " IS GREATEST"	Labels the answer.
410 GO TO 110	Returns for more data.
500 DATA 7, 3, 8, -9.8, 6.1, 2	Supplies two sets of data.
900 END	

```
RUN
7 3 8                          First set of three numbers
8 IS GREATEST
-9.8, 6.1, 2                   Second set of three numbers
6.1 IS GREATEST
OUT OF DATA                    Some computers display an error message.
```

If the numbers are too close together on your monitor, substitute commas for the semicolons in line 120.

For each set of data, tell what the computer will display and which lines of the program will be skipped, or not executed.
1. 500 DATA 56, 65, 31, 91, 6, 28
2. 500 DATA 8, 6, 4, 10, 15, 20, 16, 18, 17
3. 500 DATA 462.5, −8170, 71043, −6, −3, −2.5
4. What will the computer display for 500 DATA 2, ,3, 7 ? Why?
5. Why must the number 27,802,376 be entered without commas?

For more information about BASIC, see the Computer Handbook at the back of the book.

Computer Activity

To some students, the opening paragraph may seem to suggest that comparing numbers is easier for a person than for a computer. However, a computer is certainly more efficient when there are many numbers to be compared or ordered.

ADDITIONAL ANSWERS

Computer Activity
1. 65 IS GREATEST
   91 IS GREATEST
   Line 350 not executed.
2. 8 IS GREATEST
   20 IS GREATEST
   18 IS GREATEST
   All lines executed.
3. 71043 IS GREATEST
   -2.5 IS GREATEST
   Lines 220, 230, 310, and 320 are not executed.
4. 3 IS GREATEST
   The computer interprets the blank between the commas as a zero. Therefore it compares 2, 0, and 3.
5. If commas are used, the computer will interpret the entry as being three different numbers.

The opening lesson of this chapter discusses rational numbers in fraction and in decimal form. The students learn an algorithm for expressing infinite repeating decimals in fraction form.

Next, square roots are studied in radical form and evaluated by using the divide-and-average method and by using tables.

The major focus of attention in the chapter is on radicals. Students learn to multiply, divide, add, and subtract expressions involving radicals; for each operation, the text carefully presents appropriate methods of simplification.

Near the close of the chapter, the Pythagorean theorem is studied; then it is applied in deriving and using the distance formula for points on a coordinate plane. The chapter ends with a lesson devoted to solving radical equations.

CHAPTER 11

Suppose the height of this tower and the distance from the end of each wire to the base of the tower are known. The length of each wire can then be computed using the Pythagorean theorem.

RADICALS

Prerequisite Skills Review

Write the letter for the correct answer.

1. Which statement is false?   a

   a. $\left(3\frac{1}{2}\right)^2 = 9\frac{1}{4}$ **b.** $\left(2\frac{1}{2}\right)^2 = 6\frac{1}{4}$ **c.** $\left(1\frac{2}{3}\right)^2 = 2\frac{7}{9}$ **d.** $\left(4\frac{1}{2}\right)^2 = 20\frac{1}{4}$

2. Which statement is false?   b

   a. $490 = 7^2 \cdot 10$ **b.** $128 = 8^2 \cdot 4$ **c.** $48 = 4^2 \cdot 3$ **d.** $27 = 3^2 \cdot 3$

3. What is the quotient? $0.8\overline{)0.1608}$ c

   a. 20.1   **b.** 2.01   **c.** 0.201   **d.** 0.21

4. What is the quotient? $0.72\overline{)16.992}$ c

   a. 0.236   **b.** 2.36   **c.** 23.6   **d.** 236

5. Which statement is false?   d

   a. $(0.08)^2 = 0.0064$ **b.** $\dfrac{7 \cdot 7^4}{7^3} = 7^2$

   c. $(3r)^4 = 81r^4$ **d.** $(ab^3c^4)^2 = a^2b^5c^6$

6. Which expression is *not* equal to 2^6?   d

   a. $2^5 \cdot 2$ **b.** $(-2)^6$ **c.** $(2^3)^2$ **d.** $2^3 \cdot 2^2$

7. Which expression is equal to $2 \cdot 2 \cdot 3 \cdot 3 \cdot 5 \cdot 5$? c

   a. $10 \cdot 6^2$ **b.** $3 \cdot 10^2$ **c.** 30^2 **d.** $2 \cdot 15^2$

8. Which statement is false?   c

   a. $(12 \cdot 10)^2 = 14,400$ **b.** $5 \cdot 5^3 \cdot 2^6 = (5^2 \cdot 2^3)^2$

   c. $70^2 = 490$ **d.** $25 \cdot 10^2 = 50^2$

9. $5 \cdot 7 \cdot 7 \cdot 2 \cdot 2 \cdot 5 \cdot 10 \cdot 7 = \underline{\ ?\ }$ d

   a. $10(2 \cdot 5 \cdot 7)^2$ **b.** $3 \cdot 70$ **c.** $10^3 \cdot 21$ **d.** $(2 \cdot 5 \cdot 7)^3$

10. If $(2, 9)$ and $(-3, 5)$ represent two ordered pairs (x_1, y_1) and (x_2, y_2), then the value of $(x_2 - x_1)^2 = \underline{\ ?\ }$. b

   a. 16   **b.** 25   **c.** 49   **d.** 64

11. If $(0, -2)$ and $(-9, -8)$ represent two ordered pairs (x_1, y_1) and (x_2, y_2), then the value of $(y_2 - y_1)^2 = \underline{\ ?\ }$. b

   a. 4   **b.** 36   **c.** 81   **d.** 100

RADICALS

395

PREREQUISITE SKILLS REVIEW

For students who need additional practice with the algebraic skills in this Prerequisite Skills Review, you may assign Follow-Up exercises on page 505 in the students' books.

An item-by-item error analysis of the Prerequisite Skills Review appears on page T27.

LESSON NOTES

The procedure for writing a rational number $\frac{a}{b}$ in decimal form should be familiar to most students from their work in earlier mathematics courses. However, it is worthwhile to emphasize that $\frac{a}{b}$ means $a \div b$; we work the example $b\overline{)a}$ to find the decimal for $\frac{a}{b}$. To find the decimal for a number such as $1\frac{2}{3}$, we can find the decimal for $\frac{2}{3}$ (0.6666 . . .) and then write the decimal for $1\frac{2}{3}$ as 1.6666 . . ., or 1.$\overline{6}$, or we can express $1\frac{2}{3}$ as $\frac{5}{3}$ and then divide 5 by 3. To find the decimal for a negative number such as $-\frac{3}{8}$, we simply find the decimal for $\frac{3}{8}$ and affix a negative sign.

In discussing the procedure for writing repeating decimals as fractions (Examples 2 and 3), be sure the students realize: The number of digits repeating in the decimal indicates the power of ten by which we multiply. If the decimal has 1 digit repeating, we multiply by 10^1, or 10; if the decimal has 2 digits repeating, we multiply by 10^2, or 100; if the decimal has 3 digits repeating, we multiply by 10^3, or 1000.

11-1 Rational Numbers as Fractions and Decimals

OBJECTIVES

To write rational numbers as fractions or decimals.
To write terminating or repeating decimals as fractions.

Baseball standings show the number of wins (**W**) and losses (**L**) for each team. These are used to find the percent of games won (**Pct.**) and the number of games behind the leader (**GB**).

All the numbers listed in the standings are *rational numbers*.

Baseball
Central League Standings

	W	L	Pct.	GB
Aces	65	45	.591	—
Bravos	66	46	.589	—
Cords	63	48	.568	2½
Larks	57	54	.514	8½
Stars	51	59	.464	14
Elves	51	59	.464	14

Recall that a *rational number* is a number that can be written as a fraction $\frac{a}{b}$, where a and b are integers, $b \neq 0$. In the standings above, the Cords have 63 wins and a winning percent of 0.568. They are $2\frac{1}{2}$ games behind the Aces.

To show that each of these numbers is a rational number, write it as a ratio of two integers.

$$63 = \frac{63}{1} \qquad 0.568 = \frac{568}{1000} \qquad 2\frac{1}{2} = \frac{5}{2}$$

When a rational number is changed to decimal form, the decimal either terminates or the digits repeat without end.

$$\frac{5}{8} \longrightarrow 8\overline{)5.000} \begin{array}{r} 0.625 \\ \hline \end{array}$$
$$\begin{array}{r} 4\ 8 \\ \hline 20 \\ 16 \\ \hline 40 \\ 40 \\ \hline 0 \end{array}$$

$$\frac{5}{6} \longrightarrow 6\overline{)5.000} \begin{array}{r} 0.833 \cdots \\ \hline \end{array}$$
$$\begin{array}{r} 4\ 8 \\ \hline 20 \\ 18 \\ \hline 20 \\ 18 \\ \hline 2 \end{array}$$

The remainder is 0. So the decimal terminates.

The remainder will never be 0. The digit 3 repeats without end.

$$\frac{5}{8} = 0.625$$

$$\frac{5}{6} = 0.8333 \ldots$$

In a repeating decimal, a bar can be used to show which digits repeat endlessly. The bar below shows that 3 repeats in the decimal 0.8333 . . .

$$\frac{5}{6} = 0.8\overline{3}$$

EXAMPLE 1 Write the next six digits for each repeating decimal.

  a. $0.\overline{54}$ **b. $0.5\overline{4}$**   **c. $0.5\overline{44}$**

  0.54545454 . . .   0.54444444 . . .   0.544544544 . . .

All integers and all mixed numbers are rational numbers. Likewise, all terminating and repeating decimals are rational numbers.
To write a repeating decimal as a fraction, study these examples.

EXAMPLE 2 Write $0.\overline{72}$ as a fraction.

  Let n = 0.727272 . . .

  Since there are two repeating digits, multiply n by 10^2, or 100.

$$100n = 72.727272 \dots$$
$$\underline{n = 0.727272 \dots} \qquad \text{Now subtract } n \text{ from } 100\,n.$$
$$99n = 72.000000 \dots$$
$$99n = 72 \qquad \text{Solve for } n.$$
$$n = \frac{72}{99} = \frac{8}{11} \qquad \text{To check that } 0.\overline{72} = \tfrac{8}{11}, \text{ divide 8 by 11.}$$

In Example 2 there were two repeating digits, so n was multiplied by 100. If three digits repeat, multiply by 10^3, or 1000. If just one digit repeats, multiply by 10.

EXAMPLE 3 Write each repeating decimal as a fraction.

  a. $0.\overline{162}$ **b. $2.3\overline{5}$**

  Let n = 0.162162 . . .   Let n = 2.3555 . . .

  Then 1000n = 162.162162 . . .   Then 10n = 23.5555 . . .

  $\underline{n = 0.162162 \dots}$ $\underline{n = 2.3555 \dots}$

  999n = 162.000000 . . .   9n = 21.2000 . . .

  $n = \dfrac{162}{999} = \dfrac{6}{37}$ $n = \dfrac{21.2}{9} = \dfrac{212}{90} = \dfrac{106}{45}$

CLASS EXERCISES

Write each rational number as a terminating or repeating decimal.

1. $\frac{3}{8}$ 0.375   **2.** $-\frac{3}{4}$ −0.75   **3.** $\frac{7}{20}$ 0.35   **4.** $\frac{3}{15}$ 0.2   **5.** $1\frac{5}{15}$ $1.\overline{3}$

Write each rational number as a fraction in simplest form.

6. 0.45 $\frac{9}{20}$ **7.** −0.005 $-\frac{1}{200}$ **8.** 1.2 $\frac{6}{5}$ **9.** $0.\overline{7}$ $\frac{7}{9}$ **10.** $0.\overline{63}$ $\frac{7}{11}$

Does the given decimal equal $0.\overline{72}$?

11. $0.72\overline{72}$ Yes   **12.** 0.72 No   **13.** $0.72\overline{72}$ No   **14.** $0.\overline{7272}$ Yes

---

ALTERNATE EXAMPLES

1. Write the next six digits for each repeating decimal.
  a. $0.\overline{37}$ 0.37373737 . . .
  b. $0.3\overline{7}$ 0.37777777 . . .
  c. $0.\overline{377}$ 0.377377377 . . .

2. Write $0.\overline{48}$ as a fraction. $\frac{16}{33}$

3. Write each repeating decimal as a fraction.
  a. $0.\overline{138}$ $\frac{46}{333}$ **b.** $6.5\overline{7}$ $\frac{296}{45}$

DAILY QUIZ

Write each rational number as a decimal.

1. $\frac{17}{20}$ **2.** $3\frac{5}{9}$ **3.** $\frac{11}{8}$

  0.85 $3.\overline{5}$ 1.375

Write each rational number as a fraction in simplest form.

4. −1.76 $-\frac{44}{25}$ **5.** $0.\overline{18}$ $\frac{2}{11}$

ASSIGNMENT GUIDE
(pages 398–400)

Minimum course: 1–37 odd
    second day: *Extra Topic*
Average course: 1–55 odd
    second day: *Extra Topic*
Maximum course: 1–53 odd,
    54–59
    second day: *Extra Topic*

ENRICHMENT ACTIVITY

Have students find the decimals for the numbers in each row and indicate whether they are terminating or repeating decimals.

a. $\dfrac{1}{8}, \dfrac{9}{25}, \dfrac{131}{200}, \dfrac{33}{32}, \dfrac{517}{500}$

0.125, 0.36, 0.655, 1.03125, 1.034; all terminating

b. $\dfrac{2}{9}, \dfrac{8}{7}, \dfrac{7}{15}, \dfrac{5}{12}, \dfrac{7}{22}$

$0.\overline{2}, 1.\overline{142857}, 0.4\overline{6}, 0.41\overline{6}, 0.3\overline{18}$; all repeating

Then have them find the prime factors of each denominator and try to formulate a generalization that indicates whether a fraction $\dfrac{a}{b}$ can be expressed as a terminating decimal or whether it has only a repeating decimal as its decimal equivalent. A number $\dfrac{a}{b}$ in simplest form has a decimal that terminates if b has no prime factors other than 2 or 5. A number $\dfrac{a}{b}$ in simplest form has a decimal that repeats if b has any prime factors other than 2 or 5.

ADDITIONAL ANSWERS

Exercises

60. No
61. $b - 1$

EXERCISES

A   Write the first ten decimal places in each decimal.

1. $0.3\overline{5}$
0.3555555555

2. $0.\overline{35}$
0.3535353535

3. $0.\overline{354}$
0.3543543543

4. $0.3\overline{54}$
0.3545454545

5. $0.\overline{69}$
0.6969696969

6. $1.2\overline{47}$
1.2474747474

7. $2.\overline{338}$
2.3383383383

8. $-3.\overline{0001}$
−3.0001001001

Write each rational number as a decimal. Then write **T** or **R** to tell whether the decimal is terminating or repeating.

9. $\dfrac{1}{3}$ $0.\overline{3}$, R   **10.** $\dfrac{2}{3}$ $0.\overline{6}$, R   **11.** $\dfrac{3}{8}$ 0.375, T   **12.** $\dfrac{5}{8}$ 0.625, T   **13.** $\dfrac{5}{4}$ 1.25, T

14. $\dfrac{7}{10}$ 0.7, T   **15.** $\dfrac{4}{9}$ $0.\overline{4}$, R   **16.** $\dfrac{8}{9}$ $0.\overline{8}$, R   **17.** $3\dfrac{4}{9}$ $3.\overline{4}$, R   **18.** $\dfrac{2}{11}$ $0.\overline{18}$, R

19. $\dfrac{6}{11}$ $0.\overline{54}$, R   **20.** $\dfrac{6}{8}$ 0.75, T   **21.** $\dfrac{7}{8}$ 0.875, T   **22.** $\dfrac{9}{8}$ 1.125, T   **23.** $1\dfrac{13}{40}$ 1.325, T

Write each rational number as a fraction in simplest form.

24. 0.67 $\dfrac{67}{100}$ **25.** 0.81 $\dfrac{81}{100}$ **26.** 7.8 $\dfrac{39}{5}$ **27.** 200 $\dfrac{200}{1}$ **28.** 0.05 $\dfrac{1}{20}$

29. 0.132 $\dfrac{33}{250}$ **30.** 1.6 $\dfrac{8}{5}$ **31.** $-2\dfrac{3}{8}$ $-\dfrac{19}{8}$ **32.** $1\dfrac{3}{4}$ $\dfrac{7}{4}$ **33.** $-5\dfrac{1}{3}$ $-\dfrac{16}{3}$

34. -15.15 $-\dfrac{303}{20}$ **35.** $0.\overline{3}$ $\dfrac{1}{3}$ **36.** $1.\overline{3}$ $\dfrac{4}{3}$ **37.** $0.\overline{6}$ $\dfrac{2}{3}$ **38.** $0.\overline{06}$ $\dfrac{2}{33}$

B   **39.** $0.\overline{83}$ $\dfrac{83}{99}$ **40.** $0.\overline{1}$ $\dfrac{1}{9}$ **41.** $0.\overline{34}$ $\dfrac{34}{99}$ **42.** $0.\overline{402}$ $\dfrac{134}{333}$ **43.** $0.08\overline{6}$ $\dfrac{13}{150}$

44. $2.\overline{36}$ $\dfrac{26}{11}$ **45.** $2.\overline{036}$ $\dfrac{226}{111}$ **46.** $2.\overline{0036}$ $\dfrac{2226}{1111}$ **47.** $0.91\overline{6}$ $\dfrac{11}{12}$ **48.** $1.8\overline{3}$ $\dfrac{11}{6}$

Which of the two decimals is greater?

49. 0.02 or $0.\overline{02}$ $0.\overline{02}$ **50.** $0.\overline{202}$ or $0.0\overline{20}$ $0.\overline{202}$ **51.** $0.0\overline{2}$ or $0.\overline{020}$ $0.0\overline{2}$

52. Show that $2.4\overline{9}$ and 2.5 are equal.
$10n = 24.999\ldots\,; n = 2.499\ldots\,; 9n = 22.5;$
$n = \dfrac{22.5}{9} = \dfrac{225}{90} = \dfrac{5}{2} = 2.5$

53. Express $\dfrac{1}{7}, \dfrac{2}{7},$ and $\dfrac{3}{7}$ as repeating decimals. Find a pattern in the repeating digits and use it to guess the decimal forms of $\dfrac{4}{7}, \dfrac{5}{7},$ and $\dfrac{6}{7}$. Divide to verify each answer. $\dfrac{1}{7} = 0.\overline{142857}; \dfrac{2}{7} = 0.\overline{285714}; \dfrac{3}{7} = 0.\overline{428571}; \dfrac{4}{7} = 0.\overline{571428};$
$\dfrac{5}{7} = 0.\overline{714285}; \dfrac{6}{7} = 0.\overline{857142}$

C   Write each answer as a repeating decimal and in fraction form.

54. $0.\overline{6} + 0.\overline{7}$ $1.\overline{4}; \dfrac{13}{9}$ **55.** $0.\overline{6} + 0.0\overline{7}$ $0.7\overline{4}; \dfrac{67}{90}$ **56.** $0.\overline{76} - 0.\overline{67}$ $0.\overline{09}; \dfrac{1}{11}$

57. $0.\overline{6} \times 0.\overline{7}$ $0.4\overline{6}; \dfrac{7}{15}$ **58.** $0.\overline{6} \div 0.\overline{7}$ $0.\overline{952380}; \dfrac{20}{21}$ **59.** $0.\overline{6} \times 0.7$ $0.5\overline{18}; \dfrac{14}{27}$

*Suppose the decimal form of the number $\dfrac{a}{b}$ is endless and repeating.

60. When b is divided into a to find the decimal form, is it possible to have 0 as the remainder in any one of the division steps?

61. What is the maximum number of digits possible in the repeating part of the decimal?

398

Scientific Notation

Powers of 10 are place values in the decimal system of numeration.

$$\left.\begin{array}{ll}\text{positive}\\ \text{powers}\\ \text{of 10}\end{array}\right\{\begin{array}{l}10^3 \quad = 1000\\ 10^2 \quad = 100\\ 10^1 \quad = 10\end{array}$$
$$10^0 \quad = 1$$
$$\left.\begin{array}{ll}\text{negative}\\ \text{powers}\\ \text{of 10}\end{array}\right\{\begin{array}{l}10^{-1} = 0.1\\ 10^{-2} = 0.01\\ 10^{-3} = 0.001\end{array}$$

Powers of 10 are also used to express numbers in *scientific notation*. Scientific notation is useful in writing very large and very small numbers.

To express a number in **scientific notation,** write it in the form $a \times 10^b$. The factor a is between 1 and 10, and the exponent b is an integer.

two million
$$\begin{aligned}2,000,000 &= 2 \times 1,000,000\\ &= 2 \times 10^6\end{aligned}$$

two millionths
$$\begin{aligned}0.000002 &= 2 \times 0.000001\\ &= 2 \times 10^{-6}\end{aligned}$$

If the given number is greater than 10, the exponent b is positive. If the given number is less than 1, the exponent b is negative.

Example 1   The speed of light is 186,000 miles per second. Write this number in scientific notation.

186,000.   Since 186,000 is greater than 10, the exponent b is posi-
↑_____| tive. The decimal point is moved 5 places, so $b = 5$.

$$186,000 = 1.86 \times 10^5$$

Example 2   Neon is a gas that is used in advertising signs. Only about 18 millionths (0.000018) of the air we breathe is neon. Write this number in scientific notation.

0.000018   Since 0.000018 is less than 1, the exponent b is nega-
|_____↑   tive. The decimal point is moved 5 places, so $b = -5$.

$$0.000018 = 1.8 \times 10^{-5}$$

Example 3   Write each number in decimal form.

a. $3.57 \times 10^6 = 3,570,000$ Multiply by the indicated power of 10.
b. $5.2 \times 10^{-8} = 0.000000052$

RADICALS

399

Extra Topic

Scientific notation is used widely in mathematics and in the sciences, so an understanding of it is important for most students.

Devote particular attention to Examples 1–3 and the sample that precedes Exercises 21–28.

Write in scientific notation.

1. 4000 4×10^0 **2.** 72,000 7.2×10^4 **3.** 550,000 5.5×10^5 **4.** 3,300,000,000
3.3×10^9

5. 0.003 3×10^{-3} **6.** 0.015 1.5×10^{-2} **7.** 0.000029 **8.** 0.000000005
2.9×10^{-5} 5×10^{-9}

9. 2,660,000   **10.** 0.1111   **11.** 0.0081   **12.** 0.00796
2.66×10^6 1.111×10^{-1} 8.1×10^{-3} 7.96×10^{-3}

13. nine million 9×10^6 **14.** eight billion 8×10^9 **15.** eight billionths 8×10^{-9}

16. 0.0000000021 inches   The radius of a hydrogen atom 2.1×10^{-9}

17. 0.0000000000000000000000000009 grams   The mass of an electron 9×10^{-28}

Write each number in decimal form.

18. 1.38×10^7 °C   The temperature at the sun's core 13,800,000° C

19. 1.5×10^{11} m   The distance from the Earth to the sun 150,000,000,000 m

20. 1.8×10^{30} kg   The mass of the sun   1,800,000,000,000,000,000,000,000,000,000 kg

Use the rules for exponents where appropriate. Write each result first in scientific notation and then in decimal form.

> **Sample** $(4.1 \times 10^3)(2 \times 10^4) = (4.1 \times 2) \times (10^3 \times 10^4)$
> $= 8.2 \times 10^7$
> $= 82,000,000$

21. $(2.3 \times 10^2)(4 \times 10^5)$ **22.** $(6 \times 10^{-5})(1.5 \times 10^{-6})$
9.2×10^7; 92,000,000 9×10^{-11}; 0.00000000009
23. $(5 \times 10^{-4})(1.2 \times 10^7)$ 6×10^3; 6000 **24.** $(8 \times 10^{-9})(1.1 \times 10^5)$ 8.8×10^{-4}; 0.00088

25. $\dfrac{6.4 \times 10^8}{1.6 \times 10^3}$ 4×10^5; 400,000   **26.** $\dfrac{2.7 \times 10^{-2}}{9 \times 10^{-6}}$ 3×10^3; 3000

27. $(1.3 \times 10^6) + (4.9 \times 10^6)$ **28.** $(8.89 \times 10^9) - (5.9 \times 10^8)$
6.2×10^6; 6,200,000 8.3×10^9; 8,300,000,000

Write each answer in scientific notation.

29. There are approximately 3×10^{19} molecules in a cubic millimeter of water. How many molecules are in a cubic centimeter of water? 3×10^{22}

30. The radioactive half-life of uranium 238 is 4,500,000,000 years. Find the number of seconds in 4,500,000,000 years. 1.42×10^{17} to 3 significant digits

31. The radioactive half-life of polonium 212 is 0.0000003 seconds. Express in years the half-life of polonium 212. 9.5×10^{-15} to 2 significant digits

32. A signal transmitted to Earth from a spaceship that is 54 million miles from Earth travels at the speed of light. Use scientific notation to find how many minutes it takes the signal to reach the Earth.   4.8 min. (to nearest tenth)

11-2 Square Roots

OBJECTIVE

To find the square root of a number and to classify it as rational or irrational.

Finding the square root of a number is the reverse of squaring a number.

$$6^2 = 36 \qquad \text{The } square \text{ of 6 is 36.}$$
$$\sqrt{36} = 6 \qquad \text{The } positive \text{ square root of 36 is 6.}$$

Since $(-6)^2$ also equals 36, both 6 and -6 are square roots of 36. But the symbol $\sqrt{36}$ refers to the *positive* square root, 6, which is also known as the *principal* square root. The symbol $-\sqrt{36}$ means the negative square root, -6. The expression $\sqrt{36}$ is called a **radical** and the symbol $\sqrt{}$ is a **radical sign.**

If $a^2 = b$, then a is a **square root** of b. Note that b cannot be negative. There is no real number whose square is negative.

EXAMPLE 1   Simplify each radical.

   a. $\sqrt{49}$ $\qquad 49 = 7 \cdot 7 = 7^2$, so $\sqrt{49} = \sqrt{7^2} = 7$

   b. $\sqrt{100}$ $\qquad 100 = 10 \cdot 10 = 10^2$, so $\sqrt{100} = \sqrt{10^2} = 10$

   c. $-\sqrt{\dfrac{4}{9}}$ $\qquad \dfrac{4}{9} = \left(\dfrac{2}{3}\right)\left(\dfrac{2}{3}\right) = \left(\dfrac{2}{3}\right)^2$, so $-\sqrt{\dfrac{4}{9}} = -\sqrt{\left(\dfrac{2}{3}\right)^2} = -\dfrac{2}{3}$

Example 1 and the definition of square root suggest the following properties of square roots.

If $n \geq 0$, then $\sqrt{n^2} = n$ and $(\sqrt{n})^2 = n$.

The quantity under the radical sign is called the **radicand.** Keep in mind that this radicand cannot be negative. You cannot take the square root of a negative number and get a real number. So radicals like $\sqrt{-25}$ have no meaning here.

EXAMPLE 2   Simplify each expression.

   a. $\sqrt{70 - 6} = \sqrt{64}$ $\qquad$ **b.** $3\sqrt{4} = 3(2)$ $\qquad$ **c.** $-\sqrt{9} = -3$
             $= 8$ $\qquad\qquad\qquad\qquad\quad = 6$

   d. $\sqrt{37} \cdot \sqrt{37} = (\sqrt{37})^2$ $\qquad$ **e.** $\sqrt{19^2} = 19$ $\qquad$ **f.** $\sqrt{5^4} = \sqrt{(5^2)^2}$
               $= 37$ $\qquad\qquad\qquad\qquad\qquad\qquad\qquad\qquad = 5^2 = 25$

A number whose square root is a whole number is called a **perfect square.** Can you give the principal square root of each of the following perfect squares?

   0   1   4   9   16   25   36   49   64   81   100   121   324   1369

WARM-UP EXERCISES

Solve.
1. $x \cdot x = 25$ 5 or -5
2. $y \cdot y = 121$ 11 or -11
3. $n \cdot n = \dfrac{1}{4}$ $\dfrac{1}{2}$ or $-\dfrac{1}{2}$
4. $x \cdot x = \dfrac{9}{16}$ $\dfrac{3}{4}$ or $-\dfrac{3}{4}$

LESSON NOTES

Discuss the model examples in detail. In Example 1c, for instance, help the students see that to find $-\sqrt{\dfrac{4}{9}}$, we begin by considering $\dfrac{4}{9}$.
Since $\dfrac{4}{9} = \left(\dfrac{2}{3}\right)\left(\dfrac{2}{3}\right) = \left(\dfrac{2}{3}\right)^2$, $\sqrt{\dfrac{4}{9}} = \dfrac{2}{3}$ and $-\sqrt{\dfrac{4}{9}} = -\dfrac{2}{3}$.

In Example 2f, point out that $5^4 = (5^2)(5^2)$, so $\sqrt{5^4} = 5^2 = 25$.

On page 402, several methods of approximating irrational square roots are discussed. The divide-and-average method is explained carefully. This procedure makes sense to most students.

ALTERNATE EXAMPLES

1. Simplify each radical.
   a. $\sqrt{64}$ 8   **b.** $\sqrt{144}$ 12
   c. $-\sqrt{\dfrac{16}{81}}$ $-\dfrac{4}{9}$

2. Simplify each expression.
   a. $\sqrt{44 - 8}$ 6   **b.** $4\sqrt{25}$ 20
   c. $-\sqrt{16}$ -4
   d. $\sqrt{29} \cdot \sqrt{29}$ 29
   e. $\sqrt{31^2}$ 31   **f.** $\sqrt{7^4}$ 49

Students frequently make errors in dealing with square roots and the symbol $\sqrt{}$. For instance, when asked for $\sqrt{100}$, they may write: 10 and -10. To help them avoid this type of error, review the idea of square roots and the definition of the radical sign. That is, point out that although 100 has two square roots (10 and -10), $\sqrt{100}$ denotes the *positive* square root of 100. Thus:

$$\sqrt{100} = 10$$

To indicate the negative square root of 100, we write $-\sqrt{100}$. Thus:

$$-\sqrt{100} = -10$$

Using BASIC

In BASIC, the function SQR(X) will compute the square root of X. However, due to the way they function internally, some computers display an approximate square root for some numbers that are perfect squares. The following program can be used to explore whether a particular computer displays approximate square roots for some numbers that are actually perfect squares.

```
10 LET X = 1
20 LET D = 3
30 PRINT X, SQR(X)
40 LET X = X + D
50 LET D = D + 2
60 FOR I = 1 TO 100
70 NEXT I
80 GO TO 30
```

The display can be speeded up or slowed down by changing line 60. To speed up the display, change line 60 as follows:

```
60 FOR I = 1 TO 50
```

To slow down the display, change line 60 as follows:

```
60 FOR I = 1 TO 200
```

Although 3 is not a perfect square, $\sqrt{3}$ is a *real* number between $\sqrt{1}$ and $\sqrt{4}$. The exact value of $\sqrt{3}$ cannot be expressed as a terminating decimal. The decimal never repeats or ends.

$$\sqrt{3} = 1.732050807\ldots$$

A nonrepeating, nonterminating decimal is not a rational number. Recall that a real number that is not rational, like $\sqrt{3}$, is an *irrational* number.

Decimal approximations for $\sqrt{3}$ may be written with as many decimal places as needed. When you square such approximations, the more decimal places used, the closer the result will be to 3.

$\sqrt{3} = 1.7$, to the nearest tenth $\qquad (1.7)^2 = 2.89$

$\sqrt{3} = 1.73$, to the nearest hundredth $\qquad (1.73)^2 = 2.9929$

$\sqrt{3} = 1.732$, to the nearest thousandth $\qquad (1.732)^2 = 2.999824$

Any number that is not a perfect square, or any fraction that cannot be expressed as a ratio of perfect squares, has an irrational square root.

$\sqrt{529}$ is rational. $\qquad \sqrt{529} = \sqrt{23^2} = 23$

$\sqrt{\dfrac{12}{75}}$ is rational. $\qquad \sqrt{\dfrac{12}{75}} = \sqrt{\dfrac{4}{25}} = \sqrt{\left(\dfrac{2}{5}\right)^2} = \dfrac{2}{5}$

$\sqrt{0.09}$ is rational. $\qquad \sqrt{0.09} = \sqrt{(0.3)^2} = 0.3$

$\sqrt{76}$ is irrational. $\qquad$ 76 is not a perfect square.

Although $\sqrt{76}$ is irrational, its value can be approximated in several ways.

- Using a calculator, $\sqrt{76} = 8.7177978$, correct to seven decimal places. If you square 8.7177978, how close do you get to 76?

- From a table of squares and square roots, $\sqrt{76} = 8.718$, to three decimal places.

N	N^2	$\sqrt{N}$
⋮	⋮	⋮
76	5776	8.718

This table shows that $\sqrt{76} = 8.718$. It also shows that $76^2 = 5776$, so $\sqrt{5776} = 76$.

- You can use the *divide-and-average method* of finding square roots. For this procedure, first choose a divisor close to the square root of 76. Then divide 76 by this number, and average the quotient and divisor. This average can then be used as a second divisor. Each time you divide and average, you get a more precise estimate of $\sqrt{76}$.

Step 1 For the first divisor, choose 9, since $\sqrt{81}$ is close to $\sqrt{76}$. Divide 76 by 9 and write the quotient with two more decimal places than the divisor. Then average the divisor and quotient.

$$9\overline{)76.00} \to 8.44 \qquad \frac{9 + 8.44}{2} = 8.72$$

402

Step 2 Use 8.72 for the second divisor.

$$\frac{8.7156 \rightarrow 8.72}{8.72\overline{)76.000000}}$$

The divisor and quotient are the same, to two decimal places. So 8.72 is the square root of 76, correct to the nearest hundredth.

CLASS EXERCISES

Find two square roots for each number.

1. 1   1, −1   **2.** 25   5, −5   **3.** 81   9, −9   **4.** 400 20, −20 **5.** 8100   90, −90

Simplify. Remember that the radical sign denotes the positive square root only.

6. $\sqrt{4}$ 2   **7.** $\sqrt{64}$ 8 **8.** $\sqrt{49}$ 7   **9.** $\sqrt{121}$ 11 **10.** $\sqrt{900}$ 30

11. $-\sqrt{36}$ −6   **12.** $4\sqrt{9}$ 12 **13.** $\sqrt{0.81}$ 0.9   **14.** $\sqrt{\frac{1}{4}}$ $\frac{1}{2}$ **15.** $9\sqrt{\frac{1}{9}}$ 3

16. $\sqrt{169-144}$ 5   **17.** $\sqrt{169}-\sqrt{144}$ 1   **18.** $\sqrt{81}-\sqrt{100}$ −1

EXERCISES

A   *Find two square roots for each number.*

1. 9   3, −3   **2.** 36   6, −6   **3.** 64   8, −8   **4.** 441 21, −21 **5.** 1600   40, −40

Simplify each expression.

6. $-\sqrt{100}$ −10   **7.** $-\sqrt{121}$−11 **8.** $\sqrt{225}$ 15   **9.** $-\sqrt{324}$−18 **10.** $\sqrt{400}$ 20

11. $-\sqrt{196}$ −14 **12.** $\sqrt{5^2}$ 5 **13.** $-\sqrt{7^2}$ −7 **14.** $-\sqrt{12^2}$ −12 **15.** $\sqrt{3^4}$ 9

16. $-\sqrt{\frac{1}{100}}$ $-\frac{1}{10}$ **17.** $\sqrt{\frac{4}{81}}$ $\frac{2}{9}$ **18.** $-\sqrt{\frac{25}{100}}$ $-\frac{1}{2}$ **19.** $\sqrt{\frac{1}{25}}$ $\frac{1}{5}$ **20.** $-\sqrt{\frac{18}{98}}$ $-\frac{3}{7}$

21. $3\sqrt{9}$ 9 **22.** $5\sqrt{81}$ 45 **23.** $-2\sqrt{4}$ −4 **24.** $\frac{1}{3}\sqrt{36}$ 2 **25.** $\frac{2}{3}\sqrt{144}$ 8

26. $\sqrt{3^2-2^3}$ 1   **27.** $\sqrt{3^2+4^2}$ 5   **28.** $\sqrt{5^2+12^2}$ 13 **29.** $\sqrt{10^2-8^2}$ 6

*Classify each number as **rational** or **irrational**.*

30. $\sqrt{5}$ Irrat. **31.** $-\sqrt{36}$ Rat. **32.** $\sqrt{81}$ Rat. **33.** $\sqrt{120}$ Irrat. **34.** $\sqrt{100}$ Rat.

35. $\sqrt{1000}$ Irrat. **36.** $\sqrt{0.25}$ Rat. **37.** $-\sqrt{0.64}$ Rat. **38.** $\sqrt{\frac{9}{16}}$ Rat. **39.** $\sqrt{\frac{1}{5}}$ Irrat.

Evaluate. Use the table of squares and square roots.

40. 27^2 729   **41.** 91^2 8281 **42.** 55^2 3025 **43.** 69^2 4761 **44.** $\sqrt{1156}$ 34

45. $\sqrt{3481}$ 59   **46.** $\sqrt{1936}$ 44 **47.** $\sqrt{5929}$ 77 **48.** $\sqrt{45}$ 6.708 **49.** $\sqrt{98}$ 9.899

RADICALS

403

EXTRA PRACTICE, page 528

50. $\sqrt{\dfrac{64}{169}}$ $\dfrac{8}{13}$ **51.** $\sqrt{\dfrac{4}{4096}}$ $\dfrac{1}{32}$ **52.** $\sqrt{\dfrac{121}{484}}$ $\dfrac{1}{2}$ **53.** $\sqrt{\dfrac{1024}{576}}$ $\dfrac{4}{3}$

B *Evaluate to the nearest hundredth. Use the divide-and-average method.*

54. $\sqrt{14}$ 3.74 **55.** $\sqrt{83}$ 9.11 **56.** $\sqrt{65}$ 8.06 **57.** $\sqrt{114}$ 10.68 **58.** $\sqrt{120}$ 10.95

Evaluate to four decimal places.

59. $\sqrt{5}$ **60.** $\sqrt{50}$ **61.** $\sqrt{500}$ **62.** $\sqrt{135}$ **63.** $\sqrt{13{,}500}$

    2.2361   7.0711   22.3607   11.6190   116.1895

C *For the following problems, write answers to the nearest tenth.*

64. A formula for force in terms of distance, mass, and velocity is given by $Fs = \frac{1}{2}mv^2$. Find v if $F = 5$, $s = 7$, and $m = 3.5$.   4.5

65. The length and width of a rectangle have the ratio 5:2. If the area of the rectangle is 600 square units, find the width and length.   Width is 15.5; length is 38.7

66. The figure at the right shows two concentric circles. The radius of the smaller circle is 3 cm. Find the radius of the larger circle if the shaded area of the ring is two times the area of the smaller circle.   5.2 cm

CHECKPOINT

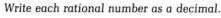

Write each rational number as a decimal.

1. $\dfrac{1}{4}$ 0.25   **2.** $\dfrac{4}{3}$ $1.\overline{3}$ **3.** $\dfrac{5}{9}$ $0.\overline{5}$ **4.** $\dfrac{1}{13}$ $0.\overline{076923}$ **5.** $\dfrac{5}{13}$ $0.\overline{384615}$

Write each rational number as a fraction in simplest form.

6. 0.77 $\dfrac{77}{100}$ **7.** 8.9 $\dfrac{89}{10}$ **8.** 0.06 $\dfrac{3}{50}$ **9.** 0.142 $\dfrac{71}{500}$ **10.** $-6.\overline{6}$ $-\dfrac{20}{3}$

Simplify. Use the table of squares and square roots where necessary.

11. 28^2 784 **12.** 92^2 8464 **13.** $\sqrt{121}$ 11 **14.** $\sqrt{484}$ 22 **15.** $\sqrt{1089}$ 33

16. $\sqrt{3364}$ 58 **17.** $\sqrt{10^2}$ 10 **18.** $-\sqrt{5^4}$ -25 **19.** $3\sqrt{16}$ 12 **20.** $\dfrac{5}{8}\sqrt{64}$ 5

21. $\sqrt{\dfrac{1}{81}}$ $\dfrac{1}{9}$ **22.** $\sqrt{\dfrac{4}{1024}}$ $\dfrac{1}{16}$ **23.** $\sqrt{\dfrac{81}{196}}$ $\dfrac{9}{14}$ **24.** $\sqrt{\dfrac{144}{576}}$ $\dfrac{1}{2}$ **25.** $\sqrt{\dfrac{9}{1225}}$ $\dfrac{3}{35}$

11-3 Simplifying Radicals: Multiplication

OBJECTIVES

To simplify radicals that have a perfect square factor.
To multiply radicals.

Simplify $\sqrt{900}$ and the product $\sqrt{9} \cdot \sqrt{100}$. Then compare the results.

$$\sqrt{900} = \sqrt{30^2} \qquad \sqrt{9} \cdot \sqrt{100} = 3 \cdot 10$$
$$= 30 \qquad\qquad\qquad\quad = 30$$

Since the values are the same, $\sqrt{900} = \sqrt{9} \cdot \sqrt{100}$. This illustrates the following property of radicals.

> **Product Property of Radicals**
>
> For $a \geq 0, b \geq 0$, $\sqrt{ab} = \sqrt{a} \cdot \sqrt{b}$ and $\sqrt{a} \cdot \sqrt{b} = \sqrt{ab}$.

This property is used in simplifying radicals and in multiplying them. A radical is not simplified if the radicand has a perfect square factor.

EXAMPLE 1   Simplify. Look for perfect square factors in the radicand. Then use the property $\sqrt{ab} = \sqrt{a} \cdot \sqrt{b}$.

a. $\sqrt{8100} = \sqrt{81 \cdot 100}$
$= \sqrt{81} \cdot \sqrt{100}$
$= 9 \cdot 10$
$= 90$

b. $\sqrt{425} = \sqrt{25 \cdot 17}$
$= \sqrt{25} \cdot \sqrt{17}$
$= 5\sqrt{17}$

EXAMPLE 2   Simplify $\sqrt{96}$.

Method I   Look for a perfect square factor in the radicand.
$$\sqrt{96} = \sqrt{16 \cdot 6} = \sqrt{16} \cdot \sqrt{6} = 4\sqrt{6}$$

Method II   Factor the radicand into prime factors.

$\sqrt{96} = \sqrt{2 \cdot 2 \cdot 2 \cdot 2 \cdot 2 \cdot 3}$ This method is longer, but it is useful when you
$= \sqrt{2^2 \cdot 2^2 \cdot 2 \cdot 3}$ do not recognize a perfect square factor in the
$= \sqrt{2^2} \cdot \sqrt{2^2} \cdot \sqrt{6}$ radicand.
$= 2 \cdot 2 \cdot \sqrt{6}$
$= 4\sqrt{6}$

WARM-UP EXERCISES

In each equation below, y stands for a perfect square. Solve.
1. $28 = x \cdot y$ $x = 7, y = 4$
2. $75 = y \cdot x$ $y = 25, x = 3$

LESSON NOTES

Notice that Examples 1 and 2 involve simplifying radicals by expressing them as $\sqrt{ab}$, where one or both of the factors are perfect squares. Thus, Examples 1 and 2 use the fact that $\sqrt{ab} = \sqrt{a} \cdot \sqrt{b}$. In contrast, Examples 3 and 4 apply the fact that $\sqrt{a} \cdot \sqrt{b} = \sqrt{ab}$.

In discussing Method II in Example 2, be sure the students understand why this procedure is useful when they do not recognize a perfect square factor in the radicand. Point out that once they have expressed the radicand as the product of prime factors, they can group these factors into numbers that are perfect squares and then simplify as shown.

ALTERNATE EXAMPLES

1. Simplify. Look for perfect square factors in the radicand. Then use the property $\sqrt{ab} = \sqrt{a} \cdot \sqrt{b}$.
   a. $\sqrt{6400}$ 80
   b. $\sqrt{575}$ $5\sqrt{23}$
2. Simplify: $\sqrt{108}$ $6\sqrt{3}$

3. Multiply.
  a. $\sqrt{5} \cdot \sqrt{7}$ $\sqrt{35}$
  b. $\sqrt{\dfrac{7}{20}} \cdot \sqrt{\dfrac{7}{5}}$ $\dfrac{7}{10}$
4. Multiply $\sqrt{18} \cdot \sqrt{20}$. Give the answer correct to the nearest hundredth.   18.97

POSSIBLE ERROR

In simplifying a radical, some students find a perfect square in the radicand but then forget to take its square root before removing it from the radical. Thus, in Class Exercise 3, they may write

$$\sqrt{27} = \sqrt{9 \cdot 3} = 9\sqrt{3}$$

(incorrect)

To help them avoid this type of error, encourage them to show each of the intermediate steps and then examine each step to be sure it makes sense.

$$\sqrt{27} = \sqrt{9 \cdot 3}$$
$$= \sqrt{9} \cdot \sqrt{3} = 3\sqrt{3}$$

Also show them that $\sqrt{27} \neq 9\sqrt{3}$, since $(9\sqrt{3})^2 = 81 \cdot 3 = 243$.

DAILY QUIZ
Simplify.
1. $\sqrt{18}$ $3\sqrt{2}$
2. $\sqrt{36} \cdot \sqrt{27}$ $18\sqrt{3}$
3. $\sqrt{8} \cdot \sqrt{16}$ $8\sqrt{2}$
4. $\sqrt{72} \cdot \sqrt{2}$ 12
5. $(\sqrt{3})^5$ $9\sqrt{3}$

ASSIGNMENT GUIDE
(pages 406–407)

Minimum course: 1–35 odd
Average course: 1–57 odd
Maximum course: 1–57 odd,
59–64

ADDITIONAL ANSWERS

Class Exercises

1. 50 **2.** 70 **3.** $3\sqrt{3}$
4. $-10\sqrt{2}$

[*Answers for Class Exercises and Exercises continue on page 407.*]

To multiply radicals, use the fact that $\sqrt{a} \cdot \sqrt{b} = \sqrt{ab}$, $a \geq 0$, $b \geq 0$.

EXAMPLE 3   Multiply.

a. $\sqrt{2} \cdot \sqrt{3} = \sqrt{2 \cdot 3} = \sqrt{6}$ **b.** $\sqrt{\dfrac{5}{3}} \cdot \sqrt{\dfrac{5}{12}} = \sqrt{\dfrac{5}{3} \cdot \dfrac{5}{12}} = \sqrt{\dfrac{25}{36}} = \dfrac{5}{6}$

EXAMPLE 4   Multiply $\sqrt{8} \cdot \sqrt{12}$. Give the answer correct to the nearest hundredth.

$$\sqrt{8} \cdot \sqrt{12} = (2\sqrt{2})(2\sqrt{3}) \qquad \text{Simplify each radical.}$$
$$= (2 \cdot 2)(\sqrt{2} \cdot \sqrt{3}) \qquad \text{Regroup the factors.}$$
$$= 4\sqrt{6}$$

The square root table gives $\sqrt{6}$ as 2.449. So $4\sqrt{6}$ is 9.796, or 9.80 to the nearest hundredth.

In the exercises, leave irrational answers in simplest radical form unless otherwise indicated.

CLASS EXERCISES

Simplify.

1. $\sqrt{2500}$ **2.** $\sqrt{4900}$ **3.** $\sqrt{27}$ **4.** $-\sqrt{200}$ **5.** $\sqrt{44}$

6. $3\sqrt{12}$ **7.** $-2\sqrt{50}$ **8.** $3\sqrt{32}$ **9.** $\sqrt{3} \cdot \sqrt{5}$ **10.** $\sqrt{7} \cdot \sqrt{9}$

11. $\sqrt{4} \cdot \sqrt{8}$ **12.** $\sqrt{3} \cdot \sqrt{18}$ **13.** $\sqrt{7} \cdot \sqrt{5}$ **14.** $\sqrt{6} \cdot \sqrt{3}$ **15.** $\sqrt{2} \cdot \sqrt{88}$

16. $\sqrt{3} \cdot \sqrt{5} \cdot \sqrt{5}$ **17.** $3\sqrt{3} \cdot 5\sqrt{3}$ **18.** $(5\sqrt{3})^2$ **19.** $(3\sqrt{5})^3$

EXERCISES

A   *Simplify.*

1. $\sqrt{1}$ **2.** $\sqrt{12}$ **3.** $\sqrt{1000}$ **4.** $\sqrt{300}$ **5.** $\sqrt{50{,}000}$

6. $\sqrt{52}$ **7.** $-\sqrt{54}$ **8.** $\sqrt{56}$ **9.** $\sqrt{75}$ **10.** $-\sqrt{96}$

11. $2\sqrt{8}$ **12.** $3\sqrt{27}$ **13.** $4\sqrt{125}$ **14.** $-5\sqrt{48}$ **15.** $\sqrt{2} \cdot \sqrt{8}$

16. $\sqrt{5} \cdot \sqrt{45}$ 15 **17.** $\sqrt{3} \cdot \sqrt{0}$ 0 **18.** $\sqrt{11} \cdot \sqrt{5}$ $\sqrt{55}$ **19.** $\sqrt{12} \cdot \sqrt{2}$ $2\sqrt{6}$

20. $\sqrt{12} \cdot \sqrt{18}$ $6\sqrt{6}$ **21.** $\sqrt{12 \cdot 18}$ $6\sqrt{6}$ **22.** $3\sqrt{5} \cdot \sqrt{60}$ $30\sqrt{3}$ **23.** $5\sqrt{3} \cdot \sqrt{60}$ $30\sqrt{5}$

24. $\sqrt{3} \cdot \sqrt{6} \cdot \sqrt{9}$ $9\sqrt{2}$ **25.** $\sqrt{5} \cdot \sqrt{10} \cdot \sqrt{12}$ $10\sqrt{6}$ **26.** $\sqrt{12} \cdot \sqrt{8} \cdot \sqrt{6}$ 24

27. $\sqrt{\dfrac{1}{3}} \cdot \sqrt{\dfrac{4}{3}}$ $\dfrac{2}{3}$ **28.** $\sqrt{\dfrac{1}{8}} \cdot \sqrt{\dfrac{8}{9}}$ $\dfrac{1}{3}$ **29.** $\sqrt{\dfrac{5}{12}} \cdot \sqrt{\dfrac{3}{20}}$ $\dfrac{1}{4}$ **30.** $\sqrt{\dfrac{3}{8}} \cdot \sqrt{\dfrac{27}{50}}$ $\dfrac{9}{20}$

Simplify. Then evaluate to two decimal places.

31. $\sqrt{300}$ **32.** $\sqrt{500}$ **33.** $\sqrt{175}$ **34.** $\sqrt{650}$ **35.** $\sqrt{637}$
$10\sqrt{3}$; 17.32 $10\sqrt{5}$; 22.36 $5\sqrt{7}$; 13.23 $5\sqrt{26}$; 25.50 $7\sqrt{13}$; 25.24

EXTRA PRACTICE, page 528

B *Simplify.*

36. $(2\sqrt{5})^2$ 20   **37.** $(\sqrt{5})^3$ $5\sqrt{5}$ **38.** $(2\sqrt{5})^3$ $40\sqrt{5}$ **39.** $2(\sqrt{5})^4$ 50

40. $(\sqrt{27})^2$ 27   **41.** $(\sqrt{12})^4$ 144   **42.** $(-\sqrt{2})^5$ $-4\sqrt{2}$ **43.** $(\sqrt{2})^6$ 8

44. $\sqrt{2}(5 + \sqrt{2})$ $5\sqrt{2}+2$ **45.** $\sqrt{5}(\sqrt{5} + \sqrt{10})$ $5+5\sqrt{2}$ **46.** $\sqrt{8}(\sqrt{4} - \sqrt{2})$ $4\sqrt{2}-4$

47. $\sqrt{3}(\sqrt{24} - \sqrt{6})$ **48.** $\sqrt{196 \cdot 10^2}$ 140   **49.** $\sqrt{1.44 \cdot 10^4}$ 120
$6\sqrt{2}-3\sqrt{2}$
50. $\sqrt{0.25 \cdot 10^6}$ **51.** $\sqrt{384 \cdot 10^4}$ $800\sqrt{6}$ **52.** $\sqrt{625 \cdot 10^6}$ 25,000
500

A formula for the volume of a cube in terms of the area of one face is
$V^2 = A^3$*. Find* V *for each value of* A*.*

53. $A = 1$ 1   **54.** $A = 3$ $3\sqrt{3}$ **55.** $A = 5$ $5\sqrt{5}$ **56.** $A = 7$ $7\sqrt{7}$

57. The area of a square tile is 360 cm². Find the length of a side correct to the nearest hundredth.   18.97 cm

58. The volume of a cone is given by the formula $V = \frac{1}{3}\pi r^2 h$.
Find the radius r if $V = 1100$ and $h = 14$. Use $\pi = \frac{22}{7}$ and
round the answer to the nearest tenth.   8.7

C *Simplify.*

Sample $(3 + \sqrt{2})^2 = 3^2 + 2 \cdot 3 \cdot \sqrt{2} + (\sqrt{2})^2 = 9 + 6\sqrt{2} + 2 = 11 + 6\sqrt{2}$

59. $(5 + \sqrt{3})^2$ $28 + 10\sqrt{3}$ **60.** $(2 - \sqrt{2})^2$ $6 - 4\sqrt{2}$ **61.** $(3\sqrt{2} + \sqrt{5})^2$ $23 + 6\sqrt{10}$

62. $(\sqrt{8} - \sqrt{5})^2$ $13 - 4\sqrt{10}$ **63.** $(7 - \sqrt{2})(7 + \sqrt{2})$ 47 **64.** $(3 - \sqrt{2})(5 - \sqrt{6})$
$15 + 2\sqrt{3} - 5\sqrt{2} - 3\sqrt{6}$

USING THE CALCULATOR

Exploring Number Sequences

Here is an interesting sequence to explore with your calculator.

	Sample	**Display**
Start with any fraction $\frac{x}{y}$.	$\frac{4}{5}$	0.8
The next term is $\frac{(x + y) + y}{x + y}$.	$\frac{(4 + 5) + 5}{4 + 5} = \frac{14}{9}$	1.5555555
Repeat the pattern to find the next term.	$\frac{(14 + 9) + 9}{14 + 9} = \frac{32}{23}$	1.3913043

1. Continue the process five more times. Write the sequence of the eight fractions and their decimal representations.

2. Choose another fraction and find the corresponding eight terms. In each sequence, do the decimals for the last terms look familiar?

LESSON NOTES

Division involving radicals is often difficult for students. Discuss each of the model examples carefully; it would be worthwhile to show the steps on the chalkboard.

As you consider Example 4c, point out the reasoning that leads us to multiply by $\sqrt{2}$. We want to rationalize the denominator; since 16 is a perfect square, we multiply by $\sqrt{2}$ and obtain $\sqrt{16}$ as the denominator, which is then simplified to 4.

As the text itself notes, the denominator of $\dfrac{\sqrt{5}}{\sqrt{8}}$ can also be rationalized by multiplying the numerator and denominator by $\sqrt{8}$. Show the steps on the chalkboard:

$$\dfrac{\sqrt{5}}{\sqrt{8}} = \dfrac{\sqrt{5}\cdot\sqrt{8}}{\sqrt{8}\cdot\sqrt{8}} = \dfrac{\sqrt{40}}{8} = \dfrac{\sqrt{4}\cdot\sqrt{10}}{8}$$

$$= \dfrac{2\sqrt{10}}{8}$$

$$= \dfrac{\sqrt{10}}{4}$$

The procedure is longer, but the answer is the same.

ALTERNATE EXAMPLES

1. Simplify.

a. $\sqrt{\dfrac{7^2}{16}}$ $\dfrac{7}{4}$ b. $\sqrt{\dfrac{12}{81}}$ $\dfrac{2\sqrt{3}}{9}$

2. Simplify: $\sqrt{6\dfrac{3}{4}}$ $\dfrac{3\sqrt{3}}{2}$

3. Simplify: $\dfrac{1}{\sqrt{5}}$ $\dfrac{\sqrt{5}}{5}$

11-4 Simplifying Radicals: Division

OBJECTIVES _____

To simplify radicals with a fraction in the radicand.
To divide radicals.

_____

How does the radical $\sqrt{\dfrac{9}{25}}$ compare with the quotient $\dfrac{\sqrt{9}}{\sqrt{25}}$?

$$\sqrt{\dfrac{9}{25}} = \sqrt{\left(\dfrac{3}{5}\right)^2} = \dfrac{3}{5} \qquad \dfrac{\sqrt{9}}{\sqrt{25}} = \dfrac{3}{5}$$

Therefore $\sqrt{\dfrac{9}{25}}$ equals $\dfrac{\sqrt{9}}{\sqrt{25}}$, since each has the value $\dfrac{3}{5}$. This suggests the following property.

Quotient Property of Radicals
For $a \geq 0$, $b > 0$, $\sqrt{\dfrac{a}{b}} = \dfrac{\sqrt{a}}{\sqrt{b}}$ and $\dfrac{\sqrt{a}}{\sqrt{b}} = \sqrt{\dfrac{a}{b}}$.

This property is used to simplify radicals with fractions and in dividing radicals. A radical is not simplified if the radicand contains a fraction.

EXAMPLE 1 Simplify.

a. $\sqrt{\dfrac{5^4}{9}} = \dfrac{\sqrt{5^4}}{\sqrt{9}} = \dfrac{5^2}{3} = \dfrac{25}{3}$ b. $\sqrt{\dfrac{18}{49}} = \dfrac{\sqrt{18}}{\sqrt{49}} = \dfrac{3\sqrt{2}}{7}$

EXAMPLE 2 Simplify $\sqrt{5\dfrac{5}{9}}$.

$$\sqrt{5\dfrac{5}{9}} = \sqrt{\dfrac{50}{9}} = \dfrac{\sqrt{50}}{\sqrt{9}} = \dfrac{5\sqrt{2}}{3}$$

A fraction in simplest form has no radical in the denominator. In the next example, the denominator contains a radicand that is not a perfect square. To simplify the radical, you must *rationalize the denominator*.

EXAMPLE 3 Simplify $\dfrac{1}{\sqrt{2}}$.

$$\dfrac{1}{\sqrt{2}} = \dfrac{1 \cdot \sqrt{2}}{\sqrt{2}\cdot\sqrt{2}} \qquad \text{Multiply the numerator and denominator by } \sqrt{2}.$$

$$= \dfrac{\sqrt{2}}{2}$$

Compare these methods of finding a decimal approximation for $\frac{1}{\sqrt{2}}$.

Method I $\frac{1}{\sqrt{2}} \approx \frac{1}{1.414}$ In this form, you must divide by 1.414.

Method II $\frac{1}{\sqrt{2}} = \frac{\sqrt{2}}{2} \approx \frac{1.414}{2}$ If you rationalize the denominator, you can divide by 2, which is easier.

Of course, when a calculator is used, Method II has little advantage. The value of $\frac{1}{\sqrt{2}}$ is 0.707, correct to the nearest thousandth.

EXAMPLE 4   Simplify.

a. $\frac{\sqrt{18}}{\sqrt{2}} = \sqrt{\frac{18}{2}} = \sqrt{9} = 3$ Use the fact that $\frac{\sqrt{a}}{\sqrt{b}} = \sqrt{\frac{a}{b}}$.

b. $\frac{\sqrt{2}}{\sqrt{3}} = \frac{\sqrt{2}\cdot\sqrt{3}}{\sqrt{3}\cdot\sqrt{3}} = \frac{\sqrt{6}}{3}$ Multiply numerator and denominator by $\sqrt{3}$.

c. $\frac{\sqrt{5}}{\sqrt{8}} = \frac{\sqrt{5}\cdot\sqrt{2}}{\sqrt{8}\cdot\sqrt{2}} = \frac{\sqrt{10}}{\sqrt{16}} = \frac{\sqrt{10}}{4}$ Multiply numerator and denominator by $\sqrt{2}$.

The denominator of $\frac{\sqrt{5}}{\sqrt{8}}$ can also be rationalized by multiplying the numerator and denominator by $\sqrt{8}$.   However, another step in simplifying would then be required.

In summary, a radical is in simplest form if
  • the radicand contains no perfect square and no fraction.
  • no denominator contains a radical.

CLASS EXERCISES

Simplify. Rationalize the denominator, where appropriate.

1. $\sqrt{\frac{4}{9}}$ $\frac{2}{3}$ **2.** $\sqrt{\frac{25}{121}}$ $\frac{5}{11}$ **3.** $\sqrt{\frac{100}{81}}$ $\frac{10}{9}$ **4.** $\sqrt{\frac{7}{64}}$ $\frac{\sqrt{7}}{8}$ **5.** $\sqrt{\frac{12}{49}}$ $\frac{2\sqrt{3}}{7}$

6. $\frac{5}{\sqrt{6}}$ $\frac{5\sqrt{6}}{6}$ **7.** $\frac{6}{\sqrt{5}}$ $\frac{6\sqrt{5}}{5}$ **8.** $\frac{3}{\sqrt{5}}$ $\frac{3\sqrt{5}}{5}$ **9.** $\frac{\sqrt{2}}{\sqrt{18}}$ $\frac{1}{3}$ **10.** $\frac{3\sqrt{2}}{\sqrt{6}}$ $\sqrt{3}$

EXERCISES

A   *Simplify.*

1. $\frac{9}{\sqrt{36}}$ $\frac{3}{2}$ **2.** $\sqrt{\frac{9}{36}}$ $\frac{1}{2}$ **3.** $\frac{9}{36}$ $\frac{1}{4}$ **4.** $\frac{\sqrt{9}}{36}$ $\frac{1}{12}$ **5.** $\sqrt{\frac{1}{25}}$ $\frac{1}{5}$

6. $\sqrt{\frac{100}{121}}$ $\frac{10}{11}$ **7.** $\frac{\sqrt{75}}{\sqrt{3}}$ 5 **8.** $\frac{\sqrt{45}}{\sqrt{5}}$ 3 **9.** $\sqrt{2\frac{1}{4}}$ $\frac{3}{2}$ **10.** $\sqrt{1\frac{11}{25}}$ $\frac{6}{5}$

11. $\frac{\sqrt{32}}{2\sqrt{2}}$ 2 **12.** $\frac{\sqrt{50}}{5}$ $\sqrt{2}$ **13.** $\frac{3\sqrt{7}}{\sqrt{28}}$ $\frac{3}{2}$ **14.** $\frac{8\sqrt{2}}{2\sqrt{8}}$ 2 **15.** $\frac{4\sqrt{7}}{8\sqrt{7}}$ $\frac{1}{2}$

RADICALS

ALTERNATE EXAMPLE

4. Simplify.

a. $\frac{\sqrt{24}}{\sqrt{6}}$ 2 **b.** $\frac{\sqrt{3}}{\sqrt{5}}$ $\frac{\sqrt{15}}{5}$

c. $\frac{\sqrt{7}}{\sqrt{12}}$ $\frac{\sqrt{21}}{6}$

POSSIBLE ERROR

Students sometimes fail to check to see that their answers meet all three conditions for the simplest form of a radical. Thus, in solving Exercise 22, they may write

$$\sqrt{\frac{1}{8}} = \frac{\sqrt{1}}{\sqrt{8}} = \frac{1}{\sqrt{8}}$$

$$= \frac{1\cdot\sqrt{8}}{\sqrt{8}\cdot\sqrt{8}} = \frac{\sqrt{8}}{8}$$

The work is correct as far as it goes, but the process has not been completed. The numerator does not meet condition 1; the radicand can be simplified further, and so can the entire expression.

Review the three conditions and be sure each condition is clear to the students. It may also be worthwhile to point out that multiplying $\frac{1}{\sqrt{8}}$ by $\frac{\sqrt{2}}{\sqrt{2}}$ would have produced the correct answer in fewer steps.

DAILY QUIZ

Simplify.

1. $\frac{5}{\sqrt{16}}$ $\frac{5}{4}$ **2.** $\frac{\sqrt{60}}{2}$ $\sqrt{15}$

3. $\frac{1}{\sqrt{7}}$ $\frac{\sqrt{7}}{7}$ **4.** $\frac{\sqrt{3}}{\sqrt{5}}$ $\frac{\sqrt{15}}{5}$

5. $\sqrt{\frac{3}{8}}\cdot\sqrt{\frac{3}{2}}$ $\frac{3}{4}$

EXTRA PRACTICE, page 529

ASSIGNMENT GUIDE
(pages 409–410)
Minimum course: 1–25 odd
second day: 2–30 even
Average course: 1–41 odd
Maximum course: 1–47 odd

ENRICHMENT ACTIVITY

Challenge your students to find the nth roots of various numbers such as $\sqrt[3]{8}$ and $\sqrt[3]{27}$. Then have them calculate quotients of the nth roots. Point out that if a and b are positive integers, $\sqrt[n]{\dfrac{a}{b}} = \dfrac{\sqrt[n]{a}}{\sqrt[n]{b}}$. Have your students use this property to simplify these radicals.

a. $\sqrt[3]{\dfrac{8}{27}}$ $\dfrac{2}{3}$ **b.** $\sqrt[4]{\dfrac{16}{625}}$ $\dfrac{2}{5}$

c. $\sqrt[5]{\dfrac{3}{32}}$ $\dfrac{\sqrt[5]{3}}{2}$ **d.** $\sqrt[6]{\dfrac{1}{2}}$ $\dfrac{\sqrt[6]{32}}{2}$

Simplify by rationalizing the denominator.

16. $\dfrac{2}{\sqrt{3}}$ $\dfrac{2\sqrt{3}}{3}$ **17.** $\dfrac{4}{\sqrt{5}}$ $\dfrac{4\sqrt{5}}{5}$ **18.** $\dfrac{5}{\sqrt{6}}$ $\dfrac{5\sqrt{6}}{6}$ **19.** $\dfrac{\sqrt{4}}{\sqrt{5}}$ $\dfrac{2\sqrt{5}}{5}$ **20.** $\dfrac{\sqrt{5}}{\sqrt{6}}$ $\dfrac{\sqrt{30}}{6}$

21. $\dfrac{2\sqrt{7}}{\sqrt{3}}$ $\dfrac{2\sqrt{21}}{3}$ **22.** $\sqrt{\dfrac{1}{8}}$ $\dfrac{\sqrt{2}}{4}$ **23.** $\sqrt{\dfrac{2}{3}}$ $\dfrac{\sqrt{6}}{3}$ **24.** $\sqrt{\dfrac{9}{10}}$ $\dfrac{3\sqrt{10}}{10}$ **25.** $\sqrt{\dfrac{3}{20}}$ $\dfrac{\sqrt{15}}{10}$

Simplify. Then use the table to evaluate to the nearest hundredth.

26. $\dfrac{1}{\sqrt{3}}$ $\dfrac{\sqrt{3}}{3}$; 0.58   **27.** $\dfrac{1}{\sqrt{5}}$ $\dfrac{\sqrt{5}}{5}$; 0.45   **28.** $\dfrac{3}{\sqrt{6}}$ $\dfrac{\sqrt{6}}{2}$; 1.22   **29.** $\dfrac{3}{\sqrt{12}}$ $\dfrac{\sqrt{3}}{2}$; 0.87   **30.** $\dfrac{\sqrt{14}}{\sqrt{21}}$ $\dfrac{\sqrt{6}}{3}$; 0.82

B   *Simplify.*

31. $\sqrt{\dfrac{1}{4} + \dfrac{1}{5}}$ $\dfrac{3\sqrt{5}}{10}$ **32.** $\sqrt{\dfrac{3}{4} + \dfrac{2}{5}}$ $\dfrac{\sqrt{115}}{10}$ **33.** $\sqrt{1 - \dfrac{1}{9}}$ $\dfrac{2\sqrt{2}}{3}$ **34.** $\sqrt{\dfrac{1}{3}} \cdot \sqrt{\dfrac{3}{5}}$ $\dfrac{\sqrt{5}}{5}$

35. $\sqrt{\dfrac{2}{5}} \cdot \sqrt{\dfrac{20}{3}}$ $\dfrac{2\sqrt{6}}{3}$ **36.** $\sqrt{\dfrac{1}{2}} \cdot \sqrt{\dfrac{2}{3}}$ $\dfrac{\sqrt{3}}{3}$ **37.** $\dfrac{\sqrt{3} + \sqrt{2}}{\sqrt{3}}$ $\dfrac{3 + \sqrt{6}}{3}$ **38.** $\dfrac{\sqrt{3} + \sqrt{10}}{\sqrt{2}}$ $\dfrac{\sqrt{6} + 2\sqrt{5}}{2}$

Simplify. Assume that the variables represent positive numbers.

39. $\sqrt{\dfrac{x^2}{y^2}}$ $\dfrac{x}{y}$ **40.** $\sqrt{\dfrac{4x^3}{y^3}}$ $\dfrac{2x\sqrt{xy}}{y^2}$ **41.** $\sqrt{\dfrac{x^2 y}{xy^2}}$ $\dfrac{\sqrt{xy}}{y}$ **42.** $\dfrac{\sqrt{8x^4 y}}{\sqrt{14xy^3}}$ $\dfrac{2x\sqrt{7x}}{7y}$

C   *Simplify and then evaluate.*

43. $x\sqrt{\dfrac{x}{9}}$ for $x = 4$ $\dfrac{x\sqrt{x}}{3}$; $\dfrac{8}{3}$ **44.** $\dfrac{\sqrt{4x^3}}{\sqrt{9x^2}}$ for $x = 9$ $\dfrac{2\sqrt{x}}{3}$; 2

45. $\sqrt{\dfrac{5x^4}{3}}$ for $x = 3$ $\dfrac{x^2\sqrt{15}}{3}$; $3\sqrt{15}$ **46.** $\sqrt{\dfrac{9x^5}{8}}$ for $x = 2$ $\dfrac{3x^2\sqrt{2x}}{4}$; 6

47. The area of an equilateral triangle is related to the length of a side by the formula $A = \dfrac{s^2\sqrt{3}}{4}$. If $A = 12\sqrt{3}$, find s. $4\sqrt{3}$

48. The shortest distance from a point (x_1, y_1) to a line $ax + by + c = 0$ is given by the formula

$$d = \dfrac{|ax_1 + by_1 + c|}{\sqrt{a^2 + b^2}}$$

Find the distance from the point $(1, 4)$ to the line $x + 2y - 2 = 0$. First determine the values of a, b, c, x_1, and y_1. Round the answer to the nearest tenth. $a = 1$; $b = 2$; $c = -2$; $x_1 = 1$; $y_1 = 4$
Distance is 3.1 to the nearest tenth.

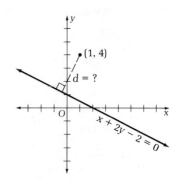

11-5 Radicals with Variables

OBJECTIVES

To multiply, divide, and simplify radicals that have variables.

WARM-UP EXERCISES

Find the correct value for n.
1. $a^3 \cdot a^3 = a^n$ $n = 6$
2. $b^4 \cdot b^4 = b^n$ $n = 8$
3. $a^{10} = a^n \cdot a^n$ $n = 5$
4. $b^6 = (b^n)^2$ $n = 3$

Is it true that $\sqrt{7^2} = 7$?   Is it true that $\sqrt{x^2} = x$?

The first equation is true, but the second equation is not always true. Does $\sqrt{x^2} = x$ if x is negative?   Let $x = -4$.

$$\sqrt{(-4)^2} \stackrel{?}{=} -4$$
$$\sqrt{16} \stackrel{?}{=} -4$$
$$4 \neq -4$$

$\sqrt{x^2} = x$ is true only when x is positive or 0. The absolute-value symbol can be used to simplify $\sqrt{x^2}$ for *all* values of x.

$$\sqrt{x^2} = |x|$$

EXAMPLE 1   Simplify each expression.

a. $\sqrt{9x^2} = 3|x|$ b. $\sqrt{\dfrac{y^4}{16}} = \dfrac{y^2}{4}$ The absolute-value symbol is unnecessary here since $\dfrac{y^2}{4}$ cannot be negative.

For most of our work in this book, we shall assume that a variable in a radicand stands for a nonnegative number, so that the absolute-value symbol will not be needed in simplifying the radical.

EXAMPLE 2   Simplify $\sqrt{25x}$, $x \geq 0$.

$\sqrt{25x} = \sqrt{25} \cdot \sqrt{x} = 5\sqrt{x}$.

EXAMPLE 3   Simplify each expression. Assume that a is nonnegative.

a. $\sqrt{a^6} = \sqrt{(a^3)^2} = a^3$ b. $\sqrt{a^7} = \sqrt{a^6 \cdot a} = \sqrt{a^6} \cdot \sqrt{a} = a^3\sqrt{a}$

EXAMPLE 4   Simplify $\sqrt{50x^8y^3}$. Assume that y is nonnegative.

$$\sqrt{50x^8y^3} = \sqrt{50} \cdot \sqrt{x^8} \cdot \sqrt{y^3}$$
$$= \sqrt{25 \cdot 2} \cdot \sqrt{(x^4)^2} \cdot \sqrt{y^2 y}$$
$$= 5\sqrt{2} \cdot x^4 \cdot y\sqrt{y} \qquad \text{Now regroup the factors.}$$
$$= 5x^4y \cdot \sqrt{2} \cdot \sqrt{y}$$
$$= 5x^4y\sqrt{2y}$$

LESSON NOTES

The introductory material on page 411 and in Example 1 are used to remind students that caution is necessary in dealing with expressions involving variables. Following this reminder, it is noted that in this book a variable in the radicand will generally be assumed to stand for a nonnegative number (thus eliminating the need for using absolute value in simplifying radicals).

Encourage the students to think through each step as they simplify radicals that involve variables. In Example 4, for instance, be sure the students understand that $\sqrt{25 \cdot 2} = \sqrt{25} \cdot \sqrt{2} = 5\sqrt{2}$ and $\sqrt{y^2y} = \sqrt{y^2} \cdot \sqrt{y} = y\sqrt{y}$. Also make it clear that x^8 is the square of x^4, so $\sqrt{x^8} = \sqrt{(x^4)^2} = x^4$.

ALTERNATE EXAMPLES

1. Simplify each expression.
   a. $\sqrt{25x^2}$ $5|x|$ b. $\sqrt{\dfrac{a^4}{49}}$ $\dfrac{a^2}{7}$
2. Simplify: $\sqrt{81x}$, $x \geq 0$ $9\sqrt{x}$
3. Simplify each expression. Assume that y is nonnegative.
   a. $\sqrt{y^8}$ y^4 b. $\sqrt{y^9}$ $y^4\sqrt{y}$
4. Simplify: $\sqrt{48x^5y^6}$ $4x^2y^3\sqrt{3x}$

5. Simplify. Assume that variables represent nonnegative numbers.

a. $\sqrt{\dfrac{5x}{6}}$ $\dfrac{\sqrt{30x}}{6}$

b. $\sqrt{\dfrac{49}{x}}$ $\dfrac{7\sqrt{x}}{x}$

c. $\dfrac{\sqrt{18y^2}}{\sqrt{2y^6}}$ $\dfrac{3}{y^2}$

DAILY QUIZ

Simplify. All variables represent positive numbers.

1. $\sqrt{100x^2}$ 10x   2. $\sqrt{y^7}$ $y^3\sqrt{y}$

3. $\sqrt{250x^6y}$ $5x^3\sqrt{10y}$

4. $\sqrt{\dfrac{3x^2}{16}}$ $\dfrac{x\sqrt{3}}{4}$

Simplify. Assume that variables and radicands represent positive numbers.

5. $\sqrt{x^2 - 2x + 1}$ $x - 1$

ASSIGNMENT GUIDE
(pages 412–413)

Minimum course: 1–31 odd
  second day: 2–30 even
Average course: 1–43 odd
Maximum course: 1–57 odd
All courses: *Checkpoint*
  review
  exercises

ADDITIONAL ANSWERS

Exercises

9. $5x^3y^3\sqrt{5x}$ 10. $2xy^2\sqrt{3xy}$

11. $4x^2y^3z^4\sqrt{3xyz}$ 12. $4xyz^2\sqrt{y}$

35. $3x\sqrt{2x - 3y}$ 36. $5y\sqrt{y + 2x}$

37. $x + 2$ 38. $2x + 3$

39. $a + b$ 40. $a + 3b$

EXAMPLE 5 Simplify. Assume that variables represent nonnegative numbers.

a. $\sqrt{\dfrac{2y}{3}} = \dfrac{\sqrt{2y}}{\sqrt{3}} = \dfrac{\sqrt{2y}\cdot\sqrt{3}}{\sqrt{3}\cdot\sqrt{3}} = \dfrac{\sqrt{6y}}{3}$ Rationalize the denominator.

b. $\sqrt{\dfrac{25}{y}} = \dfrac{5}{\sqrt{y}} = \dfrac{5\sqrt{y}}{\sqrt{y}\cdot\sqrt{y}} = \dfrac{5\sqrt{y}}{y}$ Rationalize the denominator.

c. $\dfrac{\sqrt{8x}}{\sqrt{2x^3}} = \sqrt{\dfrac{8x}{2x^3}} = \sqrt{\dfrac{4}{x^2}} = \dfrac{2}{x}$ Use the property $\dfrac{\sqrt{a}}{\sqrt{b}} = \sqrt{\dfrac{a}{b}}$.

CLASS EXERCISES

Simplify. All variables represent positive numbers.

1. $\sqrt{x^4}$ x^2 2. $\sqrt{x^7}$ $x^3\sqrt{x}$ 3. $\sqrt{y^{20}}$ y^{10} 4. $\sqrt{y^{21}}$ $y^{10}\sqrt{y}$ 5. $\sqrt{25y}$ $5\sqrt{y}$

6. $\sqrt{7x^2}$ $x\sqrt{7}$ 7. $\sqrt{3y^3}$ $y\sqrt{3y}$ 8. $\sqrt{x^6y^7}$ $x^3y^3\sqrt{y}$ 9. $\dfrac{1}{\sqrt{x}}$ $\dfrac{\sqrt{x}}{x}$ 10. $\dfrac{x}{\sqrt{x^5}}$ $\dfrac{\sqrt{x}}{x^2}$

11. $\sqrt{27}\cdot\sqrt{x^5}$ 12. $\sqrt{8}\cdot\sqrt{4y^4}$ 13. $3\sqrt{x}\cdot\sqrt{3y}$ 14. $\sqrt{3x}\cdot3\sqrt{y}$
  $3x^2\sqrt{3x}$ $4y^2\sqrt{2}$ $3\sqrt{3xy}$ $3\sqrt{3xy}$

EXERCISES

A   Simplify. All variables represent positive numbers.

1. $\sqrt{9x^2}$ $3x$ 2. $\sqrt{36x^4}$ $6x^2$ 3. $\sqrt{20x^6}$ $2x^3\sqrt{5}$ 4. $\sqrt{400x^3}$ $20x\sqrt{x}$

5. $\sqrt{2x^2}$ $x\sqrt{2}$ 6. $\sqrt{12x^2y^2}$ $2xy\sqrt{3}$ 7. $\sqrt{6x^3y^2}$ $xy\sqrt{6x}$ 8. $\sqrt{x^3y^3}$ $xy\sqrt{xy}$

9. $\sqrt{125x^7y^6}$ 10. $\sqrt{12x^3y^5}$ 11. $\sqrt{48x^5y^7z^9}$ 12. $\sqrt{16x^2y^3z^4}$

13. $2\sqrt{2x}\cdot\sqrt{x}$ $2x\sqrt{2}$ 14. $\sqrt{2}\cdot\sqrt{2x}$ $2\sqrt{x}$ 15. $\sqrt{2x}\cdot\sqrt{2x}$ $2x$ 16. $4x\sqrt{2x^4y}$ $4x^3\sqrt{2y}$

17. $\sqrt{3x}\cdot\sqrt{y}$ $\sqrt{3xy}$ 18. $3\sqrt{x}\cdot\sqrt{3y}$$3\sqrt{3xy}$ 19. $x^2\sqrt{y^9}$ $x^2y^4\sqrt{y}$ 20. $\sqrt{3x^2}\cdot\sqrt{3y^2}$ $3xy$

21. $\sqrt{\dfrac{x}{25}}$ $\dfrac{\sqrt{x}}{5}$ 22. $\sqrt{\dfrac{x^2}{36}}$ $\dfrac{x}{6}$ 23. $\sqrt{\dfrac{x^3}{49}}$ $\dfrac{x\sqrt{x}}{7}$ 24. $\sqrt{\dfrac{x^4}{64}}$ $\dfrac{x^2}{8}$

25. $\sqrt{\dfrac{3x^2}{4}}$ $\dfrac{x\sqrt{3}}{2}$ 26. $\dfrac{\sqrt{3x^2}}{4}$ $\dfrac{x\sqrt{3}}{4}$ 27. $3\sqrt{\dfrac{x^2}{4}}$ $\dfrac{3x}{2}$ 28. $\sqrt{\dfrac{3}{4x^2}}$ $\dfrac{\sqrt{3}}{2x}$

29. $\sqrt{3x^2}\cdot3\sqrt{y^4}$ $3xy^2\sqrt{3}$ 30. $\sqrt{xy}\cdot\sqrt{yz}$ $y\sqrt{xz}$ 31. $\sqrt{2x}(32 + \sqrt{8xy})$
                                  $32\sqrt{2x} + 4x\sqrt{y}$

B Simplify. Assume that variables and radicands represent positive numbers.

Sample $\sqrt{4a^2x^2 - 36a^2y^2} = \sqrt{4a^2(x^2 - 9y^2)} = \sqrt{4a^2}\cdot\sqrt{x^2 - 9y^2} = 2a\sqrt{x^2 - 9y^2}$

32. $\sqrt{ax^2 + bx^2}$ $x\sqrt{a + b}$ 33. $\sqrt{a^2b^2 + a^2c^2}$ $a\sqrt{b^2+c^2}$ 34. $\sqrt{4m^2 - 16n^2}$ $2\sqrt{m^2 - 4n^2}$

35. $\sqrt{18x^3 - 27x^2y}$ 36. $\sqrt{25y^3 + 50xy^2}$ 37. $\sqrt{x^2 + 4x + 4}$

38. $\sqrt{4x^2 + 12x + 9}$ 39. $\sqrt{a^2 + 2ab + b^2}$ 40. $\sqrt{a^2 + 6ab + 9b^2}$

Simplify and evaluate. Round irrational answers to the nearest tenth.

41. $2\sqrt{a}\cdot\sqrt{3a^3}$ for $a = 2$ $2a^2\sqrt{3}$; 13.9 42. $\sqrt{a^3b}\cdot\sqrt{ab^3}$ for $a = 3$ and $b = 2$ a^2b^2; 36

43. $\sqrt{12a^3}\cdot\sqrt{3ab^2}$ for $a = 2$ and $b = 3$ 44. $2\sqrt{a^2 + 8a + 16}$ for $a = 5$ $2a + 8$; 18
  $6a^2b$; 72

EXTRA PRACTICE, page 529

C The area of a square is given. Find the length of a side *s* and the perimeter *p*. Write answers in simplified radical form.

45. Area = $68x^4y^2$ **46.** Area = $27xy^2$

$s = \underline{\ ?\ }$ $2x^2y\sqrt{17}$ $s = \underline{\ ?\ }$ $3y\sqrt{3x}$

$p = \underline{\ ?\ }$ $8x^2y\sqrt{17}$ $p = \underline{\ ?\ }$ $12y\sqrt{3x}$

Multiply. Assume that *p* and *q* are nonnegative.

47. $(\sqrt{p} + q)(\sqrt{q} + p)$ **48.** $\sqrt{p}(p - \sqrt{p})$ $p\sqrt{p} - p$ **49.** $\sqrt{p}(\sqrt{p} - \sqrt{q})$ $p - \sqrt{pq}$

$p + q$

Simplify. Note any restrictions on the variables.

Samples   **a.** $\sqrt{x^4y^2} = x^2|y|$ **b.** $\sqrt{12ab^6} = (2\sqrt{3})\sqrt{a}|b^3|$

$= 2\sqrt{3a}|b^3|,\ a \geq 0$

50. $\sqrt{16a^2b^6}$ $4|ab^3|$ **51.** $\sqrt{100xy^8}$ **52.** $\sqrt{50x^3y^4}$ **53.** $\sqrt{242p^2q^3}$

$10y^4\sqrt{x}$; $x \geq 0$ $5xy^2\sqrt{2x}$; $x \geq 0$ $11|p|q\sqrt{2q}$; $q \geq 0$

For what values of the variable does each radical represent a real number?

Sample $\sqrt{x^2 - 25}$ represents a real number if $x^2 - 25$ is nonnegative.

$x^2 - 25 \geq 0$

$x^2 \geq 25$

$x \geq 5$ or $x \leq -5$

54. $\sqrt{x^2 - 9}$ **55.** $\sqrt{a - 5}$ **56.** $\sqrt{9 - x^2}$ **57.** $\sqrt{y + 2}$ **58.** $\sqrt{y^2 + 2}$

$x \geq 3$ or $a \geq 5$ $x \leq 3$ and $y \geq -2$ All values of y

$x \leq -3$ $x \geq -3$

CHECKPOINT

Write each rational number as a decimal.

1. $\dfrac{91}{100}$ 0.91 **2.** $\dfrac{11}{4}$ 2.75 **3.** $\dfrac{5}{3}$ $1.\overline{6}$ **4.** $\dfrac{7}{3}$ $2.\overline{3}$ **5.** $\dfrac{7}{9}$ $0.\overline{7}$

6. Write $2.\overline{83}$ as a fraction. $\dfrac{281}{99}$

Simplify. Assume that variables represent positive numbers.

7. $\sqrt{50}$ $5\sqrt{2}$ **8.** $\sqrt{500}$ $10\sqrt{5}$ **9.** $5\sqrt{20}$ $10\sqrt{5}$ **10.** $4\sqrt{27}$ $12\sqrt{3}$ **11.** $-3\sqrt{28}$
$-6\sqrt{7}$

12. $\dfrac{4}{\sqrt{144}}$ $\frac{1}{3}$ **13.** $\sqrt{\dfrac{4}{144}}$ $\frac{1}{6}$ **14.** $\dfrac{4}{144}$ $\frac{1}{36}$ **15.** $\dfrac{\sqrt{4}}{144}$ $\frac{1}{72}$ **16.** $\sqrt{\dfrac{121}{169}}$ $\frac{11}{13}$

17. $\dfrac{\sqrt{125}}{\sqrt{5}}$ 5 **18.** $\sqrt{\dfrac{3}{5}}$ $\frac{\sqrt{15}}{5}$ **19.** $\sqrt{\dfrac{5}{7}}$ $\frac{\sqrt{35}}{7}$ **20.** $\dfrac{1}{\sqrt{8}}$ $\frac{\sqrt{2}}{4}$ **21.** $\sqrt{\dfrac{48}{27}}$ $\frac{4}{3}$

22. $\sqrt{25x^2}$ $5x$ **23.** $\sqrt{3x^2}$ $x\sqrt{3}$ **24.** $\sqrt{64x^4}$ $8x^2$ **25.** $\sqrt{900x^3}$ **26.** $\sqrt{72x^5y^7}$
$30x\sqrt{x}$ $6x^2y^3\sqrt{2xy}$

27. $\sqrt{18x^2y^2}$ $3xy\sqrt{2}$ **28.** $\sqrt{x^5y^5}$ $x^2y^2\sqrt{xy}$ **29.** $\sqrt{3} \cdot \sqrt{3x}$ $3\sqrt{x}$ **30.** $3\sqrt{3x} \cdot \sqrt{x}$
$3x\sqrt{3}$

RADICALS   **413**

ENRICHMENT ACTIVITY

Tell your students to determine the conditions on *a* and *b* for which each of these radicals represents a real number.

a. $\sqrt{a + b}$ $a + b \geq 0$

b. $\sqrt{a^2 + b^2}$ All real numbers *a* and *b*

c. $\sqrt{a^2 - b^2}$ $|a| \geq |b|$

d. $\sqrt{a^3 - b^3}$ $a \geq b$

Then have them make up examples to demonstrate such situations. Have the students exchange examples and identify the permissible values for the variables. For instance, $\sqrt{2^2 - x^2}$ is a real number for $-2 \leq x \leq 2$.

Checkpoint

Students may check their answers with those given in the back of their books.

LESSON NOTES

As you develop this lesson, stress that adding or subtracting radicals is similar to adding or subtracting like terms. For instance, point out that adding $\sqrt{2}$ and $2\sqrt{2}$ is similar to adding x and $2x$. To help make the use of the distributive property clear, it may be worthwhile to remind students that just as $x = 1x$, $\sqrt{2} = 1\sqrt{2}$. Then the application of the distributive property can be illustrated as shown below:

$$x + 2x = 1x + 2x$$
$$= (1 + 2)x$$
$$= 3x$$
$$\sqrt{2} + 2\sqrt{2} = 1\sqrt{2} + 2\sqrt{2}$$
$$= (1 + 2)\sqrt{2}$$
$$= 3\sqrt{2}$$

Be sure the students understand that the distributive property can be applied to radicals only when the radicands are the same.

ALTERNATE EXAMPLES

1. Simplify each expression.
   a. $5\sqrt{3} + 3\sqrt{3}$ $8\sqrt{3}$
   b. $4\sqrt{20} + 2\sqrt{5}$ $10\sqrt{5}$

2. Simplify $6\sqrt{x} + \sqrt{x^3}$
   when $x \geq 0$. $(6 + x)\sqrt{x}$

3. Simplify : $\sqrt{26} - \sqrt{10}$
   $\sqrt{26} - \sqrt{10}$

11-6 Sums and Differences of Radicals

OBJECTIVE

To add and subtract expressions with radicals.

Here is one way to find the approximate value of $\sqrt{2} + \sqrt{8}$. This sequence of steps can be used with most calculators.

You can also write $\sqrt{2} + \sqrt{8}$ in a simpler form, using just one radical. To do this, simplify $\sqrt{8}$. Then use the distributive property.

$$\sqrt{2} + \sqrt{8} \quad = \quad \sqrt{2} + 2\sqrt{2} \qquad \sqrt{8} = 2\sqrt{2}$$
$$= \quad (1 + 2)\sqrt{2} \qquad \text{Use the distributive property. Factor out the common factor } \sqrt{2}.$$
$$= \quad 3\sqrt{2} \qquad \text{Simplified form of } \sqrt{2} + \sqrt{8}$$

On your calculator you will find that the approximations for $\sqrt{2} + \sqrt{8}$ and $3\sqrt{2}$ are the same.

A sum or difference of radicals cannot always be simplified. But whenever the terms have a common radical factor, you can simplify the expression.

EXAMPLE 1   Simplify each expression.

   a. $3\sqrt{5} + 4\sqrt{5} = (3 + 4)\sqrt{5}$
   $\qquad\qquad\qquad = 7\sqrt{5}$

   b. $5\sqrt{12} + 2\sqrt{3} = 10\sqrt{3} + 2\sqrt{3}$ $5\sqrt{12} = 5\sqrt{4}\sqrt{3} = 5(2\sqrt{3}) = 10\sqrt{3}$
   $\qquad\qquad\qquad\quad = (10 + 2)\sqrt{3}$
   $\qquad\qquad\qquad\quad = 12\sqrt{3}$

Use the same procedure with variables.

EXAMPLE 2   Simplify $3\sqrt{x} - \sqrt{x^3}$ when $x \geq 0$.

$$3\sqrt{x} - \sqrt{x^3} = 3\sqrt{x} - \sqrt{x^2 x}$$
$$= 3\sqrt{x} - x\sqrt{x}$$
$$= (3 - x)\sqrt{x}$$

EXAMPLE 3   Simplify $\sqrt{35} - \sqrt{6}$.

Neither term can be simplified and the terms have no common factors. So the expression is already in simplest radical form.

CLASS EXERCISES

Simplify.

1. $2\sqrt{3} + 3\sqrt{3}$ $5\sqrt{3}$ 2. $6\sqrt{2} + 5\sqrt{2}$ $11\sqrt{2}$ 3. $4\sqrt{5} - 3\sqrt{5}$ $\sqrt{5}$ 4. $7\sqrt{7} + \sqrt{7}$ $8\sqrt{7}$

5. $5\sqrt{20} - 2\sqrt{5}$ $8\sqrt{5}$ 6. $8\sqrt{8} + \sqrt{2}$ $17\sqrt{2}$ 7. $\sqrt{12} - \sqrt{3}$ $\sqrt{3}$ 8. $\sqrt{48} + \sqrt{75}$ $9\sqrt{3}$

EXERCISES

A

Simplify. Assume that variables represent positive numbers.

1. $6\sqrt{2} + 2\sqrt{2}$ $8\sqrt{2}$ 2. $4\sqrt{5} + 6\sqrt{5}$ $10\sqrt{5}$ 3. $8\sqrt{3} - 3\sqrt{3}$ $5\sqrt{3}$

4. $4\sqrt{6} - 3\sqrt{6}$ $\sqrt{6}$ 5. $8\sqrt{5} - \sqrt{5}$ $7\sqrt{5}$ 6. $\sqrt{11} + 11\sqrt{11}$ $12\sqrt{11}$

7. $13\sqrt{7} - 6\sqrt{7}$ $7\sqrt{7}$ 8. $9\sqrt{12} - 7\sqrt{12}$ $4\sqrt{3}$ 9. $12\sqrt{3} - 7\sqrt{3} + \sqrt{3}$ $6\sqrt{3}$

10. $5\sqrt{x} - 9\sqrt{x}$ $-4\sqrt{x}$ 11. $3\sqrt{x} + \sqrt{x}$ $4\sqrt{x}$ 12. $12\sqrt{x} - 7\sqrt{x}$ $5\sqrt{x}$

13. $\sqrt{8} + \sqrt{2}$ $3\sqrt{2}$ 14. $\sqrt{3} + \sqrt{12}$ $3\sqrt{3}$ 15. $\sqrt{5} + \sqrt{125}$ $6\sqrt{5}$

16. $\sqrt{1000} - \sqrt{10}$ $9\sqrt{10}$ 17. $2\sqrt{3} + \sqrt{12}$ $4\sqrt{3}$ 18. $5\sqrt{3} - \sqrt{27}$ $2\sqrt{3}$

19. $4\sqrt{8} - 3\sqrt{2}$ $5\sqrt{2}$ 20. $15\sqrt{32} - \sqrt{72}$ $54\sqrt{2}$ 21. $\sqrt{100{,}000} - \sqrt{10}$ $99\sqrt{10}$

22. $\sqrt{2} + 2\sqrt{8} + 3\sqrt{18}$ 23. $4\sqrt{3} + 7\sqrt{12} - 5\sqrt{75}$ 24. $\sqrt{20} + \sqrt{45} + \sqrt{80}$
   $14\sqrt{2}$ $-7\sqrt{3}$ $9\sqrt{5}$

B

25. $\sqrt{x^3} - \sqrt{x}$ $(x-1)\sqrt{x}$ 26. $5\sqrt{x^3} + 3\sqrt{x}$ $(5x+3)\sqrt{x}$ 27. $\sqrt{x^2 y} + \sqrt{y}$ $(x+1)\sqrt{y}$

28. $\sqrt{x^3 y^2} + \sqrt{x^2 y^3}$ 29. $3\sqrt{x^3} - \sqrt{3x^3}$ 30. $\sqrt{4x^3 y^2} - \sqrt{8x^5 y^4}$
   $xy(\sqrt{x} + \sqrt{y})$ $x(3\sqrt{x} - \sqrt{3x})$ $2xy(\sqrt{x} - xy\sqrt{2x})$

Simplify. Then evaluate to the nearest hundredth. Use the square root table or your calculator.

31. $4\sqrt{5} + \sqrt{20}$ $6\sqrt{5}$; 13.42 32. $3\sqrt{27} - \sqrt{3}$ $8\sqrt{3}$; 13.86

33. $3\sqrt{2} + 4\sqrt{50} - 2\sqrt{200}$ $3\sqrt{2}$; 4.24 34. $\sqrt{10} + \sqrt{4000} + \sqrt{900{,}000}$
                              $321\sqrt{10}$; 1015.09

C

Simplify. Assume that variables represent positive numbers.

35. $\sqrt{40} - 2\sqrt{90} + \sqrt{\dfrac{2}{5}}$ 36. $3\sqrt{75} - 2\sqrt{27} + \sqrt{48}$ 37. $\sqrt{98} + \dfrac{1}{3}\sqrt{72} - 2\sqrt{\dfrac{1}{8}}$
   $-3\frac{4}{5}\sqrt{10}$ $13\sqrt{3}$ $8\frac{1}{2}\sqrt{2}$

38. $3\sqrt{28} + 4\sqrt{\dfrac{1}{7}} + \sqrt{112}$ 39. $\sqrt{x} + \sqrt{x^3} + \sqrt{x^5}$ 40. $\sqrt{12x} - \sqrt{75x^3} + \sqrt{\dfrac{3}{x}}$

41. $\sqrt{(x+y)^3} - \sqrt{x+y}$ 42. $\sqrt{a^5} - 4\sqrt{a^3} + 4\sqrt{a}$

43. $\sqrt{18} - \sqrt{\dfrac{1}{3}} + \sqrt{12} - \sqrt{\dfrac{1}{8}}$ 44. $\sqrt{12a^4 + 48a^3 + 48a^2} - \sqrt{12a^4 + 12a^3 + 3a^2}$

45. Solve for x and check: $4x\sqrt{3} + 2\sqrt{75} = \sqrt{12}$ $x = -2$

46. Show that $1 + \sqrt{5}$ is a root of the equation $x^2 - 2x - 4 = 0$.
   $(1+\sqrt{5})^2 - 2(1+\sqrt{5}) - 4 \overset{?}{=} 0$; $1 + 2\sqrt{5} + 5 - 2 - 2\sqrt{5} - 4 \overset{?}{=} 0$; $0 = 0$ ✔

RADICALS   415

DAILY QUIZ

Simplify. Assume that variables represent positive numbers.

1. $5\sqrt{7} + 6\sqrt{7}$ $11\sqrt{7}$
2. $18\sqrt{2} - 10\sqrt{2}$ $8\sqrt{2}$
3. $\sqrt{12} + \sqrt{27}$ $5\sqrt{3}$
4. $\sqrt{72} - 5\sqrt{18}$ $-9\sqrt{2}$
5. $7\sqrt{x^3} - 3\sqrt{x}$ $(7x - 3)\sqrt{x}$

ASSIGNMENT GUIDE
(page 415)

Minimum course: 1–23 odd
     second day: 2–30 even
Average course: 1–35 odd
Maximum course: 7–45 odd

ENRICHMENT ACTIVITY

Have students investigate how to simplify radicals within radicals. Encourage them to make up other examples such as these to test one another's skill.

1. $\sqrt{\sqrt{64}}$ $= \sqrt{8} = 2\sqrt{2}$
2. $\sqrt{16 + \sqrt{81}}$ $= \sqrt{16 + 9}$
               $= \sqrt{25} = 5$
3. $\sqrt{\sqrt{36} + \sqrt{9}}$ $= \sqrt{6 + 3}$
               $= \sqrt{9} = 3$
4. $\sqrt{\sqrt{81} - \sqrt{25}}$ $= \sqrt{9 - 5}$
               $= \sqrt{4} = 2$
5. $\sqrt{57 - \sqrt{49}}$ $= \sqrt{57 - 7}$
               $= \sqrt{50} = 5\sqrt{2}$
6. $\sqrt{4 + \sqrt{32}}$ $= \sqrt{4 + 4\sqrt{2}}$
               $= \sqrt{4(1 + \sqrt{2})}$
               $= 2\sqrt{1 + \sqrt{2}}$

ADDITIONAL ANSWERS

Exercises

38. $10\frac{4}{7}\sqrt{7}$
39. $\sqrt{x}(1 + x + x^2)$
40. $\left(2 - 5x + \dfrac{1}{x}\right)\sqrt{3x}$
41. $(x + y - 1)\sqrt{x + y}$
42. $(a - 2)^2\sqrt{a}$
43. $2\frac{3}{4}\sqrt{2} + 1\frac{2}{3}\sqrt{3}$
44. $3a\sqrt{3}$

EXTRA PRACTICE, page 529

LESSON NOTES

In developing the Pythagorean theorem, it would be worthwhile to begin by drawing the right triangle on the board; then draw the square on each side. In that way, the students will be able to see the relationship more clearly. You may also wish to use a 3-4-5 right triangle on the chalkboard so that all of the lengths of the sides are rational numbers.

The converse of the Pythagorean theorem is stated on page 417 and applied in Example 4. Exercises 14–19 also apply the converse.

POSSIBLE ERROR

A common error made in using the Pythagorean theorem $a^2 + b^2 = c^2$ is to treat the unknown as if it were always the length of the hypotenuse. This type of error would lead students to write the equation for Example 2 as:

$6^2 + 10^2 = x^2$ (incorrect)

Emphasize to the students that they must *think* about each situation *before* they write the equation. Also, to help students avoid operating by rote, discuss a few examples in which right triangles are shown with their hypotenuses in horizontal or vertical positions.

11-7 The Pythagorean Theorem

OBJECTIVE

To apply the Pythagorean theorem and its converse.

In a right triangle, the side opposite the right angle is called the **hypotenuse.** It is always the longest side. The other two sides are called the **legs.**

The right triangle shown here has legs of 2 and 5 units. The squares on the legs have areas of 4 and 25 square units respectively.

By counting, you can show that the area of the square on the hypotenuse is 29 square units. But this is the same as the sum of the areas of the squares on the two legs.

$$2^2 + 5^2 = c^2$$
$$4 + 25 = 29$$
$$29 = 29$$

This illustrates a property of all right triangles, which is known as the *Pythagorean* theorem.

The Pythagorean Theorem

If in a right triangle the legs measure a units and b units and the hypotenuse measures c units, then
$$a^2 + b^2 = c^2$$

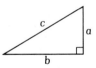

The Pythagorean theorem is often stated briefly as follows.

The square of the hypotenuse of a right triangle is equal to the sum of the squares of the legs.

If you know the lengths of any two sides of a right triangle, you can find the length of the third side by using the Pythagorean theorem.

416

EXAMPLE 1

Find c, the length of the hypotenuse.

The legs have lengths 12 and 5 units.

$a^2 + b^2 = c^2$ Pythagorean theorem

$12^2 + 5^2 = c^2$

$c^2 = 169$ Use the positive square root of 169,

$c = 13$ since a length must be positive.

The length of the hypotenuse is 13 units.

EXAMPLE 2

Find x.

$6^2 + x^2 = 10^2$

$36 + x^2 = 100$

$x^2 = 64$

$x = 8$

EXAMPLE 3

Find the length of a diagonal of a square 3 meters on a side.

The diagonal is the hypotenuse of a right triangle.

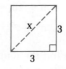

$x^2 = 3^2 + 3^2$

$x^2 = 18$

$x = \sqrt{18}$, or $3\sqrt{2}$

The length of the diagonal is $3\sqrt{2}$ meters. This is approximately 4.24 meters.

The *converse* of the Pythagorean theorem is also true: *If a, b, and c are the measures of the sides of a triangle such that $a^2 + b^2 = c^2$, then the triangle is a right triangle with c the hypotenuse.*

You can use the converse of the Pythagorean theorem to check whether a triangle is a right triangle.

EXAMPLE 4

Is $\triangle PQR$ a right triangle?

See whether the triangle satisfies the condition $a^2 + b^2 = c^2$, where c is the longest side.

Does $16^2 + 30^2$ equal 34^2?

$256 + 900 = 1156$

$1156 = 1156$ ✔

Therefore, $\triangle PQR$ is a right triangle, with right angle at Q.

RADICALS

1. Find c, the length of the hypotenuse. The legs have lengths 9 and 12 units.
$c = 15$

2. Find x.
$8^2 + x^2 = 17^2$
$x = 15$

3. Find the length of a diagonal of a square 5 meters on a side.
$x = \sqrt{50}$ or $5\sqrt{2}$; approximately 7.07 meters

4. Is $\triangle KLM$ a right triangle? See whether the triangle satisfies the condition $a^2 + b^2 = c^2$, where c is the longest side.
Yes; $\triangle KLM$ is a right triangle.

Solve. The variables represent lengths of sides of a right triangle.

1. $5^2 + b^2 = 13^2$ 12
2. $0^2 + 8^2 = c^2$ 10

Find the length of the third side of each right triangle. Write irrational answers in simplest radical form.

3.   **4.**

5. Find the area of this right triangle.

ASSIGNMENT GUIDE
(pages 418–420)
Minimum course: 1–19 odd
Average course: 1–27 odd
    second day: 2-28 even
Maximum course: 1–27 odd
    second day: 20–28 even,
        29–37

CLASS EXERCISES

For each right triangle, the measures of two sides are given. Find the measure of the third side. Write irrational numbers in radical form.

	a	b	c	
1.	3	4	?	5
2.	7	24	?	25
3.	6	5	?	$\sqrt{61}$
4.	2	9	?	$\sqrt{85}$

	a	b	c	
5.	8	?	10	6
6.	?	24	26	10
7.	?	5	8	$\sqrt{39}$
8.	11	?	12	$\sqrt{23}$

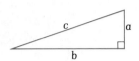

The lengths of three sides of a triangle are given. Tell whether or not the triangle is a right triangle.

9. 16, 30, 34   Yes   **10.** 10, 20, 30   No   **11.** 35, 12, 37   Yes

EXERCISES

A   Solve.

1. $9 + 16 = c^2$ 5   **2.** $64 + 36 = c^2$ 10

3. $a^2 + 7^2 = 25^2$ 24   **4.** $b^2 + 12^2 = 15^2$ 9

Find the length of the third side of each right triangle. Write irrational answers in simplest radical form.

5.   **6.**   **7.**

8.   **9.**   **10.**

11.   **12.**   **13.**

      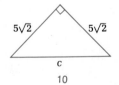

418   CHAPTER 11

The lengths of the three sides of a triangle are given. Tell whether the triangle is a right triangle.

14. 15, 20, 25   Yes   **15.** 7, 12, 14   No   **16.** 9, 40, 41   Yes

17. 20, 30, 36   No   **18.** 24, 45, 51   Yes   **19.** 13, 16, 21   No

B *Find **c**, the length of the diagonal of each rectangle. Give your answer to the nearest tenth of a centimeter.*

20.

7cm
8.1 cm

21.

2 cm
3.6 cm

22.

9 cm
9.1 cm

Find the area of each right triangle. Use one leg as the base and the other as the height. Write irrational numbers as decimals, correct to the nearest hundredth.

23.

9 cm²

24.

120 cm²

25.

$3\sqrt{85}$; 27.66 cm²

26. The base lines in softball are each 60 feet long and form a square. How far is it from home to second base? Give your answer to the nearest foot.
85 ft

27. A support wire on a radio antenna forms a right triangle with the antenna and the ground. If the wire is 85 meters long and it meets the ground 40 meters from the center of the base, find the height of the antenna.   75 m

28. A kite is in the shape of an equilateral triangle. If each side of the triangle is 120 cm, find the height of the triangle to the nearest cm.   104 cm

---

ENRICHMENT ACTIVITY

Have your students explore an extension of the Pythagorean theorem from 2 to 3 dimensions.

1. What is the longest stick that will fit in a rectangular box measuring 3 × 4 × 12 inches?   13 in.

2. Find the length of a diagonal in a cube that measures 2 inches on each edge. $2\sqrt{3}$ in.

3. What are the lengths of the four diagonals through a rectangular box measuring *a* by *b* by *c*?
$d = \sqrt{a^2 + b^2 + c^2}$; all 4 diagonals are the same length.

In these problems, round irrational answers to the nearest hundredth.

29. A ladder reaches 18 feet up a wall. If the ladder is 20 feet long, how far is its base from the foot of the wall? 8.72 ft

30. A square has a perimeter of 24 meters. How long is a diagonal? 8.49 m

31. A square has an area of 100 cm². Find the length of a diagonal. 14.14 cm

32. A square has a diagonal 5 meters long. How long are its sides? 3.54 m

33. A square has a diagonal 7 feet long. Find the area of the square. 24.5 ft²

34. A rectangle is twice as long as it is wide. If its perimeter is 42 inches, what is the length of a diagonal? 15.65 in.

Draw a 2-by-1 rectangle on a number line. Use the Pythagorean theorem to find the length of its diagonal, $\sqrt{5}$. Then use a compass to locate the corresponding point on the number line.

 By a similar method, locate the following points on separate number lines.   Figures needed to locate the points are described below.

35. $\sqrt{2}$
1-by-1 square

36. $\sqrt{10}$
1-by-3 rectangle

37. $\sqrt{20}$
2-by-4 rectangle

*38. Triangle *ABC* has a right angle at *C*, with *AC* = 32 and *AB* = 40. If *P* is on side $\overline{AC}$ such that *PA* = *PB*, find the length of these equal segments.   25

═EXTRA TOPIC═

Pythagorean Triples

A **Pythagorean triple** is a set of three positive integers that satisfy the Pythagorean relation. One familiar triple is 3, 4, 5. Multiples of these numbers, such as 6, 8, 10 and 9, 12, 15 are also Pythagorean triples. Triples that have no common factors are called *primitive* Pythagorean triples.
   Euclid (323 B.C.) gave the following method for finding all such triples.

   Let *u* and *v* be relatively prime, one even and one odd, with *u* > *v*.
   Then all primitive Pythagorean triples can be expressed in the form

$$2uv \qquad u^2 - v^2 \qquad u^2 + v^2$$

*Verify that these values for **u** and **v** yield Pythagorean triples.*

1. 2 and 1   **2.** 3 and 2   **3.** 4 and 3

4. 4 and 1   **5.** 5 and 2   **6.** 7 and 4

7. The Pythagoreans knew that the expressions $2n + 1$, $2n^2 + 2n$, and $2n^2 + 2n + 1$ yield primitive Pythagorean triples when *n* is a positive integer. Verify this when *n* has the values 1, 2, 3, 4, 5, and 10.

420

Using Proof

A **proof** is a logical argument that leads from a given or established statement to a new result. In developing a proof, only previously established results or definitions can be used as reasons. Here we will outline the proof of the Pythagorean theorem. Some basic algebra and the area formulas for squares and triangles will be used as our previously established results.

We will use an arbitrary right triangle with legs of lengths a and b, and with hypotenuse of length c.

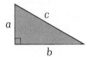

Start with two squares, each with sides $a + b$, as shown below. Their areas have been divided into square and triangular regions in two different ways.

 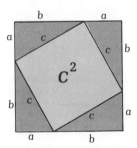

1. Express the area of each square in terms of a and b by finding the product $(a + b)(a + b)$.

2. Now express each area in a different way, using the sums of the areas of the regions into which it has been divided. Why must these new expressions be equal?

3. Subtract the areas of the four right triangles from each expression. Do you get $a^2 + b^2 = c^2$?

Since the areas of the original squares are the same, the resulting areas with the triangles removed must also be the same.

Strategies for Problem Solving

This *Strategies for Problem Solving* contains one of the many proofs of the Pythagorean theorem that have been discovered over many centuries. The advantage of this proof is that it is visual, rather than purely abstract, as many proofs are.

ADDITIONAL ANSWERS

Strategies for Problem Solving

1. $a^2 + 2ab + b^2$
2. Left square:
   $$a^2 + b^2 + 4\left(\tfrac{1}{2}ab\right)$$
   $$= a^2 + b^2 + 2ab$$
   Right square:
   $$c^2 + 4\left(\tfrac{1}{2}ab\right) = c^2 + 2ab$$
   The areas of the two large squares are equal, so
   $$a^2 + b^2 + 2ab = c^2 + 2ab$$
3. Yes
   $$a^2 + b^2 + 2ab - 2ab$$
   $$= c^2 + 2ab - 2ab$$
   $$a^2 + b^2 = c^2$$

WARM-UP EXERCISES

Find the positive number that is a solution for the equation. Give the answer in simplest radical form.

1. $c^2 = 1^2 + 4^2$ $\sqrt{17}$
2. $d^2 = 2^2 + 2^2$ $2\sqrt{2}$

LESSON NOTES

Example 1 prepares the students for the introduction of the distance formula on page 423. As you discuss the distance formula, be sure the students understand that either of the two points can be used as the point with coordinates (x_1, y_1); then the coordinates of the other point are (x_2, y_2). This idea is emphasized in Example 2. To help the students understand, show that using $(4, 3)$ as (x_1, y_1) and $(-2, 1)$ as (x_2, y_2) result in the same answer for Example 2:

$$d = \sqrt{(-2 - 4)^2 + (1 - 3)^2}$$
$$= \sqrt{(-6)^2 + (-2)^2}$$
$$= \sqrt{36 + 4}$$
$$= \sqrt{40} = 2\sqrt{10}$$

Stress that no matter which point is selected for (x_1, y_1), the same order must be used in working with the x- and y-coordinates.

In working the exercises, the students use the distance formula in a variety of situations. To solve Exercise 26, the students can begin by finding the fourth vertex. They can do this by using a sketch and reasoning as follows: The x-coordinate of C is 4 more than the x-coordinate of B; the y-coordinate of C is 2 more than the y-coordinate of B. Since a similar relationship must exist between point D and point A, the coordinates of D are $(1, 7)$.

ALTERNATE EXAMPLE

1. Find the distance d between $(-2, 3)$ and $(2, 8)$.
   $\sqrt{41}$; approximately 6.4

11-8 The Distance Formula

OBJECTIVE

To find the distance between any two points on the coordinate plane.

The distance between A and B can be found by counting 6 units across. Likewise, the distance between B and C is 8 units, counting down.

Can you find the distance from A to C?

You cannot find it directly by counting, but you can use the Pythagorean theorem.

Triangle ABC is a right triangle, and the distance d from A to C is the length of the hypotenuse.

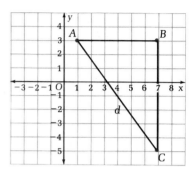

$$d^2 = 6^2 + 8^2$$
$$d^2 = 36 + 64$$
$$d^2 = 100$$
$$d = 10$$

EXAMPLE 1   Find the distance d between $(-3, 1)$ and $(2, 4)$.

Draw the right triangle shown. The distance needed is the length of the hypotenuse.

Find the lengths of the legs first. Then use the Pythagorean theorem.

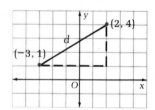

The length of the horizontal leg is 5.   Subtract the x-coordinates.
$$2 - (-3) = 5$$

The length of the vertical leg is 3.   Subtract the y-coordinates.
$$4 - 1 = 3$$

$$d^2 = 5^2 + 3^2$$
$$d^2 = 34$$
$$d = \sqrt{34}$$

The exact length is $\sqrt{34}$.
This is approximately 5.8.

Example 1 illustrates a method that can be used to find the distance between any two points (x_1, y_1) and (x_2, y_2). Let d be the distance between the points. Then

$$d^2 = (x_2 - x_1)^2 + (y_2 - y_1)^2$$

Solving for d results in the distance formula.

The Distance Formula

The distance between two points (x_1, y_1) and (x_2, y_2) is given by the formula

$$d = \sqrt{(x_2 - x_1)^2 + (y_2 - y_1)^2}$$

EXAMPLE 2   Find the distance d between $(-2, 1)$ and $(4, 3)$.

Choose either point as (x_1, y_1). Then the other point is (x_2, y_2).

$d = \sqrt{(x_2 - x_1)^2 + (y_2 - y_1)^2}$ The distance formula
$d = \sqrt{[4 - (-2)]^2 + [3 - 1]^2}$ Let $(x_1, y_1) = (-2, 1)$.
$d = \sqrt{6^2 + 2^2}$ Let $(x_2, y_2) = (4, 3)$.
$d = \sqrt{40}$
$d = 2\sqrt{10}$, or approximately 6.3

CLASS EXERCISES

Find the distance between each pair of points. Write irrational answers in simplest radical form.

1. A, B $\sqrt{2}$ 2. B, C $2\sqrt{5}$
3. C, D $2\sqrt{2}$ 4. D, E 5
5. E, F 4 6. F, G $\sqrt{17}$
7. G, H 6 8. H, J $5\sqrt{2}$
9. J, K $2\sqrt{2}$ 10. K, M $2\sqrt{5}$

EXERCISES

A   *Find the distance between each pair of points. Express irrational answers in simplest radical form.*

1. $(-7, 0), (-3, 0)$ 4 2. $(0, 0), (5, 5)$ $5\sqrt{2}$ 3. $(2, -3), (2, 5)$ 8
4. $(3, -4), (-4, -4)$ 7 5. $(1, 5), (-3, 2)$ 5 6. $(7, -8), (3, -5)$ 5

RADICALS

EXTRA PRACTICE, page 529

7. $(-4, -3), (-2, 2)$ $\sqrt{29}$ **8.** $(1, 6), (9, 0)$ 10   **9.** $(6, -2), (9, 3)$ $\sqrt{34}$

10. $(0, 3), (-4, 6)$ 5   **11.** $(2, -5), (-3, 7)$ 13   **12.** $(5, -8), (-1, 3)$ $\sqrt{157}$

13. $(-1, -6), (7, 0)$ 10   **14.** $(5, -3), (-6, 2)$ $\sqrt{146}$ **15.** $(1, 2), (3, 4)$ $2\sqrt{2}$

B

*Express irrational answers in simplest radical form and in decimal
form to the nearest tenth.*

16. Find the perimeter of a triangle with ver-
    tices at $A(-2, 1)$, $B(1, -2)$, and $C(5, 2)$.
    $12\sqrt{2}$; 17.0

17. Find the perimeter of a quadrilateral with
    vertices at $A(-2, 2)$, $B(2, 6)$, $C(5, 3)$, and $D(1, -1)$. $14\sqrt{2}$; 19.8

18. Find the perimeter of a quadrilateral with vertices at $E(10, -3)$,
    $F(2, 1)$, $G(1, -1)$, and $H(5, -3)$. $5 + 7\sqrt{5}$; 20.7

19. Three vertices of a rectangle are $R(-3, 5)$, $S(1, 5)$, and $T(-3, -4)$.
    Find the coordinates of the fourth vertex, U. Then find the length of
    a diagonal. $(1, -4)$; $\sqrt{97}$; 9.8

C

A triangle has vertices at $A(6, 3)$, $B(4, -3)$, and $C(2, 1)$.

20. Show that the triangle is a right triangle. Use the converse of the
    Pythagorean theorem. $AC = 2\sqrt{5}$, $BC = 2\sqrt{5}$, $AB = 2\sqrt{10}$; $(2\sqrt{5})^2 + (2\sqrt{5})^2 \overset{?}{=} (2\sqrt{10})^2$;
    $20 + 20 = 40$ ✓
21. Find the area of the triangle. Use the legs as base and height.   10 sq. units

22. Given a right triangle with vertices at $A(-4, -5)$, $B(-4, 7)$, and
    $C(4, 7)$, find the area and perimeter of the triangle.   Perimeter $= 20 + 4\sqrt{13}$; 34.4 units
    Area $= 48$ sq. units
23. Find the radius of the circle with center at $(1, 2)$, $(-3, 7)$
    and passing through the point $(-3, 7)$.
    $\sqrt{41}$; 6.4

24. A diameter of a circle has endpoints at $(-2, -2)$ and $(6, 2)$. Find
    the length of a radius of the circle. $2\sqrt{5}$; 4.5

25. For what values of a is $(-5, -3)$ ten units from $(a, 5)$?   1, −11

26. Three vertices of a square are $A(-3, 5)$, $B(-1, 1)$, and $C(3, 3)$. Find
    the coordinates of the fourth vertex, D. Then find the length of a
    diagonal and the area of the square. $D(1, 7)$; $2\sqrt{10}$, 6.3; 20 sq. units

27. The sides of a quadrilateral lie on the lines $x + y = 6$, $x - y = 6$,
    $x + y = -6$, and $x - y = -6$. Draw this quadrilateral. Then find its
    perimeter and area.

CHAPTER 11

11-9 Solving Radical Equations

OBJECTIVE

To solve equations that contain radicals with variables.

An equation with a variable in a radicand is called a **radical equation**. Such an equation can be solved by squaring.

EXAMPLE 1   Solve $\sqrt{x} = 3$.

$$\sqrt{x} = 3$$
$$(\sqrt{x})^2 = 3^2 \qquad \text{Square each side.}$$
$$x = 9$$

Check $\sqrt{9} \overset{?}{=} 3$
$$3 = 3 \; ✔$$

The solution is 9.

Sometimes you have to isolate the radical expression first. To do this, the addition property of equality is used in the next example.

EXAMPLE 2   4 more than the square root of n is 11. Find n.

$$\sqrt{n} + 4 = 11$$
$$\sqrt{n} = 7 \qquad \text{Isolate the radical on one side.}$$
$$n = 49 \qquad \text{Square each side.}$$

Check   Four more than the square root of 49 is $\sqrt{49} + 4 = 7 + 4 = 11 \; ✔$

EXAMPLE 3   Solve $\sqrt{n + 4} = 11$.

$$\sqrt{n + 4} = 11$$
$$n + 4 = 121 \qquad \text{Square each side.}$$
$$n = 117$$

Check $\sqrt{117 + 4} \overset{?}{=} 11$
$$\sqrt{121} \overset{?}{=} 11$$
$$11 = 11 \; ✔$$

The solution is 117.

Squaring each side of an equation can be helpful, but the new equation is not always equivalent to the original equation. *Extraneous* roots that do not satisfy the original equation may be introduced. Hence, a check is essential.

EXAMPLE 4   Solve $\sqrt{n} + 8 = 3$.

$$\sqrt{n} + 8 = 3$$
$$\sqrt{n} = -5$$
$$n = 25$$

Check $\sqrt{25} + 8 \overset{?}{=} 3$
$$5 + 8 \overset{?}{=} 3$$
$$13 = 3 \quad \text{False}$$

25 is not a solution.
The equation has no solution.

RADICALS

WARM-UP EXERCISES

Square each expression.
1. $\sqrt{x}$ x
2. $\sqrt{y + 3}$ $y + 3$
3. $5\sqrt{y}$ $25y$
4. $\sqrt{x - 2}$ $x - 2$

LESSON NOTES

In discussing the model examples, emphasize the importance of checking each number that is obtained to see whether it is a solution of the original equation or problem. The paragraph that precedes Example 4 introduces the concept of *extraneous* roots. Then, in Example 4, we find that 25 is an extraneous root. After discussing Example 4, point out that the second step in the solution ($\sqrt{n} = -5$) could have served as a warning that the original equation had no solution. Since $\sqrt{n}$ can never be negative, $\sqrt{n} = -5$ has no solution (and $\sqrt{n} + 8 = 3$ is equivalent to $\sqrt{n} = -5$).

ALTERNATE EXAMPLES

1. Solve: $\sqrt{x} = 5$ $x = 25$
2. 8 more than the square root of n is 14. Find n. $n = 36$
3. Solve: $\sqrt{n - 9} = 12$ $n = 153$

4. Solve: $\sqrt{n} - 2 = -5$ No solution
**For an example in which the radical has a numerical coefficient, use
$$4\sqrt{n} = 3$$
$$16n = 9$$
$$n = \frac{9}{16}$$

(See Exercises 5, 6, 13, 15, 16, 18, 19, 21, 34.)

Solve and check.
1. $\sqrt{x} = 4$ 16
2. $\sqrt{3x} = 6$ 12
3. $\sqrt{5x} = -10$ No sol.
4. $3\sqrt{x} + 2 = 11$ 9
5. $\sqrt{x + 2} = 3\sqrt{2}$ 16

ASSIGNMENT GUIDE
(page 426)
Minimum course: omit
Average course: 1–31 odd
Maximum course: 1–43 odd

ENRICHMENT ACTIVITY

Have your students explore the solutions to equations such as these:
1. $\sqrt[3]{x} = 4$
   $x = 64$ (Cube both sides.)
2. $\sqrt[3]{x - 2} = -5$
   $x - 2 = -5$ (Cube both sides.)
   $x = -123$
3. $\sqrt[4]{x} + 1 = -2$
   $\sqrt[4]{x} = -3$ (Raise both sides
   $x = 81$ to the fourth
   power.)

The x-values for the first two problems satisfy the equations, so they *are* solutions. However, we must reject $x = 81$ as a possible solution to the third problem because it does not satisfy the original equation. There is no solution to problem 3.

Let your students try to discover when extraneous roots may occur in solving radical equations. When both sides of an equation are raised to an even power, extraneous roots may occur. When both sides of an equation are raised to an odd power, extraneous roots do not occur.

CLASS EXERCISES

Solve and check. Remember to isolate the radical if necessary.

1. $\sqrt{y} = 9$ 81
2. $5 = \sqrt{y}$ 25
3. $\sqrt{y} = 0$ 0
4. $\sqrt{y + 1} = 4$ 15
5. $\sqrt{y - 2} = 8$ 66
6. $\sqrt{2y + 1} = 5$ 12
7. $\sqrt{y} - 1 = 5$ 36
8. $2 + \sqrt{y} = 3$ 1
9. $\sqrt{y + 4} = 4$ 12

EXERCISES

A   Solve and check.

1. $\sqrt{x} = 7$ 49
2. $\sqrt{5x} = 5$ 5
3. $\sqrt{4x} = 8$ 16
4. $\sqrt{3x} = -6$ No solution
5. $2\sqrt{x} = 3$ $\frac{9}{4}$
6. $3\sqrt{x} = \frac{1}{2}$ $\frac{1}{36}$
7. $\sqrt{x} - 1 = 4$ 25
8. $9 + \sqrt{x} = 10$ 1
9. $\sqrt{2x + 3} = 5$ 2
10. $\sqrt{8x} - 9 = -1$ 8
11. $\sqrt{2 + x} = -5$ No solution
12. $\sqrt{3x - 8} = 2$ 4
13. $2\sqrt{x} + 3 = 9$ 9
14. $\sqrt{2x + 3} = 9$ 39
15. $2\sqrt{x + 3} = 9$ $\frac{69}{4}$

B
16. $\dfrac{\sqrt{x}}{5} = 2$ 100
17. $\sqrt{\dfrac{z}{2}} = \dfrac{1}{2}$ $\frac{1}{2}$
18. $-2\sqrt{\dfrac{z}{8}} = 15$ No solution
19. $\dfrac{\sqrt{m - 1}}{2} = 5$ 101
20. $\sqrt{\dfrac{2m + 3}{5}} = 1$ 1
21. $2\sqrt{\dfrac{m + 1}{3}} = 4$ 11
22. $\sqrt{n^2} = 200$ 200 or -200
23. $\sqrt{4n^2} = \dfrac{1}{3}$ $\frac{1}{6}$ or $-\frac{1}{6}$
24. $\sqrt{2x} = 3\sqrt{2}$ 9
25. $\sqrt{x} = 6\sqrt{3}$ 108
26. $\sqrt{x - 5} = 2\sqrt{5}$ 25

27. 6 times the square root of some number is 54. Find the number.   81
28. 8 less than the square root of some number is 73. What is the number?   6561
29. The square root of the sum of 3 and a number is 8. What is the number?   61
30. If 8 is subtracted from n, the square root of the difference is 12. Find n.   152
31. Find a number such that 7 more than twice its square root is 7.   0
32. 5 decreased by the square root of twice a number equals 1. Find the number.   8

C   Solve and check.

33. $\sqrt{x^2} = -3$ No solution
34. $5\sqrt{x^2} = 6$ $\frac{6}{5}$ or $-\frac{6}{5}$
35. $\sqrt{x^2} + 7 = 13$ 6 or -6
36. $\sqrt{x^2} + 1 = -1$ No solution
37. $\sqrt{2x^2 - 4} = x$ 2
38. $\sqrt{3x^2 - 18} = x$ 3
39. $\sqrt{2x - 2} = \sqrt{x + 1}$ 3
40. $\sqrt{x - 3} = \sqrt{x + 3}$ No solution
41. $\sqrt{x + 3} + x = 3$ 1
42. $\sqrt{x + 5} - 3 = x$ -1
43. $\sqrt{x + 12} - x = 10$ -8
44. $6 - \sqrt{x + 6} = 3x$ $\frac{10}{9}$

*45. $\sqrt{22 + \sqrt{7 + \sqrt{x - 1}}} = 7$ 521,285

CHAPTER 11

EXTRA PRACTICE, page 529

Archaeology

Applications

You may wish to discuss this *Applications* page to provide a glimpse of one of the many fascinating facts that are found in the history of mathematics. We generally credit Pythagoras with the right-triangle rule; however mathematicians in ancient Babylon were aware of aspects of right-triangle relationships 1200 years before Pythagoras was born!

Archaeologists sometimes use mathematics in order to translate or decipher inscriptions. The records of many ancient civilizations show how people recorded time according to the motion of the sun, moon, and planets.

Other findings reveal how they computed and measured.

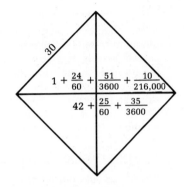

This is a sketch of an ancient Babylonian tablet that dates to 1700 B.C. It shows three numbers written on the side and diagonal of a square, and nothing more. Yet, when the cuneiform writing was translated, it turned out to be a remarkable find.

This is what it says. Can you discover its meaning?

The figure on the tablet shows a square and its diagonals.

1. How long is the diagonal of a 1-unit square? $\sqrt{2}$, or about 1.414 units

2. How long is the diagonal of a square measuring 30 units on each side? $30\sqrt{2}$, or about 42.426 units

3. Use your calculator to evaluate the sums of the two sets of fractions shown in the sketch above. How do their decimal values compare with your answers to Questions 1 and 2?   The decimal values are close to the answers to Questions 1 and 2.

4. Explain the meaning of the numbers on this ancient Babylonian tablet.   They represent the length of a diagonal of a 1-unit square and the length of a diagonal of a 30-unit square.

These exercises review basic algebraic skills.

Simplify.

1. $-2a^2 - (-2a)^2$ $-6a^2$

2. $x(x - 3) - 2(5 - x) - (x^2 - 1)$
$-x - 9$

3. $\dfrac{1 - x[3(5 - x)] - 1}{3x}$ $x - 5$

4. $\dfrac{3}{5} \cdot \sqrt{60}$ $\dfrac{6\sqrt{15}}{5}$

5. $\sqrt{20} + \sqrt{45}$ $5\sqrt{5}$

Evaluate when $a = -5$, $b = -3$, and $c = -1$.

6. $a^3b^4c^5$ 10,125

7. $\dfrac{ab^2 + bc^2}{abc}$ $\dfrac{48}{15}$

Solve for x.

8. $3(x - 1) + 5(x + 1) = 6x$

9. $x^2 - 3x = 18$ 6 or -3

10. $|3x - 5| = 10$ 5 or $-\dfrac{5}{3}$

11. Solve the system:
$x - y = 4$
$5x - 3y = 0$ $(-6, -10)$

12. Find the slope of the line that contains the points $(-6, 3)$ and $(-5, 2)$. -1

13. Write the equation, in slope-intercept form, of the line that has an x-intercept of 5 and a y-intercept of 3. $y = -\dfrac{3}{5}x + 3$

Factor completely.

14. $x^2 + \dfrac{1}{2}x + \dfrac{1}{16}$ $\left(x + \dfrac{1}{4}\right)^2$

15. $4x^2 - 2x - 2$ $2(2x + 1)(x - 1)$

16. $x^5 - 9x^3$ $x^3(x + 3)(x - 3)$

17. Multiply: $(x^2 + 1)(x^2 - x - 1)$
$x^4 - x^3 - x - 1$

Solve. Graph the solution set on a number line.

18. $-2 < 3 - 5x < 13$
$-2 < x < 1$

19. $|x - 1| > 3$ $x > 4$ or $x < -2$

20. Find the measure of the hypotenuse of a right triangle with legs that measure $\sqrt{54}$ and $\sqrt{96}$. Give your answer in simplest radical form. $5\sqrt{6}$

428

CHAPTER 11 REVIEW

VOCABULARY

square root (p. 401)
principal square root (p. 401)
radical (p. 401)
radical sign, $\sqrt{}$ (p. 401)
radicand (p. 401)
rationalizing the denominator (p. 408)

Pythagorean theorem (p. 416)
hypotenuse (p. 416)
legs of a right triangle (p. 416)
radical equation (p. 425)
extraneous roots (p. 425)

SUMMARY

In this chapter, repeating decimals are introduced in the further exploration of rational numbers. Irrational numbers are reviewed and discussed, mainly as square roots. Operations with radicals are examined, beginning with multiplication and division. This is followed by the addition and subtraction of radical expressions. As an application of radicals, the Pythagorean theorem is used to derive the distance formula. This formula is used to find lengths of segments and to determine whether a triangle is a right triangle.

REVIEW EXERCISES

11-1   *Write each rational number as a decimal.*

1. $1\dfrac{17}{20}$ 1.85
2. $\dfrac{7}{12}$ $0.58\overline{3}$
3. $\dfrac{3}{11}$ $0.\overline{27}$
4. $\dfrac{7}{15}$ $0.4\overline{6}$

Write each rational number as a fraction in simplest form.

5. 1.8 $\dfrac{9}{5}$
6. $5.\overline{3}$ $\dfrac{16}{3}$
7. $0.\overline{7}$ $\dfrac{7}{9}$
8. $0.1\overline{30}$ $\dfrac{43}{330}$

11-2   *Simplify.*

9. $\sqrt{64}$ 8
10. $-\sqrt{25}$ -5
11. $\sqrt{200}$ $10\sqrt{2}$
12. $\sqrt{108}$ $6\sqrt{3}$

13. $\sqrt{27}$ $3\sqrt{3}$
14. $3\sqrt{32}$ $12\sqrt{2}$
15. $\sqrt{5776}$ 76
16. $\sqrt{13^2 - 5^2}$ 12

Extra Topic   *Write in scientific notation.*

17. 7000 7×10^3
18. 320,000 3.2×10^5
19. 0.067 6.7×10^{-2}
20. 0.000004 4×10^{-6}

21. Write 4.1×10^{-3} in decimal form. 0.0041

11-3   *Simplify.*

22. $\sqrt{20}$ $2\sqrt{5}$
23. $4\sqrt{80}$ $16\sqrt{5}$
24. $-7\sqrt{300}$ $-70\sqrt{3}$
25. $\dfrac{1}{2}\sqrt{72}$ $3\sqrt{2}$

26. $\sqrt{5}\sqrt{3}$ $\sqrt{15}$
27. $\sqrt{12}\sqrt{18}$ $6\sqrt{6}$
28. $\sqrt{45}\sqrt{27}$ $9\sqrt{15}$
29. $6\sqrt{12}\sqrt{8}$ $24\sqrt{6}$

428

11-4 *Simplify.*

30. $\sqrt{\dfrac{4}{64}}$ $\frac{1}{4}$ **31.** $\dfrac{1}{\sqrt{3}}$ $\frac{\sqrt{3}}{3}$ **32.** $\dfrac{\sqrt{8}}{2}$ $\sqrt{2}$ **33.** $\sqrt{\dfrac{5}{3}}$ $\frac{\sqrt{15}}{3}$

34. $\sqrt{\dfrac{7}{12}}$ $\frac{\sqrt{21}}{6}$ **35.** $\dfrac{2}{3}\sqrt{\dfrac{18}{27}}$ $\frac{2\sqrt{6}}{9}$ **36.** $\dfrac{\sqrt{72}}{\sqrt{27}}$ $\frac{2\sqrt{6}}{3}$ **37.** $\sqrt{6\dfrac{1}{8}}$ $\frac{7\sqrt{2}}{4}$

11-5 *Simplify. All variables represent positive numbers.*

38. $\sqrt{4x^2}$ $2x$ **39.** $\sqrt{100x^4}$ $10x^2$ **40.** $\sqrt{8x^3}$ $2x\sqrt{2x}$ **41.** $3\sqrt{x}\,\sqrt{3x}$ $3x\sqrt{3}$

42. $\sqrt{\dfrac{x^2}{10}}$ $\frac{x\sqrt{10}}{10}$ **43.** $5xy\sqrt{75y^5}$ **44.** $-2x\sqrt{x^{10}}$ $-2x^6$ **45.** $5x\sqrt{5x}\,\sqrt{5x^2}$

            $25xy^3\sqrt{3y}$ $25x^2\sqrt{x}$

11-6   **46.** $5\sqrt{6} - 2\sqrt{6}$ $3\sqrt{6}$ **47.** $3\sqrt{3} + \sqrt{12}$ $5\sqrt{3}$ **48.** $7\sqrt{24} - 5\sqrt{54}$ $-\sqrt{6}$

          49. $2\sqrt{125} - 3\sqrt{20}$ $4\sqrt{5}$ **50.** $\sqrt{x} + \sqrt{x^5}$ $(1 + x^2)\sqrt{x}$ **51.** $\sqrt{x^5y^4} + \sqrt{x^4y^5}$

                                                              $x^2y^2(\sqrt{x} + \sqrt{y})$

11-7 *Solve for **x**, using the Pythagorean theorem. Write irrational answers in simplest radical form.*

52. 15

53. $\sqrt{19}$

54. $6\sqrt{3}$

55. The two legs of a right triangle are 16 m and 30 m long. Find the length of the hypotenuse.   34 m

56. The hypotenuse of a right triangle is 10 cm long. The two legs are equal in length. Find the length of each leg. $5\sqrt{2}$ cm; $5\sqrt{2}$ cm

57. A triangle has sides 24, 7, and 25 units long. Show why the triangle is or is not a right triangle. $7^2 + 24^2 \overset{?}{=} 25^2$; $49 + 576 \overset{?}{=} 625$; $625 = 625$ ✔   The triangle is a right triangle.

11-8 *Find the distance between each pair of points. Express irrational answers in simplest radical form.*

58. $(4, 5)$, $(10, -3)$ 10 **59.** $(2, -7)$, $(-3, -3)$ $\sqrt{41}$ **60.** $(-3, 2)$, $(6, -1)$ $3\sqrt{10}$

61. The distance between two points, $(2, 4)$ and $(8, y)$, is $\sqrt{37}$. Find two possible values for y. $y = 3$ or $y = 5$

11-9 *Solve for **x** and check.*

62. $3\sqrt{x} = 12$ 16 **63.** $\sqrt{\dfrac{x}{5}} + 3 = 0$ No solution   **64.** $\sqrt{3 + 2x} = 4$ $\frac{13}{2}$

65. $\sqrt{2x} = -10$ No solution   **66.** $2\sqrt{x - 3} = 5$ $\frac{37}{4}$ **67.** $\sqrt{8x} = 3$ $\frac{9}{8}$

CHAPTER 11 TEST

11-1 Write each rational number as a terminating or repeating decimal.

1. $1\frac{3}{5}$ 1.6

2. $\frac{11}{9}$ $1.\bar{2}$

3. $\frac{9}{11}$ $0.\overline{81}$

Write each rational number as a fraction in simplest form.

4. 0.6 $\frac{3}{5}$

5. $0.\bar{6}$ $\frac{2}{3}$

6. $1.\overline{06}$ $\frac{35}{33}$

Simplify each expression. All variables represent positive numbers.

11-2   **7.** $-\sqrt{144}$ -12 **8.** $\frac{1}{2}\sqrt{64}$ 4

11-3   **9.** $\sqrt{90}$ $3\sqrt{10}$ **10.** $-\sqrt{5}\sqrt{10}$ $-5\sqrt{2}$

11-4   **11.** $\frac{3}{\sqrt{3}}$ $\sqrt{3}$ **12.** $\frac{3}{4}\sqrt{\frac{27}{12}}$ $\frac{9}{8}$

11-5   **13.** $\sqrt{144x^4}$ $12x^2$ **14.** $\sqrt{16x^3}$ $4x\sqrt{x}$

15. $3\sqrt{8x}$ $6\sqrt{2x}$ **16.** $\sqrt{\frac{5}{x}}$ $\frac{\sqrt{5x}}{x}$

11-6   **17.** $6\sqrt{8} + 2\sqrt{8}$ $16\sqrt{2}$ **18.** $\sqrt{12} - \sqrt{27}$ $-\sqrt{3}$

11-7 Solve for **x**. Write irrational answers in simplest radical form.

19.

(triangle with legs 10 and 24, hypotenuse x)

26

20.

$3\sqrt{2}$

21.

$2\sqrt{10}$

22. A triangle has sides that are 21, 28, and 35 units long. Show that it is a right triangle. $(21)^2 + (28)^2 \stackrel{?}{=} (35)^2$; $441 + 784 \stackrel{?}{=} 1225$; $1225 = 1225$ ✔
∴ The triangle is a right triangle.

11-8   **23.** Find the distance between $(-2, 3)$ and $(5, 11)$. Express your answer in simplest radical form. $\sqrt{113}$

11-9 Solve.

24. $\sqrt{5x - 6} = 3$ 3   **25.** $3\sqrt{2x} = 4$ $\frac{8}{9}$

430

Is It a Right Triangle?

Is a triangle with sides of 15, 112, and 113 a right triangle? The computer seems ideal for solving problems of this type. The program below is designed to determine whether or not $15^2 + 112^2 = 113^2$.

Before entering the program, determine which symbol your computer uses for exponentiation. If necessary, replace the symbol ↑ in line 200 with either ∧ or **.

The Program	What It Does
``` 100 REM RIGHT TRIANGLE? ```	
``` 110 READ A, B, C ```	Reads three values in order, from left to right, from the DATA statement.
``` 120 DATA 15, 112, 113 ```	
``` 200 IF A ↑ 2 + B ↑ 2 = C ↑ 2 THEN 310 ```	If $a^2 + b^2 = c^2$, jumps to line 310; if not, continues to line 300.
``` 300 PRINT "NOT A "; ```	
``` 310 PRINT "RIGHT TRIANGLE." ```	
``` 400 GO TO 110 ```	Returns for more data.
``` 900 END ```	

When the above program is RUN, some computers will display RIGHT TRIANGLE; others will display NOT A RIGHT TRIANGLE. Incorrect output on some computers is due to the way they perform computations. On one computer PRINT 7 ↑ 2 displays 49.0000001. Even when the exact answer is displayed on the monitor, the computer may be storing an approximate value internally. One way to deal with this difficulty is to rewrite line 200 as:

```
IF A * A + B * B = C * C THEN 310
```

Multiplication usually gives an exact answer, while raising to a power may not.

Another method is to take advantage of the fact that the values computed are very close to exact. We therefore allow a small tolerance, such as 0.0001. Line 200 may be replaced with:

```
200 LET X = A ↑ 2 + B ↑ 2

210 LET Y = C ↑ 2

220 IF ABS(X - Y) < .0001 THEN 310
```

Test all versions of the above program with the following data. Tell which triples represent sides of a right triangle.

1. 120 DATA 39, 80, 89, 85, 132, 157
2. 120 DATA 60, 91, 109, 36, 77, 85, 48, 55, 71

3. When we know that the results of the computation must be integers, we can use rounding to deal with inexact results. Revise the above program and use rounding in lines 200 to 220.

For more information about BASIC, see the Computer Handbook at the back of the book.

Computer Activity

It may be worthwhile to discuss lines 200, 300, and 310 in the program. According to the instruction in line 200, if $a^2 + b^2 = c^2$, then the program goes immediately to line 310 and RIGHT TRIANGLE is printed. If $a^2 + b^2 \neq c^2$, then the program goes to line 300 and NOT A is printed; then, as per the direction in line 310, RIGHT TRIANGLE is printed; thus, the phrase NOT A RIGHT TRIANGLE is displayed.

ADDITIONAL ANSWERS

Computer Activity

1. Both triples represent sides of a right triangle.
2. The first two triples represent sides of a right triangle. The triple 48, 55, 71 does not represent the sides of a right triangle.
3. ```
   200 LET X = INT(A ↑
       2 + B ↑ 2 + .5)
   210 LET Y = INT(C ↑
       2 + .5)
   220 IF X = Y THEN
       310
   ```
   ```

In many school systems, this chapter may be the final unit in a first-year algebra course.

The chapter begins with an introduction to functions and the notation for a function. Thereafter, it presents a study of quadratic equations and their graphs in the coordinate plane.

Next, the students learn to solve a quadratic equation of the form $ax^2 + bx + c = 0$ by completing the square; this leads, in turn, to the solution of such equations by the quadratic formula. The discriminant $b^2 - 4ac$ is studied and used to determine the number and characteristics of the roots of quadratic equations.

This chapter closes with lessons that deal with problem solving and direct and inverse variation.

CHAPTER 12

The altitude of the sky diver can be found by using a quadratic equation. This equation would include the number of seconds that have passed since he jumped, his initial downward velocity, and the altitude of the plane.

QUADRATIC FUNCTIONS AND EQUATIONS

Prerequisite Skills Review

Write the letter for the correct answer.

1. Simplify $\dfrac{-2 - 1.4}{2}$.   c

   a. -2.7 **b.** -2.4 **c.** -1.7 **d.** -0.8

2. If $x = -3$, then $x^2 + 2x - 3 = \underline{\ ?\ }$.   c

   a. -18 **b.** -3 **c.** 0 **d.** 12

3. $x^2 + 4x - 3 = \underline{\ ?\ }$ b

   a. $(x + 2)^2 + 7$ **b.** $(x + 2)^2 - 7$ **c.** $(x - 2)^2 - 1$ **d.** $(x + 4)^2 - 19$

4. If $x = \dfrac{-8 + \sqrt{64 - (4)(3)(-2)}}{6}$, then $x = \underline{\ ?\ }$.   a

   a. $\dfrac{-4 + \sqrt{22}}{3}$ **b.** $\dfrac{-4 + 2\sqrt{22}}{3}$ **c.** $\dfrac{-4 + \sqrt{10}}{3}$ **d.** $\dfrac{-4 + 2\sqrt{10}}{3}$

5. $\dfrac{6 - \sqrt{20}}{2} = \underline{\ ?\ }$ b

   a. $3 - 2\sqrt{5}$ **b.** $3 - \sqrt{5}$ **c.** $3 - \sqrt{10}$ **d.** $3 - \sqrt{20}$

6. Which expression is negative for all values of x?   d

   a. $6 - x$ **b.** $-2x$ **c.** $5x$ **d.** $-3x^2 - 1$

7. Which expression is nonnegative for all values of x?   a

   a. $(x - 10)^2$ **b.** $\dfrac{1}{2}x$ **c.** $-x - 3$ **d.** $x + 15$

8. What is the missing term? $(2n + 7)^2 = 4n^2 + \underline{\ ?\ } + 49$ d

   a. 0 **b.** $7n$ **c.** $14n$ **d.** $28n$

9. Which trinomial is *not* a trinomial square?   d

   a. $x^2 - 8x + 16$ **b.** $x^2 + 10x + 25$
   c. $9x^2 + 6x + 1$ **d.** $x^2 - 4x - 4$

10. Which equation is equivalent to the proportion $\dfrac{7}{9} = \dfrac{x}{4}$?   b

    a. $7x = 36$ **b.** $9x = 28$ **c.** $4x = 63$ **d.** $x + 9 = 11$

11. Solve for the positive value of n: $\dfrac{4}{n^2} = \dfrac{1}{2}$ b

    a. 8 **b.** $2\sqrt{2}$ **c.** $\sqrt{2}$ **d.** 4

PREREQUISITE SKILLS REVIEW

For students who need additional practice with the algebraic skills in this Prerequisite Skills Review, you may assign Follow-Up exercises on pages 505–506 in the students' books.

An item-by-item error analysis of the Prerequisite Skills Review appears on page T28.

Evaluate each expression for $x = 3$.

1. $x - 5$ $\quad -2$

2. $5x - 4$ $\quad 11$

3. $5 - 2x$ $\quad -1$

LESSON NOTES

Any set of ordered pairs (x, y) is a relation. When a relation is such that each value of x has one and only one corresponding value of y, then the relation is a *function*.

The vertical line test is a convenient method of recognizing which graphs represent functions. As you discuss the figures on page 435, be sure the students understand that when a vertical line intersects a graph in more than one point, there is more than one y-value for the given value of x. Thus, the graph is not that of a function. Notice that the vertical line test is used in Class Exercises 4–6 and in Exercises 5–7.

Note, in Exercises 36–39, the more able students informally explore composite functions. No terminology is introduced; the aim is simply to enable these students to explore ideas independently. In each of these exercises, the students should discover that $f(g(x))$ is not the same as $g(f(x))$. (At a later level, the students will find that $f(g(x)) = g(f(x))$ if $f(x)$ and $g(x)$ are inverse functions.)

12-1 Functions and Function Notation

OBJECTIVES

To tell whether a set of ordered pairs of numbers is a function.

To tell whether a graph represents a function.

To use the notation $f(x)$ in evaluating functions.

You have already learned how to draw the graph of a linear equation. Consider, for example, the graph of $y = x + 1$.

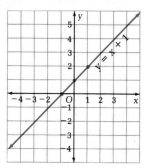

When $x = -1$, $y = 0$

When $x = 0$, $y = 1$

When $x = 1$, $y = 2$

So the graph contains points $(-1, 0)$, $(0, 1)$, and $(1, 2)$. Note that for each value of x, there is one and only one value of y. When this is so, we say that the graph represents a *function*.

> A **function** is a set of ordered pairs of numbers such that for each first number there is exactly one second number.

Each of the following sets of number pairs is a function.

$$\{(1, 1), (2, 2), (3, 3), (4, 4), (5, 5)\}$$
$$\{(-2, 1), (-1, 0), (0, -1), (1, -2), (2, -3)\}$$

Can you tell why the set $\{(-2, -1), (-2, 1), (0, 0), (1, 2), (2, 3)\}$ is not a function? For $x = -2$, there are two values for y, -1 and 1. Although this set of ordered pairs is not a function, it is called a *relation*. Every set of ordered pairs is a **relation** but not every relation is a function.

The equation $y = x + 1$ gives a rule that assigns a unique y-value to each x-value. Therefore the equation *defines* a function. However, we often speak informally of the rule as the function.

We sometimes say that y is a function of x, and use the symbol $f(x)$ in place of y. The symbol $f(x)$ is read **f of x,** or **f at x.** It does not mean f times x.

In function notation we write $y = x + 1$ as $f(x) = x + 1$.

The symbol $f(2)$ indicates the value of the function when $x = 2$. Thus for $f(x) = x + 1$,

$$f(2) = 2 + 1 = 3 \qquad \text{This is read } f \text{ of 2 is equal to 3.}$$

Similarly,

$$f(-1) = -1 + 1 = 0 \quad \text{and} \quad f(9) = 9 + 1 = 10$$

Other letters may also be used in function notation.

434

EXAMPLE 1   Let $g(x) = 3x - 5$.

   a. Find $g(-1)$. $g(-1) = 3(-1) - 5 = -8$

   b. Find $g(0)$. $g(0) = 3(0) - 5 = -5$

   c. Find $g(4)$. $g(4) = 3(4) - 5 = 7$

EXAMPLE 2   Let $f(x) = x^2 + 2x - 3$.

   a. Find $f(1)$. $f(1) = 1^2 + 2(1) - 3 = 0$

   b. Find $f(-2)$. $f(-2) = (-2)^2 + 2(-2) - 3 = -3$

   c. Find $f(2)$. $f(2) = 2^2 + 2(2) - 3 = 5$

   d. Find $-f(2)$. $-f(2) = -[2^2 + 2(2) - 3] = -5$

                  Note that $-f(2) \neq f(-2)$.

It is possible to tell whether a graph represents a function by using a **vertical line test.**   The graph represents a function if any vertical line intersects the graph in, at most, one point. Consider these graphs.

The graph represents a function. Every vertical line intersects the graph in only one point. For each x, there is only one y.

The graph does not represent a function. A vertical line can be drawn to intersect the graph in two points.

The following graphs represent functions.

The graphs below do not represent functions. Do you see why not?

Determine if each set of ordered
pairs is or is not a function. If not,
explain why not.

1. {(−2, 3), (5, −1), (2, 5)} Yes

2. {(−4, 1), (1, 6), ((−4, 3)}
No. When $x = −4$, y has two
values, 1 and 3.

Given the function $f(x) = 4x − 3$,
evaluate the function for the given
values of x.

3. $f(0)$ −3

4. $f(−1)$ −7

5. $f(2) − f(−2)$ 16

ASSIGNMENT GUIDE
(pages 436–437)

Minimum course: 1–19
Average course: 1–23 odd,
24–29
Maximum course: 1–29 odd,
30–39

ENRICHMENT ACTIVITY

Have students study the Challenge
that appears on page 437. Then ask
them to graph the relations defined
by the following equations:

1. $|x| + |y| = 3$ **2.** $|x| − |y| = 3$
3. $|x + y| = 3$ **4.** $|x − y| = 3$

1.

2.

3.

4.

CLASS EXERCISES

Tell whether each set of ordered pairs is a function. If not, explain why not.

1. {(1, 3), (2, 5), (3, −1), (4, 5)} Yes

2. {(1, 1), (2, 1), (3, 1), (4, 1), (5, 1)} Yes

3. {(1, 1), (1, 2), (1, 3), (1, 4), (1, 5)} No, since different y-values correspond to $x = 1$.

Use the vertical line test to tell whether each graph represents a function. If not, explain why not.

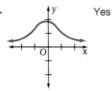

4. Yes **5.** No. A vertical line crosses the graph twice. **6.** Yes

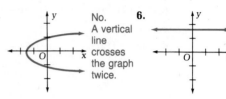

For each function, find the indicated values.

$f(x) = x^2 + 3x − 2$

$g(x) = x^2 − x$

7. $f(3)$ 16 **8.** $f(0)$ −2 **9.** $f(−2)$ −4 **10.** $−f(−2)$ 4

11. $g(3)$ 6 **12.** $g(1)$ 0 **13.** $g(0)$ 0 **14.** $g(−3)$ 12

EXERCISES

A

Tell whether each set of ordered pairs is a function. If not, explain why not.

1. {(−1, 2), (0, 1), (1, 0), (2, 1), (3, 2), (4, 3)} Yes

2. {(−5, 0), (−1, 1), (0, 2), (0, −1), (1, 1)} No; when $x = 0$, y has values 2 and −1.

3. {(−3, 1), (−1, −1), (0, 2), (1, 2), (2, 3)} Yes

4. {(1, 1), (2, 2), (3, 3), (4, 4), (5, 5)} Yes

Use the vertical line test to tell whether each graph represents a function. If not, explain why not.

5. Yes **6.** Yes **7.** No. A vertical line can cross the graph at many points.

436

CHAPTER 12

EXTRA PRACTICE, pages 529–530

For each function, find the indicated values.

$f(x) = 3x - 1$ **8.** $f(0)$ -1 **9.** $f(-2)$ -7 **10.** $f(3)$ 8 **11.** $f\left(\dfrac{1}{2}\right)$ $\dfrac{1}{2}$

$g(x) = 3 - 2x$ **12.** $g(1)$ 1 **13.** $g(2)$ -1 **14.** $g(-2)$ 7 **15.** $g\left(\dfrac{3}{2}\right)$ 0

$f(x) = x^2 + x + 1$ **16.** $f(1)$ 3 **17.** $f(-1)$ 1 **18.** $f(5)$ 31 **19.** $f(-5)$ 21

$g(x) = 2x^2 - x + 3$ **20.** $g(0)$ 3 **21.** $g(2)$ 9 **22.** $g(-2)$ 13 **23.** $g(-1)$ 6

B

For each function, evaluate **a.** $f(2) + f(3)$ **b.** $\dfrac{f(2)}{f(3)}$ **c.** $f\left(\dfrac{2}{3}\right)$

24. $f(x) = 2x - 1$ **25.** $f(x) = 5 - x$ **26.** $f(x) = 3x^2$

27. $f(x) = x^2 + 4$ **28.** $f(x) = 2x^2 - 1$ **29.** $f(x) = x^2 - x + 1$

C

Let $f(x) = 3x - 5$ and $g(x) = 5x - 9$. Evaluate each of the following.

30. $f(3) + g(2)$ 5 **31.** $f(-3) + g(-2)$ -33 **32.** $f(0) - g(0)$ 4

33. $f(x) + g(x)$ $8x - 14$ **34.** $f(x) - g(x)$ $-2x + 4$ **35.** $f(x) \cdot g(x)$ $15x^2 - 52x + 45$

36. $f(g(3))$ 13 **37.** $g(f(3))$ 11 **38.** $f(g(-3))$ -77
    Hint: Work within inner parentheses first.

39. Use $f(x)$ and $g(x)$, as given above. Then compare $f(g(x))$ with $g(f(x))$.

*40. Let $g(x) = x^2$. Evaluate and simplify the quotient $\dfrac{g(x) - g(4)}{x - 4}$; $x \neq 4$. $x + 4$

*41. Let $g(x) = \frac{1}{x}$. Evaluate and simplify $g(3 + x) \cdot [g(3) + g(x)]$; $x \neq 0$. $\frac{1}{3x}$

CHALLENGE

Absolute-Value Function

The absolute-value function is described by the equation $y = |x|$. Using a
table of values as a guide, we can graph the function.

x	-2	-1	0	1	2
y	2	1	0	1	2

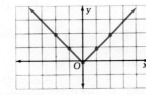

As the table suggests, there is just one y-
value for each given x-value. Use the vertical line test to show that this is the graph
of a function.

Draw each graph. Tell whether the graph represents a function.

  1. $y = |x - 1|$ **2.** $y = |x + 2|$ **3.** $x = |y|$ **4.** $y = -|x|$

QUADRATIC FUNCTIONS AND EQUATIONS   **437**

Evaluate each expression for $x = 5$.
1. $5x^2$ 125
2. $\frac{1}{2}x^2$ $12\frac{1}{2}$
3. $-2x^2$ -50

LESSON NOTES

In this lesson students work with quadratic equations of the form $y = ax^2$. Discuss the graph of $y = x^2$ (in which $a = 1$) in detail. Help the students see that the y-axis is the axis of symmetry. Be sure, too, that the students understand why the vertex (0, 0) is a minimum point. (Since x^2 cannot be negative, y cannot be negative.)

Example 1 shows that $y = -x^2$ is congruent to $y = x^2$, but the vertex (0, 0) is a maximum point.

Example 2 shows that different values of a affect the "spread" of the parabola.

Before proceeding to the exercises, have the students carefully study the summary at the bottom of page 439.

POSSIBLE ERROR

When substituting in a quadratic equation such as $y = 2x^2$, some students make errors by squaring the entire expression $2x$ rather than just the x-value. For example, when $x = 2$, they may write

$$y = 2x^2 = 4^2 = 16$$
(incorrect)

Remind the students that an expression such as $2x^2$ means $2(x \cdot x)$. (In contrast, $2x$ squared would be written as $(2x)^2$.)

12-2 The Quadratic Equation: $y = ax^2$

OBJECTIVES

To graph equations of the form $y = ax^2$.
To state the domain and range of functions of the form $f(x) = ax^2$.

The graph of a linear equation in two variables is a straight line. The graph of a **quadratic equation** such as $y = x^2$ is a curve.

This curve passes through the origin since $y = 0$ when $x = 0$. Also note that y cannot be negative since x^2 must be positive or 0.

We need to locate a sufficient number of points in order to draw the graph. Then we plot these points and connect them with a smooth curve.

The coordinates of some points are shown in the table below.

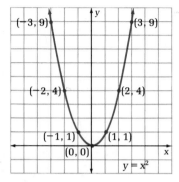

x	-3	-2	-1	0	1	2	3
y	9	4	1	0	1	4	9

The equation $y = x^2$ defines a function and can be written as $f(x) = x^2$. The graph of the function is a **parabola** with the y-axis as its **axis of symmetry.** The y-axis acts as a mirror to divide the curve into two symmetric parts. Note that

$$f(1) = f(-1) = 1$$
$$f(2) = f(-2) = 4$$
$$f(3) = f(-3) = 9$$

In general, for any x-value,

$$f(x) = f(-x) = x^2$$

The point (0, 0) is the **vertex** of the parabola. It is the *minimum point* of the curve, the point for which y has its least value.

For the function $f(x) = x^2$, the variable x can be replaced by any real number. This set of allowable replacements for x is the **domain** of the function.

Since x^2 must be positive or 0, it follows that y, or $f(x)$, must be positive or 0. The set of corresponding values for y is the **range** of the function. The range consists of all nonnegative numbers.

In brief,

Function: $f(x) = x^2$, or $y = x^2$
Domain: x is any real number.
Range: All $y \geq 0$

EXAMPLE 1   Graph $y = -x^2$. Then state the domain and range.

First, list some points on the graph in a table of values.

x	−3	−2	−1	0	1	2	3
y	−9	−4	−1	0	−1	−4	−9

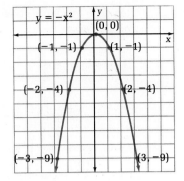

Then plot the points and draw a smooth curve through them.

The domain of the function $f(x) = -x^2$ is the set of real numbers. The range is the set of numbers that are negative or 0. That is, all $y \leq 0$.

Notice that the graph of $y = -x^2$ is congruent to the graph of $y = x^2$, but has been reflected about the x-axis. The vertex is still (0, 0), but here it is a *maximum* point of the parabola, the point for which y has its greatest value.

EXAMPLE 2   Graph each equation.

a. $y = \frac{1}{2}x^2$

x	−4	−2	0	2	4
y	8	2	0	2	8

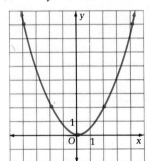

The graph does not rise as rapidly as that for $y = x^2$. Each y-value for $y = x^2$ has been multiplied by $\frac{1}{2}$.

b. $y = 2x^2$

x	−2	−1	0	1	2
y	8	2	0	2	8

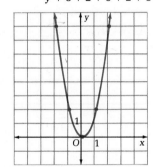

The graph rises more rapidly than that for $y = x^2$. Each y-value for $y = x^2$ has been multiplied by 2.

In summary, the graph of $y = ax^2$ is a parabola, $a \neq 0$.
The vertex is the origin and the y-axis is the axis of symmetry.
If $a > 0$, the vertex is the minimum point and the graph opens upward.
If $a < 0$, the vertex is the maximum point and the graph opens downward.
Domain: x is any real number.
Range: All $y \geq 0$, if $a > 0$.
All $y \leq 0$, if $a < 0$.

QUADRATIC FUNCTIONS AND EQUATIONS   **439**

1. Graph $y = -\frac{1}{2}x^2$. Then state the domain and range. First, list some points on the graph in a table of values.

x	−2	−1	0	1	2
y	−2	$-\frac{1}{2}$	0	$-\frac{1}{2}$	−2

The domain of the function $y = -\frac{1}{2}x^2$ is the set of real numbers. The range is the set of numbers that are negative or 0. That is, $f(x) \leq 0$, or $y \leq 0$.

2. Graph each equation.

a. $y = \frac{1}{4}x^2$

x	−4	−2	0	2	4
y	4	1	0	1	4

b. $y = 3x^2$

x	−2	−1	0	1	2
y	12	3	0	3	12

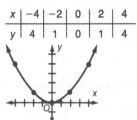

1. Graph $y = x^2$ and $y = \frac{1}{4}x^2$ on the same set of axes.

2. Complete the table for $y = \frac{1}{3}x^2$ and sketch the curve.

x	-2	-1	0	1	2
y	$\frac{4}{3}$	$\frac{1}{3}$	0	$\frac{1}{3}$	$\frac{4}{3}$

State the domain and range of each function.

3. $f(x) = x^2 + 1$
   D: x is any real number.
   R: $f(x) \geq 1$

4. $f(x) = -x^2$
   D: x is any real number.
   R: $f(x) \leq 0$

5. Give the coordinates of the vertex of $y = -4x^2$ and tell whether it is a maximum or a minimum point.
   (0, 0); maximum

ASSIGNMENT GUIDE
(pages 440–441)

Minimum course: 1–6
Average course: 1–10,
         11–17 odd
Maximum course: 1–14 odd,
         15–22
All courses: *Checkpoint*
         review
         exercises

ADDITIONAL ANSWERS

Exercises

See page 441.

CLASS EXERCISES

Match each quadratic equation with its graph.

1. $y = 3x^2$ *d*   **2.** $y = -3x^2$ *a*   **3.** $y = \frac{1}{3}x^2$ *b*   **4.** $y = -\frac{1}{3}x^2$ *c*

a.

b.

c.

d.
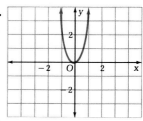

EXERCISES

A   *Graph each pair of quadratic equations on the same set of axes.*

1. $y = x^2$ and $y = \frac{1}{2}x^2$ **2.** $y = x^2$ and $y = 2x^2$

3. $y = -x^2$ and $y = -2x^2$ **4.** $y = -x^2$ and $y = -\frac{1}{2}x^2$

Complete each table of values for the given function. Then draw the graph.

5. $y = \frac{1}{5}x^2$

x	-2	-1	0	1	2
y	$\frac{4}{5}$	?	?	?	?
		$\frac{1}{5}$	0	$\frac{1}{5}$	$\frac{4}{5}$

6. $y = 5x^2$

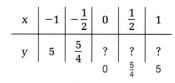

x	-1	$-\frac{1}{2}$	0	$\frac{1}{2}$	1
y	5	$\frac{5}{4}$	?	?	?
			0	$\frac{5}{4}$	5

B   *Graph the function defined by each equation.*

7. $y = 4x^2$ **8.** $y = \frac{1}{4}x^2$ **9.** $y = -4x^2$ **10.** $y = -\frac{1}{4}x^2$

EXTRA PRACTICE, page 530

State the domain and the range for each function.

11. $f(x) = 2x^2$ **12.** $f(x) = -2x^2$ **13.** $f(x) = \frac{1}{2}x^2$ **14.** $f(x) = -\frac{1}{2}x^2$

Give the coordinates of the vertex for each parabola. Tell whether it is a minimum or a maximum point.

15. $y = 5x^2$ **16.** $y = -\frac{1}{4}x^2$ **17.** $y = \frac{1}{2}x^2$ **18.** $y = -3x^2$

   (0, 0), min.   (0, 0), max.   (0, 0), min.   (0, 0), max.

 Prepare a table of values and graph each function.

19. $y = x^2 + 1$ **20.** $y = x^2 + 2$ **21.** $y = x^2 - 1$ **22.** $y = -x^2 + 1$

*23. Solve the system of equations by two methods: $\begin{array}{l} y = \frac{1}{4}x^2 \\ 2y - x = 4 \end{array}$

   a. Graph each equation on the same set of axes and write the coordinates of the intersection points.
   b. Solve the system algebraically.

CHECKPOINT

Tell whether each set of ordered pairs is a function. If not, explain why not.

1. $\{(-3, -1), (-2, 0), (-2, -3)\}$ **2.** $\{(-3, 0), (-2, -1), (0, -1)\}$

Use the vertical line test to tell whether each graph represents a function. If not, explain why not.

3.   **4.**   **5.**   **6.**

Let **f(x) = 3x² − 2x + 5**. Evaluate each of the following.

7. $f(0)$ 5   **8.** $f(1)$ 6   **9.** $f(-1)$ 10   **10.** $f(a)$ $3a^2 - 2a + 5$

11. $f(2)$ 13   **12.** $f(-2)$ 21   **13.** $f\left(\frac{1}{3}\right)$ $4\frac{2}{3}$ **14.** $f\left(-\frac{1}{3}\right)$ 6

15. Graph the parabolas $y = 8x^2$ and $y = -\frac{1}{8}x^2$ on the same set of axes and tell whether the vertex is a minimum or a maximum point. Then state the domain and range of each function.

QUADRATIC FUNCTIONS AND EQUATIONS   **441**

ENRICHMENT ACTIVITY

Have students research and report on applications of the parabola. Among the applications they may find is the use of the parabola in parabolic arches (in bridge construction). The parabola is also used in parabolic reflectors in telescopes.

Checkpoint
Students may check their answers with those given in the back of their books.

ADDITIONAL ANSWERS
Exercises
1.

2.

3.

4.

[Answers for the Exercises continue on page A12.]

Checkpoint
See page A13.

Evaluate each expression for $x = 2$.
1. $x^2 - 4$ 0
2. $-x^2 + 5$ 1
3. $2x^0 - 6$ 2

LESSON NOTES

In the introductory paragraphs dealing with $y = x^2 + 1$, the text points out that $y = x^2 + 1$ is congruent to $y = x^2$, but translated one unit up. Example 1 uses $y = -x^2 - 1$ to illustrate the general way in which the graph can be derived from the graph of $y = x^2$.

Discuss the generalization about $y = ax^2 + k$ in detail. Whereas $y = ax^2$ has its vertex at $(0, 0)$, $y = ax^2 + k$ has its vertex at $(0, k)$. If $a > 0$, the parabola opens upward; if $a < 0$, the parabola opens downward.

Exercises 31–36 anticipate the next lesson. Able students should be allowed to solve these exercises by using any method they wish. They can simply substitute appropriate values for x, construct a table, and then plot points in order to sketch each graph.

ALTERNATE EXAMPLE

1. Graph: $y = -x^2 - 2$

12-3 The Quadratic Equation: $y = ax^2 + k$

OBJECTIVE

To graph an equation of the form $y = ax^2 + k$.

We have seen that the graph of $y = ax^2$ is a parabola with vertex at $(0, 0)$.

For $a > 0$, the vertex is a minimum point.

For $a < 0$, the vertex is a maximum point.

Now consider an equation of the form $y = ax^2 + k$, such as $y = x^2 + 1$. To graph this equation, you can construct a table of values and plot points. However, it is useful to note that the graph will be congruent to that for $y = x^2$, but shifted, or translated, one unit up. The vertex is $(0, 1)$, the minimum point of the parabola.

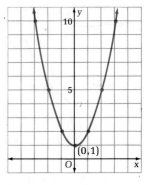

$y = x^2 + 1$

x	-3	-2	-1	0	1	2	3
y	10	5	2	1	2	5	10

Domain: x is any real number.   Range: All $y \geq 1$
The graph shows that y cannot be less than 1.

EXAMPLE 1   Graph $y = -x^2 - 1$.

A table of values can always be used as an aid in graphing. However, this equation can be graphed by thinking of these three steps.

Step 1 Graph $y = x^2$.   **Step 2** Reflect about the x-axis.   **Step 3** Translate one unit down.

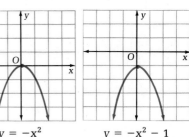

$y = x^2$ $y = -x^2$ $y = -x^2 - 1$

In general, the graph of $y = ax^2 + k$ is a parabola with vertex at $(0, k)$. The vertex is a minimum point for $a > 0$ and it is a maximum point for $a < 0$. The shape of the curve depends on the value of a. In the next example, $a = 2$.

442

EXAMPLE 2 Graph $y = 2x^2 - 1$. Then state the domain and range of the function.

The graph is congruent to that for $y = 2x^2$, but translated one unit down. It is helpful to plot a few points before drawing the graph.

x	-2	-1	0	1	2
y	7	1	-1	1	7

$(0, -1)$

Function: $f(x) = 2x^2 - 1$, or $y = 2x^2 - 1$

Domain: x is any real number.

Range: $f(x) \geq -1$, or all $y \geq -1$

Note that the axis of symmetry is the line $x = 0$, or the y-axis.

EXAMPLE 3 Graph. **a.** $y = x^2 - 2$ **b.** $y = -x^2 + 3$

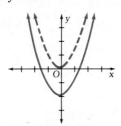

Show the graph of $y = x^2$ with a dashed curve. Then translate 2 units down.

Show the graph of $y = -x^2$ with a dashed curve. Then translate 3 units up.

CLASS EXERCISES

Match each graph with its equation.

1. b

2. a

3. d

4. c

a. $y = x^2 - 2$
b. $y = -x^2 - 2$
c. $y = x^2 + 2$
d. $y = -x^2 + 2$

Copy and complete.

5. The graph of $y = x^2 + 3$ is congruent to $y = x^2$ but translated _?_ units _?_ .
    3   up

6. The graph of $y = x^2 - 3$ is congruent to _?_ but translated _?_ units _?_ .
    $y = x^2$ 3   down

7. The graph of $y = -x^2 + 3$ is congruent to $y = -x^2$ but translated _?_ units _?_ .
    3   up

8. The graph of $y = -x^2 - 3$ is congruent to _?_ but translated _?_ units _?_ .
    $y = -x^2$ 3   down

3. Graph the function $y = x^2 - 4$.

4. Identify the vertex of the parabola $y = -x^2 - 2$. Is it a minimum or a maximum point?

$(0, -2)$; maximum

5. Graph the function $y = -\frac{1}{4}x^2 - 2$. Identify the domain and range.

Domain: x is a real number.
Range: $y \le -2$

ASSIGNMENT GUIDE
(page 444)

Minimum course: 1–8, 9, 12, 15, 18, 21, 23
Average course: 1–29 odd
Maximum course: 1–37 odd

ENRICHMENT ACTIVITY

Have the students tell whether each of the following equations defines a function. (A table of values and a graph may be used to determine the answer.)

1. $x = y^2$ No
2. $x = 2y^2 + 1$ No

ADDITIONAL ANSWERS

Exercises

See page A13.

EXERCISES

A   *Match each graph with its equation.*

a. $y = \frac{1}{2}x^2 + 1$ **b.** $y = \frac{1}{2}x^2 - 1$ **c.** $y = -\frac{1}{2}x^2 + 1$ **d.** $y = -\frac{1}{2}x^2 - 1$

1.
b
2.
a
3.
d
4.
c

5. The graph of $y = x^2 - 5$ is congruent to ? but translated ? units ? .
$y = x^2$ 5   down
6. The graph of $y = x^2 + 5$ is congruent to ? but translated ? units ? .
$y = x^2$ 5   up
7. The graph of $y = -x^2 - 5$ is congruent to ? but translated ? units ? .
$y = -x^2$ 5   down
8. The graph of $y = -x^2 + 5$ is congruent to ? but translated ? units ? .
$y = -x^2$ 5   up

Graph the function defined by each equation.

9. $y = x^2 + 2$ **10.** $y = x^2 - 2$ **11.** $y = -x^2 + 2$

12. $y = -x^2 - 2$ **13.** $y = -2x^2 + 3$ **14.** $y = 2x^2 - 3$

15. $y = \frac{1}{2}x^2 - 2$ **16.** $y = -\frac{1}{2}x^2 + 2$ **17.** $y = \frac{1}{2}x^2 - 3$

18. $y = \frac{1}{2}x^2 + 2$ **19.** $y = -\frac{1}{2}x^2 - 2$ **20.** $y = -\frac{1}{2}x^2 + 3$

Identify the vertex for each parabola. Is it a minimum or a maximum point?

21. $y = 3x^2 - 5$ **22.** $y = 5x^2 + 2$ **23.** $y = -2x^2 - 3$ **24.** $y = -x^2 + 4$
$(0, -5)$; min. $(0, 2)$; min. $(0, -3)$; max. $(0, 4)$; max.

B   *Graph each function and state **a.** the domain.   **b.** the range.*

25. $f(x) = x^2 + 3$ **26.** $f(x) = x^2 - 3$ **27.** $f(x) = -x^2 + 3$

28. $f(x) = -x^2 - 3$ **29.** $f(x) = 2x^2 + 5$ **30.** $f(x) = -\frac{1}{2}x^2 - 5$

C   *Graph.*

31. $y = (x - 1)^2$ **32.** $y = (x + 1)^2$ **33.** $y = (x - 2)^2$

34. $y = (x + 2)^2$ **35.** $y = -(x - 1)^2$ **36.** $y = -(x + 1)^2$

37. Consider equations of the form $y = ax^2 + 1$.
   a. If a is positive but gets close to 0, what happens to the graph?
   b. If a is negative but gets close to 0, what happens to the graph?
   c. If $a = 0$, what happens to the graph?

CHAPTER 12

EXTRA PRACTICE, page 530

12-4 The Quadratic Equation: $y = a(x - h)^2 + k$

OBJECTIVE

Given an equation in the form $y = a(x - h)^2 + k$, to identify the vertex and axis of symmetry and to graph the equation.

You have seen how to graph quadratic equations of the form $y = ax^2 + k$ by translating $y = ax^2$ up or down. Now let us consider the graph of an equation in the form $y = a(x - h)^2$. The graph is congruent to that of $y = ax^2$, but translated $|h|$ units left or right. Compare the graphs of $y = (x - 2)^2$ and $y = (x + 2)^2$.

$y = (x - 2)^2$

x	0	1	2	3	4
y	4	1	0	1	4

The vertex is (2, 0).

The axis of symmetry is $x = 2$.

$y = (x + 2)^2$

x	-4	-3	-2	-1	0
y	4	1	0	1	4

The vertex is (-2, 0).

The axis of symmetry is $x = -2$.

Both $y = (x - 2)^2$ and $y = (x + 2)^2$ have the form $y = (x - h)^2$. When h is -2, the equation is $y = [x - (-2)]^2$, or $y = (x + 2)^2$. Each graph is congruent to $y = x^2$.

EXAMPLE 1   On the same set of axes, draw the graphs of $y = x^2$, $y = (x + 5)^2$, and $y = (x - 4)^2$.

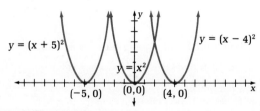

To graph an equation of the form $y = a(x - h)^2 + k$, begin with the graph for $y = ax^2$. Then translate the curve $|h|$ units right or left, and $|k|$ units up or down. The value for a determines the shape of the curve. When $a = 1$, the curve is congruent to that for $y = x^2$.

QUADRATIC FUNCTIONS AND EQUATIONS

445

WARM-UP EXERCISES

Find the value of y when $x = 3$.
1. $y = (x - 1)^2$ 4
2. $y = (x - 1)^2 + 2$ 6
3. $y = (x - 3)^2$ 0
4. $y = (x - 3)^2 - 1$ -1

LESSON NOTES

In this lesson, students learn another way in which the graph of a parabola may be translated, this time by a horizontal shift to the left or to the right. The form of the quadratic equation now becomes $y = a(x - h)^2 + k$, and the vertex is located at the point (h, k). This is illustrated in Example 1. Examples 2 and 3 are important because they involve both horizontal and vertical translations.

Example 4 and Exercises 33–37 require the students to reverse their thought processes and derive the equations from descriptions of the graphs. To solve Exercise 38 or Exercise 39, students must substitute the coordinates of the given point for x and y in the equation and then solve the equation for k or h.

The C Exercises involve quadratic inequalities. You may wish to point out that a parabola such as $y = x^2$ separates the plane into three sets of points: the parabola itself where $y = x^2$; the "inside" of the parabola, where $y > x^2$; and the "outside" of the parabola, where $y < x^2$.

ALTERNATE EXAMPLE

1. On the same set of axes, draw the graphs of $y = x^2$, $y = (x + 3)^2$, and $y = (x - 3)^2$.

$y = (x + 3)^2$ $y = (x - 3)^2$

2. Graph: $y = (x - 2)^2 + 2$

(2, 2)

3. Graph: $y = -(x - 2)^2 + 3$

(2, 3)

4. Write the equation of the graph described. Then identify the equation of the axis of symmetry and the coordinates of the vertex.

a. The graph of $y = x^2$ is translated 6 units left.
Equation: $y = (x + 6)^2$
Axis: $x = -6$
Vertex: $(-6, 0)$

b. The graph of $y = -\frac{1}{2}x^2$ is translated 2 units to the right and 3 units up.
Equation: $y = -\frac{1}{2}(x - 2)^2 + 3$
Axis: $x = 2$
Vertex: $(2, 3)$

POSSIBLE ERROR

When graphing a quadratic function such as $y = (x - 2)^2$, students tend to shift the graph of $y = x^2$ to the left instead of to the right. Likewise, they incorrectly shift $y = (x + 2)^2$ to the right.

You can correct this error by suggesting that they always locate the vertex as the first step in graphing a quadratic function.

EXAMPLE 2   Graph $y = (x - 3)^2 + 1$.

Step 1	Step 2	Step 3
Graph $y = x^2$.	Translate 3 units right.	Translate 1 unit up.

$y = x^2$ $y = (x - 3)^2$ (3, 1) $y = (x - 3)^2 + 1$

(3, 0)

Vertex: (3, 1)

Axis of symmetry: x = 3

Domain: x is any real number.

Range: All $y \geq 1$

EXAMPLE 3   Graph $y = -(x + 3)^2 + 2$.

Show the graph of $y = -x^2$ with a dashed curve. Then translate 3 units left and 2 units up.

(−3, 2)

EXAMPLE 4   Write the equation of the graph described. Then identify the equation of the axis of symmetry and the coordinates of the vertex.

a. The graph of $y = 2x^2$ is translated 10 units left.
Equation: $y = 2(x + 10)^2$
Axis: $x = -10$
Vertex: $(-10, 0)$

b. The graph of $y = -\frac{1}{2}x^2$ is translated 3 units right and 4 units up.
Equation: $y = -\frac{1}{2}(x - 3)^2 + 4$
Axis: $x = 3$
Vertex: $(3, 4)$

In general, consider a quadratic equation in the **h, k** form.

$$y = a(x - h)^2 + k, \quad a \neq 0$$

The graph is a parabola.
The vertex is (h, k) and the axis of symmetry is $x = h$.
If $a > 0$, the vertex is a minimum point and the graph opens upward.
If $a < 0$, the vertex is a maximum point and the graph opens downward.
Domain: x is any real number.
   Range: All $y \geq k$, if $a > 0$
           All $y \leq k$, if $a < 0$

CLASS EXERCISES

Identify *a.* the coordinates of the vertex. *b.* the equation of the axis of symmetry. Is the vertex a minimum or a maximum point?

1. $y = (x - 2)^2 + 5$
  (2, 5); $x = 2$; min.
2. $y = (x + 2)^2 - 5$
  (−2, −5); $x = -2$; min.
3. $y = (x + 1)^2 + 3$
  (−1, 3); $x = -1$; min.
4. $y = (x - 1)^2 - 3$
  (1, −3); $x = 1$; min.
5. $y = 2(x - 3)^2 + 4$
  (3, 4); $x = 3$; min.
6. $y = 2(x + 3)^2 - 4$
  (−3, −4); $x = -3$; min.
7. $y = -2(x + 4)^2 - 3$
  (−4, −3); $x = -4$; max.
8. $y = -2(x - 4)^2 + 3$
  (4, 3); $x = 4$; max.
9. $y = 3(x - 2)^2 - 1$
  (2, −1); $x = 2$; min.

EXERCISES

A

Match each graph with its equation.

1. *c*
(−1, 2)

2. *a*
(1, 2)

a. $y = (x - 1)^2 + 2$

b. $y = (x + 1)^2 - 2$

c. $y = -(x + 1)^2 + 2$

d. $y = -(x - 1)^2 - 2$

3. *b*
(−1, −2)

4. *d*
(1, −2)

Identify *a.* the coordinates of the vertex. *b.* the equation of the axis of symmetry. Is the vertex a minimum or a maximum point?

5. $y = (x + 1)^2 + 1$

6. $y = (x + 1)^2 - 1$

7. $y = (x - 1)^2 - 1$

8. $y = (x - 1)^2 + 1$

9. $y = 2(x + 3)^2 - 1$

10. $y = 2(x - 3)^2 + 1$

11. $y = -2(x + 3)^2 + 1$

12. $y = -2(x - 3)^2 - 1$

13. $y = -(x + 2)^2 - 3$

Copy and complete.

14. The graph of $y = (x - 3)^2 + 5$ is congruent to $y = x^2$ but is translated _?_ units to the _?_ and _?_ units _?_. 3; right; 5; up

15. The graph of $y = -(x + 3)^2 - 5$ is congruent to _?_ but is translated _?_ units to the _?_ and _?_ units _?_. $y = -x^2$; 3; left; 5; down

16. The graph of $y = (x + 5)^2 - 3$ is congruent to _?_ but is translated _?_ units to the _?_ and _?_ units _?_. $y = x^2$; 5; left; 3; down

17. The graph of $y = -(x - 5)^2 + 3$ is congruent to _?_ but is translated _?_ units to the _?_ and _?_ units _?_. $y = -x^2$; 5; right; 3; up

EXTRA PRACTICE, page 530

DAILY QUIZ

Identify the coordinates of the vertex and the equation of the axis of symmetry. Is the vertex a minimum or a maximum point?

1. $y = (x + 2)^2 + 2$
  (−2, 2); $x = -2$; minimum
2. $y = 3(x + 4)^2 - 2$
  (−4, −2); $x = -4$; minimum
3. Graph: $y = -(x - 3)^2 - 1$

4. Copy and complete.
The graph of $y = (x - 3)^2 + 1$ is congruent to $y = x^2$ but is translated _?_ units to the right and _?_ units up. 3; 1

5. State the domain and range of $f(x) = (x - 4)^2 + 3$.
Domain: x is any real number.
Range: $y \geq 3$

ASSIGNMENT GUIDE
(pages 447–448)

Minimum course: 1–17 odd
  second day: 6–12 even,
    19–31 odd
Average course: 1–31 odd
  second day: 33–43
Maximum course: 1–25 odd,
    27–32
  second day: 33–46

ADDITIONAL ANSWERS

Exercises
5. a. (−1, 1) **b.** $x = -1$ min.
6. a. (−1, −1) **b.** $x = -1$ min.
7. a. (1, −1) **b.** $x = 1$ min.
8. a. (1, 1) **b.** $x = 1$ min.
9. a. (−3, −1) **b.** $x = -3$ min.
10. a. (3, 1) **b.** $x = 3$ min.

[Answers continue on page 448.]

[Answers continue on page A14.]

Graph.

18. $y = (x - 2)^2 + 1$
19. $y = (x + 2)^2 - 1$
20. $y = (x + 1)^2 - 2$
21. $y = (x - 1)^2 + 2$
22. $y = -(x - 1)^2 + 1$
23. $y = -(x + 1)^2 - 1$
24. $y = -(x - 2)^2 - 2$
25. $y = -(x + 2)^2 + 2$
26. $y = (x + 3)^2 + 2$

B   *For each function, state   **a.** the domain.   **b.** the range.*

27. $f(x) = (x - 3)^2 + 4$
28. $f(x) = (x + 3)^2 - 4$
29. $f(x) = 2(x - 1)^2 + 5$
30. $f(x) = -2(x + 1)^2 - 5$
31. $f(x) = -(x + 1)^2 - 2$
32. $f(x) = -(x - 1)^2 + 3$

Write the equation of the graph described. Then identify the equation of the axis of symmetry and the coordinates of the vertex.

33. The graph of $y = 2x^2$ is translated 2 units right and 3 units down.

34. The graph of $y = \frac{1}{2}x^2$ is translated 2 units left and 3 units up.

35. The graph of $y = -x^2$ is translated 5 units left and 4 units down.

36. The graph of $y = -3x^2$ is translated 5 units right and 4 units up.

37. The graph of $y = 3x^2$ is translated 4 units left and 1 unit up.

38. Find the value for k so that the graph of $y = (x - 1)^2 + k$ will pass through the point $(2, -6)$. -7

39. Find values for h so that the graph of $y = (x - h)^2 - 7$ will pass through the point $(-1, 2)$. $-4; 2$

*Match each graph of $y = a(x - h)^2 + k$ with the correct values for **a**, **h**, and **k**.*

a. $a > 0, h > 0, k < 0$
b. $a < 0, h < 0, k > 0$
c. $a > 0, h < 0, k > 0$
d. $a < 0, h > 0, k < 0$

40.
b

41.
c

42.
d

43.
a

C   The graph of $y = x^2$ is shown as a dashed curve. The shaded region above the curve is the graph of $y > x^2$. To show the graph of $y \geq x^2$, we use a solid curve rather than a dashed one. The unshaded region is the graph of $y < x^2$.

Graph each of the following by shading the appropriate region.

44. $y \leq -2x^2$
45. $y > \frac{1}{2}x^2 - 2$
46. $y \leq -(x - 2)^2 + 3$
*47. $y \geq x^2 - 1$ and $y \leq -x^2 + 1$
*48. $y \geq x^2 - 1$ or $y \leq -x^2 + 1$

CHAPTER 12

12-5 Completing the Square

OBJECTIVES

To solve quadratic equations by completing the square.
To write the equation $y = ax^2 + bx + c$ in h, k form.

Quadratic equations of the form $ax^2 + bx + c = 0$, were solved by factoring. However, not every quadratic can be factored by using integers. Consider:

$$x^2 - 6x + 7 = 0$$

Since we cannot factor easily, we will use a method known as **completing the square.** First, collect all the variables on one side of the equation.

$$
\begin{aligned}
x^2 - 6x &= -7 \\
x^2 - 6x + 9 &= -7 + 9 \qquad &&\text{Add 9 to each side.} \\
(x - 3)^2 &= 2 \qquad &&\text{The left side is now a perfect square.} \\
x - 3 &= \pm\sqrt{2} \qquad &&\text{If } x^2 = k, \text{ then } x = \pm\sqrt{k}. \\
x &= 3 \pm \sqrt{2} \qquad &&\text{Solve for } x.
\end{aligned}
$$

The equation has two solutions, $3 + \sqrt{2}$ and $3 - \sqrt{2}$.

Adding 9 to $x^2 - 6x$ was an example of *completing the square.* The trinomial $x^2 - 6x + 9$ is the square of $(x - 3)$. In general,

$$x^2 - 2hx + h^2 = (x - h)^2$$

The constant term, h^2, is the square of one-half the coefficient of x. $\left[\frac{1}{2}(2h)\right]^2 = h^2$

EXAMPLE 1   Complete the square.

a. $x^2 + 8x +$?

$$\frac{1}{2}(8) = 4; \quad 4^2 = 16$$

$$x^2 + 8x + 16 = (x + 4)^2$$

b. $x^2 - 3x +$?

$$\frac{1}{2}(3) = \frac{3}{2}; \quad \left(\frac{3}{2}\right)^2 = \frac{9}{4}$$

$$x^2 - 3x + \frac{9}{4} = \left(x - \frac{3}{2}\right)^2$$

EXAMPLE 2   Write $y = x^2 + 4x - 1$ in h, k form. Then draw the graph.

$$
\begin{aligned}
y &= x^2 + 4x - 1 \\
y &= (x^2 + 4x + \underline{\ ?\ }) - 1 \qquad &&\text{Take } \tfrac{1}{2} \text{ of 4 and square it: } 2^2 = 4. \\
y &= (x^2 + 4x + 4) - 1 - 4 \qquad &&\text{Add 4 within the parentheses to complete the} \\
y &= (x + 2)^2 - 5 \qquad &&\text{square, but then also subtract 4. Why?}
\end{aligned}
$$

The equation $y = x^2 + 4x - 1$ is equivalent to the equation $y = (x + 2)^2 - 5$.

In this h, k form we recognize the graph as a parabola with vertex $(-2, -5)$ and with axis of symmetry $x = -2$. The vertex is the minimum point of the curve.

QUADRATIC FUNCTIONS AND EQUATIONS

449

3. Write $y = -2x^2 - 8x - 7$ in h, k form. Then describe its graph.
$y = -2(x + 2)^2 + 1$
Vertex: $(-2, 1)$
Axis of symmetry: $x = -2$
Since a is negative, the curve opens downward, and 1 is the maximum value of y. This occurs at the vertex, when $x = -2$.

4. Use the formula to write the equation of the axis of symmetry for the graph of $y = 3x^2 - 6x + 1$. Find the coordinates of the vertex.
Axis of symmetry: $x = 1$
Vertex: $(1, -2)$

POSSIBLE ERROR

The following sequence of steps illustrates a common error made by students in completing the square:

$y = -2x^2 - 4x + 7$
$y = -2(x^2 + 2x) + 7$
$y = -2(x^2 + 2x + 1) + 7 - 1$
(incorrect)

Here students have incorrectly added a -1 to offset "the addition of 1" in completing the square. However, because of the -2 coefficient preceding the parentheses, -2 was actually added in order to complete the square. This must be offset by the addition of 2. Thus, the third step should be:

$y = -2(x^2 + 2x + 1) + 7 + 2$

DAILY QUIZ

1. Copy and complete to form a perfect trinomial square.
$x^2 + 6x + \underline{\ ?\ }$ $x^2 + 6x + 9$
2. Solve by completing the square.
$x^2 - 4x + 2 = 0$ $2 \pm \sqrt{2}$

[Daily Quiz continues on page 451.]

The process of completing the square has been used in two ways. We used it to solve a quadratic equation of the form $ax^2 + bx + c = 0$ and to rewrite an equation of a quadratic function, $y = ax^2 + bx + c$, in h, k form. The h, k form was then used in drawing the graph.

EXAMPLE 3   Write $y = -2x^2 - 4x + 7$ in h, k form. Then describe its graph.

$y = -2x^2 - 4x + 7$
$y = -2(x^2 + 2x + \underline{\ ?\ }) + 7$ Factor -2 from the first two terms.
$y = -2(x^2 + 2x + 1) + 7 + 2$ Add 1 within the parentheses to complete the square. But then add 2 outside the parentheses. Why?
$y = -2(x + 1)^2 + 9$

Vertex: $(-1, 9)$ Axis of symmetry: $x = -1$

Since a is negative, the curve opens downward, and 9 is the maximum value of y. This occurs at the vertex, when $x = -1$.

The equation of the axis of symmetry for $y = ax^2 + bx + c$ can be written in terms of a and b. Since the equations $y = ax^2 + bx + c$ and $y = ax^2 + bx$ have the same axis of symmetry, we will write $y = ax^2 + bx$ in h, k form.

$$y = ax^2 + bx \longrightarrow y = a\left(x^2 + \frac{b}{a}x + \underline{\ ?\ }\right) \longrightarrow y = a\left(x + \frac{b}{2a}\right)^2 + \text{some constant}$$

In this case, h is $-\frac{b}{2a}$, so the equation of the axis of symmetry is

$$x = -\frac{b}{2a}$$

EXAMPLE 4   Use the formula to write the equation of the axis of symmetry for the graph of $y = 2x^2 - 4x + 5$. Find the coordinates of the vertex.

$a = 2$, $b = -4$, $c = 5$ List the values of a, b, and c in the equation.

$x = -\dfrac{-4}{4} = 1$ Substitute in the formula $x = -\frac{b}{2a}$.

$x = 1$ The axis of symmetry is $x = 1$.

$y = 2(1)^2 - 4(1) + 5 = 3$ The vertex is located at $(1, 3)$.

CLASS EXERCISES

Tell what must be added to make each trinomial a perfect square.

1. $x^2 + 6x + \underline{\ ?\ }$ 9
2. $x^2 + 4x + \underline{\ ?\ }$ 4
3. $x^2 + 2x + \underline{\ ?\ }$ 1

4. $x^2 - 6x + \underline{\ ?\ }$ 9
5. $x^2 - 4x + \underline{\ ?\ }$ 4
6. $x^2 - 2x + \underline{\ ?\ }$ 1

7. $x^2 + 8x + \underline{\ ?\ }$ 16
8. $x^2 - 10x + \underline{\ ?\ }$ 25
9. $x^2 - 3x + \underline{\ ?\ }$ $\frac{9}{4}$

10. $x^2 - 5x + \underline{\ ?\ }$ $\frac{25}{4}$
11. $x^2 + x + \underline{\ ?\ }$ $\frac{1}{4}$
12. $x^2 - x + \underline{\ ?\ }$ $\frac{1}{4}$

EXERCISES

A

Copy and complete to form a trinomial square.

1. $x^2 + 10x + \underline{?}$
$x^2 + 10x + 25$
4. $x^2 - 14x + \underline{?}$
$x^2 - 14x + 49$

2. $x^2 + 12x + \underline{?}$
$x^2 + 12x + 36$
5. $x^2 - 20x + \underline{?}$
$x^2 - 20x + 100$

3. $x^2 - 8x + \underline{?}$
$x^2 - 8x + 16$
6. $x^2 - 7x + \underline{?}$
$x^2 - 7x + \frac{49}{4}$

Solve each equation by completing the square.

7. $x^2 - 4x + 1 = 0$
$2 + \sqrt{3},\ 2 - \sqrt{3}$
10. $x^2 + 2x - 5 = 0$
$-1 + \sqrt{6},\ -1 - \sqrt{6}$
13. $x^2 - 8x = 2$
$4 + 3\sqrt{2},\ 4 - 3\sqrt{2}$

8. $x^2 + 4x - 3 = 0$
$-2 + \sqrt{7},\ -2 - \sqrt{7}$
11. $x^2 - 6x + 2 = 0$
$3 + \sqrt{7},\ 3 - \sqrt{7}$
14. $x^2 + 4x = -2$
$-2 + \sqrt{2},\ -2 - \sqrt{2}$

9. $x^2 + 6x - 5 = 0$
$-3 + \sqrt{14},\ -3 - \sqrt{14}$
12. $x^2 - 5x + 1 = 0$
$\frac{5 + \sqrt{21}}{2},\ \frac{5 - \sqrt{21}}{2}$
15. $x^2 = 3 - x$
$\frac{-1 + \sqrt{13}}{2},\ \frac{-1 - \sqrt{13}}{2}$

Write in **h, k** form.

16. $y = x^2 + 4x - 3$
$y = (x + 2)^2 - 7$
19. $y = x^2 - 2x + 6$
$y = (x - 1)^2 + 5$
22. $y = 2x^2 - 8x + 7$
$y = 2(x - 2)^2 - 1$

17. $y = x^2 - 6x + 1$
$y = (x - 3)^2 - 8$
20. $y = x^2 + 10x - 9$
$y = (x + 5)^2 - 34$
23. $y = 2x^2 + 6x + 1$
$y = 2\left(x + \frac{3}{2}\right)^2 - \frac{7}{2}$

18. $y = x^2 + 8x + 7$
$y = (x + 4)^2 - 9$
21. $y = x^2 - 3x + 5$
$y = \left(x - \frac{3}{2}\right)^2 + \frac{11}{4}$
24. $y = -2x^2 - 8x + 5$
$y = -2(x + 2)^2 + 13$

B

Write each equation in **h, k** form. Then write the coordinates of the vertex and the equation of the axis of symmetry, and draw the graph.

25. $y = x^2 - 8x + 1$
26. $y = x^2 - 5x$
27. $y = 2x^2 - 12x + 3$

28. $y = -x^2 - 2x + 7$
29. $y = -2x^2 - 4x + 9$
30. $y = \frac{1}{2}x^2 - x + 5$

Use the formula $x = -\frac{b}{2a}$ to find the equation of the axis of symmetry. Then find the coordinates of the vertex. Is the vertex a minimum or a maximum point?

31. $y = x^2 + 4x - 2$
$x = -2,\ (-2, -6),$ min.
34. $y = 2x^2 - 6x + 1$
$x = \frac{3}{2};\ \left(\frac{3}{2}, -\frac{7}{2}\right);$ min.

32. $y = -x^2 + 2x + 4$
$x = 1,\ (1, 5),$ max.
35. $y = 3x^2 - 2x - 5$
$x = \frac{1}{3};\ \left(\frac{1}{3}, -\frac{16}{3}\right);$ min.

33. $y = x^2 + 6x$
$x = -3,\ (-3, -9),$ min.
36. $y = -x^2 + 5x - 7$
$x = \frac{5}{2};\ \left(\frac{5}{2}, -\frac{3}{4}\right);$ max.

C

Write each equation in **h, k** form. Then set **y = 0** to find the **x**-intercepts of the graph.

Sample $y = x^2 - 4x - 8 = (x - 2)^2 - 12$

Let $y = 0$. Then $(x - 2)^2 - 12 = 0$

$(x - 2)^2 = 12$

$x - 2 = \pm\sqrt{12}$

$x = 2 \pm 2\sqrt{3}$

37. $y = x^2 - 6x + 5$
38. $y = x^2 + x - 6$
39. $y = x^2 - 5x + 3$

40. $y = 2x^2 + 3x - 2$
41. $y = -2x^2 - 5x + 1$
42. $y = -\frac{1}{2}x^2 + x - 3$

*43. Write the equation $y = ax^2 + bx + c$ in h, k form. Then give the coordinates of the vertex.

QUADRATIC FUNCTIONS AND EQUATIONS

451

LESSON NOTES

In this lesson we develop the *quadratic formula* by applying the method of completing the square to the general quadratic equation $ax^2 + bx + c = 0$. In developing the formula, it will be worthwhile to show completing the square for an equation having specific values for a, b, and c. For example, use $2x^2 - x - 1 = 0$ ($a = 2$, $b = -1$, $c = -1$). Then, alongside this, duplicate each step in turn, using the letters a, b, and c.

As shown in Example 1, students must first decide correctly on the values of a, b, and c before using the formula. Plus and minus signs have to be watched carefully.

To find the x-intercepts when graphing a parabola, we let $y = 0$ in the function, and solve the resulting equation for x, as shown in Example 2. The graph in Example 3 has no x-intercepts because the equation has no real solution.

Exercise 39 develops two interesting properties of a quadratic equation.

12-6 The Quadratic Formula

OBJECTIVE

To solve equations of the form $ax^2 + bx + c = 0$ by using the quadratic formula.

The graph of $y = x^2 - 2x - 2$ crosses the y-axis at $(0, -2)$. You can estimate the x-intercepts from the graph. However, to find the x-intercepts algebraically, let $y = 0$.

$$0 = x^2 - 2x - 2$$

Solve this equation by completing the square.

$$x^2 - 2x - 2 = 0$$
$$x^2 - 2x = 2$$
$$x^2 - 2x + 1 = 2 + 1 \qquad \text{Complete the square on the left.}$$
$$(x - 1)^2 = 3$$
$$x - 1 = \pm\sqrt{3}$$
$$x = 1 \pm \sqrt{3}$$

$x = 1 + \sqrt{3}$ or $x = 1 - \sqrt{3}$ Since $\sqrt{3} \approx 1.7$, the x-intercepts are 2.7 and -0.7, correct to the nearest tenth.

We will now use this method to develop a formula for solving any quadratic equation $ax^2 + bx + c = 0$.

$$ax^2 + bx + c = 0$$
$$x^2 + \frac{b}{a}x = -\frac{c}{a} \qquad \text{Subtract } c \text{ from each side of the equation and divide by } a. \text{ Then complete the square on}$$
$$x^2 + \frac{b}{a}x + \left(\frac{b}{2a}\right)^2 = \frac{b^2}{4a^2} - \frac{c}{a} \qquad \text{the left by adding } \left(\frac{b}{2a}\right)^2 \text{ to each side.}$$
$$\left(x + \frac{b}{2a}\right)^2 = \frac{b^2 - 4ac}{4a^2}$$
$$x + \frac{b}{2a} = \frac{\pm\sqrt{b^2 - 4ac}}{2a}$$
$$x = \frac{-b + \sqrt{b^2 - 4ac}}{2a} \quad \text{or} \quad x = \frac{-b - \sqrt{b^2 - 4ac}}{2a}$$

These solutions for x are expressed in terms of coefficients a, b, and c. The two solutions are combined in the quadratic formula.

The Quadratic Formula

If $ax^2 + bx + c = 0$, $a \neq 0$, then $x = \dfrac{-b \pm \sqrt{b^2 - 4ac}}{2a}$.

CHAPTER 12

EXAMPLE 1

Solve $x^2 - 10x + 23 = 0$ for x. Use the quadratic formula.

$$x = \frac{-(-10) \pm \sqrt{(-10)^2 - 4(1)(23)}}{2(1)} \qquad a = 1, b = -10, c = 23$$

$$x = \frac{10 \pm \sqrt{100 - 92}}{2}$$

$$x = \frac{10 \pm \sqrt{8}}{2}$$

$$x = \frac{10 \pm 2\sqrt{2}}{2}$$

$$x = 5 + \sqrt{2} \quad \text{or} \quad x = 5 - \sqrt{2}$$

Check each solution by substitution in the original equation.

$(5 + \sqrt{2})^2 - 10(5 + \sqrt{2}) + 23 = 25 + 10\sqrt{2} + 2 - 50 - 10\sqrt{2} + 23 = 0$ ✔

$(5 - \sqrt{2})^2 - 10(5 - \sqrt{2}) + 23 = 25 - 10\sqrt{2} + 2 - 50 + 10\sqrt{2} + 23 = 0$ ✔

The solutions, or *roots*, are $5 + \sqrt{2}$ and $5 - \sqrt{2}$.

EXAMPLE 2

Find the x-intercepts for the graph of $y = 4x^2 + 4x - 15$.

Let $y = 0$ and solve the equation $4x^2 + 4x - 15 = 0$.

$$x = \frac{-4 \pm \sqrt{16 - 4(4)(-15)}}{2(4)} \qquad a = 4, b = 4, c = -15$$

$$x = \frac{-4 \pm \sqrt{16 + 240}}{8}$$

$$x = \frac{3}{2} \quad \text{or} \quad x = -\frac{5}{2}$$

The x-intercepts are $\frac{3}{2}$ and $-\frac{5}{2}$.   Check that $y = 0$ when $x = \frac{3}{2}$ or $-\frac{5}{2}$.

EXAMPLE 3

Where does the graph of $y = 2x^2 - 4x + 5$ cross the x-axis?

Solve $2x^2 - 4x + 5 = 0$.

Use the quadratic formula. $a = 2, b = -4, c = 5$

$$x = \frac{4 \pm \sqrt{16 - 40}}{4}$$

$$x = \frac{4 \pm \sqrt{-24}}{4}$$

$(0, 5)$

$(1, 3)$

Since $\sqrt{-24}$ is not a real number, we say that the equation $2x^2 - 4x + 5 = 0$ has *no solution*. Thus the graph of $y = 2x^2 - 4x + 5$ does not cross the x-axis.

QUADRATIC FUNCTIONS AND EQUATIONS

453

ASSIGNMENT GUIDE
(pages 454–455)

Minimum course: 1–23 odd
second day: 12–28 even
Average course: 1–29 odd
Maximum course: 1–29 odd,
34–37
All courses: *Strategies
for Problem
Solving*

ENRICHMENT ACTIVITY

Challenge the students to find a rational approximation of the positive number x named by the infinite expression below:

$$x = \sqrt{1 + \sqrt{1 + \sqrt{1 + \ldots}}}$$

The three dots are used to indicate that the pattern continues forever.

By squaring both sides of the equation, we obtain:

$$x^2 = 1 + \sqrt{1 + \sqrt{1 + \sqrt{1 + \ldots}}}$$

Note that the right member of the equation is equivalent to $1 + x$ (the original expression added to 1). Thus, we have $x^2 = 1 + x$, a quadratic equation that can be solved, yielding the roots $\dfrac{1 \pm \sqrt{5}}{2}$. Since x must be positive, only $\dfrac{1 + \sqrt{5}}{2}$ is a solution for the problem. A rational approximation of the solution is 1.62.

ADDITIONAL ANSWERS

Exercises

See page A15.

Using BASIC

This program can be used to solve quadratic equations of the form $ax^2 + bx + c$.

```
10  PRINT "ENTER A, B, C"
20  INPUT A, B, C
30  LET D = B * B
    - 4 * A * C
40  IF D < 0 THEN 90
```

[*Using BASIC* continues on page 455.]

CLASS EXERCISES

*Use the quadratic formula to solve for **x**.*

1. $x^2 - x - 2 = 0$ 2, −1   **2.** $x^2 + 3x + 2 = 0$ −1, −2   **3.** $x^2 + 5x + 6 = 0$ −2, −3

4. $x^2 - x - 6 = 0$ 3, −2   **5.** $x^2 - 2x - 15 = 0$ 5, −3   **6.** $x^2 + 2x - 8 = 0$ 2, −4

7. $2x^2 + x - 1 = 0$ $\frac{1}{2}$, −1   **8.** $2x^2 - 3x + 1 = 0$ 1, $\frac{1}{2}$ **9.** $2x^2 - x - 6 = 0$ 2, $-\frac{3}{2}$

10. $2x^2 + x - 6 = 0$ −2, $\frac{3}{2}$ **11.** $3x^2 + x - 2 = 0$ −1, $\frac{2}{3}$ **12.** $3x^2 - 5x + 2 = 0$ 1, $\frac{2}{3}$

EXERCISES

A   *Use the quadratic formula to solve for **x**.*

1. $x^2 - 3x - 10 = 0$ 5, −2   **2.** $x^2 - 7x + 10 = 0$ 2, 5   **3.** $x^2 - 4x + 3 = 0$ 1, 3

4. $x^2 + 2x - 3 = 0$ 1, −3   **5.** $x^2 - 4x - 5 = 0$ 5, −1   **6.** $x^2 + 6x + 5 = 0$ −1, −5

7. $2x^2 - x - 1 = 0$ 1, $-\frac{1}{2}$ **8.** $2x^2 - 3x - 2 = 0$ 2, $-\frac{1}{2}$ **9.** $2x^2 + 5x - 3 = 0$ $\frac{1}{2}$, −3

10. $2x^2 + 7x + 3 = 0$ **11.** $3x^2 + 2x - 1 = 0$ −1, $\frac{1}{3}$ **12.** $3x^2 + 7x + 2 = 0$ −2, $-\frac{1}{3}$
   −3, $-\frac{1}{2}$

*Write each equation in the form $ax^2 + bx + c = 0$. Then solve for **x**.*

13. $x^2 - 3x = 1$ **14.** $x^2 + 5x = 5$ **15.** $x^2 + 5x = -14$

16. $x^2 + x = 3$ **17.** $2x^2 + x = 1$ **18.** $2 = 3x^2 + 2x$

19. $3x^2 - 1 = x$ **20.** $2x^2 = 2 - x$ **21.** $2x^2 = 8x - 5$

22. $3x = 2 - x^2$ **23.** $x + 3 = 2x^2$ **24.** $1 - 3x^2 = 2x$

B   *Find the **x**-intercepts, if any, for the graph of each equation.*

25. $y = x^2 + 5x + 6$ −2, −3   **26.** $y = x^2 + 2x + 1$ −1   **27.** $y = x^2 - x - 12$ 4, −3

28. $y = 2x^2 + 3x + 1$ −1, $-\frac{1}{2}$ **29.** $y = 4x^2 - 6x + 9$ **30.** $y = -2x^2 - x + 3$ 1, $-\frac{3}{2}$
                               No x-intercepts

31. $y = -x^2 + x - 2$ **32.** $y = x^2 + x - 3$ **33.** $y = 2x^2 + x + 2$

   No x-intercepts $\frac{-1 \pm \sqrt{13}}{2}$ No x-intercepts

C   *Solve for **x**.*

34. $(3x + 1)^2 - (2x - 1)^2 + 5 = 0$ −1   **35.** $x - \dfrac{3}{x} = \dfrac{2x - 5}{x}$ No solution (no real number solution)

36. $(2x - 1)(3x + 2) = x^2 + 4$ 1, $-\frac{6}{5}$ **37.** $x^4 - 3x^2 - 10 = 0$ $\sqrt{5}, -\sqrt{5}$
                                                  (The other two solutions are not real numbers.)

*38. The graph of $x^2 + y^2 + 6x - 6y - 7 = 0$ is a curve that intersects each axis in two points. Find the x- and y-intercepts. $x = -7, x = 1; y = 7, y = -1$

*39. Use the roots of $ax^2 + bx + c = 0$ to find general formulas for   **a.** the sum of the roots and   **b.** the product of the roots. Then test these formulas on the solutions for Exercises 1–9.

454   CHAPTER 12

EXTRA PRACTICE, page 530

Using a New Point of View

Sometimes a problem can be solved by changing one's perspective—by looking at the problem from a different or unexpected point of view. For example, suppose you are asked to solve this inequality:

$$x^2 + 2x - 3 < 0$$

One method has already been presented on page 381. Such problems were solved using the number line. The thinking was "one-dimensional." Now let's do the unexpected and change the problem to two dimensions by letting $y = f(x) = x^2 + 2x - 3$. We graph this function by using the methods of this chapter.

$$y = x^2 + 2x - 3$$
$$y = (x^2 + 2x + 1) - 3 - 1$$
$$y = (x + 1)^2 - 4$$

The graph is a parabola with vertex at $(-1, -4)$. The axis of symmetry is $x = -1$.

From the graph we see that the curve is below the x-axis between $x = -3$ and $x = 1$. That is, $f(x) < 0$ for $-3 < x < 1$. From this we may conclude that

$$x^2 + 2x - 3 < 0 \quad \text{when} \quad -3 < x < 1$$

This is the solution to the original inequality. It may also be written in the form $x > -3$ *and* $x < 1$.

We also see from the graph that $f(x) \geq 0$ when $x \leq -3$ or $x \geq 1$. This gives the solution to the inequality $x^2 + 2x - 3 \geq 0$.

Solutions to these inequalities can be shown on the number line.

$$x^2 + 2x - 3 < 0$$
Solution: $-3 < x < 1$

$$x^2 + 2x - 3 \geq 0$$
Solution: $x \leq -3$ or $x \geq 1$

If r_1 and r_2 are roots of $ax^2 + bx + c = 0$, and $a > 0$, and $r_1 < r_2$, then $ax^2 + bx + c < 0$ for $r_1 < x < r_2$ and $ax^2 + bx + c > 0$ for $x < r_1$ or $x > r_2$.

A similar generalization can be written for the case where a is negative.

Solve and graph each inequality on a number line.

1. $x^2 - 4 < 0$
   $-2 < x < 2$
2. $x^2 + 6x + 5 > 0$
   $x < -5$ or $x > -1$
3. $x^2 - 5x + 6 \geq 0$
   $x \leq 2$ or $x \geq 3$
4. $x^2 + x - 6 \leq 0$
   $-3 \leq x \leq 2$
5. $x^2 - 6x + 9 > 0$
   $x < 3$ or $x > 3$
6. $x^2 - 2x + 3 < 0$
   $\emptyset$ (no real-number solution)

Strategies for Problem Solving

This Strategies for Problem Solving page illustrates the value of imagination in problem solving. As the example shows, a quadratic equation or inequality in one variable (for example, $x^2 - x - 2 > 0$ or $x^2 - 4 \leq 0$) can be solved by thinking of a quadratic function of the form $y = ax^2 + bx + c$. This function is obtained by replacing 0 with y. The different portions of the graph of this function reveal the solutions of $f(x) < 0$, $f(x) = 0$, and $f(x) > 0$.

In doing the exercises, the students should replace 0 with y and then graph the resulting quadratic function. Then, the portion of the parabola that satisfies the original inequality will reveal the solution.

ADDITIONAL ANSWERS

Strategies for Problem Solving

1. $-2 \quad 2$

2. $-5 \quad -1$

3. $2 \quad 3$

4. $-3 \quad 2$

5. 3

Using BASIC (continued)

```
50   LET X1 =
     (-B + SQR(D))/(2 * A)
60   LET X2 =
     (-B - SQR(D))/(2 * A)
70   PRINT "ROOTS ARE ";
     X1; " AND "; X2
80   GO TO 100
90   PRINT "NO SOLUTION"
100  PRINT "ANOTHER?
     (1 = YES, 0 = NO)"
110  INPUT Z
120  IF Z = 1 THEN 10
900  END
```

WARM-UP EXERCISES

For each quadratic equation, identify the values of *a*, *b*, and *c*.

1. $3x^2 - 2x + 1 = 0$
   $a = 3; b = -2; c = 1$
2. $x^2 = 2x$
   $a = 1; b = -2; c = 0$
3. $5x^2 + x = 3$
   $a = 5; b = 1; c = -3$

LESSON NOTES

Students already know that if $\sqrt{x}$ is to be a real number, then *x* cannot be less than 0. Also, if *x* is a perfect square, the expression is a rational number; if *x* is not a perfect square, the expression is an irrational number.

In this lesson we note that the expression $b^2 - 4ac$ is under the sign $\sqrt{}$; so if $b^2 - 4ac$ is negative, then $\sqrt{b^2 - 4ac}$ is not a real number and the equation has no real roots. Moreover, as the text notes, if $b^2 - 4ac > 0$, then the equation has two real roots; if $b^2 - 4ac = 0$, then the equation has one root.

Carefully discuss the chart on page 457 as well as the summary statements that precede the Class Exercises.

ALTERNATE EXAMPLE

Use the discriminant to tell the number of roots of the equation
$3x^2 - 2x - 1 = 0$.
$b^2 - 4ac = 16$
Since $b^2 - 4ac > 0$, there are two roots. Since 16 is a perfect square, the roots are rational.

12-7 The Discriminant

OBJECTIVES _____

To evaluate the discriminant $b^2 - 4ac$.
To determine the number of roots of the equation $ax^2 + bx + c = 0$.

_____

Most of the quadratic equations so far have had either one or two solutions. But sometimes a given equation has no real-number solution.

Solve $x^2 + 2x + 4 = 0$. Use the formula $x = \dfrac{-b \pm \sqrt{b^2 - 4ac}}{2a}$.

$$x = \frac{-2 \pm \sqrt{2^2 - 4(1)(4)}}{2(1)} \qquad a = 1, b = 2, c = 4$$

$$x = \frac{-2 \pm \sqrt{-12}}{2} \qquad \begin{array}{l}\sqrt{-12}\text{ is not a real number. There are no}\\ \text{real-number roots.}\end{array}$$

The fact that the equation $x^2 + 2x + 4 = 0$ has no roots is evident when you look at the graph of $y = x^2 + 2x + 4 = (x + 1)^2 + 3$.

x	-3	-2	-1	0	1
y	7	4	3	4	7

There are no x-intercepts. That is, there are no x-values for which $y = 0$.

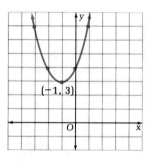

You can tell whether a quadratic equation has two, one, or no roots by evaluating the radicand in the quadratic formula. This quantity, $b^2 - 4ac$, is called the **discriminant** of the quadratic equation. Consider any quadratic equation in the form $ax^2 + bx + c = 0$.

If $b^2 - 4ac > 0$, then the equation has two roots.
If $b^2 - 4ac = 0$, then the equation has one root.
If $b^2 - 4ac < 0$, then the equation has no real root.

EXAMPLE

Use the discriminant to tell the number of roots of the equation $2x^2 - 5x - 1 = 0$.

Evaluate the discriminant $b^2 - 4ac$; $a = 2$, $b = -5$, and $c = -1$.

$$b^2 - 4ac = (-5)^2 - 4(2)(-1) = 25 + 8 = 33$$

Since $b^2 - 4ac > 0$, there are two roots.
Also, since 33 is not a perfect square, the roots are irrational.

456

$y = ax^2 + bx + c$ or $f(x) = ax^2 + bx + c$	Discriminant $b^2 - 4ac$	No. of roots of $ax^2 + bx + c = 0$	Graph of function
$y = x^2 - 8x + 15$	4	$x^2 - 8x + 15 = 0$ two rational roots, since 4 is a perfect square $x = 3$ or $x = 5$	two x-intercepts
$y = x^2 - 4x + 1$	12	$x^2 - 4x + 1 = 0$ two irrational roots; 12 is not a perfect square $x = 2 + \sqrt{3}$ or $x = 2 - \sqrt{3}$	two x-intercepts
$y = x^2 + 8x + 16$	0	$x^2 + 8x + 16 = 0$ one rational root $x = -4$	one x-intercept
$y = x^2 + 2x + 4$	-12	$x^2 + 2x + 4 = 0$ no real roots	no x-intercepts

DAILY QUIZ

Use the values of the discriminant to decide the number of roots of each equation.
1. $x^2 - 6x + 10 = 0$ None
2. $x^2 + 8x + 16 = 0$ 1
3. $x^2 + x + 4 = 0$ None
4. $-x^2 + 4x + 2 = 0$ 2
5. Determine the number of x-intercepts, if any, for $y = x^2 - 5x - 7$.   2

To summarize, the discriminant gives the following information about the roots of the quadratic equation $ax^2 + bx + c = 0$:

If $b^2 - 4ac$ is positive, there are two roots.
These roots are rational if $b^2 - 4ac$ is a perfect square.
If $b^2 - 4ac$ is 0, there is one root, sometimes called a *double root*.
If $b^2 - 4ac$ is negative, there is no real root.

CLASS EXERCISES

Use the value of the discriminant to tell the number of roots of each equation.

1. $x^2 - 5x - 8 = 0$ 2
2. $x^2 + 7x + 13 = 0$ None
3. $x^2 - 8x + 16 = 0$ 1
4. $3x^2 + x - 1 = 0$ 2
5. $4x^2 - 3x + 2 = 0$ None
6. $-x^2 = 2x - 3$ 2

QUADRATIC FUNCTIONS AND EQUATIONS

457

Minimum course: omit
Average course: 1–21 odd
Maximum course: 7–25 odd,
26–29
Average course: } Checkpoint
Maximum course: } review
exercises

ENRICHMENT ACTIVITY

As a challenge, introduce the concept of the imaginary number i. For example, using the quadratic formula, show that the solution of the equation $x^2 + x + 1 = 0$ is $x = \dfrac{-1 \pm \sqrt{-3}}{2}$. Since the radicand is a negative number, there is no real solution. However, if we invent the imaginary number $i = \sqrt{-1}$, then $\sqrt{-3}$ becomes $\sqrt{3}i$, and the solution of the equation becomes $x = \dfrac{-1 \pm \sqrt{3}i}{2}$.

Suggest that students read about and prepare a report on imaginary and complex numbers.

ADDITIONAL ANSWERS

Exercises

1. 1; rational
2. 2; rational
3. 2; irrational
4. None
5. 1; rational
6. 2; rational
7. 1; rational
8. 2; rational
9. None
10. 1; rational
11. 2; rational
12. 2; rational

Checkpoint

See page A16.

Checkpoint

Students may check their answers with those given in the back of their books.

EXERCISES

A Use the value of the discriminant to tell the number of real roots of each equation. State whether the roots are rational or irrational.

1. $x^3 - 6x + 9 = 0$ 2. $x^2 + 8x + 15 = 0$ 3. $x^2 + 5x - 2 = 0$

4. $x^2 + x + 3 = 0$ 5. $x^2 + 10x + 25 = 0$ 6. $x^2 + 4x - 21 = 0$

7. $4x^2 - 4x + 1 = 0$ 8. $6x^2 + 7x - 3 = 0$ 9. $3x^2 + x + 2 = 0$

10. $-4x^2 + 4x - 1 = 0$ 11. $2x^2 + x = 10$ 12. $3x^2 = 2 - x$

From the graph, tell what must be true about $b^2 - 4ac$.

13.   14.   15.   16.

0   Positive   Negative   0

B Determine the number of x-intercepts for the graph of each equation.

17. $y = x^2 - 5x + 6$ 2   18. $y = x^2 - 4$ 2   19. $y = x^2 + 8x + 16$ 1

20. $y = x^2 + 4x - 2$ 2   21. $y = x^2 - 2x + 4$ None   22. $y = x^2 - 3x - 40$ 2

23. $y = -x^2 - x + 5$ 2   24. $y = 2x^2 - 3x + 1$ 2   25. $y = -2x^2 - x + 2$ 2

C Find the values of k if the graph of the equation has only one x-intercept.

26. $y = x^2 + kx + 4$ 4 or -4 27. $y = 9x^2 - kx + 4$ 28. $y = x^2 - 3x + k$ $\frac{9}{4}$
                                  12 or -12

29. For what values of k must the parabola $y = 25x^2 + 10kx + 9$ lie above the x-axis, for all x? $-3 < k < 3$

CHECKPOINT

1. For the parabola $y = -4(x - 4)^2 - 2$, identify **a.** the coordinates of the vertex. **b.** the equation of the axis of symmetry. Is the vertex a minimum or a maximum point? V: (4, -2); axis: $x = 4$; max. pt.

2. Write $y = 2x^2 - 12x + 3$ in h, k form. Then graph the parabola.

Write each equation in the form $ax^2 + bx + c = 0$. Then solve for x.

3. $x^2 - 5x = 3$ $x = \frac{5 \pm \sqrt{37}}{2}$ 4. $2x^2 = 4 - 3x$ $x = \frac{-3 \pm \sqrt{41}}{4}$ 5. $3 - 5x^2 = 4x$ $x = \frac{-2 \pm \sqrt{19}}{5}$
   $x^2 - 5x - 3 = 0$ $2x^2 + 3x - 4 = 0$ $5x^2 + 4x - 3 = 0$

6. How many real roots has the equation $3x^2 + 12x + 12 = 0$?
   One, since the discriminant $= 144 - 4(3)(12) = 0$

458

EXTRA PRACTICE, page 531

12-8 Problem Solving: Using Quadratic Equations

WARM-UP EXERCISES

1. If the perimeter of a triangle is 12 cm and two of the sides measure 3 cm and 4 cm, what is the measure of the third side? 5 cm
2. If the legs of a right triangle measure 5 cm and 12 cm, what is the measure of the hypotenuse? 13 cm

OBJECTIVE

To solve problems using quadratic equations.

We are now ready to solve many types of problems that give rise to quadratic equations. Some quadratic equations can be solved by factoring, but all of them can be solved by using the quadratic formula.

LESSON NOTES

In this lesson we use the quadratic formula in problem solving. The essential steps in solving a problem are recalled in Example 1.

• Read the problem to find the key ideas.

• Use a variable to represent the unknown quantity that is being sought.

• Write an equation.

• Find a solution. Be sure to check solutions which are possible in the context of the problem situation.

• Answer the question.

EXAMPLE 1

Strategy: Draw a figure. Express the legs in terms of a variable and use the Pythagorean theorem.

One leg of a right triangle is 1 cm longer than the other. Find the lengths of the legs if the hypotenuse is 29 cm long.

Read the problem to find the key ideas.

The length of the hypotenuse of a right triangle is given. To find the lengths of the legs, the Pythagorean theorem can be used.

Use a variable.

Let x = the length of the shorter leg.

Then $x + 1$ = the length of the longer leg.

Write an equation.

$$x^2 + (x + 1)^2 = 29^2$$ Pythagorean theorem

Find the solution.

$$x^2 + x^2 + 2x + 1 = 841$$

$$2x^2 + 2x - 840 = 0$$

$$x^2 + x - 420 = 0$$

Each term is a multiple of 2, so the equation can be simplified.

$$x = \frac{-1 \pm \sqrt{1 + 1680}}{2}$$

Use the quadratic formula, with $a = 1$, $b = 1$, $c = -420$.

$$x = \frac{-1 \pm \sqrt{1681}}{2}$$

$$x = \frac{-1 \pm 41}{2}$$

$$x = \frac{-1 + 41}{2} \text{ or } x = \frac{-1 - 41}{2}$$

$$x = 20 \quad \text{or} \quad x = -21$$

The length of a leg cannot be negative. Thus we reject the solution $x = -21$. The only possible solution is $x = 20$.

To check, refer to the original problem.

$$20^2 + 21^2 = 400 + 441 = 841 \; ✔$$

Answer the question.

The legs are 20 cm and 21 cm long.

Be alert for students who may not complete the last step. In Example 1, for instance, we cannot give the answer as $x = 20$ or $x = 21$. We must give an answer that makes sense in the problem situation.

Example 3 shows how we can use the ordinate of the vertex of a parabola to indicate the maximum value of h, the height. This occurs at the time value, t, indicated by the abscissa of the vertex.

ALTERNATE EXAMPLE

1. One leg of a right triangle is 2 cm shorter than the other. Find the lengths of the legs if the hypotenuse is 10 cm long.
   The legs are 6 cm and 8 cm long.

QUADRATIC FUNCTIONS AND EQUATIONS

459

2. The difference between a number and its reciprocal is 5. Find the number.

$$\frac{5 + \sqrt{29}}{2} \text{ or } \frac{5 - \sqrt{20}}{2}$$

3. A ball is thrown straight upward. The height up in feet is given by the formula $h = 32t - 16t^2$. What is the maximum height it can reach? How long does it take to reach this height?

The maximum height is 16 feet. This is reached after 1 second.

POSSIBLE ERROR

When using a quadratic equation to solve a word problem, students are often careless in interpreting the roots of the equation. For instance, in solving Exercise 12, they may give the answer as $x = 20$ or $x = -17$. However, the problem deals with a square piece of cloth, so a negative length of cloth is not sensible. Emphasize the need to make sure the "answer" makes sense in the problem situation.

DAILY QUIZ

1. If 6 times a number is added to the square of the number, the sum is 135. Find the number. -15 or 9.

2. Find two numbers if their sum is 29 and the sum of their squares is 425. 16 and 13

3. The sum of a number and 5 times its reciprocal is 6. Find the number. 5

4. The hypotenuse of a right triangle is 15 cm. How long are the legs if one is 3 cm longer than the other? 9 and 12

5. The perimeter of a right triangle is 96 in. If the hypotenuse is 40 in., how long are the other two sides? 24 in. and 32 in.

EXAMPLE 2 The difference between a number and its reciprocal is 3. Find the number.

Use a variable. Let n = the number.

Write an equation. $n - \dfrac{1}{n} = 3$ \qquad The reciprocal of n is $\frac{1}{n}$.

Find the solution. $n^2 - 1 = 3n$ \qquad Multiply by the LCD, which is n.

$n^2 - 3n - 1 = 0$ \qquad $a = 1, b = -3, c = -1$

$n = \dfrac{3 \pm \sqrt{9 + 4}}{2}$

$n = \dfrac{3 + \sqrt{13}}{2}$ or $n = \dfrac{3 - \sqrt{13}}{2}$

There are two solutions. The check is left to you.

Answer the question. The number is $\dfrac{3 + \sqrt{13}}{2}$ or $\dfrac{3 - \sqrt{13}}{2}$.

EXAMPLE 3 A ball is thrown straight upward. Its height in feet is given by the formula $h = 48t - 16t^2$ where t is the number of seconds it has been in the air. What is the maximum height it can reach? How long does it take to reach this height?

Write the formula. $h = -16t^2 + 48t$

Find the solution. The question calls for the maximum value of a quadratic function. So, find the coordinates of the vertex of the graph, which is a parabola.

$h = -16(t^2 - 3t + \underline{\ ?\ })$

$h = -16\left(t^2 - 3t + \dfrac{9}{4}\right) + 16\left(\dfrac{9}{4}\right)$

$h = -16\left(t - \dfrac{3}{2}\right)^2 + 36$

The vertex is $\left(\dfrac{3}{2}, 36\right)$.

Answer the question. The maximum height is 36 ft. This is reached after $1\frac{1}{2}$ sec.

CLASS EXERCISES

A right triangle has a perimeter of 56 in. and a hypotenuse of 25 in.

1. The sum of the lengths of the two legs = $\underline{\ ?\ }$. 31 in.

2. If the length of one leg is represented by x the length of the other leg can be represented by $31 - x$. Use the Pythagorean theorem to write an equation. Then solve for x.
$x^2 + (31 - x)^2 = 25^2$; $x = 7$ or $x = 24$

3. What is the value of $31 - x$? What are the lengths of the legs?
If $x = 7$, $31 - x = 24$; If $x = 24$, $31 - x = 7$. The lengths of the legs are 7 in. and 24 in.

4. Check your answer.
Check: $7^2 + 24^2 = 49 + 576 = 625 = 25^2$ and $7 + 24 = 31$

EXERCISES

A

1. If 8 times a number is added to the square of the number, the sum is 425. Find the numbers.   17 or −25

2. Find two numbers if their sum is 28 and the sum of their squares is 400.   12 and 16

3. The sum of a number and 6 times its reciprocal is 5. Find the number.   3 or 2

4. The hypotenuse of a right triangle is 17 cm. How long are the legs if one is 7 cm longer than the other?   8 cm and 15 cm

5. The perimeter of a right triangle is 84 in. If the hypotenuse is 35 in., how long are the other two sides?   21 in. and 28 in.

6. The sum of a number and its reciprocal is $2\frac{1}{6}$. What is the number? $\frac{3}{2}$ or $\frac{2}{3}$

7. Find two consecutive integers such that the sum of their squares is 313.
12 and 13 or −12 and −13

8. The product of two consecutive integers is 132. Find the integers.
11 and 12, or −11 and −12

9. The length of a rectangular lawn is 2 yd more than 3 times its width. The area is 85 yd². Find the length and the width of the lawn.
Width, 5 yd; length 17 yd

10. A 50-in. piece of wire is bent to form a rectangle with area 156 in.². Find the dimensions of the rectangle.   12 in. by 13 in.

11. When 8 is divided by a certain number, the result is the same as when 12 is subtracted from the number and this difference is divided by 8. Find the number.   16 or −4

12. A 3-inch strip is cut from one side of a square piece of cloth. The remaining rectangle has an area of 340 in.². How long was a side of the original square piece of cloth?   20 in.

B

13. The sum of what number and its reciprocal is 3? Check each answer. $\frac{3 + \sqrt{5}}{2}$ or $\frac{3 - \sqrt{5}}{2}$

14. The sum of the first n even integers greater than 0 is given by the formula $S = n(n + 1)$. How many of these integers add up to 1640?   40

15. The sum of the whole numbers, 1, 2, 3, . . . to n inclusive, is given by the formula $S = \frac{1}{2}n(n + 1)$. Find n if S is 120.   15

16. The number of diagonals of a polygon of n sides is given by the formula $d = \frac{1}{2}n(n - 3)$.

   a. How many diagonals does a 5-sided polygon have?   5

   b. If a polygon has 20 diagonals, how many sides does it have?   8

QUADRATIC FUNCTIONS AND EQUATIONS

461

EXTRA PRACTICE, page 531

ENRICHMENT ACTIVITY

Have the students study the following table which is based on the quadratic equation, $y = x^2 + x + 1$.

x	y	First differences	Second differences
1	3		
2	7	4	
3	13	6	2
4	21	8	2
5	31	10	2

Tell the students that if the second differences in a set of values are constant, then the values can be represented by a quadratic function.

Have the students try to discover a formula that fits this set of values:

t	1	2	3	4	5
s	16	64	144	256	400

The formula is $s = 16t^2$. This formula describes the distance in feet, s, that a body falls in a vacuum in a given number of seconds, t.

17. The perimeter of a right triangle is 36 cm and one of the legs is 3 cm longer than the other. Find the lengths of the three sides. 9 cm, 12 cm, 15 cm

18. When a stone is thrown upward, its height h feet after t seconds can be found from the formula $h = 80t - 16t^2$.

   a. After 2 seconds, how high is the stone? 96 ft

   b. When $h = 0$, find two values for t. What do these answers mean? $t = 0$; $t = 5$; The height is 0 ft before the stone is thrown (0 sec) and after it falls to the ground (5 sec).

   c. What is the greatest height the stone can reach? 100 ft

19. An object is projected vertically upward. Its height after t seconds is h meters. This height can be determined from the formula $h = 40t - 5t^2$.

   a. How long does it take the object to reach a height of 60 meters? 2 sec
After how many more seconds is the height 60 meters again? After 4 more sec

   b. Show that the object cannot reach a height of 90 meters.

                                        Maximum height is 80 meters.

C   **20.** A group of students hired a bus for a trip to an amusement park. They shared the $150 cost equally, but if 5 more people had joined the group, each person would have paid $1 less. How many students went on the trip? 25

21. It took a rowboat 4 hours longer than a motorboat to travel 10 miles around a lake. If the motorboat went 5 times as fast as the rowboat, how long did it take the rowboat? 5 hours

22. Emilio entered a 400-meter track event. It would have taken him 30 seconds less time to complete the race if he had run 3 meters per second faster. How fast did he run? 5 meters per second

23. A square garden is bordered on three sides by a path 1 yard wide. The area of the path is $\frac{5}{9}$ the area of the garden. Find the length of a side of the garden. 6 yd

***24.** A triangle of area 27 cm² is inscribed in a square 8 cm on a side. Two vertices of this triangle are on sides of the square and the third vertex is at a corner. Of the three right triangles that remain, one has sides x and $2x$ cm long, as shown. Find x. 3

25. A group of students formed a business to manufacture yo-yos. They found that the daily cost C of manufacturing n of these items is given by the formula $C = n^2 - 8n + 25$. How many yo-yos should they manufacture each day so as to keep the cost to a minimum? 4

***26.** Suppose that 80 meters of fencing is used to enclose a rectangular garden. One side of the garden is to be against the side of a house. What are the dimensions of the garden that will give a maximum area? 20 meters by 40 meters

462

12-9 Direct Variation

OBJECTIVES

To express direct variation in equation form.
To solve problems involving direct variation.

The scale for a map indicates a *direct variation* between distance on the map and actual distance. For example, if 1 centimeter represents 5 kilometers, then 10 centimeters represent 50 kilometers.

$$\frac{1 \text{ cm}}{5 \text{ km}} = \frac{10 \text{ cm}}{50 \text{ km}}$$

km 0   5   10   15

Two variables, y and x, **vary directly** if the ratio of y to x is always the same number. This direct variation can be expressed by the equations

$$\frac{y}{x} = k \quad \text{or} \quad y = kx$$

The constant k is called the *constant of variation*, $k \neq 0$.

EXAMPLE 1   Express each direct variation in the form $y = kx$.

   a. C varies directly as d.   **b. F varies directly as a.**

     $C = kd$ $F = ka$

EXAMPLE 2   If y varies directly as x, and $y = 15$ when $x = 20$,   **a.** find the constant of variation and express the variation in equation form.   **b.** find y when $x = 32$.

   a. $y = kx$ y varies directly as x.

     $15 = k(20)$ Substitute $y = 15$ and $x = 20$.

     $k = \dfrac{15}{20} = \dfrac{3}{4}$

     $y = \dfrac{3}{4}x$ Substitute $\frac{3}{4}$ for k in $y = kx$.

   b. $y = \dfrac{3}{4}(32)$

     $y = 24$

Direct variation can also be expressed in proportion form. Suppose that y varies directly as x, and that (x_1, y_1) and (x_2, y_2) represent corresponding nonzero values for x and y, then we can write the following proportion.

$$\frac{y_1}{x_1} = \frac{y_2}{x_2}$$ Each ratio is equal to the constant k, so the ratios are equal to each other.

Therefore it can also be said that y is *directly proportional* to x.

QUADRATIC FUNCTIONS AND EQUATIONS   **463**

3. At any given moment, lengths of shadows of buildings vary directly as their heights. If a building 80 feet high casts a shadow 20 ft long, how tall is a building that casts a 15 ft shadow?
60 ft high

If y varies directly as x, and $x = 5$ when $y = 25$, complete the following:

1. If $x = 10$, then $y = \underline{?}$ 50
2. If $x = 15$, then $y = \underline{?}$ 75
3. If $y = 35$, then $x = \underline{?}$ 7
4. If $y = 1.25$, then $x = \underline{?}$ 0.25
5. The distance between two cities is 36 miles. They are $8\frac{1}{4}$ inches apart on a map. What is the distance between two cities that are $5\frac{1}{2}$ inches apart on the map?   24 miles

---

ASSIGNMENT GUIDE
(pages 464–465)

Minimum course: omit
Average course: 1–17 odd
Maximum course: 1–9 odd,
1–19

EXAMPLE 3

At any given moment, lengths of the shadows of buildings vary directly as their heights. If a building 100 ft high casts a shadow 50 ft long, how tall is a building that casts an 80-ft shadow?

Use a proportion

$$\frac{x_1}{y_1} = \frac{x_2}{y_2}$$

Substitute $x_1 = 50$, $y_1 = 100$, and $x_2 = 80$.

$$\frac{50}{100} = \frac{80}{y_2}$$

$$50y_2 = 8000$$

$$y_2 = 160 \qquad \text{The building is 160 ft high.}$$

$y_1 = 100$ $y_2 = ?$

$x_1 = 50$ $x_2 = 80$

Since $y = 100$ when $x = 50$, the equation for Example 3 is $y = 2x$.

The graph of $y = 2x$ is a line with slope 2 that passes through the origin. Therefore this direct variation is a *linear function*.

The graph of any statement of direct variation is a straight line through the origin. The equation can be written in the form $y = kx$, where k is the *slope* of the line.

CLASS EXERCISES

If y varies directly as x, and $y = 20$ when $x = 5$, find y for each value of x.

1. $x = 1$ 4   **2.** $x = 6$ 24   **3.** $x = 30$ 120   **4.** $x = 200$ 800   **5.** $x = \frac{1}{2}$ 2

6. If y varies directly as x, and $y = 4$ when $x = 12$,
  a. find the constant of variation and express the variation in equation form. $\frac{1}{3}$; $y = \frac{1}{3}x$
  b. find y when $x = 21$.   7

EXERCISES

A   If y varies directly as x, and $x = 3$ when $y = 9$, complete the following.

1. If $x = 10$, then $y = \underline{?}$.   30   **2.** If $x = 15$ then $y = \underline{?}$.   45

3. If $y = 33$, then $x = \underline{?}$.   11   **4.** If $y = 1.8$, then $x = \underline{?}$.   0.6

If y varies directly as x, and $y = 12$ when $x = 8$, find:

5. y when $x = 32$ 48   **6.** y when $x = 16$ 24   **7.** y when $x = 18$ 27

8. y when $x = 40$ 60   **9.** x when $y = 18$ 12   **10.** x when $y = 72$ 48

EXTRA PRACTICE, page 531

B

11. The distance between two cities is 24 miles. They are $5\frac{1}{4}$ in. apart on the map. Find the distance between two cities that are $3\frac{1}{2}$ in. apart. **16 mi**

12. Two disks are cut from the same piece of sheet metal. If a disk 4 inches in diameter weighs 4.8 pounds, find the diameter of a disk weighing 14.7 pounds. Assume that the weight w varies directly as the square of the diameter d. **7 in.**

13. A piece of land is shown on a map as a rectangle 1 centimeter long and $\frac{1}{2}$ centimeter wide. What is the area of this land in square kilometers if 1 centimeter on the map represents 10 kilometers? **50 km²**

14. The air pressure p within an automobile tire varies directly as the absolute temperature t, given in degrees Kelvin. If the air pressure in a tire is 30 pounds per square inch at 280° Kelvin, what is the pressure at 315°? **$33\frac{3}{4}$ lb**

*In the following exercises, **y** varies directly as the square of **x**, so that $y = kx^2$. Find the constant k and express the variation in equation form.*

15. $y = 32$ when $x = 4$ **16.** $y = 36$ when $x = 6$ **17.** $y = 27$ when $x = 3$
  $y = 2x^2$ **$y = x^2$**   **$y = 3x^2$**

18. If d varies directly as the square of t, and $d = 2$ when $t = 1$, find d when $t = 3$. **18**

C

19. The surface area of a sphere varies directly as the square of its radius, and the volume varies directly as the cube of its radius. If the radius of a sphere is 5 in., the surface area is 314 in.² and the volume is 524 in.³. Find the surface area and the volume of a sphere with a 10-in. radius. **Surface area, 1256 in.²; volume, 4192 in.³**

USING THE CALCULATOR

Direct Variation

The area A of a regular pentagon varies directly as the square of a side s. If $s = 3$, $A = 15.48$.

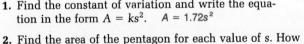

1. Find the constant of variation and write the equation in the form $A = ks^2$. **$A = 1.72s^2$**

2. Find the area of the pentagon for each value of s. How does A change when s is multiplied by 2? **A is multiplied by 4.**

  a. $s = 2$ 6.88   **b.** $s = 4$ 27.52   **c.** $s = 8$ 110.08   **d.** $s = 16$ 440.32

3. Find the length of a side for each value of A. Round your answers to the nearest tenth. How does s change when A is multiplied by 9? **s is multiplied by 3.**

  a. $A = 5$ 1.7   **b.** $A = 45$ 5.1   **c.** $A = 405$ 15.3   **d.** $A = 3645$ 46.0

QUADRATIC FUNCTIONS AND EQUATIONS

465

Find the missing factors.
1. $(6)(8) = (12)(\underline{?})$ 4
2. $(-2)(10) = (4)(\underline{?})$ −5
3. $\left(\dfrac{1}{2}\right)(8) = (-4)(\underline{?})$ −1

LESSON NOTES

In this lesson we introduce *inverse variation*. Here, the constant of variation, *k*, is a product. If $x \cdot y$ is always the same number, then *y* varies inversely with *x*. Thus, the formula for inverse variation is $xy = k$, or $y = \dfrac{k}{x}$.

Inverse variation can be expressed by the proportion $\dfrac{x_1}{x_2} = \dfrac{y_2}{y_1}$. However, students tend to confuse the terms of an inverse proportion, so they are safer using the $xy = k$ method of solution shown in Examples 2 and 3.

Following Example 3, the graph of an inverse variation is identified as a hyperbola, and the equation $xy = 1$ is graphed. In discussing the graph of $xy = 1$, point out that the graph lies only in the first and third quadrants. This is because a positive product can result only from two positive factors ($x > 0$ and $y > 0$) or from two negative factors ($x < 0$ and $y < 0$).

ALTERNATE EXAMPLES

1. Express each inverse variation in the form $xy = k$.
   a. *M* varies inversely as *n*.
   b. *S* varies inversely as *t*.
   a. $Mn = k$ b. $St = k$
2. If *x* and *y* vary inversely, and if $x = 0.2$ when $y = 40$, find the constant of variation. $k = 8$

12-10 Inverse Variation

OBJECTIVES

To express inverse variation in equation form.
To solve problems involving inverse variation.

The three rectangles have the same area, 1 square unit. The length decreases as the width increases while the product, *lw*, stays the same.

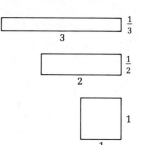

$$lw = 1$$

For all rectangles with the same area, the length and width *vary inversely*.

l	3	2	1
w	$\dfrac{1}{3}$	$\dfrac{1}{2}$	1

Two variables, x and y, **vary inversely** if their product is always the same.

$$xy = k \quad \text{or} \quad y = \dfrac{k}{x}$$

The constant value k is the *constant of variation*, $k \neq 0$.

EXAMPLE 1   Express each inverse variation in the form $xy = k$.

   a. *A* varies inversely as *v*.   **b.** *C* varies inversely as *s*.
   $Av = k$ $Cs = k$

With one pair of corresponding values, you can find the constant k.

EXAMPLE 2   If x and y vary inversely, and x = 0.3 when y = 15, find the constant of variation and write the variation in equation form.

$$xy = k \qquad x \text{ and } y \text{ vary inversely.}$$
$$(0.3)(15) = k \qquad \text{Substitute } x = 0.3 \text{ and } y = 15.$$
$$4.5 = k$$
$$xy = 4.5, \text{ or } y = \dfrac{4.5}{x}$$

Inverse variation can also be expressed in terms of equal products. If (x_1, y_1) and (x_2, y_2) represent corresponding values of x and y, inverse variation can be expressed as follows.

$$x_1 y_1 = x_2 y_2 \qquad \begin{array}{l}\text{Each product is equal to } k, \text{ so the products} \\ \text{are equal to each other.}\end{array}$$

466

EXAMPLE 3 Suppose that y varies inversely as x, and $x = 5$ when $y = 2$. Find x when $y = 4$.

$$xy = k \qquad \text{Find the constant of variation, } k.$$
$$(5)(2) = k \qquad \text{Substitute } x = 5 \text{ and } y = 2.$$
$$10 = k$$

Then the equation is $xy = 10$, or $y = \frac{10}{x}$.

$$x \cdot 4 = 10 \qquad \text{Substitute } y = 4.$$
$$x = \frac{5}{2}$$

Therefore when $y = 4$, $x = \frac{5}{2}$.

To solve for x in Example 3, you can also use the equation $x_1 y_1 = x_2 y_2$. Substitute the three given values, $x_1 = 5$, $y_1 = 2$, and $y_2 = 4$. Then $(5)(2) = (x_2)(4)$. So $x_2 = \frac{5}{2}$.

The graph of an inverse variation is neither a straight line nor a parabola. The graph of $xy = k$ is called a **hyperbola.**

The graph of $xy = 1$ is shown here.

x	-3	-2	-1	$-\frac{1}{2}$	$\frac{1}{2}$	1	2	3
y	$-\frac{1}{3}$	$-\frac{1}{2}$	-1	-2	2	1	$\frac{1}{2}$	$\frac{1}{3}$

Notice that for each value of x there is only one value of y. Therefore the hyperbola represents a function, where $y = \frac{1}{x}$. In function notation, $f(x) = \frac{1}{x}$. The domain, however, is not the set of all real numbers since x cannot be 0.

Domain: x is any real number except 0.
Range: y is any real number except 0.

CLASS EXERCISES

*Suppose that **y** varies inversely as **x**, and **x** = 2 when **y** = 1. Complete the following.*

1. If $x = 4$, then $y = \underline{\ ?\ }$. $\frac{1}{2}$
2. If $x = 8$, then $y = \underline{\ ?\ }$. $\frac{1}{4}$
3. If $y = 2$, then $x = \underline{\ ?\ }$. 1
4. If $y = \frac{1}{5}$, then $x = \underline{\ ?\ }$. 10
5. If x and y vary inversely, and $x = 17$ when $y = 3$, find the constant of variation. 51
6. If r and t vary inversely, and $r = 60$ when $t = 3$, find r when $t = 4$. 45

QUADRATIC FUNCTIONS AND EQUATIONS

467

ENRICHMENT ACTIVITY

In this lesson, students have learned that the graph of $xy = k$ is a hyperbola. Suggest that they graph the following relations by plotting points:

1. $\dfrac{x^2}{4} - \dfrac{y^2}{1} = 1$ 2. $\dfrac{y^2}{4} - \dfrac{x^2}{1} = 1$

Give the hint that each will graph into a hyperbola symmetric to the axes. (A hyperbola is a set of points such that the difference of the distances from two fixed points, called the foci, is constant.)

ADDITIONAL ANSWERS

Exercises

17.

18.

[*Answers continue on page A16.*]

EXERCISES

A *y varies inversely as* **x**, *and* **x** = 40 *when* **y** = 2. *Complete the following.*

1. If x = 2, then y = _?_ . 40

2. If x = 4, then y = _?_ 20

3. If x = 16, then y = _?_ . 5

4. If y = 1, then x = _?_ . 80

If **a** *and* **b** *vary inversely, and* **a** = $\frac{1}{2}$ *when* **b** = 2, *find:*

5. b when $a = \dfrac{1}{3}$ 3

6. a when $b = \dfrac{1}{2}$ 2

7. b when $a = 10$ $\frac{1}{10}$

Write an equation to express each inverse variation. Use **k** *as a constant.*

8. The frequency of radio waves f varies inversely as their wavelength l. $fl = k$ or $f = \frac{k}{l}$

9. The speed of a gear wheel r varies inversely as the number of teeth n.
$rn = k$ or $r = \frac{k}{n}$

B *Identify each equation as representing direct or inverse variation.*

10. $A = 35w$ Direct

11. $P = 1.25C$ Direct

12. $81 = rt$ Inverse

13. $y = \dfrac{16}{x}$ Inverse

14. Find the constant of variation if x varies inversely as y and x = -5 when y = 8. -40

15. If n varies inversely as y and n = 20 when y = 0.35, find y when n = 2. 3.5

16. If gas is held at a constant temperature, the pressure varies inversely as its volume. If the pressure is 40 pounds per square inch when the volume is 80 cubic inches, find the pressure when the volume is 200 cubic inches. 16 lb per sq in.

Graph each statement of inverse variation. Let some **x**-*values be* $\pm\frac{1}{4}$, ±1, *and* ±4.

17. $xy = 2$

18. $xy = 4$

19. $xy = -1$

20. $xy = -2$

C 21. The two types of variation can be combined. For example, electrical resistance in a wire R varies directly as the length of the wire l and inversely as the square of the diameter d. This can be expressed as $R = \dfrac{kl}{d^2}$. If 4250 ft of $\frac{5}{32}$-inch wire has a resistance of 13.6 ohms, how long would a $\frac{3}{16}$-inch wire have to be in order to have a resistance of 4.2 ohms? 1890 ft

*22. The weight, w pounds, of a person h miles above the surface of the earth varies inversely as the square of his distance from the center of the earth. The radius of the earth is about 4000 miles, so that a person h miles above the surface is $(4000 + h)$ miles from the center. If a person weighs 180 pounds on the surface of the earth, where $h = 0$, what is his weight in a space capsule 500 miles above the earth? Round your answer to the nearest ten pounds. 140 pounds

CHAPTER 12

EXTRA PRACTICE, page 531

Navigation

How far away is the horizon? To a navigator, the horizon is the line where the land or sea appears to meet the sky. The distance to the horizon depends on the height of the observer's eye above the surface of the earth. The greater the height, the greater is the visible distance.

The distance to the horizon *varies directly* as the square root of the height of the observer.

Let d be the distance, in nautical miles, to the horizon.

Let h be the height, in feet, of the observer's eyes above sea level.

$$\text{Then } d = 1.17 \sqrt{h}$$

Example   The eye level of an observer standing on the deck of a ship is 50 feet above sea level. How far is it to the horizon line?

$$d = 1.17\sqrt{h}$$
$$= 1.17\sqrt{50}$$
$$= 1.17(7.07)$$
$$= 8.27$$

The distance to the horizon is about 8.3 nautical miles.
A nautical mile is about 6080 feet.

*Find **d**, the distance to the horizon, for each of the following values of **h**. Give your answers to the nearest tenth of a nautical mile.*

1. $h = 25$ ft   5.9   **2.** $h = 10,000$ ft   117   **3.** $h = 40$ ft   7.4

The same formula applies for the horizon line as seen from an airplane.

4. A jetliner is flying at an altitude of 35,000 feet. How far away is the horizon?   219 nautical miles, to the nearest mile (218.9 to nearest tenth)

5. A pilot sights a city on the horizon that he knows is some 37 nautical miles away. How high is he flying?

Applications

On this Applications page, the text introduces a formula that is used in navigation. Students should be encouraged to *understand* the formula $d = 1.7\sqrt{h}$, not merely to compute with it.

Have them note that as h increases, d also increases. That is, the greater the height of the observer, the greater the visible distance. For this reason, lookouts on sailing ships were always posted high on a mast.

ADDITIONAL ANSWERS

Applications

5. 1000 feet, to the nearest foot (999.8 to the nearest tenth)

Simplify.

1. $\dfrac{8x^2 - 8}{4x - 4}$ $2(x + 1)$

2. $\sqrt{81} \div 3^2 + \sqrt{4} \cdot 2^3$ 17

3. $\sqrt{8a^4b^7}$ $2a^2b^3\sqrt{2b}$

4. $\dfrac{1}{a - b} + \dfrac{1}{b - a}$ 0

Evaluate when $a = 4$, $b = 3$, and $c = 2$.

5. $\dfrac{a + (-b) - (-c)}{-bc}$ $-\dfrac{1}{2}$

6. $abc - ab - a$ 8

7. $\sqrt{a^2b^2} - \sqrt{b^2c^2}$ 6

Solve for x.

8. $x^2 - 8x = 0$ $0, 8$

9. $\sqrt{x - 1} = 2x$
   No real-number solution

10. $x^2 - x - 1 = 0$ $\dfrac{1 \pm \sqrt{5}}{2}$

11. $x^2 + x + 1 = (x + 1)^2 - x$
    Identity

12. $\sqrt{4 - 2x} = 8$ -30

[*Maintaining Skills continues on page 471.*]

ADDITIONAL ANSWERS

Review Exercises

10–12.

CHAPTER 12 REVIEW

VOCABULARY

function (p. 434)
relation (p. 434)
vertical line test (p. 435)
quadratic equation (p. 438)
parabola (p. 438)
axis of symmetry (p. 438)
vertex of a parabola (p. 438)
minimum point (p. 438)
domain of a function (p. 438)
range of a function (p. 438)

maximum point (p. 439)
h, k form of a quadratic
   equation (p. 446)
completing the square (p. 449)
quadratic formula (p. 452)
discriminant (p. 456)
direct variation (p. 463)
inverse variation (p. 466)
hyperbola (p. 467)

SUMMARY

Quadratic equations of the form $y = ax^2 + bx + c$ are used in the study of the function concept and to introduce the function notation $f(x)$. The h, k form of such equations makes it possible to obtain the graphs of parabolas by using translations of $y = ax^2$ that have already been graphed. This form also identifies the vertex and axis of symmetry of the parabola. The problem of finding the x-intercepts of the parabola leads to the solution of quadratic equations in one variable. Through a process known as "completing the square," a new method of solving these equations is presented, and the quadratic formula is developed. This formula is then used in solving quadratic equations. A study of direct and inverse variation completes this chapter.

REVIEW EXERCISES

12-1   *Use the vertical line test to tell whether each graph represents a function.*

1. No

2. Yes

3. Yes

Tell whether each set of ordered pairs is a function.

4. $\{(1, 2), (3, 4), (4, 4), (5, 2)\}$ Yes

5. $\{(1, 2), (1, 3), (1, 4), (-1, 5)\}$ No

Let $f(x) = 3x^2 + 4x - 5$. Evaluate each of the following.

6. $f(0)$ -5

7. $f(3)$ 34

8. $f(-3)$ 10

9. $f(c)$ $3c^2 + 4c - 5$

12-2   *Graph each equation on the same set of axes.*

10. $y = -x^2$

11. $y = 2x^2$

12. $y = -\dfrac{1}{2}x^2$

For each function: **a.** Identify the vertex and the axis of symmetry. **b.** Tell whether the vertex is a maximum or a minimum point. **c.** Draw the graph.

12-3   **13.** $y = 2x^2 + 3$ **14.** $y = x^2 - 9$ **15.** $y = -\frac{1}{2}x^2 + 3$

12-4   **16.** $y = (x - 3)^2 + 4$ **17.** $y = -3(x + 2)^2 + 5$ **18.** $y = -\frac{1}{3}(x + 1)^2 - 3$

12-5   Solve for **x** by completing the square.

19. $x^2 - 10x = 10$ $5 \pm \sqrt{35}$ **20.** $x^2 + 4x + 5 = 0$ **21.** $x^2 - 1 = 2x$ $1 \pm \sqrt{2}$
No (real number) solution

22. $x^2 - 8x + 15 = 0$ 3; 5   **23.** $x^2 + 5x = -\dfrac{25}{4}$ $-\frac{5}{2}$ **24.** $x^2 = 3x + 5$ $\dfrac{3 \pm \sqrt{29}}{2}$

Write each equation in **h, k** form. Then: **a.** Write the coordinates of the vertex and the equation of the axis of symmetry. **b.** State the domain and the range.

25. $y = x^2 - 6x + 2$ **26.** $y = -3x^2 + 6x + 1$ **27.** $y = 2x^2 + 10x + 1$

28. $y = -2x^2 + 4x + 3$ **29.** $y = -\frac{1}{2}x^2 + 4x + 5$ **30.** $y = 5x^2 - x + 3$

12-6   Use the quadratic formula to solve for **x**.

31. $x^2 + 5x - 2 = 0$ **32.** $2x^2 = 6x + 8$ **33.** $9x^2 + 4 = 12x$

34. $8x^2 - 2x - 1 = 0$ **35.** $3x^2 - 5 = 8x$ **36.** $-5x^2 + 7x = 2$

12-7   Use the value of the discriminant to tell the number of roots of each equation.

37. $2x^2 + 7x + 6 = 0$ **38.** $-9x^2 + 6x - 1 = 0$ **39.** $5x^2 - 3x + 2 = 0$
$b^2 - 4ac = 1; 2$ $b^2 - 4ac = 0; 1$ $b^2 - 4ac = -31; 0$

40. $3x^2 - 5x + 8 = 0$ **41.** $-7x^2 + 3x + 4 = 0$ **42.** $4x^2 = 4x - 1$
$b^2 - 4ac = -71; 0$ $b^2 - 4ac = 121; 2$ $b^2 - 4ac = 0; 1$

12-8   **43.** The product of two consecutive odd integers is 195. Find the integers.
      13, 15, or −15, −13

44. One leg of a right triangle is 7 cm longer than the other leg. The hypotenuse is 1 cm longer than twice the smaller leg. How long is each side?   8, 15, 17

45. The sum of a number and its reciprocal is $2\frac{4}{15}$. Find the number. $\frac{3}{5}$ or $\frac{5}{3}$

12-9   **46.** If p varies directly as q, and $p = 8$ when $q = 10$, find p when $q = 35$.   28

47. If y varies directly as x, and $y = 16$ when $x = 12$, find y when $x = 18$.   24

48. If y varies directly as x, and $x = 7$ when $y = 17\frac{1}{2}$, find x when $y = 175$.   70

12-10   **49.** If r varies inversely as s, and $r = 5$ when $s = 2$, find s when $r = -10$.   −1

50. Find the constant of variation if x varies inversely as y, and $x = -7$ when $y = 9$.   −63

51. If x and y vary inversely, and $x = 3$ when $y = 8$, find y when $x = 2$.   12

52. The graph of an inverse variation is a curve called a(n) _?_. The graph that represents a direct variation is a(n) _?_.   hyperbola; straight line

REVIEW   **471**

10. Maximum

11. Minimum

12. Minimum

13. a. $(-3, -19)$; $x = -3$
b. Domain: x is any real number.
Range: $f(x) \geq -19$
14. a. $(-1, 4)$; $x = -1$
b. Domain: x is any real number.
Range: $f(x) \leq 4$

CHAPTER 12 TEST

12-1 Use the vertical line test to tell whether each graph represents a function.

1. Yes

2. No

3. 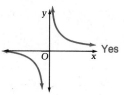 Yes

Let $f(x) = 4 - 3x^2$. Evaluate each of the following.

4. $f(0)$ 4   **5.** $f(2)$ -8 **6.** $f(-1)$ 1

12-2
12-3
12-4 Give the coordinates of the vertex for each parabola.

7. $y = 3x^2$ $(0, 0)$ **8.** $y = x^2 - 2$ $(0, -2)$ **9.** $y = (x + 2)^2$ $(-2, 0)$

12-3
12-4 For each parabola, tell whether the vertex is a maximum or a minimum point. Sketch each graph.

10. $y = -x^2 + 1$ **11.** $y = x^2 - 1$ **12.** $y = 2(x - 1)^2 - 5$

12-5 Write each equation in h, k form. Then: **a.** Write the coordinates of the vertex and the equation of the axis of symmetry. **b.** State the domain and the range for each function.

13. $y = 2x^2 + 12x - 1$ **14.** $y = -x^2 - 2x + 3$

Solve each equation by completing the square.

15. $x^2 - 4x = 2$ $2 \pm \sqrt{6}$ **16.** $x^2 = 3 - x$ $\frac{-1 \pm \sqrt{13}}{2}$ **17.** $x^2 + 48 = 14x$ $8; 6$

12-6 Use the quadratic formula to solve for x.

18. $x^2 + x - 5 = 0$ $\frac{-1 \pm \sqrt{21}}{2}$ **19.** $3x^2 - 2x = 1$ $1; -\frac{1}{3}$ **20.** $-2x^2 + 5 = 0$ $\pm\frac{\sqrt{10}}{2}$

12-7 **21.** Find the value of the discriminant and use it to determine the number of roots of the equation $x^2 - 3x - 6 = 0$. $b^2 - 4ac = 33; 2$

12-8 **22.** The sum of a number and the reciprocal of 3 times the number is $\frac{13}{6}$. Find the number. $\frac{1}{6}$ or 2

12-9 If y varies directly as x, and $x = 8$ when $y = 4$, find y for each value of x.

23. $x = -1$ $-\frac{1}{2}$ **24.** $x = 6a$ $3a$

12-10 **25.** If y varies inversely as x, and $y = 4$ when $x = 1$, find x when $y = 8$. $\frac{1}{2}$

Weightlessness

Astronauts undergo lengthy training to learn to deal with the problem of weightlessness. The weight of an object in space decreases as the distance from earth increases. The weight in space W at a distance of m miles above the earth's surface is given by $W = \dfrac{16{,}000{,}000p}{16{,}000{,}000 + 8000m + m^2}$, where p is the weight on earth.

In BASIC, commas separate entries (in INPUT and DATA statements) and displays (in PRINT statements). Commas may not be used in a number such as 16,000,000. The computer expresses such numbers in a form similar to scientific notation. 16,000,000 is expressed in scientific notation as 1.6×10^7 and in BASIC as 1.6E+07. The number 0.000042 is expressed as 4.2E−05 in BASIC.

This program uses BASIC E notation to compute weight in space.

The Program	What It Does
`100 REM WEIGHT IN SPACE`	
`110 PRINT "WEIGHT ON EARTH";`	
`120 INPUT P`	Waits for input.
`130 PRINT "HOW MANY MILES UP";`	
`140 INPUT M`	
`200 LET N = P * 1.6E+07`	Computes numerator of the formula.
`210 LET D = 1.6E+07 + 8000 * M + M ↑ 2`	Computes the denominator.
`220 LET W = N/D`	Determines weight in space.
`230 PRINT "WEIGHT IN SPACE IS "; W`	
`240 PRINT`	Leaves a blank line.
`300 PRINT "ANOTHER? (1 = YES, 0 = NO)"`	
`310 INPUT Z`	
`320 IF Z = 1 THEN 110`	
`900 END`	

Write each of these BASIC numerals in standard form.

1. 5.7E+08   2. 1.67E+12   3. 3E−06   4. 8.5E−09

An astronaut weighs 180 pounds on the earth. What will the astronaut weigh at each of these distances above the earth?

5. 2000 miles   80 lb   6. 4000 miles   45 lb   7. 8000 miles   20 lb
8. 16,000 miles   7.2 lb   9. 56,000 miles   0.8 lb   10. 36,000 miles   1.8 lb

11. Who weighs more, a 144-pound explorer 20,000 miles above the earth, or a 169-pound explorer who is 22,000 miles up?   Each weighs 4 pounds.

12. Combine the computation in lines 200, 210, and 220 into one line. Is the program now easier to understand? Why?

For more information about BASIC, see the Computer Handbook at the back of the book.

This chapter provides a brief introduction to right-triangle trigonometry. In many school systems, trigonometry is considered to be an optional topic in a first year algebra course.

The opening lesson of the chapter provides a review of angles and their properties. Next, similar triangles are discussed, and the lengths and angle measures of corresponding parts of the triangles are found through the use of similarity properties. This leads the way for a presentation of the sine, cosine, and tangent ratios associated with an acute angle in a right triangle.

To help students gain an understanding of trigonometric ratios, the text devotes special attention to these ratios for special angles, such as 30°, 45°, and 60°. Thereafter, the work is generalized for any acute angle; the students work with tables of trigonometric ratios and use the concepts and skills in solving problems involving indirect measurement.

CHAPTER 13

A ship may change course several times while traveling from one port to another. Using trigonometry, the distance from the ship to its home port can be calculated if the distance traveled at each bearing is known.

TRIGONOMETRY

Prerequisite Skills Review

PREREQUISITE SKILLS REVIEW

For students who need additional practice with the algebraic skills in this Prerequisite Skills Review, you may assign Follow-Up exercises on page 506 in the students' books.

An item-by-item error analysis of the Prerequisite Skills Review appears on page T29.

Write the letter for the correct answer.

1. To rationalize the denominator, multiply $\frac{1}{\sqrt{3}}$ by _?_. **c**

   a. $\sqrt{3}$ **b.** $\frac{1}{\sqrt{3}}$ **c.** $\frac{\sqrt{3}}{\sqrt{3}}$ **d.** $\frac{3}{\sqrt{3}}$

2. The reciprocal of $\frac{\sqrt{2}}{2}$ is _?_. **c**

   a. $\frac{-\sqrt{2}}{2}$ **b.** $\frac{1}{2\sqrt{2}}$ **c.** $\sqrt{2}$ **d.** $\frac{1}{\sqrt{2}}$

3. Simplify $\frac{6}{\sqrt{3}}$. **c**

   a. 2   **b.** $3\sqrt{3}$ **c.** $2\sqrt{3}$ **d.** $\frac{2\sqrt{3}}{3}$

4. Which statement is false? **d**

   a. $4\sqrt{5} > 8$ **b.** $\sqrt{3} < 2$ **c.** $\frac{1}{\sqrt{2}} = \frac{\sqrt{2}}{2}$ **d.** $\frac{1}{2\sqrt{5}} < \frac{\sqrt{5}}{10}$

5. Which expressions are equal to 10^2? **d**
   I. $6^2 + 8^2$ II. $3^2 + 7^2$ III. $(\sqrt{10})^2 + (3\sqrt{10})^2$

   a. I only   **b.** I, II, and III   **c.** I and II only   **d.** I and III only

6. If $2^2 + (2\sqrt{3})^2 = c^2$, then $|c| = $ _?_. **c**
   a. $2 + 2\sqrt{3}$ **b.** $6\sqrt{3}$ **c.** 4   **d.** 8

7. Solve for x. **b**
   a. 5   **b.** $3\sqrt{5}$

   c. $5\sqrt{3}$ **d.** $\sqrt{53}$

8. If $a = \frac{b}{c}$, express c in terms of a and b. **a**

   a. $c = \frac{b}{a}$ **b.** $c = \frac{a}{b}$ **c.** $c = a - b$ **d.** $c = ab$

9. $\left(\frac{a}{c}\right)^2 + \left(\frac{b}{c}\right)^2 = $ _?_ **d**

   a. $\frac{a^2 + b^2}{2c^2}$ **b.** $\left(\frac{a+b}{c}\right)^2$ **c.** $\frac{1}{2}$ **d.** 1

WARM-UP EXERCISES

Solve.

1. $x + 53 = 90$ 37
2. $112 + y = 180$ 68
3. $4x + x = 180$ 36

LESSON NOTES

The geometric ideas in this lesson should be familiar to most students. However, be sure the students understand the various terms and the angle relationships. For example, point out that supplementary angles need not have a common vertex and a common side that lies between the other sides. (That is, they need not be adjacent angles.) Angles such as these are supplementary.

Similarly, as an illustration in the text indicates, complementary angles need not have a common vertex and a common side that lies between the other sides.

ALTERNATE EXAMPLE

1. The sum of the complement and the supplement of an angle is 170°. What is the measure of the angle?
   50°

13-1 Angles and Their Properties

OBJECTIVE

To solve problems that involve angle measures.

The angle shown here may be read as *angle KLM*, as *angle MLK*, or simply as *angle L*.

∠KLM, ∠MLK, or L

It is necessary to use three letters only when there may be some doubt as to which angle is being considered. In this figure, ∠C, might refer to more than one angle. Therefore we use ∠ACD for the angle marked 1, and ∠BCD for the angle marked 2.

∠ACD = 30°

You have probably learned how to use a protractor to measure angles. In this next figure, ∠ACD measures 30°.

Notice that there are two readings where CD crosses the protractor. The measure of ∠BCD is 150°. The sum of the measures of the two angles is 180°, and they are called supplementary angles.

Two angles are **supplementary angles** *if the sum of their measures is 180°.*

In the next figure, ∠1 + ∠2 = 90°. Also ∠A + ∠B = 90°. When the sum of the measures of two angles is 90°, they are called *complementary angles*.

Two angles are **complementary angles** *if the sum of their measures is 90°.*

EXAMPLE 1   The sum of the complement and the supplement of an angle is 190°. What is the measure of the angle?

Let x represent the measure of the angle.
Then 90 − x represents the complement of the angle and
   180 − x represents the supplement.

$(90 - x) + (180 - x) = 190$
$270 - 2x = 190$
$-2x = -80$
$x = 40$

Check   The complement of 40° is 50°. The supplement of 40° is 140°.

$50° + 140° = 190°$

Therefore the measure of the angle is 40°.

We will be working with triangles throughout this chapter. Here are some special types of triangles.

Equilateral triangle
$\angle A = \angle B = \angle C$
$AB = BC = AC$

Isosceles triangle
$\angle L = \angle M$
$KL = KM$

Right triangle
$\angle Z$ is a right angle (90°)
$x^2 + y^2 = z^2$

One property is common to all triangles. Whatever the size or shape of the triangle, the sum of the measures of the three angles is always the same.

The sum of the measures of the angles of a triangle is 180°.

To show this, you can measure the angles of a triangle, or try the activity suggested on page 478. Later you will prove this fact in your geometry course.

EXAMPLE 2 The angle measures of a triangle are x°, 3x°, and 5x°. Find the number of degrees in each angle.

$$x + 3x + 5x = 180 \qquad \text{The sum of the measures of the three angles is 180°.}$$
$$9x = 180$$
$$x = 20$$

Then $3x = 60$ and $5x = 100$.   **Check** 20° + 60° + 100° = 180° ✔
The measures of the three angles are 20°, 60°, and 100°.

CLASS EXERCISES

Find the measure of the complement of each angle.

1. 50°   40°   **2.** 85°   5°   **3.** 15°   75°   **4.** n° (90 − n)°   **5.** 2n° (90 − 2n)°

Find the measure of the supplement of each angle.

6. 145°   35°   **7.** 105°   75°   **8.** 29°   151°   **9.** x°   (180 − x)°   **10.** (3x + 10)°   (170 − 3x)°

EXERCISES

A   *Find the measure of the complement of each angle.*

1. 10°   80°   **2.** 17°   73°   **3.** 47°   43°   **4.** 5y°   (90 − 5y)°   **5.** (y + 25)°   (65 − y)°

Find the measure of the supplement of each angle.

6. 19°   161°   **7.** 128°   52°   **8.** 137°   43°   **9.** 7n°   (180 − 7n)°   **10.** (2n − 45)°   (225 − 2n)°

TRIGONOMETRY   477

ALTERNATE EXAMPLE

2. The angles of a triangle are represented by x°, 2x°, and 3x°. Find the number of degrees in each angle.   30°, 60°, 90°

DAILY QUIZ

Find the number of degrees in the described angles.
1. Two complementary angles have measures x° and 8x°.
   10°, 80°
2. Two supplementary angles have measures x° and 8x°.
   20°, 160°
3. Two complementary angles have measures in the ratio 4:11.
   24°, 66°
4. The angles of a triangle have measures of x°, (12x + 8)°, and (x − 10)°.   13°, 164°, 3°
5. The measure of an angle is 20° less than the measure of its complement. Find the measure of the supplement of the angle.
   145°

EXTRA PRACTICE, pages 531–532

ENRICHMENT ACTIVITY

Use the Activity to illustrate the fact that the sum of the measures of the angles of a triangle is 180°. Then illustrate an informal proof of this fact by using an approach that students will encounter in geometry. First define alternate interior angles formed by parallel lines as being equal in measure.

Have the students use alternate interior angles to show that the three angles of a triangle form a straight angle of 180°. The initial step is to draw a line through the vertex parallel to the base of the triangle.

$$\angle 1 + \angle 2 + \angle 3 = 180°$$

ADDITIONAL ANSWERS

Exercises
See page A17.

Activity
See page A17.

Find the number of degrees in the angles described.

11. Two complementary angles have measures of x° and 5x°. 15°, 75°

12. Two supplementary angles have measures of x° and 5x°. 30°, 150°

13. Two complementary angles have measures in the ratio 1 : 2. 30°, 60°

14. Two complementary angles have measures of x° and (3x − 10)°. 25°, 65°

15. The angles of a triangle have measures of x°, (10x + 6)°, and (x − 2)°. $14\frac{2}{3}°$, $152\frac{2}{3}°$, $12\frac{2}{3}°$

16. The angles of a triangle have measures of x°, 2x°, and $1\frac{1}{2}x°$. 40°, 80°, 60°

17. The measures of the angles of a triangle are consecutive integers.
    59°, 60°, 61°

18. One of the equal angles of an isosceles triangle measures 43°. Find the measures of the other angles. 94°, 43°

19. The base angles of an isosceles triangle are the equal angles. The measure of the third angle is one-half that of one of the base angles. Find the measure of each angle in the triangle. 36°, 72°, 72°

20. The measure of an angle is 10° less than the measure of its complement. Find the measure of the supplement of the angle. 140°

21. For a certain angle, the sum of the complement of the angle, the supplement of the angle, and the square of the measure of the angle is 318°. Find the measure of the angle. 8°

22. In △XYZ, the measure of ∠Z is 3 more than 5 times the measure of ∠Y, and the measure of ∠X is 7 less than twice the measure of ∠Y. Find the measures of ∠X, ∠Y, and ∠Z. ∠Y = 23° ∠Z = 118°, ∠X = 39°

*23. Show that the measures of the angles of a triangle cannot be consecutive odd integers.

ACTIVITY

Paper Folding

Cut out a triangular piece of paper. Label the vertices A, B, and C. Locate point P on BC by folding BC over on itself so that the crease goes through A. AP is called an *altitude* of △ABC. Now fold the vertices A, B, and C onto point P.

Notice that the sum of the measures of the three angles is 180°. That is, $\angle A + \angle B + \angle C = 180°$.

Here is a challenge for you. Use these figures to demonstrate that the formula for the area of a triangle is $A = \frac{1}{2} \times \text{base} \times \text{height}$ ($A = \frac{1}{2}bh$).

CHAPTER 13

13-2 Similar Triangles

OBJECTIVE

To find lengths and angle measures, using similar triangles.

In the photograph and its enlargement the triangular sails have the same shape. Two triangles with the same shape are **similar.**

$$\triangle ABC \text{ is similar to } \triangle XYZ$$

$$\triangle ABC \sim \triangle XYZ$$

If two triangles are similar, then each angle of one triangle has the same measure as each angle of the other. The pairs of angles with equal measures are called **corresponding angles.** The sides opposite corresponding angles are called **corresponding sides,** and their lengths are proportional. That is,

$$\frac{AB}{XY} = \frac{BC}{YZ} = \frac{AC}{XZ}$$

In the triangles at the right, $\angle C$ and $\angle R$ are corresponding angles. The sides opposite them, AB and PQ, are corresponding sides. Also, $\angle B$ corresponds to $\angle Q$ and $\angle A$ corresponds to $\angle P$.

Compare the ratios of the corresponding sides.

$$\frac{AB}{PQ} = \frac{8}{12} = \frac{2}{3} \qquad \frac{BC}{QR} = \frac{18}{27} = \frac{2}{3} \qquad \frac{AC}{PR} = \frac{20}{30} = \frac{2}{3}$$

Therefore $\dfrac{AB}{PQ} = \dfrac{BC}{QR} = \dfrac{AC}{PR}$.

In summary: If two triangles are similar, then the corresponding angles are equal in measure. The corresponding sides are proportional.

EXAMPLE 1 $\triangle ABC \sim \triangle XYZ$. Find x and y.

The lengths of corresponding sides AB and XY are known. $AB = 9$ and $XY = 6$. Use the ratio $\frac{AB}{XY}$ to find x and y.

$$\frac{AB}{XY} = \frac{BC}{YZ} \qquad\qquad \frac{AB}{XY} = \frac{AC}{XZ}$$

$$\frac{9}{6} = \frac{12}{x} \qquad\qquad\qquad \frac{9}{6} = \frac{15}{y}$$

$$9x = 72 \qquad\qquad\qquad 9y = 90$$

$$x = 8 \qquad\qquad\qquad\quad y = 10$$

TRIGONOMETRY

479

LESSON NOTES

As you develop the fact that corresponding sides of similar triangles are proportional, you may wish to point out that the way in which we name similar triangles indicates the corresponding parts of the triangles. That is, if we say that triangle ABC is similar to triangle PQR, we are indicating that the corresponding angles are $\angle A$ and $\angle P$, $\angle B$ and $\angle Q$, and $\angle C$ and $\angle R$. Similarly, the corresponding sides are segments AB and PQ, BC and QR, and CA and RP. Make sure the students understand the way small marks have been used to indicate equal angle measures in triangles ABC and PQR.

It may also be worthwhile to discuss similarity and congruence. If two triangles have the same shape, they are similar; if two triangles have the same shape and size, they are congruent. Thus, if two triangles are congruent, they are also similar. However, if two triangles are similar, they are not necessarily congruent.

ALTERNATE EXAMPLE

1. $\triangle ABC \sim \triangle JKL$. Find a and b.
   $a = 18$, $b = 12$

EXAMPLE 2

As an airplane takes off, its angle of climb is 5.7°. After flying 1000 ft, its altitude, or height above the ground, is 100 ft. What will its altitude be when it has flown another 2000 ft at the same angle?

Since $\triangle ABC \sim \triangle ADE$, the corresponding sides are proportional.

$\dfrac{BC}{DE} = \dfrac{AB}{AD}$

$\dfrac{100}{h} = \dfrac{1000}{3000}$

$\dfrac{100}{h} = \dfrac{1}{3}$

$h = 300$

The altitude of the airplane will be 300 ft.

CLASS EXERCISES

For each pair of similar triangles, list the corresponding angles and sides.

For each pair of similar triangles, find **x** and **y**.

3. $x = 12, y = 6$ **4.** $x = 4\frac{4}{5}, y = 6\frac{2}{3}$

EXERCISES

A   Complete each proportion for similar triangles **ABC** and **XYZ**.

1. $\dfrac{AB}{XY} = \dfrac{BC}{?}$ YZ   **2.** $\dfrac{AC}{XZ} = \dfrac{?}{YZ}$ BC   **3.** $\dfrac{AB}{?} = \dfrac{AC}{XZ}$ XY

For each pair of similar triangles, find **x** and **y**.

4. $x = 10, y = 6$ **5.** $x = 5, y = 8$

CHAPTER 13

6.

$x = 6, y = 15$

7.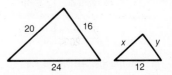

$x = 8, y = 21$

8. A tree casts a shadow 16 meters long. At the same time, a vertical stick that is 3 meters high casts a shadow 4 meters long. Find the height of the tree.   **12 meters**

9. Find the height of a tree that casts a 24-foot shadow at the same time that a yardstick casts a 4-foot shadow.   **18 ft**

10. The sides of a triangular park are 200, 250, and 350 yd long. On a map, if the longest side measures 7 cm, find the measures of the other two sides.   **4 cm, 5 cm**

11. The sides of a triangle are 8, 7, and 5 in. long. Find the lengths of the sides of a similar triangle if its longest side is 10 in. $8\frac{3}{4}$ in., $6\frac{1}{4}$ in.

12. Triangle *PQR* is similar to triangle *STV*. Find the perimeter of triangle *STV*.   **52 units**

*Triangles **ABC** and **DEF** are similar, with dimensions as shown.*

13. Can you find the length of *BC*?   **No.** Explain why or why not.
The length of *EF* is not given.

14. What is the relationship between the lengths of *BC* and *EF*? Their ratio is $\frac{3}{4}$.

15. Suppose the length of *BC* is 9 units. What is the length of *EF*?
12 units

16. Triangle *ABC* is similar to triangle *AXY*. *XY* = 3, *BC* = 8, and *AB* = 12. Find *AX*. $4\frac{1}{2}$

17. Similar triangles *PMN* and *PRS* were used to find the distance across a lake. Find the distance *MN*.   **88 m**

*18. On the coordinate plane, △*ABC* has vertices *A*(2, 1), *B*(4, 1), and *C*(4, 2). In a similar triangle *A'B'C'*, the vertices corresponding to *A* and *B* are *A'*(6, 3) and *B'*(12, 3). What are the coordinates of *C'*? Two answers are possible. Find both of them.   **(12, 6) or (12, 0)**

DAILY QUIZ (continued)

3. These triangles are similar. Find *x* and *y*.   *x* = 10, *y* = 8

4. A tree casts a shadow 24 meters long. At the same time, a vertical stick 2 meters high casts a shadow 3 meters long. Find the height of the tree.
16 meters

5. The sides of a triangular park are 150, 200, and 250 yd long. On a map, if the longest side measures 5 inches, find the measures of the other two sides.
3 inches, 4 inches

ASSIGNMENT GUIDE
(pages 480–481)

Minimum course: omit
Average course: omit
Maximum course: 1–9 odd,
10–17

ENRICHMENT ACTIVITY

Have students conduct an activity that is based on Exercise 8 of this lesson. On a sunny day, suggest that they go outside, stand a yardstick perpendicular to the ground, and measure the length of its shadow. Then have them measure the length of the shadow of some other object, such as a flagpole, and write a proportion to find the height of the object. Have several students conduct this experiment individually and then compare their results.

In right triangle *ABC*, find the ratio of:

1. $\dfrac{\text{length of side } BC}{\text{length of side } AB} \quad \dfrac{4}{5}$

2. $\dfrac{\text{length of side } AC}{\text{length of side } AB} \quad \dfrac{3}{5}$

3. $\dfrac{\text{length of side } BC}{\text{length of side } AC} \quad \dfrac{4}{3}$

LESSON NOTES

Discuss each of the model examples in detail. In considering Example 1, you may wish to have the students identify

the side opposite ∠*A*   side *BC*
the side adjacent to ∠*A*   side *AC*
the side opposite ∠*B*   side *AC*
the side adjacent to ∠*B*   side *BC*

It may also be worthwhile to draw a right triangle in this position on the chalkboard:

Then, using this triangle, have the students identify the hypotenuse, the side opposite a given acute angle, and the side adjacent to the given angle.

ALTERNATE EXAMPLE

1. Find the values of each trigonometric ratio for angles *D* and *E*.

$\sin D = \dfrac{3}{5} \qquad \sin E = \dfrac{4}{5}$

$\cos D = \dfrac{4}{5} \qquad \cos E = \dfrac{3}{5}$

$\tan D = \dfrac{3}{4} \qquad \tan E = \dfrac{4}{3}$

13-3 Trigonometric Ratios

OBJECTIVE

To express the sine, cosine, and tangent of an acute angle in terms of the sides of a right triangle.

Triangle *ABC* is a right triangle with right angle *C*. Recall that the side opposite the right angle is the *hypotenuse*, and that the two perpendicular sides are the *legs* of the triangle. In △*ABC*,

a is the length of the leg opposite ∠*A*,

b is the length of the leg adjacent to ∠*A*,

c is the length of the hypotenuse.

Ratios of the lengths of sides of a right triangle have special names.

Ratio	Name	Abbreviation
$\dfrac{\text{length of leg opposite } \angle A}{\text{length of hypotenuse}}$	sine of ∠*A*	sin *A*
$\dfrac{\text{length of leg adjacent to } \angle A}{\text{length of hypotenuse}}$	cosine of ∠*A*	cos *A*
$\dfrac{\text{length of leg opposite } \angle A}{\text{length of leg adjacent to } \angle A}$	tangent of ∠*A*	tan *A*

The sine, cosine, and tangent ratios are called **trigonometric ratios.** For ∠*A* in △*ABC*, these ratios may be expressed as follows.

$$\sin A = \dfrac{a}{c} \qquad \cos A = \dfrac{b}{c} \qquad \tan A = \dfrac{a}{b}$$

EXAMPLE 1   Find the value of each trigonometric ratio for angles *A* and *B*.

$$\mathbf{\sin A} = \dfrac{a}{c} = \dfrac{5}{13} \qquad \mathbf{\sin B} = \dfrac{b}{c} = \dfrac{12}{13}$$

$$\mathbf{\cos A} = \dfrac{b}{c} = \dfrac{12}{13} \qquad \mathbf{\cos B} = \dfrac{a}{c} = \dfrac{5}{13}$$

$$\mathbf{\tan A} = \dfrac{a}{b} = \dfrac{5}{12} \qquad \mathbf{\tan B} = \dfrac{b}{a} = \dfrac{12}{5}$$

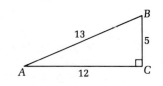

Trigonometric ratios depend on the size of an angle, not on the size of the triangle. In the figure below, $\triangle ABC$ and $\triangle AB'C'$ are right triangles with a common acute angle A. Any two such triangles are similar.

Since $\triangle ABC \sim \triangle AB'C'$, we know that corresponding sides are proportional.

$$\frac{BC}{AB} = \frac{B'C'}{AB'} = \sin A$$

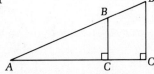

Thus the sine ratio depends only on the size of a given angle, and not on the size of the triangle. This is also true for the cosine and tangent ratios.

$$\frac{AC}{AB} = \frac{AC'}{AB'} = \cos A \qquad \frac{BC}{AC} = \frac{B'C'}{AC'} = \tan A$$

EXAMPLE 2

Find $\cos R$ to two decimal places.

Since $\cos R = \frac{1}{t}$, find t first.

$t^2 = 2^2 + 1^2$ Pythagorean theorem
$t^2 = 4 + 1$
$t^2 = 5$
$t = \sqrt{5}$

$$\cos R = \frac{1}{\sqrt{5}} = \frac{1}{\sqrt{5}} \cdot \frac{\sqrt{5}}{\sqrt{5}} = \frac{\sqrt{5}}{5} \approx \frac{2.236}{5} \approx 0.447$$

$\cos R = 0.45$ to two decimal places

CLASS EXERCISES

Find the value of each trigonometric ratio.

1. $\sin D$ $\frac{15}{17}$
2. $\cos D$ $\frac{8}{17}$
3. $\tan D$ $\frac{15}{8}$
4. $\sin F$ $\frac{8}{17}$
5. $\cos F$ $\frac{15}{17}$
6. $\tan F$ $\frac{8}{15}$

EXERCISES

A

Find the value of each trigonometric ratio.

1. $\sin A$ $\frac{3}{5}$
2. $\cos A$ $\frac{4}{5}$
3. $\tan A$ $\frac{3}{4}$
4. $\sin B$ $\frac{4}{5}$
5. $\cos B$ $\frac{3}{5}$
6. $\tan B$ $\frac{4}{3}$

TRIGONOMETRY

483

EXTRA PRACTICE, page 532

483

For each triangle find sin A, cos A, and tan A. Express irrational answers in simplest radical form.

7.
$\sin A = \frac{3}{5}$; $\cos A = \frac{4}{5}$; $\tan A = \frac{3}{4}$

8.
$\sin A = \frac{7}{25}$; $\cos A = \frac{24}{25}$; $\tan A = \frac{7}{24}$

9.
$\sin A = \frac{\sqrt{2}}{2}$; $\cos A = \frac{\sqrt{2}}{2}$; $\tan A = 1$

10.
$\sin A = \frac{\sqrt{3}}{2}$; $\cos A = \frac{1}{2}$; $\tan A = \sqrt{3}$

11.
$\sin A = \frac{2}{3}$; $\cos A = \frac{\sqrt{5}}{3}$; $\tan A = \frac{2\sqrt{5}}{5}$

12.
$\sin A = \frac{1}{2}$; $\cos A = \frac{\sqrt{3}}{2}$; $\tan A = \frac{\sqrt{3}}{3}$

For each triangle find sin B, cos B, and tan B. Express irrational answers in simplest radical form.

13.
$\sin B = \frac{40}{41}$; $\cos B = \frac{9}{41}$; $\tan B = \frac{40}{9}$

14.
$\sin B = \frac{\sqrt{11}}{6}$; $\cos B = \frac{5}{6}$; $\tan B = \frac{\sqrt{11}}{5}$

15.
$\sin B = \frac{5\sqrt{34}}{34}$; $\cos B = \frac{3\sqrt{34}}{34}$; $\tan B = \frac{5}{3}$

B

$\triangle ABC$ is a right triangle with right angle C. Use the Pythagorean theorem to find the length of the missing side. Then find sin A, cos A, and tan A.

16. $a = 3$, $b = 4$ **17.** $a = 5$, $c = 13$

18. $b = 12$, $c = 15$ **19.** $a = 2$, $b = 3$

20. $a = 3$, $c = 8$ **21.** $b = 5$, $c = 10$

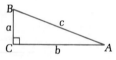

Use the figure at the right to verify each of the following.

22. $(\sin A)^2 + (\cos A)^2 = 1$ **23.** $\sin A = \cos B$

24. $\tan A = \dfrac{\sin A}{\cos A}$ **25.** $(\tan A)(\tan B) = 1$

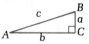

C

26. In $\triangle ABC$, $\angle C = 90°$, $\tan A = \frac{3}{4}$, and $AC = 12$. Find BC and AB. $BC = 9$, $AB = 15$

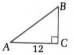

27. In right triangle XYZ, $\angle Z = 90°$ and $\sin X = \frac{5}{13}$. Find cos X. Then find tan Y. $\frac{12}{13}; \frac{12}{5}$

28. Express each ratio in terms of x.
   a. sin A   **b.** cos A   **c.** tan A

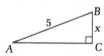

CHAPTER 13

13-4 Trigonometric Ratios of Special Angles

OBJECTIVE

To use trigonometric ratios of 30°, 45°, and 60° angles.

An *isosceles right triangle* has two legs of equal length. The two equal angles measure 45°. If we let $AC = BC = x$, we can solve for the hypotenuse c in terms of x.

$$c^2 = x^2 + x^2 \qquad \text{Pythagorean theorem}$$
$$c^2 = 2x^2$$
$$c = \sqrt{2x^2}$$
$$c = x\sqrt{2}$$

We can now find the trigonometric ratios for an angle of 45°.

$$\sin 45° = \sin A = \frac{x}{c} = \frac{x}{x\sqrt{2}} = \frac{1}{\sqrt{2}} = \frac{\sqrt{2}}{2}$$

$$\cos 45° = \cos A = \frac{\sqrt{2}}{2}. \qquad \text{Why?}$$

$$\tan 45° = \tan A = \frac{x}{x} = 1$$

It helps to remember these ratios if we use a triangle with legs of 1 unit.

$$\sin 45° = \frac{1}{\sqrt{2}} = \frac{\sqrt{2}}{2}$$

$$\cos 45° = \frac{1}{\sqrt{2}} = \frac{\sqrt{2}}{2}$$

$$\tan 45° = \frac{1}{1} = 1$$

If a decimal approximation is needed, use $\sqrt{2} = 1.414$ (correct to three decimal places). Then $\sin 45° = \cos 45° = \frac{1.414}{2} = 0.707$.

For convenience, we now use "$=$" instead of "$\approx$" in giving the approximate values for trigonometric ratios.

Another special right triangle is the *30°-60°-90° trian-gle*. In such a triangle, the side opposite the 30° angle is one-half the length of the hypotenuse.

To see why this is so, imagine $\triangle ABC$ reflected over side AC, forming $\triangle ABB'$, an equilateral triangle with $AB = BB' = AB'$.   Since $BC = \frac{1}{2}BB'$, then $BC = \frac{1}{2}AB$.

If we let $BC = x$ and $AB = 2x$, we can solve for b.

$$x^2 + b^2 = (2x)^2 \qquad \text{Pythagorean theorem}$$
$$x^2 + b^2 = 4x^2$$
$$b^2 = 3x^2$$
$$b = x\sqrt{3}$$

WARM-UP EXERCISES

Solve. Each variable represents the length of a side of a right triangle.
1. $1^2 + 1^2 = c^2$ $c = \sqrt{2}$
2. $1^2 + b^2 = 2^2$ $b = \sqrt{3}$

LESSON NOTES

By focusing on the trigonometric ra-tios of 30°, 45°, and 60° angles, the text makes it possible for students to apply the sine, cosine, and tan-gent definitions without having to consult a table of values for trig-onometric ratios. (In the next lesson, the students learn to use such a ta-ble.)

In considering the Class Exer-cises, be sure the students under-stand what is meant by simplest radical form. The answer may have a radical in it, but a radical may not appear in the denominator of a frac-tion.

We can now find the trigonometric ratios of angles of 30° and 60°. It is easier, however, to think of a right triangle in which the shorter leg x is equal to 1.

$$\sin 30° = \frac{1}{2} \qquad\qquad \sin 60° = \frac{\sqrt{3}}{2}$$

$$\cos 30° = \frac{\sqrt{3}}{2} \qquad\qquad \cos 60° = \frac{1}{2}$$

$$\tan 30° = \frac{1}{\sqrt{3}} = \frac{\sqrt{3}}{3} \qquad \tan 60° = \sqrt{3}$$

These ratios can now be used to find the lengths of sides of a right triangle that contains a 30°, 45°, or 60° angle.

EXAMPLE 1

Find x. Leave the answer in simplest radical form.

The problem involves the hypotenuse and the leg adjacent to the 30° angle. Use the cosine ratio.

$$\cos 30° = \frac{x}{18}$$
$$x = 18(\cos 30°)$$
$$x = 18\left(\frac{\sqrt{3}}{2}\right) = 9\sqrt{3}$$

EXAMPLE 2

A kite is held at the end of a 100-meter string. The string forms a 45° angle with the ground. Find the height of the kite.

The problem involves the hypotenuse and the leg opposite the 45° angle. Use the sine ratio.

$$\sin 45° = \frac{x}{100}$$
$$x = 100(\sin 45°)$$
$$x = 100\left(\frac{\sqrt{2}}{2}\right)$$
$$x = 50\sqrt{2}$$
$$x = 50(1.414) \quad \text{Use } \sqrt{2} = 1.414.$$
$$x = 70.7 \qquad \text{To the nearest meter, the kite is 71 m high.}$$

Some problems involve an **angle of elevation** through which you look up at an object, or an **angle of depression** through which you look down at an object.

CHAPTER 13

EXAMPLE 3

From a point 50 ft from the base of a tower, the angle of elevation of the top is 60°. Find the height of the tower to the nearest foot.

The problem involves the two legs of a right triangle, so use the tangent ratio.

$$\tan 60° = \frac{x}{50}$$

$$x = 50(\tan 60°)$$

$$x = 50\sqrt{3}$$

$$x = 50(1.732) \quad \text{Use } \sqrt{3} = 1.732.$$

$$x = 86.6 \quad \text{The tower is 87 ft high, to the nearest ft.}$$

CLASS EXERCISES

Find **x.** *Leave irrational answers in simplest radical form.*

1.
5

2.
$\frac{20\sqrt{3}}{3}$

3.
$25\sqrt{3}$

4.
$8\sqrt{3}$

EXERCISES

A *Find* **x.** *Leave irrational answers in simplest radical form.*

1.
$16\sqrt{2}$

2.
$9\sqrt{2}$

3.
$21\sqrt{3}$

4.
18

5.
$15\sqrt{3}$

6.
$18\sqrt{3}$

7.
$30\sqrt{3}$

8.
$40\sqrt{2}$

B *Find each answer correct to the nearest whole number.*

9. A ladder leans against a wall and forms a 60° angle with the ground. If the ladder is 30 feet long, how high up the wall will it reach? 26 ft

10. Find the height of a kite when a 300-foot string forms the given angle with the ground. **a.** 30° **b.** 45° **c.** 60°
150 ft   212 ft   260 ft

11. The diagonal of a square forms a 45° angle with each side. The length of a side of the square is 5 feet. Find the length of the diagonal. 7 ft

TRIGONOMETRY

487

EXTRA PRACTICE, pages 532–533

DAILY QUIZ

Find *x*. Leave irrational answers in simplest radical form.

1.
$x = 8\sqrt{2}$

2.
$x = 24$

3.
$x = 20\sqrt{3}$

4.
$x = 13$

5. The hypotenuse of a 30°-60°-90° triangle is 36 feet. Find the perimeter of the triangle to the nearest whole number.   85 ft

ASSIGNMENT GUIDE
(pages 487–488)

Minimum course: omit
Average course: omit
Maximum course: 1–15 odd, 16–23

ENRICHMENT ACTIVITY

Have the students work the Challenge on page 488. Then ask them which of the following are identities for right triangle *ABC*.

1. $\dfrac{\cot A - 1}{1 - \tan A} \stackrel{?}{=} \dfrac{\csc A}{\sec A}$ Identity

2. $\dfrac{\sin A + \cos A}{\sin A - \cos A} \stackrel{?}{=} \dfrac{\sec A + \csc A}{\sec A - \csc A}$ Identity

3. $\dfrac{1}{\sec A + \tan A} \stackrel{?}{=} \dfrac{2 - \sin A}{\cos A}$ Not an identity

4. $\dfrac{\sec A - \cos A}{(\tan A)^2} \stackrel{?}{=} \dfrac{(\tan A)^2}{\sec A}$ Not an identity

5. $\dfrac{1 - \cos A}{\sin A} \stackrel{?}{=} \dfrac{(\sin A)^2}{1 + \cos A}$ Not an identity

12. The hypotenuse of a 30°-60°-90° triangle is 24 feet. Find the perimeter of the triangle. 57 ft

13. The shorter leg of a 30°-60°-90° triangle is 4 meters long. Find the length of the hypotenuse. 8 m

14. A roof has a 30° slope. How much does the roof rise for each 10 feet of horizontal distance? 6 ft

15. From a point 130 feet from the base of a building, the angle of elevation to the top is 30°. How high is the building? 75 ft

C

16. From two campsites due east of a 400-ft tower, the angles of elevation to the top of the tower are 30° and 60°. How far apart are the campsites? 462 ft

17. An airport marker is sighted from a plane flying at an altitude of 7000 feet. If the angle of depression to the marker is 30°, what is the air distance from the plane to the marker? 14,000 ft

By substitution, verify each of the following statements.

18. $(\sin 30°)^2 + (\cos 30°)^2 = 1$ $\frac{1}{4} + \frac{3}{4} = 1$ **19.** $(\sin 60°)^2 + (\cos 60°)^2 = 1$ $\frac{3}{4} + \frac{1}{4} = 1$

20. $(\sin 45°)^2 + (\cos 45°)^2 = 1$ **21.** $\sin 60° = 2(\sin 30°)(\cos 30°)$

22. $\tan 30° = \dfrac{\sin 30°}{\cos 30°}$ **23.** $1 - \dfrac{(\cos 30°)^2}{1 + \sin 30°} = \sin 30°$

*24. $\triangle ABC$ is a 30°-60°-90° triangle with $\angle C = 90°$. $AB = \frac{4}{\sqrt{3}}$, $AC = \frac{2}{\sqrt{3}}$, and $BC = 2$. If P is the point on BC such that $AP = PB$, show that $\sin \angle CAP$ is $\frac{1}{2}$.

CHALLENGE

More Trigonometric Ratios

Other trigonometric ratios are reciprocals of sin A, cos A, and tan A.

cotangent of $\angle A = \cot A = \dfrac{1}{\tan A}$

secant of $\angle A = \sec A = \dfrac{1}{\cos A}$

cosecant of $\angle A = \csc A = \dfrac{1}{\sin A}$

Use $\triangle ABC$ to verify each of the following.

1. $(\tan A)^2 + 1 = (\sec A)^2$ **2.** $1 + (\cot A)^2 = (\csc A)^2$

3. $\dfrac{1 - \csc A}{\cot A} = \dfrac{\sin A - 1}{\cos A}$ **4.** $\dfrac{\csc A + 1}{\csc A - 1} = (\sec A + \tan A)^2$

13-5 Using Trigonometric Ratios

OBJECTIVE _____

To solve problems, using the table of trigonometric ratios.

_____

The table on page 547 gives values of trigonometric ratios for angles from 0° to 90°. Most of these values are approximations.

To find tan 35°, look for 35° in the column headed *Angle*. Then look across to the column headed *Tangent*.

$$\tan 35° = 0.7002$$

To find x° if sin x° = 0.6018, locate .6018 in the column headed *Sine*. The corresponding angle is 37°. Therefore

$$\sin 37° = 0.6018$$

Angle	Sine	Cosine	Tangent
33°	.5446	.8387	.6494
34°	.5592	.8290	.6745
35°	.5736	.8192	**.7002**
36°	.5878	.8090	.7265
37°	**.6018**	.7986	.7536
38°	.6157	.7880	.7813
39°	.6293	.7771	.8098
40°	.6428	.7660	.8391

With the aid of the table on page 547, we are now able to work with angles other than 30°, 45°, and 60°.

EXAMPLE 1 At a point on the ground 60 meters from the base of a flagpole, the angle of elevation to the top is 40°. How high is the flagpole?

The problem involves the two legs of the right triangle. Use the tangent ratio.

$$\tan 40° = \frac{x}{60}$$

$$x = 60(\tan 40°)$$
$$x = 60(0.8391)$$
$$x = 50.346 \qquad \text{The flagpole is approximately 50 ft high.}$$

EXAMPLE 2 From the top of a building, the angle of depression to a certain point on the ground is 35°. If the building is 125 feet high, how far is the point from the base of the building?

The angle of depression is 35°. Notice that the complement of this angle is 55°.

$$\tan 55° = \frac{x}{125}$$

$$x = 125(\tan 55°)$$
$$x = 125(1.4281)$$
$$x = 178.5125$$

To the nearest foot, the point is 179 feet from the base of the building.

TRIGONOMETRY   **489**

LESSON NOTES (continued)

Note that Example 3 involves deciding which of two entries in the table is closer to the computed value of the cosine. Be sure the students understand why the required angle is 32°, to the nearest degree.

Starred problem 34 is very challenging. Take time to point out that the two angles of depression are measured in the same vertical plane.

ALTERNATE EXAMPLE

3. Find x to the nearest degree. 51°, to the nearest degree

POSSIBLE ERROR

Students often make errors in working with problems involving angles of elevation and depression. The errors usually stem from a failure to visualize the physical situation correctly and then use the appropriate data. For instance, in Example 2, if no figure were given, they might write:

$$\tan 35° = \frac{x}{125} \quad \text{(incorrect)}$$

Stress the importance of visualizing the situation and showing it in an appropriate diagram.

DAILY QUIZ

Find the value of each ratio. Use the table on page 547.
1. sin 43°   0.6820
2. tan 27°   0.5095
Find x to the nearest degree.
3. cos x = 0.9328   21°
4. tan x = 0.7560   37°
5. A 30-foot ladder is placed against a wall. It forms an angle of 44° with the ground. To the nearest whole number, how far up the wall does the ladder reach?   21 ft

EXAMPLE 3   Find x to the nearest degree.

Use the cosine ratio, which involves the adjacent leg and the hypotenuse.

$$\cos x° = \frac{8.5}{10}$$

$\cos x° = 0.85$, or 0.8500

Now look at the table on page 547.   In the column headed *Cosine*, .8500 is not shown. It is between the entries .8572 and .8480, but it is closer to .8480.

Therefore the required angle is 32°, to the nearest degree.

CLASS EXERCISES

Find the value of each ratio. Use the table.

1. sin 41°   0.6561   **2.** cos 37°   0.7986   **3.** tan 18°   0.3249   **4.** sin 79°   0.9816

5. cos 63°   0.4540   **6.** tan 81°   6.3138   **7.** cos 23°   0.9205   **8.** tan 53°   1.3270

Find x to the nearest degree.

9. cos x = 0.4540   63°   **10.** sin x = 0.9120   66°   **11.** tan x = 0.3000   17°

EXERCISES

A   *Find the value of each ratio. Use the table.*

1. sin 27°   0.4540   **2.** cos 49°   0.6561   **3.** tan 12°   0.2126   **4.** tan 87°   19.0811

5. cos 39°   0.7771   **6.** sin 71°   0.9455   **7.** tan 7°   0.1228   **8.** cos 12°   0.9781

Find x to the nearest degree.

9. sin x = 0.2920   17°   **10.** tan x = 0.2522   14°   **11.** cos x = 0.9845   10°

Find the value of x to the nearest tenth.

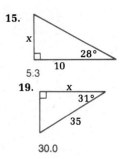

12. 8.5   **13.** 12.0   **14.** 37.2   **15.** 5.3

16. 26.7   **17.** 23.0   **18.** 40.7   **19.** 30.0

490

CHAPTER 13

Find the value of **x** *to the nearest degree.*

20.

37°

21.

40°

22.

22°

23.

49°

Find lengths to the nearest whole number and angles to the nearest degree.

24. A 25-foot ladder is placed against a wall. It forms an angle of 27° with the wall. How far up the wall does the ladder reach?   22 ft

25. A surveyor, standing 40 meters from the base of a building, finds that the angle of elevation to the top is 38°. How tall is the building?   31 m

26. A 70-foot wire is attached to the top of a 30-foot pole and fastened to the ground at the other end. What angle does the wire make with the ground?   25°

27. The angle of elevation of a plane from point *X* on the ground is 32°. The plane is directly above point *Y* on the ground, which is 800 meters from *X*. Find the height of the plane. 500 m

28. A flagpole casts a shadow 13 feet long. The angle of elevation of the top of the pole from the end of the shadow is 62°. Find the height of the pole.   24 ft

29.

Find *x*°, the inclination of the roof. 37°

30.

Find the width *x* of the river.   89 ft

31. From a lookout point in a lighthouse, the angle of depression of a floating object is 13°. The lookout point is 250 feet above the level of the water. Find the horizontal distance from the lighthouse to the object.   1083 ft

32. On the coordinate plane, a line through the origin passes through the point (8, 5).   What angle does the line make with the x-axis?   32°

*33. From a point on the ground, the angle of elevation to the top of a hill is 27°. Another point, in the same direction from the hill, is 1000 feet from the base of the hill. From the second point, the angle of elevation to the top of the hill is 47°. Find the distance between the two points.   1104 ft

*34. From the top of a 200-foot cliff, a surveyor locates two points on opposite banks of a river. The angle of depression to the nearer point is 55°. The angle of depression to the point on the opposite side of the river is 28°. How wide is the river between these two points?   236 ft

ASSIGNMENT GUIDE
(pages 490–492)

Minimum course: omit
Average course: omit
Maximum course: 1–31 odd, 32,
*Strategies
for Problem
Solving*

ENRICHMENT ACTIVITY

Have students study the table of trigonometric values to see what relationships they can discover. For example, they should notice the following facts:

As the angle ranges in value from 0° to 90°:

• The value of the sine varies from 0 to 1.

• The value of the cosine varies from 1 to 0.

• The value of the tangent increases in value from 0 toward the infinite. (At 90°, the tangent is undefined.)

Challenge the students to use a right triangle to verify that the sine of an angle is equal to the cosine of its complement and that the cosine of an angle is equal to the sine of its complement.

STRATEGIES for PROBLEM SOLVING

Relating a New Problem to a Familiar One

Can you find the length of side $\overline{AB}$ in the figure shown?

The difficulty is that $\triangle ABC$ is *not* a right triangle. However, we will try to relate this problem to right triangles, with which we are already familiar.

The clue is to draw an auxiliary line. We will draw $\overline{CP}$ at right angles to side $\overline{AB}$. Now we can proceed as follows.

$$\cos 74° = \frac{m}{50} \qquad \cos 37° = \frac{n}{80}$$
$$m = 50(\cos 74°) \qquad n = 80(\cos 37°)$$
$$m = 50(0.2756) \qquad n = 80(0.7986)$$
$$m = 13.780 \qquad n = 63.888$$

To the nearest foot, $AB = m + n = 14 + 64 = 78$ feet.

Let us now draw a general triangle ABC. In the figure, $\overline{CP}$ is drawn at right angles to $\overline{AB}$. Let $CP = h$ and use the *sine ratio* in each right triangle.

$$\sin A = \frac{h}{b} \qquad \sin B = \frac{h}{a}$$
$$b(\sin A) = h \qquad a(\sin B) = h$$

Since both products are equal to h,

$$a(\sin B) = b(\sin A)$$

$$\frac{a(\sin B)}{\sin A} = b \qquad \text{Divide each side by } \sin A.$$

$$\frac{a}{\sin A} = \frac{b}{\sin B} \qquad \text{Divide each side by } \sin B.$$

We can extend this equality and state the **Law of Sines** for any triangle ABC.

$$\frac{a}{\sin A} = \frac{b}{\sin B} = \frac{c}{\sin C}$$

Now try these. Use the Law of Sines to find **x** to the nearest foot or degree.

CHAPTER 13

Architecture

Architects choose the pitch, or slope, of a roof when designing a house. Some of the choices available are given in the diagram.

Here is one of the formulas used.

$$\text{Slope} = \frac{\text{rise}}{\text{run}} = \frac{\text{rise}}{\frac{1}{2}\,\text{span}}$$

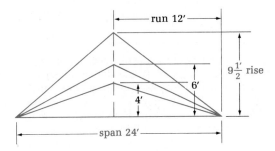

Example   The highest roof shown has a span of 24′ and a rise of $9\frac{1}{2}′$.

a. Find the slope.

$$\text{Slope} = \frac{9\frac{1}{2}}{\frac{1}{2}(24)} = \frac{9\frac{1}{2}}{12} = 0.7917 \qquad \text{Give the ratio to four decimal places.}$$

b. Find the angle that the roof makes with the ceiling rafters.

$\tan A = 0.7917$

$\angle A = 38°$ In the table, the angle whose tangent is closest to 0.7917 is 38°. (tan 38° = 0.7813)

1. A roof has a span of 18′ and a rise of 3′. Find its slope and its angle with the ceiling rafters.   Slope $= \frac{1}{3} = 0.3333$; angle is 18°

2. A roof has a span of 40′ and a slope of $\frac{2}{5}$. Find its rise.   8′

3. A roof has a run of 18′ and makes an angle of 35° with the ceiling rafters. Find its rise to the nearest inch.   151 in.

Applications

This Applications page illustrates the fact that trigonometry is essential in architecture and in the construction trade.

If photographs of pitched-roof houses can be obtained, students might be asked to make measurements to calculate roof slopes. They should also see that different slopes have different degrees of eye-appeal.

These exercises review basic algebraic skills.

1. Simplify:

$$6 - 2^2 \cdot \sqrt{25} - 2^3 \div \sqrt{\frac{1}{4}}$$

00

2. If $(-4, n)$ is a solution of $y = 6 - 3x$, what is the value of n? 18

3. Simplify: $\dfrac{x^2 + 14x + 49}{x^2 - 49}$

$\dfrac{x + 7}{x - 7}$

4. Evaluate $-a^2 - a(1 - a)$ when $a = -2$. 2

5. Evaluate $(2)(\sin 30°)$. 1

Solve for x.

6. $2x^2 - 9x + 4 = 0$ $\dfrac{1}{2}$ or 4

7. $3x^2 - x - 5 = 0$ $\dfrac{1 \pm \sqrt{61}}{6}$

8. $\sqrt{x + 1} + x = 1$ 0

9. Subtract $3x^2 - 5x - 4$ from $x^2 + x - 3$. $-2x^2 + 6x + 1$

Factor completely.

10. $7x^2 - 63$ $7(x + 3)(x - 3)$

11. $4x^2 - 26x + 12$
$(4x - 2)(x - 6)$

12. $3x^2 - 4x - 15$
$(3x + 5)(x - 3)$

13. Solve the system:
$2x + y = -9$
$y = x + 3$ $(-4, -1)$

[*Maintaining Skills continues on page 495.*]

CHAPTER 13 REVIEW

VOCABULARY

supplementary angles (p. 476)
complementary angles (p. 476)
similar triangles (p. 479)
corresponding angles (p. 479)
corresponding sides (p. 479)
trigonometric ratios (p. 482)
sine, sin (p. 482)

cosine, cos (p. 482)
tangent, tan (p. 482)
isosceles right triangle (p. 485)
30°-60°-90° right triangle (p. 485)
angle of elevation (p. 486)
angle of depression (p. 486)

SUMMARY

The chapter begins with a review of the degree measure of angles. After establishing properties of similar triangles, the sine, cosine, and tangent trigonometric ratios are defined. These definitions are made for acute angles within right triangles. The trigonometric ratios of the special angles of 30°, 45°, and 60° are found and then used to determine the measures of unknown sides of right triangles. Trigonometric ratios of angles with measures between 0° and 90° are found in a table of ratios, and are used in solving problems that involve right triangles.

REVIEW EXERCISES

13-1 **1.** Find the number of degrees in each of two complementary angles that have measures of $2x°$ and $3x°$. 36°; 54°

2. Find the number of degrees in each of two supplementary angles that have measures of $(2x + 10)°$ and $(3x - 15)°$. 84°; 96°

3. Find the number of degrees in each angle of a triangle if their measures are $(2x + 9)°$, $(x - 12)°$, and $(3x + 15)°$. 16°, 65°, 99°

13-2 *For each pair of similar triangles, find x and y.*

4.

$x = 18, y = 24$

5.

$x = 12, y = 30$

6.

$x = 30°, y = 50°$

7.

$x = 68°, y = 22°$

494

13-3   *Use the Pythagorean theorem to find the length of the missing side of each right triangle. Then find sin A, cos A, and tan A. Express irrational answers in simplest radical form.*

8.

$AC = \sqrt{13}$;

$\sin A = \frac{3\sqrt{13}}{13}$,

$\cos A = \frac{2\sqrt{13}}{13}$,

$\tan A = \frac{3}{2}$

9.

$BC = 5$;

$\sin A = \frac{5}{13}$,

$\cos A = \frac{12}{13}$,

$\tan A = \frac{5}{12}$

10.

$AB = \sqrt{51}$; $\sin A = \frac{7}{10}$,

$\cos A = \frac{\sqrt{51}}{10}$, $\tan A = \frac{7\sqrt{51}}{51}$

13-4   *From a point 100 feet from the base of a building, the angle of elevation to the bottom of a radio antenna is 45°. The angle of elevation to the top of the radio antenna, from the same point, is 60°. Give answers, correct to the nearest whole number, to the following questions.*

11. How far is it from the point on the ground to the bottom of the radio antenna?   141'

12. How far is it from the point on the ground to the top of the radio antenna?   200'

13. How high is the building?   100'

14. How far is it from the base of the building to the top of the radio antenna?   173'

15. How high is the radio antenna?   73'

⊢———100'———⊣

13-5   *Find x to the nearest whole number or to the nearest degree. Use the table on page 547.*

16.

$x = 9$

17.

$x = 67°$

18.

$x = 7$

19. The top of a 5-meter ladder rests against a wall. The bottom of the ladder makes a 70° angle with the ground. How high up the wall does the ladder reach? Give your answer to the nearest tenth of a meter.   4.7 meters (appr. 470 cm)

REVIEW   **495**

14. Find the *x*- and *y*-intercepts of the line $3y = x - 4$.

x-int. = 4, y-int. = $-\frac{4}{3}$

15. Solve this compound inequality and graph the solution:

$x + 1 > 5$ or $1 - x > -3$

x > 4 or x < 4

16. Simplify: $\sqrt{32x} - \sqrt{\frac{x}{2}}$ $\frac{7\sqrt{2x}}{2}$

17. Solve for *x*.

28   *x*   14   30°

18. Write the equation, in standard form, of the line that has a slope of $\frac{1}{2}$ and a y-intercept of $\frac{1}{3}$.

$3x - 6y = -2$

19. If the diagonal of a square measures 14 cm, what is the measure of each side of the square? $7\sqrt{2}$ cm

20. 20 gallons of a saltwater solution contain 5 gallons of salt. How much water must evaporate from the solution for it to become a 50% saltwater solution?   10 gallons

13-1   **1.** Two complementary angles have measures of $(3x + 5)°$ and $(8x - 3)°$. Find the number of degrees in each angle.   29°; 61°

13-2   For each pair of similar triangles, find **x** and **y**.

2.

3.

4.

$x = 80, y = 24$ $x = 9, y = 6$ $x = 115°, y = 45°$

13-3   Complete each ratio for right triangle **ABC**.

5. $\sin A$ $\frac{a}{c}$

6. $\cos A$ $\frac{b}{c}$

7. $\tan B$ $\frac{b}{a}$

Find each trigonometric ratio.

8. $\sin F$ $\frac{3}{5}$

10. $\tan F$ $\frac{3}{4}$

9. $\sin D$ $\frac{4}{5}$

11. $\cos D$ $\frac{3}{5}$

13-4   Find each value. Simplify all radicals.

12. $\sin 30°$ $\frac{1}{2}$ **13.** $\tan 45°$ 1 **14.** $\cos 45°$ $\frac{\sqrt{2}}{2}$

15. $\sin 60°$ $\frac{\sqrt{3}}{2}$ **16.** $\sin 45°$ $\frac{\sqrt{2}}{2}$ **17.** $\tan 30°$ $\frac{\sqrt{3}}{3}$

13-5   **18.** Find the value of x to the nearest tenth.   14.7

19. Find the value of x to the nearest degree.   16°

20. Find the distance AB across a lake if the distance from B to C is 300 meters and $\angle C = 42°$. Give your answer to the nearest meter.   270 m

Arithmetic Mean

Teachers and students often compute the *average*, or *mean*, of a set of grades. A program can be used that automatically counts the number of entries. To achieve this we use a "counter." Line 110, below, sets the counter to zero. As each number is entered, line 230 adds one to the counter K.

Since the computer does not know when we have entered the last value, we program it to recognize a signal, or *flag*. In this program, −1 is used as the flag to tell the computer to compute the mean.

The Program	What It Does
100 REM MEAN	
110 LET K = 0	Sets counter to zero.
120 LET T = 0	Sets total to zero.
130 PRINT "ENTER ONE NUMBER"	
140 PRINT "AT A TIME."	
150 PRINT "FOR MEAN, ENTER -1"	If N is the flag, −1, the last
200 INPUT N	number has been entered.
210 IF N = -1 THEN 300	
220 LET T = T + N	Adds entry to previous total.
230 LET K = K + 1	Increases counter by one.
240 GO TO 200	Returns for next entry.
300 LET A = T/K	Computes the arithmetic mean.
310 PRINT "THE MEAN IS "; A	
400 PRINT "ANOTHER? (1 = YES, 0 = NO)"	
410 INPUT Z	
420 IF Z = 1 THEN 110	
900 END	

The program is in sections, or "modules," which begin at lines 100, 200, 300, and 400. This makes the program easier to understand and to modify.

1. What is the purpose of line 120? Will the program function properly if it is omitted? Why?

What will be displayed for each of these sets of entries?

2. 56, 34, 19, 67, 34, −1   42   3. 44, 69, 103, 56, −1   68

4. 9.25, 6.75, 6.5, −1   7.5   5. 80, 85, 85, 90, 94, 100, −1   89

6. Write a line 305 to round the mean to the nearest tenth.

7. The mean of 90, 85, and 89 is 88. Modify the program so that it will display:

```
3 NUMBERS ENTERED
THEIR SUM IS 264
THEIR MEAN IS 88
```

For more information about BASIC, see the Computer Handbook at the back of the book.

Computer Activity

In many computer programs, a "counter" and a "flag" are very useful devices. Take time to be sure the students understand the ideas.

ADDITIONAL ANSWERS

Computer Activity

1. Line 120 sets the total of the numbers at 0.
   No. For each group of numbers to be averaged, we must begin with total set at 0.

6. 305   LET A
   = INT(A * 10 +
   .5)/10

7. 303   PRINT K;
   " NUMBERS
   ENTERED"

    306   PRINT "THEIR
   SUM IS "; T

    310   PRINT "THEIR
   MEAN IS "; A

PART I

Write the letter for the correct answer.

Chap. 2   **1.** Evaluate: $2b - a$ if $a = -2$ and $b = -3$ a

    a. -4 **b.** 4 **c.** 8 **d.** -3 **e.** 1

Chap. 3   **2.** Solve for x: $1 - 2(x + 1) = -4(2 - x)$ e

    a. $-\dfrac{2}{7}$ **b.** $-\dfrac{7}{2}$ **c.** $-\dfrac{5}{6}$ **d.** $\dfrac{6}{7}$ **e.** $\dfrac{7}{6}$

Chap. 6   **3.** Solve for x: $2x^2 = 5x$ e

    a. $-2; -5$ **b.** $2; 5$ **c.** $0; -\dfrac{5}{2}$ **d.** $2; 0$ **e.** $0; \dfrac{5}{2}$

Chap. 8   **4.** Multiply: $\left(\dfrac{x^2 + x - 12}{x + 2}\right)\left(\dfrac{4 - x^2}{x^2 - 5x + 6}\right)$ d

    a. $x + 4$ **b.** $x - 4$ **c.** $4x$ **d.** $-x - 4$ **e.** $-x + 4$

    5. Divide: $\dfrac{(a - 2)^2}{3ab} \div \dfrac{a^2 - 4}{12a^2}$ c

    a. $-\dfrac{4a}{b}$ **b.** $\dfrac{(a - 2)^3(a + 2)}{36a^3b}$ **c.** $\dfrac{4a(a - 2)}{b(a + 2)}$ **d.** -1 **e.** $\dfrac{4a}{b}$

Chap. 9   **6.** Solve for x: $\dfrac{1}{x} + \dfrac{3}{2x} = \dfrac{1}{x + 1}$ d

    a. $\dfrac{1}{3}$ **b.** $\dfrac{5}{3}$ **c.** $-\dfrac{1}{3}$ **d.** $-\dfrac{5}{3}$ **e.** $-\dfrac{3}{5}$

    7. 2.4 is what percent of 3?   b

    a. 75%   **b.** 80%   **c.** 85%   **d.** 83%   **e.** 87%

Chap. 10   **8.** If $a \le b$, then $-4a \;\underline{\ ?\ }\; -4b$.   d

    a. $=$ **b.** $>$ **c.** $<$ **d.** $\ge$ **e.** $\le$

Chap. 11   **9.** Simplify: $(1 + \sqrt{3})(1 - \sqrt{3})$ b

    a. 1 **b.** -2 **c.** -8 **d.** 8 **e.** 2

    10. Simplify: $\sqrt{18x^8}$ e

    a. $2x^4\sqrt{3}$ **b.** $3x^2\sqrt{2}$ **c.** $3x^2$ **d.** $9x^4$ **e.** $3x^4\sqrt{2}$

    11. Simplify: $\dfrac{1}{\sqrt{x}}$ d

    a. $\dfrac{1}{x}$ **b.** x **c.** $\sqrt{x}$ **d.** $\dfrac{\sqrt{x}}{x}$ **e.** $\dfrac{x^2}{x}$

Chap. 12   **12.** If x varies directly as y, and $x = 5$ when $y = 4$, find y when $x = 1$.   e

    a. 20   **b.** $\dfrac{6}{5}$ **c.** $\dfrac{5}{6}$ **d.** $\dfrac{5}{4}$ **e.** $\dfrac{4}{5}$

PART II

Chap. 4 Write an equation of a line, given a point on the line and its slope.

13. (3, 0); m = 2
$y = 2x - 6$

14. (−1, 2); m = −1
$y = -x + 1$

15. (−1, −1); m = 0 $y = -1$

Chap. 5
Chap. 6 Simplify.

16. $-2(x^3y)^2(xy^5)(-xy)$
$2x^8y^8$

17. $6x(x - 1) + 5x^2$
$11x^2 - 6x$

18. $(5x + 3)(3x - 2)$
$15x^2 - x - 6$

19. $(x - 3)^2 - (x + 1)^2$
$-8x + 8$

20. $\dfrac{48x^2y^3}{8x^2y}$ $6y^2$

21. $\dfrac{-121x^2y^2z^2}{11x^5y^2z}$ $\dfrac{-11z}{x^3}$

Factor completely.

Chap. 6 **22.** $x^2 - 12xy + 36y^2$
$(x - 6y)^2$

23. $27x^3 - 3x$
$3x(3x - 1)(3x + 1)$

24. $5x^2 - 8x - 4$
$(5x + 2)(x - 2)$

25. Solve for x: $3x^2 + x = 2$ $\frac{2}{3}; -1$

Chap. 7 **26.** Solve the system of equations:
$\begin{aligned} 3x + y &= 2 \\ 2x + 3y &= -8 \end{aligned}$ (2, −4)

Chap. 8 **27.** Divide: $x^2 + 3x - 1$ by $x + 2$ $x + 1 - \dfrac{3}{x + 2}$

28. Add: $\dfrac{x}{x^2 + 7x + 12} + \dfrac{3}{x + 3}$ $\dfrac{4}{x + 4}$

29. Subtract: $\dfrac{3x + 2y}{3y} - \dfrac{x + 2y}{6x}$ $\dfrac{6x^2 + 3xy - 2y^2}{6xy}$

Chap. 9 **30.** A car, averaging 40 mph, left a city at noon. A second car left the same city 15 minutes later and traveled at 48 mph in the same direction. At what time did the second car overtake the first? 1:30 P.M.

Chap. 10 Solve and graph each compound inequality.

31. $3x + 2 > 14$ or $x - 5 < -2$

32. $6 - x \leq 5$ and $2 - 5x > -13$

Chap. 11 Simplify.

33. $9\sqrt{12} + 4\sqrt{48}$ $34\sqrt{3}$

34. $7\sqrt{12}\sqrt{8}$ $28\sqrt{6}$

35. $-3x\sqrt{8x^5} + 2x^2\sqrt{50x^3}$
$4x^3\sqrt{2x}$

36. Solve for x: $-8 + \sqrt{x + 1} = -5$ 8

Chap. 12 For each parabola: **a.** Write the coordinates of the vertex and tell whether it is a maximum or a minimum point. **b.** Draw the graph.

37. $y = 3(x - 2)^2$

38. $y = -(x + 1)^2 + 2$

39. $y = 2x^2 - 8x + 9$

40. If x varies inversely as y, and x = 4 when y = 9, find y when x = 1. 36

Chap. 13 Find **x** to the nearest foot or to the nearest degree.

41.

42.

43.
70′
x°
90′
90°
39°

499

PREREQUISITE SKILLS REVIEW FOLLOW-UP

Chapter One

1. a. $13 - 2\frac{1}{4} = $ _?_ $10\frac{3}{4}$ **b.** $7\frac{1}{2} - 6\frac{2}{3} = $ _?_ $\frac{5}{6}$

2. a. $\frac{1}{5} + \frac{1}{3} = $ _?_ $\frac{8}{15}$ **b.** $\frac{3}{4} + \frac{1}{3} = $ _?_ $1\frac{1}{12}$

3. a. $\frac{3}{5} \times 9 = $ _?_ $5\frac{2}{5}$ **b.** $4 \times \frac{5}{8} = $ _?_ $2\frac{1}{2}$

4. a. $\frac{2}{3} \times \frac{5}{7} = $ _?_ $\frac{10}{21}$ **b.** $\frac{1}{3} \times \frac{3}{5} = $ _?_ $\frac{1}{5}$

5. a. $\frac{3.7}{10} = $ _?_ 0.37 **b.** $\frac{0.385}{10} = $ _?_ 0.0385

6. a. $3.6 - 2 = $ _?_ 1.6 **b.** $9 - 1.4 = $ _?_ 7.6

7. Simplify.

  a. $\frac{0.3}{0.5}$ $\frac{3}{5}$ **b.** $\frac{3 \times 11}{5 \times 11}$ $\frac{3}{5}$

  c. $\frac{3 + 2}{5 + 2}$ $\frac{5}{7}$ **d.** $\frac{3 \div 5}{5 \div 5}$ $\frac{3}{5}$

8. a. $0.7 \div 0.14 = $ _?_ 5

  b. $36 \div 0.6 = $ _?_ 60

  c. $7.8 \div 12 = $ _?_ 0.65

  d. $9.36 \div 1.3 = $ _?_ 7.2

9. a. $1.45 \times 10 = $ _?_ 14.5

  b. $36.2 \times 100 = $ _?_ 3620

  c. $0.43 \times 10 = $ _?_ 4.3

  d. $4.21 \times 1000 = $ _?_ 4210

10. a. 15 less 7 is _?_ . 8

  b. 7 less than 15 is _?_ . 8

  c. 7 subtracted from 15 is _?_ . 8

  d. 15 subtracted from 27 is _?_ . 12

Chapter Two

1. a. $\frac{1}{2}$ of _?_ is equal to $\frac{1}{6}$. $\frac{1}{3}$

  b. $\frac{1}{4}$ of _?_ is equal to $\frac{1}{20}$. $\frac{1}{5}$

2. a. The opposite of $|5| + |-2|$ is _?_ . -7

  b. The opposite of $|-6| - |-2|$ is _?_ . -4

3. a. $\frac{3.8}{0.52} = \frac{?}{0.052}$ 0.38 **b.** $\frac{3.8}{0.52} = \frac{3.80}{?}$ 0.52

  c. $\frac{3.8}{0.52} = \frac{?}{52}$ 380 **d.** $\frac{3.8}{0.52} = \frac{3800}{?}$ 520

4. Simplify.

  a. $\frac{8 + 12}{4} + 8 + \frac{12}{4}$ 16

  b. $\frac{15 + 20}{5} + 15 + \frac{20}{5}$ 26

5. a. $18 \div 6 \div 3 + 3 = $ _?_ 4

  b. $15 \div 3 + 2 \times 4 = $ _?_ 13

6. a. $\frac{1}{4}(200 + 16) = $ _?_ 54

  b. $\frac{1}{4}(200) + 16 = $ _?_ 66

7. a. $(5)(0) = $ _?_ 0 **b.** $\frac{(5)(8)}{8} = $ _?_ 5

  c. $1 \div 5 = $ _?_ 0.2, or $\frac{1}{5}$ **d.** $\frac{5 + 3}{3} = $ _?_ $2\frac{2}{3}$

8. a. If $a = 3$ and $b = 0.2$, then

  $\frac{1}{a} + \frac{1}{b} = $ _?_ . $5\frac{1}{3}$

  b. If $a = 0.4$ and $b = 2$, then

  $\frac{1}{a} + \frac{1}{b} = $ _?_ . 3

9. If $x = 3$ and $y = \frac{1}{3}$, then:

  a. $xy = $ _?_ 1 **b.** $x - y = $ _?_ $2\frac{2}{3}$

  c. $x - 3y = $ _?_ 2 **d.** $x - 9y = $ _?_ 0

10. If $n = 3$, then:

  a. $5(6n - 4n) = $ _?_ 30

  b. $30n - 20n = $ _?_ 30

  c. $37n - n = $ _?_ 108

  d. $6(5n - 4n) = $ _?_ 18

Chapter Three

1. **a.** If 4 times a number is 156, then $\frac{1}{3}$ of the number is _?_ . 13

   b. If 3 times a number is 354, then $\frac{1}{2}$ of the number is _?_ . 59

2. **a.** If $\frac{1}{3}$ of a number is 6.1, then 2 times the number is _?_ . 36.6

   b. If $\frac{1}{4}$ of a number is 1.7, then 3 times the number is _?_ . 20.4

3. *Simplify.*

   a. $\frac{1}{5} - \frac{1}{4}\left(3 - \frac{1}{3}\right)$ $-\frac{7}{15}$

   b. $\frac{1}{8} - \frac{1}{5}\left(4 - \frac{1}{4}\right)$ $\frac{-5}{8}$

4. **a.** If $x = 200$, then
   $8x + 5(1000 - x) = $ _?_ . 5600

   b. If $x = 500$, then
   $3x + 3(2000 - x) = $ _?_ . 6000

5. *Simplify, or write **undefined**.*

   a. $(6 - 6)5$ 0   **b.** $4 - 3\left(\frac{4}{3}\right)$ 0

   c. $\frac{10}{3(3) - 9}$ Undefined   **d.** $\frac{3(2) - 6}{7}$ 0

6. *If $x = -2$, then:*

   a. $2x - 4 = $ _?_ -8

   b. $12 - 2x = $ _?_   16

   c. $-2(2 - x) = $ _?_ -8

   d. $8(1 + x) = $ _?_ -8

7. **a.** $(-3)\left(-\frac{1}{3}\right) = $ _?_   1

   b. $\left(\frac{5}{9}\right)\left(1\frac{4}{5}\right) = $ _?_   1

8. **a.** If $n = 3.2$, then $\frac{3}{3 - n} = $ _?_ . -15

   b. If $n = 8.3$, then $\frac{6}{8 - n} = $ _?_ . -20

9. **a.** $\frac{5}{2}\left(n + \frac{1}{2}\right) = $ _?_ $+ $ _?_ $\frac{5}{2}n + \frac{5}{4}$

   b. $\frac{5}{2}n + \frac{1}{2} = \frac{1}{2}($ _?_ $+ 1)$ $5n$

   c. $\frac{3}{2}(3n - 1) = $ _?_ $- $ _?_ $\frac{9}{2}n - \frac{3}{2}$

   d. $\frac{6}{7}n + \frac{3}{7} = $ _?_ $(2n + 1)$ $\frac{3}{7}$

10. *Multiply.*

    a. $\frac{2}{5}(10 - 5x)$ **b.** $\frac{2}{3}(6x - 3)$

    $4 - 2x$ $4x - 2$

Chapter Four

1. **a.** $\frac{3}{4}(3) - 2 = $ _?_ $\frac{1}{4}$

   b. $\frac{2}{5}(3) - 1 = $ _?_ $\frac{1}{5}$

2. **a.** $-\frac{2}{3}(9) + 2 = $ _?_ -4

   b. $-\frac{4}{5}(15) + 12 = $ _?_   0

3. **a.** $\frac{-3 - 2}{6 - 3} = $ _?_ $\frac{-5}{3}$, or $-1\frac{2}{3}$

   b. $\frac{-3 - (-2)}{6 - (-3)} = $ _?_ $-\frac{1}{9}$

   c. $\frac{-3 - 2}{-6 - 3} = $ _?_ $\frac{5}{9}$

   d. $\frac{-3 - 2}{6 - (-3)} = $ _?_ $\frac{-5}{9}$

4. **a.** If $a = 2$ and $b = -3$, then
   $\frac{a - b}{a + b} = $ _?_ . -5

   b. If $a = -4$ and $b = 3$, then
   $\frac{a + b}{a - b} = $ _?_ . $\frac{1}{7}$

5. *Simplify.*

   a. $\frac{2 - 4}{3 - 5}$ 1   **b.** $\frac{-3 - 6}{-9 + 5}$ $\frac{9}{4}$, or $2\frac{1}{4}$

   c. $\frac{8 - (-3)}{4 - 7}$ $-\frac{11}{3}$ **d.** $\frac{4 - (-3)}{-4 - 3}$ -1

6. **a.** $\frac{x - 1}{-9}$ is equal to $-\frac{1}{3}$ if $x = $ _?_ . 4

   b. $\frac{x - 4}{-12}$ is equal to $\frac{1}{2}$ if $x = $ _?_ . -2

PREREQUISITE SKILLS FOLLOW-UP

EXTRA PRACTICE SETS

COMPUTER HANDBOOK

TABLES

GLOSSARY

ANSWERS TO CHECKPOINTS

ANSWERS TO SELECTED EXERCISES

INDEX

PREREQUISITE SKILLS FOLLOW-UP

7. a. If $x = -4$ and $y = 1$, then
$2x - y = \underline{\ ?\ }$. -9

b. If $x = 3$ and $y = -5$, then
$3x - y = \underline{\ ?\ }$. 14

8. a. If $-3x + 4y = 10$ and $y = 0$, then
$x = \underline{\ ?\ }$. -6

b. If $2x - 5y = -10$ and $x = 0$, then
$y = \underline{\ ?\ }$. 2

9. Solve for *b* in terms of *a*.

a. $4 - b = a$
$b = 4 - a$

b. $2a - b = 3$
$b = 2a - 3$

10. a. If $7b - 4g = 15$ and $b = 1$, then
$g = \underline{\ ?\ }$. -2

b. If $3t - 5r = 14$ and $t = 3$, then
$r = \underline{\ ?\ }$. -1

Chapter Five

1. a. $(-3)^3 = \underline{\ ?\ }$ -27 **b.** $(-1)^4 = \underline{\ ?\ }$ 1

2. a. $-2(-2)^5 = \underline{\ ?\ }$ 64 **b.** $-3(-4)^2 = \underline{\ ?\ }$ -48

3. a. $(0.1)^4 = \underline{\ ?\ }$ 0.0001 **b.** $(0.01)^2 = \underline{\ ?\ }$
0.0001

4. a. $[3(-1)]^2 + 3(-1) = \underline{\ ?\ }$ 6

b. $[2(-2)]^2 + 2(-2) = \underline{\ ?\ }$ 12

5. a. $\frac{1}{3}(-3)^3 = \underline{\ ?\ }$ -9 **b.** $\frac{1}{4}(-4)^2 = \underline{\ ?\ }$ 4

6. a. $6\left(9 + \frac{1}{2}\right) - \frac{1}{2} = \underline{\ ?\ }$ $56\frac{1}{2}$

b. $10\left(8 + \frac{1}{5}\right) - \frac{1}{5} = \underline{\ ?\ }$ $81\frac{4}{5}$

7. a. $4 - 4(4)^2 = \underline{\ ?\ }$ **b.** $2 - 2(2)^3 = \underline{\ ?\ }$
-60 -14

8. Simplify.

a. $7t + 9t$ $16t$ **b.** $5a + 6a$ $11a$

9. Using exponents, write an equivalent expression in simplest form.

a. $2 \cdot x \cdot x \cdot x + 3 \cdot x \cdot x + 2 \cdot x \cdot x$ $2x^3 + 5x^2$

b. $5 \cdot x \cdot x \cdot x \cdot x + 3 \cdot x \cdot x \cdot x + 7 \cdot x \cdot x \cdot x$
$5x^4 + 10x^3$

10. Simplify.

a. $7x^2 + 3(x^2 - 3x)$ $10x^2 - 9x$

b. $6x^2 + 4(2x^2 - 3)$ $14x^2 - 12$

11. Simplify if possible, or use the distributive property in reverse.

a. $7xy - 14x$ **b.** $4rs + 4st$
$7x(y - 2)$ $4s(r + t)$

12. Simplify.

a. $3df - 4df + 3f$ $-df + 3f$

b. $-4rt + 3rt - 5r$
$-rt - 5r = -r(t + 5)$

13. a. The length of a rectangle is 3 more than twice its width x. An expression for the area is $\underline{\ ?\ }$. $x(2x + 3)$

b. The width of a rectangle is 4 less than half its length y. An expression for the area is $\underline{\ ?\ }$. $y\left(\frac{1}{2}y - 4\right)$

Chapter Six

1. a. $-14y = -2(\underline{\ ?\ })$ $7y$

b. $-12t = -3(\underline{\ ?\ })$ $4t$

2. a. $x^3y = (\underline{\ ?\ })xy$ x^2 **b.** $r^5s = (\underline{\ ?\ })rs$ r^4

3. a. $(2 + 5)^2 = 2^2 + \underline{\ ?\ } + 5^2$ $2 \cdot 2 \cdot 5$, or 20

b. $(7 + 3)^2 = 7^2 + \underline{\ ?\ } + 3^2$ $2 \cdot 7 \cdot 3$, or 42

4. a. $(9 - 1)^2 = 9^2 - \underline{\ ?\ } + (-1)^2$ $2 \cdot 9 \cdot 1$, or 18

b. $(6 - 2)^2 = 6^2 - \underline{\ ?\ } + (-2)^2$ $2 \cdot 6 \cdot 2$, or 24

5. a. $4x(3 - x) = \underline{\ ?\ }$ $12x - 4x^2$

b. $2y(7 - 3y) = \underline{\ ?\ }$ $14y - 6y^2$

6. a. $a - b = -(b - \underline{\ ?\ })$ a

b. $r - t = \underline{\ ?\ }(t - r)$ -1

7. a. $9(x - b) - 7(x - b) = 2(\underline{\ ?\ })$ $x - b$

b. $6(y - a) - 2(y - a) = 4(\underline{\ ?\ })$ $y - a$

8. Evaluate for the given value.

a. $x(x - 3) - 3(x - 3)$ when $x = 13$ 100

b. $x(x - 5) - 5(x - 5)$ when $x = 16$ 121

9. Multiply.

a. $(2x + 5)(2x - 3)$ $4x^2 + 4x - 15$

b. $(3x - 5)(x + 2)$ $3x^2 + x - 10$

10. Multiply.

a. $3(x - 4)(x - 3)$ $3x^2 - 21x + 36$

b. $2(x - 2)(x + 1)$ $2x^2 - 2x - 4$

PREREQUISITE SKILLS REVIEW FOLLOW-UP

Is 2 a solution of the equation? Is −3?

11. a. $x^2 - 5x + 6 = 0$ 2 is; −3 is not.

b. $x^2 + x - 6 = 0$ Yes, both 2 and −3

12. a. $x^2 - 2x = 0$ **b.** $x^2 + 3x = 0$
2 is; −3 is not.   −3 is; 2 is not.

13. *Multiply.*

a. $3x(3x^3 - 2x^2)$ **b.** $4x(x^3 - 5x)$
$9x^4 - 6x^3$ $4x^4 - 20x^2$

Chapter Seven

Complete for the given point in the coordinate plane.

1. a. (5, 0) lies on the _?_ axis. x-

b. (0, −2) lies on the _?_ axis. y-

2. a. (3, −1) is in quadrant _?_ . IV

b. (−6, −6) is in quadrant _?_ . III

3. a. The line with equation $y = 3$ is parallel to the _?_ axis. x-

b. Is the line with equation $y = x$ parallel to the x-axis? No

4. a. The line with equation $x = -8$ is parallel to the _?_ axis. y-

b. Is the line with equation $x + y = 5$ parallel to the y-axis? No

5. *Find the slope of the line that contains the given points.*

a. (2, 4) and (0, 6) −1

b. (−7, 3) and (1, 11) 1

6. *Find the slope of the line.*

a. $2y = x - 5$ $\frac{1}{2}$ **b.** $3y + x = 7$ $-\frac{1}{3}$

7. *Find the y-intercept of the line.*

a. $y = x - 3$ −3   **b.** $x + 3y = 3$ 1

8. *Find the slope and the y-intercept of the line.*

a. $x + y = 2$ −1; 2 **b.** $y = 3x - 2$ 3; −2

c. $y - 3x = 2$ 3; 2 **d.** $y = 2x - 3$ 2; −3

Does the point with the given coordinates lie on the given line?

9. a. $y = 5x - 2$ (0, 2) No

b. $y = 2x + 3$ $\left(-\frac{3}{2}, 0\right)$ Yes

10. a. $y - x = 5$ (−1, 6) No

b. $y + 2x = 2$ (2, −2) Yes

11. a. $x = 3$ (−3, 3) No

b. $y + 3x = 0$. (3, −1) No

12. *A line passes through the points with coordinates (0, 5) and (1, 6).*

a. The slope of the line is _?_ . 1

b. The y-intercept of the line is _?_ . 5

c. Can the equation of the line be $x + y = 5$? No

d. Can the equation of the line be $y = x + 5$? Yes

Chapter Eight

1. a. $\frac{5}{7}(7) =$ _?_ 5 **b.** $10\left(\frac{5}{2}\right) =$ _?_ (5) 5

c. $8\left(\frac{3}{7}\right) = \frac{24}{?}$ 7 **d.** $9\left(\frac{x}{y}\right) = \frac{?}{y}$ 9x

2. *Simplify.*

a. $\frac{4 - (-3)}{10 - 3}$ 1 **b.** $\frac{8 - 1}{8}$ $\frac{7}{8}$

c. $\frac{5 - 6}{6 - 5}$ −1 **d.** $\frac{2(-3)}{3(-2)}$ 1

3. *Write in simplest form.*

a. $\frac{15}{40}$ $\frac{3}{8}$ **b.** $\frac{3\left(\frac{1}{5}\right)}{8\left(\frac{1}{5}\right)}$ $\frac{3}{8}$ **c.** $\frac{3\frac{1}{5}}{8\frac{1}{5}}$ $\frac{16}{41}$ **d.** $\frac{3.75}{10}$ $\frac{3}{8}$

4. *For what value of x is the fraction undefined?*

a. $\frac{3 - x}{x}$ 0 **b.** $\frac{x + 1}{2x - 3}$ $\frac{3}{2}$

PREREQUISITE SKILLS FOLLOW-UP

EXTRA PRACTICE SETS

COMPUTER HANDBOOK

TABLES

GLOSSARY

ANSWERS TO CHECKPOINTS

ANSWERS TO SELECTED EXERCISES

INDEX

PREREQUISITE SKILLS FOLLOW-UP

5. *Factor, if possible.*

a. $x^2 + 4$ Not factorable **b.** $x^2 - 4$ $(x + 2)(x - 2)$

c. $5x - 20$ $5(x - 4)$ **d.** $x^2 - 9$ $(x + 3)(x - 3)$

6. *Factor.*

a. $x^2 + x - 2$ $(x - 1)(x + 2)$ **b.** $x^2 - x - 12$ $(x - 4)(x + 3)$

7. *Find the missing trinomial factor.*

a. $-3x^2 + 12x - 12 = -3(\underline{\ ?\ })$ $x^2 - 4x + 4$

b. $-2x^2 + 6x + 8 = -2(\underline{\ ?\ })$ $x^2 - 3x - 4$

8. a. The opposite of $x - 5$ is $\underline{\ ?\ } + 5$. $-x$

b. The opposite of $a - b$ is $\underline{\ ?\ } - a$. b

c. The opposite of $y - 2$ is $-(\underline{\ ?\ })$. $y - 2$

d. The opposite of $\underline{\ ?\ }$ is $x + y$. $-x - y$

9. *Multiply.*

a. $(2x - 4)(2x - 4)$ $4x^2 - 16x + 16$

b. $(3x + 5)(3x + 5)$ $9x^2 + 30x + 25$

Chapter Nine

1. a. If $x = -3$, then $\dfrac{5 - x}{2} = \underline{\ ?\ }$. 4

b. If $x = -6$, then $\dfrac{14 - x}{4} = \underline{\ ?\ }$. 5

2. *Simplify.*

a. $-12x\left(\dfrac{1}{4}\right)$ $-3x$ **b.** $-15x\left(-\dfrac{3}{5}\right)$ $9x$

3. a. $60\left(\dfrac{3}{4}\right) = 15(\underline{\ ?\ })$ 3

b. $6\left(3 - \dfrac{1}{2}\right) = 18 - \underline{\ ?\ }$ 3

c. $12\left(\dfrac{x}{3}\right) = \underline{\ ?\ }(x)$ 4

d. $16\left(\dfrac{5 - y}{8}\right) = 10 - \underline{\ ?\ }$ $2y$

Simplify.

4. a. $3(x - 1)\left(\dfrac{2x}{x - 1}\right)$ $6x$

b. $3x(2x + 3)\left(\dfrac{5x}{2x + 3}\right)$ $15x^2$

5. a. $10\left(\dfrac{3x - 7}{5}\right)$ $6x - 14$ **b.** $4\left(\dfrac{5 + 8x}{2}\right)$ $10 + 16x$

6. a. $\left[\dfrac{10 - 4\left(\frac{1}{4}\right)}{3}\right]$ -3

b. $-\left[\dfrac{16 - 5\left(\frac{1}{5}\right)}{5}\right]$ -3

Find the least common multiple of:

7. a. 2, 5, 15 30 **b.** 3, 7, 14 42

8. a. $(x - 2)^2$ and $3(x - 2)$ $3(x - 2)^2$

b. $x(y - 3)^2$ and $x^2(y - 3)$ $x^2(y - 3)^2$

9. *Find the LCD of:*

a. $\dfrac{5}{2x + 6}$ and $\dfrac{3x}{x^2 + 6x + 9}$ $2(x + 3)^2$

b. $\dfrac{2x}{x^2 - 7x + 12}$ and $\dfrac{1}{x^2 - 16}$ $(x - 3)(x - 4)(x + 4)$

10. *Rewrite without fractions.*

a. $8\left(\dfrac{x + 2}{4}\right) = 8\left(\dfrac{1}{2}\right)$ $2x + 4 = 4$

b. $10\left(\dfrac{x - 1}{2}\right) = 15\left(\dfrac{1}{5}\right)$ $5x - 5 = 3$

Chapter Ten

1. *Use < or > to complete.*

a. $0.1 \underline{\ ?\ } 0.01$ > **b.** $\dfrac{5}{12} \underline{\ ?\ } \dfrac{11}{12}$ <

c. $\dfrac{1}{2} \underline{\ ?\ } \dfrac{1}{3}$ > **d.** $\dfrac{1}{5} \underline{\ ?\ } \dfrac{1}{12}$ >

2. *Arrange from least to greatest.*

a. 0.081, 0.1, 0.009 0.009, 0.081, 0.1

b. 0.1, 0.053, 0.006 0.006, 0.053, 0.1

3. a. $|5 - 2| = |-5 + \underline{\ ?\ }|$ 2 or 8

b. $-|3 - 7| = \underline{\ ?\ }$ -4

c. $\left|-\dfrac{3}{5} \cdot 10\right| = \underline{\ ?\ }$ 6

d. $\left|\dfrac{2}{3} - \dfrac{1}{6}\right| = \underline{\ ?\ }$ $\frac{1}{2}$

4. Simplify.

  a. $|5 - 3| - |3 - 5|$ 0

  b. $|6 - 12| - |12 - 6|$ 0

Solve for the variable.

5. a. $|x| - 5 = 10$ **b.** $|x| + 3 = 7$
      15, −15   4, −4

6. a. $6 - 2y = 1$ $\frac{5}{2}$ **b.** $8 - 3y = 4$ $\frac{4}{3}$

7. a. $5 - \frac{1}{4}x = 7$ −8   **b.** $2 - \frac{1}{3}x = 5$ −9

Express in slope-intercept form.

8. a. $-y = 2x + 7$ $y = -2x - 7$

  b. $-y = -\frac{1}{2}x - 3$ $y = \frac{1}{2}x + 3$

9. a. $3x - y = 4(2 + x)$ $y = -x - 8$

  b. $2x - 2y = 3(5 - 2x)$ $y = 4x - \frac{15}{2}$

10. Does the point with the given coordinates lie on the line whose equation is given?

  a. $x - y = 4$; $(0, 4)$ No

  b. $2x - 3y = 5$; $(4, -1)$ No

11. Find the **x**- and **y**-intercepts.

  a. $x + 3y = 6$ x-int. = 6; y-int. = 2

  b. $y = -2x - 1$ x-int. = $-\frac{1}{2}$; y-int. = −1

  c. $\frac{x}{3} + \frac{y}{2} = 1$ x-int. = 3; y-int. = 2

12. What is the point of intersection of the lines with the given equations?

  a. $y = 5x$ and $3x + y = -8$ $(-1, -5)$

  b. $y = 3x - 2$ and $x = -y$ $\left(\frac{1}{2}, -\frac{1}{2}\right)$

Chapter Eleven

1. Write the answer as a mixed number.

  a. $\left(1\frac{1}{2}\right)^2 = \underline{\ ?\ }$ $2\frac{1}{4}$ **b.** $\left(5\frac{1}{2}\right)^2 = \underline{\ ?\ }$ $30\frac{1}{4}$

2. a. $5^2 \cdot 3 = \underline{\ ?\ }$ 75   **b.** $6^2 \cdot 4 = \underline{\ ?\ }$ 144

Divide.

3. a. $0.5\overline{)0.3515}$ 0.703   **b.** $0.6\overline{)1.2018}$ 2.003

4. a. $0.38\overline{)10.336}$ 27.2   **b.** $0.91\overline{)3.9767}$ 4.37

Simplify.

5. a. $(0.04)^2$ 0.0016   **b.** $(2x)^5$ $32x^5$

  c. $\dfrac{8 \cdot 8^3}{8^2}$ 64   **d.** $(x^2yz^5)^2$ $x^4y^2z^{10}$

6. a. $x^5 \cdot x$ x^6 **b.** $(-3)^4$ 81

  c. $(x^4)^3$ x^{12} **d.** $x^4 \cdot x^3$ x^7

7. Write the prime factorization for the expression.

  a. $12 \cdot 5^2$ $2^2 \cdot 3 \cdot 5^2$ **b.** $3 \cdot 10^2$ $2^2 \cdot 3 \cdot 5^2$

  c. 30^2 $2^2 \cdot 3^2 \cdot 5^2$ **d.** $5 \cdot 6^2$ $2^2 \cdot 3^2 \cdot 5$

8. a. $(30)^2 = \underline{\ ?\ }$ 900   **b.** $(15 \cdot 10)^2 = \underline{\ ?\ }$ 22,500

  c. $15 \cdot 10^2 = \underline{\ ?\ }$ 1500   **d.** $\dfrac{6^6 \cdot 3^8}{6^3 \cdot 3^4} = (\underline{\ ?\ })^2$

9. a. $(2 \cdot 3 \cdot 5)^2 = (2 \cdot 3 \cdot 5)(\underline{\ ?\ } \cdot \underline{\ ?\ } \cdot \underline{\ ?\ })$ $2 \cdot 3 \cdot 5$

  b. $(2 \cdot 5 \cdot 11)^3 =$
     $2 \cdot 2 \cdot \underline{\ ?\ } \cdot 5 \cdot 5 \cdot \underline{\ ?\ } \cdot 11 \cdot 11 \cdot \underline{\ ?\ }$ 2; 5; 11

The ordered pairs represent (x_1, y_1) and (x_2, y_2). Find $(x_2 - x_1)^2$ and $(y_2 - y_1)^2$.

10. a. $(6, -1)$ and $(-2, 0)$ $(x_2 - x_1)^2 = 64$; $(y_2 - y_1)^2 = 1$

  b. $(-2, -3)$ and $(0, -8)$ $(x_2 - x_1)^2 = 4$; $(y_2 - y_1)^2 = 25$

11. a. $(4, 0)$ and $(-5, -7)$ $(x_2 - x_1)^2 = 81$; $(y_2 - y_1)^2 = 49$

  b. $(-9, 1)$ and $(-6, -4)$ $(x_2 - x_1)^2 = 9$; $(y_2 - y_1)^2 = 25$

Chapter Twelve

1. Simplify.

  a. $\dfrac{-3 - 2.4}{3}$ −1.8   **b.** $\dfrac{-4 - 1.6}{4}$ −1.4

2. a. If $x = -2$, then $x^2 + 3x + 2 = \underline{\ ?\ }$.   0

  b. If $x = -4$, then $x^2 + 2x - 4 = \underline{\ ?\ }$.   4

Simplify.

3. a. $(x - 3)^2 + 4$ $x^2 - 6x + 13$ **b.** $(x + 2)^2 - 6$ $x^2 + 4x - 2$

4. a. $\dfrac{-6 + \sqrt{36 - 4(2)(-3)}}{4}$ $\dfrac{-3 + \sqrt{15}}{2}$

  b. $\dfrac{-4 - \sqrt{16 - 4(3)(-3)}}{6}$ $\dfrac{-2 - \sqrt{13}}{3}$

5. a. $\dfrac{15 - \sqrt{18}}{3}$ $5 - \sqrt{2}$ **b.** $\dfrac{12 - \sqrt{8}}{2}$ $6 - \sqrt{2}$

PREREQUISITE SKILLS FOLLOW-UP

EXTRA PRACTICE SETS

COMPUTER HANDBOOK

TABLES

GLOSSARY

ANSWERS TO CHECKPOINTS

ANSWERS TO SELECTED EXERCISES

INDEX

PREREQUISITE SKILLS FOLLOW-UP

6. Will **all**, **some**, or **no** values of **x** make the expression negative?

   a. $5x$ Some   **b.** $-3x$ Some

   c. $5 - x$ Some   **d.** $-(x^2 + 1)$ All

7. Will **all**, **some**, or **no** values of **x** make the expression nonnegative?

   a. $(x - 4)^2$ All   **b.** $\frac{1}{4}x$ Some

   c. $-x - 2$ Some   **d.** $x + 9$ Some

8. a. $(3n + 5)^2 = 9n^2 + \underline{\ ?\ } + 25$ $30n$

   b. $(4n + 2)^2 = 16n^2 + \underline{\ ?\ } + 4$ $16n$

9. Factor the trinomial only if it is a trinomial square.

   a. $x^2 - 6x + 9$ **b.** $4x^2 + 4x + 1$

   c. $x^2 - 4x + \frac{(x-3)^2}{4}$ **d.** $x^2 - 9x \stackrel{(2x+1)^2}{-} 9$

   $(x - 2)^2$ Not a trinomial square

10. Rewrite, without fractions.

   a. $\frac{3}{8} = \frac{x}{7}$ $8x = 21$ **b.** $\frac{2}{5} = \frac{x}{6}$ $5x = 12$

11. Solve for the positive value of **n**.

   a. $\frac{3}{n^2} = \frac{1}{4}$ $2\sqrt{3}$ **b.** $\frac{2}{n^2} = \frac{1}{9}$ $3\sqrt{2}$

Chapter Thirteen

1. To rationalize the denominator:

   a. Multiply $\frac{1}{\sqrt{5}}$ by $\underline{\ ?\ } \cdot \frac{\sqrt{5}}{\sqrt{5}}$

   b. Multiply $\frac{\sqrt{3}}{\sqrt{7}}$ by $\underline{\ ?\ } \cdot \frac{\sqrt{7}}{\sqrt{7}}$

2. Give the simplest form of the reciprocal.

   a. $\frac{\sqrt{3}}{3}$ $\sqrt{3}$ **b.** $\frac{\sqrt{5}}{10}$ $2\sqrt{5}$

3. Simplify: **a.** $\frac{5}{\sqrt{5}}$ $\sqrt{5}$ **b.** $\frac{4}{\sqrt{8}}$ $\sqrt{2}$

4. Use $<$, $>$, or $=$ to make the sentence true.

   a. $6\sqrt{5} \ \underline{\ ?\ }\ 12$ $>$ **b.** $\sqrt{8} \ \underline{\ ?\ }\ 3$ $<$

   c. $\frac{1}{\sqrt{3}} \ \underline{\ ?\ }\ \frac{\sqrt{3}}{3}$ $=$ **d.** $\frac{1}{3\sqrt{2}} \ \underline{\ ?\ }\ \frac{\sqrt{2}}{6}$ $=$

   e. $9 \ \underline{\ ?\ }\ \sqrt{3}$ $>$

5. Use $=$ or $\neq$ to make the sentence true.

   a. $3^2 + 4^2 \ \underline{\ ?\ }\ 5^2$ $=$

   b. $2^2 + 3^2 \ \underline{\ ?\ }\ 5^2$ $\neq$

   c. $5^2 + 12^2 \ \underline{\ ?\ }\ 13^2$ $=$

   d. $(\sqrt{5})^2 + (2\sqrt{5})^2 \ \underline{\ ?\ }\ 5^2$ $=$

6. Give positive values for **c**.

   a. If $4^2 + (2\sqrt{5})^2 = c^2$, then $c = \underline{\ ?\ }$. 6

   b. If $5^2 + (2\sqrt{6})^2, = c^2$, then $c = \underline{\ ?\ }$. 7

   c. If $3^2 + (3\sqrt{5})^2 = c^2$, then $c = \underline{\ ?\ }$. $3\sqrt{6}$

7. Solve for **x**.

   a.   **b.**

     $8\sqrt{2}$ $3\sqrt{2}$

8. Express **x** in terms of **t** and **y**.

   a. $t = \frac{y}{x}$ $x = \frac{y}{t}$ **b.** $\frac{t}{x} = y$ $x = \frac{t}{y}$

9. Add or subtract, and simplify.

   a. $\left(\frac{x}{r}\right)^2 + \left(\frac{y}{r}\right)^2$ 1

   b. $\left(\frac{r}{x}\right)^2 - \left(\frac{y}{x}\right)^2$ 1

EXTRA PRACTICE SETS

EXTRA PRACTICE SETS

PREREQUISITE SKILLS FOLLOW-UP

COMPUTER HANDBOOK

TABLES

GLOSSARY

ANSWERS TO CHECKPOINTS

ANSWERS TO SELECTED EXERCISES

INDEX

CHAPTER 1

1-1 *Simplify.*

1. $3 + 9 - 6$ 6	**2.** $5 - 2 + 8$ 11	**3.** $4 \times 3 - 7$ 5
4. $12 - 3 \times 4$ 0	**5.** $10 \div 2 + 9$ 14	**6.** $8 - 4 \div 2$ 6
7. $5 \times 4 \div 5$ 4	**8.** $5 + (7 - 4)$ 8	**9.** $8 \times (15 - 7)$ 64
10. $(4 + 10) \div 2$ 7	**11.** $5 \times (3 + 2) \div 5$ 5	**12.** $11 - (4 - 2) \div 2$ 10

13. $\dfrac{45 \div (10 - 7)}{5} \div 3$ 1   **14.** $18.5 + \dfrac{(0.5 - 0.2)}{0.3}$ 19.5   **15.** $\dfrac{12 - 4 \times 2}{1 + 6 \div 2} + 5$ 6

16. $48 - [(15 - 10) \times 5]$ 23   **17.** $[18 - (6 + 1)] \times 3$ 33   **18.** $6 \times [16 - (3 + 7)]$ 36

1-2 *Evaluate each expression for the given value of the variable.*

19. $12 - (3 + n)$ 5 if $n = 4$	**20.** $4(a + 2)$ 44 if $a = 9$	**21.** $d(d + 8)$ 65 if $d = 5$
22. $7(28 - 3p)$ 49 if $p = 7$	**23.** $16 \div (m + 2)$ 2 if $m = 6$	**24.** $9(5 - x) - 7$ 11 if $x = 3$
25. $\dfrac{3b - 2}{4}$ 4 if $b = 6$	**26.** $\dfrac{8z + 14}{z}$ 10 if $z = 7$	**27.** $\dfrac{2s + 7}{s + 1}$ 3 if $s = 4$

Evaluate. Let $a = 6$, *and* $b = 4$.

28. $5a - b$ 26	**29.** $2ab$ 48	**30.** $b(a - 3)$ 12
31. $a(b + 9)$ 78	**32.** $4(2a + 8b)$ 176	**33.** $15a - 3b$ 78
34. $(4a)(ba)$ 576	**35.** $3 + 6ab$ 147	**36.** $\dfrac{8 + b}{a}$ 2
37. $\dfrac{a(a + b)}{3b}$ 5	**38.** $\dfrac{ab + 16}{a + b}$ 4	**39.** $\dfrac{ab}{2a - (b + 4)}$ 6

Evaluate. Let $x = 2$, $y = 4$, *and* $z = 10$.

40. xyz 80	**41.** $x(z - y)$ 12	**42.** $2x + 3y - z$ 6
43. $z(x + y)$ 60	**44.** $x(4y - z)$ 12	**45.** $5xy + z$ 50
46. $xy(z + 4)$ 112	**47.** $y(x + z - 7)$ 20	**48.** $\dfrac{x + y + z}{8}$ 2
49. $\dfrac{yz}{x}$ 20	**50.** $\dfrac{x + 3y}{z - 3}$ 2	**51.** $\dfrac{y(42 - x)}{z}$ 16

EXTRA PRACTICE   **507**

1-3   *Evaluate each algebraic expression if x = 4.*

52. x^2 16   **53.** x^4 256   **54.** $3x^2$ 48   **55.** $(5x)^2$ 400

56. $\dfrac{3x^3}{2x^2}$ 6   **57.** $\dfrac{x^2}{2}$ 8   **58.** $\dfrac{x^3 - 18}{x^2}$ 1   **59.** $\dfrac{x(x^2 - 9)}{x + 3}$ 4

Evaluate each algebraic expression if a = 2 and b = 3.

60. $a^2 + b^3$ 31   **61.** ab^2 18   **62.** $(b - a)^2$ 1   **63.** a^2b^2 36

64. $5b^2$ 45   **65.** $4(ab)^2$ 144   **66.** $5a^2b$ 60   **67.** $(3b)^3$ 729

1-5   *Is the number in parentheses a solution of the equation? Write **yes** or **no**.*

68. $2(n + 4) = 14$; (3)   Yes   **69.** $98 + 3c = 113$; (4)   No

70. $50 - (5 + x) = 38$; (7) Yes   **71.** $5(n - 4) = 40$; (12) Yes

72. $\dfrac{a + 2}{2} - 5 = 7$; (4)   No   **73.** $\dfrac{2(3x + 5)}{17} = 2$; (4)   Yes

74. $\dfrac{x + 3}{2x - 6} = 2$; (5)   Yes   **75.** $\dfrac{n + 12}{n} = 12$; (12)   No

1-9   *Use > or < to complete each sentence.*

76. $8 \underline{\ ?\ } -2$ >   **77.** $-15 \underline{\ ?\ } -8$ <   **78.** $5 \underline{\ ?\ } -9$ >

79. $\dfrac{1}{2} \underline{\ ?\ } \dfrac{1}{8}$ >   **80.** $-1.2 \underline{\ ?\ } -1.0$ <   **81.** $\dfrac{3}{5} \underline{\ ?\ } -\dfrac{4}{5}$ >

82. $4\dfrac{1}{4} \underline{\ ?\ } 3\dfrac{3}{4}$ >   **83.** $1\dfrac{1}{2} \underline{\ ?\ } 1.2$ >   **84.** $-12 \underline{\ ?\ } 1$ <

1-6   *Using **n** as the variable, write an equation for each problem. Then solve it.*

85. A number is 15 less than 12 increased by 42. What is the number?
$n = (12 + 42) - 15$; 39

86. Some number less the sum of 38 and 12 is 26. What is the number?
$n - (38 + 12) = 26$; 76

87. Some number less the difference between 39 and 15 is 24. What is the number? $n - (39 - 15) = 24$; 48

88. Laura's earnings decreased by $26 to $65 a week. What was she earning before the decrease? $n - \$26 = \$65$; $91

89. Monique bought 6 of the same item for $11.10. What was the price per item?
$\$11.10 \div 6 = n$; $1.85

90. A certain amount divided by 10 is $12.00. What is the amount? $n \div 10 = \$12$; $120

91. Eleven years ago, Cliff was 15. How old is he now? $n - 11 = 15$; 26

92. Ted is 36, or 3 times Gwen's age. How old is Gwen? $36 = 3n$; 12

93. June is $\frac{1}{3}$ as old as her grandfather, who is 75. How old is June? $n = \frac{1}{3}(75)$; 25

94. Three weeks ago today it was September 10. What is the date today?
$n - 21 = 10$; October 1

EXTRA PRACTICE

2-2 *Find the sum.*

1. $13 + (-5)$ 8   **2.** $-35 + 12$ -23 **3.** $6 + (-8)$ -2

4. $-100 + (-18)$ -118 **5.** $79 + (-40)$ 39   **6.** $-14 + (-33)$ -47

7. $-2 + 3 + (-14)$ -13 **8.** $9 + (-5) + (-36)$ -32

9. $(-50) + (-20) + 17$ -53 **10.** $30 + (-29) + 54$ 55

11. $-7 + 8 + 21$ 22   **12.** $-49 + 2 + (-86)$ -133

13. $-4 + (-5) + 16$ 7   **14.** $28 + (-7) + (-40)$ -19

Find the solution.

15. $x + (-3) = 7$ 10   **16.** $x + 8 = -6$ -14 **17.** $x + (-5) = -15$ -10

18. $-8 + x = 0$ 8   **19.** $-x + 9 = 2$ 7   **20.** $-12 + x = -4$ 8

21. $4 + x = 28$ 24   **22.** $-x + (-3) = -123$ 120   **23.** $-9 + x = 10$ 19

2-3 *Simplify.*

24. $8 - 5$ 3   **25.** $2 - 7$ -5 **26.** $0 - 9$ -9 **27.** $4 - 4$ 0

28. $-3 - 5$ -8 **29.** $9 - 5$ 4   **30.** $3 - 6$ -3 **31.** $6 - (-9)$ 15

32. $-8 - 7$ -15 **33.** $-2 - (-5)$ 3   **34.** $-2 - (-3)$ 1   **35.** $0 - (-4)$ 4

36. $12 - 8 - 3 + 5$ 6   **37.** $-6 - 5 - (-8) + 12$ 9

38. $11 + 8 + 9 - 2 - (-3)$ 29   **39.** $30 - (-10) + 6 - 8 + 12$ 50

40. $-(-12) + 3 - [6 - (-11 - 3)]$ -5 **41.** $15 + 7 - 6 + 5 - (-8)$ 29

Evaluate for $x = 2$, $y = -4$, and $z = 3$.

42. $x + (-y) + z$ 9   **43.** $x + y + z$ 1   **44.** $x - (-y) - z$ -5

45. $x + y - z$ -5 **46.** $x - y - z$ 3   **47.** $-x - y + z$ 5

48. $-x + y - z$ -9 **49.** $x - y + z$ 9   **50.** $-x - (-y) + z$ -3

2-4 *Use the distributive property to rewrite each expression.*

51. $8(m + n)$ $8m + 8n$ **52.** $6(a - b)$ $6a - 6b$ **53.** $0.5(x - 2)$ $0.5x - 1.0$

54. $3.5(s - t)$ $3.5s - 3.5t$ **55.** $7(x - 3)$ $7x - 21$ **56.** $9(5 + x)$ $45 + 9x$

57. $7(c + d - 5)$ $7c + 7d - 35$ **58.** $9(s - 5)$ $9s - 45$ **59.** $4.2(a + b + 3)$ $4.2a + 4.2b + 12.6$

60. $\frac{1}{2}\left(\frac{3}{4} - c\right)$ $\frac{3}{8} - \frac{1}{2}c$ **61.** $\frac{2}{3}\left(9 + p\right)$ $6 + \frac{2}{3}p$ **62.** $3\left(\frac{1}{2} - y\right)$ $1\frac{1}{2} - 3y$

EXTRA PRACTICE

PREREQUISITE SKILLS FOLLOW-UP

EXTRA PRACTICE SETS

COMPUTER HANDBOOK

TABLES

GLOSSARY

ANSWERS TO CHECKPOINTS

ANSWERS TO SELECTED EXERCISES

INDEX

EXTRA PRACTICE SETS

2-5 *Simplify.*

63. $3b + 4b$ $7b$ **64.** $-6x - x$ $-7x$ **65.** $-8c + c$ $-7c$ **66.** $-3d - 5d$ $-8d$

67. $8u + (-u)$ $7u$ **68.** $9n^2 + n^2$ $10n^2$ **69.** $5st - 11st$ $-6st$ **70.** $-m - 2m$ $-3m$

71. $10t - 5t - 11t$ $-26t$ **72.** $-3x - (-4x) + 1 - 8n$ $x + 1 - 8n$

73. $d + (-3d) - (-5d)$ $3d$ **74.** $s^2 + 3t - (-3s^2) - 4t$ $4s^2 - t$

75. $c + \dfrac{c}{5} - \dfrac{c}{10}$ $1\frac{1}{10}c$ **76.** $-3ab - a + b - ab$ $-4ab - a + b$

2-6 *Evaluate when* $x = -3$ *and* $y = 7$.

77. $6x$ -18 **78.** $-2x + 5$ 11 **79.** $7x - 8y$ -77 **80.** x^2 9

81. $y^2 + 4$ 53 **82.** xy^2 -147 **83.** $3y - 2x$ 27 **84.** $10 - 3x$ 19

85. x^2y 63 **86.** $xy - 11$ -32 **87.** $(xy)^2$ 441 **88.** $7x - (2y)^2$ -217

2-7 *Simplify.*

89. $-(-b)$ b **90.** $-(-d + 2)$ $d - 2$ **91.** $-(x - y)$ $-x + y$

92. $-(-3 + f)$ $3 - f$ **93.** $-(xy + z)$ $-xy - z$ **94.** $-n - n + 2m - 5n$ $2m - 7n$

95. $5 - (x - 1)$ $6 - x$ **96.** $-[a - (-c)]$ $-a - c$ **97.** $-[-3 - (-b)]$ $3 - b$

2-8 *Evaluate when* $x = -3$ *and* $y = 6$.

98. $\dfrac{x}{6}$ $-\frac{1}{2}$ **99.** $\dfrac{y}{x}$ -2 **100.** $\dfrac{y}{-x}$ 2 **101.** $\dfrac{3y}{2x}$ -3

102. $\dfrac{x + y}{3y}$ $\frac{1}{6}$ **103.** $\dfrac{5x + 3}{-2y}$ 1 **104.** $\dfrac{xy^2}{x^3}$ 4 **105.** $\dfrac{(2x)^2}{6y}$ 1

Evaluate when $a = \frac{1}{2}$, $b = -2$, *and* $c = \frac{1}{3}$.

106. $\dfrac{-12c}{-4}$ 1 **107.** $\dfrac{ab}{b}$ $\frac{1}{2}$ **108.** $\dfrac{-54c}{9}$ -2 **109.** $\dfrac{20a}{-4}$ $-\frac{5}{2}$

110. $\dfrac{4a^2b^3}{2ab}$ 4 **111.** $\dfrac{18ac}{-9c}$ -1 **112.** $\dfrac{a^2b^2}{ab}$ -1 **113.** $\dfrac{abc}{ac}$ -2

2-9 *Solve each problem.*

114. From a reading of $-18°C$, the temperature rose $6°$ and then dropped $20°$. What was the final temperature? $-32°C$

115. The temperature was $4°C$ at 10 P.M. It dropped $3°$ in each of the next three hours. How much below $0°$ was the temperature at midnight? At 1 A.M.? $2°$; $5°$

116. Starting from the dock, Denise rowed 825 yards upstream, then 915 yards downstream. At that point, how far was Denise from the dock? In which direction, upstream or downstream?   90 yards; downstream

EXTRA PRACTICE

117. On Tuesday the stock market average stood at 1,150. On Wednesday it dropped 7 points. On Thursday it rose 12 points. What was the average on Thursday? 1,155

118. The football is on your team's 45-yard line. On the next play you gain 3 yards. Where is the ball now? Your team's 48-yard line

119. Find the profit on a loaf of bread that costs 55¢ to make but sells for 98¢. 43¢

120. Product A costs $3.20 per kilogram. Product B costs twice as much, and Product C costs $\frac{1}{2}$ as much. Find the cost of each.
Product B, $6.40; product C, $1.60

121. Anthony has $451.86 in his account. On Monday he makes a withdrawal of $78.00. On Thursday he deposits $125.00. How much is in his account on Thursday? $498.86

122. Degrees Fahrenheit is 32° more than $\frac{9}{5}$ times degrees Celsius. Express 15°C in degrees Fahrenheit. 59°F

123. The range r is the highest value h minus the lowest value l. Find the range if the highest value is 26.9 and the lowest is −15.8. 42.7

CHAPTER 3

3-3 *Solve each equation and check.*

1. $x + 5 = 14$ 9   **2.** $n - 3 = 12$ 15   **3.** $8 + c = -6$ −14

4. $y - 10 = -1$ 9   **5.** $a - (-5) = 0$ −5   **6.** $-6 + b = -5$ 1

7. $x + (-4) = 9$ 13   **8.** $5 = c - 11$ 16   **9.** $0 = f - 7$ 7

10. $x + 0.5 = -4$ −4.5   **11.** $-2 + s = 18$ 20   **12.** $-21 = c - 8$ −13

13. $9 = n - (-5)$ 4   **14.** $-6 = t + (-5)$ −1   **15.** $b - (-2) = 12$ 10

16. $5.4 = -35.0 + c$ 40.4   **17.** $-2.5 = f - 1.0$ −1.5   **18.** $6.4 = x + 2$ 4.4

19. $-3.7 = y + 6.1$ −9.8   **20.** $m - 2.3 = -4.0$ −1.7   **21.** $-18.5 = 3.2 + c$ −21.7

22. $-\frac{4}{5} = n - \left(-\frac{1}{5}\right)$ −1   **23.** $n - \frac{1}{4} = \frac{1}{2}$ $\frac{3}{4}$ **24.** $\frac{4}{5} + n = -\frac{1}{3}$ $-1\frac{2}{15}$

25. $-\frac{1}{4} = x - \frac{1}{2}$ $\frac{1}{4}$ **26.** $-2\frac{1}{3} + x = 4\frac{2}{3}$ 7   **27.** $d + \frac{3}{4} = \frac{1}{2}$ $-\frac{1}{4}$

3-5 *Solve and check.*

28. $5y = 35$ 7   **29.** $\frac{x}{6} = 2$ 12   **30.** $\frac{b}{7} = -3$ −21

31. $-91 = -7n$ 13   **32.** $5d = 125$ 25   **33.** $-10w = 100$ −10

PREREQUISITE SKILLS FOLLOW-UP

EXTRA PRACTICE SETS

COMPUTER HANDBOOK

TABLES

GLOSSARY

ANSWERS TO CHECKPOINTS

ANSWERS TO SELECTED EXERCISES

INDEX

EXTRA PRACTICE SETS

34. $8b = -64$ -8 **35.** $-6n = -72$ 12 **36.** $28 = -4b$ -7

37. $\dfrac{c}{-2} = 4$ -8 **38.** $-5 = \dfrac{a}{8}$ -40 **39.** $\dfrac{s}{4} = -123$ -492

40. $\dfrac{x}{3} - \dfrac{1}{2}$ $1\frac{1}{2}$ **41.** $-\dfrac{1}{3} = \dfrac{n}{2}$ $-\frac{2}{3}$ **42.** $\dfrac{b}{8} = -2.1$ -16.8

43. $-1.7x = 6.8$ -4 **44.** $-16.8 = -5.6n$ 3 **45.** $8.4c = -42$ -5

46. $28 = \dfrac{b}{4.9}$ 137.2 **47.** $\dfrac{d}{-4.5} = 0.6$ -2.7 **48.** $-2.1 = \dfrac{x}{1.2}$ -2.52

49. $-8n = 96$ -12 **50.** $-55 = -1.1n$ 50 **51.** $-20b = -74$ 3.7

52. $\dfrac{x}{-5} = \dfrac{4}{5}$ -4 **53.** $\dfrac{c}{3} = 19$ 57 **54.** $-\dfrac{1}{4} = \dfrac{x}{12}$ -3

3-6   **55.** $4x + 1 = 29$ 7 **56.** $6a - 3 = 33$ 6 **57.** $5n + 2 = -33$ -7

58. $3t - 1 = -16$ -5 **59.** $42 = 6b - 6$ 8 **60.** $18 = 3x - 15$ 11

61. $12 = 2x + 4$ 4 **62.** $7y + 8 = 50$ 6 **63.** $-19 = 4c + 29$ -12

64. $\dfrac{1}{2}x + 3 = 9$ 12 **65.** $2x + \dfrac{2}{3} = 2\dfrac{2}{3}$ 1 **66.** $\dfrac{1}{4}x - 4 = 5$ 36

67. $-3s + 1 = 10$ -3 **68.** $-4x - 2 = 14$ -4 **69.** $2.5b + 3 = -13$ -6.4

70. $0.4 - 1.2x = 4.0$ -3 **71.** $3t - 1 = -10$ -3 **72.** $12 = 5p - 3$ 3

73. $-5 = 4 + 3x$ -3 **74.** $45 = -9 + 9c$ 6 **75.** $-x + 5 = 10$ -5

76. $\dfrac{x}{2} - 1 = 4$ 10 **77.** $-y + 6 = \dfrac{1}{3}$ $5\frac{2}{3}$ **78.** $\dfrac{3}{5}a + 6 = 18$ 20

79. $253 = 3.5x + 1$ 72 **80.** $0.5 - 1.5d = 3.5$ -2 **81.** $-33.2 = -18.2 + 5b$ -3

3-7   **82.** $2(x + 9) = 24$ 3 **83.** $6(c - 3) = 54$ 12 **84.** $-7(-a - 10) = 28$ -6

85. $\dfrac{4b}{5} = 8$ 10 **86.** $\dfrac{6x}{9} = -2$ -3 **87.** $\dfrac{12a}{-6} = 4$ -2

88. $3x + 2 = 4x$ 2 **89.** $-3d - 15 = 2d$ -3 **90.** $12p = 32 - 4p$ 2

91. $\dfrac{1}{2}x + 1 = x - 5$ 12 **92.** $y + 2 = \dfrac{1}{3}y - 4$ -9 **93.** $-\left(x + \dfrac{3}{4}\right) = 4\dfrac{1}{4}$ -5

94. $6\left(c - \dfrac{2}{3}\right) = -34$ -5 **95.** $8\left(b + \dfrac{1}{8}\right) = 33$ 4 **96.** $3(a - 4) = -8$ $1\frac{1}{3}$

97. $a + (a - 2) = 10$ 6 **98.** $4 - (3x + 6) = -11$ 3

99. $5 + 8(c - 3) = 77$ 12 **100.** $5p - (3 + p) = -31$ -7

101. $2(n - 7) = 42 - 2n$ 14 **102.** $3c + 27 = 7c - 1$ 7

103. $4(t + 2) = 2(t - 4)$ -8 **104.** $6x - 5 = 5(x + 1)$ 10

3-8 *Write an equation to solve each problem. Check the answer.*

105. Kate's age is 25 years less than three times Joanie's age. If Joanie is 14, how old is Kate?   17

106. Todd is 9 years older than Jeri. Their ages add to 33. How old is each one?   12; 21

107. A stack of nickels and dimes has a total value of $3.00. Find the number of each if there are three times as many nickels as dimes.
36 nickels; 12 dimes

108. Some nickels, dimes, and quarters have a total value of $3.90. There are four times as many nickels as quarters, and two times as many nickels as dimes. Find the number of each type of coin.   24 nickels; 12 dimes; 6 quarters

109. A rectangle is 15 meters longer than it is wide. Find its length and width if the perimeter is 102 meters.   Length is 33 m; width is 18 m.

110. The perimeter of a rectangle is 18 centimeters. If the length is 11 centimeters less than four times the width, find the length and width.
Length is 5 cm; width is 4 cm.

111. Two consecutive odd integers add to 204. Find the integers.   101, 103

112. Find three consecutive integers if the sum of the second two larger integers is equal to three times the first integer.   3, 4, 5

113. John is 12 years older than Barry. In 6 years John will be twice as old as Barry will be then. How old is each one now?   John is 18. Barry is 6.

114. If the sum of four consecutive even integers is decreased by 30, the result is equal to the fourth integer. Find the four integers.   8, 10, 12, 14

CHAPTER 4

4-3 *Graph each equation. First plot and label at least three points on the graph.*

1. $y = x + 6$ 2. $y = 3x$ 3. $y = x - 2$ 4. $y = -3x$

5. $y = 4x + 5$ 6. $y = -2x - 2$ 7. $y = -3x + 1$

*Is the given ordered pair a solution of the equation? Write **yes** or **no**.*

8. $y = \frac{1}{2}x$ (6, 3)   Yes   9. $y = \frac{1}{4}x - 2$ (−4, 3)   No

10. $2x + 3y = 15$ (0, 5)   Yes   11. $3x - y = 8$ (4, 6)   No

12. $y = \frac{1}{3}x + \frac{2}{3}$ (4, 2)   Yes   13. $4x + 6y = 3$ $\left(\frac{1}{2}, \frac{1}{6}\right)$ Yes

14. $5x - y = 8$ (3, 7)   Yes   15. $3x + y = 9$ (3, 1)   No

16. $x - 4y = 16$ (0, −4)   Yes   17. $2x - y = 10$ (−5, 5)   No

18. $4x + 3y = 29$ (5, −3)   No   19. $x - y = 8$ (4, −4)   Yes

EXTRA PRACTICE

PREREQUISITE SKILLS FOLLOW-UP

EXTRA PRACTICE SETS

COMPUTER HANDBOOK

TABLES

GLOSSARY

ANSWERS TO CHECKPOINTS

ANSWERS TO SELECTED EXERCISES

INDEX

EXTRA PRACTICE SETS

ADDITIONAL ANSWERS

Chapter 4 Extra Practice

1.

2.

3.

4.

5.

6.

[Answers continue on page 514.]

ADDITIONAL ANSWERS
(continued)

7.

55. $y = 2x - 4$
slope: 2   y-int.: −4

56. $y = -\frac{1}{3}x + 5$
slope: $-\frac{1}{3}$ y-int.: 5

57. $y = x$
slope: 1   y-int.: 0

58. $y = 3x - 5$
slope: 3   y-int.: −5

59. $y = \frac{1}{4}x + \frac{1}{4}$
slope: $\frac{1}{4}$ y-int.: $\frac{1}{4}$

60. $y = \frac{3}{5}x - 6$
slope: $\frac{3}{5}$ y-int.: −6

61. $y = -\frac{2}{3}x - \frac{1}{3}$
slope: $-\frac{2}{3}$ y-int.: $-\frac{1}{3}$

62. $y = x + 8$
slope: 1   y-int.: 8

63. $y = \frac{1}{6}x + 2$
slope: $\frac{1}{6}$ y-int.: 2

64. $y = \frac{1}{7}x - 3$
slope: $\frac{1}{7}$ y-int.: −3

65. $y = -3x + 9$
slope: −3   y-int.: 9

66. $y = x + \frac{1}{2}$
slope: 1   y-int.: $\frac{1}{2}$

[*Answers continue on page 515.*]

4-4   *Find the slope of the line through the two given points.*

20. (3, 6), (2, 5)   1   **21.** (−3, 0), (7, 5) $\frac{1}{2}$ **22.** (3, −3), (6, 12)   5

23. (−3, −2), (−8, 8)   −2   **24.** (−4, 1), (0, 4) $\frac{3}{4}$ **25.** (4, 7), (−2, 7)   0

26. (5, 9), (0, 5) $\frac{4}{5}$ **27.** (1, 1), (3, 7)   3   **28.** (1, 8), (5, −8)   −4

29. (0, 1), (8, 1)   0   **30.** (−9, 3), (0, 0) $-\frac{1}{3}$ **31.** (4, 5), (0, −7)   3

32. (0, 0), $\left(\frac{1}{3}, -\frac{1}{4}\right)$ $-\frac{3}{4}$ **33.** $\left(\frac{1}{8}, \frac{1}{4}\right), \left(\frac{5}{8}, \frac{3}{4}\right)$ 1   **34.** (4, 4), (10, 8) $\frac{2}{3}$

4-5   *Find the x-intercept and the y-intercept for each equation.*

35. $y = 2x + 3$ **36.** $x + y = 10$ **37.** $y = -3x$ 0; 0 **38.** $4x = 6y$ 0; 0
$-1\frac{1}{2}$; 3   10; 10

39. $y = \frac{1}{2}x - 7$ 7; −7 **40.** $y = -5x$ 0; 0 **41.** $2.5x = 4y$ 0; 0 **42.** $3x + 2y = 18$ 6; 9

43. $y = 6x$ 0; 0 **44.** $y = x + 3$ −3; 3 **45.** $y = -x + 1$ 1; 1 **46.** $x + y = -8$ −8; −8

47. $x - 2y = -\frac{1}{4}$ **48.** $y - 3 = \frac{2}{3}x$ **49.** $y - x = \frac{3}{4}$ $-\frac{3}{4}$; $\frac{3}{4}$ **50.** $y - \frac{1}{2}x = 9$ −18; 9
$-\frac{1}{4}$; $\frac{1}{8}$ $-4\frac{1}{2}$; 3

51. $x - y - 6 = 1$ **52.** $4x - 2y = 8$ **53.** $2x - y = -3$ **54.** $4x + 1.5y = 12$ 3; 8
7; −7   2; −4 $-1\frac{1}{2}$; 3

4-6   *Rewrite in slope-intercept form. Then find the slope and the y-intercept.*

55. $2x - y = 4$ **56.** $3y + x = 15$ **57.** $x - y = 0$

58. $y - 3x = -5$ **59.** $4y - x = 1$ **60.** $3x - 5y = 30$

61. $4x + 6y = -2$ **62.** $x - y = -8$ **63.** $6y - x = 12$

64. $x - 7y = 21$ **65.** $y + 3x = 9$ **66.** $2x - 2y = -1$

67. $5y - 10x = 6$ **68.** $2x - y = -7$ **69.** $5y + 4x = 20$

Use the slope and the y-intercept to graph each equation.

70. $y = 2x + 4$ **71.** $y = x - 6$ **72.** $y = -3x$ **73.** $y = 5x - 2$

74. $y = \frac{1}{2}x$ **75.** $y = \frac{1}{3}x + \frac{1}{2}$ **76.** $y = 2x - \frac{1}{4}$ **77.** $y = -\frac{1}{2}x + 5$

4-7   *The slope and one point on a line are given. Find the y-intercept. Then write an equation for the line.*

78. m = 3; (1, 3)   **79.** m = 2; (−3, 0)   **80.** m = 4; (0, 4)

81. m = −6; (5, 0)   **82.** m = 0; (2, −2)   **83.** m = −2; (−1, 5)

84. m = −3; (−1, 2)   **85.** m = −1; (3, 4)   **86.** m = 6; (0, 3)

87. $m = \frac{1}{2}$; (4, 4)   **88.** $m = \frac{4}{3}$; (6, −3)   **89.** $m = \frac{1}{4}$; (−5, 1)

4-8 Write the equation, in slope-intercept form, of the line passing through the given pair of points.

90. $(4, 1)$, $(0, 5)$ **91.** $(2, -1)$, $(6, 7)$ **92.** $(4, 3)$, $(7, 4)$

93. $(0, 0)$, $(-3, -2)$ **94.** $(4, 1)$, $(5, -4)$ **95.** $(3, -4)$, $(-2, 6)$

96. $(3, -6)$, $(-5, 2)$ **97.** $(2, 4)$, $(3, 6)$ **98.** $(-1, 0)$, $(0, 3)$

99. $(3, 1)$, $(5, 2)$ **100.** $(0, 0)$, $(-1, 2)$ **101.** $(5, 0)$, $(0, 1)$

Write each equation in standard form.

102. $y = 3x + 5$ **103.** $y = -x - 5$ **104.** $y = \frac{3}{2}x - 6$

105. $y = -x + 4$ **106.** $y = 2x - 3$ **107.** $y = 4x + 2$

108. $y = \frac{1}{2}x + 6$ **109.** $y = \frac{4}{3}x + 4$ **110.** $y = -\frac{1}{4}x - 8$

CHAPTER 5

5-1 Simplify each polynomial. Then give the degree.

1. $3x + 5 - x + 10$ $2x + 15; 1$ **2.** $12a + 2a^2 + a^2 - 3a$ $3a^2 + 9a; 2$

3. $6 - 7c + 3c^2 + 6c$ $3c^2 - c + 6; 2$ **4.** $y + y^4 - y^2 - y^4 + 3y^2$ $2y^2 + y; 2$

5. $x^2 - 5x + 2x^2 + 3x - 10$
   $3x^2 - 2x - 10; 2$
6. $t^3 + 4t^2 - 2t^3 + 3t^3 + 6$
   $4t^3 + 2t^2 + 6; 3$
7. $2s^2 + s^3 + s^2 - s^3 + 3s^2$ $6s^2; 2$
8. $4.3h + 3.4h^2 - 1.5h + h^2$
   $4.4h^2 + 2.8h; 2$
9. $2x^3 + 2x - 3x + x^4 - x^3 - 4x^4$
   $-3x^4 + x^3 - x; 4$
10. $3p - 2p^2 + 4p - 5p^2 + p^2 + 6p$
   $-6p^2 + 13p; 2$

5-2 Add.

11. $\begin{array}{r} 2x^2 + 6 \\ 5x^2 - 5 \\ \hline 7x^2 + 1 \end{array}$ **12.** $\begin{array}{r} -4b + 3 \\ 5b - 11 \\ \hline b - 8 \end{array}$ **13.** $\begin{array}{r} 2b^2 + 4b - 2 \\ b^2 - 3b + 8 \\ \hline 3b^2 + b + 6 \end{array}$

14. $\begin{array}{r} 3s^2 + 6s - 7 \\ -2s^2 \quad\quad + 9 \\ \hline s^2 + 6s + 2 \end{array}$ **15.** $\begin{array}{r} 5.4x + 3y + 0.5 \\ -1.7x - 2y + 1.6 \\ \hline 3.7x + y + 2.1 \end{array}$ **16.** $\begin{array}{r} 3a + 5b - 7c \\ 4a - 8b + 3c \\ \hline 7a - 3b - 4c \end{array}$

Subtract.

17. $\begin{array}{r} 4p^2 - 8 \\ 2p^2 - 5 \\ \hline 2p^2 - 3 \end{array}$ **18.** $\begin{array}{r} -3x^2 + 7 \\ - x^2 + 5 \\ \hline -2x^2 + 2 \end{array}$ **19.** $\begin{array}{r} 5n + 6c \\ -3n - 2c \\ \hline 8n + 8c \end{array}$

20. $\begin{array}{r} 0.1a - 3b + 6 \\ 3.5a + 2b - 10 \\ \hline -3.4a - 5b + 16 \end{array}$ **21.** $\begin{array}{r} - n^2 \quad\quad + 6 \\ 4n^2 + 3n - 10 \\ \hline -5n^2 - 3n + 16 \end{array}$ **22.** $\begin{array}{r} a \quad\quad + 8c \\ -4a + 5b \\ \hline 5a - 5b + 8c \end{array}$

EXTRA PRACTICE

515

PREREQUISITE SKILLS FOLLOW-UP

EXTRA PRACTICE SETS

COMPUTER HANDBOOK

TABLES

GLOSSARY

ANSWERS TO CHECKPOINTS

ANSWERS TO SELECTED EXERCISES

INDEX

EXTRA PRACTICE SETS

ADDITIONAL ANSWERS (continued)

67. $y = 2x + \frac{6}{5}$

   slope: 2 y-int.: $\frac{6}{5}$

68. $y = 2x + 7$
   slope: 2 y-int.: 7

69. $y = -\frac{4}{5}x + 4$

   slope: $-\frac{4}{5}$ y-int.: 4

70.

71.

72.

73.

[Answers continue on page A18.]

Simplify.

23. $(x^2 + 3) + (2x^2 - 1)$ $\quad 3x^2 + 2$

24. $(5c + 9) - (-3c + 4)$ $\quad 8c + 5$

25. $(9s + 1) - (3s - 5)$ $\quad 6s + 6$

26. $(-3n^2 + 2n + 3) - (n^2 + 1 - 3n)$
$-4n^2 + 5n + 2$

27. $(-p + 5) + (2p - 4)$ $\quad p + 1$

28. $(2u - b) - (5c + b) + (a + 3b)$
$3a + b - 5c$

29. $(3m + n) - (m - n) + (2m + n)$
$4m + 3n$

30. $(5c^2d - 4d) - (3c^2d + 3d)$ $\quad 2c^2d - 7d$

31. $(s^2 - 3 + s) + (2s^2 + 7s - 1)$
$3s^2 + 8s - 4$

32. $(6x^2 + 1) - (x - 2) + (x^2 + 2x)$
$7x^2 + x + 3$

5-3 *Simplify.*

33. $(a^2)(a^4)$ $\quad a^6$

34. $(-p^3)(-p)$ $\quad p^4$

35. $(2c^2)(3c^4)$ $\quad 6c^6$

36. $(-3b^2)(4b^2)$ $\quad -12b^4$

37. $(5a^2b)(3a^3b^2)$ $\quad 15a^5b^3$

38. $(7x^3)(5x^3)(4x^3)$ $\quad 140x^9$

39. $(5x^3b)(-6xb^2)(xb)$
$-30x^5b^4$

40. $(-yz^3)(5y^2z)(-z^4)$ $\quad 5y^3z^8$

41. $(-2ab)(-3b)(-5abc)$
$-30a^2b^3c$

42. $(-0.5c^3)(-0.6cd^2)$
$0.3c^4d^2$

43. $-1(x^3)(-x^6)$ $\quad x^9$

44. $h^4(2h^3)(-5h)$ $\quad -10h^8$

45. $(6.75)^3(6.75)^4$ $\quad (6.75)^7$

46. $(-b^3)(-5a^2bc^2)(-abc)$ $\quad -5a^3b^5c^3$

5-4 **47.** $(3x)^3$ $\quad 27x^3$

48. $(-5b)^2$ $\quad 25b^2$

49. $(-c^2)^2$ $\quad c^4$

50. $(x^3)^2$ $\quad x^6$

51. $(cd)^5$ $\quad c^5d^5$

52. $(6h)^3$ $\quad 216h^3$

53. $(-4ab)^2$ $\quad 16a^2b^2$

54. $(3a^2c)^3$ $\quad 27a^6c^3$

55. $3x(-4x)^3$ $\quad -192x^4$

56. $(5c)^2(2d^3)^4$ $\quad 400c^2d^{12}$

57. $a^2(ab)^4$ $\quad a^6b^4$

58. $2x(x^2y)^2(-xy)^3$ $\quad -2x^8y^5$

59. $-x(5xy)^2$ $\quad -25x^3y^2$

60. $(ab)^2(a^3b)^3(ab)^4$ $\quad a^{15}b^9$

5-5 *Multiply.*

61. $x(4x - 6)$ $\quad 4x^2 - 6x$

62. $2c(4c + 2)$ $\quad 8c^2 + 4c$

63. $(2b - 3)5b$ $\quad 10b^2 - 15b$

64. $-n(5n + 2)$ $\quad -5n^2 - 2n$

65. $-d(4d^2 + 1)$ $\quad -4d^3 - d$

66. $(x^2 - 5)3x$ $\quad 3x^3 - 15x$

67. $x(x^3 + 3x - 5)$ $\quad x^4 + 3x^2 - 5x$

68. $5(c^3 + cd + 5d^2)$ $\quad 5c^3 + 5cd + 25d^2$

69. $3xy(x^2 + y^2)$ $\quad 3x^3y + 3xy^3$

70. $(5p^2 - 3pq + 4p^3)(-5p)$
$-25p^3 + 15p^2q - 20p^4$

71. $5(d^3 - 5d + 18)$ $\quad 5d^3 - 25d + 90$

72. $-3x^2y(x + 2xy - 4x^2y^4)$
$-3x^3y - 6x^3y^2 + 12x^4y^5$

Simplify. Remember to combine like terms.

73. $3 + 4(5x + 8)$ $\quad 20x + 35$

74. $a(5a + 3) - a(4a - 7)$ $\quad a^2 + 10a$

75. $d(5c^2 + c^3) + cd(5c + c^2)$
$10c^2d + 2c^3d$

76. $-5b(3c + 2) + b(5c - 7)$ $\quad -10bc - 17b$

77. $mn(m - n) + mn(2m + 3n)$
$3m^2n + 2mn^2$

78. $7 - 6(3x + 11)$ $\quad -18x - 59$

79. $-5(a + 3) - a(a + 7)$
$-a^2 - 12a - 15$

80. $xy(x^2 + 4x - 2) + xy(x - 3)$
$x^3y + 5x^2y - 5xy$

5-6 *Multiply. Combine like terms when possible.*

81. $(x + 5)(x + 3)$

82. $(b + 2)(b - 4)$

83. $(5c + 1)(c - 6)$

84. $(d - 3)(d + 4)$

85. $(x + 4y)(x - 2y)$

86. $(b^2 + 3)(b - 6)$

87. $(x + 1)(x^2 + 3x - 5)$

88. $(c + 3)(c^2 - c - 4)$

89. $(x - y)(3x^2 - xy + y^3)$

90. $(c + 3d)(c^2 + 5cd - 8d^2)$

91. $(1.5a - 3)(2.0a + 7)$

92. $(2s + t)(s^2 + 5st - 4t^2)$

5-7 *Multiply by inspection.*

93. $(x + 3)(x + 4)$

94. $(a + 2)(a - 5)$

95. $(c - 5)(c - 3)$

96. $(2p + 1)(p - 3)$

97. $(y - 6)(y + 4)$

98. $(5x - 4)(2x + 3)$

99. $(2a - 1)(2a - 1)$

100. $(c - 4d)(c + 3d)$

101. $(x - y)(2x + y)$

102. $(m + 5n)(m + 5n)$

103. $(5s - t)(4s + 2t)$

104. $(p^2 - 3)(2p^2 + 4)$

105. $(x^2 + 2)(x^2 - 4)$

106. $(3u - v)(u + 3v)$

107. $(a^2 + b^2)(a^2 - b^2)$

108. $\left(\dfrac{1}{3}c + d\right)\left(\dfrac{1}{3}c - d\right)$

109. $\left(a + \dfrac{1}{4}\right)\left(a - \dfrac{1}{4}\right)$

110. $\left(\dfrac{1}{2}b + 2c\right)\left(\dfrac{1}{2}b + 2c\right)$

5-8 *Solve for **x** and check. If no solution exists, write **no solution**. If the equation is an identity, write **identity**.*

111. $4(10 - n) = 32$ 2

112. $5x + 2(x - 1) = 19$ 3

113. $2(c - 5) + c = 2c - 2$ 8

114. $8(x + 2) - 4 = 8x + 12$ Identity

115. $6(n - 4) = 4(n - 1)$ 10

116. $x^2 + x(2x + 4) = 4 + 3x^2 + 2x$ 2

117. $3(2x + 4) = 2(3x + 6) + 5$ No solution

118. $(3x + 2)^2 = (9x - 2)(x + 2)$ 2

119. $2(8x - 3.5) = 3(4x + 3)$ 4

120. $x(x + 7) = (x + 4)(x + 3)$ No solution

121. $2(n - 3) = 3(n - 6)$ 12

122. $15 - 3(x - 1) = -5x - 2(-9 - x)$ Identity

5-9 *Solve.*

123. The square of 7 less than a number is equal to 7 less than the square of the number. What is the number?   4

124. Find three consecutive even integers if the square of the second less the square of the first is 3 times the third.   8, 10, 12

125. Find five consecutive odd integers if the square of the fifth equals 40 more than the square of the third.   −1, 1, 3, 5, 7

126. A rectangle is 15 cm longer than it is wide. If the width is increased by 3 cm and the length is decreased by 5 cm, the area remains the same. What is the perimeter of the original rectangle?   90 cm

127. Marty made a print in art class that is 4 inches longer than it is wide. He framed it with a border that is 4 inches wide. If the area of the border is 224 square inches, what are the dimensions of the print?   8 in. by 12 in.

PREREQUISITE SKILLS FOLLOW-UP

EXTRA PRACTICE SETS

COMPUTER HANDBOOK

TABLES

GLOSSARY

ANSWERS TO CHECKPOINTS

ANSWERS TO SELECTED EXERCISES

INDEX

EXTRA PRACTICE SETS

ADDITIONAL ANSWERS

Chapter 5 Extra Practice

87. $x^3 + 4x^2 - 2x - 5$

88. $c^3 + 2c^2 - 7c - 12$

89. $3x^3 - 4x^2y + xy^2 + xy^3 - y^4$

90. $c^3 + 8c^2d + 7cd^2 - 24d^3$

91. $3.0a^2 + 4.5a - 21$

92. $2s^3 + 11s^2t - 3st^2 - 4t^3$

93. $x^2 + 7x + 12$

94. $a^2 - 3a - 10$

95. $c^2 - 8c + 15$

96. $2p^2 - 5p - 3$

97. $y^2 - 2y - 24$

98. $10x^2 + 7x - 12$

99. $4a^2 - 4a + 1$

100. $c^2 - cd - 12d^2$

101. $2x^2 - xy - y^2$

102. $m^2 + 10mn + 25n^2$

103. $20s^2 + 6st - 2t^2$

104. $2p^4 - 2p^2 - 12$

105. $x^4 - 2x^2 - 8$

106. $3u^2 + 8uv - 3v^2$

107. $a^4 - b^4$

108. $\dfrac{1}{9}c^2 - d^2$

109. $a^2 - \dfrac{1}{16}$

110. $\dfrac{1}{4}b^2 + 2bc + 4c^2$

128. Linda spent Thursday, Friday, and Saturday nights in a country inn. The inn charges $12 extra per night on weekends (Friday and Saturday nights). If Linda's bill was $96, what is the inn's charge for a room on a weekday night? $24

129. At the park, Tony rode his bicycle from the tennis courts to the swimming pool, and from there to the track, a total of 1,524 yards. If the first part of his ride was 3 times as long as the second, how many yards was the ride from the pool to the track?   381 yards

130. Ralph has a vegetable garden that is x feet wide and x + 14 feet long. He increases the width by 6 feet. If the area added to the garden is 384 square feet, what was the original area?   3,200 sq ft

CHAPTER 6

6-2   *Simplify each expression. Assume that no denominator is 0.*

1. $\dfrac{5a}{a}$ 5   **2.** $\dfrac{3xy}{y}$ $3x$ **3.** $\dfrac{14bc}{-2c}$ $-7b$ **4.** $\dfrac{d^3}{d^2}$ d

5. $\dfrac{-15x^4}{3x^2}$ $-5x^2$ **6.** $\dfrac{a^4b^3}{a^2b^2}$ a^2b **7.** $\dfrac{st^2}{st}$ t **8.** $\dfrac{9a^3c^2}{-3ac}$ $-3a^2c$

9. $\dfrac{-16m^5n^2}{-4m^3n^2}$ $4m^2$ **10.** $\dfrac{50p^5q^6}{-10pq^3}$ $-5p^4q^3$ **11.** $\dfrac{20a^7b^3}{5a^2b^2}$ $4a^5b$ **12.** $\dfrac{-18uv^5}{3uv^3}$ $-6v^2$

13. $\dfrac{33x^5yz^4}{-11x^4yz^3}$ $-3xz$ **14.** $\dfrac{8a^4b^2c}{2abc}$ $4a^3b$ **15.** $\dfrac{-4q^3r^4s^5t^6}{2qst}$ $-2q^2r^4s^4t^5$ **16.** $\dfrac{f^3g^2h^5}{-f^2h}$ $-fg^2h^4$

Find the missing factors.

17. $15a^5 = 5a^2(\underline{\ ?\ })$ $3a^3$ **18.** $10x^4 = 2x^3(\underline{\ ?\ })$ $5x$ **19.** $-12ab^3 = (\underline{\ ?\ })2b$ $-6ab^2$

20. $9c^6d^3 = 9cd(\underline{\ ?\ })$ c^5d^2 **21.** $-4m^3n = -2mn(\underline{\ ?\ })$ $2m^2$ **22.** $x^5y^6z^4 = xyz(\underline{\ ?\ })$ $x^4y^5z^3$

23. $4c^2d^5 + 7c^5d = 2c(\underline{\ ?\ }) + (\underline{\ ?\ })7d$ $2cd^5; c^5$

24. $12a^5b^6c^3 - 6a^2b^3c = 4abc^3(\underline{\ ?\ }) - 3ac(\underline{\ ?\ })$ $3a^4b^5; 2ab^3$

6-3   *Factor completely, and check.*

25. $2x + 12$ $2(x + 6)$ **26.** $9x - 3$ $3(3x - 1)$ **27.** $4c + 12$ $4(c + 3)$ **28.** $5b - 15$ $5(b - 3)$

29. $15a^2 - 45a$ **30.** $10cd + 16c$ **31.** $6x^3 + 4x$ **32.** $-7d^2 + 35d$

33. $2x^4 + 6x - 10$ **34.** $84 + 14s + 7s^4$ **35.** $4a^3r^2 + 12a^2r + 60r$

36. $30a^3 + 12a^4b^2 + 18a^2b$ $6a^2(5a + 2a^2b^2 + 3b)$

37. $15s^8t^4 - 35s^3t^2 + 40s^7t$ $5s^3t(3s^5t^3 - 7t + 8s^4)$

38. $8x^8y^6z^3 - 12x^2y^3z + 20x^5yz$ $4x^2yz(2x^6y^5z^2 - 3y^2 + 5x^3)$

6-4   Factor.

39. $n(n + 2) + 5(n + 2)$ $(n + 5)(n + 2)$

40. $4c(c^2 - 7) + 3d(c^2 - 7)$
      $(4c + 3d)(c^2 - 7)$

41. $ab + 5b + 3a + 15$ $(b + 3)(a + 5)$

42. $mn + n^2 + 4m + 4n$ $(n + 4)(m + n)$

43. $y^2 + yz + 4y + 4z$ $(y + 4)(y + z)$

44. $20 - cd + 5c - 4d$ $(5 - d)(c + 4)$

45. $yz^2 + 4y + 7z^2 + 28$ $(y + 7)(z^2 + 4)$

46. $s^2t - 8 + 2t - 4s^2$ $(t - 4)(s^2 + 2)$

47. $4u^2 - 3vw - 3uv + 4uw$
      $(4u - 3v)(u + w)$

48. $c^2 + 4ab - ac - 4bc$
      $(a - c)(4b - c)$

6-5   Factor.

49. $x^2 - 25$

50. $16 - b^2$

51. $9a^2 - 36$

52. $4c^2 - 4d^2$

53. $9s^2 - 49t^2$

54. $16y^2 - 64z^2$

55. $h^2 - 400$

56. $144x^2 - 81y^2$

57. $a^2 - 100b^2$

Factor completely.

58. $c^3 - 16c$

59. $4b^3 - 64b$

60. $3p^3 - 27p$

61. $6b^3 - 96b$

62. $3a^3 - 27a$

63. $2a^3 - 50ab^2$

64. $4st^2 - 196s^3$

65. $4d^3 - 36c^2d$

66. $18x^2y - 32y^3$

6-6   **67.** $x^2 + 6x + 9$

68. $p^2 - 4p + 4$

69. $16g^2 + 8g + 1$

70. $4n^2 + 4n + 1$

71. $4a^2 - 28a + 49$

72. $36t^2 - 60t + 25$

73. $x^2 + 4xy + 4y^2$

74. $9c^2 + 12cd + 4d^2$

75. $9a^2 + 6ab + b^2$

76. $2h^3 + 4h^2 + 2h$

77. $4c^3 - 8c^2 + 4c$

78. $-3x^3 - 18x^2 - 27x$

79. $c^3 + 4c^2d + 4cd^2$

80. $16s^3 + 80s^2t + 100st^2$

6-7   Factor. Check by multiplying.

81. $x^2 + 5x + 6$

82. $c^2 - 9c + 20$

83. $d^2 + 9d + 8$

84. $x^2 - 15x + 54$

85. $x^2 - x - 12$

86. $p^2 + p - 30$

87. $b^2 - 9b - 36$

88. $a^2 + 3a - 70$

89. $y^2 + 3y - 40$

90. $t^2 - 3t + 2$

91. $h^2 - 3h - 28$

92. $b^2 - 5b + 6$

93. $s^2 - st - 6t^2$

94. $x^2 - 2xy - 3y^2$

95. $c^2 + 3cd + 2d^2$

6-8   **96.** $2x^2 + 9x + 4$

97. $8x^2 + 16x + 6$

98. $3x^2 + 33x + 30$

99. $5x^2 - 17x + 6$

100. $10x^2 - 27x + 18$

101. $8x^2 - 12x + 4$

102. $3x^2 - 2x - 5$

103. $4x^2 - x - 14$

104. $6x^2 - 4x - 2$

105. $25x^2 + 5x - 6$

106. $24x^2 + 28x - 20$

107. $35x^2 - 57x + 18$

108. $16x^2 + 20x - 36$

109. $10x^2 + 11x - 18$

110. $28x^2 + 20x + 3$

EXTRA PRACTICE

519

PREREQUISITE SKILLS FOLLOW-UP

EXTRA PRACTICE SETS

COMPUTER HANDBOOK

TABLES

GLOSSARY

ANSWERS TO CHECKPOINTS

ANSWERS TO SELECTED EXERCISES

INDEX

EXTRA PRACTICE SETS

ADDITIONAL ANSWERS

Chapter 6 Extra Practice

49. $(x - 5)(x + 5)$

50. $(4 + b)(4 - b)$

51. $9(a - 2)(a + 2)$

52. $4(c - d)(c + d)$

53. $(3s - 7t)(3s + 7t)$

54. $16(y - 2z)(y + 2z)$

55. $(h - 20)(h + 20)$

56. $9(4x + 3y)(4x - 3y)$

57. $(a + 10b)(a - 10b)$

58. $c(c - 4)(c + 4)$

59. $4b(b - 4)(b + 4)$

60. $3p(p - 3)(p + 3)$

61. $6b(b - 4)(b + 4)$

62. $3a(a - 3)(a + 3)$

63. $2a(a - 5b)(a + 5b)$

64. $4s(t - 7s)(t + 7s)$

65. $4d(d - 3c)(d + 3c)$

66. $2y(3x - 4y)(3x + 4y)$

67. $(x + 3)^2$

68. $(p - 2)^2$

69. $(4g + 1)^2$

70. $(2n + 1)^2$

[Answers continue on page 520.]

71. $(2a - 7)^2$
72. $(6t - 5)^2$
73. $(x + 2y)^2$
74. $(3c + 2d)^2$
75. $(3a + b)^2$
76. $2h(h + 1)^2$
77. $4c(c - 1)^2$
78. $-3x(x + 3)^2$
79. $c(c + 2d)^2$
80. $4s(2s + 5t)^2$
81. $(x + 2)(x + 3)$
82. $(c - 4)(c - 5)$
83. $(d + 1)(d + 8)$
84. $(x - 6)(x - 9)$
85. $(x - 4)(x + 3)$
86. $(p + 6)(p - 5)$
87. $(b - 12)(b + 3)$
88. $(a + 10)(a - 7)$
89. $(y + 8)(y - 5)$
90. $(t - 2)(t - 1)$
91. $(h - 7)(h + 4)$
92. $(b - 3)(b - 2)$
93. $(s - 3t)(s + 2t)$
94. $(x - 3y)(x + y)$
95. $(c + d)(c + 2d)$
96. $(2x + 1)(x + 4)$
97. $(2x + 3)(4x + 2)$
98. $(3x + 3)(x + 10)$
99. $(5x - 2)(x - 3)$
100. $(2x - 3)(5x - 6)$
101. $(8x - 4)(x - 1)$
102. $(3x - 5)(x + 1)$
103. $(4x + 7)(x - 2)$
104. $(6x + 2)(x - 1)$
105. $(5x + 3)(5x - 2)$
106. $(8x - 4)(3x + 5)$
107. $(5x - 6)(7x - 3)$
108. $(4x + 9)(4x - 4)$
109. $(x + 2)(10x - 9)$
110. $(2x + 1)(14x + 3)$

6-9 *Factor completely.*

111. $12x^2 - 3$ $3(2x + 1)(2x - 1)$
112. $4x^2 + 4x - 224$ $4(x + 8)(x - 7)$
113. $6a^2 + 7a - 3$ $(2a + 3)(3a - 1)$
114. $5x^2 + 10x - 15$ $5(x + 3)(x - 1)$
115. $3x^3 + 36x^2 + 108x$ $3x(x + 6)^2$
116. $8s^3t - 128st^3$ $8st(s + 4t)(s - 4t)$
117. $8b(b + 3) + 4(b + 3)$ $4(2b + 1)(b + 3)$
118. $36x^2 + 6x - 6$ $6(3x - 1)(2x + 1)$
119. $a^2b^2 - 4b^2 - 16a^2 + 64$
   $(a + 2)(a - 2)(b + 4)(b - 4)$
120. $16x^4 - 8x^2 + 1$ $[(2x + 1)(2x - 1)]^2$

6-10 *Solve by factoring, and check. Be sure that one side of the equation is 0 before you factor.*

121. $x^2 + 6x = 0$ $0; -6$
122. $x^2 - 36 = 0$ $6; -6$
123. $27x^2 + 9x = 0$ $0; -\frac{1}{3}$
124. $2x^2 - 8x = 0$ $0; 4$
125. $x^2 - 10x = 0$ $0; 10$
126. $4x^2 - 16 = 0$ $-2; 2$
127. $x^3 - x^2 - 2x = 0$ $0; 2; -1$
128. $3x^2 - 14x = 5$ $-\frac{1}{3}; 5$
129. $x^3 - 4x^2 = 12x$ $0; 6; -2$
130. $x^2 + 6x + 9 = 0$ -3
131. $x^2 + 10x = -25$ -5
132. $x^2 - 4x = -4$ 2
133. $3x^2 + x = 4$ $-1\frac{1}{3}; 1$
134. $x^2 + 14x = -49$ -7
135. $x^2 + 4x - 21 = 0$ $-7; 3$
136. $4x^2 + 4x = -1$ $-\frac{1}{2}$
137. $x^3 + 10x^2 = -21x$ $0; -7; -3$
138. $x^2 + 20x = -100$ -10

6-11 *Solve. Show all solutions if more than one is possible.*

139. If 14 is added to the square of a number, the result is 30. Find the number.   4 or -4

140. Find two positive integers if their difference is 13 and their product is 300.   12 and 25

141. Three times the square of a number is equal to 4 times the number. What is the number?   0 or $\frac{4}{3}$

142. Five times a number is 3 less than twice its square. Find the number.   3 or $-\frac{1}{2}$

143. The product of two consecutive odd integers is 575. What are the integers?   23 and 25, or -23 and -25

144. If the sides of a square are multiplied by 6, the area of the new square is 560 cm^2 greater than the original square. What is the length of a side of the original square?   4 cm

CHAPTER 7

7-1 *Determine whether the given point is a solution of the system of equations.*

1. $(4, 6)$; $x + y = 10$
   $2y - x = 8$ Yes
2. $(1, 2)$; $x + 6y = 13$
   $y = -x + 3$ Yes
3. $(0, 8)$; $x - 2y = -16$
   $y + 2x = 0$ No
4. $(3, 5)$; $2x + 3y = 21$
   $y = x + 2$ Yes

Determine whether the system has a solution or not. Find the solution, if it exists, by graphing.

5. $y - 4x = 1$
$y + 10 = 4x$ No solution

6. $2x - 4y = -2$
$3y = 14 - x$ (5, 3)

7. $2y = 6x + 10$
$y - 3x = 8$
No solution

7-2 *Solve each system of equations by the substitution method.*

8. $y = 2x + 7$
$4x = y - 6$ $\left(\frac{1}{2}, 8\right)$

9. $2y = 20 - 2x$
$4y - 3x = 26$ (2, 8)

10. $y - 7 = 5x$
$2y = 10x - 2$ No solution

11. $2x - y = -2$
$3y - 4x = 8$
(1, 4)

12. $9x + 3y = 6$
$5x - y = -2$ (0, 2)

13. $y + 2 = 4x$
$6y - 1 = 24x$
No solution

14. $3x = y - 4$
$3y = 15x + 10$ $\left(\frac{1}{3}, 5\right)$

15. $x - y = 0$
$y - 2x = -4$
(4, 4)

7-3 *Solve and check each system. Use addition, subtraction, or substitution.*

16. $2x + y = 6$
$3x - y = -1$ (1, 4)

17. $-6x + 2y = 10$
$6x + 6y = 14$ $\left(-\frac{2}{3}, 3\right)$

18. $5x + y = -9$
$5x - 3y = 7$ (-1, -4)

19. $2y + x = 12$
$4x = 2y - 2$ (2, 5)

20. $0.2x + y = 2.8$
$0.2x = y + 1.6$ (11, 0.6)

21. $\frac{1}{3}x + \frac{5}{6}y = 6$
$\frac{1}{3}x + \frac{1}{6}y = 2$ (3, 6)

7-4 *Solve each system, using multiplication with addition. Then check.*

22. $4x + 2y = 14$
$3x - y = -2$ (1, 5)

23. $x - 3y = -7$
$-2x + 4y = 6$ (5, 4)

24. $6x + 3y = 9$
$4x - y = 0$ $\left(\frac{1}{2}, 2\right)$

25. $5x + 3y = -14$
$4x - 4y = 8$ (-1, -3)

26. $2x + 6y = 2$
$3x - 7y = -29$ (-5, 2)

27. $1.6x - 0.4y = 2.4$
$2.5x + 0.5y = 1.5$
(1, -2)

28. $9x + 3y + 51 = 0$
$6x + 10y + 26 = 0$
(-6, 1)

29. $2x = 11 - y$
$y = x - 10$ (7, -3)

30. $3(2x + 4) = 30y$
$4(2x - 6) = 20y$
(8, 2)

7-5 *Classify each system of equations. Then solve it if a unique solution exists.*

31. $3x - y = -3$
$y + 4 = 3x$ Inconsist.; indep.

32. $2x + 4y = 12$
$x - 3y = -9$ Consistent; indep. (0,3)

33. $y = 4x - 7$
$12x = 3y + 21$
Consist.; dep.

34. $4x + 5y = 14$
$7x + 6y = 8$ Consistent; indept. (-4, 6)

35. $3(2x + 9) = 3y$
$12 = 2x - y$ Inconsist.; indep.

36. $4(2x - 6) = -2y$
$5x + 2 = 3y$
Consistent; indep. (2, 4)

7-6 *Solve, using a system of equations.*

37. The sum of two numbers is 75. Twice the larger number is equal to 8 times the smaller number. Find the numbers.   15 and 60

38. The sum of two numbers is 105. Three times the first number equals 250 minus 2 times the second number. Find the numbers.   40 and 65

39. The difference between two numbers is 24. Four times the larger number is equal to 12 times the smaller number. Find the numbers.   12 and 36

EXTRA PRACTICE

521

PREREQUISITE SKILLS FOLLOW-UP

EXTRA PRACTICE SETS

COMPUTER HANDBOOK

TABLES

GLOSSARY

ANSWERS TO CHECKPOINTS

ANSWERS TO SELECTED EXERCISES

INDEX

EXTRA PRACTICE SETS

ADDITIONAL ANSWERS

Chapter 7 Extra Practice

6.
(5, 3)

40. Chang is 6 years less than 4 times as old as Jill. The sum of their ages is 29. How old is each?   Chang is 22. Jill is 7.

41. Mark is 7 years older than Betty. In 2 years Mark will be twice as old as Betty. How old are they now?   Mark is 12. Betty is 5.

42. A rectangle has a perimeter of 22 inches. If the length were increased an amount equal to the width, the perimeter would be 28 inches. Find the length and width.   Length is 8″. Width is 3″.

43. The length of a rectangle is twice its width. If its length is increased by 18 inches, the rectangle would be 5 times as long as it is wide. Find the dimensions of the rectangle.   Length is 12″. Width is 6″.

44. Boxes of large eggs cost 99¢. Boxes of jumbo eggs cost $1.19. Carlos spent $5.55 for some of both sizes. He spent $1.59 more on the jumbo eggs. How many boxes of each size did he buy?
Carlos bought 2 boxes of large eggs and 3 boxes of jumbo eggs.

45. A dozen ears of corn and 6 lemons cost $1.68. The lemons cost 48¢ less than the corn. Find the price of one ear of corn and the price of one lemon.   One ear of corn costs 9¢; one lemon costs 10¢.

7-7 **46.** Sixty coins in nickels and dimes have a total value of $4.25. How many nickels and how many dimes are there?   35 nickels, 25 dimes

47. A pile of dimes and quarters contains 35 coins. There are 3 more dimes than quarters. What is the total value of the coins? $5.90

48. Inez has some nickels and quarters. There are 50 coins in all, with $1.00 more in nickels than in quarters. How many of each are there?
45 nickels, 5 quarters

49. In a two-digit number, the units digit is 5 more than the tens digit. Three times the tens digit is 1 less than the units digit. Find the number.   27

50. The sum of the digits of a two-digit number is 12. If the digits are interchanged, the number is increased by 36. Find the number.   48

51. A three-digit number has a 2 for its tens digit. The sum of the digits is 7 and the number is 31 times the units digit. Find the number.   124

CHAPTER 8 ────────────────────────────

8-1 *Simplify.*

1. $\dfrac{5x}{25x^4}$ $\dfrac{1}{5x^3}$ **2.** $\dfrac{6a^7b^3}{2ab^2}$ $3a^6b$ **3.** $\dfrac{9(c-d)}{18(c-d)}$ $\dfrac{1}{2}$

4. $\dfrac{4x^2-4}{x+1}$ $4(x-1)$ **5.** $\dfrac{3x^2+6x}{x}$ $3(x+2)$ **6.** $\dfrac{x+4}{x^2-16}$ $\dfrac{1}{x-4}$

7. $\dfrac{2x^2+2x-4}{x+2}$ $2(x-1)$ **8.** $\dfrac{4x^2-14x-30}{(x-5)(x+1)}$ $\dfrac{2(2x+3)}{x+1}$ **9.** $\dfrac{9x-6}{3x^2+10x-8}$ $\dfrac{3}{x+4}$

EXTRA PRACTICE

8-2

10. $\dfrac{7-x}{x^2-49}$ $-\dfrac{1}{x+7}$ **11.** $\dfrac{x-24}{-2x+48}$ $-\dfrac{1}{2}$ **12.** $\dfrac{-b^2-b+12}{b^2+8b+16}$ $\dfrac{-b+3}{b+4}$

13. $\dfrac{-h^2+4h+21}{-h-3}$ $h-7$ **14.** $\dfrac{9-x^2}{(x-3)^2}$ $\dfrac{-3-x}{x-3}$ **15.** $\dfrac{-5x+30}{-3x+18}$ $1\frac{2}{3}$

16. $\dfrac{-x^2+x+42}{x^2-8x+7}$ $\dfrac{-x-6}{x-1}$ **17.** $\dfrac{x-1}{-2x^2+5x-3}$ $\dfrac{1}{-2x+3}$ **18.** $-\dfrac{-3n^2-5n+2}{n+2}$ $3n-1$

8-3 Multiply. Simplify your answers.

19. $\dfrac{2a^2}{6}\cdot\dfrac{a^3}{a^4}$ $\dfrac{a}{3}$ **20.** $\dfrac{2x^2y}{4x}\cdot\dfrac{9y^3}{3xy}$ $\dfrac{3y^3}{2}$ **21.** $\dfrac{x^2-16}{3x}\cdot\dfrac{9x^2}{x+4}$ $3x(x-4)$

22. $\dfrac{h^2-4}{16h^2+32h+15}\cdot\dfrac{12h+15}{4-h^2}$ $\dfrac{-3}{4h+3}$ **23.** $\dfrac{x^2+5xy+6y^2}{x+3y}\cdot\dfrac{x}{x^2-4y^2}$ $\dfrac{x}{x-2y}$

24. $\dfrac{x^2-9}{x^2-1}\cdot\dfrac{x^2+x}{2x^2-6x}$ $\dfrac{x+3}{2(x-1)}$ **25.** $\dfrac{x^2-1}{3x^2+3x}\cdot\dfrac{4x}{x^2-x}\cdot\dfrac{2x}{4}$ $\dfrac{2}{3}$

8-4 Divide and simplify.

26. $\dfrac{4a^3}{5b}\div\dfrac{2a^2}{15b}$ $6a$ **27.** $\dfrac{3x}{x+1}\div\dfrac{9}{4x+1}$ $\dfrac{x(4x+1)}{3(x+1)}$ **28.** $\dfrac{c^2-4}{3c+15}\div\dfrac{c+2}{c+5}$ $\dfrac{c-2}{3}$

29. $\dfrac{x^2+2x-3}{4}\div\dfrac{5x-5}{12}$ $\dfrac{3(x+3)}{5}$ **30.** $\dfrac{3t+3}{t^2-9}\div\dfrac{3t^2-12t-15}{t^2-t-12}$ $\dfrac{t-4}{(t-3)(t-5)}$

31. $\dfrac{a^2-b^2}{a^2-2ab+b^2}\div\dfrac{5a+5b}{2a-2b}$ $\dfrac{2}{5}$ **32.** $\dfrac{c+2}{c^2+4c}\div\dfrac{c^2-c-6}{3c+12-c^2-4c}$ $-\dfrac{1}{c}$

8-5 Divide.

33. $\dfrac{2x^2+2x}{x}$ $2x+2$ **34.** $\dfrac{10x^3+15x}{5x}$ $2x^2+3$ **35.** $\dfrac{x^2-x-6}{x-3}$ $x+2$

36. $\dfrac{x^2+5x+12}{x+3}$ $x+2+\dfrac{6}{x+3}$ **37.** $\dfrac{x^3-5x^2+11x-10}{x-2}$ x^2-3x+5 **38.** $\dfrac{x^3-12}{x-4}$ $x^2+4x+16+\dfrac{52}{x-4}$

39. $(x^3+4x^2+9x+10)\div(x+2)$ x^2+2x+5 **40.** $(x^3-2x^2+x+6)\div(x+1)$ $x^2-3x+4+\dfrac{2}{x+1}$

8-6 Add or subtract. Write answers in simplest form.

41. $\dfrac{12x}{10xy}-\dfrac{7x}{10xy}$ $\dfrac{1}{2y}$ **42.** $\dfrac{4y^2}{2y+1}-\dfrac{1}{2y+1}$ $2y-1$ **43.** $\dfrac{3}{x^2-9}+\dfrac{x}{x^2-9}$ $\dfrac{1}{x-3}$

44. $\dfrac{x^2+3x}{x+4}-\dfrac{3x+16}{x+4}$ $x-4$ **45.** $\dfrac{y^2-3y}{y+1}-\dfrac{4}{y+1}$ $y-4$ **46.** $\dfrac{5}{x-5}-\dfrac{x}{x-5}$ -1

8-7 Combine and simplify.

47. $\dfrac{7c-3}{c}+4$ $\dfrac{11c-3}{c}$ **48.** $\dfrac{5x}{4x^2}-\dfrac{x}{2x}+\dfrac{1}{2}$ $\dfrac{5}{4x}$ **49.** $\dfrac{4}{5x}-\dfrac{1}{3}$ $\dfrac{12-5x}{15x}$

50. $\dfrac{3}{x+2}+\dfrac{4}{x-2}$ **51.** $\dfrac{1}{x+4}-\dfrac{5}{x-7}$ **52.** $\dfrac{b}{b-2}-\dfrac{8}{b^2-4}$

PREREQUISITE SKILLS FOLLOW-UP

EXTRA PRACTICE SETS

COMPUTER HANDBOOK

TABLES

GLOSSARY

ANSWERS TO CHECKPOINTS

ANSWERS TO SELECTED EXERCISES

INDEX

EXTRA PRACTICE SETS

ADDITIONAL ANSWERS

Chapter 8 Extra Practice

50. $\dfrac{7x+2}{(x+2)(x-2)}$

51. $\dfrac{-4x-27}{(x+4)(x-7)}$

52. $\dfrac{b+4}{b+2}$

EXTRA PRACTICE

53. $\dfrac{x+3}{x}$

54 $\dfrac{x-1}{x-4}$

55. $\dfrac{x+4}{x}$

59. $\dfrac{x-4}{2(x-2)}$

60. $\dfrac{2c+1}{c}$

61. $\dfrac{-1}{2x+4}$

62. $\dfrac{4x}{x+3}$

63. $\dfrac{-3}{2(x+1)}$

53. $\dfrac{3x+6}{x^2+2x}+1$

54. $\dfrac{x}{x-4}-\dfrac{x+1}{x^2-3x-4}$

55. $\dfrac{6x+8}{x^2+2x}+\dfrac{x}{x+2}$

8-8

56. $\dfrac{4}{5b}+\dfrac{7}{10b}$ $\dfrac{3}{2b}$

57. $\dfrac{2}{4a^2}-\dfrac{1}{2a}$ $\dfrac{1-a}{2a^2}$

58. $\dfrac{x-2}{x+2}+\dfrac{6}{x}$ $\dfrac{x^2+4x+12}{x(x+2)}$

59. $\dfrac{x}{2x+4}-\dfrac{4}{x^2-4}$

60. $\dfrac{c+b}{c^2+bc}+\dfrac{2c+2b}{c+b}$

61. $\dfrac{8}{4x^2-16}-\dfrac{1}{2x-4}$

62. $\dfrac{4x}{x-4}-\dfrac{28x}{x^2-x-12}$

63. $\dfrac{x+1}{x^2+2x+1}-\dfrac{5}{2x+2}$

8-9 Simplify.

64. $\dfrac{1-\dfrac{3}{x}}{1-\dfrac{9}{x^2}}$ $\dfrac{x}{x+3}$

65. $\dfrac{\dfrac{4}{5x}}{\dfrac{16}{10x^2}}$ $\dfrac{x}{2}$

66. $\dfrac{\dfrac{3x-15}{2y}}{\dfrac{x-5}{4y}}$ 6

67. $\dfrac{\dfrac{4x^2}{x^2-y^2}}{\dfrac{2x}{x-y}}$ $\dfrac{2x}{x+y}$

68. $\dfrac{\dfrac{12-4x}{3x}}{\dfrac{2x-6}{9x}}$ -6

69. $\dfrac{\dfrac{x^2+2x}{y}}{\dfrac{x^2-4}{3y}}$ $\dfrac{3x}{x-2}$

70. $\dfrac{\dfrac{1}{y^2}-\dfrac{1}{x^2}}{\dfrac{y}{x}-\dfrac{x}{y}}$ $-\dfrac{1}{xy}$

71. $\dfrac{\dfrac{4x^4}{2x^2+10x+12}}{\dfrac{2x^3}{x+3}}$ $\dfrac{x}{x+2}$

CHAPTER 9

9-1 Solve and check.

1. $\dfrac{3}{4}y=\dfrac{3}{2}$ 2

2. $3\dfrac{1}{2}-\dfrac{n}{3}=\dfrac{1}{2}$ 9

3. $\dfrac{x}{3}+\dfrac{3x}{2}=11$ 6

4. $\dfrac{3x}{8}-\dfrac{5x}{4}=\dfrac{21}{8}$ -3

5. $\dfrac{2y}{5}-\dfrac{y}{2}=14-\dfrac{4y-1}{7}$ 30

6. $\dfrac{3x-2}{3}-1=\dfrac{9-2x}{3}+\dfrac{x}{2}$ 4

9-2 Solve and check. Write **no solution** if none exists.

7. $\dfrac{4}{x}+\dfrac{1}{2x}=\dfrac{1}{6}$ 27

8. $\dfrac{x}{2}+\dfrac{3x}{x-6}=\dfrac{2}{x-6}$ 2; -2

9. $\dfrac{-5}{x+5}=\dfrac{x}{x+5}$ No solution

10. $\dfrac{7}{x+3}-\dfrac{x}{x^2+7x+12}=\dfrac{4}{x+4}$ -8

11. $\dfrac{8+x}{x^2-9}=\dfrac{3}{x-3}-\dfrac{2}{x+3}$ No solution

9-3

12. What number added to both the numerator and the denominator of $\dfrac{4}{7}$ results in a new fraction that equals $\dfrac{2}{3}$?   2

13. The denominator of a certain fraction is 2 more than the numerator. If the denominator is increased by 5 and the numerator is decreased by 1, then the new fraction equals $\dfrac{1}{5}$. Find the original fraction. $\dfrac{3}{5}$

14. The denominator of a fraction is 5 more than 5 times its numerator. If 3 is added to the numerator and 10 is subtracted from the denominator, the result is 1. Find the fraction. $\dfrac{2}{15}$

EXTRA PRACTICE

15. The sum of the reciprocals of two consecutive even integers is $\frac{5}{12}$. Find the integers. **4 and 6**

16. The sum of a fraction and twice its reciprocal is $\frac{33}{10}$. Find the fraction. $\frac{4}{5}$ or $\frac{5}{2}$

9-4 **17.** Alan can trim the hedges in 3 hours. If Stan helps, they can finish in 2 hours. How long would it take Stan to complete the job working alone? **6 hours**

18. Steve can pave the school parking lot in 8 hours. If Julio helps, they can finish in 3 hours. How long would it take Julio to do the job alone?
$4\frac{4}{5}$ hours, or 4 hours 48 minutes

19. Yolanda can rake the yard in 2 hours, and Sue can do the same job in 3 hours. If they work together, how long does the job take?
$1\frac{1}{5}$ hours, or 1 hour 12 minutes

20. Lizzie and Tai working together can weed their garden in 5 hours. Tai can do the job herself in $\frac{1}{2}$ the time it would take Lizzie. How long would it take each girl to weed the garden alone?
Lizzie, 15 hours; Tai, $7\frac{1}{2}$ hours, or 7 hours 30 minutes

21. Mr. Robinson can mow the lawn in one-third the time it takes Mr. Calvino to mow it. It takes 1 hour to finish when both men mow. How long would it take each man working alone?
Mr. Robinson, $1\frac{1}{3}$ hours, or 1 hour 20 minutes; Mr. Calvino, 4 hours

9-5 **22.** Two numbers in the ratio 7 to 8 have a sum of 135. Find the numbers.
63 and 72

23. A moped can travel 375 miles on 5 gallons of gasoline. How far can it travel on 12 gallons? **900 miles**

24. There are 600 students in a high school. The ratio of students who ride a school bus to those who don't is 3 to 2. How many students ride a school bus?
360

25. Posters are selling at 4 for $6.00. What is the price for 15? **$22.50**

26. The difference between two numbers is 12, and the ratio of the smaller number to the larger number is 3:5. Find the numbers. **18 and 30**

9-6 **27.** A $145 radio is on sale at a discount of 25%. How much do you save? **$36.25**

28. The price of a record that normally sells for $8.99 is reduced 30%. What is the sale price? **$6.29**

29. Raquel receives a 15% commission, or 75¢, on each ticket she sells. What is the price of a ticket? **$5**

30. A certain company charges students $12 for a magazine subscription that normally sells for $15. What percent is the discount? **20%**

31. Lani bought a sweater at a 15% discount for $29.75. What was the original price? **$35**

9-7 **32.** Two thousand dollars is deposited at $7\frac{1}{4}$% interest per year. How much interest is earned in 9 months? **$108.75**

33. How long will it take a $700 investment to earn $147 interest at a yearly interest rate of $5\frac{1}{4}$%? **4 years**

PREREQUISITE SKILLS FOLLOW-UP

EXTRA PRACTICE SETS

COMPUTER HANDBOOK

TABLES

GLOSSARY

ANSWERS TO CHECKPOINTS

ANSWERS TO SELECTED EXERCISES

INDEX

EXTRA PRACTICE SETS

34. Find the interest on $2,500 borrowed for 9 months at an interest rate of 1.2% per month. $270

35. Part of Mr. Linh's $15,000 is invested in one account at 9% interest per year, and the rest is invested in another account at $5\frac{1}{4}$% interest per year. The total annual income from both accounts is $1,237.50. How much is invested at each rate? $12,000 at 9%; $3,000 at $5\frac{1}{4}$%

36. Twenty-eight hundred dollars is invested in a 12-month savings certificate that earns 9% interest per year. The interest earned the first year is added to the original $2,800 investment. At the same rate, how much interest will be earned the second year? What is the total interest earned for the 2 years? $274.68; $526.68

9-8 **37.** A 2-cup mixture of vinegar and oil is 55% vinegar. How much oil must be added to obtain a 25% mixture? $2\frac{2}{5}$ cups

38. A 454-gram blend of butter and margarine is 50% butter. How much margarine must be added to make a blend that is 20% butter? 681 g

39. How many quarts of milk that are 2% butterfat must be added to 12 quarts of 36%-butterfat cream to obtain a 26%-butterfat cream? 5 quarts

40. A mixture of bran flakes and raisins weighs 108 grams. Forty percent of this weight is in raisins. If 18 grams of flakes are eaten, what percent of the remaining mixture is raisins? 48%

41. A scientist has a 40% saltwater solution and a 60% saltwater solution. How many ounces of each must be mixed to produce 32 ounces of a 45% saltwater solution? 24 ounces of 40% sol.; 8 ounces of 60% sol.

9-9 **42.** A truck and a van are traveling west. At 2 P.M., the truck was 25 miles west of the van. Later, the van passed the truck. At what time did the van pass the truck if the truck's average speed was 45 mph and the van's was 50 mph? 7 P.M.

43. Two joggers start at the same time and travel toward each other from opposite ends of a road 15 miles long. One travels 1.5 times as fast as the other. Find the average speed of both if they meet in 1 hour. 9 mph and 6 mph

44. Kim lives 8 km from the skating rink. She walks for 20 minutes at 6 km/h and then rides her skateboard until she reaches the rink 30 minutes later. Find her speed on the skateboard. 12 km/h

45. Yesterday it took Cleon 30 minutes to drive to the mall in a rainstorm. Today, he increased his speed by 9 mph and made the trip in 20 minutes. How far does Cleon live from the mall? 9 miles

46. A car left Seaville at 8 A.M. and traveled due north at 80 km/h. At 10:30 A.M. a second car left the station and traveled the same route at 110 km/h. At what time will the faster car overtake the slower one? 5:10 P.M.

EXTRA PRACTICE

CHAPTER 10

10-1 *Write **true** or **false**.*

1. $-7 < 5$ True **2.** $4 < -8$ False **3.** $0 \leq 1$ True **4.** $-6 \geq -6$ True

5. $-\frac{1}{2} > -\frac{1}{4}$ False **6.** $5.5 > 5.25$ True **7.** $-3 \geq 2$ False **8.** $0 \geq -5$ True

Graph each inequality.

9. $x < 2$ **10.** $x > 0$ **11.** $x \leq -7$ **12.** $x \geq -0.5$

10-2 *Solve.*

13. $x + 7 > 2$ **14.** $y - 4 < -6$ **15.** $x - 1 \leq 3$

16. $3y + 2 < 8 + 2y$ **17.** $4x - 1 > 3x + 7$ **18.** $9y + 3 \geq 8y + 6$

19. $2(3x + 2) \leq 5x + 4$ **20.** $3(y - 6) > 2y - 2$ **21.** $4(x + 3) < 3x + 10$

22. $y + 5 \not> 6$ **23.** $2x - 10 \not\geq x - 2$ **24.** $3(x + 2) \not\leq 4(x + 3)$

10-3 **25.** $4x > 24$ **26.** $3b \leq 15$ **27.** $-10c < 100$ **28.** $-\frac{3}{4}y \geq -6$

29. $3x + 2 > 8$ **30.** $6 - 2x \leq 10$ **31.** $5x + 1 \geq 16$ **32.** $9 - 7x < 30$

33. $\frac{-x}{3} \geq -3$ $x \leq 9$ **34.** $-5 - 4x \leq 11$ $x \geq -4$ **35.** $6x + 1 \not\geq 2x + 5$ $x < 1$

36. $3x + 2 \not< 5x - 8$
$x \leq 5$
37. $7x + 1 \leq 3x - 15$
$x \leq -4$
38. $-4(x + 2) > -2(x - 6)$
$x < -10$

10-5 *Solve and graph each compound inequality on a number line.*

39. $-1 < x - 3 < 0$ **40.** $15 \leq 3x < 21$

41. $27 < 9 - 3x < 33$ **42.** $2x \leq 14$ or $x - 6 > 10$

43. $2x + 5 > -5$ or $x - 11 > -4$ **44.** $2x + 5 > -5$ and $x - 11 > -4$

10-6 **45.** $|c - 1| < 4$ **46.** $|h + 6| \geq 8$ **47.** $|5x| > 10$

48. $|3 - 3x| > 15$ **49.** $\left|\frac{2}{3}x\right| \leq 2$ **50.** $|2x + 1| \leq 3$

10-7 *Graph.*

51. $y < 2x - 5$ **52.** $y - x \geq 3$ **53.** $4x - 2y \leq 8$ **54.** $5y + 10x - 20 > 0$

10-8 *Graph each system of inequalities.*

55. $y < 2x$
$y \geq x + 1$
56. $y > 5 - x$
$y < 2$
57. $x + y \leq -1$
$x - y \geq 3$
$x > 2$
58. $3x + y > 1$
$x - y \leq 4$
$-x < 4$

PREREQUISITE SKILLS FOLLOW-UP

EXTRA PRACTICE SETS

COMPUTER HANDBOOK

TABLES

GLOSSARY

ANSWERS TO CHECKPOINTS

ANSWERS TO SELECTED EXERCISES

INDEX

EXTRA PRACTICE SETS

ADDITIONAL ANSWERS

Chapter 10 Extra Practice

9.

10.

11.

12.

13. $x > -5$ **14.** $y < -2$
15. $x \leq 4$ **16.** $y < 6$
17. $x > 8$ **18.** $y \geq 3$
19. $x \leq 0$ **20.** $y > 16$
21. $x < -2$ **22.** $y \leq 1$
23. $x < 8$ **24.** $-6 > x$

[*Answers continue on page 528.*]

25. $x > 6$ **26.** $b \leq 5$
27. $c > -10$ **28.** $y \leq 8$
29. $x > 2$ **30.** $x \geq -2$
31. $x \geq 3$ **32.** $x > -3$

39. $2 < x < 3$

40. $5 \leq x < 7$

41. $-6 > x > -8$

42. $x \leq 7$ or $x > 16$

43. $x > -5$

[Answers continue on A18.]

Chapter 11 Extra Practice
6. $\dfrac{151}{30}$ **7.** $\dfrac{37}{33}$ **8.** $\dfrac{2039}{999}$
9. $\dfrac{23}{15}$ **10.** $\dfrac{41}{3330}$

10-4   *Use an inequality to solve each problem.*

59. The sum of two consecutive even integers is no greater than 86. Find the largest pair of such integers possible.   42, 44

60. Three times the product of 8 and a number is at least 168. Find the smallest such number possible.   7

61. The sum of four consecutive integers is less than 126. Find the greatest integers for which this is possible.   29, 30, 31, 32

62. Five times the sum, 3 plus 6 times an integer, is greater than 255. Find the smallest such integer possible.   9

63. The area of a square is at least 144 cm². What is the shortest possible length of each side?   12 cm

64. Bill is 7 years younger than Susan. The sum of their ages is no less than 36. What is the youngest that each could be?   Bill, $14\frac{1}{2}$; Susan, $21\frac{1}{2}$

65. The length of a rectangle is twice its width. If the perimeter of the rectangle is no more than 48 inches, what is the greatest possible length of the rectangle?   16 inches

66. Two cyclists pass each other and continue in opposite directions. One travels at 15 mph and the other at 20 mph. How long must they travel to be at least 42 miles apart? $1\frac{1}{5}$ hours, or 1 hour 12 minutes

CHAPTER 11

11-1   *Write each rational number as a fraction in simplest form.*

1. 0.43 $\frac{43}{100}$ **2.** 60 $\frac{60}{1}$ **3.** 5.8 $\frac{29}{5}$ **4.** 0.02 $\frac{1}{50}$ **5.** $0.\overline{1}$ $\frac{1}{10}$

6. $5.0\overline{3}$ **7.** $1.\overline{12}$ **8.** $2.\overline{041}$ **9.** $1.5\overline{3}$ **10.** $0.0\overline{123}$

11-2   *Simplify each expression.*

11. $\sqrt{196}$ 14   **12.** $-\sqrt{4^2}$ -4 **13.** $\sqrt{2^4}$ 4   **14.** $-\sqrt{\dfrac{1}{16}}$ $-\frac{1}{4}$ **15.** $\sqrt{\dfrac{9}{36}}$ $\frac{1}{2}$

16. $-4\sqrt{100}$ -40 **17.** $\dfrac{1}{4}\sqrt{64}$ 2   **18.** $\sqrt{6^2 + 8^2}$ 10   **19.** $\sqrt{5^3 - 2^2}$ 11

Evaluate to the nearest hundredth. Use the divide-and-average method.

20. $\sqrt{19}$ 4.36   **21.** $\sqrt{58}$ 7.62   **22.** $\sqrt{103}$ 10.15   **23.** $\sqrt{15}$ 3.87   **24.** $\sqrt{128}$ 11.31

11-3   *Simplify.*

25. $\sqrt{63}$ $3\sqrt{7}$ **26.** $\sqrt{80}$ $4\sqrt{5}$ **27.** $\sqrt{275}$ $5\sqrt{11}$ **28.** $\sqrt{18}$ $3\sqrt{2}$ **29.** $\sqrt{640}$ $8\sqrt{10}$

30. $\sqrt{12} \cdot \sqrt{5}$ $2\sqrt{15}$ **31.** $4\sqrt{2} \cdot \sqrt{54}$ $24\sqrt{3}$ **32.** $4(\sqrt{6})^3$ $24\sqrt{6}$ **33.** $(-\sqrt{8})^4$ 64

34. $\sqrt{3}(4 + \sqrt{3})$ $4\sqrt{3} + 3$ **35.** $\sqrt{7}(\sqrt{7} + \sqrt{75})$ $7 + 5\sqrt{21}$ **36.** $\sqrt{12}(\sqrt{8} - \sqrt{3})$ $4\sqrt{6} - 6$

528

ADDITIONAL ANSWERS

Chapter 11 Extra Practice
54. $2x\sqrt{y + 3z}$
55. $4c\sqrt{c - 2b}$
56. $c + 5d$

11-4 37. $\dfrac{3}{\sqrt{9}}$ 1 38. $\dfrac{\sqrt{30}}{\sqrt{5}}$ $\sqrt{6}$ 39. $\dfrac{\sqrt{45}}{\sqrt{3}}$ $\sqrt{15}$ 40. $\sqrt{\dfrac{5}{6}}$ $\dfrac{\sqrt{30}}{6}$ 41. $\sqrt{\dfrac{3}{4}}$ $\dfrac{\sqrt{3}}{2}$

42. $\sqrt{\dfrac{2}{3}} \cdot \sqrt{\dfrac{1}{4}}$ $\dfrac{\sqrt{6}}{6}$ 43. $\dfrac{\sqrt{5} + \sqrt{20}}{\sqrt{5}}$ 3 44. $\sqrt{\dfrac{1}{2}} \cdot \sqrt{\dfrac{4}{3}}$ $\dfrac{\sqrt{6}}{3}$ 45. $\dfrac{\sqrt{5} + \sqrt{12}}{\sqrt{2}}$ $\dfrac{\sqrt{10} + 2\sqrt{6}}{2}$

11-5 Simplify. All variables and radicands represent positive numbers.

46. $\sqrt{16x^2}$ $4x$ 47. $\sqrt{12x^4}$ $2x^2\sqrt{3}$ 48. $\sqrt{96x^2y^6}$ $4xy^3\sqrt{6}$ 49. $2x^3\sqrt{2x^2y^9}$ $2x^4y^4\sqrt{2y}$

50. $\sqrt{\dfrac{5x^3}{9}}$ $\dfrac{x\sqrt{5x}}{3}$ 51. $\sqrt{\dfrac{1}{6x^2}}$ $\dfrac{\sqrt{6}}{6x}$ 52. $2\sqrt{\dfrac{x^4}{49}}$ $\dfrac{2x^2}{7}$ 53. $\dfrac{\sqrt{6x}}{\sqrt{4x^8}}$ $\dfrac{\sqrt{6x}}{2x^4}$

54. $\sqrt{4x^2y + 12x^2z}$ 55. $\sqrt{16c^3 - 32bc^2}$ 56. $\sqrt{c^2 + 10cd + 25d^2}$

11-6 57. $9\sqrt{3} - 6\sqrt{3}$ $3\sqrt{3}$ 58. $8\sqrt{x} + 3\sqrt{x}$ $11\sqrt{x}$ 59. $5\sqrt{10} + \sqrt{40}$ $7\sqrt{10}$

60. $7\sqrt{5} - 2\sqrt{20}$ $3\sqrt{5}$ 61. $\sqrt{x^3} - 4\sqrt{x}$ $(x - 4)\sqrt{x}$ 62. $2\sqrt{x^3} + 6\sqrt{x}$ $(2x + 6)\sqrt{x}$

63. $6\sqrt{x^2y} + \sqrt{y}$ 64. $\sqrt{2x^5} + \sqrt{12x^3}$ 65. $\sqrt{x^5y^4} - \sqrt{x^3y^3}$
   $(6x + 1)\sqrt{y}$ $x(x\sqrt{2x} + 2\sqrt{3x})$ $xy(xy\sqrt{x} - \sqrt{xy})$

11-7 Find the length of the third side of each right triangle. Write irrational answers in simplest radical form.

66.
2√2
2

67.
3√5

68.
2√2
4

11-8 Find the distance between each pair of points. Express irrational answers in simplest radical form.

69. $(3, 2), (5, 0)$ $2\sqrt{2}$ 70. $(-2, 2), (1, -2)$ 5 71. $(4, -7), (8, 6)$ $\sqrt{185}$

72. $(1, 9), (-2, 7)$ $\sqrt{13}$ 73. $(0, 4), (-5, -6)$ $5\sqrt{5}$ 74. $(5, 7), (-7, -9)$ 20

75. $(-3, 2), (1, 2)$ 4 76. $(8, -9), (7, -4)$ $\sqrt{26}$ 77. $(-1, -6), (-5, -8)$ $2\sqrt{5}$

11-9 Solve and check.

78. $\sqrt{2x} = 4$ 8 79. $\sqrt{x} + 2 = 10$ 64 80. $\sqrt{x} - 3 = 1$ 16

81. $5 + \sqrt{x} = 2$ No solution 82. $\sqrt{9 - 2x} = 3$ 0 83. $\sqrt{4x + 8} = 10$ 23

84. $\dfrac{\sqrt{x}}{3} = 2$ 36 85. $\sqrt{\dfrac{x + 3}{2}} = 2$ 5 86. $\sqrt{x + 4} = 2\sqrt{7}$ 24

CHAPTER 12

12-1 Evaluate each function for the given values.

$f(x) = 4x - 3$ 1. $f(3)$ 9 2. $f(1)$ 1 3. $f(0)$ −3 4. $f\left(\dfrac{1}{4}\right)$ −2

EXTRA PRACTICE

PREREQUISITE SKILLS FOLLOW-UP

EXTRA PRACTICE SETS

COMPUTER HANDBOOK

TABLES

GLOSSARY

ANSWERS TO CHECKPOINTS

ANSWERS TO SELECTED EXERCISES

INDEX

EXTRA PRACTICE SETS

21.

22.

23.

24.

25.

26.

[Answers continue on page 531.]

$f(x) = 5 - 8x$ **5.** $f(-2)$ 21 **6.** $f\left(\dfrac{1}{2}\right)$ 1 **7.** $f(1)$ −3 **8.** $f(-1)$ 13

$f(x) = 2x^2$ **9.** $f(4)$ 32 **10.** $f(-3)$ 18 **11.** $f(0)$ 0 **12.** $f\left(\dfrac{1}{2}\right)$ $\dfrac{1}{2}$

$f(x) - x^2 + 3x - 4$ **13.** $f(2)$ 6 **14.** $f(1)$ 0 **15.** $f(-5)$ 6 **16.** $f(-3)$ −4

$f(x) = 9x^2 - 5$ **17.** $f(0)$ −5 **18.** $f\left(\dfrac{1}{3}\right)$ −4 **19.** $f(-3)$ 76 **20.** $f(-1)$ 4

12-2 Graph the function defined by each equation.

21. $y = x^2$ **22.** $y = -\dfrac{1}{8}x^2$ **23.** $y = -\dfrac{1}{3}x^2$ **24.** $2x^2$

12-3 **25.** $y = x^2 + 4$ **26.** $y = -x^2 - 1$ **27.** $y = -2x^2 - 2$ **28.** $y = \dfrac{1}{2}x^2 + 3$

12-4 Write the equation of the graph described. Then identify the equation of the axis of symmetry and the coordinates of the vertex.

29. The graph of $y = 4x^2$ is translated 2 units left and 1 unit up.

30. The graph of $y = \dfrac{1}{3}x^2$ is translated 3 units right and 4 units down.

31. The graph of $y = -2x^2$ is translated 4 units right and 5 units up.

32. The graph of $y = -\dfrac{1}{4}x^2$ is translated 1 unit left and 5 units down.

12-5 Write in **h, k** form. Then write the coordinates of the vertex and the equation of the axis of symmetry.

33. $y = x^2 + 4x + 5$ **34.** $y = x^2 - 6x + 1$ **35.** $y = 4x^2 - 8x + 3$

36. $y = -3x^2 - 12x + 2$ **37.** $y = -x^2 + 4x + 9$ **38.** $y = \dfrac{1}{4}x^2 - x + 7$

Use the formula $x = -\dfrac{b}{2a}$ to find the equation of the axis of symmetry. Then find the coordinates of the vertex. Is the vertex a minimum or a maximum point?

39. $y = x^2 + 8x + 2$ **40.** $y = -x^2 - 2x + 5$ **41.** $y = 3x^2 + 6x - 4$

42. $y = x^2 - 5x + 3$ **43.** $y = x^2 + 3x - 9$ **44.** $y = -4x^2 + 8x + 10$

12-6 Write each equation in the form $ax^2 + bx + c = 0$. Then solve for **x**.

45. $x^2 - 7x = -6$ **46.** $-2 + 5x^2 = -3x$ **47.** $-7 = 14x + 7x^2$

48. $-6x - 15 = 2x^2$ **49.** $4x^2 + x = 5$ **50.** $7x = -11 - x^2$

Find the **x**-intercepts, if any, for the graph of each equation.

51. $y = x^2 + 12x + 32$ **52.** $y = 4x^2 + 6x + 2$ **53.** $y = 2x^2 - 12x + 18$

54. $y = 3x^2 - x + 2$ **55.** $y = 3x^2 + 6x + 2$ **56.** $y = 2x^2 + 6x + 10$

12-7 Use the discriminant to determine the number of **x**-intercepts for the graph of each equation.

57. $y = 2x^2 + 8x + 3$ 2   **58.** $y = 3x^2 - 6x + 7$ **59.** $y = 5x^2 + 2x - 4$ 2

60. $y = x^2 + 6x + 9$ 1   **61.** $y = -3x^2 - 5x + 1$ **62.** $y = -6x^2 - 3x - 7$ None
                      None

63. $y = 2x^2 + 7x + 3$ 2   **64.** $y = -16x^2 + 8x - 1$ **65.** $y = x^2 + 10x + 8$ 2
                  2   1

12-9 If **y** varies directly as **x**, and **y** = 18 when **x** = 6, find:

66. y when x = 15   45   **67.** x when y = 57   19   **68.** y when x = 2.9   8.7

69. x when y = 49.5   16.5   **70.** x when y = 123   41   **71.** y when x = 0.36   1.08

72. y when x = 66   198   **73.** y when x = 46   138   **74.** x when y = 2.1   0.7

12-10 If **a** and **b** vary inversely, and **a** = $\frac{3}{4}$ when **b** = 8, find:

75. b when a = 2   3   **76.** a when b = 12   0.5   **77.** b when a = 4   1.5

78. a when b = 1   6   **79.** b when a = 8   0.75   **80.** b when a = 3   2

81. Find the constant of variation if x varies inversely as y and x = −2 when y = $\frac{1}{4}$. $-\frac{1}{2}$

82. Find the constant of variation if y varies inversely as x and y = 6 when x = 3.   18

83. If c varies inversely as d and c = 5 when d = 1, find d when c = 4.   1.25

84. If b varies inversely as a and b = 2.5 when a = 0.5, find b when a = 5.   0.25

12-8   **85.** The sum of a number and 5 times its reciprocal is 6. Find the number.   1 or 5

86. The hypotenuse of a right triangle is 10 cm long. How long are the legs if one is 2 cm longer than the other?   6 cm, 8 cm

87. Find two consecutive even integers such that the sum of their squares is 1460.   26 and 28, or −28 and −26

88. The product of two consecutive odd integers is 143. Find the integers.   11 and 13, or −13 and −11

89. When 12 is divided by a certain number, the result is the same as when 18 is added to the number and this sum is divided by 12. Find the number.   6 or −24

90. The perimeter of a right triangle is 12 inches, and one of the legs is 1 inch longer than the other. Find the lengths of the three sides.   3 in., 4 in., 5 in.

CHAPTER 13

13-1 Find the number of degrees in the angles described.

1. Two complementary angles have measures of x° and 4x°.   18°, 72°

2. Two supplementary angles have measures in the ratio 1:8.   20°, 160°

EXTRA PRACTICE   **531**

PREREQUISITE SKILLS FOLLOW-UP
EXTRA PRACTICE SETS
COMPUTER HANDBOOK
TABLES
GLOSSARY
ANSWERS TO CHECKPOINTS
ANSWERS TO SELECTED EXERCISES
INDEX
EXTRA PRACTICE SETS

ADDITIONAL ANSWERS

Chapter 12 Extra Practice (continued)

27.

28.

29. $y = 4(x + 2)^2 + 1$
Axis: $x = -2$
Vertex: $(-2, 1)$

30. $y = \frac{1}{3}(x - 3)^2 - 4$
Axis: $x = 3$
Vertex: $(3, -4)$

31. $y = -2(x - 4)^2 + 5$
Axis: $x = 4$
Vertex: $(4, 5)$

32. $y = -\frac{1}{4}(x + 1)^2 - 5$
Axis: $x = -1$
Vertex: $(-1, -5)$

[Answers continue on page A19.]

13. $c = 15$

$\sin A = \dfrac{3}{5}$

$\cos A = \dfrac{4}{5}$

$\tan A = \dfrac{3}{4}$

14. $b = 3\sqrt{3}$

$\sin A = \dfrac{1}{2}$

$\cos A = \dfrac{\sqrt{3}}{2}$

$\tan A = \dfrac{\sqrt{3}}{3}$

15. $a = 4$

$\sin A = \dfrac{4}{5}$

$\cos A = \dfrac{3}{5}$

$\tan A = \dfrac{4}{3}$

16. $c = \sqrt{53}$

$\sin A = \dfrac{2\sqrt{53}}{53}$

$\cos A = \dfrac{7\sqrt{53}}{53}$

$\tan A = \dfrac{2}{7}$

17. $b = 2\sqrt{21}$

$\sin A = \dfrac{2}{5}$

$\cos A = \dfrac{\sqrt{21}}{5}$

$\tan A = \dfrac{2\sqrt{21}}{21}$

18. $a = 12\sqrt{2}$

$\sin A = \dfrac{2\sqrt{2}}{3}$

$\cos A = \dfrac{1}{3}$

$\tan A = 2\sqrt{2}$

3. Two supplementary angles have measures of x° and (3x + 20)°.   40°, 140°

4. Two complementary angles have measures of x° and (7x − 22)°.   14°, 76°

5. The angles of a triangle have measures of x°, $3\frac{3}{4}$x°, and $4\frac{1}{4}$x°.   20°, 75°, 85°

6. The measure of an angle is 110° less than its supplement. Find the measure of its complement. 55°

7. One of the equal angles of an isosceles triangle measures 70°. Find the measures of the other angles. 70°, 40°

8. The base angles of an isosceles triangle are the equal angles. The measure of the third angle is $5\frac{1}{5}$ times that of one of the base angles. Find the measure of each angle in the triangle.   25°, 25°, 130°

13-2 *For each pair of similar triangles, find **x** and **y**.*

9.   x = 6, y = 9

10.   x = 7, y = 6

11.   x = 12.5, y = 12

12.   x = 8, y = 4

13-3 △**ABC** *is a right triangle with right angle* **C**. *Use the Pythagorean theorem to find the length of the missing side. Then find sin **A**, cos **A**, and tan **A**.*

13. $a = 9, b = 12$ **14.** $a = 3, c = 6$ **15.** $b = 3, c = 5$

16. $a = 2, b = 7$ **17.** $a = 4, c = 10$ **18.** $b = 6, c = 18$

13-4 *Find **x**. Leave irrational answers in simplest radical form.*

19.

20.

21.

22.

Find each answer correct to the nearest whole number.

23. Find the height of a kite when a 440-foot string forms a 60° angle with the ground.   381 ft

24. The longer leg of a 30°-60°-90° triangle is 6 meters long. Find the length of the shorter leg.   3 m

25. From a point 12 meters from the base of a building, the angle of elevation to the top is 60°. How high is the building?   21 m

13-5   *Find the value of **x** to the nearest tenth.*

26.
36.3

27.
19.0

28.
17.9

29.
26.6

*Find the value of **x** to the nearest degree.*

30.

31.

32.

33.

Find each length to the nearest whole number and each angle to the nearest degree.

34. A 10-meter board is leaning against a wall. It forms an angle of 65° with the ground. How far up the wall does the board reach?   9 m

35. A 40-foot ladder is placed against a building. It reaches 30 feet up the wall. What is the angle of elevation?   49°

36. From a lookout point in a lighthouse, the angle of depression to an anchor on the beach below is 20°. The lookout point is 225 feet in the air. Find the horizontal distance from the lighthouse to the anchor.   618 ft

PREREQUISITE SKILLS FOLLOW-UP

EXTRA PRACTICE SETS

COMPUTER HANDBOOK

TABLES

GLOSSARY

ANSWERS TO CHECKPOINTS

ANSWERS TO SELECTED EXERCISES

INDEX

EXTRA PRACTICE SETS

COMPUTER HANDBOOK

I. Working with BASIC

BASIC is the most popular computer language because it is easy to learn and to use. Computers, however, vary slightly in the BASIC they use. The explanations and programs in this book are designed for use with as many different computers as possible, and can be understood when no computer is available. Because many computers display only capital letters, the programs are written in capitals.

If you enter a program into a computer and find that it does not run properly, first check to see that every line was entered correctly. Even the slightest mistake in entering a program may prevent it from running or may cause an erroneous result. If you still encounter difficulty, consult the section "Some Differences in BASICs" on page 545. Also consult the manual for the computer you are using.

II. Writing a Program

In BASIC, each statement is given a line number. We usually number the statements using multiples of ten. This makes it easy to insert additional statements into the program.

The information immediately following the characters REM does not affect the program itself. This allows you to include comments that make the program easier to read and understand.

Here is a program, written in the language of BASIC, that calculates and displays the sum of two numbers. The PRINT instruction commands the computer to display what follows it on the monitor or TV screen. In order to display words or symbols, we must enclose them in quotation marks, as in line 50. When no quotation marks are used, as in line 60, only the value of S will be displayed on the monitor.

The Program	What It Does
`10   REM PROGRAM ONE`	Gives the program a title.
`20   LET A = 72`	Assigns the value 72 to A.
`30   LET B = 48`	Assigns the value 48 to B.
`40   LET S = A + B`	Assigns their sum to S.
`50   PRINT "THE SUM IS"`	Displays a message.
`60   PRINT S`	Displays the value of S.
`70   PRINT`	Leaves a blank line.
`90   END`	Ends the program.

The A, B, and S are called *variables*. In BASIC, a variable is the name of a location in the computer's memory where a number is stored. Line 20 assigns the number 72 to memory location A.

534

After you have entered the program, you must enter the command RUN. This instructs the computer to run the program, starting with the lowest line number. Here is a sample run of PROGRAM ONE.

```
RUN
THE SUM IS
120
```

If we wish the output to be displayed on one line, as

```
THE SUM IS 120
```

we can combine lines 50 and 60 by using a semicolon.

```
50 PRINT "THE SUM IS "; S
```

EXERCISES *Insert these lines into PROGRAM ONE.*

```
75  LET D = A - B
80  PRINT "THE DIFFERENCE IS"
85  PRINT D
```

1. When the revised program is run, what number will be stored in memory location D? 24

2. How many numbers will the revised program instruct the computer to display?
Two numbers (S and D)
3. Why will the value of S be printed before the value of D?
Line 60 is executed before line 85.
4. Write a program in BASIC that instructs the computer to find and display the sum and the difference of 775 and 499.

III. Numerical Expressions in BASIC

To perform operations in BASIC, five symbols are used.

+ addition   * multiplication
- subtraction   / division
↑ raising to a power

Note: Some computers use the symbol ∧ for raising a number to a power, while others use the symbol **. Check your user's manual.

Examples

Arithmetic Expression	Equivalent BASIC Expression
$24 + 16$	$24 + 16$
$50 - 39$	$50 - 39$
6×15	$6 * 15$
$72 \div 12$	$72 / 12$
15^2	$15 \uparrow 2$

The order of operations in BASIC is the same as in algebra.

1. Perform the operations within grouping symbols first, starting with the innermost grouping symbol.
2. Raise a number to a power.
3. Multiply and divide in order, from left to right.
4. Add and subtract in order, from left to right.

PREREQUISITE SKILLS FOLLOW-UP

EXTRA PRACTICE SETS

COMPUTER HANDBOOK

TABLES

GLOSSARY

ANSWERS TO CHECKPOINTS

ANSWERS TO SELECTED EXERCISES

INDEX

COMPUTER HANDBOOK

ADDITIONAL ANSWERS

Exercises

```
4. 10  REM PROGRAM TWO
   20  LET A = 775
   30  LET B = 499
   40  LET S = A + B
   50  PRINT "THE SUM
       IS "; S
   60  PRINT
   70  LET D = A - B
   80  PRINT "THE DIF
       FERENCE IS "; D
   90  END
```

Since parentheses are the only grouping symbols used in BASIC, we use parentheses within parentheses. Two or more terms in the numerator or denominator of a fraction must be grouped within parentheses.

Examples	Arithmetic Expression	Equivalent BASIC Expression	Value
	$8 \times (20 - 13)$	$8 * (20 - 13)$	56
	$7 + 9 \times 10$	$7 + 9 * 10$	97
	$50 - 3^2$	$50 - 3 \uparrow 2$	41
	$\dfrac{6 + 9}{8 - 3}$	$(6 + 9)/(8 - 3)$	3
	$\dfrac{3 \times (8 + 2)}{5}$	$3 * (8 + 2)/5$	6
	$5 \times [10 - (15 - 8)]$	$5 * (10 - (15 - 8))$	15

EXERCISES   *Write the value of each BASIC expression.*

1. 4 * 17   68   **2.** 36/4   9   **3.** 8 ↑ 2   64   **4.** 20 − (4 + 8)   8
5. 2 * 8 ↑ 2   128   **6.** 12 + 6 * 8   60   **7.** 100 − 64/4 84   **8.** 65/(10 + 3)   5
9. (18 + 12)/(40 − 25) 2 **10.** (13 − 9) ↑ 3 64 **11.** 50/5 ↑ 2   2 **12.** 6 * (3 + 7)/12   5

IV. Algebraic Expressions

A statement in BASIC may look like an algebraic equation, yet have a totally different meaning and use. For example:

```
70   LET X = X + 2
```

In algebra, the equation x = x + 2 can never be true. In BASIC, the statement LET X = X + 2 tells the computer to take the value stored in memory location X, increase it by 2, and store the result as the new value for X. On many computers, LET may be omitted.

The left side of a LET statement in BASIC may contain only a variable. The computer evaluates the expression on the right side of the equal sign and assigns that value to the variable on the left side.

The multiplication symbol * must always be used in BASIC.

Examples	Algebraic Expression	Equivalent BASIC Expression
	$5a$	$5 * A$
	$3(r - 4)$	$3 * (R - 4)$
	$6x^2$	$6 * X \uparrow 2$
	$ax^2 + bx - c$	$A * X \uparrow 2 + B * X - C$

EXERCISES   *Tell what output will be displayed.*

```
1. 10   LET R = 12
   20   LET R = 5 * R
   30   PRINT R
   90   END  60
```

```
2. 10   LET T = 4
   20   LET Q = T ↑ 2 + 3 * T
   30   PRINT "Q EQUALS "
   40   PRINT Q
   90   END   Q EQUALS
                  28
```

536

Write each of the following in BASIC.

3. $7t$ $7 * T$ **4.** $3x^2$ $3 * X \uparrow 2$ **5.** $6b + 4$ $6 * B + 4$ **6.** $4(a + 3)$ $4 * (A + 3)$

7. $2x^3$ **8.** $y^2 - 2y$ **9.** $8a(a - 5)$ **10.** $m^2 - 3m + 4$
   $2 * X \uparrow 3$ $Y \uparrow 2 - 2 * Y$ $8 * A * (A - 5)$ $M \uparrow 2 - 3 * M + 4$

Note: Because of the way some computers function, the command
PRINT 7 ↑ 2 may result in a display of 49.0000001. To avoid this,
most programs in this book use multiplication to raise a number to a
power. Thus, 7^2 is programmed as $7 * 7$ rather than as $7 \uparrow 2$.

V. Using INPUT Statements

An INPUT statement causes the computer to stop and wait for an entry. On most
computers, a question mark is displayed to indicate that the computer is waiting
for you to input a value. After an appropriate entry has been made, the computer
continues to the next instruction. Here is a program that computes and displays
the area of a square after you enter the length of its side.

The Program	What It Does
10 REM AREA OF SQUARE	Tells what the program will compute.
20 PRINT "ENTER LENGTH OF SIDE"	Reminds you what to enter.
30 INPUT S	Waits for you to enter the length.
40 LET A = S * S	Computes $A = s^2$.
50 PRINT "AREA IS "; A	Displays the output.
90 END	Ends the program.

Here is a sample run when the length of a side is 8.

```
RUN
ENTER LENGTH OF SIDE
? 8
AREA IS 64
```
You must enter 8 before the computer will proceed.

Sometimes we wish to enter (input) two or more values. On most
computers this can be done with one INPUT statement. The numbers
entered must be separated by commas. The following program illustrates a multiple INPUT statement.

The Program	What It Does
10 REM AREA OF RECTANGLE	Tells what the program will compute.
20 PRINT "ENTER LENGTH, WIDTH"	Prompts you to enter the dimensions.
30 INPUT L, W	Waits for you to enter the length and width, separated by a comma.
40 LET A = L * W	Computes $A = lw$.
50 PRINT "AREA IS "; A	
90 END	

Here is a sample run; the length is 9, the width is 6.

```
RUN
ENTER LENGTH, WIDTH
? 9, 6
AREA IS 54
```
You must enter 9, 6 before the computer will proceed.

PREREQUISITE SKILLS FOLLOW-UP

EXTRA PRACTICE SETS

COMPUTER HANDBOOK

TABLES

GLOSSARY

ANSWERS TO CHECKPOINTS

ANSWERS TO SELECTED EXERCISES

INDEX

COMPUTER HANDBOOK

EXERCISES   *Here is a program for finding the volume of a cylinder.*

```
10   REM VOLUME OF CYLINDER
20   PRINT "ENTER RADIUS, HEIGHT"
30   INPUT R, H
40   LET V = 3.14 * R * R * H
50   PRINT "VOLUME IS "; V
90   END
```

1. What does the computer display if you enter the values 5, 6?   VOLUME IS 471
2. How would you enter $r = 12$ and $h = 15$? What will be the output? 12, 15; VOLUME IS 6782.4
3. What is the output if you enter 15, 12?   VOLUME IS 8478
4. Write a program that uses the formula $S = 2\pi r(r + h)$ to find the surface area of a cylinder when you input the radius and height.

VI. Using GO TO Statements

It is often necessary to have the computer repeat the same set of instructions over and over again. The instruction GO TO (or GOTO on some computers) can be used to direct the computer to do this. The following program directs the computer to display the counting numbers.

The Program	What It Does
`10   REM COUNTING NUMBERS`	
`20   LET N = 1`	Assigns the value 1 to N.
`30   PRINT N`	Displays the number in N.
`40   LET N = N + 1`	Adds 1 to N; assigns new value to N.
`50   GO TO 30`	Jumps back to line 30 and prints the new value
`90   END`	assigned to N.

When the computer reaches line 50, it jumps back, or "loops," to line 30. The program will display 1, 2, 3, 4, 5, . . . and continue without ever reaching END. The computer is in an "infinite loop."

EXERCISES   *What will the computer display when each of the following programs is entered and run?*

1.
```
10   LET N = 2
20   PRINT N
30   LET N = N + 2
40   GO TO 20
90   END   2, 4, 6, 8, . . .
              (Multiples of 2)
```
2.
```
10   LET N = 2
20   PRINT N
30   LET N = N + 2
40   GO TO 10
90   END   2, 2, 2, 2, . . .
```
3.
```
10   LET N = 0
20   LET N = N + 7
30   PRINT N
40   GO TO 20
90   END   7, 14, 21, 28, . . .
              (Multiples of 7)
```
4.
```
10   LET N = 66
20   GO TO 40
30   PRINT N
40   LET N = N + N
90   END   No values will be displayed.
```
5. Write a program that displays the positive multiples of 5.
6. Write a program that begins by displaying 100 and counts backwards.

VII. Using FOR. . .NEXT Statements

One way to avoid an infinite loop is to use a FOR. . .NEXT statement. Such a statement tells the computer to repeat a group of instructions a specified number of times. The following program instructs the computer to display the counting numbers from 5 through 8.

The Program	What It Does
10 REM FIVE TO EIGHT	
20 FOR N = 5 TO 8 STEP 1	Assigns the value 5 to N. Increases this value by 1 each time it loops back.
30 PRINT N	Displays the number in N.
40 NEXT N	Jumps back to line 20 to assign the next value to N.
50 PRINT	Leaves a blank line.
60 PRINT "FINISHED."	Displays FINISHED to show that the computer has left (exited) the loop.
90 END	

```
RUN
  5
  6
  7
  8

FINISHED
```

Lines 20 and 40 set up a loop. The computer begins with N = 5. When line 40 is reached, the computer loops back to line 20 and increases the value of N by 1 (STEP 1). Once the last value for N has been reached, line 40 permits the computer to exit, or leave, the loop and continue to lines 50 through 90.

If we omit "STEP 1" in a FOR. . .NEXT statement, the computer will automatically increase the variable by one each step. By placing an appropriate value after "STEP", we can instruct the computer to increase or decrease the value of the variable by any number we choose. These programs illustrate two uses of FOR. . .NEXT. . .STEP.

```
10  REM MULTIPLES OF FIVE       10  REM BACKWARDS
20  FOR F = 5 TO 20 STEP 5      20  FOR B = 6 TO 3 STEP -1
30  PRINT F                     30  PRINT B
40  NEXT F                      40  NEXT B
90  END                         90  END
    RUN                             RUN
     5                               6
    10                               5
    15                               4
    20                               3
```

EXERCISES   *What numbers will be output when each program is run?*

```
1. 10   FOR Z = 1 TO 7          2. 10   FOR J = 25 TO 30
   20   PRINT Z                    20   PRINT J - 12
   30   NEXT Z                     30   NEXT J
   90   END   1, 2, 3, 4, 5, 6, 7  90   END   13, 14, 15, 16, 17, 18
```

PREREQUISITE SKILLS FOLLOW-UP

EXTRA PRACTICE SETS

COMPUTER HANDBOOK

TABLES

GLOSSARY

ANSWERS TO CHECKPOINTS

ANSWERS TO SELECTED EXERCISES

INDEX

COMPUTER HANDBOOK

```
3. 10   FOR M = 2 TO 22 STEP 4      4. 10   FOR A = 10 TO 60 STEP 10
   20   PRINT M                        20   PRINT A * A
   30   NEXT M                         30   NEXT A
   90   END   2, 6, 10, 14, 18, 22     90   END   100, 400, 900, 1600, 2500, 3600
5. 10   FOR N = 2 TO -2 STEP -1     6. 10   FOR K = 10 TO 0 STEP -2
   20   PRINT N + 2                    20   PRINT K
   30   NEXT N                         30   NEXT K
   90   END   4, 3, 2, 1, 0            90   END   10, 8, 6, 4, 2, 0
```

Write a program that uses a FOR. . .NEXT statement to display the:

7. multiples of ten from 100 to 200.

8. whole numbers from 20 back to 10.

VIII. Using IF. . .THEN Statements

When a program uses an IF. . .THEN statement, the computer may give the impression that it is thinking. Actually the computer is only comparing two quantities, using one of these symbols:

=	is equal to	< >	is not equal to
>	is greater than	> =	is greater than or equal to
<	is less than	< =	is less than or equal to

To see how an IF. . .THEN statement works, compare these two programs for counting.

```
10   REM COUNT              10   REM COUNT TO TEN
20   LET K = 1             20   LET K = 1
30   REM LOOP BEGINS       30   REM LOOP BEGINS
40   PRINT K               40   PRINT K
50   LET K = K + 1         50   LET K = K + 1
60   GO TO 40              60   IF K <= 10 THEN 40
90   END                   90   END
```

The first program, COUNT, puts the computer into an infinite loop. Each time it reaches line 60, the computer loops back to line 40. As a result, the program never ends.

In the second program, COUNT TO TEN, line 60 tests the value in K. As long as the value in K is 10 or less, the computer loops back to line 40. But as soon as the value of K is greater than 10, the computer ignores the THEN command and goes to line 90, ending the program.

Note: The programs in this book use only line numbers after THEN. Some computers, however, require a GO TO statement. If your computer does not accept line 60 in the above program, make this change:

```
60   IF K <= 10 THEN GO TO 40
```

540

Study the two programs that follow and note how the location of the IF...THEN statement affects the output.

```
10   REM COUNT BY FIVE        10   REM COUNT BY FIVE
20   LET N = 5                20   LET N = 5
30   PRINT N                  30   PRINT N
40   IF N = 20 THEN 90        40   LET N = N + 5
50   LET N = N + 5            50   IF N < 20 THEN 30
60   GO TO 30                 90   END
90   END
```

```
RUN                          RUN
  5      The computer continues      5      The computer jumps to
 10         in a loop until N        10         line 90 and ends the
 15         equals 20 and 20 has     15         program without
 20         been displayed.                     displaying 20.
```

EXERCISES   *What numbers will be displayed when each program is run?*

```
1. 10   REM COUNT BY TEN       2. 10   REM COUNT BY TEN
   20   LET A = 0                 20   LET A = 0
   30   PRINT A                   30   PRINT A
   40   IF A = 50 THEN 90         40   IF A > 50 THEN 90
   50   LET A = A + 10            50   LET A = A + 10
   60   GO TO 30                  60   GO TO 30
   90   END   0, 10, 20, 30, 40, 50    90   END   0, 10, 20, 30, 40, 50, 60
```

```
3. 10   REM COUNT BY TEN       4. 10   REM COUNT BY TEN
   20   LET A = 0                 20   LET A = 0
   30   PRINT A                   30   PRINT A
   40   LET A = A + 10            40   LET A = A + 10
   50   IF A < 50 THEN 30         50   IF A <= 50 THEN 30
   90   END   0, 10, 20, 30, 40     90   END   0, 10, 20, 30, 40, 50
```

5. Show what the output will be when this program is run.

```
10   REM MULTIPLES OF EIGHT
20   LET T = 1
30   PRINT 8 * T
40   LET T = T + 1
50   IF T < 10 THEN 30
90   END   8, 16, 24, ..., 64, 72
```

IX. Using READ—DATA Statements

READ—DATA statements are often used to enter data into a computer. The programs that follow, and the sample run for each, show how READ—DATA statements can be used. Note that the DATA statement may appear anywhere in the program before the END statement.

PREREQUISITE SKILLS FOLLOW-UP

EXTRA PRACTICE SETS

COMPUTER HANDBOOK

TABLES

GLOSSARY

ANSWERS TO CHECKPOINTS

ANSWERS TO SELECTED EXERCISES

INDEX

COMPUTER HANDBOOK

The Program	What It Does
10 REM AREA OF SQUARE	
20 READ S	The computer reads one value at a time, left to right, from the DATA statement.
30 DATA 16, 12.5	Values must be separated by commas.
40 PRINT "SIDE IS "; S	Displays current value of S taken from the DATA statement.
50 LET A = S * S	Computes $A = s^2$
60 PRINT "AREA IS "; A	Displays current value of A.
70 PRINT	Leaves a blank line.
80 GO TO 20	Returns for more data.
90 END	

```
      RUN
      SIDE IS 16
      AREA IS 256

      SIDE IS 12.5
      AREA IS 156.25

      OUT OF DATA
```

Displays output for first value in DATA statement.

Displays output for second value in DATA statement.

Some computers display an error message when out of data.

The Program	What It Does
100 REM VOLUME OF PRISM	
110 READ L, W, H	Reads three consecutive values from the DATA statement.
120 PRINT "LENGTH IS "; L	Displays the values currently in L, W, and H.
130 PRINT "WIDTH IS "; W	
140 PRINT "HEIGHT IS "; H	
150 LET V = L * W * H	Computes $V = lwh$.
160 PRINT "VOLUME IS "; V	Displays current value of V.
170 PRINT	Leaves a blank line.
180 GO TO 110	Returns for more data.
190 DATA 24, 12, 15	Gives dimensions of a prism.
900 END	

```
      RUN
      LENGTH IS 24
      WIDTH IS 12
      HEIGHT IS 15
      VOLUME IS 4320

      OUT OF DATA
```

Displays output for set of three values in DATA statement.

When a great many values are to be entered, you may use as many DATA statements as necessary.

EXERCISES

1. In the program AREA OF SQUARE, change line 30 to:

                30   DATA 21, 9, 7.5

What areas will be displayed when this revised program is run?

542

2. In the program VOLUME OF PRISM, change line 190 to:

```
190  DATA 7, 5, 4, 30, 24, 25, 6, 4, 3.5
```

What volumes will be displayed when this revised program is run?

3. Suppose the following is entered as line 190:

```
190  DATA -10, -8, -6, +3, -2, -1
```

a. What will the computer display?   VOLUME IS −480   VOLUME IS 6

b. Can a prism have negative dimensions?   No

c. Can a prism have a negative volume?   No

d. Does the output always indicate when the input is invalid?   No

e. What does this illustrate about the relationship between the input and the output of a computer program?

X. Using Exponential Notation

Computers often display numbers in an exponential form that is very similar to scientific notation.

Standard Notation	Scientific Notation	Exponential Notation in BASIC
3,000,000	3×10^6	3E+06
575,000,000,000	5.75×10^{11}	5.75E+11
0.0002	2×10^{-4}	2E−04
0.00425	4.25×10^{-3}	4.25E−03

EXERCISES   *Write each of the following in standard notation.*

1. 8E+09   **2.** 4E+13   **3.** 6.8E+07   **4.** 7.245E+12

5. 6E−06   **6.** 3E−09   **7.** 5.6E−08   **8.** 1.33E−10

Write each of the following in BASIC exponential notation.

9. 60,000   6E+04   **10.** 75,000,000,000   7.5E+10   **11.** 5,675,000,000   5.675E+09

12. 0.0000000004   4E−10   **13.** 0.00000475   4.75E−06   **14.** 0.000000067   6.7E−08

XI. Using BASIC Functions

In BASIC, a number of programs, called functions, are stored inside the computer. They can be used by entering the appropriate keyword.

Function	Mathematical Symbol	BASIC Keyword
Absolute Value	$\lvert x \rvert$	ABS(X)
Greatest Integer	$[x]$	INT(X)
Square Root	$\sqrt{x}$	SQR(X)

ABS(X) causes the computer to obtain the absolute value of X.

     LET N = ABS(−19) sets N equal to 19.

Examples
```
PRINT ABS(26)      PRINT ABS(-3)      PRINT ABS(-2.5)
 26                 3                  2.5
```

COMPUTER HANDBOOK   **543**

PREREQUISITE SKILLS FOLLOW-UP

EXTRA PRACTICE SETS

COMPUTER HANDBOOK

TABLES

GLOSSARY

ANSWERS TO CHECKPOINTS

ANSWERS TO SELECTED EXERCISES

INDEX

COMPUTER HANDBOOK

ADDITIONAL ANSWERS

Exercises (Top of page)

2. VOLUME IS 140
    VOLUME IS 18000
    VOLUME IS 84

3e. Unless the input is tested for validity, the computer will execute it and the output may be invalid.

Exercises (Middle of page)

1. 8,000,000,000

2. 40,000,000,000,000

3. 68,000,000

4. 7,245,000,000,000

5. 0.000006

6. 0.000000003

7. 0.000000056

8. 0.000000000133

INT(X) causes the computer to obtain the greatest integer that is not greater than X. For a decimal numeral, this has the effect of always rounding down to the next lower integer.

LET N = INT(−15.5) sets N equal to −16

Examples

```
PRINT INT(6)        PRINT INT(2.7)       PRINT INT(0.25)
6                   2                    0

PRINT INT(-5)       PRINT INT(-1.8)      PRINT INT(-0.4)
-5                  -2                   -1
```

SQR(X) causes the computer to obtain the square root of X. If X is negative, the computer displays an error message.

LET N = SQR(49) sets N equal to 7.

Examples

```
PRINT SQR(144)      PRINT SQR(6.25)      PRINT SQR(-16)
12                  2.5                  ERROR
```

EXERCISES   *What will the computer display for each entry?*

1. PRINT ABS(−6)   6   2. PRINT ABS(12.8)   12.8   3. PRINT INT(4.8)   4
4. PRINT INT(−7.1)   −8   5. PRINT INT(0.75)   0   6. PRINT INT(−0.25)   −1
7. PRINT INT(−13)   −13   8. PRINT SQR(64)   8   9. PRINT SQR(−9)   Error

XII. Using Rounding

Because all numbers entered into a computer are converted to base two internally, the results may not always be exact. Some computers are more precise in computation than others. One method of handling this is to round off the results displayed or stored in the computer.

The following BASIC statements can be used to round numbers. In each, the variable N to the right of the equal sign represents the number before rounding. The N to the left of the equal sign represents the rounded number.

To the nearest hundred: N = INT(N/100 + .5) * 100
To the nearest ten: N = INT(N/10 + .5) * 10
To the nearest unit: N = INT(N + .5)
To the nearest tenth: N = INT(N * 10 + .5)/10
To the nearest hundredth: N = INT(N * 100 + .5)/100

EXERCISES   *Write an expression in BASIC to round the number **N***

1. to the nearest thousand.
   R = INT(N/1000 + .5) * 1000

2. to the nearest ten-thousandth.
   R = INT(N * 10000 + .5)/10000

Examine the precision of your computer by running these two programs.

```
10   REM TENTHS TEST          10   REM POWERS TEST
20   FOR N = 1 TO 25 STEP .1  20   FOR N = 1 TO 20
40   PRINT N                  30   PRINT N ↑ 2, N ↑ 3
50   NEXT N                   40   NEXT N
90   END                      90   END
```

544

3. All numerals displayed by TENTHS TEST should have a maximum of one digit to the right of the decimal point. If not, write a new line 30 that will round N to the nearest tenth.
4. All numerals displayed by POWERS TEST should be whole numbers. If not, write a program that computes the second and third powers of the numbers from 1 to 20, and displays the exact values.

XIII. Some Differences in BASICs

When a program has a statement that does not run on your computer, the following may help you to modify the program.

1. Instead of using ↑ to indicate raising to a power, some computers use ∧ or **.
2. On most computers, if you do not assign a value to a variable (as in LET X = 5), the computer automatically assigns the value zero. On a few computers, however, a program will not run unless you assign a value for each variable used in the program.
3. On most computers the command PRINT 2.6−2.5 will result in a display of .1. But on some, the display will be .0999999996. To avoid difficulties caused by inexact answers, you may have to round the results. (See Section XII, Using Rounding)
4. Some computers do not permit multiple INPUT statements. On these computers, write a separate statement for each variable. Instead of 40 INPUT A, B   use   40 INPUT A
                                           45 INPUT B
5. If a computer rejects GO TO, use GOTO.
6. If a computer rejects a statement such as IF A = 8 THEN 60 use   IF A = 8 THEN GO TO 60.
7. For a computer without READ-DATA capability, use LET statements or INPUT statements to enter the values.
8. Each computer divides the screen display into "zones." However, the number of zones and their size vary widely. In a PRINT statement, a variable or message following a comma will be printed in the next zone. See your computer manual for further explanation.
9. A semicolon in a PRINT statement that displays a variable has a different effect on different computers. The command PRINT 9; 6 may give any of these displays: 96   9 6   9   6   See your computer manual for further explanation.
10. Different computers give different "error messages." See your computer manual for an explanation.

   As you work with a computer, keep in mind that several different programs can usually be written to solve a problem. The programs in this book were selected because they are easy to understand or because they illustrate certain BASIC commands and programming techniques. Once you learn to program in BASIC, you may be able to write programs that are shorter and more efficient.

PREREQUISITE SKILLS FOLLOW-UP

EXTRA PRACTICE SETS

COMPUTER HANDBOOK

TABLES

GLOSSARY

ANSWERS TO CHECKPOINTS

ANSWERS TO SELECTED EXERCISES

INDEX

COMPUTER HANDBOOK

ADDITIONAL ANSWERS

Exercises

3–4. Students' results and programs may vary.

SQUARES AND SQUARE ROOTS

No.	Square	Square Root	No.	Square	Square Root	No.	Square	Square Root
1	1	1.000	51	2,601	7.141	101	10,201	10.050
2	4	1.414	52	2,704	7.211	102	10,404	10.100
3	9	1.732	53	2,809	7.280	103	10,609	10.149
4	16	2.000	54	2,916	7.348	104	10,816	10.198
5	25	2.236	55	3,025	7.416	105	11,025	10.247
6	36	2.449	56	3,136	7.483	106	11,236	10.296
7	49	2.646	57	3,249	7.550	107	11,449	10.344
8	64	2.828	58	3,364	7.616	108	11,664	10.392
9	81	3.000	59	3,481	7.681	109	11,881	10.440
10	100	3.162	60	3,600	7.746	110	12,100	10.488
11	121	3.317	61	3,721	7.810	111	12,321	10.536
12	144	3.464	62	3,844	7.874	112	12,544	10.583
13	169	3.606	63	3,969	7.937	113	12,769	10.630
14	196	3.742	64	4,096	8.000	114	12,996	10.677
15	225	3.873	65	4,225	8.062	115	13,225	10.724
16	256	4.000	66	4,356	8.124	116	13,456	10.770
17	289	4.123	67	4,489	8.185	117	13,689	10.817
18	324	4.243	68	4,624	8.246	118	13,924	10.863
19	361	4.359	69	4,761	8.307	119	14,161	10.909
20	400	4.472	70	4,900	8.367	120	14,400	10.954
21	441	4.583	71	5,041	8.426	121	14,641	11.000
22	484	4.690	72	5,184	8.485	122	14,884	11.045
23	529	4.796	73	5,329	8.544	123	15,129	11.091
24	576	4.899	74	5,476	8.602	124	15,376	11.136
25	625	5.000	75	5,625	8.660	125	15,625	11.180
26	676	5.099	76	5,776	8.718	126	15,876	11.225
27	729	5.196	77	5,929	8.775	127	16,129	11.269
28	784	5.292	78	6,084	8.832	128	16,384	11.314
29	841	5.385	79	6,241	8.888	129	16,641	11.358
30	900	5.477	80	6,400	8.944	130	16,900	11.402
31	961	5.568	81	6,561	9.000	131	17,161	11.446
32	1,024	5.657	82	6,724	9.055	132	17,424	11.489
33	1,089	5.745	83	6,889	9.110	133	17,689	11.533
34	1,156	5.831	84	7,056	9.165	134	17,956	11.576
35	1,225	5.916	85	7,225	9.220	135	18,225	11.619
36	1,296	6.000	86	7,396	9.274	136	18,496	11.662
37	1,369	6.083	87	7,569	9.327	137	18,769	11.705
38	1,444	6.164	88	7,744	9.381	138	19,044	11.747
39	1,521	6.245	89	7,921	9.434	139	19,321	11.790
40	1,600	6.325	90	8,100	9.487	140	19,600	11.832
41	1,681	6.403	91	8,281	9.539	141	19,881	11.874
42	1,764	6.481	92	8,464	9.592	142	20,164	11.916
43	1,849	6.557	93	8,649	9.644	143	20,449	11.958
44	1,936	6.633	94	8,836	9.695	144	20,736	12.000
45	2,025	6.708	95	9,025	9.747	145	21,025	12.042
46	2,116	6.782	96	9,216	9.798	146	21,316	12.083
47	2,209	6.856	97	9,409	9.849	147	21,609	12.124
48	2,304	6.928	98	9,604	9.899	148	21,904	12.166
49	2,401	7.000	99	9,801	9.950	149	22,201	12.207
50	2,500	7.071	100	10,000	10.000	150	22,500	12.247

TABLE OF SINES, COSINES, AND TANGENTS

Angle	Sine	Cosine	Tangent	Angle	Sine	Cosine	Tangent
0°	.0000	1.0000	.0000	45°	.7071	.7071	1.0000
1	.0175	.9998	.0175	46	.7193	.6947	1.0355
2	.0349	.9994	.0349	47	.7314	.6820	1.0724
3	.0523	.9986	.0524	48	.7431	.6691	1.1106
4	.0698	.9976	.0699	49	.7547	.6561	1.1504
5	.0872	.9962	.0875	50	.7660	.6428	1.1918
6	.1045	.9945	.1051	51	.7771	.6293	1.2349
7	.1219	.9925	.1228	52	.7880	.6157	1.2799
8	.1392	.9903	.1405	53	.7986	.6018	1.3270
9	.1564	.9877	.1584	54	.8090	.5878	1.3764
10	.1736	.9848	.1763	55	.8192	.5736	1.4281
11	.1908	.9816	.1944	56	.8290	.5592	1.4826
12	.2079	.9781	.2126	57	.8387	.5446	1.5399
13	.2250	.9744	.2309	58	.8480	.5299	1.6003
14	.2419	.9703	.2493	59	.8572	.5150	1.6643
15	.2588	.9659	.2679	60	.8660	.5000	1.7321
16	.2756	.9613	.2867	61	.8746	.4848	1.8040
17	.2924	.9563	.3057	62	.8829	.4695	1.8807
18	.3090	.9511	.3249	63	.8910	.4540	1.9626
19	.3256	.9455	.3443	64	.8988	.4384	2.0503
20	.3420	.9397	.3640	65	.9063	.4226	2.1445
21	.3584	.9336	.3839	66	.9135	.4067	2.2460
22	.3746	.9272	.4040	67	.9205	.3907	2.3559
23	.3907	.9205	.4245	68	.9272	.3746	2.4751
24	.4067	.9135	.4452	69	.9336	.3584	2.6051
25	.4226	.9063	.4663	70	.9397	.3420	2.7475
26	.4384	.8988	.4877	71	.9455	.3256	2.9042
27	.4540	.8910	.5095	72	.9511	.3090	3.0777
28	.4695	.8829	.5317	73	.9563	.2924	3.2709
29	.4848	.8746	.5543	74	.9613	.2756	3.4874
30	.5000	.8660	.5774	75	.9659	.2588	3.7321
31	.5150	.8572	.6009	76	.9703	.2419	4.0108
32	.5299	.8480	.6249	77	.9744	.2250	4.3315
33	.5446	.8387	.6494	78	.9781	.2079	4.7046
34	.5592	.8290	.6745	79	.9816	.1908	5.1446
35	.5736	.8192	.7002	80	.9848	.1736	5.6713
36	.5878	.8090	.7265	81	.9877	.1564	6.3138
37	.6018	.7986	.7536	82	.9903	.1392	7.1154
38	.6157	.7880	.7813	83	.9925	.1219	8.1443
39	.6293	.7771	.8098	84	.9945	.1045	9.5144
40	.6428	.7660	.8391	85	.9962	.0872	11.4301
41	.6561	.7547	.8693	86	.9976	.0698	14.3007
42	.6691	.7431	.9004	87	.9986	.0523	19.0811
43	.6820	.7314	.9325	88	.9994	.0349	28.6363
44	.6947	.7193	.9657	89	.9998	.0175	57.2900
45	.7071	.7071	1.0000	90	1.0000	.0000	

PREREQUISITE SKILLS FOLLOW-UP

EXTRA PRACTICE SETS

COMPUTER HANDBOOK

TABLES

GLOSSARY

ANSWERS TO CHECKPOINTS

ANSWERS TO SELECTED EXERCISES

INDEX

TABLES

GLOSSARY

abscissa (p. 128)   The x-coordinate, or first number, in an ordered pair (x, y). The abscissa of (2, −3) is 2.

absolute value (p. 32)   The distance of a number n from 0 on the number line, written as $|n|$.

absolute-value function (p. 437)   The function described by the equation $y = |x|$ (or $f(x) = |x|$).

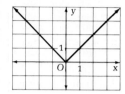

addition property of equality (p. 87)   For real numbers a, b, and c:

$$\text{If } a = b, \text{ then } a + c = b + c.$$

addition property of inequality (p. 366)   For real numbers a, b, and c:

$$\text{If } a < b, \text{ then } a + c < b + c.$$
$$\text{If } a > b, \text{ then } a + c > b + c.$$

addition property of opposites (p. 45)   For any number a:

$$a + (-a) = (-a) + a = 0$$

addition property of zero (p. 45)   For any number a:

$$a + 0 = 0 + a = a$$

additive identity (p. 44)   Zero is the additive identity. Adding 0 to the number produces the same number: $n + 0 = n$.

additive inverse (p. 44)   The opposite of a number. The additive inverse of a is −a. $a + (-a) = 0$

algebraic expression (p. 5)   An expression that involves variables, such as:

$$5n \qquad 3x + 5 \qquad a(2 - a) \qquad \frac{6 + 3m}{m - 5}$$

associative properties (p. 34)   For real numbers a, b, and c:

$$(a + b) + c = a + (b + c) \text{ and } (ab)c = a(bc)$$

average (p. 73)   A measure of central tendency; a typical value. The average that is used most often is the *mean*, which is the sum of the numbers divided by the number of numbers.

axes (p. 124)   In a coordinate plane, the horizontal number line is called the x-axis and the vertical number line is called the y-axis.

axis of symmetry (p. 438)   For a parabola of the form $y = x^2$, the vertical line through the vertex.

base (p. 8)   A number or variable used as a factor in an exponential expression. In $2^5 = 2 \cdot 2 \cdot 2 \cdot 2 \cdot 2$, the base is 2.

binomial (p. 166)   A polynomial with two terms. $3x^2 - 2$ is a binomial.

closure properties (p. 34)   The sum or product of two real numbers is a real number.

commutative properties (p. 34)   For real numbers a and b:

$$a + b = b + a \text{ and } ab = ba$$

complementary angles (p. 476)   Two angles, the sum of whose measures is 90°.

completing the square (p. 449)   Adding a constant to an expression of the form $ax^2 + bx$ to create a trinomial square.

complex fraction (p. 312)   A fraction that contains another fraction in the numerator or the denominator.

compound inequality (pp. 375, 376)   Two inequalities combined into one sentence by the connective words *and* or *or*.

$$x < 4 \text{ } and \text{ } x > 2 \qquad x > 7 \text{ } or \text{ } x < 1$$

conjunction (p. 375)   A compound sentence that uses the connective word *and*.

consecutive even numbers (p. 22)   Even numbers that differ by 2, such as 12, 14, 16, 18. If n is even, then the next consecutive even number is $n + 2$.

consecutive numbers (p. 21)   Consecutive numbers differ by 1, such as 101, 102, 103, 104. If n is a whole number or integer, the next consecutive number is $n + 1$.

consecutive odd numbers (p. 22)   Odd numbers that differ by 2, such as 13, 15, 17, 19. If n is odd, the next consecutive odd number is $n + 2$.

consistent system of equations (p. 268)   A system that has at least one solution.

constant of variation (pp. 463, 466)   The constant k in the equations $y = kx$ and $xy = k$.

constant term, or **constant** (p. 59)   A number alone, such as 25 in the expression $3x^2 + 25$.

coordinate (p. 28)   A number associated with a point on a number line. The coordinate of A is -2.

$$\overset{\textstyle A}{\underset{\textstyle -4\,-3\,-2\,-1\ 0\ \ 1\ \ 2\ \ 3\ \ 4}{\longleftrightarrow}}$$

coordinate plane (p. 124)   A plane with two axes. Points are located relative to a horizontal x-axis and a vertical y-axis.

coordinates of a point (p. 128)   An ordered pair (x, y) that locates a point in a coordinate plane.

corresponding angles (p. 479)   In two congruent or similar triangles, the pairs of angles with equal measures.

corresponding sides (p. 479)   In two congruent or similar triangles, the sides opposite pairs of angles that have equal measures.

cosine (p. 482)   For an acute angle A in a right triangle:

$$\text{cosine of } \angle A = \cos A = \frac{\text{length of leg adjacent to } \angle A}{\text{length of hypotenuse}}$$

degree of a monomial (p. 166)   The sum of the exponents of the variables. The degree of $6abc^2$ is 4.

degree of a polynomial in one variable (p. 167)   The greatest exponent of the variable that appears when the polynomial is in simplified form. The degree of $6x^5 - 3x^3$ is 5.

PREREQUISITE SKILLS FOLLOW-UP

EXTRA PRACTICE SETS

COMPUTER HANDBOOK

TABLES

GLOSSARY

ANSWERS TO CHECKPOINTS

ANSWERS TO SELECTED EXERCISES

INDEX

GLOSSARY

dependent system of equations (p. 269)   A system that has identical graphs for each of its equations, such as: $\begin{array}{l} y = x \\ x - y = 0 \end{array}$

direct variation (p. 463)   Two variables, y and x, vary directly if $y = kx$, where k is a constant.

discriminant (p. 456)   The quantity $b^2 - 4ac$ of the quadratic equation $ax^2 + bx + c = 0$. The discriminant of $3x^2 - 2x + 1 = 0$ is $(-2)^2 - 4(3)(1)$, or -8.

disjunction (p. 376)   A compound sentence that uses the connective word or.

distance formula (p. 423)   The distance between points (x_1, y_1) and (x_2, y_2) is:

$$\sqrt{(x_2 - x_1)^2 + (y_2 - y_1)^2}$$

distributive property (p. 55)   For real numbers a, b, and c:

$$a(b + c) = ab + ac \text{ and } (b + c)a = ba + ca$$

domain of a function (p. 438)   The set of replacements allowed for x in the ordered pairs (x, y) of the function

empty set (p. 90)   The set that contains no members. The symbol for the empty set is $\emptyset$.

equation (p. 14)   Two expressions with an equal sign between them.

equilateral triangle (p. 477)   A triangle with all sides of equal length.

equivalent equations (p. 87)   Equations that have the same solutions. $x + y = 8$ and $y = -x + 8$ are equivalent equations.

equivalent expressions (p. 60)   Expressions that have the same value for any replacement of the variable or variables.

evaluate (p. 5)   To evaluate an algebraic expression, replace each variable with the number it represents, and simplify.

even number (p. 22)   A member of the set 0, 2, 4, 6, 8, ...

exponent (p. 8)   A number that tells how many times the base is used as a factor. In $2^5 = 2 \cdot 2 \cdot 2 \cdot 2 \cdot 2$, the exponent is 5.

extraneous root (pp. 325, 425)   A number that appears to be a root but does not satisfy a given equation.

extremes of a proportion (p. 335)   In the proportion $a : b = c : d$, a and d are the extremes.

factor (p. 8)   Each of the numbers or variables used in a product.

factored form (p. 204)   A number or algebraic expression written as a product of its factors.

function (p. 434)   A set of ordered pairs of numbers such that for each first number there is exactly one second number.

function notation (p. 434)   The symbol $f(x)$ is read "f of x" or "f at x." If $f(x) = x^2 + 3$, then $f(2) = 2^2 + 3 = 7$.

greatest common factor for integers (p. 205)   The greatest factor that is common to each of the integers. The greatest common factor of 12 and 18 is 6.

greatest common factor for the terms of a polynomial (p. 213)   The product of the greatest common factor of the coefficients times the highest powers of the variables common to all terms. The greatest common factor of $12x^3y^2$ and $18xy^3$ is $6xy^2$.

550

grouping symbols (p. 3)   Parentheses, brackets, or fraction bars used to set off an expression.

half-plane (p. 383)   A line separates a plane into two regions, each called a half-plane.

hyperbola (p. 467)   The graph of an inverse variation such as $xy = 1$.

hypotenuse (p. 416)   The side opposite the right angle in a right triangle.

identity (p. 191)   An equation that is true for all replacements of the variable.
$2x = x + x$ is an identity.

inconsistent system of equations (p. 268)   A system of equations that has no solution, such as: $\begin{array}{l} y = 2x \\ y = 2x + 1 \end{array}$

independent system of equations (p. 268)   A system that has different graphs for each of its equations, such as: $\begin{array}{l} y = 3x \\ x + y = 4 \end{array}$

inequality (pp. 25, 362)   A sentence that contains an inequality symbol, such as $x > 2$ or $x \le -3$.

integer (p. 25)   A member of the set: $\{\ldots, \ ^-3, \ ^-2, -1, 0, \ ^+1, \ ^+2, \ ^+3, \ldots\}$.

intersection (p. 374)   The set of elements that belong to *each* of two or more sets. The intersection of $A = \{1, 2, 3, 4\}$, $B = \{1, 3, 5\}$, and $C = \{1, 2, 4\}$ is $\{1\}$.

inverse operations (pp. 92, 100)   Adding a number and subtracting the same number are inverse operations. Dividing by a number and multiplying by the same number are also inverse operations. Each operation "undoes" the other.

inverse variation (p. 466)   Two variables, y and x, vary inversely if $xy = k$, where k is a constant.

irrational number (p. 28)   A real number that cannot be expressed as a ratio of two integers.

isosceles triangle (p. 477)   A triangle that has two sides of equal length.

least common denominator (p. 309)   For fractions, the least common multiple of the denominators.

least common multiple (p. 309)   For several positive integers, the least number that is a multiple of each of the positive integers. The least common multiple of 9 and 15 is 45.

legs of a right triangle (p. 416)   The two sides adjacent to the right angle.

like terms (p. 59)   Terms that are identical or differ only in their numerical coefficients, such as $3x$, $7x$, and $-5x$. Like terms may also be called *similar* terms.

linear equation (p. 132)   An equation in two variables whose graph is a straight line. Such equations are also called first-degree equations since the variables occur in the first degree only.

PREREQUISITE SKILLS FOLLOW-UP

EXTRA PRACTICE SETS

COMPUTER HANDBOOK

TABLES

GLOSSARY

ANSWERS TO CHECKPOINTS

ANSWERS TO SELECTED EXERCISES

INDEX

GLOSSARY

maximum point of a parabola (p. 439)   The point of the curve for which the function has its greatest value

means of a proportion (p. 335)   In the proportion $a:b = c:d$, b and c are the means.

minimum point of a parabola (p. 438)   The point of the curve for which the function has its least value.

monomial (p. 166)   A constant, a variable, or the product of a constant and variables.

multiplication properties of 1 and −1 (p. 66)   For any number a:

$$a = 1(a) = a(1)$$
$$-a = -1(a) = a(-1)$$
$$(-1)(-a) = -(-a) = a$$

multiplication property of equality (p. 96)   For real numbers a, b, and c:

$$\text{If } a = b, \text{ then } ac = bc.$$

multiplication property of inequality (p. 368)   For real numbers a, b, and c:

When c is positive: If $a < b$, then $ac < bc$.
If $a > b$, then $ac > bc$.
When c is negative: If $a < b$, then $ac > bc$.
If $a > b$, then $ac < bc$.

multiplicative identity (p. 66)   The multiplicative identity is 1. Multiplying a number by 1 produces the same number: $1(a) = a$.

multiplicative inverse (p. 69)   The reciprocal of a nonzero number. The multiplicative inverse of a is $\frac{1}{a}$. $a \cdot \frac{1}{a} = 1$

numerical coefficient (p. 59)   The numerical factor of a term. In the term $5x^2y$, the numerical coefficient is 5.

numerical expression (p. 2)   An expression involving numbers, such as $9 + 6$ or 3×5.

odd number (p. 22)   A member of the set: $\{1, 3, 5, 7, 9, \ldots\}$.

open sentence (p. 14)   An equation or inequality that contains a variable.

opposite (p. 25)   The opposite, or additive inverse, of a number is the same distance as the number from the origin on a number line, but in the opposite direction. The opposite of a number a is $-a$. $a + (-a) = 0$

order of operations (pp. 3, 9)   First simplify expressions set off by grouping symbols. Next raise to a power, then multiply and divide, in order from left to right. Then add and subtract, in order from left to right.

ordered pair (p. 125)   A pair of numbers, usually (x, y), in which the order is x first and y second.

ordinate (p. 128)   The y-coordinate, or second number, in an ordered pair (x, y). The ordinate of $(2, -3)$ is -3.

origin (pp. 25, 124)   The point corresponding to zero on a number line. The intersection of the x- and y-axes, $(0, 0)$, in a coordinate plane.

parabola (p. 438)   The graph of a quadratic function of the form $y = ax^2 + bx + c$, $a \neq 0$.

parallel lines (p. 145)   Lines with the same slope but different y-intercepts. Lines in a plane that never meet, including pairs of vertical lines.

perfect square (p. 401)   A number whose positive square root is a whole number.

polynomial (p. 166)   A monomial or the sum of terms each of which is a monomial, such as $4x^3 - 3x^2 - 2x + 5$.

power (pp. 8, 211) x^n is read as the "the nth power of x." It denotes a product that shows x used as a factor n times. By definition, $x^0 = 1$ and $x^{-n} = \frac{1}{x^n}$, $x \neq 0$.

prime factorization (p. 205)   A number written as a product of prime factors. The prime factorization of 36 is $2^2 \cdot 3^2$.

prime number (p. 204)   A positive integer that has exactly two different factors, itself and 1.

proportion (p. 335)   An equation stating that two ratios are equal.

proportion property (p. 336)   For real numbers a, b, c, and d with $b \neq 0$ and $d \neq 0$:

$$\text{If } \frac{a}{b} = \frac{c}{d}, \text{ then } ad = bc.$$

Pythagorean theorem (p. 416)   In a right triangle, with legs a and b and hypotenuse c, $a^2 + b^2 = c^2$.

quadrant (p. 128)   One of four regions formed in a coordinate plane by the x- and y-axes.

quadratic equations (pp. 438, 452)   Second-degree equations of the form:

$$ax^2 + bx + c = 0 \text{ or of the form } y = ax^2 + bx + c; a \neq 0$$

quadratic formula (p. 452)   If $ax^2 + bx + c = 0$, $a \neq 0$, then:

$$x = \frac{-b \pm \sqrt{b^2 - 4ac}}{2a}$$

radical (p. 401)   An expression such as $\sqrt{37}$. The symbol $\sqrt{}$ is a radical sign.

radical equation (p. 425)   An equation with a variable in the radicand.

radicand (p. 401)   The quantity under a radical sign. In $\sqrt{37}$, the radicand is 37.

range of a function (p. 438)   The set of replacements for y in the ordered pairs (x, y) of the function.

ratio (p. 335)   A comparison of two numbers by division. The ratio of a to b is $\frac{a}{b}$.

rational expression (p. 286)   An expression of the form $\frac{a}{b}$ where a and b are polynomials.

PREREQUISITE SKILLS FOLLOW-UP

EXTRA PRACTICE SETS

COMPUTER HANDBOOK

TABLES

GLOSSARY

ANSWERS TO CHECKPOINTS

ANSWERS TO SELECTED EXERCISES

INDEX

GLOSSARY

rational number (p. 28)   A number that can be expressed as a ratio of two integers.

rationalize the denominator (p. 408)   A process of rewriting a fraction so that the new denominator is a rational number.

real number (p. 29)   A member of the set of rational numbers or the set of irrational numbers. A number that corresponds to a point on a number line.

reciprocal (p. 69)   The reciprocal, or multiplicative inverse, of a nonzero number a is $\frac{1}{a}$. $a \cdot \frac{1}{a} = 1$

reflexive property of equality (p. 35)   For any real number a, $a = a$.

relation (p. 434)   A set of ordered pairs of numbers.

replacement set (p. 90)   A set of numbers that may be used as replacements for a variable.

right triangle (p. 416)   A triangle that contains a 90°, or right, angle.

root (p. 14)   A solution of an equation.

scientific notation (p. 399)   A number in the form $a \times 10^b$ where a is between 1 and 10 and b is an integer. In scientific notation, 360,000 is 3.6×10^5 and 0.0023 is 2.3×10^{-3}.

similar terms (p. 59)   See like terms.

similar triangles (p. 479)   Triangles that have the same shape. The statement $\triangle ABC \sim \triangle XYZ$ is read as "Triangle ABC is similar to triangle XYZ." For these triangles, $\angle A = \angle X$, $\angle B = \angle Y$, and $\angle C = \angle Z$.

sine (p. 482)   For an acute angle A in a right triangle:

$$\text{sine of } \angle A = \sin A = \frac{\text{length of leg opposite } \angle A}{\text{length of hypotenuse}}$$

slope-intercept form of a linear equation (p. 145)   The form $y = mx + b$, where m is the slope and b is the y-intercept of the line. $y = 3x + 4$ is the slope-intercept form of $6x - 2y = -8$.

slope of a line (p. 136)   For points (x_1, y_1) and (x_2, y_2) on a line, the slope is $\frac{y_2 - y_1}{x_2 - x_1}$. The slope of a horizontal line is 0. The slope of a vertical line is not defined.

solution (pp. 14, 362)   A replacement for a variable that makes an equation or an inequality true. A solution of an equation may also be called a *root* of the equation.

solution of a linear equation in two variables (p. 133)   An ordered pair that satisfies the equation.

solution of a system of two equations in two unknowns (p. 254)   An ordered pair that satisfies both equations.

solution set (p. 90)   Those elements of the replacement set of a variable that make an equation or inequality true.

square root (p. 401)   If $a^2 = b$, then a is a square root of b. Since $5^2 = 25$, 5 is a square root of 25. -5 is also a square root of 25.

standard form of a linear equation (p. 152)   The form $Ax + By = C$ where A and B are not both 0.

supplementary angles (p. 476)   Two angles the sum of whose measures is 180°.

symmetric property of equality (p. 35)   For real numbers a and b:

$$\text{If } a = b, \text{ then } b = a.$$

system of equations (p. 254)   A set of equations in two or more variables for which a common solution is sought.

tangent (p. 482)   For an acute angle A in a right triangle:

$$\text{tangent of } \angle A = \tan A = \frac{\text{length of leg opposite } \angle A}{\text{length of leg adjacent to } \angle A}$$

term (p. 59)   A number, a variable, or the product or quotient of numbers and variables.

transitive property of equality (p. 35)   For real numbers a, b, and c:

$$\text{If } a = b \text{ and } b = c, \text{ then } a = c.$$

transitive property of inequality (p. 363)   For real numbers a, b, and c:

$$\text{If } a < b \text{ and } b < c, \text{ then } a < c.$$
$$\text{If } a > b \text{ and } b > c, \text{ then } a > c.$$

trichotomy property (p. 363)   For real numbers a and b:

$$a < b, a = b, \text{ or } a > b.$$

trinomial (p. 166)   A polynomial with three terms. $3x^5 + 4x^2 - 3x$ is a trinomial.

trinomial square (p. 223)   A trinomial of the form $a^2 + 2ab + b^2$ or $a^2 - 2ab + b^2$, which is the square of a binomial.

union (p. 374)   The set of elements that belong to at least one of two or more sets. The union of $A = \{1, 2, 3, 4\}$, $B = \{1, 3, 5\}$, and $C = \{1, 2, 4\}$ is $\{1, 2, 3, 4, 5\}$.

variable (p. 5)   A symbol, usually a letter, used to represent numbers.

vertex of a parabola (p. 438)   The minimum or maximum point of the parabola.

vertical line test (p. 435)   A graph represents a function if any vertical line intersects the graph in at most one point.

whole number (p. 21)   A member of the set: $\{0, 1, 2, 3, \ldots\}$.

x-axis (p. 128)   The horizontal number line in a coordinate plane.

x-coordinate (p. 128)   The first number in an ordered pair (x, y). The x-coordinate is also called the *abscissa*.

x-intercept (p. 141)   The x-coordinate of the point where a line or curve crosses the x-axis; that is, the x-coordinate when $y = 0$. The x-intercept of $x + 2y = 4$ is 4.

y-axis (p. 128)   The vertical number line in a coordinate plane.

y-coordinate (p. 128)   The second number in an ordered pair (x, y). The y-coordinate is also called the *ordinate*.

y-intercept (p. 141)   The y-coordinate of the point where a line or curve crosses the y-axis; that is, the y-coordinate when $x = 0$. The y-intercept of $x + 2y = 4$ is 2.

zero product rule (p. 236)   For real numbers a and b:

$$\text{If } ab = 0, \text{ then } a = 0 \text{ or } b = 0.$$
$$\text{If } a = 0 \text{ or } b = 0, \text{ then } ab = 0.$$

PREREQUISITE SKILLS FOLLOW-UP

EXTRA PRACTICE SETS

COMPUTER HANDBOOK

TABLES

GLOSSARY

ANSWERS TO CHECKPOINTS

ANSWERS TO SELECTED EXERCISES

INDEX

GLOSSARY

ANSWERS TO CHECKPOINTS

CHAPTER 1
Page 16. **1.** 10 **2.** 16 **3.** 10 **4.** 0
5. 49 **6.** 12 **7.** 15 **8.** 1 **9.** 36 **10.** 32
11. 192 **12.** 80 **13.** 52 **14.** 144
15. 72 **16.** 8
Page 31. **1.** 3 **2.** 0 **3.** 10 **4.** 7 **5.** 1
6. 108 **7.** $2x$ **8.** $x + 2$ **9.** $x - 2$ **10.** $\dfrac{x}{2}$
11. $x + 5 = 13; x = 8$ **12.** $x - 11 = 21;$
$x = 32$ **13.** $3x = 51; x = 17$ **14.** 0, 1, 2
15. 3, 4, 5, 6, $\cdots$ **16.** 1, 2, 3, 6 **17.** 1,
2 **18.** 0, 1, 2, 3

CHAPTER 2
Page 58. **1.** -2 **2.** -5 **3.** 3 **4.** -21
5. 0 **6.** 12 **7.** 8 **8.** -10 **9.** -12
10. 19 **11.** 13 **12.** -8 **13.** -73
14. 14 **15.** 1 **16.** 0 **17.** 23 **18.** 80
19. -14 **20.** -8 **21.** -11 **22.** -0.5
23. 5.5 **24.** -5.5 **25.** -5.5 **26.** -5.5
27. -0.5 **28.** 5.5 **29.** 5.5 **30.** 4 **31.** a
32. $4x + 12$ **33.** $15x + 15y$ **34.** $xy - 7x$
35. $xy + xz$
Page 72. **1.** 23 **2.** -19 **3.** 16 **4.** 18
5. -2 **6.** 48 **7.** -48 **8.** -48 **9.** 48
10. -2 **11.** $\dfrac{1}{8}$ **12.** -6 **13.** -6
14. $3x + 3$ **15.** $4a + 4b$ **16.** $6g + 2g$
17. $qr - qt$ **18.** -10 **19.** 2 **20.** 3
21. 4 **22.** $18x$ **23.** $-18y$ **24.** $-8a$
25. $-30k^2$ **26.** $-6 - 16h$ **27.** Cannot be
simplified **28.** -60 **29.** 4 **30.** 17 **31.** 7

CHAPTER 3
Page 95. **1.** $x + 17 = 29$
2. $x - 12 = 10$ **3.** $3 + x = -2$
4. $6 - x = 8$ **5.** Three times some number is equal to 18. **6.** Five more than
twice a number is equal to 16. **7.** Four
times the sum of n and 2 is equal to 10.
8. 11 **9.** 7.8 **10.** 5.4 **11.** -2.3 **12.** 15
13. -8 **14.** $\dfrac{1}{8}$ **15.** $\dfrac{1}{2}$ **16.** $-\dfrac{1}{6}$

17. $x - 13 = 9;$ 22 **18.** $11 + x = 4;$ 7
19. $1 = x + (-8);$ 9
20. $3 = x - (-8);$ -5
Page 110. **1.** -30 **2.** -1 **3.** 3 **4.** -9
5. $\dfrac{1}{8}$ **6.** 8 **7.** 6 **8.** 5 **9.** 8 **10.** -26
11. 4 **12.** 2 **13.** 3 **14.** 3 **15.** 12
16. -3 **17.** -2 **18.** -13
19. $8x - 50 = 6;$ 7 **20.** $3(x + 2) = 9;$ 1
21. $2x - 15 = 75;$ 45
22. $\dfrac{1}{2}(x + 13) = 3(1 - x);$ -1

CHAPTER 4
Page 135. **1.** $(-4, 1)$ **2.** $(-4, -1)$
3. $(-2, 3)$ **4.** $(0, -3)$ **5.** $(4, -1)$
6. $(4, 1)$ **7.** $(-1, 0)$ **8.** $(2, 4)$ **9.** I
10. x-axis **11.** III **12.** x and y axes
13. II **14.** IV **15.** y-axis **16.** I
17. Points will vary.

18. Points will vary.

19. **20.**

21.

22. Yes **23.** Yes **24.** No

Page 148. **1.** IV **2.** $\frac{11}{7}$ **3.** 0

4. $-\frac{12}{11}$ **5.** $-\frac{1}{3}$; 1 **6.** -2; 4 **7.** 6; -3

8. 2; 3 **9.** -4; 0

10. $\frac{2}{3}$; -3

11. $-\frac{3}{2}$

CHAPTER 5

Page 177. **1.** $5x$; 1 **2.** $-10x$; 1
3. $-5x^3 + 25x$; 3 **4.** $7x + 3$; 1 **5.** $-4x^4$;
4 **6.** -2; 0 **7.** 10 **8.** $13x - y - 2$
9. $-x + 2y + 7z$ **10.** $x^2 - y^2$
11. $x^2 - x - 30$ **12.** $35a^6$ **13.** $-3x^8$
14. $6a^2b$ **15.** $4ab^3$ **16.** $3x^5y^6$ **17.** $8x^3y^2$
18. x^8 **19.** x^5 **20.** 7^{11} **21.** a^{x+y}

Page 192. **1.** $7x - 11$; -25 **2.** $-3x +$
3; 9 **3.** $-4x - 1$; 7 **4.** $-2a - 6$
5. $-4x + y$ **6.** a^5b^5 **7.** a^2b^5 **8.** $-24x^{10}$
9. $x^{12}y^{11}$ **10.** $-16x - 1$ **11.** 0
12. $2x^2 + 3x - 2$ **13.** $2x^2 - 5x + 3$
14. $9x^2 - 6x + 1$ **15.** $6x^2 - 17x + 12$
16. $6x^2 + 10x + 4$ **17.** $16x^2 - 9$ **18.** 6
19. $\frac{1}{2}$ **20.** $-\frac{2}{3}$ **21.** 1

ANSWERS TO CHECKPOINTS

CHAPTER 6

Page 222. **1.** 9 **2.** 52 **3.** 19 **4.** 6
5. $6x$ **6.** -3 **7.** $5z^5$ **8.** $2xz$
9. $6(x + 3)$ **10.** $5(x + 2)$ **11.** $5(2x - 1)$
12. $9x(x - 3)$ **13.** $-3x^2(x - 1)$, or
$3x^2(-x + 1)$ **14.** $13x^2(3x^2 + 2)$
15. $7x(-2x + 1)$ **16.** $14x(2x^2 - 1)$
17. $3x(3x^2 - 2x + 1)$ **18.** $(x - 7)(x + 7)$
19. $2(x^2 + y^2)$ **20.** $(2x + 5)(y - 3)$
21. $(y - 1)(1 + x)$ **22.** $(y + 2)(x + 3)$
23. $(2 - x)(2 + x)$ **24.** $(3x - 4)(3x + 4)$
25. $(4x - 3y)(4x + 3y)$
26. $(10x - 1)(10x + 1)$
27. $x(x - 9)(x + 9)$ **28.** $3x(x - 3)(x + 3)$
29. $2(11 - x)(11 + x)$
30. $5y(x - 5y)(x + 5y)$

Page 235 **1.** $9z^3$ **2.** $\frac{7x^2}{4}$ **3.** $-2yz$
4. $\frac{xz^3}{7}$ **5.** $4x^3z^2w$ **6.** $2xz$ **7.** $-3x^2y$

8. $-3xyz$ **9.** $3x(2x + 1)$ **10.** $x^4(x^2 + 1)$
11. $6x^2(8x - 3)$ **12.** $4x(x - 2)$
13. $(x + 2)(x + 2y)$ **14.** $(x - ac)(x - ab)$
15. $(5x - y)(5x + y)$ **16.** $4(3 - 2x)(3 + 2x)$
17. $x(x - 4)(x + 4)$ **18.** $4(x - 5)(x + 5)$
19. $(4x^2 + 9)(2x - 3)(2x + 3)$
20. $(5x - y)(5x + y)(25x^2 + y^2)$
21. $(x + 8)^2$ **22.** $(4x - 3)^2$ **23.** $2x(2x - 3)^2$
24. $(x - 7)(x + 3)$ **25.** $(x + 8)(x - 3)$
26. $(3x - 2)(x - 1)$ **27.** $(3x + 1)(3x + 8)$

CHAPTER 7

Page 263.

1. $(3, 1)$

2. $(1, -1)$

3. $(1, 6)$

PREREQUISITE SKILLS FOLLOW-UP

EXTRA PRACTICE SETS

COMPUTER HANDBOOK

TABLES

GLOSSARY

ANSWERS TO CHECKPOINTS

ANSWERS TO SELECTED EXERCISES

INDEX

ANSWERS TO CHECKPOINTS

4. $(-4, -1)$ **5.** $(0, 1)$ **6.** $(4, 1)$
7. $(2, -2)$ **8.** $(-1, 0)$ **9.** $(2, -5)$
10. $(6, 0)$

Page 271.

1. $(3, -2)$ **2.** $(4, -4)$

3. $(-2, 3)$

4. $(6, 1)$; consistent; independent

5. Inconsistent; independent **6.** $\left(\dfrac{1}{4}, \dfrac{1}{2}\right)$; consistent; independent **7.** $(-4, 3)$; consistent; independent **8.** Consistent; dependent **9.** $\left(-\dfrac{7}{4}, 2\right)$; consistent; independent **10.** $x = 7$; $y = 10$

CHAPTER 8

Page 304. **1.** $\dfrac{5}{21}$ **2.** $-\dfrac{1}{12}$ **3.** xy

4. -3 **5.** $\dfrac{5}{16}$ **6.** $\dfrac{1}{2}$ **7.** $\dfrac{4}{5x^2y}$

8. $\dfrac{(x-6)^2}{(x+2)^2}$ **9.** $\dfrac{x}{4}$ **10.** $\dfrac{1}{x-3}$ **11.** $x - 3$

12. $x + 3 + \dfrac{5}{x-1}$ **13.** $x + 2 - \dfrac{17}{x+4}$

14. $2x - 5 + \dfrac{15}{3x+2}$

Page 311. **1.** $\dfrac{2y}{3x^2}$ **2.** $x - 2y$ **3.** $\dfrac{x-1}{x+1}$

4. $\dfrac{2}{x+1}$ **5.** $\dfrac{x^2}{3(x+1)}$ **6.** $\dfrac{x+4}{(x-3)^2}$

7. $x - 1$ **8.** $\dfrac{2x+9}{(x-3)(x+3)}$ **9.** $\dfrac{5}{2(x+1)}$

CHAPTER 9

Page 329. **1.** 1 **2.** 5 **3.** No solution

4. 1 **5.** 1.8, or $\dfrac{9}{5}$ **6.** 2 **7.** 4 **8.** -4

9. 3 **10.** $\dfrac{8}{13}$

Page 342. **1.** 54 **2.** 1 **3.** 3 **4.** $\dfrac{5}{9}$

5. 9 **6.** $-\dfrac{1}{2}$ **7.** -1; -2 **8.** 20% **9.** 40

10. $250.50 **11.** 11% **12.** $573.05

CHAPTER 10

Page 370.

1. $x \geq 3$

2. $x < -1$

3. $x > 6$

4. $x > 2$

5. $x < -2$

6. $x < 2$

7. $x \geq -1$

8. $x \geq 5$

9. $x \leq 17$

10. $x \leq -8$

11. $x > 3$

12. $x < 5$

13. $x \leq 4$

14. $x > 26$

Page 385.

1. $1 < x < 3$

2. $-5 \leq x < -3$

3. $-1 < x < 2$

558

4. $x > 2$ or $x < -3$ ◄———○————○——►
$\qquad\qquad\qquad -3 \qquad 2$

5. $1 \leq x \leq 3$ ◄———●————●——►
$\qquad\qquad\qquad 1 \qquad 3$

6. $1 < x < 3$ ◄———○————○——►
$\qquad\qquad\qquad 1 \qquad 3$

7. $x > 3$ or $x < 1$ ◄———○————○——►
$\qquad\qquad\qquad 1 \qquad 3$

8. $x \leq 1$ or $x \geq 5$ ◄———●————●——►
$\qquad\qquad\qquad 1 \qquad 5$

9. $\dfrac{3}{4} < x < \dfrac{7}{4}$ ◄———○————○——►
$\qquad\qquad\qquad \frac{3}{4} \qquad \frac{7}{4}$

CHAPTER 11

Page 404. **1.** 0.25 **2.** $1.\overline{3}$ **3.** $0.\overline{5}$

4. $0.\overline{076923}$ **5.** $0.\overline{384615}$ **6.** $\dfrac{77}{100}$ **7.** $\dfrac{89}{10}$

8. $\dfrac{3}{50}$ **9.** $\dfrac{71}{500}$ **10.** $-\dfrac{20}{3}$ **11.** 784

12. 8464 **13.** 11 **14.** 22 **15.** 33

16. 58 **17.** 10 **18.** -25 **19.** 12 **20.** 5

21. $\dfrac{1}{9}$ **22.** $\dfrac{1}{16}$ **23.** $\dfrac{9}{14}$ **24.** $\dfrac{1}{2}$ **25.** $\dfrac{3}{35}$

Page 413. **1.** 0.91 **2.** 2.75 **3.** $1.\overline{6}$

4. $2.\overline{3}$ **5.** $0.\overline{7}$ **6.** $\dfrac{281}{99}$ **7.** $5\sqrt{2}$ **8.** $10\sqrt{5}$

9. $10\sqrt{5}$ **10.** $12\sqrt{3}$ **11.** $-6\sqrt{7}$ **12.** $\dfrac{1}{3}$

13. $\dfrac{1}{6}$ **14.** $\dfrac{1}{36}$ **15.** $\dfrac{1}{72}$ **16.** $\dfrac{11}{13}$ **17.** 5

18. $\dfrac{\sqrt{15}}{5}$ **19.** $\dfrac{\sqrt{35}}{7}$ **20.** $\dfrac{\sqrt{2}}{4}$ **21.** $\dfrac{4}{3}$

22. $5x$ **23.** $x\sqrt{3}$ **24.** $8x^2$ **25.** $30x\sqrt{x}$

26. $6x^2y^3\sqrt{2xy}$ **27.** $3xy\sqrt{2}$ **28.** $x^2y^2\sqrt{xy}$

29. $3\sqrt{x}$ **30.** $3x\sqrt{3}$

CHAPTER 12

Page 441 **1.** No. When $x = -2$, y has different values, 0 and -3 **2.** Yes
3. Yes **4.** No. A vertical line can intersect the graph in two places. **5.** No. A vertical line can intersect the graph in two places. **6.** Yes **7.** 5 **8.** 6 **9.** 10

10. $3a^2 - 2a + 5$ **11.** 13 **12.** 21

13. $4\dfrac{2}{3}$ **14.** 6 **15.** Vertex is $(0, 0)$. It is a maximum point for $y = -\dfrac{1}{8}x^2$ and a minimum point for $y = 8x^2$.

$y = 8x^2 \rightarrow$ D: x is any real number
$\qquad\qquad$ R: $y \geq 0$

$y = -\dfrac{1}{8}x^2 \rightarrow$ D: x is any real number
$\qquad\qquad$ R: $y \leq 0$

Page 458. **1.** $(4, -2)$; $x = 4$; max. pt.
2. $y = 2(x - 3)^2 - 15$

3. $x^2 - 5x - 3 = 0$; $x = \dfrac{5 \pm \sqrt{37}}{2}$

4. $2x^2 + 3x - 4 = 0$; $x = \dfrac{-3 \pm \sqrt{41}}{4}$

5. $5x^2 + 4x - 3 = 0$; $x = \dfrac{-2 \pm \sqrt{19}}{5}$

6. One, since the discriminant $=$ $144 - 4(3)(12) = 0$.

PREREQUISITE SKILLS FOLLOW-UP

EXTRA PRACTICE SETS

COMPUTER HANDBOOK

TABLES

GLOSSARY

ANSWERS TO CHECKPOINTS

ANSWERS TO SELECTED EXERCISES

INDEX

ANSWERS TO CHECKPOINTS

559

ANSWERS TO SELECTED EXERCISES

CHAPTER 1

Page 1. Prerequisite Skills Review
1. b **2.** d **3.** c **4.** b **5.** b **6.** a **7.** b
8. b **9.** c **10.** d
Page 3. Class Exercises 1. 9 **3.** 23
5. 7 **7.** 6 **9.** 2 **11.** 6 **13.** 30 **15.** 17
Page 4. Exercises 1. 9 **3.** 18 **5.** 8
7. 5 **9.** 7 **11.** 9 **13.** 8 **15.** 1 **17.** 8
19. 16 **21.** 0 **23.** 24 **25.** 2 **27.** 5
29. 34 **31.** 0 **33.** 6 **35.** 1 **37.** 11
39. 13 **41.** 10 **43.** 4 **45.** 4 **47.** 126
49. 44 **51.** 66 **53.** 4 **55.** 77 **57.** 14
59. c **61.** b **63.** $(12 \times 2) + 6$;
$12 \times (2 + 6)$ **65.** $48 - [(28 - 10) \times 2]$;
$[48 - (28 - 10)] \times 2$
Page 6. Class Exercises 1. 11 **3.** 36
5. 9 **7.** 19 **9.** 2 **11.** 12 **13.** 2 **15.** 2
Pages 6–7. Exercises 1. 17 **3.** 6
5. 40 **7.** 37 **9.** 10 **11.** 18 **13.** 5
15. 12 **17.** 2 **19.** 60 **21.** 3 **23.** 72
25. 24 **27.** 8 **29.** 3 **31.** 8 **33.** 42
35. 216 **37.** 18 **39.** 180 **41.** 2 **43.** 3
45. 75 **47.** 280 **49.** 97 **51.** 56 **53.** 2
55. 7 **57.** 23 **59.** $\frac{3}{8}$, or 0.375
Page 9. Class Exercises 1. 25 **3.** 27
5. 81 **7.** 100 **9.** x^3 **11.** ab^4
Page 10. Exercises 1. 8 **3.** 9 **5.** 1
7. 243 **9.** 144 **11.** 16 **13.** 21 **15.** 3
17. 2 **19.** x^6 **21.** $3xz^2$ **23.** $4d^2$
25. $(7e)^3$ **27.** $(5s)^2$ **29.** 12 **31.** 216
33. 32 **35.** 512 **37.** 48 **39.** 192
41. 3600 **43.** 32 **45.** $a^2 + b^2 = 20$
47. $a^2b^2 = 64$ **49.** 1.728
Page 12. Class Exercises 1. 20 **3.** 8
5. $x + 5$ **7.** $5 + x$ **9.** $5x + 5$
11. $5 - \frac{x}{5}$
Pages 12–13. Exercises 1. 14 **3.** 45
5. $6n$ **7.** $6 - n$ **9.** $6n + 6$ **11.** $\frac{6}{n}$, or
$6 \div n$ **13.** $a + 15$ **15.** $\frac{8}{a}$ **17.** $6a + 7$

10. $\frac{11}{a + 6}$ **21.** 5 more than a number
23. 5 less than a number **25.** $x \div y$, or $\frac{x}{y}$
27. 6 more than 5 times p **29.** 5 times
the sum of r and 6 **31.** $x^2 + 1$
33. $(x + y)^2$ **35.** $y - x^4$ **37.** $s - 6$
39. $2s$
Page 15. Class Exercises 1. Yes
3. Yes **5.** No **7.** 2 **9.** 2 **11.** 3
Pages 15–16. Exercises 1. Yes
3. No **5.** Yes **7.** 2 **9.** 1 **11.** 3 **13.** 1
15. 2 **17.** 3 **19.** 3 **21.** 2 **23.** No
25. No **27.** Yes **29.** No **31.** Yes
33. Yes **35.** Yes **37.** No **39.** Yes
41. 0; 3 **43.** 0; 1 **45.** 4; 5 **47.** 7
49. 9 **51.** 3 **53.** 7 **55.** 4 **57.** 6
Page 18. Class Exercises 1. Sub.; 25
3. Add.; 28 **5.** Div.; 50 **7.** Mult.; 180
9. $n + 3 = 17$; 14 **11.** $n = 4(9)$; 36
13. $4 + 4(7) = n$; 32; Aug. 1
Pages 19–20. Exercises 1. Add.; 96
3. Sub.; 40 **5.** Div.; 11 **7.** Mult.; 80
9. Div.; 5 **11.** Add., sub.; 55
13. $n + 18 = 35$; \$17 **15.** $8n = 1.20$; 15¢
17. $12n = 600$; \$50 **19.** $\frac{n}{25} = 6$; \$150
21. $n + 16 = 40$; 24 **23.** $6n = 96$; 16
25. 66 **27.** 1732 **29.** $6\frac{1}{2}$¢, or 6.5¢
31. \$6.84 **33.** 1980 **35.** 1981; 1988;
1989 **37.** 1980; 1982 **39.** Franklin
Roosevelt; 2 years
Page 22. Class Exercises 1. 84; yes
3. 4.2; no **5.** 4; yes **7.** 2; yes
9. 0, 1, 2, $\cdots$, 24 **11.** All whole numbers: 0, 1, 2, $\cdots$ **13.** All whole numbers: 0, 1, 2, $\cdots$ **15.** 0, 3, 6, 9, $\cdots$
Page 23. Exercises 1. No **3.** Yes
5. No **7.** 99; yes **9.** 49; yes **11.** 0; yes
13. 2; yes **15.** All whole numbers
17. No values **19.** 1, 2, 5, 10 **21.** 0, 1,
2, 3, 4, 5 **23.** 998, 1000, 1002

25. $n + 2, n + 4, n + 6$ **27.** $n + 1,$
$n + 2, n + 3$ **29.** Even **31.** Odd
33. Odd **35.** Even **37.** $n + 4, n + 6,$
$n + 8$ **39.** $0, 8, 16, \cdots$
41. $0, 3, 6, 9, \cdots$ **43.** $0, 1, 2, \cdots$

Page 26. Class Exercises **1.** Yes
3. No **5.** Yes **7.** $^-9$ **9.** 1 **11.** $A = $
$^-8; B = ^-2; C = 0; D = 4; E = 12$

Page 27. Exercises **1.** 13, 49, 0 **3.** 2
5. 257 **7.** $A = ^-6; B = ^-3; C = 1; D = 7$

9.

$-5\ -4\ -3\ -2\ -1\ 0\ 1\ 2\ 3\ 4\ 5$

$-5\ -4\ -3\ -2\ -1\ 0\ 1\ 2\ 3\ 4\ 5$

11. 9, 10, 11, 12, 13 **13.** $^-5, ^-4, ^-3$
15. True **17.** $^-7, ^-4, ^-1, 0, 1, 3$
19. 0, 6 **21.** $^+9$ **23.** $^-5000$ **25.** $^-2$
27. $n + 1, n + 2$ **29.** $n + 1, n + 3$
31. Odd

Pages 29–30. Class Exercises **1.** B
3. A **5.** 1, 2 **7.** 1, 2 **9.** $^-2, ^-1.7, 1.5, 3$

Pages 30–31. Exercises **1.** G **3.** J
5. C

7.

$-5\ -4\ -3\ -2\ -1\ 0\ 1\ 2\ 3\ 4\ 5$

9. $\dfrac{3}{10}$ **11.** $-\dfrac{65}{100}$ **13.** $>$ **15.** $<$ **17.** $<$

19. $>$ **21.** $>$ **23.** $^-5, ^-3, 8$ **25.** $^-1, -\dfrac{1}{2}, 0$

27. $^-1.1, ^-0.8, 0.9$ **29.** $^-\pi, ^-\sqrt{3}, ^-1.5,$

$^-1\dfrac{4}{9}, ^-\sqrt{2}$ **31.** F **33.** B **35.** H **37.** A

39. $^-1\dfrac{5}{8}$ **41.** $^-4$ **43.** Positive **45.** Negative

Page 33. Class Exercises **1.** 6 **3.** 3
5. 7 **7.** 3 **9.** 1 **11.** 1, $^-1$ **13.** 1, $^-1$

Page 33. Exercises **1.** 5 **3.** 12.7
5. 0 **7.** 10 **9.** 0 **11.** 8 **13.** 21 **15.** 15
17. 27 **19.** 1 and $^-1$ **21.** None **23.** 1
and $^-1$ **25.** 7 and $^-7$ **27.** 9 and $^-9$
29. Negative values **31.** Positive and
negative values and 0

Page 35. Class Exercises
1. Comm. for add. **3.** Assoc. for mult.
5. Assoc. for add. **7.** Comm. for add.
9. Symmetric

Page 36. Exercises **1.** Assoc. for add.
3. Assoc. for mult. **5.** Assoc. for mult.
7. Assoc. for add. **9.** Assoc. for mult.
11. Closure for mult. **13.** Symmetric
15. Reflexive **17.** 15; 15; assoc. for add.
19. 2.1; 2.1; comm. for add. **21.** 60; 60;
assoc. for mult. **23.** 6; 6; comm. for
mult. **25.** $6\dfrac{3}{4}; 6\dfrac{3}{4}$; comm. for add.

27. $2\dfrac{1}{4}$ **29.** 0.4 **31.** 67 **33.** No

35. No **37.** Yes

Pages 38–40. Review Exercises **1.** 8
3. 24 **5.** 90 **7.** 35 **9.** 40 **11.** 15
13. 64 **15.** 160 **17.** 8 **19.** $(x + y) - 1$
21. $2(x + 12)$ **23.** 5 **25.** $n + 16 = 39$;
23 **27.** $\dfrac{n}{12} = 7$; \$84 **29.** 0, 1, 2, 3, 4, 5

31. 1, 2, 3, 4, 6, 12 **33.** Yes **35.** Yes
37. -5 **39.** 0 **41.** $>$ **43.** $<$ **45.** 0.6
47. 11 **49.** Commut. prop. for mult.
51. Assoc. prop. for mult. **53.** Reflexive
55. Symmetric

CHAPTER 2
Page 43. Prerequisite Skills Review
1. d **2.** d **3.** c **4.** b **5.** b **6.** c **7.** c
8. a **9.** d **10.** d

Pages 45–46. Class Exercises **1.** -6
3. 15 **5.** $1 + 4 = 5$ **7.** 5 **9.** -6 **11.** 2
13. 0 **15.** 2 **17.** 3.2 **19.** -8 **21.** 2

23. $-\dfrac{1}{4}$ **25.** $-4\dfrac{1}{4}$

Page 46. Exercises **1.** $(-2) + (-2) = $
-4 **3.** 4 **5.** -2 **7.** -6 **9.** -2 **11.** 2

13. -5 **15.** 4 **17.** -10 **19.** $4\dfrac{1}{2}$

21. -3.3 **23.** -8 **25.** -25 **27.** -1

29. 3 **31.** -37 **33.** 10.1 **35.** $8\dfrac{1}{4}$

37. $2\dfrac{4}{5}$ **39.** $3\dfrac{1}{5}$ **41.** $36 + 4 + (-3) + $
$(-6) + 17 = 48$; on 48-yard line

Page 48. Class Exercises **1.** $+$ **3.** $-$
5. $-$ **7.** 6 **9.** -30 **11.** 14 **13.** -13

15. $-7\dfrac{1}{2}$ **17.** -5 **19.** -7 **21.** -3

PREREQUISITE SKILLS FOLLOW-UP

EXTRA PRACTICE SETS

COMPUTER HANDBOOK

TABLES

GLOSSARY

ANSWERS TO CHECKPOINTS

ANSWERS TO SELECTED EXERCISES

INDEX

ANSWERS TO SELECTED EXERCISES

Pages 48–49. Exercises 1. -58 **3.** 1
5. -108 **7.** -29 **9.** -100 **11.** -42
13. 80 **15.** -320 **17.** -6 **19.** 18
21. -17 **23.** 3 **25.** 35 **27.** 15
29. -22 **31.** -3 **33.** 73 **35.** -9.5
37. 65 **39.** 5 **41.** 7 **43.** -28
45. Pos. **47.** Neg. **49.** 0 **51.** -2
53. -5 **55.** -2 **57.** 4 **59.** $-2\frac{1}{4}$
61. $2\frac{3}{4}$ **63.** $1\frac{3}{4}$ **65.** 20 yards;
downstream **67.** $-18, 21, -24, 27, -30,$
$33, -36, 39, -42, 45, -48, 51, -54, 57$

Pages 51–52. Class Exercises 1. $3 +$
$(-5) = -2; 3 - 5 = -2$ **3.** $9 + (-5) = 4$
5. $9 + 5 = 14$ **7.** $5 + (-9) = -4$
9. $5 + 9 = 14$ **11.** -4 **13.** $6\frac{1}{2}$
15. -14 **17.** 2 **19.** -13

Pages 52–53. Exercises 1. $2 + (-3) =$
-1 **3.** $-2 + (-3) = -5$ **5.** 3 **7.** 0
9. -5 **11.** -8 **13.** -5 **15.** -15 **17.** 8
19. 3 **21.** $2\frac{1}{2}$ **23.** -1 **25.** 2 **27.** 10
29. 8 **31.** 12 **33.** 14 **35.** -14 **37.** -4
39. 9.6 **41.** -4 **43.** -12 **45.** 2
47. 31 **49.** -15.4 **51.** 9; -13; no
53. $57.8 - (-84.4) = 142.2; 142.2°$
55. Comm. prop. for add.; assoc. prop.
for add.; add. prop. of opposites; add.
prop. of 0 **57.** 105 **59.** 7

Pages 56–57. Class Exercises 1. 3
3. 5 **5.** 3 **7.** $3x + 12$ **9.** $\frac{2}{3}y + \frac{2}{3}k$
11. $11x - 11y$ **13.** $xt - 5t$ **15.** 25
17. $132 + 60 = 192$ **19.** $96 - 40 = 56$

Pages 57–58. Exercises 1. 4 **3.** 14; 14
5. 8 **7.** $3p + 3q$ **9.** $6m + 6t$
11. $ax + ap$ **13.** $ax - ap$ **15.** $3x - 3y$
17. $8x - 8r$ **19.** $\frac{1}{2}x + 4$ **21.** $3y - 15$
23. $6a + 6b + 6c$ **25.** $7k + 7n + 14$
27. y **29.** p **31.** x **33.** 15; x
35. $0.7t + 0.7k$ **37.** $0.2y + 5$
39. $8y - 2$ **41.** $\frac{2}{3}x + 4$ **43.** $80 + 20 =$
100 **45.** $4(2000 + 500 + 70 + 3) =$
$8000 + 2000 + 280 + 12 = 10,292$

47. $8(100 - 2) = 800 - 16 = 784$
49. $10(200 - 1) = 2000 - 10 = 1990$
51. $7(500 - 1) = 3500 - 7 = 3493$
53. $50(2000 + 1) = 100,000 + 50 =$
$100,050$ **55.** $3(4 + 7) = 12 + 21 = 33;$
$3(4 + 7) = 3(11) = 33$ **57.** $10(5 + 15) =$
$50 + 150 = 200; 10(5 + 15) = 10(20) =$
200 **59.** $(7 + 11)2 = 14 + 22 = 36;$
$(7 + 11)2 = 18(2) = 36$
61. $\left(\frac{1}{2} + \frac{1}{4}\right)20 = 10 + 5 = 15;$
$\left(\frac{1}{2} + \frac{1}{4}\right)20 = \frac{3}{4}(20) = 15$
63. $5(9 + 8 - 7) = 45 + 40 - 35 = 50;$
$5(9 + 8 - 7) = 5(10) = 50$

Page 60. Class Exercises 1. Yes
3. No **5.** No **7.** Yes **9.** $1a$, or a
11. $-3c$

Pages 60–61. Exercises 1. $a, -4a$
3. $ab, -ab, 6ab$ **5.** $9x$ **7.** $5x$ **9.** $-11y$
11. $6xy$ **13.** $2xy$ **15.** b **17.** $-2r$ **19.** 0
21. Cannot be simplified **23.** $7x$ **25.** 0
27. $-2b$ **29.** $10st$ **31.** $-32w$
33. $-5pqr$ **35.** $-6n + 4$ **37.** $3mn +$
$m - 6$ **39.** $6x^2 - 3x - 10$ **41.** $-25x -$
2 **43.** $1\frac{3}{4}x$ **45.** $4a + \frac{1}{3}$ **47.** $10x - 6$
49. $3n + 3$ **51.** $6w$ **53.** $12x$

Page 64. Class Exercises 1. -56
3. $\frac{6}{100}$ **5.** 30 **7.** -24 **9.** 200
11. -5000 **13.** -21 **15.** 12

Pages 64–65. Exercises 1. 63 **3.** -63
5. 500 **7.** -5000 **9.** 0 **11.** 60 **13.** 24
15. -900 **17.** 1200 **19.** 25 **21.** 30
23. 24 **25.** -21 **27.** -39 **29.** 75
31. 25 **33.** 225 **35.** 150 **37.** 900
39. 64 **41.** -78 **43.** 0 **45.** $7x + 1$
47. $9y - 36$ **49.** $2x - 28$ **51.** $2n^2$; 18
53. $-1n - 3$; 0 **55.** $5n^3$; -135
57. False **59.** False **61.** True
63. $6[12.40 - 2(5)]$; \$14.40

Page 67. Class Exercises 1. 26 **3.** 14
5. $-x + y$ **7.** $x - y - 5$ **9.** 3 **11.** 15
13. -7 **15.** -1

562

Pages 67–68. Exercises 1. 14 **3.** 6
5. $-x + 8$; 11 **7.** $x + 8$; 5 **9.** $-x +$
18; 21 **11.** 42 **13.** -250 **15.** -40
17. -5 **19.** 85 **21.** -121 **23.** $-y$
25. $x - y + z$ **27.** $-xy + z$ **29.** $-x +$
$y - z$ **31.** $-3y + 5$ **33.** $3x - 8$
35. $-(a + b - c - d + e)$
$= (-1)(a + b - c - d + e)$
Mult. prop. of -1
$= (-1)[a + b + (-c) + (-d) + e]$
Subtr. rule
$= (-1)a + (-1)b + (-1)(-c) +$
$(-1)(-d) + (-1)e$ Distr. prop.
$= -a - b + c + d - e$
Mult. prop. of -1
37. $-a(-b)$
$= (-1)(a)(-1)(b)$ Mult. prop. of -1
$= (-1)(-1)(a)(b)$ Comm. prop. for mult.
$= ab$ Mult. prop. of -1

Page 70. Class Exercises 1. $-12\left(\dfrac{1}{3}\right) =$
-4 **3.** $48 \times \left(-\dfrac{1}{6}\right) = -8$ **5.** $18\left(-\dfrac{1}{6}\right) =$
-3 **7.** $(200 - 500)\dfrac{1}{60} = -5$ **9.** 6
11. -1

Pages 71–72. Exercises 1. $80\left(\dfrac{1}{5}\right) = 16$
3. $80\left(-\dfrac{1}{5}\right) = -16$ **5.** $400\left(\dfrac{1}{20}\right) = 20$
7. $-400\left(\dfrac{1}{20}\right) = -20$ **9.** $24\left(\dfrac{1}{6}\right) = 4$
11. $-48\left(-\dfrac{1}{8}\right) = 6$ **13.** $-60\left(-\dfrac{1}{5}\right) = 12$
15. $-63\left(\dfrac{1}{7}\right) = -9$ **17.** -15 **19.** 4
21. -4 **23.** -2 **25.** -1 **27.** 1 **29.** -3
31. 36 **33.** $4 \cdot \dfrac{1}{2} = 2$ **35.** $\dfrac{1}{4} \cdot 2 = \dfrac{1}{2}$
37. 0 **39.** Undefined **41.** 1 **43.** -10
45. $-\dfrac{5}{8}$ **47.** $-\dfrac{1}{4}$ **49.** $\dfrac{5}{8}$ **51.** $\dfrac{5}{2}$ **53.** 1;
4; No **55.** $-\dfrac{1}{36}$ **57.** $-\dfrac{4x}{y}$; 6 **59.** $\dfrac{4}{x}$; 2
61. $-\dfrac{5(x + y)}{x}$; $-12\dfrac{1}{2}$

Page 75. Class Exercises 1. Yes; No
3. Answers may vary. Sample: Let $x =$
boiling pt. of oxygen; $y =$ boiling pt. of
hydrogen. **5.** $-183°C$

Pages 75–76. Exercises 1. $-6°C$
3. $10°$ below $0°C$ **5.** $-8°C$ **7.** $C =$
$\dfrac{5}{9}(F - 32)$; about $29°C$ **9.** 1.8 mm
11. Solid **13.** $70°$ **15.** $a = 3(c - 24)$
17. $d = \dfrac{1}{4}e$ **19.** $f = 3d$ **21.** 0.09 g;
1.977 g

Pages 78–80. Review Exercises 1. 12
3. -7 **5.** 3.8 **7.** Neg. **9.** Pos. **11.** Neg.
13. 0 **15.** 8 **17.** -24 **19.** $3.5 - 0.7x$
21. $-17a^2$ **23.** $-8c$ **25.** $5z - 3$
27. 300 **29.** -54 **31.** 70 **33.** 81
35. -13 **37.** -50 **39.** $-h$; 1
41. $2g - h$; -5 **43.** $-gh + h$; -4
45. 24 **47.** -35 **49.** -1 **51.** $\dfrac{1}{2}$
53. $-\dfrac{7}{13}$ **55.** 3 **57.** 4 **59.** 5 **61.** \$66
63. \$680.41

CHAPTER 3
Page 83. Prerequisite Skills Review
1. a **2.** b **3.** a **4.** c **5.** c **6.** b **7.** b
8. d **9.** d **10.** b
Page 85. Class Exercises 1. $a + 16 =$
84 **3.** $\dfrac{c}{4} = 7$ **5.** $6e = -78$ **7.** 9 decreased by the number n equals 17.
9. 14 times the number n equals 84.
Pages 85–86. Exercises 1. $6 - y = -3$
3. $x + 7 = 3\dfrac{1}{2}$ **5.** $2 + p = -1$ **7.** $9r = 3$
9. $66 - b = -6.5$ **11.** $5c + 5 = 8$
13. The sum of the number n and 14
equals 39. **15.** 3 increased by some
number n equals 21. **17.** 5 times the
number n equals 65. **19.** Twice some
number n plus 3 equals 25. **21.** $P = 4s$
23. $V = lwh$ **25.** $C = (212 - 32)\dfrac{5}{9}$
27. $y + (y - 10) = 36$
29. $m(m + 3) = 550$

Pages 88–89. Class Exercises **1.** -7; 12 **3.** -5; -4 **5.** 9; 12 **7.** 6; 14 **9.** 12; 23 **11.** 9; 16

Pages 89–90. Exercises **1.** -2 **3.** -9 **5.** 7 **7.** -4 **9.** -8 **11.** 4 **13.** 14 **15.** 27 **17.** -13 **19.** 19.25 **21.** -11 **23.** 13 **25.** 9 **27.** 24 **29.** $-3\frac{1}{2}$ **31.** $-6\frac{1}{2}$ **33.** 0.5 **35.** $10\frac{1}{4}$ **37.** 89 **39.** -77 **41.** -2.5 **43.** -0.2 **45.** -2.8 **47.** $-\frac{5}{6}$ **49.** $-\frac{2}{9}$ **51.** $\frac{2}{3}$ **53.** $a = 10 - b$ **55.** $a = b + 20$ **57.** $a = -b - 30$ **59.** $y = 18 - x$ **61.** $y = 8 - x$ **63.** $y = 24 - x$ **65.** $b = p - a - c$ **67.** Add. prop. of equality; add. prop. of opposites; add. prop. of 0 **69.** $-x$; $-x$; 4; -3; 4; -3; 1

Pages 93–94. Class Exercises **1.** 10 **3.** 4 **5.** -8 **7.** -16 **9.** 3 **11.** 5 **13.** 13 **15.** 1.5

Pages 94–95. Exercises **1.** 6 **3.** 20 **5.** -25 **7.** 0 **9.** -1 **11.** $8\frac{1}{2}$ **13.** 15 **15.** 1 **17.** -5 **19.** -8 **21.** 1.0 **23.** 6 **25.** 0 **27.** 10.8 **29.** 13 **31.** 21 **33.** -3 **35.** -8 **37.** -1 **39.** -34.7 **41.** 0.2 **43.** $-\frac{5}{6}$ **45.** $\frac{1}{6}$ **47.** $\frac{1}{6}$ **49.** $174.95 + t = 187.25$; \$12.30 **51.** $s = p - 8$ **53.** $s = 4 - p$ **55.** -18 **57.** 3 **59.** 7 **61.** 7

Page 98. Class Exercises **1.** Mult. by $\frac{1}{4}$. **3.** Mult. by $-\frac{1}{2}$. **5.** Mult. by 2. **7.** Mult. by $-\frac{5}{3}$. **9.** 3 **11.** 3 **13.** $\frac{4}{3}$ **15.** $-\frac{2}{3}$

Pages 98–99. Exercises

	Multiply by	Solution
1.	$\frac{1}{7}$	3
3.	$\frac{1}{4}$	$\frac{15}{2}$
5.	$\frac{1}{9}$	0
7.	$\frac{1}{5}$	-11
9.	$-\frac{1}{12}$	5
11.	$\frac{1}{6}$	-7
13.	$\frac{1}{16}$	6
15.	$\frac{1}{4}$	-13
17.	$-\frac{1}{21}$	21
19.	$\frac{1}{40}$	-5
21.	$\frac{1}{64}$	$-\frac{1}{8}$
23.	$\frac{7}{8}$	49
25.	$-\frac{1}{3}$	$-\frac{4}{3}$
27.	$-\frac{1}{12}$	$\frac{3}{2}$
29.	$\frac{1}{8}$	-90
31.	$-\frac{1}{900}$	$-\frac{9}{100}$

33. 8 **35.** -20 **37.** 64 **39.** -25 **41.** $-\frac{10}{27}$ **43.** 0.02 **45.** 2.2 **47.** -100 **49.** -3 **51.** -2 **53.** $\frac{1}{2}$ **55.** 6 **57.** $\frac{1}{3}$ **59.** Mult. prop. of equality; assoc. prop. of mult; def. of reciprocals; mult. prop. of 1

Page 101. Class Exercises **1.** 16 **3.** -21 **5.** -120 **7.** -2 **9.** 60 **11.** $\frac{2}{5}$ **13.** 7 **15.** $\frac{3}{20}$ **17.** $-\frac{1}{3}$ **19.** -5

Pages 101–102. Class Exercises **1.** 35 **3.** 42 **5.** -30 **7.** 48 **9.** -72 **11.** 140 **13.** -6 **15.** 6 **17.** 9 **19.** $\frac{1}{8}$ **21.** 248 **23.** 128 **25.** -52 **27.** -20 **29.** 3 **31.** 31 **33.** -16 **35.** 9 **37.** 135 **39.** -65 **41.** $\frac{4}{3}$ **43.** -13 **45.** -261

47. 59　**49.** −14　**51.** −19　**53.** 2

55. −2　**57.** −$\frac{1}{8}$　**59.** 15.3　**61.** −28.8

63. −3.72　**65.** −2　**67.** −3　**69.** −12

71. 3.4x = 105.4; 31　**73.** h = $\frac{A}{b}$

75. d = $\frac{C}{\pi}$　**77.** t = $\frac{d}{r}$　**79.** b = ac

81. −$\frac{7}{2}$　**83.** 6　**85.** m = $\frac{E}{c^2}$; E = mc²

Page 105. Class Exercises　1. 3n + 6 = 30　**3.** $\frac{n}{6}$ + 4 = 10　**5.** 4　**7.** −2　**9.** −2
11. −12　**13.** 2$\frac{1}{2}$　**15.** 25

Pages 105–106. Exercises　1. 5a + 3 = 28　**3.** 2$\frac{1}{2}$c + 6 = 31　**5.** $\frac{e}{3}$ − 7 = 12
7. 2　**9.** −1　**11.** 3　**13.** 4　**15.** 6　**17.** 3
19. 6　**21.** 35　**23.** 20　**25.** 3$\frac{1}{2}$　**27.** 15
29. 2n + 6 = 24; 9　**31.** 5n − 9 = 76; 17
33. 2x + 18 = 150; 66　**35.** 2x + 50 = 500; 225　**37.** 2x + 25 = −5; −15　**39.** $\frac{4}{3}$
41. −12　**43.** 5　**45.** 4　**47.** x = $\frac{c-b}{a}$
49. x = $\frac{b}{c-a}$

Page 109. Class Exercises　1. 6　**3.** −4
5. 5　**7.** 3　**9.** 3　**11.** 12

Pages 109–110. Exercises　1. 1　**3.** −1
5. −3　**7.** 18　**9.** 60　**11.** −1　**13.** −2
15. −2　**17.** 16　**19.** 3　**21.** −10　**23.** 11
25. 2　**27.** $\frac{5}{4}$　**29.** −$\frac{1}{2}$　**31.** 2　**33.** 4
35. −15　**37.** −2　**39.** −4　**41.** 83
43. 2　**45.** 33　**47.** −9　**49.** 5　**51.** 13
53. −2　**55.** $6420

Page 113. Class Exercises　1. n + 1
3. 2n + 1 = 97; 48, 49　**5.** 10　**7.** Width is 94 m; length is 106 m.

Pages 113–114. Exercises　1. Dean is 23. Alison is 16.　**3.** 14　**5.** 72 nickels; 64 dimes　**7.** 20 pennies; 10 nickels
9. Width is 9$\frac{1}{2}$ cm; length is 14$\frac{1}{2}$ cm.
11. 18, 20　**13.** 15, 17　**15.** 9, 9, 12

17. Merv is 13. Mel is 29.　**19.** 63, 65, 67

Pages 116–118. Review Exercises
1. y + 11 = 15　**3.** 10y = 2700
5. 8(y + 5) = 200　**7.** 12　**9.** −0.6
11. −11　**13.** −7.6　**15.** −3.7　**17.** −$\frac{1}{2}$
19. 12　**21.** 2.6　**23.** −11　**25.** −8
27. −1.3　**29.** 2$\frac{1}{2}$　**31.** 12.25n = 49; 4
33. 4　**35.** −9　**37.** 20　**39.** 4x + 15 = 47; 8　**41.** 2x + (−3) = 11; 7　**43.** 2.8 = $\frac{7x}{13}$; 5.2　**45.** −12　**47.** 0　**49.** 2　**51.** 12
53. 45　**55.** −25　**57.** 7　**59.** 20, 21
61. 9 nickels, 3 dimes, 1 quarter

Pages 120–121. Cumulative Review
1. b　**3.** e　**5.** d　**7.** d　**9.** d　**11.** b
13. c　**15.** Dist. prop. of mult. over add.
17. Comm. for mult.　**19.** 12　**21.** 10
23. 5x − 20　**25.** 1　**27.** 144　**29.** 3
31. $.35n　**33.** 20　**35.** −3　**37.** $\frac{1}{2}$　**39.** 4
41. 0　**43.** −1　**45.** 14 units and 18 units
47. 2n + 7 = 39; n = 16
49. 5(n + 3) = 2n; n = −5

CHAPTER 4
Page 123. Prerequisite Skills Review
1. a　**2.** b　**3.** d　**4.** d　**5.** c　**6.** d　**7.** d
8. b　**9.** c　**10.** a

Page 126. Class Exercises
1. Right 5, up 4　**3.** Left 1, up 3
5. Left 5, down 2　**7.** Right 1, down 6
9. No move right or left, up 3　**11.** Left 2, no move up or down　**13.** (−1, 1)
15. (0, 3)　**17.** (3, 0)　**19.** (0, −3)

Pages 126–127. Exercises　1. No move right or left, down 2　**3.** Left 4, down 1　**5.** No move right or left, up 2　**7.** No move right, left, up, or down
9. Right 1$\frac{1}{2}$, up 1　**11.** Right $\frac{3}{4}$, down $\frac{1}{4}$　**13.** (−2, 1)　**15.** (0, −3)
17. (−1, −1)　**19.** (−4, 0)　**21.** $\left(3, \frac{1}{2}\right)$

ANSWERS TO SELECTED EXERCISES

565

PREREQUISITE SKILLS FOLLOW-UP

EXTRA PRACTICE SETS

COMPUTER HANDBOOK

TABLES

GLOSSARY

ANSWERS TO SELECTED CHECKPOINTS

ANSWERS TO SELECTED EXERCISES

INDEX

ANSWERS TO SELECTED EXERCISES

23. G **25.** B **27.** F **29.** K **31.** E
33. C
35–45.

47. A four-pointed star.

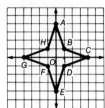

49. 7 units **51.** 16 units **53.** (4, 4)
55. −6

Page 130. Class Exercises **1.** I
3. II **5.** IV **7.** III **9.** x-axis
11.

Pages 130–131. Exercises **1.** III
3. I **5.** IV **7.** x-axis **9.** III **11.** II
13.   **15.**

17. IV **19.** y **21.** horizontal
23. Answers will vary: (3, 1), (2, 0),
(0, −2), (−3, −5)

25. Answers will vary: (−4, −2), (0, 0),
(2, 1), (4, 2)

27. I **29.** IV **31.** I or III

Page 133. Class Exercises
1. −2; 0; 2; 4 **3.** 6; 4; 2; 0; −2; −4

5. No **7.** Yes

Pages 134–135. Exercises
1. −1; 0; 1; 2; 3; 4; 5 **3.** 5; 4; 3; 2; 1; 0;
−1

5.   **7.**

9.   **11.**

13.   **15.**

ANSWERS TO SELECTED EXERCISES

17. **19.**

21. **23.**

25. **27.**

29. No **31.** No **33.** Yes **35.** Yes
37. Yes **39.** Yes **41.** −1 **43.** m
45. p **47.** (−1, 1)

Page 138. Class Exercises 1. $\frac{3}{4}$

3. $\frac{2}{3}$ **5.** 0 **7.** 1 **9.** $\frac{2}{5}$ **11.** −1 **13.** 2

15. −5 **17.** $-\frac{4}{3}$

Pages 139–140. Exercises 1. $\frac{3}{4}$ **3.** $\frac{1}{2}$

5. $\frac{3}{5}$ **7.** $-\frac{5}{2}$ **9.** 1 **11.** −2 **13.** $\frac{1}{2}$

15. $\frac{5}{3}$ **17.** 2 **19.** 1 **21.** 0 **23.** 1 **25.** 0

27. a **29.** e **31.** a and e

33.

35. **37.**

39. $\frac{b}{a}$ **41.** (4, 2), (2, 10), (−6, −4)

Page 142. Class Exercises 1. x-int.
−2; y-int. 1 **3.** x-int. 3; y-int. 2
5. x-int. $-\frac{5}{2}$; y-int. 5 **7.** x-int. 1; y-int.
1 **9.** x-int. −2; y-int. 2

Pages 142–143. Exercises 1. 1; 2
3. −2; −1 **5.** 4 **7.** 6 **9.** −3 **11.** 0
13. −1 **15.** −2 **17.** $-\frac{1}{2}$ **19.** $-\frac{1}{2}$
21. $\frac{5}{2}$; −5 **23.** $-\frac{4}{5}$; −4 **25.** $-\frac{1}{3}$; 1
27. 0; 0 **29.** 2; 2 **31.** 3; −3 **33.** $-\frac{1}{4}$;
$\frac{1}{2}$ **35.** $\frac{5}{2}$; $\frac{5}{3}$ **37.** −3; $\frac{3}{4}$ **39.** −0.3; 0.5

41. $\frac{5}{2}$

43. y-int. 2 **45.** y-int. −1 **47.** x-int. 6;
y-int. −3 **49.** x-int. 2; y-int. 4

51. x-int. 4;
y-int. 6

PREREQUISITE SKILLS FOLLOW-UP

EXTRA PRACTICE SETS

COMPUTER HANDBOOK

TABLES

GLOSSARY

ANSWERS TO CHECKPOINTS

ANSWERS TO SELECTED EXERCISES

INDEX

ANSWERS TO SELECTED EXERCISES

53. x-int. −1; y-int. 5

55. x-int. 5; y-int. 3

57. x-int. 6; y-int. −4

Page 146. Class Exercises 1. $\frac{1}{2}$; 0

3. 2; 9 **5.** $-\frac{1}{3}$; 2 **7.** $\frac{2}{3}$; 3

9. $y = 4x + 1$ **11.** $y = x + 4.5$

13. $y = -3x + 9$; −3, 9

15. $y = -x + 3$; −1, 3

Pages 147–148. Exercises 1. Slope −2, y-int. 0 **3.** Slope 5, y-int. −2

5. Slope $\frac{2}{3}$, y-int. 0 **7.** Slope $\frac{1}{2}$, y-int. −1 **9.** $y = 3x$ **11.** $y = -3x - 5$

13. $y = 3$ **15.** $y = \frac{1}{4}x + 3$

17. $y = -\frac{2}{3}x - 5$ **19.** $y = 1.2x + 1$

21. $y = -4x + 7$, $m = -4$, $b = 7$

23. $y = 3x + 4$, $m = 3$, $b = 4$

25. $y = \frac{3}{2}x + \frac{2}{5}$, $m = \frac{3}{2}$, $b = \frac{2}{5}$

27. $y = \frac{1}{2}x + \frac{1}{2}$, $m = \frac{1}{2}$, $b = \frac{1}{2}$

29. $y = 4x + 6$, $m = 4$, $b = 6$

31. $y = \frac{1}{3}x - 4$, $m = \frac{1}{3}$, $b = -4$

33.

35.

37.

39.

41. 3 **43.** 0 **45.** They do. $m = 2$

47. They do. $m = -\frac{1}{2}$

49. For side *DE*, $m = \frac{3}{2}$. For side *EF*, $m = \frac{1}{5}$. For side *DF*, $m = -\frac{2}{3}$.

51. $y = 4x + 2$

53. $y + 2x = 2$, or $y = -2x + 2$

55. False **57.** True **59.** True

Page 150. Class Exercises **1.** $b = -1$; $y = 3x - 1$ **3.** $b = -6$; $y = -x - 6$

5. $b = -1$; $y = \frac{3}{5}x - 1$

Pages 150–151. Exercises **1.** $b = 2$; $y = x + 2$ **3.** $b = -4$; $y = \frac{1}{2}x - 4$

5. $b = -3$; $y = -2x - 3$ **7.** $b = -\frac{1}{2}$; $y = \frac{1}{2}x - \frac{1}{2}$ **9.** $b = 3$; $y = 3$

11. $y - 3x = 4$, or $y = 3x + 4$

13. $3x + 2y = 0$, or $y = -\frac{3}{2}x$

15. $y = x - 1$

17. $y = \frac{1}{2}x - 2$

19. $2x + 3y = 12$ or $y = -\frac{2}{3}x + 4$

21. $y = ax - e$ **23.** -3 **25.** 5
27. $m(x - x_1) = y - y_1$, or $y - y_1 = m(x - x_1)$ **29.** $y + \frac{1}{4} = \frac{3}{4}\left(x - \frac{1}{2}\right)$
31. $m = 1$; $y - 1 = 1(x - 1)$; $y = x$
33. $y + 7 = -\frac{5}{2}(x - 3)$

Page 153. Class Exercises **1.** 1

3. $y = x - 1$ **5.** $-\frac{1}{2}$ **7.** $y = -\frac{1}{2}x + 1$

Pages 153–154. Exercises **1.** 2
3. $y = 2x - 3$ **5.** $y = x - 2$

7. $y = \frac{1}{3}x + 1$ **9.** $y = 2x - 3$

11. $y = -\frac{3}{4}x - \frac{5}{2}$ **13.** $y = \frac{3}{2}x$

15. $x + y = 8$ **17.** $2x - y = -6$

19. $x - 3y = 12$ **21.** $2x + 3y = 6$

23. $3x + 2y = -7$

25. $2x + 3y = 15$

27. $2x + 3y = -4$

29. $2x + y = -7$

PREREQUISITE SKILLS FOLLOW-UP

EXTRA PRACTICE SETS

COMPUTER HANDBOOK

TABLES

GLOSSARY

ANSWERS TO CHECKPOINTS

ANSWERS TO SELECTED EXERCISES

INDEX

ANSWERS TO SELECTED EXERCISES

31. $3x - y = 15$

33. $4x + y = -4$ **35.** $y = -\frac{3}{2}x + 3$

37. $y = \frac{3}{2}x + 3$ **39.** $y = 4$ **41.** $y = \frac{2}{3}x$

43. $y = -4x - \frac{1}{3}$ **45.** $y = -2x + \frac{63}{10}$

47. $y = x + d - c$ **49.** Negative

51. Positive **53.** $\dfrac{y_1 - y_2}{x_1 - x_2}; \dfrac{y - y_1}{x - x_1};$

$y - y_1 = \left(\dfrac{y_1 - y_2}{x_1 - x_2}\right)(x - x_1)$

55. $y - 2 = \left(\dfrac{2 - (-8)}{7 - 5}\right)(x - 7)$, or
$y - 2 = 5(x - 7)$

Page 157. Class Exercises 1. $y = 0$;
slope is 0 **3.** $x = 0$; slope is undefined
5. $y = 0$; slope is 0 **7.** a. $y = 4$;
b. $x = -8$; c. $x = -4$; d. $y = -1$;
e. $x = 5$; f. $x = 7$

Pages 157–158. Exercises 1. Undefined **3.** 0 **5.** Undefined **7.** 0
9. Undefined **11.** 0 **13.** $y = 1$
15. $y = 6$ **17.** $y = 0$ **19.** $y = -4$
21. $x = 0$ **23.** $x = 9$

25.

27.

29.

31.

33. $y = 6$ **35.** $x = 3$ **37.** $x = 0$
39. Yes **41.** No **43.** No **45.** No
47. Yes **49.** No **51.** Yes **53.** No
55. $y = -\frac{1}{2}$ **57.** $x = \frac{5}{6}$ and $x = -\frac{1}{6}$
59. $(4, 4)$

Pages 160–162. Review Exercises
1. $(0, 2)$ **3.** $(-2, 0)$ **5.** $(2, 0)$ **7.** I
9. II **11.** IV **13.** Points may vary.

15. Yes **17.** $-\frac{1}{3}$ **19.** 3 **21.** 0 **23.** 3; 21

25. 2; 3 **27.** $-\frac{7}{5}$ **29.** 15; −37 **31.** 72;
101 **33.** $y = x + 18$

35. $y = -\frac{1}{2}x + 4$ **37.** $y = \frac{1}{2}x + \frac{3}{2}$

39. $y = -x + 1$ **41.** $y = x + 4$
43. $y = -4x + 3$ **45.** $y = -\frac{2}{3}x - \frac{1}{3}$
47. $5x + 10y = 4$ **49.** 0; $y = 5$ **51.** 0;
$y = -7$

CHAPTER 5
Page 165. Prerequisite Skills Review
1. d **2.** b **3.** c **4.** c **5.** c **6.** d **7.** b
8. b **9.** a **10.** d **11.** d **12.** d **13.** b
Pages 167–168. Class Exercises
1. Binomial **3.** Monomial **5.** Trinomial
7. $a^2 + 3a$; 2 **9.** $4x + 9$; 1
11. $-t^2 - 3t - 4$; 2 **13.** $y^3 + 15y^2$; 3
15. $-3b^4 + 4b$; 4 **17.** 6

Pages 168–169. Exercises 1. Binomial
3. None of these **5.** Monomial
7. $2x + 2$; 1 **9.** $x^2 - 2x$; 2 **11.** $6y^2$; 2
13. $4x^3 - 6x$; 3 **15.** $2y^2 + 4y$; 2
17. $x^3 - x^2 + x - 1$; 3 **19.** $2x^5$; 5

21. 7 **23.** 2 **25.** 1 **27.** $2\frac{1}{4}$
29. $x^3 - 8x^2 + 17x - 10$; 3

31. $a^4 + 2a^2 + 2a - 1$; 4 **33.** $-2\frac{1}{2}x + 3$;
1 **35.** $x^3 - 2x^2 + 13x + 10$; 3
37. $-4x^4 - 3x^3 + 22x^2 - 14x$; 4 **39.** 1
41. 25 **43.** -76 **45.** 44 **47.** -4

49. -27 **51.** $23\frac{5}{8}$ **53.** $3x^4 + 6x^2y - 27y^2$
55. $6x + 2$; -16; 2 **57.** $9x + 3$; -24; 3
59. $7x^2 + 4x$; 51; 0 **61.** $3x^2 + 8x$; 3; 0
63. $x = 11$ **65.** $n = -64$ **67.** -14
69. 0

Page 171. Class Exercises 1. $7x + 14$
3. $6x^2 + 3x - 5$ **5.** $23x + 8$
7. $-5n^2 - 3n + 5$ **9.** $8x^2 - 5x$
11. $15a - 2$ **13.** $a^2 - b^2$
15. $5x - 7y + 6z$

Pages 172–173. Exercises 1. $6x^2 + 9x$
3. $12n + 8$ **5.** $8x^2 + 3x - 2$ **7.** $1.6a +$
$3b + 0.8$ **9.** $7x + 1\frac{1}{2}y - 6\frac{3}{4}z$
11. $3a + 9$ **13.** $5a^2 + 2a + 6$
15. $2x + 3y$ **17.** $-5n^2 - 5m + 8$
19. $2x - 2$ **21.** $10x - 2$ **23.** $8r + 4$
25. $-8y - 10$ **27.** $a^2 - b^2$ **29.** $20b - 2c$
31. $21b$ **33.** $-2x - 5y$
35. $-8xy + 14x + 3$ **37.** $7x^2 + 7x + 4$
39. $-4a^3 + a^2 + a$ **41.** $-2x - 2y$
43. $-11a - 12$ **45.** $x^3 - 7x^2 - 6x + 1$
47. $5x^2 - xy - y^2$ **49.** $8x + 2$; 26
51. $x + 2y + 3z$ **53.** $x^4 + 9x^3 + 14x^2 -$
$4x - 8$ **55.** $5a^2 + b^2 + 5c^2$
57. $-a^2 + a + 1$
Page 175. Class Exercises 1. 5^5
3. $(-4)^7$ **5.** b^{22} **7.** $(0.4)^6$ **9.** $-6y^2$
11. $3x^2$ **13.** $4ab^3$ **15.** $3a^2b^4$ **17.** False
19. True **21.** False
Pages 175–177. Exercises 1. 2^7 **3.** 2^7
5. b^9 **7.** x^5 **9.** y^5 **11.** $\left(\frac{2}{3}\right)^5$ **13.** False

15. False **17.** $-d^2$ **19.** $-x^3$ **21.** t^6
23. x^4 **25.** $3x^3$ **27.** $-3x^8$ **29.** $6a^2b$
31. $-8b^4$ **33.** x^5y^6 **35.** $-4x^4y^3$
37. $-4x^3y^4$ **39.** $-21a^{10}$ **41.** $20x^4y^4$
43. n^6 **45.** $24a^3b^3$ **47.** $3t^8u^3$
49. $-15a^4bc^3$ **51.** $x^3y^3z^3$ **53.** $(0.5)^7$
55. $-24a^3b^2c$ **57.** xy^4z^4 **59.** 6×10^7;
60,000,000 **61.** 3×10^9; 3,000,000,000
63. 9.02×10^{11}; 902,000,000,000 **65.** $9x^5$
67. $4a^4$ **69.** $7x^4y^4$ **71.** 0 **73.** x^{a+1}
75. x^{a+b} **77.** x^{2n} **79.** 3^{7x} **81.** x^m
83. a^{7m+1} **85.** $(a + 1)^{n+2}$ **87.** $15x^3y^2$;
12,000 sq. units
Page 179. Class Exercises 1. 10^6
3. 10^{14} **5.** $9a^2$ **7.** -27 **9.** $-32n^5$
11. a^8b^{12}

Pages 179–180. Exercises 1. 5^6 **3.** 5^{20}
5. $16a^2$ **7.** $16n^2$ **9.** $25x^2$ **11.** $4y^2$
13. t^4 **15.** $-t^6$ **17.** a^2b^2 **19.** $25a^2$
21. $a^3b^3c^3$ **23.** $-x^3y^3$ **25.** $125x^6$
27. $-27a^3$ **29.** a^8b^4 **31.** $125x^{12}y^9$
33. $32a^{15}b^{10}$ **35.** $\frac{9}{25}a^{10}b^6$ **37.** False; 3^{20}
39. True **41.** False; 30^2 **43.** $-54x^4y^3$
45. $a^{12}b^4$ **47.** $243n^3w^4$ **49.** $-x^7y^{11}$
51. x^8y^7 **53.** 6.25×10^6; 6,250,000
55. 2.985984×10^{12}; 2,985,984,000,000
57. $28x^3y^3$ **59.** 0 **61.** 0 **63.** $24x^3y^6$;
192 **65.** a^{n^2} **67.** $-8a^{3x}$ **69.** $2^{12} = 4096$
71. $x^{24}y^4$ **73.** Answers will vary. Let
$a = 3$, $b = 2$, $c = 3$. Then

$$(a^b)^c = (3^2)^3 = 9^3 = 729;$$
$$a^{(b^c)} = 3^{(2^3)} = 3^8 = 6561.$$

Since $729 \neq 6561$, $(a^b)^c \neq a^{(b^c)}$.

Page 182. Class Exercises 1. $6x^2 + 4x$
3. $3x^3 + 3x^2$ **5.** $2t^2 - 4t$ **7.** $-2x^2 - 2xy$
9. $x^4y - x^3y^2$ **11.** $x^5 - x^8$

Page 183. Exercises 1. $3x^2 + 2x$
3. $15x^2 + 20x$ **5.** $4y^2 - 32y$
7. $28y^2 - 21y$ **9.** $-3n^2 - 27n$
11. $n^3 - 3n$ **13.** $-20x^2 + 12xy$
15. $2x^3 - 8x^2 + 6x$ **17.** $2r^2 - 2rt + 6t^2$
19. $n^3 + 5n^2 + 2n$ **21.** $-3 - n + n^2$
23. $2a^3b - 2ab^3$ **25.** $-12x^3 + 8x^2y -$
$10xy^2$ **27.** $-a^4b^4 - 2a^3b^3 + a^2b^2$
29. $-3a^3b + 6a^3b^3 - 9a^4b^4$

PREREQUISITE SKILLS FOLLOW-UP

EXTRA PRACTICE SETS

COMPUTER HANDBOOK

TABLES

GLOSSARY

ANSWERS TO CHECKPOINTS

ANSWERS TO SELECTED EXERCISES

INDEX

ANSWERS TO SELECTED EXERCISES

31. $-12x^3y^2 + 18x^2y^3 - 24x^3y^3 + 6x^4y^4$

33. $4h^5 - h^4 + \frac{1}{4}h^3 - 16h^2 + 4h$

35. $6y + 35$ **37.** $2a + 6$ **39.** t
41. $v^2 - 16y$ **43.** $2x^2y$ **45.** $2x^4 +$
$7x^3 + 2x^2 - 23x - 36$ **47.** 0 **49.** 2
51. $6x^2 + \pi x^2 - 14x$, or $(6 + \pi)x^2 - 14x$

53. $\frac{1}{2}x^2 + 3x$

Page 185. Class Exercises **1.** $x + 9$
3. 2 **5.** $x^2 + 8x + 15$ **7.** $n^2 - 5n + 4$
9. $2x^2 - 15x + 25$ **11.** $6x^2 + 23x + 20$
13. $9x^2 - 18x + 8$

Pages 185–186. Exercises **1.** $x^2 +$
$6x + 8$ **3.** $x^2 + 10x + 21$ **5.** $y^2 + 3y +$
2 **7.** $r^2 + 5r + 6$ **9.** $x^2 + 2x - 8$
11. $2x^2 + 13x - 24$ **13.** $2x^2 + 3x - 2$
15. $6x^2 - 19x + 10$ **17.** $8x^2 - 22x + 15$
19. $10x^2 + 21x - 10$ **21.** $9x^2 - 12x + 4$
23. $6x^2 + 13x - 5$ **25.** $6x^3 + 15x^2 +$
$8x + 4$ **27.** $x^3 + 2x^2 - 2x - 1$
29. $2a^2 - 11ab + 15b^2$
31. $c^2 + 3cd + 2d^2$ **33.** $4a^2 - b^2$
35. $ac + bc + ad + bd$ **37.** $ac - bc +$
$ad - bd$ **39.** $ab - 2b - 2a + 4$
41. $a^4 - 36$ **43.** $n^4 + 8n^2 + 16$
45. $a^4 - b^4$ **47.** $a^4 - 4a^2b^2 + 4b^4$

49. $9x^4 - 4y^4$ **51.** $\frac{3}{8}x^2 + 13x + 32$

53. $3x^2 + 0.2x - 0.01$ **55.** $a^3 - 9a^2b +$
$27ab^2 - 27b^3$ **57.** $x^3 + y^3$ **59.** $-4x - 10$
61. $3x^2 + 5x - 5$ **63.** $6a - 2$
65. $24a^3 - 46a^2 + 29a - 6$
67. $a^3 - 3a^2b + 3ab^2 - b^3$
69. $x^3 + 8$ **71.** $-4s^3 - 4s^2t + st^2 + t^3$
73. $-x^8 + 1$

Page 188. Class Exercises **1.** 16
3. $6x^2$ **5.** 25 **7.** $x^2 + 5x + 6$ **9.** $x^2 -$
$6x + 8$ **11.** $x^2 + 4x - 21$

Pages 188–189. Exercises **1.** $9x$ **3.** 15
5. 100 **7.** $x^2 + 8x + 15$ **9.** $x^2 + 12x +$
35 **11.** $y^2 - 5y + 6$ **13.** $y^2 - 5y - 6$
15. $y^2 - 4$ **17.** $x^2 - 4x - 5$ **19.** $x^2 +$
$10x + 21$ **21.** $x^2 + 4x - 21$ **23.** $y^2 -$
$y - 20$ **25.** $x^2 - 64$ **27.** $9x^2 - 16$
29. $4y^2 + 3y - 27$ **31.** $a^2 - 81b^2$
33. $16x^2 - y^2$ **35.** $x^2 + 6x + 9$

37. $n^2 + 10n + 25$ **39.** $x^2 - 12x + 36$
41. $n^2 + 20n + 100$ **43.** $9x^2 + 12x + 4$
45. $81x^2 - 36x + 4$ **47.** $a^2 + 4ab + 4b^2$
49. $60x^2 + 41x - 3$ **51.** $x^4 + 5x^2 + 6$

53. $-n^2 + 49$ **55.** $n^2 - \frac{1}{4}$ **57.** $9a^2 +$
$2a + \frac{1}{9}$ **59.** $(40 + 1)^2 = 1681$

61. $(90 - 1)^2 = 7921$ **63.** $\frac{1}{4}x^2 - 1$

65. $x^2 - \frac{1}{3}x + \frac{1}{36}$ **67.** $6x^4 - x^2 - 35$

69. $a^2x^4 - b^2$ **71.** $x^6 - y^4$
73. $-15x^2 - 13x + 6$ **75.** $4a^6 + 12a^3 +$
9 **77.** $x^2 - 0.2x + 0.01$

Page 191. Class Exercises **1.** 7 **3.** 4
5. 1 **7.** No solution **9.** Identity

Pages 191–192. Exercises **1.** 3 **3.** 2
5. -4 **7.** 5 **9.** -9 **11.** 7 **13.** No

solution **15.** Identity **17.** $-\frac{3}{2}$

19. Identity **21.** No solution

23. Identity **25.** $\frac{1}{5}$ **27.** $-\frac{1}{5}$ **29.** 1

31. Identity **33.** Identity

Page 194. Class Exercises **1.** $2x + 1$
3. $6x + 2 = 32$ **5.** 5 cm; 11 cm

Pages 194–196. Exercises **1.** $x + 10$
3. $x + 2; x + 7$ **5.** $x(x + 10) =$
$(x + 2)(x + 7)$ **7.** 24 in. **9.** $2\frac{1}{2}; 11\frac{1}{2}$ in.

11. -2 **13.** 650 m **15.** 7, 9, 11, 13
17. \$6 per hr **19.** 144 sq. units
21. $x = 330$; \$330; \$80; Answers may vary.

Pages 198–200. Review Exercises
1. Binomial **3.** Trinomial **5.** $2x^2 + 2x$;
2 **7.** $x^4 + 8x^2$; 4 **9.** -11 **11.** -1
13. $-x^3 - 2x^2 - 5x + 13$ **15.** $x + 8$
17. $2x^2 - 17x + 17$ **19.** n^9 **21.** $-21x^6$
23. $-28x^6$ **25.** $-6x^8$ **27.** x^6
29. $-8a^3b^{12}$ **31.** $a^{11}b^{10}$ **33.** $10x^2 - 2x$
35. $3x^3 - 6x^2 + 9x$ **37.** $6xy^3 - 8x^2y^2$
39. $6x^4y - 9x^3y + 15x^2$ **41.** $4x^2 - 6x$
43. $-2x^2 + 5x$ **45.** $25t^4 - t^2$
47. $x^2 + x - 56$ **49.** $x^2 + 16x + 63$
51. $15x^2 - 23x + 4$ **53.** $12 - 39x + 30x^2$
55. $25x^2 - 40xy + 16y^2$ **57.** $4x^2 -$
$4x + 1$ **59.** $3x^3 + 14x^2 + x - 2$

61. $r^2 - 4s^2$ **63.** $x^2 + 10x + 25$
65. $9x^2 - 24x + 16$ **67.** 11 **69.** Identity
71. No solution **73.** 4 **75.** 5

CHAPTER 6
Page 203. Prerequisite Skills Review
1. a **2.** b **3.** b **4.** d **5.** b **6.** c **7.** d
8. a **9.** a **10.** c **11.** a **12.** d **13.** c
Pages 205–206. Class Exercises **1.** $1 \cdot 6$,
$2 \cdot 3$ **3.** $1 \cdot 10, 2 \cdot 5$ **5.** $1 \cdot 21, 3 \cdot 7$ **7.** 1,
2, 7, 14 **9.** 1, 2, 4, 5, 10, 20 **11.** Prime
13. Prime **15.** Not prime **17.** $3 \cdot 11$
19. 2^6 **21.** 2 **23.** 7 **25.** 11 **27.** 6
Pages 206–207. Exercises **1.** $1 \cdot 7$
3. $1 \cdot 14, 2 \cdot 7$ **5.** $1 \cdot 19$ **7.** $1 \cdot 26, 2 \cdot 13$
9. $1 \cdot 43$ **11.** $1 \cdot 62, 2 \cdot 31$ **13.** $1 \cdot 74, 2 \cdot 37$
15. $1 \cdot 48, 2 \cdot 24, 3 \cdot 16, 4 \cdot 12, 6 \cdot 8$ **17.** 1,
2, 4 **19.** 1, 2, 5, 10 **21.** 1, 31 **23.** 1, 5,
25 **25.** 1, 3, 7, 21 **27.** Prime **29.** Prime
31. $3 \cdot 5$ **33.** 2^5 **35.** $5 \cdot 19$ **37.** 3^4
39. 2^7 **41.** 3 **43.** 8 **45.** 6 **47.** 12
49. $1 \cdot 169, 13 \cdot 13$ **51.** $1 \cdot 211$ **53.** $1 \cdot 455$,
$5 \cdot 91, 7 \cdot 65, 13 \cdot 35$ **55.** $2^2 \cdot 3 \cdot 5 \cdot 7$
57. $2^2 \cdot 3^2 \cdot 5^2$ **59.** $2 \cdot 11^3$ **61.** $2 \cdot 5 \cdot 11^2$
63. 6 **65.** 16 **67.** 9 **69.** (1)(15),
$(-1)(-15), (3)(5), (-3)(-5)$ **71.** (1)(-99),
$(-1)(99), (3)(-33), (-3)(33), (9)(-11)$,
$(-9)(11)$ **73.** $15{,}873 \times 7$ **75.** $15{,}873 \times$
5×7 **77.** 444,444 **79.** 777,777
81. 999,999
Page 209. Class Exercises **1.** 6 **3.** $5x$
5. n^6 **7.** $-\dfrac{2}{x}$ **9.** $3x$ **11.** $2ab$
Pages 209–210. Exercises **1.** $2a$
3. $3x$ **5.** $7y$ **7.** $3a^2$ **9.** $-y^5$ **11.** $3x$
13. $18xy^4$ **15.** a^3b **17.** $5y$ **19.** -3
21. $-4b$ **23.** $\dfrac{1}{2n^3}$ **25.** $4x^3$ **27.** $-\dfrac{x^5}{2}$
29. a^2b **31.** $2x^2y^6$
33. $-7a^4b^2$ **35.** $2a^2b$ **37.** $\dfrac{5a^2}{3}$
39. $\dfrac{xy^3}{8}$ **41.** $2ac$ **43.** $-3hr$ **45.** $-\dfrac{1}{2}$
47. $7z^6$ **49.** $3y$ **51.** a^3c **53.** x^4z
55. $2ab; 2ab$ **57.** $9xy^3; 16$ **59.** $3x^2y$;
$3x^2y; 3x^2y$ **61.** $x; 4$ **63.** $2x + 3; 2x + 3$

Page 214. Class Exercises **1.** a **3.** $5xy$
5. $2(2y + 3)$ **7.** $x(x + 2)$ **9.** $3rs(2s - 3)$
11. $b^2(x + 1)$
Pages 214–215. Exercises **1.** $14n^2$
3. axy **5.** $6(x + 2)$ **7.** $7(y - 4)$
9. $5(2y + 5)$ **11.** $4x(2x - 5)$
13. $12(2a - 1)$ **15.** $x(x + 6)$
17. $a(8b + 1)$ **19.** $7a(3b + 1)$
21. $5t(2t - 1)$ **23.** $10a(4x + 3)$
25. $3x^2(x - 2)$ **27.** $13a(3 + 5a)$
29. $18h(3x^2 - 2)$ **31.** $3(x^2 - 2x + 3)$
33. $2x(3x^2 - 4x + 2)$
35. $15(4 + 3b + 2b^3)$ **37.** $3(-2x + 1)$,
$-3(2x - 1)$ **39.** $a(-1 + 3a), -a(1 - 3a)$
41. $2(-3x - 1), -2(3x + 1)$
43. $y(-y + 1), -y(y - 1)$
45. $4t(15t^3 - at + 3)$
47. $3x(3x^3 - 6x^2 + 4x - 10)$
49. $xy(6x^4 - 15x^3y + 20x^2y^2 + 6y^4)$
51. $21x^2y^2(4x^6y^3 + 5x - 3y)$
53. $y^2(y + 1)$ **55.** $4b^3 + b^2 - 2$
57. $n^2 + 5n + 2$ **59.** $(3a - 2b)$ dollars
61. $8k^2(4 - \pi)$
Page 217. Class Exercises
1. $(x + 3)(x + 4)$ **3.** $(2x - 5)(x + 7)$
5. $(x^2 + 2)(y + 9)$ **7.** $(x + y)(x - y)$
9. $(3 + a)(x - 4)$ **11.** $(x - y)(x + 3)$
Pages 217–218. Exercises
1. $(x + 3)(y + 2)$ **3.** $(x - 6)(2y + 1)$
5. $(y - 4)(x + 5)$ **7.** $(a^2 + 4)(a + b)$
9. $(x - y)(x + 1)$ **11.** $(y + 2)(x + 3)$
13. $(2x + 1)(y + 6)$ **15.** $(a + 3)(a + b)$
17. $(y + 2)(3x + 5)$ **19.** $(x + 5)(x + 3y)$
21. $(1 + x)(y + 1)$ **23.** $(x - y)(x + 2)$
25. $(a - 7)(a + 2b)$ **27.** $(x^2 + 1)(y - 9)$
29. $(y - b)(x + a)$ **31.** $(x^2 + r)(y - s)$
33. $(a + b)(p - q)$ **35.** $(5 - x)(3 - y)$ or
$(x - 5)(y - 3)$ **37.** $(4 - 3y)(1 - x)$ or
$(3y - 4)(x - 1)$ **39.** $(ab + c)(a + bc)$
41. $b^2(6 + b)(a + b)$
43. $3x(x + 1)(y - 4x)$
45. $4(2 - y^2)(1 + x)$ **47.** $(x + 3)(x + 4)$
49. $(x + 2)(x - 3)$ **51.** $(x - 3)(x - 7)$
Page 220. Class Exercises **1.** y, y
3. $5b, 5b$ **5.** $(x + 4)(x - 4)$
7. $(x + h)(x - h)$ **9.** $(8 + b)(8 - b)$
11. $(9a + 2)(9a - 2)$

PREREQUISITE SKILLS FOLLOW-UP

EXTRA PRACTICE SETS

COMPUTER HANDBOOK

TABLES

GLOSSARY

ANSWERS TO CHECKPOINTS

ANSWERS TO SELECTED EXERCISES

INDEX

ANSWERS TO SELECTED EXERCISES

13. $(11p + 12q)(11p - 12q)$
15. $(x + 100)(x - 100)$

    Pages 220–222. Exercises   **1.** $n - 3$
3. $2p - 5$ **5.** $4 + y$ **7.** 1   **9.** $49a^2$
11. $(x + 2)(x - 2)$ **13.** $(x + 6)(x - 6)$
15. $(h + 10)(h - 10)$ **17.** $(11 + t)(11 - t)$
19. $(3a + b)(3a - b)$
21. $(3h + 1)(3h - 1)$ **23.** $(5 + 8t)(5 - 8t)$
25. $(x + 14b)(x - 14b)$
27. $(p + 12q)(p - 12q)$
29. $(3a + 2)(3a - 2)$
31. $(5u + 4t)(5u - 4t)$
33. $(11x + 30y)(11x - 30y)$
35. $y(y + 5)(y - 5)$ **37.** $3(a + 3)(a - 3)$
39. $7h(h + 2)(h - 2)$
41. $7a(b + 3a)(b - 3a)$
43. $a(4 + ab)(4 - ab)$
45. $3a(3a + 11b)(3a - 11b)$
47. $2ab(ac + 4b)(ac - 4b)$ **49.** 80
51. 99,980,000   **53.** 2
55. $(x^2 + 4)(x + 2)(x - 2)$
57. $(1 + 9h^2)(1 + 3h)(1 - 3h)$
59. $x(x + 6)$
61. $(x^4 + 16)(x^2 + 4)(x + 2)(x - 2)$
63. $\left(\dfrac{1}{2}y + 3\right)\left(\dfrac{1}{2}y - 3\right)$
65. $(x + 0.1)(x - 0.1)$
67. $(x + y)(x - y)$; 70 cm²; 672 cm²
69. $\pi(R + 5r)(R - 5r)$; 11,304

    Page 224. Class Exercises   **1.** $x^2 +$
$16x + 64$ **3.** $4x^2 - 12x + 9$ **5.** $(y - 3)^2$
7. $(n + 6)^2$ **9.** $2n; (n + 1)^2$ **11.** $14n;$
$(n - 7)^2$ **13.** $18y; (y - 9)^2$

    Pages 224–225. Exercises   **1.** $x^2 +$
$12x + 36$ **3.** $81x^2 - 36x + 4$ **5.** $(x + 2)^2$
7. $(3x - 1)^2$ **9.** $(x + 15)^2$ **11.** $(a - 12)^2$
13. $(7x + 3)^2$ **15.** $(2x - 5y)^2$ **17.** $18x;$
$(x + 9)^2$ **19.** $4y; (2y + 1)^2$ **21.** $30x;$
$(3x + 5)^2$ **23.** $25; (x - 5)^2$ **25.** $9;$
$(x - 3)^2$ **27.** $25y^2; (3x + 5y)^2$ **29.** $49x^2;$
$(7x + 3)^2$ **31.** $t^2; (9n + t)^2$
33. $h(h + 5)^2$
35. $2x(3x - 1)^2$ **37.** $-9x(x + 1)^2$
39. $x^2y^2(xy^2 - 11z)^2$
41. $(x - 1 + a)(x - 1 - a)$
43. $(n + 7 + x)(n + 7 - x)$
45. $(x + 14)(x - 4)$ **47.** $(3x + 4)(3x - 2)$

49. $\left(2x - \dfrac{1}{4}\right)^2$ **51.** $(2x - 0.5)^2$

53. $\left(3x - \dfrac{2}{3}\right)^2$

    Page 227. Class Exercises   **1.** 1; 7
3. 5; 8   **5.** 6; 1   **7.** $(x + 1)(x + 2)$
9. $(x - 1)(x - 3)$ **11.** $(x - 3)(x + 4)$

    Pages 227–228. Exercises   **1.** 2; 4
3. 12; 2   **5.** 7; 6   **7.** $(x + 2)(x + 4)$
9. $(x + 1)(x + 9)$ **11.** $(x - 1)(x - 9)$
13. $(x - 6)(x - 17)$ **15.** $(x - 5)(x + 9)$
17. $(x + 1)(x - 19)$ **19.** $(y - 5)(y - 19)$
21. $(w + 3)(w + 48)$ **23.** $(r + 2)(r + 13)$
25. $(t - 1)(t - 43)$ **27.** $(b + 2)(b + 9)$
29. $(h - 3)(h - 3)$ **31.** $(x - 7)$
33. $(x - y)(x + 2y)$ **35.** $(a + 2b)(a + 3b)$
37. $(a + 2b)(a - 3b)$ **39.** $(x + n)(x - 4n)$
41. $(y - 3b)(y - 8b)$
43. $x(x - 1)(x - 17)$ **45.** $3(a - 2)(a - 9)$
47. $7x^2(x - 1)(x + 5)$

    Page 230. Class Exercises
1. $(2x + 1)(x + 3)$ **3.** $(3x - 1)(x - 2)$
5. $(2x + 1)(x - 3)$

    Page 231. Exercises   **1.** $2x, x$ **3.** $5x, x$
5. $2x, x$ **7.** 3, 3   **9.** $(3x + 2)(x + 2)$
11. $(3x - 2)(x - 1)$ **13.** $(5x - 12)(x + 1)$
15. $(5x + 4)(x + 3)$ **17.** $(3x + 1)(x - 2)$
19. $(2x + 1)(3x - 5)$
21. $(3x + 2)(2x + 5)$
23. $(4x + 3)(4x + 3)$
25. $(x - 3)(8x - 3)$
27. $(3x - 10)(2x - 1)$
29. $(3x + 2)(2x - 3)$
31. $(7x - 8)(3x + 1)$
33. $(x + 1)(4x + 3)$
35. $(7x + 4)(4x - 1)$ **37.** Not factorable
39. Not factorable   **41.** $2(3x + 5)(x + 1)$
43. $9x(x + 1)(x + 1)$
45. $2y(7x + 4)(2x - 1)$
47. $6x(2x + 3)(x - 1)$
49. $2(7x + 4y)(x - y)$ **51.** $x^2y(5x + 4y)^2$
53. $(3n - 5)$ hours

    Page 234. Class Exercises   **1.** GCF;
$c(1 - x)$ **3.** GCF; $2x(x - 8)$ **5.** GCF;
$4(x^2 + 36)$ **7.** Common binomial factor;
$(4a - 9)(1 + b)$ **9.** Trinomial;
$(a - 7)(a - 11)$

574

Pages 234–235. Exercises 1. $s(1 + r)$
3. $5x(x + 3)$ **5.** $2(10 + y)(10 - y)$
7. $6\pi(R + r)(R - r)$
9. $5(5n + 11)(5n - 11)$
11. $2ab(a^2 + b^2)(a + b)(a - b)$
13. $(x + 2)(y - 2)$ **15.** $(t + h)(x + 2)$
17. $(x - 7)^2$ **19.** $(5x - y)^2$
21. $x(x - 15)(x - 4)$
23. $2(x + 10)(x + 2)$
25. $-3(x + 2)(x + 7)$ **27.** $2(3x + 4)^2$
29. $-1(5x - y)^2$ **31.** $-2(x + 17)(x - 5)$
33. $x^2(3x + 5)(x + 11)$ **35.** $5x(2x - 3)^2$
37. $(x + 1)(x + 2)$ **39.** $(n + 1)(n - 1)^2$
41. $x(x + 1)(x - 1)(x - 2)$
43. $(x + 1)(x - 1)(y + 3)(y - 3)$
45. $(4 + x - y)(4 - x + y)$
47. $(2x + y + 2)(2x - y)$
49. $(3a - b + 16)(3a - b - 16)$
51. $(x + 3y + 3a + b)(x + 3y - 3a - b)$
53. $2(a + b + c - d)(a + b - c + d)$
55. $(x + 1)(x - 2)$ **57.** $2(3x + 7)(2x + 7)$

Page 237. Class Exercises 1. $-3; -5$
3. $7; 0$ **5.** $\frac{1}{3}; 0$ **7.** $-3; 0$ **9.** $1; 3$
11. $5; -5$ **13.** $5; -2$

Pages 238–239. Exercises 1. $3; 7$ **3.** $3, 4$
5. $4; 0$ **7.** $7; 0$ **9.** $0; -\frac{3}{2}$ **11.** $9; 0$
13. $4; 0$ **15.** $3; 0$ **17.** $1; -4$ **19.** $5; -2$
21. $9; -3$ **23.** $7; 0$ **25.** $3; -1$ **27.** $2; 4$
29. $6; 0$ **31.** $9; -4$ **33.** $1; -1$ **35.** $4; -4$
37. -3 **39.** -1 **41.** $11; -1$ **43.** $3; \frac{1}{2}$
45. $-1; 0$ **47.** $6; -6; 0$ **49.** $-2; -1; 0$
51. $3; 0$ **53.** $5; -6; 0$ **55.** $2; -2$ **57.** $5; -2$ **59.** $11, 12$ or $-11, -12$ **61.** 8 by 8
cm **63.** -1 **65.** $10; -2$ **67.** $-7; 6$
69. $0; 4; -3$ **71.** $3; -3; -4$ **73.** $7; -7; -3$ **75.** $1; -4$

Page 242. Class Exercises 1. 4
3. $n(n + 4) - 60 = 0; 6$ or -10 **5.** $6, 10$
Pages 242–244. Exercises 1. 6 or -6 **3.** 8
5. 7 and 12 **7.** -20 and -18 or 18 and 20
9. 0 or $\frac{1}{2}$ **11.** 7 **13.** Length is 14 yd; width
is 7 yd. **15.** 1 ft **17.** 9 and 11, or -13

and -11 **19.** 7 or 0 **21.** $6, 8,$ and $10,$ or
$-2, 0,$ and 2 **23.** 2 **25.** Square is 7 ft on
a side. Rectangle is 9 ft by 5 ft. **27.** Maria
is 9. John is 11. **29.** $\frac{5}{2}$

Pages 246–248. Review Exercises
1. $1 \cdot 84; 2 \cdot 42; 3 \cdot 28; 4 \cdot 21; 6 \cdot 14; 7 \cdot 12$
3. $2^2 \cdot 3 \cdot 7$ **5.** 12 **7.** $2xy$ **9.** $-\frac{x^7}{2}$
11. $\frac{2}{3ab^3}$ **13.** $4y^2$ **15.** $4(2a - b)$
17. $4x(3x - 2y)$ **19.** $9x(x^2 - x - 1)$
21. $2 + x$ **23.** $x(2 - x)$
25. $(3x + 5)(3x - 2)$ **27.** $(x - 2y)(x + 5)$
29. $(y - 10)(y + 10)$ **31.** $(5x - 7)(5x + 7)$
33. $(x - 9y)(x + 9y)$
35. $(20a - 1)(20a + 1)$ **37.** $14x; (x - 7)^2$
39. $1; (9x + 1)^2$ **41.** $(2x - 7)^2$
43. $4(x + 4)^2$ **45.** $(2x - 3y)^2$
47. $(x + 4)(x + 8)$ **49.** $(x - 7)(x + 3)$
51. $(y - 9)(y - 10)$ **53.** $(x + 3)(x + 5)$
55. $(2x - 7)(x + 1)$ **57.** $(5x - 3)(x + 1)$
59. $(3x + 7)(x + 4)$ **61.** $(9x + 2)(x - 1)$
63. $(4x + 3)(x + 2)$
65. $2x(x^2 + 1)(x + 3)$ **67.** $x = -4$ or
$x = 3$ **69.** $x = 0$ or $x = 2$ or $x = -2$
71. $x = \frac{2}{3}$ or $x = -\frac{5}{2}$ **73.** 9 and 15, or
-15 and -9 **75.** $0, 2, 4,$ or $4, 6, 8$

Pages 250–251. Cumulative Review
1. a **3.** b **5.** d **7.** e **9.** c **11.** d
13. c **15.** 18 **17.** 4 **19.** -7 **21.** $-62x$
23. $-\frac{3x}{2}$ **25.** $-6xy$ **27.** 14 **29.** -40
31. -110 **33.** -6 **35.** -5 **37.** 3
39. $-\frac{1}{3}$ **41.** $y = \frac{1}{2}x + 1$
43. $y = -x + 1$ **45.** $y = \frac{3}{2}x - 3$

47. $-24x^4y^3$ **49.** $8x^2 + 10x - 7$
51. $4x^2 + 12x + 9$ **53.** $(n + 7)^2$
55. $(3x - 2)(x + 4)$

PREREQUISITE SKILLS FOLLOW-UP

EXTRA PRACTICE SETS

COMPUTER HANDBOOK

TABLES

GLOSSARY

ANSWERS TO CHECKPOINTS

ANSWERS TO SELECTED EXERCISES

INDEX

ANSWERS TO SELECTED EXERCISES

CHAPTER 7
Page 253. Prerequisite Skills Review
1. d **2.** b **3.** c **4.** d **5.** a **6.** c **7.** a
8. d **9.** b **10.** c **11.** a **12.** d
Page 255. Class Exercises **1.** (-2, 1)
3. (1, 0)
Pages 256–257. Exercises **1.** (2, 4)
3. (2, 4)
5. (2, 1)

7. (2, 1)   **9.** (6, 4)

11. $\left(\frac{1}{2}, \frac{1}{2}\right)$

13. Yes **15.** Yes **17.** No
19. (1, 1)   **21.** (2, 2)

23. No solution **25.** No solution

27. (3, 0)

29. No solution
31. (3, 2)   **33.** (3, -1)

35. No solution
37. (2, -3)   **39.** (-1, -1)

41. (2, 2)

43. x + y = 12   x = y + 4
Numbers are 8 and 4.

45. 9

Page 259. Class Exercises **1.** x = y + 8
3. x = 3 **5.** (3, -5) **7.** 3y + 4

Page 260. Exercises **1.** $\left(4\frac{1}{2}, 2\right)$

3. (2, 6) **5.** (-5, -1) **7.** $\left(2\frac{1}{2}, 2\frac{1}{2}\right)$
9. (2, 0) **11.** (2, 2) **13.** (0, 1) **15.** No
solution **17.** No solution **19.** (1, -1)
21. (0, -2) **23.** (3, -1) **25.** $\left(2, -\frac{1}{3}\right)$

27. No solution **29.** $\left(\dfrac{13}{5}, -\dfrac{9}{5}\right)$ **31.** The equations are equivalent. Any solution of one equation is a solution of the other.

33. $\left(-\dfrac{5}{7}, \dfrac{10}{7}\right)$ **35.** $(118, -41, -7)$

Page 262. Class Exercises 1. $(1, 1)$
3. $(-2, 3)$ **5.** $(-1, -1)$ **7.** $(3, 2)$
9. $(2, -1)$

Pages 262–263. Exercises 1. $(1, 1)$
3. $(0, 2)$ **5.** $(3, 0)$ **7.** $(2, -3)$ **9.** $(0, 0)$

11. $\left(-\dfrac{1}{2}, -\dfrac{5}{2}\right)$ **13.** $(-3, -3)$ **15.** $(3, 2)$

17. $\left(6\dfrac{1}{2}, 1\dfrac{1}{2}\right)$ **19.** $\left(\dfrac{1}{2}, -8\right)$ **21.** $(4, 2)$

23. $\left(4, \dfrac{4}{5}\right)$ **25.** $(20, 32)$ **27.** $(9, -6)$

Page 265. Class Exercises 1. Mult. (2) by 3; $(3, 2)$ **3.** Mult. (1) by 3; Mult. (2) by -5; $(3, 1)$ **5.** Mult. (1) by 5; Mult. (2) by 4; $(-3, 1)$

Pages 265–267. Exercises 1. $(3, -3)$
3. $(5, 4)$ **5.** $(6, -2)$ **7.** $(28, 7)$ **9.** $\left(\dfrac{5}{2}, 4\right)$
11. $(13, -2)$ **13.** $(7, -3)$ **15.** $(-1, 2)$
17. $(1, -1)$ **19.** $(-3, -5)$ **21.** $\left(\dfrac{1}{4}, \dfrac{1}{2}\right)$
23. $(-2, -2)$ **25.** $(-2, 4)$ **27.** $(12, -9)$
29. $(0, -2)$ **31.** $(7, -9)$ **33.** $(1, 1)$
35. $(2, -1)$ **37.** $(-1, -1)$ **39.** $(3, 0)$
41. $(8, 0)$ **43.** $(0, 2)$ **45.** $(4, 3)$
47. $(2, 3)$ **49.** $\left(\dfrac{1}{7}, \dfrac{1}{4}\right)$

Page 270. Class Exercises 1. Inconsistent; independent **3.** Consistent; dependent **5.** Inconsistent; independent
7. Consistent; dependent
9. Consistent; independent
11. $(7, -1)$

Pages 270–271. Exercises 1. $(5, 3)$; consistent; independent
3. Inconsistent; independent
5. $(-1, 2)$; consistent; independent
7. $(2, 3)$; consistent; independent
9. Inconsistent; independent
11. Inconsistent; independent

13. One sol. **15.** One sol. **17.** Inf. many sol. **19.** No sol. **21.** Inf. many sol.
23. $(0, 2)$; consistent; independent
25. Inconsistent; independent
27. $(-7, 13)$; consistent; independent
29. $(2, -4)$; consistent; independent
31. Inconsistent; independent
33. $(21, 3)$; consistent; independent
35. None **37.** Infinitely many solutions
Page 273. Class Exercises 1. 7 and 16
3. 40 and 76 **5.** Andy, 7; Amy, 20
7. One orange costs 12¢; one grapefruit costs 30¢.

Pages 274–275. Exercises 1. 38 and 27
3. 5 and 20 **5.** Denise is 8. Derek is 24.
7. $8\dfrac{1}{2}$ ft; $11\dfrac{1}{2}$ ft **9.** Width is 12″. Length is 31″. **11.** 125 and 10 **13.** 15 and 6
15. Peter is 7. Ben is 1. **17.** 13 of the 17¢ stamps, 18 of the 20¢ stamps
19. Dan is 8. Cary is 14. **21.** Length is 9 in. Width is 6 in. **23.** 16 and 52

25. Smaller 4″; larger 8″ **27.** Dog is $\dfrac{1}{3}$ yr old. Amy is $17\dfrac{2}{3}$ yr old.

Page 277. Class Exercises 1. 24
Pages 277–278. Exercises 1. 57 **3.** 85
5. $3.45 **7.** 15; 11 **9.** 25 quarters, 35 dimes **11.** 93 **13.** 18 quarters, 15 nickels **15.** 8 quarters, 20 dimes **17.** 365

**Pages 280–282. Review Exercises
1.** $(1, -2)$ **3.** $(-1, -5)$ **5.** $(0, 3)$

7. No **9.** Yes **11.** $\left(\dfrac{1}{2}, -\dfrac{1}{2}\right)$ **13.** $(2, 5)$
15. $(-2, 3)$ **17.** $(2, 2)$ **19.** $(-2, 3)$
21. $(-1, -2)$ **23.** Ind.: 17, 18, 19, 20, 21, Dep.: 22 **25.** Consistent, independent **27.** Inconsistent, independent
29. length 14; width 10 **31.** 9 nickels, 14 dimes; $1.85

PREREQUISITE SKILLS FOLLOW-UP

EXTRA PRACTICE SETS

COMPUTER HANDBOOK

TABLES

GLOSSARY

ANSWERS TO CHECKPOINTS

ANSWERS TO SELECTED EXERCISES

INDEX

ANSWERS TO SELECTED EXERCISES

CHAPTER 8

Page 285. Prerequisite Skills Review
1. a **2.** c **3.** d **4.** c **5.** c **6.** b **7.** c
8. c **9.** d

Page 288. Class Exercises 1. It is undefined when x = 0. **3.** 8 **5.** 7 **7.** 7; $\frac{3}{5}$ **9.** x − y; $\frac{4}{3}$

Pages 288–289. Exercises 1. 0 **3.** −6
5. −4; 5 **7.** 3; −3 **9.** a^3; $\frac{1}{4a^3}$ **11.** $7n^3$; $\frac{1}{3n^5}$
13. x; $\frac{a-1}{a-2}$ **15.** c − 1; $\frac{2}{a}$ **17.** 2; $\frac{3}{x+2}$
19. 3; $\frac{a-2b}{3x-4}$ **21.** x + 3; x + 2 **23.** a − 4; $\frac{a-3}{a+4}$ **25.** n − 4; $\frac{1}{n-5}$ **27.** a − 1; $\frac{3}{a+7}$ **29.** a + 5; $\frac{a-5}{a+8}$ **31.** $\frac{2x}{x+3}$; −1
33. $\frac{3(x+1)}{x-2}$; 0 **35.** $\frac{1}{2b}$; $a \neq 0, b \neq 0$
37. 2(x + 1); x ≠ 1 **39.** $\frac{x+6}{3ax}$; $a \neq 0$, x ≠ 0, x ≠ −5 **41.** $\frac{2x-1}{x-3}$; x ≠ 3, x ≠ $-\frac{1}{2}$
43. $\frac{a(n+3)}{n-1}$; n ≠ 1, n ≠ −3 **45.** $\frac{1}{3x}$; x ≠ 0, x ≠ −4 **47.** $\frac{1}{x(x-1)}$; x ≠ 0, x ≠ 1, x ≠ −1 **49.** $\frac{6}{x-2}$; x ≠ 2, x ≠ 5
51. In simplest form **53.** In simplest form **55.** $\frac{3}{y-3}$ **57.** $\frac{a-9}{5a-1}$
61. $\frac{x}{(x^2+2)(3x-2)}$; x ≠ $\frac{2}{3}$
63. $\frac{x}{2x-3}$; x ≠ $\frac{3}{2}$ **65.** $\frac{x}{(x+1)^2}$; x ≠ −1

Page 291. Class Exercises 1. 5 **3.** 10
5. (x − 1) **7.** (x − 2) **9.** 2 **11.** −1
13. −2

Pages 291–292. Exercises 1. −x − 1
3. (x − 2) **5.** 2xy **7.** −1 **9.** −1
11. $-\frac{1}{2}$ **13.** $-\frac{1}{2}$ **15.** x − 1

17. $\frac{1}{3(1+x)}$ **19.** −a − 1, or −1(a + 1)
21. n − 3 **23.** $\frac{-1}{x-2}$ **25.** $\frac{a-1}{2(a+4)}$
27. $\frac{h-3}{h+3}$ **29.** −1 **31.** −x − 7
33. $\frac{4(2-a)}{a^2+4}$ **35.** −(x + 3) **37.** −y − 1

Page 294. Class Exercises 1. $\frac{5}{2}$ **3.** $\frac{1}{6}$
5. $\frac{x^2}{y^3}$ **7.** $\frac{x-3}{6}$ **9.** $\frac{2b}{a(x-1)}$ **11.** $\frac{a}{a-b}$

Pages 294–295. Exercises 1. $\frac{1}{12}$ **3.** $\frac{3}{10}$
5. $-\frac{2}{45}$ **7.** $\frac{1}{4}$ **9.** $\frac{32}{9}$ **11.** $\frac{8x^2}{15}$ **13.** 1
15. $-\frac{2yz^2}{x^2}$ **17.** $\frac{15}{112}$ **19.** $\frac{3}{2}$ **21.** $\frac{12}{5}$
23. $\frac{c}{d}$ **25.** $\frac{8x^2}{15}$ **27.** $\frac{1}{5}$ **29.** 6x
31. $\frac{2}{x(x-5)}$ **33.** $x^2(x+4)$
35. $\frac{-(1+x)}{2x(x-1)}$ **37.** $\frac{y+1}{y}$
39. $\frac{3(x-1)(x+3)}{2(x+2)(x+4)}$ **41.** $-\frac{(a+b)(a+5)}{(a-b)(a-2)}$
43. $-\frac{(x-5)}{2x}$ **45.** $\frac{x^2+y^2}{2xy}$ **47.** $\frac{a+2b}{2a+b}$
49. $\frac{3(x-2)}{x-6}$ **51.** $\frac{8000x^2}{x+10}$ cm³

Page 297. Class Exercises 1. 4 **3.** 4
5. $\frac{10}{21x}$ **7.** 25 **9.** x + 1 **11.** x + 2
13. $-\frac{1}{2}$ **15.** $\frac{1}{(a+b)(a-b)}$

Pages 297–298. Exercises 1. $\frac{1}{8}$ **3.** 9
5. −4 **7.** $\frac{9x}{10}$ **9.** a. 3; b. $12x^2$
11. a. $\frac{a^3b^3}{c^2}$; b. $\frac{a}{b}$ **13.** a. 1; b. $\frac{x^2}{y^2}$
15. a. $\frac{xy}{z}$; b. $\frac{xz}{y}$ **17.** $\frac{3}{2}$ **19.** $\frac{x-2}{4}$ **21.** $\frac{4}{x}$
23. $\frac{3}{2x}$ **25.** $\frac{1}{a+2}$ **27.** 1 **29.** $\frac{1}{2(x-2)}$

31. $\dfrac{1}{x}$ **33.** $\dfrac{1}{x}$ **35.** $\dfrac{5t(t-2)}{(t+2)(t-4)}$

37. $\dfrac{x+y}{x^2+y^2}$ **39.** $\dfrac{-1}{3(5+2x)}$ **41.** $\dfrac{x+2y}{x-2y}$

43. 1 **45.** $\dfrac{x-4}{x^2}$ **47.** $\dfrac{-x-2}{x}$ or $\dfrac{-(x+2)}{x}$

Page 300. Class Exercises 1. $3x-2$
3. $3x^2-1$ **5.** $x-3y$ **7.** $x-5$
9. $x-2$ **11.** $x+3$

Page 301. Exercises 1. x^2+10
3. $-2x^2-x+3$ **5.** $-1+x+3x^2$
7. $x-5$ **9.** $x+7$ **11.** $x-1-\dfrac{2}{x-1}$
13. $x-2+\dfrac{10}{x+4}$ **15.** $x-16+\dfrac{88}{x+6}$
17. $3x-10+\dfrac{60}{x+5}$ **19.** $x^2-5x+13-\dfrac{27}{x+2}$ **21.** x^2+4x+4 **23.** $x-4-\dfrac{4}{2x+1}$ **25.** $2x^3+3x^2+2x+3+\dfrac{16}{2x-3}$
27. $x^2-x+1-\dfrac{2}{x+1}$ **29.** $4x^2-4x+1$ **31.** $x^2+x-1-\dfrac{x+2}{x^2+1}$ **33.** $2x^3+4x^2+x+2+\dfrac{4x+8}{x^2-2x}$ **35.** $x^2-2x+1+\dfrac{2}{x^2-2x+1}$ **37.** $(x+1)(x+2)$

Page 303. Class Exercises 1. $\dfrac{5}{4}$ **3.** 0
5. $\dfrac{3a}{5}$ **7.** $\dfrac{6}{x}$ **9.** $\dfrac{1}{3}$ **11.** $\dfrac{a}{a^2+1}$ **13.** 1

Pages 303–304. Exercises 1. 1 **3.** -1
5. $\dfrac{5a}{7}$ **7.** $\dfrac{-2a}{9}$ **9.** $-\dfrac{x}{5}$ **11.** $\dfrac{y}{10}$ **13.** $-\dfrac{1}{x}$
15. $-\dfrac{h}{3}$ **17.** 4 **19.** $\dfrac{7}{y}$ **21.** $\dfrac{5+x}{x-1}$ **23.** 1
25. $\dfrac{1}{h+1}$ **27.** $\dfrac{1}{x+2}$ **29.** $x+2$
31. $a-2$ **33.** -2 **35.** $-a$ **37.** $\dfrac{a+b}{ab}$
39. $2x-1$ **41.** $x-5$ **43.** $y+2$
45. x^2-1 **47.** $\dfrac{3+\pi}{x}$

Page 306. Class Exercises 1. $\dfrac{2}{12}$
3. $\dfrac{15x}{12}$ **5.** $\dfrac{4n+4}{12}$ **7.** $\dfrac{8}{15}$ **9.** $\dfrac{1}{24}$
11. $\dfrac{2a-15}{3a}$ **13.** $\dfrac{x^2+2x-2}{2x}$

Page 307. Exercises 1. $\dfrac{12x}{27x}$ **3.** $\dfrac{54}{27x}$
5. $\dfrac{21}{27x}$ **7.** $\dfrac{13}{8}$ **9.** $-\dfrac{1}{72}$ **11.** $\dfrac{125}{24}$ or $5\dfrac{5}{24}$
13. $\dfrac{5}{2}$ or $2\dfrac{1}{2}$ **15.** $\dfrac{x^2+10}{2x}$ **17.** $\dfrac{17}{12x}$
19. $\dfrac{1+5x}{x}$ **21.** $\dfrac{4y-x}{y}$ **23.** $\dfrac{2x^2+1}{2x}$
25. $\dfrac{x^2+2x+3}{x^3}$ **27.** $\dfrac{6h+10}{(h+1)(h+2)}$
29. $\dfrac{x-6}{6(x+1)}$ **31.** $\dfrac{x+2}{x}$ **33.** $\dfrac{t+5}{t}$
35. $\dfrac{2(5h-4)}{(h-1)^2}$ **37.** $\dfrac{3(x+3)}{(x-5)(x+5)}$
39. $\dfrac{a}{a-2}$ **41.** $\dfrac{x^2-2}{(x+1)^2}$ **45.** $\dfrac{13}{12n}$

Page 310. Class Exercises 1. 70 **3.** $24x$
5. $15x^3y^2$ **7.** $24;\dfrac{5}{24}$ **9.** $12;\dfrac{7y}{12}$ **11.** $xy;\dfrac{y+x}{xy}$ **13.** $(a+b)^2;\dfrac{a^2}{(a+b)^2}$ **15.** $15x;\dfrac{8}{15}$

Pages 310–311. Exercises 1. 24
3. $105x$ **5.** $5a^2b$ **7.** $40;\dfrac{11}{40}$ **9.** $10;\dfrac{71}{10}$
11. $4;\dfrac{3n}{4}$ **13.** $14;\dfrac{3a}{14}$ **15.** $ab;\dfrac{4+b}{ab}$
17. $6n;\dfrac{1}{2n}$ **19.** $24;\dfrac{29}{24}$ **21.** $6a^2;\dfrac{6-a}{3a^2}$
23. $(a-1)(a+1);\dfrac{5}{a-1}$
25. $4(x-1)(x+3);\dfrac{1}{4(x+3)}$
27. $\dfrac{5a}{4(a+2b)}$ **29.** $\dfrac{t-4}{t}$ **31.** $\dfrac{5}{2(2-x)}$
33. $\dfrac{-5}{2(x+3)}$ **35.** $\dfrac{h(h+1)}{(h-1)^2}$ **37.** $\dfrac{3n-1}{n(n-1)}$
39. $\dfrac{x}{x-2}$

Page 313. Class Exercises 1. $\dfrac{3}{8}$ **3.** $\dfrac{a}{bc}$
5. $\dfrac{3}{7}$ **7.** $\dfrac{7}{144}$

ANSWERS TO SELECTED EXERCISES

579

PREREQUISITE SKILLS FOLLOW-UP

EXTRA PRACTICE SETS

COMPUTER HANDBOOK

TABLES

GLOSSARY

ANSWERS TO SELECTED CHECKPOINTS

ANSWERS TO SELECTED EXERCISES

INDEX

ANSWERS TO SELECTED EXERCISES

Pages 313–314. Exercises 1. $\frac{2}{3}$ 3. $\frac{12}{25}$

5. $\frac{ad}{bc}$ 7. $\frac{x+3}{2}$ 9. $\frac{4}{3}$ 11. $b+a$

13. $\frac{x+y}{x-y}$ 15. 4 17. $\frac{x}{x+1}$ 19. $\frac{2-n}{10}$

21. $\frac{3}{22}$ 23. $\frac{21}{16}$ 25. $\frac{y+x}{x}$ 27. $\frac{x}{x+2}$

29. $\frac{-1}{3x}$ 31. $\frac{ab}{b-a}$ 33. $\frac{2(x-3)}{x(x+3)}$ 35. 1

37. $\frac{x}{x+1}$ 39. $\frac{5}{x-3}$

Pages 316–318. Review Exercises 1. 0

3. None 5. -1 7. $-\frac{1}{x-3}$ 9. -1

11. $\frac{9}{x^2}$ 13. $\frac{1}{a(b+3)}$ 15. 1

17. $\frac{(x-3)(x+2)}{(x^2+4)(x-2)(x+3)}$ 19. $\frac{6}{x}$ 21. $\frac{6}{5}$

23. $x-5+\frac{14}{x+3}$ 25. $2x-17+\frac{108}{x+6}$

27. $3x+20+\frac{110}{x-5}$

29. $x^2-4x+7-\frac{8}{x+1}$ 31. $\frac{-2x}{7}$

33. $x+3$ 35. $\frac{x-2}{x}$ 37. $\frac{1}{x-3}$

39. $-\frac{5}{36}$ 41. $\frac{3y+4}{xy}$ 43. $\frac{-(x^2+y^2)}{(x+y)(x-y)}$

45. $\frac{x(2x-11)}{(x+2)(x-1)}$ 47. $3x; \frac{2x+5}{3x}$

49. $(x-2)(x+2); \frac{4x+1}{(x-2)(x+2)}$

51. $(x-2)^2; \frac{x^2}{(x-2)^2}$

53. $2(x-1)(x+1); \frac{3x^2-10x+11}{2(x-1)(x+1)}$

55. $\frac{1}{6x^2y}$ 57. $\frac{x-2}{3}$ 59. $\frac{x}{y(x-y)}$

61. $\frac{1}{2(x+3)^2(x^2+6x+24)}$

CHAPTER 9
Page 321. Prerequisite Skills Review
1. c 2. b 3. d 4. b 5. a 6. d 7. b
8. c 9. a 10. a

Page 323. Class Exercises 1. 5 3. $\frac{1}{4}$
5. 2 7. 4

Page 323. Exercises 1. 2 3. 5 5. -1
7. 5 9. 4 11. -15 13. 2 15. -1
17. -3 19. -1 21. 48
23. Alma $150, Ben $75, Carol $50

25. 5, -5 27. $\frac{1}{3}$

29. $x=-\frac{7}{8}y; y=-\frac{8}{7}x$

Page 325. Class Exercises 1. 10 3. 19
5. -4 7. 7 9. 8 11. 9

Page 326. Exercises 1. 2 3. 6 5. 9

7. -2 9. $\frac{1}{2}$ 11. No solution 13. 5, -5

15. 1 17. -1 19. No solution 21. 7

23. 1, $-\frac{5}{2}$ 25. -2 27. 5 29. 2 and 8

Page 328. Class Exercises 1. $x+2$
3. $x=3$

Pages 328–329. Exercises 1. 5 3. $\frac{5}{9}$

5. 9 7. $\frac{23}{7}$ 9. 3 11. $\frac{4}{7}$ 13. $\frac{5}{9}$

Page 332. Class Exercises

1. $\frac{1}{3}; \frac{2}{3}; \frac{x}{3}$ 3. $\frac{9}{20}$ 5. 6

Pages 332–333. Exercises 1. 6 hours

3. $3\frac{1}{3}$ hours, or 3 hr 20 min 5. $2\frac{2}{9}$ hours

7. Older sister, 4 hours; younger sister,

12 hours 9. $4\frac{1}{2}$ hours 11. Faster mower,

$10\frac{1}{2}$ hours; slower mower, 21 hours

13. Cold-water faucet, 2 minutes; hot-

water faucet, 6 minutes 15. $2\frac{1}{6}$ hours

17. $2\frac{2}{3}$ hours

Page 337. Class Exercises 1. $\frac{7}{3}$ 3. $\frac{6}{1}$

5. m: 3, 16; e: 24, 2 7. m: q, r; e: p, s
9. 8 11. 25

Pages 337–338. Exercises 1. 6 3. 45
5. 56 7. 3 9. 3 11. 7 13. 9

15. -143 17. $\frac{4}{3}; \frac{3}{4}$ 19. $\frac{2}{1}$ 21. $\frac{2}{3}$ 23. 16

25. $\frac{1}{5}$ 27. 60 km 29. 150 31. 1800

Democrats, 1500 Republicans **33.** 50, 35
35. \$15.50 **37.** \$18,000, \$24,000,

\$33,000 **39.** $\frac{1}{2}$

41.
$$\frac{a}{b} = \frac{c}{d}$$
$$ad = bc$$
$$\frac{ad}{cd} = \frac{bc}{cd}$$
$$\frac{a}{c} = \frac{b}{d}$$

43.
$$\frac{a}{b} = \frac{c}{d}$$
$$ad = bc$$
$$\frac{ad}{cd} = \frac{bc}{cd}$$
$$\frac{a}{c} = \frac{b}{d}$$
$$\frac{a}{c} - 1 = \frac{b}{d} - 1$$
$$\frac{a}{c} - \frac{c}{c} = \frac{b}{d} - \frac{d}{d}$$
$$\frac{a - c}{c} = \frac{b - d}{d}$$

Page 340. Class Exercises 1. 0.25; 25%

3. $\frac{27}{100}$; 0.27 **5.** $0.\overline{6}$, or $0.66\frac{2}{3}$; $66\frac{2}{3}$%

7. $\frac{1}{8}$; $12\frac{1}{2}$% **9.** $\frac{3}{50}$; 0.06 **11.** 8.4

13. 1.21 **15.** 30

Pages 341–342. Exercises 1. 85%
3. 90% **5.** 150% **7.** 6% **9.** 81.25%
11. 80% **13.** 85% **15.** 75% **17.** 45
19. 380 **21.** 200 **23.** 912 **25.** 2.5%
27. 12% **29.** \$16 **31.** \$5.94 (rounded
up) **33.** \$3.43 **35.** \$1250 **37.** \$60
39. \$5400; \$5961.60; 89% appr. **41.** 30%
43. 1500%

Page 344. Class Exercises 1. \$108
3. \$216 **5.** 2 years **7.** \$32
Page 345. Exercises 1. \$33.60
3. \$226.80 **5.** \$1250 **7.** \$3125 **9.** $\frac{1}{3}$

year, or 4 months **11.** \$3600 at $8\frac{1}{4}$%;

\$1600 at 7% **13.** \$138.34; \$265.84
15. \$3200 at 8%; \$4800 at 7.6%
17. \$24,000 at 12%; \$18,000 at $10\frac{1}{2}$%

Page 347. Class Exercises 1. 0.5 g
3. 1.6 g **5.** 1.44 **7.** $0.15(x + 8)$
Page 348. Exercises 1. 20 g **3.** 50.4 oz
5. 40 g of each solution **7.** $18\frac{3}{4}$ lb of
20% oats; $31\frac{1}{4}$ lb of 28% oats **9.** 2 qt
11. 50 kg of 6% copper alloy; 25 kg of
18% copper alloy
Page 350. Class Exercises 1. distance
3. $15t = 20\left(3\frac{1}{2} - t\right)$
Pages 350–352. Exercises 1. $2\frac{1}{2}$ hours
3. 16 km/h, 32 km/h **5.** $66\frac{2}{3}$ miles
7. $3\frac{1}{2}$ hours **9.** 11.45 A.M. **11.** Car,
54 km/h; boat, 24 km/h **13.** 700 mph
15. 40 minutes **17.** 50 mph

Pages 354–355. Review Exercises 1. $\frac{5}{2}$
3. $\frac{5}{6}$ **5.** 15 **7.** 40 **9.** -10 **11.** 6
13. 12 **15.** 17 **17.** $\frac{3}{8}$ **19.** 16, 18
21. $\frac{6}{5}$ hr, or 1 hr 12 min **23.** $\frac{7}{3}$ **25.** $-\frac{5}{4}$
27. wz **29.** 416 miles **31.** 6.25%
33. 50¢ **35.** \$5000 @ 11%, \$2200 @ 6%
37. 4 lb cashews, 6 lb peanuts **39.** 5 hr
Pages 358–359. Cumulative Review
1. a **3.** d **5.** e **7.** e **9.** a **11.** $\frac{8}{3}$
13. $x = \frac{8}{5}$ **15.** $4x + 1$ **17.** $\frac{x - 5}{x - 3}$ **19.** 1
21. $x + 7$ **23.** $\frac{16x + 2}{3x}$ **25.** $\frac{7}{2}$ **27.** $\frac{x}{x + 1}$
29. $(3x + 1)(x - 5)$ **31.** $\left(\frac{1}{2}, \frac{3}{4}\right)$
33. 72 quarters, 98 dimes **35.** 1 **37.** $\frac{5}{2}$
39. $2; -\frac{1}{2}$

CHAPTER 10
Page 361. Prerequisite Skills Review
1. b **2.** a **3.** c **4.** a **5.** d **6.** c **7.** b
8. b **9.** c **10.** d **11.** c **12.** b
Page 364. Class Exercises 1. h is
greater than 2 **3.** x is less than or equal
to 9 **5.** $h > -1$ **7.** $x \geq 21$ **9.** False
11. True **13.** c **15.** b

PREREQUISITE SKILLS FOLLOW-UP

EXTRA PRACTICE SETS

COMPUTER HANDBOOK

TABLES

GLOSSARY

ANSWERS TO CHECKPOINTS

ANSWERS TO SELECTED EXERCISES

INDEX

ANSWERS TO SELECTED EXERCISES

Pages 364–365. Exercises **1.** < **3.** >
5. > **7.** > **9.** = **11.** = **13.** < **15.** <
17. < **19.** < **21.** True **23.** False
25. False **27.** x > 1 **29.** x > −3
31. x < 3 **33.** x ≤ $4\frac{2}{3}$ **35.** x > $−1\frac{3}{4}$

37.
1   3   5

39.
3   5   7

41.
−4   −2   0

43.
−5   −3   −1

45.
−2   0   2

47.
−3   −2   −1

49.
−1   0

51.
1   2

53.
0   2   4

55.
−6   −4   −2

57.
0   2

59. Since $a < b$ and $a − 1 < a$, then
$a − 1 < b$ **61.** Since $a < b$ and
$a − 3 < a$, then $a − 3 < b$ **63.** No.
Example: x = 0, y = −1

Page 367. Class Exercises **1.** Add 4;
x < 11 **3.** Add 8; x ≥ 7

Page 367. Exercises
1. x > 2
2

3. a < −1
−1

5. c ≥ 2
2

7. x ≤ 7
7

9. x > 4
4

11. p < 19
19

13. e **15.** d **17.** b **19.** x < 12
21. x < −8 **23.** y > −4 **25.** x ≥ 11
27. x > −23
29.
$$5x > 4x$$
$$5x − 4x > 4x − 4x$$
$$x > 0$$
31. False **33.** True

Page 369. Class Exercises **1.** Mult. by
$\frac{1}{3}$; no **3.** Mult. by $\frac{3}{2}$; no **5.** Mult. by
$−\frac{1}{3}$; yes **7.** Mult. by −1; yes **9.** < 5
11. ≤ −7

Pages 369–370. Exercises **1.** x ≥ 7
3. b ≤ 5 **5.** y > 4 **7.** t > −2 **9.** y ≤ 4
11. p ≤ 6
13. x > 2
2

15. x < 2
2

17. x ≥ −1
−1

19. x ≥ 3
3

21. x < 3
3

23. x > 0
0

25. x ≥ −7 **27.** x ≥ 16 **29.** x < −1
31. x < −2 **33.** x > 3 **35.** x ≥ 8
37. x > 2 **39.** {x | x ≥ 10}
41. {x | x ≥ −15} **43.** x > 0 **45.** x < 0
47. $a^2 < a$

Page 373. Class Exercises
1. x + 3 ≥ 17; Numbers greater than or
equal to 14; 14 **3.** n + (n + 2) < 32;
(13, 15), (11, 13), (9, 11), (7, 9), (5, 7),
(3, 5), (1, 3); (13, 15) **5.** 4x − 6 ≥ 10; 4

Pages 373–374. Exercises
1. 3n + 2 ≤ 17; Numbers less than or
equal to 5; 5 **3.** 4(5 + x) ≥ 80; Numbers
greater than or equal to 15; 15 **5.** 10
7. 2 **9.** 8, 10, 12 **11.** 4 **13.** 12, 13, 14,
15, 16, 17 **15.** 84; 109 (not possible if
the highest possible test score is
100) **17.** 24

Page 377. Class Exercises
1. 6 < x < 10 **3.** 0 < x < 1.5
5. y > −8 and y ≤ 3
7.
−3   1

9.
−2   2

11.
−11   8

13. Yes **15.** Yes

582

Page 378. Exercises **1.** $-6, 10$ **3.** 1

5.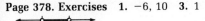

7.

9.

11. $1 < x < 5$ **13.** $x > 3$ or $x < -3$
15. $-2 \le x < 1$ **17.** $2 < x < 4$ **19.** All
real numbers **21.** $\{-8, -7, -6, -5, -4, -3, -2, -1, 0\}$ **23.** $\{\ldots, -8, -7, -6, -5, 6, 7, 8, \ldots\}$ **25.** All integers

27. $3 \ge x \ge -4$

29. $-1 \le x \le 2$

31. $-2 < x < 1$

33. $x > 1$ or $x < -3$

35. $x > 3$ or $x < 3$

37. $x > 8$ or $x < 8$

39. $x > -7$ or $x < -7$

41. $1 \le x < 3$

43.   **45.**

47. $x \ge 2$ or $x \le -2$

49. $x < 4$ and $x > -2$

Page 380. Class Exercises **1.** $-2 < x < 2$ **3.** $s > 1$ or $s < -1$ **5.** $-2 < y - 1 < 2$ **7.** $|x| \le 2$ **9.** $|x| \ge \frac{1}{2}$

Pages 380–381. Exercises **1.** $-9 \le x \le 9$ **3.** $-87 < y < 87$ **5.** $y - 5 \ge 1$ or $y - 5 \le -1$ **7.** $|x| < 8$ **9.** $|x| > 1.3$
11. $|x| \le 2$
13. $-1 < y < 3$

15. $-6 \le x \le 2$

17. $9 < x < 11$

19. $-1 < x < 1$

21. $-2 < x < 2$

23. $x \ge 3$ or $x \le -3$

25. $3 < x < 7$

27. $-1 < x < 2$

29. $x \ge 1$ or $x \le -2$

31. $0 \le x \le 4$

33. $x > 3\frac{1}{2}$ or $x < -4\frac{1}{2}$

35. $\emptyset$ **37.** $x > 0$ or $x < 0$ **39.** $0 < x < 2$
41. $|x - 5| < 3$ **43.** $\left| x + \frac{1}{2} \right| < 2\frac{1}{2}$

Page 384. Class Exercises
1. $y = -x + 1$, dashed

3. $y = x - 1$, dashed

5. $y = x$, solid

PREREQUISITE SKILLS FOLLOW-UP

EXTRA PRACTICE SETS

COMPUTER HANDBOOK

TABLES

GLOSSARY

ANSWERS TO CHECKPOINTS

ANSWERS TO SELECTED EXERCISES

INDEX

ANSWERS TO SELECTED EXERCISES

7. y = x − 3, dashed

9. Yes **11.** Yes

Pages 384–385. Exercises

1.

3.

5.

7.

9.

11.

13.

15.

17.

19.

21.

23.

25.

27.

29. y < x **31.** x < −1 **33.** y ≥ x + 2

35.

37.

39.

41.

43.

45.

47.

49.

51.

21.

23.

Page 387. Class Exercises   **1.** b   **3.** c

5.

7.

25.

Pages 387–388. Exercises

1.

3.

Pages 390–391. Review Exercises   **1.** <
3. >   **5.** $x \geq 4$ **7.** $x \geq 2$

9. $x < 6$

11. $x < -8$

13. $x \geq 7$

15. $x < -\frac{4}{3}$

5.

7.

17. $x < -2$

19. $x \geq -24$

21. $5(6 + 2x) \geq 60$; Numbers greater than
or equal to 3; 3   **23.** $4\frac{1}{2}$ cm

9.

11.

25. $-\frac{1}{2} < x < 1$

27. $-2 < x < 14$

29. $-\frac{3}{2} \leq x < -\frac{3}{4}$

31. $x \leq 2$ and $x \geq 1$, or $1 \leq x \leq 2$

13.

33. $-3 \leq x \leq 3$

35. $1 < x < \frac{11}{3}$

37. $-\frac{1}{2} < x < 2$

15. $y < 2$; $y > 2x - 2$ **17.** $y \geq 0$;
$y \geq -x + 2$ **19.** $y \geq -2$; $y \leq -x + 1$;
$y \leq x + 1$

39. $x > 12$ or $x < 0$

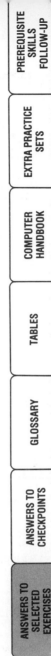

PREREQUISITE SKILLS FOLLOW-UP

EXTRA PRACTICE SETS

COMPUTER HANDBOOK

TABLES

GLOSSARY

ANSWERS TO CHECKPOINTS

ANSWERS TO SELECTED EXERCISES

INDEX

41. $y > \frac{1}{2}x$ **43.** $y \le -x + 2$

45.   **47.**

49.   **51.**

53.   **55.**

CHAPTER 11
Page 395. Prerequisite Skills Review
1. a **2.** b **3.** c **4.** c **5.** d **6.** d **7.** c
8. c **9.** d **10.** b **11.** b

Page 397. Class Exercises **1.** 0.375
3. 0.35 **5.** $1.\overline{3}$ **7.** $-\frac{1}{200}$ **9.** $\frac{7}{9}$ **11.** Yes
13. No

Page 398. Exercises **1.** 0.3555555555
3. 0.3543543543 **5.** 0.6969696969
7. 2.3383383383 **9.** $0.\overline{3}$, R **11.** 0.375, T
13. 1.25, T **15.** $0.\overline{4}$, R **17.** $3.\overline{4}$, R
19. $0.\overline{54}$, R **21.** 0.875, T **23.** 1.325, T
25. $\frac{81}{100}$ **27.** $\frac{200}{1}$ **29.** $\frac{33}{250}$ **31.** $-\frac{19}{8}$
33. $-\frac{16}{3}$ **35.** $\frac{1}{3}$ **37.** $\frac{2}{3}$ **39.** $\frac{83}{99}$ **41.** $\frac{34}{99}$
43. $\frac{13}{150}$ **45.** $\frac{226}{111}$ **47.** $\frac{11}{12}$ **49.** $0.0\overline{2}$
51. $0.\overline{02}$ **53.** $\frac{1}{7} = 0.\overline{142857}$; $\frac{2}{7} = 0.\overline{285714}$;
$\frac{3}{7} = 0.\overline{428571}$; $\frac{4}{7} = 0.\overline{571428}$;

$\frac{5}{7} = 0.\overline{714285}$; $\frac{6}{7} = 0.\overline{857142}$ **55.** $0.7\overline{4}$; $\frac{67}{90}$
57. $0.4\overline{6}$; $\frac{7}{15}$ **59.** $0.5\overline{18}$; $\frac{14}{27}$

Page 403. Class Exercises **1.** 1, 1
3. 9, −9 **5.** 90, −90 **7.** 8 **9.** 11
11. −6 **13.** 0.9 **15.** 3 **17.** 1

Pages 403–404. Exercises **1.** 3, −3
3. 8, −8 **5.** 40, −40 **7.** −11 **9.** −18
11. −14 **13.** −7 **15.** 9 **17.** $\frac{2}{9}$ **19.** $\frac{1}{5}$
21. 9 **23.** −4 **25.** 8 **27.** 5 **29.** 6
31. Rat. **33.** Irrat. **35.** Irrat. **37.** Rat.
39. Irrat. **41.** 8281 **43.** 4761 **45.** 59
47. 77 **49.** 9.899 **51.** $\frac{1}{32}$ **53.** $\frac{4}{3}$
55. 9.11 **57.** 10.68 **59.** 2.2361
61. 22.3607 **63.** 116.1895 **65.** Width is
15.5; length is 38.7

Page 406. Class Exercises **1.** 50
3. $3\sqrt{3}$ **5.** $2\sqrt{11}$ **7.** $-10\sqrt{2}$ **9.** $\sqrt{15}$
11. $4\sqrt{2}$ **13.** $\sqrt{35}$ **15.** $4\sqrt{11}$ **17.** 45
19. $135\sqrt{5}$

Pages 406–407. Exercises **1.** 1
3. $10\sqrt{10}$ **5.** $100\sqrt{5}$ **7.** $-3\sqrt{6}$ **9.** $5\sqrt{3}$
11. $4\sqrt{2}$ **13.** $20\sqrt{5}$ **15.** 4 **17.** 0
19. $2\sqrt{6}$ **21.** $6\sqrt{6}$ **23.** $30\sqrt{5}$ **25.** $10\sqrt{6}$
27. $\frac{2}{3}$ **29.** $\frac{1}{4}$ **31.** $10\sqrt{3}$; 17.32 **33.** $5\sqrt{7}$;
13.23 **35.** $7\sqrt{13}$; 25.24 **37.** $5\sqrt{5}$
39. 50 **41.** 144 **43.** 8 **45.** $5 + 5\sqrt{2}$
47. $6\sqrt{2} - 3\sqrt{2}$ **49.** 120 **51.** $800\sqrt{6}$
53. 1 **55.** $5\sqrt{5}$ **57.** 18.97 cm
59. $28 + 10\sqrt{3}$ **61.** $23 + 6\sqrt{10}$ **63.** 47

Page 409. Class Exercises **1.** $\frac{2}{3}$ **3.** $\frac{10}{9}$
5. $\frac{2\sqrt{3}}{7}$ **7.** $\frac{6\sqrt{5}}{5}$ **9.** $\frac{1}{3}$

Pages 409–410. Exercises **1.** $\frac{3}{2}$ **3.** $\frac{1}{4}$
5. $\frac{1}{5}$ **7.** 5 **9.** $\frac{3}{2}$ **11.** 2 **13.** $\frac{3}{2}$ **15.** $\frac{1}{2}$
17. $\frac{4\sqrt{5}}{5}$ **19.** $\frac{2\sqrt{5}}{5}$ **21.** $\frac{2\sqrt{21}}{3}$ **23.** $\frac{\sqrt{6}}{3}$
25. $\frac{\sqrt{15}}{10}$ **27.** $\frac{\sqrt{5}}{5}$; 0.45 **29.** $\frac{\sqrt{3}}{2}$; 0.87
31. $\frac{3\sqrt{5}}{10}$ **33.** $\frac{2\sqrt{2}}{3}$ **35.** $\frac{2\sqrt{6}}{3}$

37. $\dfrac{3 + \sqrt{6}}{3}$ **39.** $\dfrac{x}{y}$ **41.** $\dfrac{\sqrt{xy}}{y}$ **43.** $\dfrac{x\sqrt{x}}{3}$;

$\dfrac{8}{3}$ **45.** $\dfrac{x^2\sqrt{15}}{3}$; $3\sqrt{15}$ **47.** $4\sqrt{3}$

Page 412. Class Exercises 1. x^2 **3.** y^{10}

5. $5\sqrt{y}$ **7.** $y\sqrt{3y}$ **9.** $\dfrac{\sqrt{x}}{x}$ **11.** $3x^2\sqrt{3x}$

13. $3\sqrt{3xy}$

Pages 412–413. Exercises 1. $3x$

3. $2x^3\sqrt{5}$ **5.** $x\sqrt{2}$ **7.** $xy\sqrt{6x}$

9. $5x^3y^3\sqrt{5x}$ **11.** $4x^2y^3z^4\sqrt{3xyz}$

13. $2x\sqrt{2}$ **15.** $2x$ **17.** $\sqrt{3xy}$

19. $x^2y^4\sqrt{y}$ **21.** $\dfrac{\sqrt{x}}{5}$ **23.** $\dfrac{x\sqrt{x}}{7}$

25. $\dfrac{x\sqrt{3}}{2}$ **27.** $\dfrac{3x}{2}$ **29.** $3xy^2\sqrt{3}$

31. $32\sqrt{2x} + 4x\sqrt{y}$ **33.** $a\sqrt{b^2 + c^2}$

35. $3x\sqrt{2x - 3y}$ **37.** $x + 2$ **39.** $a + b$

41. $2a^2\sqrt{3}$; 13.9   **43.** $6a^2b$; 72

45. $2x^2y\sqrt{17}$; $8x^2y\sqrt{17}$ **47.** $p + q$

49. $p - \sqrt{pq}$ **51.** $10y^4\sqrt{x}$; $x \geq 0$

53. $11|p|q\sqrt{2q}$; $q \geq 0$ **55.** $a \geq 5$

57. $y \geq -2$

Page 415. Class Exercises 1. $5\sqrt{3}$

3. $\sqrt{5}$ **5.** $8\sqrt{5}$ **7.** $\sqrt{3}$

Page 415. Exercises 1. $8\sqrt{2}$ **3.** $5\sqrt{3}$

5. $7\sqrt{5}$ **7.** $7\sqrt{7}$ **9.** $6\sqrt{3}$ **11.** $4\sqrt{x}$

13. $3\sqrt{2}$ **15.** $6\sqrt{5}$ **17.** $4\sqrt{3}$ **19.** $5\sqrt{2}$

21. $99\sqrt{10}$ **23.** $-7\sqrt{3}$ **25.** $(x - 1)\sqrt{x}$

27. $(x + 1)\sqrt{y}$ **29.** $x(3\sqrt{x} - \sqrt{3x})$

31. $6\sqrt{5}$; 13.42   **33.** $3\sqrt{2}$; 4.24

35. $-3\dfrac{4}{5}\sqrt{10}$ **37.** $8\dfrac{1}{2}\sqrt{2}$

39. $\sqrt{x}(1 + x + x^2)$

41. $(x + y - 1)\sqrt{x + y}$

43. $2\dfrac{3}{4}\sqrt{2} + 1\dfrac{2}{3}\sqrt{3}$ **45.** $x = -2$

Page 418. Class Exercises 1. 5

3. $\sqrt{61}$ **5.** 6   **7.** $\sqrt{39}$ **9.** Yes   **11.** Yes

Pages 418–420. Exercises 1. 5   **3.** 24

5. 15   **7.** 8   **9.** $\sqrt{41}$ **11.** $2\sqrt{2}$ **13.** 10

15. No   **17.** No   **19.** No   **21.** 3.6 cm

23. 9 cm^2 **25.** $3\sqrt{85}$; 27.66 cm^2

27. 75 m   **29.** 8.72 ft   **31.** 14.14 cm

33. 24.5 ft^2 **35.** Figure needed to locate
the points: 1-by-1 square   **37.** Figure
needed to locate the points: 2-by-4 rectangle

Page 423. Class Exercises 1. $\sqrt{2}$
3. $2\sqrt{2}$ **5.** 4   **7.** 6   **9.** $2\sqrt{2}$

Pages 423–424. Exercises 1. 4   **3.** 8

5. 5   **7.** $\sqrt{29}$ **9.** $\sqrt{34}$ **11.** 13   **13.** 10

15. $2\sqrt{2}$ **17.** $14\sqrt{2}$; 19.8   **19.** $(1, -4)$;

$\sqrt{97}$; 9.8   **21.** 10 sq. units   **23.** $\sqrt{41}$; 6.4

25. 1, -11

27. Perimeter: $24\sqrt{2}$ units; 33.9 units
   Area: 72 square units

Page 426. Class Exercises 1. 81   **3.** 0
5. 66   **7.** 36   **9.** 12

Page 426. Exercises 1. 49   **3.** 16   **5.** $\dfrac{9}{4}$

7. 25   **9.** 2   **11.** No solution   **13.** 9

15. $\dfrac{69}{4}$ **17.** $\dfrac{1}{2}$ **19.** 101   **21.** 11   **23.** $\dfrac{1}{6}$ or

$-\dfrac{1}{6}$ **25.** 108   **27.** 81   **29.** 61   **31.** 0

33. No solution   **35.** 6 or -6 **37.** 2

39. 3   **41.** 1   **43.** -8

Pages 428–429. Review Exercises

1. 1.85   **3.** $0.\overline{27}$ **5.** $\dfrac{9}{5}$ **7.** $\dfrac{7}{9}$ **9.** 8

11. $10\sqrt{2}$ **13.** $3\sqrt{3}$ **15.** 76

17. 7×10^3 **19.** 6.7×10^{-2} **21.** 0.0041

23. $16\sqrt{5}$ **25.** $3\sqrt{2}$ **27.** $6\sqrt{6}$

29. $24\sqrt{6}$ **31.** $\dfrac{\sqrt{3}}{3}$ **33.** $\dfrac{\sqrt{15}}{3}$ **35.** $\dfrac{2\sqrt{6}}{9}$

37. $\dfrac{7\sqrt{2}}{4}$ **39.** $10x^2$ **41.** $3x\sqrt{3}$

43. $25xy^3\sqrt{3y}$ **45.** $25x^2\sqrt{x}$ **47.** $5\sqrt{3}$

49. $4\sqrt{5}$ **51.** $x^2y^2(\sqrt{x} + \sqrt{y})$ **53.** $\sqrt{19}$

55. 34 m

57. $7^2 + 24^2 \stackrel{?}{=} 25^2$
   $49 + 576 \stackrel{?}{=} 625$
   $\qquad 625 = 625$ ✔
   The triangle is a right triangle.

59. $\sqrt{41}$ **61.** $y = 3$ or $y = 5$ **63.** No

solution   **65.** No solution   **67.** $\dfrac{9}{8}$

PREREQUISITE SKILLS FOLLOW-UP

EXTRA PRACTICE SETS

COMPUTER HANDBOOK

TABLES

GLOSSARY

ANSWERS TO CHECKPOINTS

ANSWERS TO SELECTED EXERCISES

INDEX

ANSWERS TO SELECTED EXERCISES

CHAPTER 12

Page 433. Prerequisite Skills Review
1. c **2.** c **3.** b **4.** a **5.** b **6.** d **7.** a
8. d **9.** d **10.** b **11.** b

Page 436. Class Exercises **1.** Yes
3. No, since different y-values correspond
to $x = 1$. **5.** No. A vertical line crosses
the graph twice. **7.** 16 **9.** -4 **11.** 6
13. 0

Pages 436–437. Exercises **1.** Yes
3. Yes **5.** Yes **7.** No. A vertical line
can cross the graph at many points.

9. -7 **11.** $\frac{1}{2}$ **13.** -1 **15.** 0 **17.** 1

19. 21 **21.** 9 **23.** 6 **25.** $5; \frac{3}{2}; 4\frac{1}{3}$

27. $21; \frac{8}{13}; 4\frac{4}{9}$ **29.** $10; \frac{3}{7}; \frac{7}{9}$ **31.** -33

33. $8x - 14$ **35.** $15x^2 - 52x + 45$
37. 11
39. $f(g(x)) = 15x - 32$
$\quad g(f(x)) = 15x - 34$
$\quad g(f(x))$ is 2 less than $f(g(x))$.

Page 440. Class Exercises **1.** d **3.** b

Pages 440–441. Exercises

1. **3.**

5. **7.**

9.

11. D: x is any real number; R: $f(x) \geq 0$
13. D: x is any real number; R: $f(x) \geq 0$
15. (0, 0), min. **17.** (0, 0), min.

19.

x	-2	-1	0	1	2
y	5	2	1	2	5

21.

x	-2	-1	0	1	2
y	3	0	-1	0	3

Page 443. Class Exercises **1.** b **3.** d
5. 3; up **7.** 3; up

Page 444. Exercises **1.** b **3.** d
5. $y = x^2$; 5; down **7.** $y = -x^2$; 5; down

9. **11.**

13. **15.**

17. **19.**

21. $(0, -5)$; min. **23.** $(0, -3)$; max.
25. D: x is any real number; R: $f(x) \geq 3$

27. D: x is any real number; R: $f(x) \leq 3$

29. D: x is any real number; R: $f(x) \geq 5$

31. **33.**

35.

37. a. The graph, which opens upward, grows wider, approaching a straight line. **b.** The graph, which opens downward, grows wider, approaching a straight line. **c.** The graph is a straight line, $y = 1$.

Page 447. Class Exercises **1.** $(2, 5)$; x = 2; min. **3.** $(-1, 3)$; x = -1; min.

5. $(3, 4)$; x = 3; min. **7.** $(-4, -3)$; x = -4; max. **9.** $(2, -1)$; x = 2; min.

Pages 447–448. Exercises **1.** c **3.** b
5. $(-1, 1)$; x = -1; min. **7.** $(1, -1)$; x = 1; min. **9.** $(-3, -1)$; x = -3; min.
11. $(-3, 1)$; x = -3; max. **13.** $(-2, -3)$; x = -2; max. **15.** $y = -x^2$; 3; left; 5; down **17.** $y = -x^2$; 5; right; 3; up

19. **21.**

23. **25.**

27. D: x is any real number; R: $f(x) \geq 4$
29. D: x is any real number; R: $f(x) \geq 5$
31. D: x is any real number; R: $f(x) \leq -2$
33. $y = 2(x - 2)^2 - 3$; x = 2; $(2, -3)$
35. $y = -(x + 5)^2 - 4$; x = -5; $(-5, -4)$
37. $y = 3(x + 4)^2 + 1$; x = -4; $(-4, 1)$
39. -4; 2 **41.** c **43.** a
45.

Page 450. Class Exercises **1.** 9 **3.** 1
5. 4 **7.** 16 **9.** $\frac{9}{4}$ **11.** $\frac{1}{4}$

Page 451. Exercises **1.** $x^2 + 10x + 25$
3. $x^2 - 8x + 16$ **5.** $x^2 - 20x + 100$
7. $2 + \sqrt{3}$, $2 - \sqrt{3}$ **9.** $-3 + \sqrt{14}$, $-3 - \sqrt{14}$ **11.** $3 + \sqrt{7}$, $3 - \sqrt{7}$

PREREQUISITE SKILLS FOLLOW-UP

EXTRA PRACTICE SETS

COMPUTER HANDBOOK

TABLES

GLOSSARY

ANSWERS TO CHECKPOINTS

ANSWERS TO SELECTED EXERCISES

INDEX

ANSWERS TO SELECTED EXERCISES

589

13. $4 + 3\sqrt{2}, 4 - 3\sqrt{2}$ **15.** $\dfrac{-1 + \sqrt{13}}{2}$,

$\dfrac{-1 - \sqrt{13}}{2}$ **17.** $y = (x - 3)^2 - 8$

19. $y = (x - 1)^2 + 5$

21. $y = \left(x - \dfrac{3}{2}\right)^2 + \dfrac{11}{4}$

23. $y = 2\left(x + \dfrac{3}{2}\right) - \dfrac{7}{2}$

25. $y = (x - 4)^2 - 15$; $(4, -15)$; $x = 4$

27. $y = 2(x - 3)^2 - 15$; $(3, -15)$; $x = 3$

29. $y = -2(x + 1)^2 + 11$; $(-1, 11)$; $x = -1$

31. $x = -2$; $(-2, -6)$; min. **33.** $x = -3$;
$(-3, -9)$; min. **35.** $x = \dfrac{1}{3}$; $\left(\dfrac{1}{3}, -\dfrac{16}{3}\right)$;
min. **37.** $y = (x - 3)^2 - 4$; $x = 5$ or
$x = 1$ **39.** $y = \left(x - \dfrac{5}{2}\right)^2 - \dfrac{13}{4}$;
$x = \dfrac{5 \pm \sqrt{13}}{2}$ **41.** $y = -2\left(x + \dfrac{5}{4}\right)^2 + \dfrac{33}{8}$;
$x = \dfrac{-5 \pm \sqrt{33}}{4}$

590

Page 454. Class Exercises 1. $2, -1$
3. $-2, -3$ **5.** $5, -3$ **7.** $\dfrac{1}{2}, -1$ **9.** $2, -\dfrac{3}{2}$
11. $-1, \dfrac{2}{3}$

Page 454. Exercises 1. $5, -2$ **3.** $1, 3$
5. $5, -1$ **7.** $1, -\dfrac{1}{2}$ **9.** $\dfrac{1}{2}, -3$ **11.** $-1, \dfrac{1}{3}$

13. $x^2 - 3x - 1 = 0$; $x = \dfrac{3 \pm \sqrt{13}}{2}$

15. $x^2 + 5x + 14 = 0$; No real-number

solution **17.** $2x^2 + x - 1 = 0$; $x = \dfrac{1}{2}$ or
$x = -1$ **19.** $3x^2 - x - 1 = 0$;

$x = \dfrac{1 \pm \sqrt{13}}{6}$ **21.** $2x^2 - 8x + 5 = 0$;

$x = \dfrac{4 \pm \sqrt{6}}{2}$ **23.** $2x^2 - x - 3 = 0$; $x = \dfrac{3}{2}$

or $x = -1$ **25.** $-2, -3$ **27.** $4, -3$
29. No x-intercepts **31.** No x-intercepts.

33. No x-intercepts **35.** No solution (no
real-number solution) **37.** $\sqrt{5}, -\sqrt{5}$

Page 457. Class Exercises 1. 2 **3.** 1
5. None
Page 458. Exercises 1. 1; Rat. **3.** 2;
Irrat. **5.** 1; Rat. **7.** 1; Rat. **9.** None
11. 2; Rat. **13.** 0 **15.** Negative **17.** 2
19. 1 **21.** None **23.** 2 **25.** 2 **27.** 12
or -12 **29.** $-3 < k < 3$
Page 460. Class Exercises 1. 31 in.
3. If $x = 7$, $31 - x = 24$; If $x = 24$,
$31 - x = 7$. The lengths of the legs are
7 in. and 24 in.
Pages 461–462. Exercises 1. 17 or
-25 **3.** 3 or 2 **5.** 21 in. and 28 in.
7. 12 and 13, or -12 and -13 **9.** Width,
5 yd; length, 17 yd **11.** 16 or -4

13. $\dfrac{3 + \sqrt{5}}{2}$ or $\dfrac{3 - \sqrt{5}}{2}$ **15.** 15

17. 9 cm, 12 cm, 15 cm **19.** a. 2 sec; After 4 more sec b. Maximum height is
80 meters. **21.** 5 hours **23.** 6 yd **25.** 4

Page 464. Class Exercises 1. 4
3. 120 **5.** 2
Pages 464–465. Exercises 1. 30 **3.** 11
5. 48 **7.** 27 **9.** 12 **11.** 16 mi
13. 50 km^2 **15.** $y = 2x^2$ **17.** $y = 3x^2$

19. Surface area, 1256 in.^{2}; volume, 4192 in.^{3}

Page 467. Class Exercises **1.** $\frac{1}{2}$ **3.** 1
5. 51

Page 468. Exercises **1.** 40 **3.** 5 **5.** 3

7. $\frac{1}{10}$ **9.** $rn = k$ or $r = \frac{k}{n}$ **11.** Direct

13. Inverse **15.** 3.5

17. **19.**

21. 1890 ft

Pages 470–471. Review Exercises
1. No **3.** Yes **5.** No **7.** 34
9. $3c^2 + 4c - 5$
10–12.

13. $(0, 3)$, $x = 0$; min.

15. $(0, 3)$, $x = 0$; max.

17. $(-2, 5)$, $x = -2$; max.

19. $5 \pm \sqrt{35}$ **21.** $1 \pm \sqrt{2}$ **23.** $-\frac{5}{2}$

25. $y = (x - 3)^2 - 7$; $(3, -7)$, $x = 3$; D: x is a real no. R: $f(x) \geq -7$

27. $y = 2\left(x + \frac{5}{2}\right)^2 - \frac{23}{2}$; $\left(-\frac{5}{2}, -\frac{23}{2}\right)$, $x = -\frac{5}{2}$; D: x is a real no. R: $f(x) \geq -\frac{23}{2}$

29. $y = -\frac{1}{2}(x - 4)^2 + 13$; $(4, 13)$, $x = 4$; D: x is a real no. R: $f(x) \leq 13$

31. $\frac{-5 \pm \sqrt{33}}{2}$ **33.** $\frac{2}{3}$ **35.** $\frac{4 \pm \sqrt{31}}{3}$

37. $b^2 - 4ac = 1$; 2 **39.** $b^2 - 4ac = -31$; 0 **41.** $b^2 - 4ac = 121$; 2 **43.** 13 and 15 or -15 and -13 **45.** $\frac{3}{5}$ or $\frac{5}{3}$ **47.** 24

49. -1 **51.** 12

CHAPTER 13
Page 475. Prerequisite Skills Review
1. c **2.** c **3.** c **4.** d **5.** d **6.** c **7.** b
8. a **9.** d
Page 477. Class Exercises **1.** $40°$
3. $75°$ **5.** $(90 - 2n)°$ **7.** $75°$
9. $(180 - x)°$
Pages 477–478. Exercises **1.** $80°$
3. $43°$ **5.** $(65 - y)°$ **7.** $52°$
9. $(180 - 7n)°$ **11.** $15°, 75°$ **13.** $30°, 60°$
15. $14\frac{2}{3}°$, $152\frac{2}{3}°$, $12\frac{2}{3}°$ **17.** $59°, 60°, 61°$
19. $36°, 72°, 72°$ **21.** $8°$
Page 480. Class Exercises
1. $\angle A$, $\angle R$; $\angle B$, $\angle S$; $\angle C$, $\angle T$
AB, RS; BC, ST; AC, RT
3. $x = 12$, $y = 6$
Pages 480–481. Exercises **1.** YZ
3. XY **5.** $x = 5$, $y = 8$ **7.** $x = 8$, $y = 21$

PREREQUISITE SKILLS FOLLOW-UP

EXTRA PRACTICE SETS

COMPUTER HANDBOOK

TABLES

GLOSSARY

ANSWERS TO CHECKPOINTS

ANSWERS TO SELECTED EXERCISES

INDEX

ANSWERS TO SELECTED EXERCISES

9. 18 ft **11.** $8\frac{3}{4}$ in., $6\frac{1}{4}$ in. **13.** No. The length of EF is not given. **15.** 12 units **17.** 88 m

Page 483. Class Exercises 1. $\frac{15}{17}$ **3.** $\frac{15}{8}$ **5.** $\frac{15}{17}$

Pages 483–484. Exercises 1. $\frac{3}{5}$ **3.** $\frac{3}{4}$ **5.** $\frac{3}{5}$ **7.** $\frac{3}{5}$; $\frac{4}{5}$; $\frac{3}{4}$ **9.** $\frac{\sqrt{2}}{2}$; $\frac{\sqrt{2}}{2}$; 1 **11.** $\frac{2}{3}$; $\frac{\sqrt{5}}{3}$; $\frac{2\sqrt{5}}{5}$ **13.** $\frac{40}{41}$; $\frac{9}{41}$; $\frac{40}{9}$ **15.** $\frac{5\sqrt{34}}{34}$; $\frac{3\sqrt{34}}{34}$; $\frac{5}{3}$

17. $b = 12$

$\sin A = \frac{5}{13}$

$\cos A = \frac{12}{13}$

$\tan A = \frac{5}{12}$

19. $c = \sqrt{13}$

$\sin A = \frac{2\sqrt{13}}{13}$

$\cos A = \frac{3\sqrt{13}}{13}$

$\tan A = \frac{2}{3}$

21. $a = 5\sqrt{3}$

$\sin A = \frac{\sqrt{3}}{2}$

$\cos A = \frac{1}{2}$

$\tan A = \sqrt{3}$

23. $\frac{a}{c} = \frac{a}{c}$ ✔

25. $\left(\frac{a}{b}\right)\left(\frac{b}{a}\right) \stackrel{?}{=} 1$

$\frac{ab}{ab} \stackrel{?}{=} 1$

$1 = 1$ ✔

27. $\frac{12}{13}$; $\frac{12}{5}$

Page 487. Class Exercises 1. 5 **3.** $25\sqrt{3}$

Pages 487–488. Exercises 1. $16\sqrt{2}$
3. $21\sqrt{3}$ **5.** $15\sqrt{3}$ **7.** $30\sqrt{3}$ **9.** 26 ft
11. 7 ft **13.** 8 m **15.** 75 ft
17. 14,000 ft **19.** $\frac{3}{4} + \frac{1}{4} = 1$
21. $\frac{\sqrt{3}}{2} \stackrel{?}{=} 2\left(\frac{1}{2}\right)\left(\frac{\sqrt{3}}{2}\right)$ **23.** $1 - \dfrac{\frac{3}{4}}{1 + \frac{1}{2}} \stackrel{?}{=} \frac{1}{2}$

$\frac{\sqrt{3}}{2} = \frac{\sqrt{3}}{2}$ ✔ $1 - \frac{1}{2} \stackrel{?}{=} \frac{1}{2}$

$\frac{1}{2} = \frac{1}{2}$ ✔

Page 490. Class Exercises 1. 0.6561
3. 0.3249 **5.** 0.4540 **7.** 0.9205 **9.** 63°
11. 17°

Pages 490–491. Exercises 1. 0.4540
3. 0.2126 **5.** 0.7771 **7.** 0.1228 **9.** 17°
11. 10° **13.** 12.0 **15.** 5.3 **17.** 23.0
19. 30.0 **21.** 40° **23.** 49° **25.** 31 m
27. 500 m **29.** 37° **31.** 1083 ft

Pages 494–495. Review Exercises
1. 36°; 54° **3.** 16°, 65°, 99° **5.** $x = 12$, $y = 30$ **7.** $x = 68°$, $y = 22°$ **9.** BC = 5; $\sin A = \frac{5}{13}$, $\cos A = \frac{12}{13}$, $\tan A = \frac{5}{12}$
11. 141′ **13.** 100′ **15.** 73′ **17.** $x = 67°$
19. 4.7 meters (appr. 470 cm)

Pages 498–499. Cumulative Review
1. a **3.** e **5.** c **7.** b **9.** b **11.** d
13. $y = 2x - 6$ **15.** $y = -1$
17. $11x^2 - 6x$ **19.** $-8x + 8$ **21.** $\dfrac{-11z}{x^3}$
23. $3x(3x - 1)(3x + 1)$ **25.** $\frac{2}{3}$; -1
27. $x + 1 - \dfrac{3}{x + 2}$ **29.** $\dfrac{6x^2 + 3xy - 2y^2}{6xy}$
31. $x > 4$ or $x < 3$

33. $34\sqrt{3}$ **35.** $4x^3\sqrt{2x}$
37. (2, 0), min.

39. (2, 1), min.

41. 4340 **43.** 39°

INDEX

Abscissa, 128
Absolute value, 32
  in equations, 33
  in inequalities, 379
Absolute-value function, 437
Activities
  adding and subtracting on
    a nomograph, 54
  angles of a triangle, 478
  linear inequalities, 388
Addition
  of polynomials, 170–171
  of radicals, 414
  of rational expressions
    common denominators,
      302–303
    different denominators,
      305–306
    least common
      denominator,
      309–310
  of real numbers, 44, 47–48
Addition or subtraction, to
  solve systems of
  equations, 261–262
Addition property
  of equality, 87
  of inequalities, 366
  of opposites, 45
  of zero, 45
Additive identity, 44
Additive inverse, 44. *See also*
  Opposite.
Algebraic expression, 5,
  11–12
  evaluating, 5
Application
  Archaeology, 427
  Architecture, 493
  Balancing a Checkbook,
    197
  Bank Interest, 245
  Break-Even Point, 279
  Carpentry, 389
  Drafting, 315
  Finance Charges, 353
  Measurement and Cost, 77
  Meteorology, 115

  Navigation, 469
  Pictorial Graphs, 37
  Taxi Fares, 159
Associative properties, 34
Average, 73, 497
Axes in the coordinate plane,
  124
Axis of symmetry, 438
  equation of, 446, 450

Base of a power, 8–9
BASIC. *See* Computer
  Activities; Computer
  Handbook.
Binomial(s), 166
  multiplying, 184, 187–188
  squaring, 188
Boundary line of a
  half-plane, 383
Break-Even Point, 279

Calculator Activities. *See*
  Using the Calculator.
Cancellation rule, 208, 286
Challenge, 10, 53, 106, 131,
  158, 173, 196, 228, 275,
  352, 437, 488
Chapter Test, 40, 80, 118, 162,
  200, 248, 282, 318, 356,
  392, 430 472, 496. *See*
  also Tests.
Checkbook, Balancing a, 197
Checkpoint
  Ch.1, 16, 31
  Ch.2, 58, 72
  Ch.3, 95, 110
  Ch.4, 135, 148
  Ch.5, 177, 192
  Ch.6, 222, 235
  Ch.7, 263, 271
  Ch.8, 304, 311
  Ch.9, 329, 342
  Ch.10, 370, 385
  Ch.11, 404, 413
  Ch.12, 441, 458
  Answers to Checkpoints,
    556–559
Circumference, 41
Closure properties, 34
Coefficient
  leading, 290
  numerical, 59, 167

Common multiple, 309
Commutative properties, 34
Complementary angles, 476
Completing the square,
  449–450
Complex fractions, 312–313
Compound inequalities,
  375–377, 382
Compound interest, 357
Computer Activity
  Arithmetic Mean, 497
  Calculating Earnings, 319
  Circumference, 41
  Compound Interest, 357
  Engine Efficiency, 81
  Equations, 119
  Factoring a Number, 249
  Is It a Right Triangle?,
    431
  Ordered Pairs, 163
  Ordering Numbers, 393
  Ulam's Conjecture, 201
  Using Formulas, 283
  Weightlessness, 473
Computer Handbook,
  534–545
Conjunction, 375, 382
Consecutive numbers
  counting, 10
  even, 22
  odd, 22, 24
  whole, 21
Consistent system of
  equations, 268
Constant, 59
Constant of variation, 463,
  466
Coordinate(s)
  of a point in the plane, 124,
    128
  of a point on the number
    line, 28
Coordinate plane, 124
Corresponding angles, 479
Corresponding sides, 479
Cosecant, 488
Cosine, 482
Cotangent, 488
Cumulative Review,
  120–121, 250–251,
  358–359, 498–499.
  See also Tests.

PREREQUISITE SKILLS FOLLOW-UP

EXTRA PRACTICE SETS

COMPUTER HANDBOOK

TABLES

GLOSSARY

ANSWERS TO CHECKPOINTS

ANSWERS TO SELECTED EXERCISES

INDEX

INDEX

of systems of linear
inequalities, 386
Greatest common factor
(GCF)
for the terms of a
polynomial, 213
for two or more positive
integers, 205
Grouping symbols, 3

h, k form of a quadratic
equation, 446
Half-plane, 383
Hyperbola, 467

Identity
additive, 44
equation, 191
multiplicative, 66
Inconsistent system of
equations, 268
Independent system of
equations, 268
Inequalities, 25
and absolute value, 379
compound, 375–377
equivalent, 366
graphs of, 362–364,
383–384, 388
in problem solving,
371–372
properties of, 363
quadratic, 381, 455, 448
solution set of, 362
solving, 366–369
systems of linear, 386
transitive property of,
363
Integers, 25
as exponents, 211–212
Intercepts, 141–142
Interest, 245, 343–344
compound, 357
Intersection of sets, 374
Inverse
additive, 44
multiplicative, 69
Inverse operations, 92, 100
Inverse variation, 466–467
Irrational numbers, 28, 402
Isosceles triangle, 477

Law of sines, 492
Least common denominator
(LCD), 309
Least common multiple, 309
Legs of a right triangle, 416
Like terms, 59, 167
Linear equation
graphing, 132–133,
141–142, 146
of horizontal and vertical
lines, 155–156
point-slope form, 151
slope-intercept form, 145
standard form, 152
two-point form, 154
writing, 149–150, 152
Linear inequalities. *See*
Inequalities.
Logic, 382

Magic square, 173, 196
Maximum point, 439, 446
Mean(s)
as an average, 73, 497
in a proportion, 335
Minimum point, 438, 446
Mixture problems, 346–347,
355, 358–359
Monomial(s), 166
degree of, 166
dividing, 208–209
multiplying, 174–175
Multiples, common, 309
Multiplication
of binomials, 184, 187–188
of a monomial and a
polynomial, 182
of monomials, 174–175
of polynomials, 182,
184–185, 187–188
of powers with the same
base, 174
of radicals, 405–406
of rational expressions,
293–294
of real numbers, 63–64
See also Product.
Multiplication property
of equality, 96
of inequalities, 368–369
of 1 and – 1, 66

Multiplicative identity, 66
Multiplicative inverse, 69

Negative integers, 25
Negative real numbers, 29
Nonrepeating,
nonterminating decimal,
402
Number line, 28–29, 124
Numbers
consecutive, 10, 21, 22, 24
counting, 10, 20, 283
even, 22
integers, 25
irrational, 28, 402
negative, 29
odd, 22, 24
opposite, 25, 28
order, 28, 393
perfect square, 228, 401
positive, 25, 29
prime, 204, 207
rational, 28, 396–397
real, 29
whole, 21
Numerical expressions, 2

Odd numbers, 22, 24
Open sentence, 14
Opposite(s), 25, 28
addition property of, 45
Order of operations, 3, 9
Ordered pair, 124–126, 128,
163
Ordering numbers, 28, 393
Ordinate, 128
Origin, 25, 124

Parabola, 438, 442, 445–446
Parallel lines, 145
Patterns, 24
Percent, 339–340
Percent of increase or
decrease, 342
Perfect square, 228, 401
trinomial square, 223–224
Perimeter, 85
Pi (π), 29
Point(s)
in the coordinate plane,
124
distance between two, 423

PREREQUISITE SKILLS FOLLOW-UP

EXTRA PRACTICE SETS

COMPUTER HANDBOOK

TABLES

GLOSSARY

ANSWERS TO CHECKPOINTS

ANSWERS TO SELECTED EXERCISES

INDEX

PHOTO CREDITS

ADDITIONAL ANSWERS

ADDITIONAL ANSWERS TO EXERCISES

Because of space limitations, answers to some exercises cannot be shown on the pupil's reduced page or in the column at the right or left of that page. Such answers are provided below and on the pages that follow.

Pages 130–131   Exercises

15.

16.

23.

24.

25.

26.

Page 131   Challenge

1.

2.

3.

Page 134   Exercises

8.

9.

10.

11.

12.

13.

14.

15.

16.

17.

18.

19.

A1

20.

(−2, 3)

O

(0, −1)   x

(2, −5)

21.

(0, 3)

(−1, 1)

(−3, −3)

x

22.

(1, 5)

(0, 2)

O   x

(−2, −4)

23.

(2, 7)

(1, 2)

x

(0, −3)

24.

(2, 7)

(1, 3)

O   x

(0, −1)

25.

(−2, 6)

(0, 2)

O   x

(2, −2)

26.

(0, 5)

(1, 0)

O   x

(2, −5)

27.

(−3, 3)

O   x

(0, −3)

(1, −5)

28.

(−2, 4)

(−1, 1)

x

(0, −2)

Page 135   Checkpoint

17.

(1, 3)

(−1, 1)   (0, 2)

O   x

(−2, 0)

18.

(1, 2)

$(\frac{1}{2}, 1)$

(0, 0)

x

(−1, −2)

19.

$(\frac{1}{2}, 6)$

(0, 4)

$(-\frac{1}{2}, 2)$

O   x

(−1, 0)

20.

(−2, 7) $(1, 5\frac{1}{2})$

(0, 6)

(2, 5)

O   x

21.

(−2, 3)

(−1, 0)   x

(0, −3)

(1, −6)

Page 143   Exercises

49.

(0, 4)

(2, 0)

O   x

50.

(0, 6)

(2, 0)

O   x

51.

(0, 6)

(4, 0)

O   x

52.

(−1, 0)

O   x

(0, −2)

53.

(0, 5)

(−1, 0)

O   x

54.

(0, 3)

(−1, 0)

O   x

A2

55.

(0, 3)

(5, 0)

56.

(0, 4)

(−2, 0)

57.

(6, 0)

(0, −4)

58.

(0, 5)

(1, 0)

Page 147 Exercises

34.

(0, −4)

35.

(0, −3)

36.

(0, −1)

37.

(0, 1)

38.

1

$\left(0, -\frac{1}{2}\right)$

39.

$\left(0, \frac{1}{2}\right)$

−1

40.

(0, 0)

1 2

Page 148 Checkpoint

8.

1

9.

1

10.

1

Page 151 Exercises

17.

1

(0, −2)

18.

2

−2

(0, −8)

19.

(0, 4)

1

20.

1

(0, −3)

28. $y + 3 = -4(x + 2)$

29. $y + \frac{1}{4} = \frac{3}{4}\left(x - \frac{1}{2}\right)$

30. $y - \frac{3}{4} = 0\left(x - \frac{2}{3}\right)$, or $y - \frac{3}{4} = 0$

31. $m = 1; y - 1 = 1(x - 1); y = x$

32. $m = -1; y - 2 = -1(x + 2); y = -x$

Pages 153–154 Exercises

26. $x - 2y = 0$

(6, 3)

(−4, −2)

27. $2x + 3y = -4$

(−2, 0)

(4, −4)

28. $0x + y = 5$, or $y = 5$

29. $2x + y = -7$

30. $4x - 3y = -17$

31. $3x - y = 15$

54. $y - 6 = -4(x - 4)$

55. $y - 2 = 5(x - 7)$

56. $y - 9 = x - 2$

Pages 157–158 Exercises

30.

31.

58.

Page 158 Challenge

Page 161 Review Exercises

35. $y = -\dfrac{1}{2}x + 4$

36. $y = 4x + 12$

37. $y = \dfrac{1}{2}x + \dfrac{3}{2}$

Page 163 Computer Activity

8. 9, −10, 7

```
-5 , -5.2
-4 , -4.3
-3 , -3.4
-2 , -2.5
-1 , -1.6
 0 ,  -.7
 1 ,   .2
 2 ,  1.1
 3 ,   2
 4 ,  2.9
 5 ,  3.8
```

9. −7, 2, −5

```
-5 , -20
-4 , -16.5
-3 , -13
-2 , -9.5
-1 , -6
 0 , -2.5
 1 ,  1
 2 ,  4.5
 3 ,  8
 4 , 11.5
 5 , 15
```

10. 6, 25, −1

```
-5 , 1.16
-4 ,  .92
-3 ,  .68
-2 ,  .44
-1 ,  .2
 0 , -.04
 1 , -.28
 2 , -.52
 3 , -.76
 4 , -1
 5 , -1.24
```

Page 183 Exercises

21. $-3 - n + n^2$

22. $c^4 - 6c^3 + 3c^2$

23. $2a^3b - 2ab^3$

24. $3y^4 - 6y^3 - 3y^2$

25. $-12x^3 + 8x^2y - 10xy^2$

26. $-4y^4z - 16y^2z^2 + 20yz^3$

27. $-a^4b^4 - 2a^3b^3 + a^2b^2$

28. $-x^2y^3 + 2xy^3 - y^5 - y^4$

29. $-3a^3b + 6a^3b^3 - 9a^4b^4$

30. $-2x^6y^6 - 6x^4y^4 + 6x^3y^3$

31. $-12x^3y^2 + 18x^2y^3 - 24x^3y^3 + 6x^4y^4$

32. $5n^4t^3 - 10n^3t^4 - 15n^2t^5 + 20n^3t^3$

33. $4h^5 - h^4 + \dfrac{1}{4}h^3 - 16h^2 + 4h$

34. $-\dfrac{1}{25}t^4 + \dfrac{1}{5}t^3 - t^2$

Page 215   Exercises

47. $3x(3x^3 - 6x^2 + 4x - 10)$
48. $10h(12h^4 + 10h^3 + 5h^2 + 1)$
49. $xy(6x^4 - 15x^3y + 20x^2y^2 + 6y^4)$
50. $7ab(a^5 + 3a^4b + 3ab^4 + b^5)$
51. $21x^2y^2(4x^6y^3 + 5x - 3y)$
52. $21x^4y^3(3x^2y^2z^4 - 5xyz^3 + 1)$

Page 221   Exercises

59. $x(x + 6)$ **60.** $a(a - 10)$
61. $(x^4 + 16)(x^2 + 4)(x + 2)(x - 2)$
62. $\left(x + \dfrac{1}{3}\right)\left(x - \dfrac{1}{3}\right)$ **63.** $\left(\dfrac{1}{2}y + 3\right)\left(\dfrac{1}{2}y - 3\right)$
64. $\left(\dfrac{1}{3}x + \dfrac{3}{2}\right)\left(\dfrac{1}{3}x - \dfrac{3}{2}\right)$ **65.** $(x + 0.1)(x - 0.1)$
66. $\dfrac{1}{5}h(x + y)(x - y)$; 4200

Pages 256–257   Exercises

10.

11.

19.

21.

24.

26.

27.

28.

30.

31.

32.

33.

34.

36.

37.

38.

39.

40.

41.

$4x + y = 10$
$(2, 2)$

42.

$3y - 15 = -x$
$(3, 4)$
$2y = x + 5$

Page 271   Checkpoint

1.

$(3, -2)$
$x - y = 5$

2.

$x + y = 0$
$2x + y = 4$
$(4, -4)$

3.

$(-2, 3)$ $y = 3$
$y - x = 5$

Page 365   Exercises

49.
-1 ⬤ 0

50.
2 3 ⬤ 4

51.
1 2 ○

52.
-2 ⬤ -1

53.
0 ○ 2 4

54.
3 ⬤ 5 7

55.
-6 -4 ○ -2

56.
5 7 ⬤ 9

57.
0 2 ⬤

Page 367   Exercises

1. ○ 2

2. ○ 3

3. ○ -1

4. ○ -2

5. ⬤ 2

6. ⬤ 3

7. ⬤ 7

8. ⬤ 11

9. ○ 4

10. ○ 8

11. ○ 19

12. ○ 0

28.
$2x < x$
$2x - x < x - x$
$x < 0$

29.
$5x > 4x$
$5x - 4x > 4x - 4x$
$x > 0$

35. (1)　　$a < b$　　　Given
(2) $a + c < b + c$　Addition prop.
(3)　　$c < d$　　　Given
(4) $b + c < b + d$　Addition prop.
(5) $a + c < b + d$　Transitive prop. from (2) and (4)

Page 370   Exercises

15.
○ 2

16.
○ -2

17.
⬤ -1

18.
⬤ 1

19.
⬤ 3

20.
⬤ 3

21.
○ 3

22.
○ 10

23.
○ 0

24.
⬤ -1

48. (1)　$0 < a$　　Given
(2)　$a < b$　　Given
(3)　$0 < b$　　Transitive property using (1) and (2)
(4) $ab > 0$　　Product of two positive numbers is positive; from (1) and (2)
(5) $\dfrac{a}{ab} < \dfrac{b}{ab}$　Mulitplication property of inequalities; $b > 0$
(6) $\dfrac{1}{b} < \dfrac{1}{a}$,　Cancellation rule; from (5)
　　or $\dfrac{1}{a} > \dfrac{1}{b}$

49. (1)　$a > b$　　Given
(2) $ac > bc$　　Multiplication property of inequalities; $c > 0$
(3)　$c > d$　　Given
(4) $bc > bd$　　Multiplication property of inequalities; $b > 0$
(5) $ac > bd$　　Transitive property from (2) and (4)

Page 370   Checkpoint

1.
⬤ 3

2. ○ -1

3. ○ 6

4. ○ 2

5. ○ -2

6. ○ 2

7. ⬤ -1

8. ⬤ 5

9. ⬤ 17

10. ○ -8

A6

11. (number line, open circle at 3)

12. (number line, open circle at 5)

13. (number line, closed dot at 4)

14. (number line, open circle at 26)

Page 378 Exercises

10. $1 < x < 3$

11. $1 < x < 5$

12. $-5 \leq x < -3$

13. $x > 3$ or $x < -3$

14. $x \leq 3$ or $x > 4$

15. $-2 \leq x < 1$

16. $12 < x \leq 15$

17. $2 < x < 4$

18. $3 > x > 2$

19. All real numbers

20. $3 < x < 4$

27. $3 \geq x \geq -4$ (number line, closed dots at −4 and 3)

28. $-1 < x < 2$ (number line, open circles at −1 and 2)

29. $-1 \leq x \leq 2$ (number line, closed dots at −1 and 2)

30. $7 > x > -1$ (number line, open circles at −1 and 7)

31. $-2 < x < 1$ (number line, open circles at −2 and 1)

32. $-3 < x \leq -\dfrac{3}{2}$ (number line, open circle at −3, closed at $-\frac{3}{2}$)

33. $x > 1$ or $x < -3$ (number line, open circles at −3 and 1)

34. $x \leq -3$ or $x \geq 5$ (number line, closed dots at −3 and 5)

35. $x > 3$ or $x < 3$ (number line, open circle at 3)

36. $1 \leq x \leq 3$ (number line, closed dots at 1 and 3)

37. $x > 8$ or $x < 8$ (number line, open circle at 8)

38. $x > 5$ or $x < 5$ (number line, open circle at 5)

39. $x > -7$ or $x < -7$ (number line, open circle at −7)

40. $x > 7$ or $x < 7$ (number line, open circle at 7)

41. $1 \leq x < 3$ (number line, closed dot at 1, open at 3)

42. $x \leq -2$ or $x > 1$ (number line, closed dot at −2, open at 1)

43. (number line, open circles at −3 and 4)

44. (number line, open circles at 1 and 2)

45. (number line, open circles at 1, 3, 5)

46. $\emptyset$

47. $x \geq 2$ or $x \leq -2$ (number line, closed dots at −2 and 2)

48. $x \leq 2$ and $x \geq -2$ (number line, closed dots at −2 and 2)

49. $x < 4$ and $x > -2$ (number line, open circles at −2 and 4)

50. $y < 2$ and $y > -2$ (number line, open circles at −2 and 2)

Pages 380–381 Exercises

25. (number line, open circles at 3 and 7)

26. (number line, closed dots at 1 and 3)

27. (number line, open circles at −1 and 2)

28. (number line, open circles at −1 and 2)

29. (number line, closed dots at −2 and 1)

30. (number line, open circles at 0 and 4)

31. (number line, closed dots at 0 and 4)

32. (number line, open circles at 1 and $\frac{5}{3}$)

33. (number line, open circles at $-4\frac{1}{2}$ and $3\frac{1}{2}$)

44. (number line, open circles at 0, $\frac{1}{2}$, $\frac{3}{2}$, 4)

Page 384 Class Exercises

1.

2.

3.

4.

5.

6.

7.

8.

1.

2.

3.

4.

5.

6.

7.

8.

9.

10.

11.

12.

13.

14.

15.

16.

17.

18.

19.

20.

21.

22.

23.

24.

25.

26.

27.

28.

35.

36.

37.

38.

39.

40.

41.

42.

43.

44.

45.

46.

47.

48.

49.

50.

51.

52.

Page 385 Checkpoint

1. $1 < x < 3$

2. $-5 \le x < -3$

3. $-1 < x < 2$

4. $x > 2$ or $x < -3$

5. $1 \le x \le 3$

6. $1 < x < 3$

7. $x > 3$ or $x < 1$

8. $x \le 1$ or $x \ge 5$

9. $\dfrac{3}{4} < x < \dfrac{7}{4}$

Page 387   Class Exercises

4.

5.

6.

7.

Pages 387–388   Exercises

1.

2.

3.

4.

5.

6.

7.

8.

9.

10.

11.

12.

13.

14.

21.

22.

23.

24.

A10

25.

26.

27.

28.

29.

Page 388   Activity

Page 391   Review Exercises

24.
-14 7

25.
$-\frac{1}{2}$ 1

26.
-1 1

27.
-2 14

28.
$-\frac{4}{3}$ $\frac{2}{3}$

29.
$-\frac{3}{2}$ $-\frac{3}{4}$

30.
-2 3

31.
1 2

32.
-1 1

33.
-3 3

34.
-4 4

35.
1 $\frac{11}{3}$

36.
$\frac{1}{3}$ $\frac{7}{3}$

37.
$-\frac{1}{2}$ 2

38.
$-\frac{10}{3}$ 2

39.
0 12

40.
-2 $\frac{1}{2}$

44.

45.

46.

47.

48.

49.

50.

51.

52.

53.

54.

55.

Page 437   Challenge

4. Yes

Pages 440–441   Exercises

5.

6.

7.

8.

9.

10.

11. D: x is any real number
R: $f(x) \geq 0$

12. D: x is any real number
R: $f(x) \leq 0$

13. D: x is any real number
R: $f(x) \geq 0$

14. D: x is any real number
R: $f(x) \leq 0$

19.

x	-2	-1	0	1	2
y	5	2	1	2	5

20.

x	-2	-1	0	1	2
y	6	3	2	3	6

21.

x	-2	-1	0	1	2
y	3	0	-1	0	3

22.

x	-2	-1	0	1	2
y	-3	0	1	0	-3

23.
a. $(4, 4)$, $(-2, 1)$
b. $x = 4$ or $x = -2$
     $y = 4$ $y = 1$

1. No. When $x = -2$, y has different values, 0 and -3.
2. Yes   3. Yes
4. No. A vertical line can intersect the graph in two places.
5. No. A vertical line can intersect the graph in two places.
6. Yes

15.

Vertex is (0, 0). It is a maximum point for $y = -\frac{1}{8}x^2$
and a minimum point for $y = 8x^2$.
$y = 8x^2 \;\rightarrow\;$ D: x is any real number.
$\qquad\qquad$ R: $y \geq 0$
$y = -\frac{1}{8}x^2 \rightarrow$ D: x is any real number.
$\qquad\qquad$ R: $y \leq 0$

Page 444   Exercises

9.

10.

11.

12.

13.

14.

15.

16.

17.

18.

19.

20.

25.

D: x is any real number.
R: $f(x) \geq 3$

26.

D: x is any real number.
R: $f(x) \geq -3$

27.

D: x is any real number.
R: $f(x) \leq 3$

28.

D: x is any real number
R: $f(x) \leq -3$

A13

29.

D: *x* is any real number.
R: $f(x) \geq 5$

30.

D: *x* is any real number.
R: $f(x) \leq -5$

31.

32.

33.

34.

35.

36.

37. a. The graph, which opens upward, grows wider, approaching a straight line.
b. The graph, which opens downward, grows wider, approaching a straight line.
c. The graph is a straight line, $y = 1$.

Page 448   Exercises

21.

22.

23.

24.

25.

26.

27. D: *x* is any real number.
R: $f(x) \geq 4$

28. D: *x* is any real number.
R: $f(x) \geq -4$

29. D: *x* is any real number.
R: $f(x) \geq 5$

30. D: *x* is any real number.
R: $f(x) \leq -5$

31. D: *x* is any real number.
R: $f(x) \leq -2$

32. D: *x* is any real number.
R: $f(x) \leq 3$

33. $y = 2(x - 2)^2 - 3$; $x = 2$; $(2, -3)$

34. $y = \frac{1}{2}(x + 2)^2 + 3$; $x = -2$; $(-2, 3)$

35. $y = -(x + 5)^2 - 4$; $x = -5$; $(-5, -4)$

36. $y = -3(x - 5)^2 + 4$; $x = 5$; $(5, 4)$

37. $y = 3(x + 4)^2 + 1$; $x = -4$; $(-4, 1)$

44.

45.

46.

47.

48.

A14

25. $y = (x - 4)^2 - 15$;

$(4, -15)$; $x = 4$

26. $y = \left(x - \dfrac{5}{2}\right)^2 - \dfrac{25}{4}$;

$\left(\dfrac{5}{2}, -\dfrac{25}{4}\right)$; $x = \dfrac{5}{2}$

27. $y = 2(x - 3)^2 - 15$;
$(3, -15)$; $x = 3$

28. $y = -(x + 1)^2 + 8$;
$(-1, 8)$; $x = -1$

29. $y = -2(x + 1)^2 + 11$;

$(-1, 11)$; $x = -1$

30. $y = \dfrac{1}{2}(x - 1)^2 + \dfrac{9}{2}$;

$\left(1, \dfrac{9}{2}\right)$; $x = 1$

37. $y = (x - 3)^2 - 4$
$x = 5$ or $x = 1$

38. $y = \left(x + \dfrac{1}{2}\right)^2 - \dfrac{25}{4}$
$x = 2$ or $x = -3$

39. $y = \left(x - \dfrac{5}{2}\right)^2 - \dfrac{13}{4}$

$x = \dfrac{5 \pm \sqrt{13}}{2}$

40. $y = 2\left(x + \dfrac{3}{4}\right)^2 - \dfrac{25}{8}$

$x = \dfrac{1}{2}$ or $x = -2$

41. $y = -2\left(x + \dfrac{5}{4}\right)^2 + \dfrac{33}{8}$

$x = \dfrac{-5 \pm \sqrt{33}}{4}$

42. $y = -\dfrac{1}{2}(x - 1)^2 - \dfrac{5}{2}$

No x-intercepts

43. $y = a\left(x + \dfrac{b}{2a}\right)^2 - \dfrac{b^2 - 4ac}{4a}$

Vertex: $\left(-\dfrac{b}{2a}, -\dfrac{b^2 - 4ac}{4a}\right)$

13. $x^2 - 3x - 1 = 0$; $x = \dfrac{3 \pm \sqrt{13}}{2}$

14. $x^2 + 5x - 5 = 0$; $x = \dfrac{-5 \pm 3\sqrt{5}}{2}$

15. $x^2 + 5x + 14 = 0$;   no real-number solution

16. $x^2 + x - 3 = 0$; $x = \dfrac{-1 \pm \sqrt{13}}{2}$

17. $2x^2 + x - 1 = 0$; $x = \dfrac{1}{2}$ or $x = -1$

18. $3x^2 + 2x - 2 = 0$; $x = \dfrac{-1 \pm \sqrt{7}}{3}$

19. $3x^2 - x - 1 = 0$; $x = \dfrac{1 \pm \sqrt{13}}{6}$

20. $2x^2 + x - 2 = 0$; $x = \dfrac{-1 \pm \sqrt{17}}{4}$

21. $2x^2 - 8x + 5 = 0$; $x = \dfrac{4 \pm \sqrt{6}}{2}$

22. $x^2 + 3x - 2 = 0$; $x = \dfrac{-3 \pm \sqrt{17}}{2}$

23. $2x^2 - x - 3 = 0$; $x = \dfrac{3}{2}$ or $x = -1$

24. $3x^2 + 2x - 1 = 0$; $x = \dfrac{1}{3}$ or $x = -1$

39. a. Sum of the roots $= -\dfrac{b}{a}$

b. Product of the roots $= \dfrac{c}{a}$

$x^2 - 3x - 10 = 0$: $5 + (-2) = 3$ and $-\dfrac{b}{a} = 3$;

$5(-2) = -10$ and $\dfrac{c}{a} = -10$

$x^2 - 7x + 10 = 0$: $2 + 5 = 7$ and $-\dfrac{b}{a} = 7$;

$2(5) = 10$ and $\dfrac{c}{a} = 10$

$x^2 - 4x + 3 = 0$: $1 + 3 = 4$ and $-\dfrac{b}{a} = 4$;

$1(3) = 3$ and $\dfrac{c}{a} = 3$

$x^2 + 2x - 3 = 0$: $1 + (-3) = -2$ and $-\dfrac{b}{a} = -2$;

$1(-3) = -3$ and $\dfrac{c}{a} = -3$

$x^2 - 4x - 5 = 0$: $5 + (-1) = 4$ and $-\dfrac{b}{a} = 4$;

$5(-1) = -5$ and $\dfrac{c}{a} = -5$

$x^2 + 6x + 5 = 0$: $(-1) + (-5) = -6$ and $-\dfrac{b}{a} = -6$;

$(-1)(-5) = 5$ and $\dfrac{c}{a} = 5$

$2x^2 - x - 1 = 0$: $1 + \left(-\dfrac{1}{2}\right) = \dfrac{1}{2}$ and $-\dfrac{b}{a} = \dfrac{1}{2}$;

$1\left(-\dfrac{1}{2}\right) = -\dfrac{1}{2}$ and $\dfrac{c}{a} = -\dfrac{1}{2}$

$2x^2 - 3x - 2 = 0$: $2 + \left(-\dfrac{1}{2}\right) = \dfrac{3}{2}$ and $-\dfrac{b}{a} = \dfrac{3}{2}$;

$2\left(-\dfrac{1}{2}\right) = -1$ and $\dfrac{c}{a} = -1$

$2x^2 + 5x - 3 = 0$: $\dfrac{1}{2} + (-3) = -\dfrac{5}{2}$ and $-\dfrac{b}{a} = -\dfrac{5}{2}$;

$\dfrac{1}{2}(-3) = -\dfrac{3}{2}$ and $\dfrac{c}{a} = -\dfrac{3}{2}$

Page 458   Checkpoint

2. $y = 2(x - 3)^2 - 15$

Page 468   Exercises

19.

20.

Page 471   Review Exercises

15. **a.** $(0, 3)$; $x = 0$
    b. Maximum

16. **a.** $(3, 4)$; $x = 3$
    b. Minimum

c.

c.

17. **a.** $(-2, 5)$; $x = -2$
    b. Maximum
    c.

18. **a.** $(-1, -3)$; $x = -1$
    b. Maximum
    c.

25. $y = (x - 3)^2 - 7$
    a. $(3, -7)$; $x = 3$
    b. D: x is any real number.
       R: $f(x) \geq -7$

26. $y = -3(x - 1)^2 + 4$
    a. $(1, 4)$; $x = 1$
    b. D: x is any real number.
       R: $f(x) \leq 4$

27. $y = 2\left(x + \dfrac{5}{2}\right)^2 - \dfrac{23}{2}$
    a. $\left(-\dfrac{5}{2}, -\dfrac{23}{2}\right)$;
       $x = -\dfrac{5}{2}$
    b. D: x is any real number.
       R: $f(x) \geq -\dfrac{23}{2}$

28. $y = -2(x - 1)^2 + 5$
    a. $(1, 5)$; $x = 1$
    b. D: x is any real number.
       R: $f(x) \leq 5$

29. $y = -\dfrac{1}{2}(x - 4)^2 + 13$
    a. $(4, 13)$; $x = 4$
    b. D: x is any real number.
       R: $f(x) \leq 13$

30. $y = 5\left(x - \dfrac{1}{10}\right)^2 + \dfrac{59}{20}$
    a. $\left(\dfrac{1}{10}, \dfrac{59}{20}\right)$; $x = \dfrac{1}{10}$
    b. D: x is any real number.
       R: $f(x) \geq \dfrac{59}{20}$

31. $x = \dfrac{-5 \pm \sqrt{33}}{2}$

32. $x = 4$ or $x = -1$

33. $x = \dfrac{2}{3}$

34. $x = \dfrac{1}{2}$ or $x = -\dfrac{1}{4}$

35. $x = \dfrac{4 \pm \sqrt{31}}{3}$

36. $x = 1$ or $x = \dfrac{2}{5}$

23. Let x, $x + 2$, and $x + 4$ represent any three consecutive odd integers.

$$x + x + 2 + x + 4 = 180$$
$$3x + 6 = 180$$
$$3x = 174$$
$$x = 58$$

58 is not an odd integer. Therefore, the measures of the angles of a triangle cannot be consecutive odd integers.

Page 478 Activity

The triangle has an area that is twice that of the folded rectangle. The area of the rectangle is length × width. But the length $= \frac{1}{2}$ the base b of the triangle, and the height $= \frac{1}{2}$ the altitude h of the triangle. Thus, the area of the triangle is $2\left(\frac{1}{2}b \times \frac{1}{2}h\right) = 2\left(\frac{1}{4}bh\right) = \frac{1}{2}bh$.

Page 484 Exercises

18. $a = 9$

$\sin A = \frac{3}{5}$

$\cos A = \frac{4}{5}$

$\tan A = \frac{3}{4}$

19. $c = \sqrt{13}$

$\sin A = \frac{2\sqrt{13}}{13}$

$\cos A = \frac{3\sqrt{13}}{13}$

$\tan A = \frac{2}{3}$

20. $b = \sqrt{55}$

$\sin A = \frac{3}{8}$

$\cos A = \frac{\sqrt{55}}{8}$

$\tan A = \frac{3\sqrt{55}}{55}$

21. $a = 5\sqrt{3}$

$\sin A = \frac{\sqrt{3}}{2}$

$\cos A = \frac{1}{2}$

$\tan A = \sqrt{3}$

22. $\left(\frac{a}{c}\right)^2 + \left(\frac{b}{c}\right)^2 \overset{?}{=} 1$

$\frac{a^2}{c^2} + \frac{b^2}{c^2} \overset{?}{=} 1$

$\frac{a^2 + b^2}{c^2} \overset{?}{=} 1$

$\frac{c^2}{c^2} \overset{?}{=} 1$

$1 = 1$ ✔

23. $\frac{a}{c} = \frac{a}{c}$ ✔

24. $\frac{a}{b} \overset{?}{=} \dfrac{\frac{a}{c}}{\frac{b}{c}}$

$\frac{a}{b} = \frac{a}{b}$ ✔

25. $\left(\frac{a}{b}\right)\left(\frac{b}{a}\right) \overset{?}{=} 1$

$\frac{ab}{ab} \overset{?}{=} 1$

$1 = 1$ ✔

28. $\sin A = \frac{x}{5}$; $\cos A = \frac{\sqrt{25 - x^2}}{5}$;

$\tan A = \frac{x\sqrt{25 - x^2}}{25 - x^2}$

Page 488 Exercises

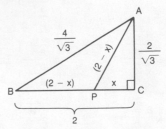

24. Method I

Let $PC = x$. In right triangle APC,

$$(2 - x)^2 = \left(\frac{2}{\sqrt{3}}\right)^2 + x^2$$

$$4 - 4x + x^2 = \frac{4}{3} + x^2$$

$$-4x = \frac{4}{3} - 4$$

$$x = \frac{2}{3} \quad \text{and} \quad 2 - x = \frac{4}{3}$$

Then $\sin \angle CAP = \frac{x}{2 - x} = \frac{2}{3} \div \frac{4}{3} = \frac{1}{2}$

Method II

Use the angles in the triangles; $\angle B = 30°$ and $\angle BAC = 60°$, from the ratios of the given sides. Then, since $BP = AP$, $\angle ABP = \angle BAP = 30°$; so $\angle CAP = 60° - 30° = 30°$. Therefore,

$\sin \angle CAP = \sin 30° = \frac{1}{2}$.

Page 488 Challenge

The Pythagorean theorem permits various substitutions:
$a^2 + b^2 = c^2$; $c^2 - a^2 = b^2$; $c^2 - b^2 = a^2$

1. $(\tan A)^2 + 1 \overset{?}{=} (\sec A)^2$

$\left(\frac{a}{b}\right)^2 + 1 \overset{?}{=} \left(\frac{1}{\frac{b}{c}}\right)^2$

$\frac{a^2}{b^2} + \frac{b^2}{b^2} \overset{?}{=} \left(\frac{c}{b}\right)^2$

$\frac{a^2 + b^2}{b^2} \overset{?}{=} \frac{c^2}{b^2}$

$\frac{c^2}{b^2} = \frac{c^2}{b^2}$ ✔

2. $1 + (\cot A)^2 \overset{?}{=} (\csc A)^2$

$1 + \left(\frac{1}{\frac{a}{b}}\right)^2 \overset{?}{=} \left(\frac{1}{\frac{a}{c}}\right)^2$

$\frac{a^2}{a^2} + \left(\frac{b}{a}\right)^2 \overset{?}{=} \left(\frac{c}{a}\right)^2$

$\frac{a^2}{a^2} + \frac{b^2}{a^2} \overset{?}{=} \frac{c^2}{a^2}$

$\frac{a^2 + b^2}{a^2} \overset{?}{=} \frac{c^2}{a^2}$

$\frac{c^2}{a^2} = \frac{c^2}{a^2}$ ✔

3. $\dfrac{1 - \csc A}{\cot A} \stackrel{?}{=} \dfrac{\sin A - 1}{\cos A}$

$$\dfrac{1 - \dfrac{1}{\frac{a}{c}}}{\dfrac{1}{\frac{a}{b}}} \stackrel{?}{=} \dfrac{\dfrac{a}{c} - 1}{\dfrac{b}{c}}$$

$$\dfrac{1 - \dfrac{c}{a}}{\dfrac{b}{a}} \stackrel{?}{=} \dfrac{\dfrac{a-c}{c}}{\dfrac{b}{c}}$$

$$\dfrac{\dfrac{a-c}{a}}{\dfrac{b}{a}} \stackrel{?}{=} \dfrac{a-c}{b}$$

$$\dfrac{a-c}{b} = \dfrac{a-c}{b} \checkmark$$

4. $\dfrac{\csc A + 1}{\csc A - 1} \stackrel{?}{=} (\sec A + \tan A)^2$

$$\dfrac{\dfrac{1}{\frac{a}{c}} + 1}{\dfrac{1}{\frac{a}{c}} - 1} \stackrel{?}{=} \left(\dfrac{1}{\frac{b}{c}} + \dfrac{a}{b}\right)^2$$

$$\dfrac{\dfrac{c}{a} + 1}{\dfrac{c}{a} - 1} \stackrel{?}{=} \left(\dfrac{c}{b} + \dfrac{a}{b}\right)^2$$

$$\dfrac{\dfrac{c+a}{a}}{\dfrac{c-a}{a}} \stackrel{?}{=} \dfrac{c^2}{b^2} + \dfrac{2ac}{b^2} + \dfrac{a^2}{b^2}$$

$$\dfrac{c+a}{c-a} \stackrel{?}{=} \dfrac{c^2 + 2ac + a^2}{b^2}$$

$$\dfrac{c+a}{c-a} \stackrel{?}{=} \dfrac{c^2 + 2ac + a^2}{c^2 - a^2}$$

$$\dfrac{c+a}{c-a} \stackrel{?}{=} \dfrac{(c+a)(c+a)}{(c-a)(c+a)}$$

$$\dfrac{c+a}{c-a} = \dfrac{c+a}{c-a} \checkmark$$

96. $y = -x - 3$

97. $y = 2x$

98. $y = 3x + 3$

99. $y = \dfrac{1}{2}x - \dfrac{1}{2}$

100. $y = -2x$

101. $y = -\dfrac{1}{5}x + 1$

102. $3x - y = -5$

103. $x + y = -5$

104. $3x - 2y = 12$

105. $x + y = 4$

106. $2x - y = 3$

107. $4x - y = -2$

108. $x - 2y = -12$

109. $4x - 3y = -12$

110. $x + 4y = -32$

Page 527   Chapter 10 Extra Practice

44. $x > 7$

45. $-3 < c < 5$

46. $h \leq -14 \text{ or } h \geq 2$

47. $x < -2 \text{ or } x > 2$

48. $x > 6 \text{ or } x < -4$

49. $-3 \leq x \leq 3$

50. $-2 \leq x \leq 1$

51.

52.

53.

54.

55.

56.

57.

Pages 513–515   Chapter 4 Extra Practice

74.

75.

76.

77.

78. $y = 3x$

79. $y = 2x + 6$

80. $y = 4x + 4$

81. $y = -6x + 30$

82. $y = -2$

83. $y = -2x + 3$

84. $y = -3x - 1$

85. $y = -x + 7$

86. $y = 6x + 3$

87. $y = \dfrac{1}{2}x + 2$

88. $y = \dfrac{4}{3}x - 11$

89. $y = \dfrac{1}{4}x + \dfrac{9}{4}$

90. $y = -x + 5$

91. $y = 2x - 5$

92. $y = \dfrac{1}{3}x + \dfrac{5}{3}$

93. $y = \dfrac{2}{3}x$

94. $y = -5x + 21$

95. $y = -2x + 2$

58.

Pages 530–532 Chapter 12 Extra Practice

33. $y = (x + 2)^2 + 1$
Vertex: $(-2, 1)$
Axis: $x = -2$

34. $y = (x - 3)^2 - 8$
Vertex: $(3, -8)$
Axis: $x = 3$

35. $y = 4(x - 1)^2 - 1$
Vertex: $(1, -1)$
Axis: $x = 1$

36. $y = -3(x + 2)^2 + 14$
Vertex: $(-2, 14)$
Axis: $x = -2$

37. $y = -(x - 2)^2 + 13$
Vertex: $(2, 13)$
Axis: $x = 2$

38. $y = \frac{1}{4}(x - 2)^2 + 6$
Vertex: $(2, 6)$
Axis: $x = 2$

39. $x = -4$
Vertex: $(-4, -14)$, min.

40. $x = -1$
Vertex: $(-1, 6)$, max.

41. $x = -1$
Vertex: $(-1, -7)$, min.

42. $x = \frac{5}{2}$
Vertex: $\left(\frac{5}{2}, \frac{-13}{4}\right)$, min.

43. $x = \frac{-3}{2}$
Vertex: $\left(\frac{-3}{2}, \frac{-45}{4}\right)$, min.

44. $x = 1$
Vertex: $(1, 14)$, max.

45. $x = 6$ or $x = 1$

46. $x = \frac{2}{5}$ or $x = -1$

47. $x = -1$

48. No real-number solution

49. $x = 1$ or $x = \frac{-5}{4}$

50. $x = \frac{-7 + \sqrt{5}}{2}$ or
$x = \frac{-7 - \sqrt{5}}{2}$

51. $x = -4$ or $x = -8$

52. $x = -\frac{1}{2}$ or $x = -1$

53. $x = 3$

54. No x-intercepts

55. $x = \frac{-6 + 2\sqrt{3}}{6}$ or $x = \frac{-6 - 2\sqrt{3}}{6}$

56. No x-intercepts